Preparing students for the world that awaits

McGraw-Hill Connect® Biology interactive learning platform provides auto-graded assessments, an adaptive diagnostic tool, lecture capture, access to instructor resources, and powerful reporting—all in an easy-to-use interface.

Learn more at www.mcgrawhillconnect.com.

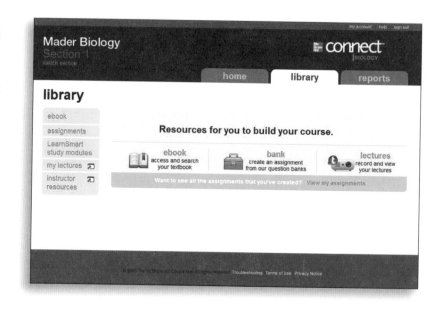

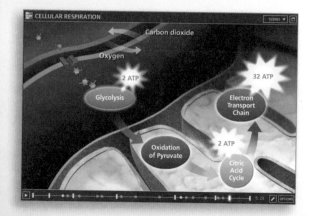

eBook

McGraw-Hill ConnectPlus® Biology provides students with all the advantages of Connect Biology, plus 24/7 online access to an eBook. This media-rich version of the book includes 3D and 2D animations, videos, virtual labs, and inline assessments placed appropriately throughout the chapter.

Assignments

Connect Biology provides a practice bank of questions that instructors can assign. Several question types are used to cover the key concepts—labeling, sequencing, classification, composition, multiple-choice, true/false, and more. Also available are animations with quizzing.

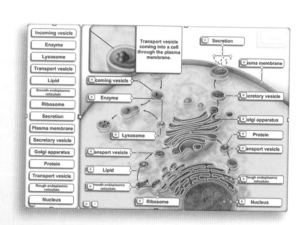

McGraw-Hill LearnSmart™ Study Modules

Powered by Connect Biology, McGraw-Hill LearnSmart™ provides students with a GPS (**G**uided **P**ath to **S**uccess). It is an adaptive diagnostic tool based on artificial intelligence that constantly assesses a student's knowledge of the course material. Sophisticated diagnostics adapt to each student's individual knowledge base, and vary the questions to determine what the student doesn't know, knows but has forgotten, and how best to match and improve their knowledge level. Students actively learn the required concepts, and instructors can get specific LearnSmart reports to monitor overall progress.

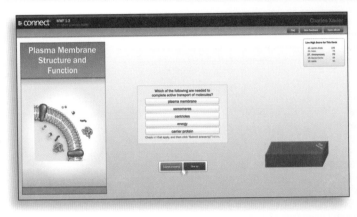

Learn Fast. Learn Easy. Learn Smart.

Learn more at www.mhlearnsmart.com.

My Lectures—Tegrity®

McGraw-Hill Tegrity® records and distributes lectures with just a click of a button. Students can view anytime/anywhere via computer, iPod, or mobile device. It indexes as it records PowerPoint® presentations and anything shown on the computer, so students can use keywords to find exactly what they want to study.

Instructor Resources

Connect Biology provides easy access to the following resources:

- Enhanced image PowerPoints with editable art
- Lecture PowerPoints with animations
- Animation PowerPoints
- Labeled and unlabeled jpeg files of art, photos, and tables from the textbook

Chapter	Enhanced Image PPTs (includes photos, and editable art)	Lecture PPTs with Animations	Animation PowerPoints	Labeled Jpeg Images	Base Art Image Files (.jpgs, no labels or leader lines)
All Chapters	Enhanced Image PPTs (707,634 KB)	Lecture Animation PPTs (649,609 KB)	Animation PPTs (1,64,060 KB)	Labeled Images (859,337 KB)	Base Images (599,793 KB)
Ch01	Ch. 1 Enhanced Image PPTs (23,977 KB)	Ch. 1 Lecture Animation PPTs (14,860 KB)	There are no Animation PPTs correlated to this chapter.	Ch. 1 Labeled Images (28,669 KB)	Ch. 1 Base Images (21,333 KB)
Ch02	Ch. 2 Enhanced Image PPTs (9,907 KB)	Ch. 2 Lecture Animation PPTs (6,012 KB)	Ch. 2 Animation PPTs (6,794 KB)	Ch. 2 Labeled Images (15,054 KB)	Ch. 2 Base Images (8,805 KB)
Ch03	Ch. 3 Enhanced Image PPTs (16,605 KB)	Ch. 3 Lecture Animation PPTs (14,220 KB)	Ch. 3 Animation PPTs (1,833 KB)	Ch. 3 Labeled Images (18,346 KB)	Ch. 3 Base Images (14,607 KB)

Powerful Reporting Solutions

Connect Biology offers detailed reporting so instructors can quickly assess how students are doing in regards to overall class performance, individual assignments, and each question.

All practice and test bank questions are tagged to the textbook by chapter, section, topic, and Bloom's level of difficulty, and aligned with the learning outcomes in the textbook to aid these reporting features.

Brief Contents

1 A View of Life   1

UNIT 1   **The Cell**   20

2 Basic Chemistry   21
3 The Chemistry of Organic Molecules   37
4 Cell Structure and Function   60
5 Membrane Structure and Function   85
6 Metabolism: Energy and Enzymes   104
7 Photosynthesis   119
8 Cellular Respiration   135

UNIT 2   **Genetic Basis of Life**   152

9 The Cell Cycle and Cellular Reproduction   153
10 Meiosis and Sexual Reproduction   171
11 Mendelian Patterns of Inheritance   192
12 Molecular Biology of the Gene   214
13 Regulation of Gene Expression   237
14 Biotechnology and Genomics   254

UNIT 3   **Evolution**   270

15 Darwin and Evolution   271
16 How Populations Evolve   289
17 Speciation and Macroevolution   306
18 Origin and History of Life   327
19 Taxonomy, Systematics, and Phylogeny   347

UNIT 4   **Microbiology and Evolution**   362

20 Viruses, Bacteria, and Archaea   363
21 Protist Evolution and Diversity   383
22 Fungi Evolution and Diversity   403

UNIT 5   **Plant Evolution and Biology**   418

23 Plant Evolution and Diversity   419
24 Flowering Plants: Structure and Organization   443
25 Flowering Plants: Nutrition and Transport   464
26 Flowering Plants: Control of Growth Responses   483
27 Flowering Plants: Reproduction   501

UNIT 6   **Animal Evolution and Diversity**   518

28 Invertebrate Evolution   519
29 Vertebrate Evolution   549
30 Human Evolution   570

UNIT 7   **Comparative Animal Biology**   586

31 Animal Organization and Homeostasis   587
32 Circulation and Cardiovascular Systems   605
33 The Lymphatic and Immune Systems   626
34 Digestive Systems and Nutrition   646
35 Respiratory Systems   663
36 Body Fluid Regulation and Excretory Systems   680
37 Neurons and Nervous Systems   693
38 Sense Organs   716
39 Locomotion and Support Systems   735
40 Hormones and Endocrine Systems   752
41 Reproductive Systems   772
42 Animal Development and Aging   795

UNIT 8   **Behavior and Ecology**   818

43 Behavioral Ecology   819
44 Population Ecology   838
45 Community and Ecosystem Ecology   857
46 Major Ecosystems of the Biosphere   883
47 Conservation of Biodiversity   907

BIOLOGY

Eleventh Edition

Sylvia S. Mader

Michael Windelspecht
Appalachian State University

With contributions by

April Cognato
Michigan State University

David Cox
Lincoln Land Community College

Jeffrey Isaacson
Nebraska Wesleyan University

Ian Quitadamo
Central Washington University

GERMANNA COMMUNITY COLLEGE
BIO 101

Boston   Burr Ridge, IL   Dubuque, IA   New York   San Francisco   St. Louis
Bangkok   Bogotá   Caracas   Lisbon   London   Madrid
Mexico City   Milan   New Delhi   Seoul   Singapore   Sydney   Taipei   Toronto

Biology, Eleventh Edition
Germanna Community College
BIO 101

This book is a McGraw-Hill Learning Solutions textbook and contains select material from *Biology*, Eleventh Edition by Sylvia S. Mader and Michael Windelspecht, with contributions by April Cognato, David Cox, Jeffrey Isaacson and Ian Quitadamo. Copyright © 2013, 2010, 2007, 2004 by The McGraw-Hill Companies, Inc. Reprinted with permission of the publisher. Many custom published texts are modified versions or adaptations of our best-selling textbooks. Some adaptations are printed in black and white to keep prices at a minimum, while others are in color.

1 2 3 4 5 6 7 8 9 0   QDB QDB   14 13 12

ISBN-13: 978-0-07-777427-1
ISBN-10: 0-07-777427-2
PART OF:
ISBN-13: 978-0-07-777428-8
ISBN-10: 0-07-777428-0

Learning Solutions Consultant: Dave Fleming
Production Editor: Larry Jackson
Printer/Binder: Quad/Graphics
Cover Photo Credits: © 2012 JupiterImages Corporation

About the Authors

Sylvia S. Mader   Sylvia S. Mader has authored several nationally recognized biology texts published by McGraw-Hill. Educated at Bryn Mawr College, Harvard University, Tufts University, and Nova Southeastern University, she holds degrees in both Biology and Education. Over the years she has taught at University of Massachusetts, Lowell; Massachusetts Bay Community College; Suffolk University; and Nathan Mayhew Seminars. Her ability to reach out to science-shy students led to the writing of her first text, *Inquiry into Life*, that is now in its thirteenth edition. Highly acclaimed for her crisp and entertaining writing style, her books have become models for others who write in the field of biology.

Although her writing schedule is always quite demanding, Dr. Mader enjoys taking time to visit and explore the various ecosystems of the biosphere. Her several trips to the Florida Everglades and Caribbean coral reefs resulted in talks she has given to various groups around the country. She has visited the tundra in Alaska, the taiga in the Canadian Rockies, the Sonoran Desert in Arizona, and tropical rain forests in South America and Australia. A photo safari to the Serengeti in Kenya resulted in a number of photographs for her texts. She was thrilled to think of walking in Darwin's steps when she journeyed to the Galápagos Islands with a group of biology educators. Dr. Mader was also a member of a group of biology educators who traveled to China to meet with their Chinese counterparts and exchange ideas about the teaching of modern-day biology.

Michael Windelspecht   As an educator, Dr. Windelspecht has taught introductory biology, genetics, and human genetics in the online, traditional, and hybrid environments at community colleges, comprehensive universities, and military institutions. For over a decade he served as the Introductory Biology Coordinator at Appalachian State University, where he directed a program that enrolled over 4,500 students annually. He was educated at Michigan State University and the University of South Florida. Dr. Windelspecht is also active in promoting the scientific literacy of secondary school educators. He has led multiple workshops on integrating water quality research into the science curriculum, and has spent several summers teaching Pakistani middle school teachers.

As an author, Dr. Windelspecht has published five reference textbooks and multiple print and online lab manuals. He served as the series editor for a ten-volume work on the human body. For years Dr. Windelspecht has been active in the development of multimedia resources for online and hybrid science classrooms. Along with his wife, Sandra, he owns a multimedia production company that actively develops and assesses the use of new technologies in the classroom.

Contributors

April Cognato serves as an Assistant Professor in the Department of Zoology at Michigan State University. She was educated at University of California–Davis, and at Texas A&M University where she earned a master's degree and Ph.D. in evolutionary biology. Dr. Cognato is an accomplished research biologist and educator. As an educator, Dr. Cognato designs and teaches introductory non-majors biology, majors biology, and genetics. In addition to her teaching assignments, Dr. Cognato has expertise in the integration of digital resources into education, and she authors fully online courses in genetics and evolution.

Dave Cox serves as Associate Professor of Biology at Lincoln Land Community College, in Springfield, Illinois. He was educated at Illinois College and Western Illinois University. As an educator, Professor Cox teaches introductory biology for non-majors in the traditional classroom format as well as in a hybrid format. He also teaches biology for majors, and marine biology and biological field studies as study-abroad courses in Belize. He serves as the Educational Director for the Sibun Education and Adventure Lodge, located in Belmopan, Belize.

Jeffrey Isaacson is an Associate Professor of Biology at Nebraska Wesleyan University, where he teaches courses in microbiology, immunology, and cell biology. He currently serves as Chair of the Undergraduate Curriculum Committee and Co-Chair of the General Education Revision Team at NWU. Dr. Isaacson was educated at Nebraska Wesleyan, Kansas State College of Veterinary Medicine, and Iowa State University. Previously, he worked as a small-animal veterinarian, and completed a post-doctoral fellowship in the Department of Immunology at the Mayo Clinic. As an author, Dr. Isaacson has served as a significant contributor and coauthor for the twelfth and thirteenth editions of Mader's *Inquiry Into Life*.

Ian Quitadamo has a dual appointment in Biological Sciences and Science Education at Central Washington University where he teaches courses in cell biology, genetics, biotechnology, and non-majors biology. In addition, he facilitates courses in teaching methodology for future science teachers and interdisciplinary content courses focused on alternative energy and sustainability. Dr. Quitadamo was educated at Washington State University where he earned an interdisciplinary Ph.D. in science, education, and technology. Dr. Quitadamo is a recipient of the Crystal Apple award for teaching excellence. He is a fourth-degree black belt in Kyokushin Karate and owns an academic consulting company.

Preface

Goals of the Eleventh Edition

The mission of Dr. Sylvia Mader's text, *Biology*, has always been to give students an understanding of biological concepts and a working knowledge of the scientific process. The concepts of biology and the methodology of science can be used to understand the particulars of new ideas or of a system, on any scale, from the cell to the biosphere.

In the twenty-first century, students are being exposed, almost on a daily basis, to exciting new discoveries and insights that, in many cases, were beyond our predictions even a few short years ago. It is our task, as instructors, not only to make these findings available to our students, but to enlighten students as to why these discoveries are important to their lives and society. At the same time, we must provide students with a firm foundation in those core principles on which biology is founded, and in doing so, provide them with the background to keep up with the many discoveries still to come. In this text, we integrate a tested, traditional learning system with modern digital and pedagogical approaches designed to stimulate and engage today's student.

The authors of the text identified several goals that guided them through the revision of *Biology*, Eleventh Edition:

1. build upon the strengths of the previous editions of the text,
2. introduce themes that connect the content of the text across multiple chapters,
3. deploy new pedagogical elements, including multimedia assets, to increase student interaction with the text,
4. develop a new series of digital assets designed to engage the modern student and provide assessment of learning outcomes.

Unit Themes

We recognize that scientific literacy is not based upon the memorization of a series of facts. Instead, learning is based on establishing associations and links between what, at first glance, appear to be diverse topics. The main themes we have chosen to emphasize include

- Evolution
- Nature of Science
- Biological Systems

The cover of this textbook, a gray wolf over a caribou skeleton with the Colorado mountain range in the background, was selected to reflect the importance of these three themes to the life sciences. By studying the historical evolutionary relationship of these species in their natural environment, biologists have been able to better understand the interdependence of the occupants of this ecosystem.

These themes are integrated into all aspects of the textbook, from the unit learning outcomes to the theme-based feature readings in the text. At the start of each chapter, "Following the Themes" introduces the relationship of the chapter's content to each of the themes. At the end of each chapter, "Connecting the Concepts with the Themes" not only reminds the student of the relationships between chapter content and the three core themes, but also acts as a prelude to topics in the next few chapters of the text. In essence, the themes act as the threads that unite the concepts throughout the text, enabling the student to see relationships from the molecular to ecosystem levels of biology.

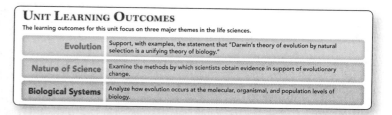

UNIT LEARNING OUTCOMES

The learning outcomes for this unit focus on three major themes in the life sciences.

Evolution	Support, with examples, the statement that "Darwin's theory of evolution by natural selection is a unifying theory of biology."
Nature of Science	Examine the methods by which scientists obtain evidence in support of evolutionary change.
Biological Systems	Analyze how evolution occurs at the molecular, organismal, and population levels of biology.

FOLLOWING the THEMES

UNIT 3 EVOLUTION — CHAPTER 15 DARWIN AND EVOLUTION

Evolution	Darwin's theory of natural selection proposes that all life on Earth descends from a common ancestor.
Nature of Science	A scientific theory, such as Darwin's theory of evolution by natural selection, is supported by abundant evidence.
Biological Systems	Evolution by natural selection comes about from interaction between the organism and its environment.

CONNECTING the CONCEPTS with the THEMES

Evolution

- All life on Earth has the same building blocks of inheritance, namely DNA, and shares in common many proteins essential to life.
- Vertebrate embryos develop the same set of features early in development, even though these features develop into very different structures in the adult.
- All animals have genes in common that control the development of the body plan. Hox genes orchestrate the development of the body plan in all animals.
- The Tree of Life project has collected information on hundreds of organisms. Anatomy, DNA, and behavior are used to trace all of life back to a single common ancestor.

Nature of Science

- Fossils provide us with a glimpse of life in the past. Transitional fossils have been discovered that support the theory of evolution via gradual changes to preexisting forms, such as alteration of hindlimbs in whale ancestors.
- At the level of the gene, small changes in the DNA sequence of switches that turn genes "on" and "off" can produce new features, such as the black spot on the wings of *Drosophila biarmipes* males that play a role in mating rituals.
- Evolution does not always occur over millions of years; it can be witnessed over a short period of time. On the Galápagos Islands, a shift in the average beak depth of ground finches can be observed as the weather changes.

Biological Systems

- Darwin proposed that natural selection is, in essence, a struggle for existence.
- Organisms tend to produce more offspring than can be supported by the environment.
- All living things require resources such as food, water, and mates in order to survive and reproduce—the intensity of competition is determined by the availability of resources in the environment.
- Natural selection operates on variation in populations. Change in the environment, both long and short term, can cause populations to evolve.

Evolution Theme

Evolutionary change, along with the mechanism of natural selection, represents the unifying concept of the biological sciences. In essence, biological evolution is the thread that links all life together. Throughout this textbook, feature readings on this theme both demonstrate the process of evolution and illustrate how scientists study and measure evolutionary change. By following this theme through the book, students develop a better understanding of why evolution is a dynamic process, and one that has shaped, and will continue to influence, life on this planet.

Nature of Science Theme

Through the processes of observation, the application of the scientific method, and the use of both inductive and deductive reasoning, scientists study life. To develop a deeper understanding of the biological sciences, students must appreciate that the study of life is a process, and that this process has application in their everyday lives. This theme focuses not only on how biologists do science, but also on the influences scientific inquiry has on our understanding of our world.

Biological Systems Theme

From cells to ecosystems, all life is interconnected. Increasingly, scientists are becoming aware that small changes in the chemical composition of an ecosystem can have a tremendous influence on the life in that ecosystem. This theme was chosen to provide a holistic approach to the study of the life sciences, by demonstrating not only that all life is interconnected, but also that the principles regulating life at the cellular level play a role in physiology and ecosystem biology as well.

Guided Chapter Tour

Pedagogy

Chapter Opener   Each chapter opener now includes two to three questions designed to integrate the subject matter into the chapter and stimulate class discussions.

Chapter Outline   The major sections that will be discussed in the chapter are listed for easy reference.

Before You Begin   The content of each chapter is linked with material from earlier in the text. The questions designate important topics that students should understand before proceeding into the chapter.

Following the Themes   The three themes are introduced at the beginning of each chapter, providing a summary of how the chapter content is linked to each of the themes.

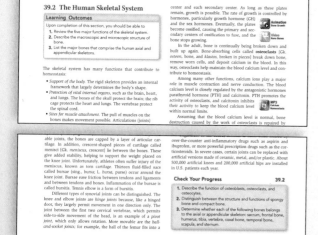

Learning Outcomes   The major goals of each section of the chapter are provided for the student. All learning outcomes may be fully assessed using McGraw-Hill Connect® Biology activities.

Media Integration   Media enhances the study of biology. Go to Connect or **www.mhhe.com/maderbiology11** to access the animations, videos, and MP3 files referenced throughout this book. Related quizzes are available through Connect® Biology for instructors to assign.

Check Your Progress   Each of the statements in this section is designed to help the student assess or apply their understanding of the material in the section.

Thematic Feature Readings

The author team has prepared feature readings to engage students in the three major themes of the textbook—evolution, nature of science, and biological systems. Each feature reading contains a series of "Questions to Consider" that may be used to stimulate classroom discussions.

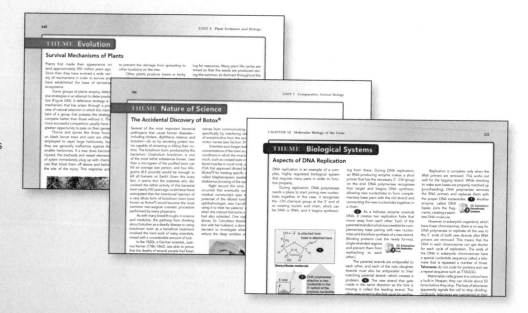

Connecting the Concepts with the Themes

At the end of each chapter, the authors have provided a brief synopsis of how each theme was integrated into the chapter. This further develops the themes as a series of learning threads, allowing the instructors and students to link related concepts more easily and facilitate the interconnectedness of the topics in the text.

Media Study Tools

This feature provides a link to the *Biology* website, which contains practice tests and other assets to assist the student in comprehending the topics of the chapter. Also present on this site are animations, videos, and multimedia assets that can help the student succeed in their study of biology. In many chapters, icons in this section direct the instructor to the presence of 3D animations that may be used in the classroom, or placed on course management systems, to further student comprehension of difficult topics.

The McGraw-Hill ConnectPlus® platform provides a media-rich eBook, interactive learning tools, and access to the LearnSmart system and Tegrity lecture-capture materials.

Summary

A concise overview of the chapter is provided in an easy-to-read paragraph style.

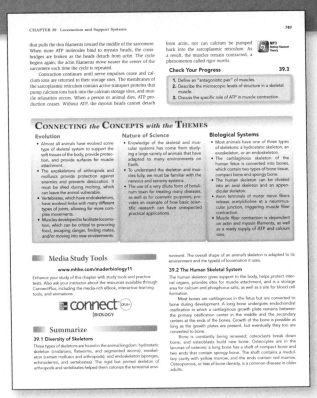

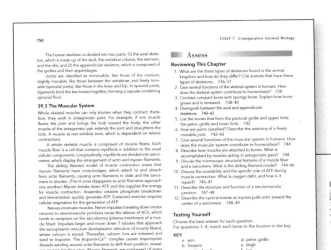

Key Terms

The glossary of this edition has been completely reworked, with a focus on reducing the key terms to those that are essential for student comprehension of the topic. All key terms in this section are linked to an updated glossary at the back of the text.

Reviewing This Chapter and Testing Yourself

Questions help students review material and prepare for tests. (See Appendix A for Testing Yourself answers.)

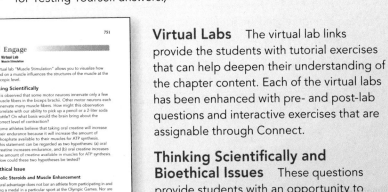

Virtual Labs

The virtual lab links provide the students with tutorial exercises that can help deepen their understanding of the chapter content. Each of the virtual labs has been enhanced with pre- and post-lab questions and interactive exercises that are assignable through Connect.

Thinking Scientifically and Bioethical Issues

These questions provide students with an opportunity to explore additional aspects of the chapter content, including bioethical issues and the design of experiments. These questions are ideal for classroom discussions.

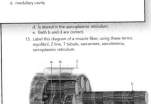

Art

Multi-Level Perspective
Illustrations depicting complex structures show macroscopic and microscopic views to help students see the relationships between increasingly detailed drawings.

Combination Art
Drawings of structures are paired with micrographs to provide the best of both perspectives: the realism of photos and the explanatory clarity of line drawings.

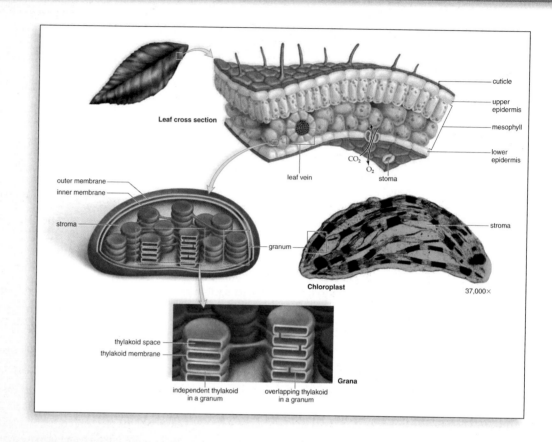

Leaf cross section

cuticle

upper epidermis

mesophyll

lower epidermis

CO_2

O_2

leaf vein

stoma

outer membrane

inner membrane

stroma

granum

stroma

Chloroplast

37,000×

thylakoid space

thylakoid membrane

independent thylakoid in a granum

overlapping thylakoid in a granum

Grana

Process Figures
Complex processes are broken down into a series of smaller steps that are easy to follow. Numbers guide readers through the process.

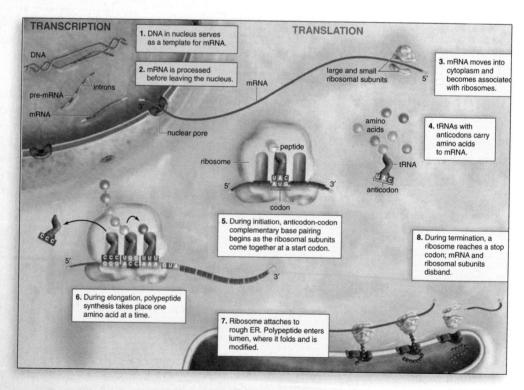

TRANSCRIPTION

TRANSLATION

DNA

1. DNA in nucleus serves as a template for mRNA.

2. mRNA is processed before leaving the nucleus.

pre-mRNA

introns

mRNA

nuclear pore

mRNA

large and small ribosomal subunits

3. mRNA moves into cytoplasm and becomes associated with ribosomes.

amino acids

4. tRNAs with anticodons carry amino acids to mRNA.

tRNA

anticodon

peptide

ribosome

codon

5. During initiation, anticodon-codon complementary base pairing begins as the ribosomal subunits come together at a start codon.

8. During termination, a ribosome reaches a stop codon; mRNA and ribosomal subunits disband.

6. During elongation, polypeptide synthesis takes place one amino acid at a time.

7. Ribosome attaches to rough ER. Polypeptide enters lumen, where it folds and is modified.

A Student's Guide to Media

Students can improve the effectiveness of their learning by integrating the digital assets of today's courses into their study habits. To facilitate this integration, the authors have prepared a video tutorial that not only outlines the role of each asset, but also explains to the student how to best utilize these materials for the comprehension of the course content. Included are descriptions on how both LearnSmart™ and Connect®, McGraw-Hill's flagship digital tools, can increase student preparedness for class as well as increase retention of difficult topics.

These assets may easily be uploaded into any course management system to provide your students with useful study tutorials.

Media Integration

As educators, the authors recognize that today's students are digital learners. Therefore, a significant new feature of this edition is the integration of media assets into the chapter content. Virtually every section of the textbook is now linked to MP3 files, animations of biological processes, and National Geographic and ScienCentral videos. In addition, McGraw-Hill's new 3D animations are integrated into the more difficult chapters of the text.

MP3 Files

These three- to five-minute audio files serve as a review of the material in the chapter, and they also assist the student in the pronunciation of scientific terms.

Animations

Drawing on McGraw-Hill's vast library of animations, the authors have selected animations that will enhance the student's understanding of complex biological processes.

3D Animations

For topics such as photosynthesis and cellular respiration, McGraw-Hill has produced a series of dynamic 3D animations that may be used both as presentation tools in the classroom, and as mini-tutorials that can be assigned within Connect or your course management system.

Videos

Two different types of movies are integrated into this edition of the text. The ScienCentral videos are short news clips on advances in the sciences. The National Geographic videos provide students with a glimpse of the complexity of life that normally would not be possible in the classroom.

Virtual Labs

These simulated experiments serve as excellent tutorials, allowing students to explore the topics covered in select chapters of the text.

Teaching and Learning Tools

McGraw-Hill Higher Education and Blackboard Have Teamed Up

The Best of Both Worlds

Blackboard®, the Web-based course-management system, has partnered with McGraw-Hill to better allow students and faculty to use online materials and activities to complement face-to-face teaching. Blackboard features exciting social learning and teaching tools that foster more logical, visually impactful, and active learning opportunities for students. You'll transform your closed-door classrooms into communities where students remain connected to their educational experience 24 hours a day.

This partnership allows you and your students access to McGraw-Hill's Connect® and McGraw-Hill Create™ right from within your Blackboard course—all with one single sign-on.

Not only do you get single sign-on with Connect and Create, you also get deep integration of McGraw-Hill content and content engines right in Blackboard. Whether you're choosing a book for your course or building Connect assignments, all the tools you need are right where you want them—inside of Blackboard.

Gradebooks are now seamless. When a student completes an integrated Connect assignment, the grade for that assignment automatically (and instantly) feeds your Blackboard grade center.

McGraw-Hill and Blackboard can now offer you easy access to industry leading technology and content, whether your campus hosts it or we do. Be sure to ask your local McGraw-Hill representative for details.

McGraw-Hill LearnSmart™

McGraw-Hill LearnSmart™ is available as an integrated feature of McGraw-Hill Connect® Biology and provides students with a GPS (Guided Path to Success) for your course. Using artificial intelligence, LearnSmart intelligently assesses a student's knowledge of course content through a series of adaptive questions. It pinpoints concepts the student does not understand and maps out a personalized study plan for success. This innovative study tool also has features that allow instructors to see exactly what students have accomplished and a built-in assessment tool for graded assignments. Visit the following site for a demonstration.
www.mhlearnsmart.com

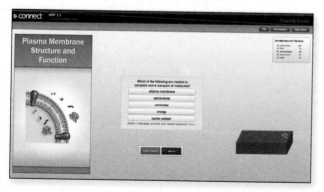

McGraw-Hill Connect® Biology

McGraw-Hill Connect® Biology provides online presentation, assignment, and assessment solutions. It connects your students with the tools and resources they'll need to achieve success.

With Connect Biology, you can deliver assignments, quizzes, and tests online. A robust set of questions and activities are presented and aligned with the textbook's learning outcomes. As an instructor, you can edit existing questions and author entirely new problems. Track individual student performance—by question, assignment, or in relation to the class overall—with detailed grade reports. Integrate grade reports easily with Learning Management Systems (LMS), such as WebCT and Blackboard—and much more.

ConnectPlus Biology provides students with all the advantages of Connect Biology, plus 24/7 online access to an eBook. This media-rich version of the book is available through the McGraw-Hill Connect platform and allows seamless integration of text, media, and assessments.

To learn more, visit
www.mcgrawhillconnect.com

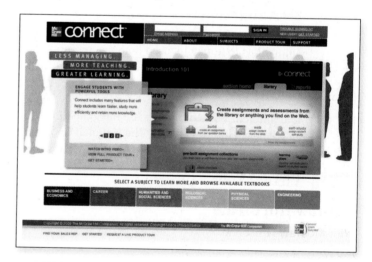

My Lectures—Tegrity®

McGraw-Hill Tegrity® records and distributes your class lecture with just a click of a button. Students can view anytime/anywhere via computer, iPod, or mobile device. It indexes as it records your PowerPoint® presentations and anything shown on your computer so students can use keywords to find exactly what they want to study. Tegrity is available as an integrated feature of McGraw-Hill Connect Biology and as a standalone.

Animations for a New Generation

Dynamic, 3D animations of key biological processes bring an unprecedented level of control to the classroom. Innovative features keep the emphasis on teaching rather than entertaining.

An options menu lets you control the animation's level of detail, speed, length, and appearance, so you can create the experience you want.

Draw on the animation using the whiteboard pen to highlight important areas.

The scroll bar lets you fast forward and rewind while seeing what happens in the animation, so you can start at the exact moment you want.

A scene menu lets you instantly jump to a specific point in the animation.

Pop-ups add detail at important points and help students relate the animation back to concepts from lecture and the textbook.

A complete visual summary at the end of the animation reminds students of the big picture.

Animation topics include: Cellular Respiration, Photosynthesis, Molecular Biology of the Gene, DNA Replication, Cell Cycle and Mitosis, Membrane Transport, and Plant Transport.

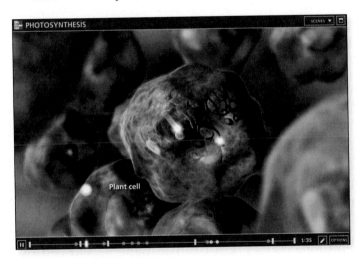

McGraw-Hill Create™

With **McGraw-Hill Create™**, you can easily rearrange chapters, combine material from other content sources, and quickly upload content you have written, like your course syllabus or teaching notes. Find the content you need in Create by searching through thousands of leading McGraw-Hill textbooks. Arrange your book to fit your teaching style. Create even allows you to personalize your book's appearance by selecting the cover and adding your name, school, and course information. Order a Create book and you'll receive a complimentary print review copy in 3–5 business days or a complimentary electronic review copy (eComp) via e-mail in minutes. Go to www.mcgrawhillcreate.com today and register to experience how McGraw-Hill Create empowers you to teach *your* students *your* way.

www.mcgrawhillcreate.com

Presentation Tools

Everything you need for outstanding presentations in one place.

www.mhhe.com/maderbiology11

FlexArt Image Powerpoints—including every piece of art that has been sized and cropped specifically for superior presentations, as well as labels that can be edited and flexible art that can be picked up and moved on key figures. Also included are tables, photographs, and unlabeled art pieces.

Lecture PowerPoints with Animations—animations illustrating important processes are embedded in the lecture material.

Animation PowerPoints—animations only are provided in PowerPoint.

Labeled JPEG Images—full-color digital files of all illustrations that can be readily incorporated into presentations, exams, or custom-made classroom materials.

Base Art Image Files—unlabeled digital files of all illustrations.

Presentation Center

In addition to the images from your book, this online digital library contains photos, artwork, animations, and other media from an array of McGraw-Hill textbooks.

Computerized Test Bank

A comprehensive bank of test questions is provided within a computerized test bank powered by McGraw-Hill's flexible electronic testing program, **EZ Test Online.** A new tagging scheme allows you to sort questions by Bloom's difficulty level, learning outcome, topic, and section. With EZ Test Online, instructors can select questions from multiple McGraw-Hill test banks or author their own, and then either print the test for paper distribution or give it online.

Instructor's Manual

The instructor's manual contains chapter outlines, lecture enrichment ideas, and discussion questions.

Laboratory Manual

The *Biology Laboratory Manual* is written by Dr. Sylvia Mader. Every laboratory has been written to help students learn the fundamental concepts of biology and the specific content of the chapter to which the lab relates, as well as gain a better understanding of the scientific method.

Companion Website

www.mhhe.com/maderbiology11

The Mader *Biology* companion website allows students to access a variety of free digital learning tools that include

- Chapter-level quizzing
- Animations and videos
- Vocabulary flashcards
- Virtual labs

Overview of Content Changes to *Biology*, Eleventh Edition

Chapter 1: A View of Life. This chapter introduces the three themes, Evolution, the Nature of Science, and Biological Systems, that will act as the focal points for the text. The virtual lab "Dependent and Independent Variables" has been added to the end of the chapter.

Unit 1: The Cell

Chapter 2: Basic Chemistry. The pH scale (Fig. 2.13) has been revised to provide students with a better understanding of acid/base relationships. The Biological Systems feature has been enhanced to include graphs of U.S. acid rain–causing emissions. **Chapter 3: The Chemistry of Organic Molecules** contains a new Nature of Science feature on fats in the diet. **Chapter 4: Cell Structure and Function.** The graphic on the endosymbiotic theory has been enhanced to include a more detailed explanation of the evolutionary significance of each stage of the process. **Chapter 5: Membrane Structure and Function** now contains links to the 3D animation "Membrane Transport." **Chapter 6: Metabolism: Energy and Enzymes** has been linked to the virtual lab "Enzyme Controlled Reactions." The 3D animation "Photosynthesis" has been integrated into **Chapter 7: Photosynthesis**. **Chapter 8: Cellular Respiration** includes links to the 3D animation "Cellular Respiration" and contains updated explanations on theoretical versus actual ATP yields.

Unit 2: Genetic Basis of Life

Chapter 9: The Cell Cycle and Cellular Reproduction has been enhanced by links to the 3D animation "Cell Cycle and Mitosis" and the virtual lab "Cell Reproduction." **Chapter 10: Meiosis and Sexual Reproduction** has been revised to include a more detailed explanation of chromosomes, including bivalent and tetrad combinations. In **Chapter 11: Mendelian Patterns of Inheritance,** an additional figure (Fig. 11.5) has been added to enhance an understanding of how the 3:1 ratio was developed using Mendel's data. The Science Focus box on Mendel's Laws and Meiosis is now integrated directly into the discussion of Mendel's laws. Two virtual labs, "Punnett Squares" and "Sex-Linked Traits," are now linked to this chapter as tutorials. Figure 12.5 of **Chapter 12: Molecular Biology of the Gene** has been revised to better indicate the directionality of the DNA molecule. In addition, Figure 12.6 has been modified to illustrate the role of RNA polymerase in DNA replication. Two 3D animations, "DNA replication" and "Molecular Biology of the Gene," have been added to the chapter. **Chapter 13: Regulation of Gene Expression** now contains a revised discussion of how sRNA molecules influence gene expression and new illustrations on the role of sRNAs in the cell (Fig. 13.9) and the action of proteasomes (Fig. 13.10). **Chapter 14: Biotechnology and Genomics** now starts with a new chapter opener on biotechnology-produced fuels. Also included is a more detailed explanation of intergenic sequences. The virtual labs "Knocking out Genes," "Gene Splicing," and "Classifying Using Biotechnology" have been linked to the chapter.

Unit 3: Evolution

Chapter 15: Darwin and Evolution has been substantially revised to better present the historical basis behind the theory of evolution to students. The chapter begins with a new article on *Tiktaalik*. New figures include Lamarck's inheritance of acquired characteristics (Fig. 15.2), the role of wingspots in *Drosophila* species (Fig. 15.11), and transitional fossils (Figs. 15.12 and 15.13). The material on Alfred Wallace is now integrated into the main text, and the evolution theme is enforced by an evolution feature reading on the "Tree of Life Project." The chapter also includes material on the criticisms of evolution. **Chapter 16: How Populations Evolve** begins with a new article on HIV. The discussion of microevolution now focuses on the peppered moth and a discussion of allele frequencies, and it includes new figures (Figs. 16.1, 16.2, 16.4, and 16.7) and a summary table (Table 16.1) to enforce these concepts. New figures on directional (Fig. 16.10) and disruptive (Fig. 16.11) selection have been added. A new Nature of Science feature reading on achromatopsia and the Pingelapese population reinforces the fact that microevolution occurs in humans. **Chapter 17: Speciation and Macroevolution** starts with a new article on micro-frogs. The chapter has been revised to include more detailed discussions on the various concepts of species, including new figures (Figs. 17.1 and 17.3). The cichlids of Africa are the focus of a new figure (Fig. 17.12) on convergent evolution. Two new feature readings are included: one of how to interpret phylogenetic trees, and a second on the genetic basis of beak shape in Galápagos finches. **Chapter 18: Origin and History of Life** has been reorganized to make a clear connection between chemical and biological evolution (Fig. 18.1). This includes more detailed discussions of the various hypotheses involved in these processes (Figs. 18.4 and 18.5). **Chapter 19: Taxonomy, Systematics, and Phylogeny** has been reorganized so that the material on the three-domain system (Section 19.2) occurs prior to the discussion of phylogeny (Section 19.3). The chapter starts with a new article on how systematics may be used in crime investigations. Figure 19.3 provides an enhanced visual explanation of classification categories, and Figure 19.5 illustrates the relationship between phylogeny, classification, and traits. A new Nature of Science feature reading examines the concept of DNA barcoding.

Unit 4: Microbiology and Evolution

Chapter 20: Viruses, Bacteria, and Archaea now begins with an article on the H1N1 virus. The structure of the influenza virus has been updated in Figure 20.1. New figures on emerging diseases (Fig. 20.5) and the features of prokaryotic cells (Fig. 20.7) have been provided. **Chapter 21: Protist Evolution and Diversity** now contains a focus on neglected tropical diseases and contains an opening article and Biological Systems feature reading on this topic. The chapter format reflects the current concept of protist "supergroups" (Table 21.1, Fig. 21.1). **Chapter 22: Fungi Evolution and Diversity** begins with an article on the use of fungal products as a form of green packaging material. Figure 22.1 now relates the fungi to the other eukaryotic supergroups. Table 22.1 has been enhanced to provide the key features of the fungal phyla.

Unit 5: Plant Evolution and Biology

Chapter 23: Plant Evolution and Diversity starts with a new article on plant diversity. A new Evolution feature on the evolutionary history of maize has been added, and the chapter includes a link to the virtual lab "Classifying Using Biotechnology." In **Chapter 24: Flowering Plants: Structure and Organization,** a new Evolution feature examines the survival mechanisms of plants. A second Nature of Science feature reading explores the many uses of bamboo in society. **Chapter 25: Flowering Plants: Nutrition and Transport** begins with a new article on artificially colored flowers. The 3D animation "Plant Transport" is integrated throughout the chapter. The chapter is linked to the virtual lab "Plant Transpiration." **Chapter 26: Flowering Plants: Control of Growth Responses** contains a new table (26.1) summarizing the major plant hormones. In **Chapter 27: Flowering Plants: Reproduction,** the Evolution feature reading has been enhanced to provide a more evolutionary perspective.

Unit 6: Animal Evolution and Diversity

For **Chapter 28: Invertebrate Evolution,** a new opener examines the fad of tapeworm diets. A new Evolution feature reading examines the genetic basis of the animal body plan. The phylogenetic tree of animals (Fig. 28.4) has been upgraded. Two virtual labs, "Earthworm Dissection" and "Classifying Arthropods," have been linked to the chapter. **Chapter 29: Vertebrate Evolution** includes a revised phylogenetic tree for the chordates (Fig. 29.4). The material on amphibian evolution (Section 29.4) has been updated to reflect recent advances in the field. The evolution of mammals (Section 29.6) now includes a timeline of important events (Fig. 29.19) and a summary table of important characteristics (Table 29.1). A new table (29.2) summarizes the major orders of placental mammals. **Chapter 30: Human Evolution** begins with a new article on the evolutionary relationship of Neandertals and *Homo sapiens*. The chapter and figures (30.4) have been upgraded to reflect changes in classification terminology. The chapter now includes a Nature of Science reading on how scientists are using comparative genomics to study similarities between the chimp and human genomes. The material on the ardipithecines and Cro-magnon *Homo sapiens* has been enhanced to focus on the significance of these groups.

Unit 7: Comparative Animal Biology

Chapter 31: Animal Organization and Homeostasis contains a new Nature of Science feature on regenerative medicine. The chapter is now linked to the virtual lab "Virtual Frog Dissection." **Chapter 32: Circulation and Cardiovascular Systems** now starts with an article on the consequences of aortic dissection. A new Nature of Science feature on the use of horseshoe crabs in cardiovascular medicine is included in the chapter. Two virtual labs, "Earthworm Dissection" and "Virtual Frog Dissection," are now linked to this chapter. **Chapter 33: The Lymphatic and Immune Systems** now begins with an article on severe combined immunodeficiency syndrome. The chapter also features a new section (33.1) on the evolution of immune systems. In addition, a new Nature of Science feature on cancer vaccines has been added to the chapter. **Chapter 34: Digestive Systems and Nutrition** begins with a new article on ruminant mammals. The chapter also includes a new Nature of Science feature on treating obesity and is linked to three virtual labs, "Earthworm Dissection," "Virtual Frog Dissection," and "Nutrition." **Chapter 35: Respiratory Systems** begins with a new article on the evolution of the diving response. The chapter also includes a new Nature of Science feature on artificial lung technology. **Chapter 36: Body Fluid Regulation and Excretory Systems** includes a new Nature of Science feature reading on the misuse of erythropoietin in sports and links to two virtual labs, "Earthworm Dissection" and "Virtual Frog Dissection." **Chapter 37: Neurons and Nervous Systems** includes a new opening article and Nature of Science feature on Parkinson disease. **Chapter 38: Sense Organs** begins with a new article on sensory perception in pit vipers. The chapter has been reorganized to include more details on sensory receptors (Section 38.1) and the somatic senses (Section 38.5). A new Nature of Science feature examines the development of artificial retinas. **Chapter 39: Locomotion and Support Systems** contains a new Nature of Science feature on diluted botulinum toxin and links to the "Muscle Stimulation" virtual lab. **Chapter 40: Hormones and Endocrine Systems** contains new images on Cushing syndrome (Fig. 40.14). **Chapter 41: Reproductive Systems** has been updated to include recent statistics on the prevalence of sexually transmitted diseases. The chapter is linked to the virtual lab "Virtual Frog Dissection." **Chapter 42: Animal Development and Aging** has been revised to include a focus on the aging process (Section 32.4).

Unit 8: Behavior and Ecology

The virtual lab "Mealworm Behavior" has been linked to **Chapter 43: Behavioral Ecology.** In **Chapter 44: Population Ecology,** a new chapter opener has been introduced that focuses on the impact of introduced species. Figure 44.7 has been modified to improve the explanation of the process of exponential growth. The comparison of the environmental impact of developed versus undeveloped countries has been enhanced by changes to Figure 44.17. The chapter is linked to the virtual lab "Population Biology." **Chapter 45: Community and Ecosystem Ecology** now opens with an article on wolves in the Yellowstone National Park, thus providing a link to the cover of the textbook. The chapter includes a new Nature of Science feature reading on global climate change and a link to the "Model Ecosystems" virtual lab. **Chapter 46: Major Ecosystems of the Biosphere** starts with a new article on the migration patterns of Canada geese. The Biological Systems feature "Biomagnification of Mercury" is new to this chapter. **Chapter 47: Conservation of Biodiversity** contains a new Nature of Science feature on floodplain restoration in the Illinois River system.

Acknowledgments

Dr. Sylvia Mader represents one of the icons of science education. Her dedication to her students, coupled to her clear, concise writing style, has benefited the education of thousands of students over the past three decades. It is an honor to continue her legacy, and to bring her message to the next generation of students. I have been privileged to work with the ultimate team of science educators—April Cognato, Dave Cox, Jeff Isaacson, and Ian Quitadamo. These dedicated and talented individuals have made a significant contribution to this text, and my abilities as a science educator have been enhanced by our teamwork. Together, we have striven to ensure that the material was written and illustrated in the familiar Mader style.

Many dedicated and talented individuals assisted in the development of *Biology*. I am very grateful for the help of so many professionals at McGraw-Hill who were involved in bringing this book to fruition. In particular, let me thank Rose Koos, the developmental editor who lent her exemplary talents, project management skills, advice, and most of all, patience, to all those who worked on this text. The biology publisher is Michael Hackett, who steadfastly encouraged and supported all aspects of this project. The desire of my editor, Eric Weber, to impact the lives of our students, is evident throughout this text. The project manager, Jayne Klein, faithfully and carefully steered the book through the publication process. Tamara Maury, the marketing manager, tirelessly promoted the text and educated the sales reps on its message.

The design of the book is the result of the creative talents of Laurie Janssen and many others who assisted in deciding the appearance of each element in the text. I was very lucky to have Jody Larson as my copyeditor, and Lauren Timmer and Dawnelle Krouse as proofreaders. Lachina Publishing Services produced this textbook, in the process emphasizing pedagogy and beauty to arrive at the best presentation on the page. Lori Hancock and Evelyn Jo Johnson did a superb job of finding just the right photographs and micrographs.

Who I am, as an educator and an author, is a direct reflection of what I have learned from my students. Education is a two-way street, and it is my honest opinion that both my professional and personal life have been enriched by my interactions with my students. They have encouraged me to learn more, teach better, and never stop questioning the world around me. I would also like to acknowledge my wife, Sandra. She has never wavered in her patience and support of my endeavors.

Michael Windelspecht, Ph.D.
Blowing Rock, NC

The eleventh edition of *Biology* would not have the same excellent quality without the input of these contributors and those of the many contributors and reviewers listed below.

McGraw-Hill's 360° Development Process is an ongoing, never-ending, market-oriented approach to building accurate and innovative print and digital products. It is dedicated to continual large-scale and incremental improvement driven by multiple customer feedback loops and checkpoints. This is initiated during the early planning stages of our new products, and intensifies during the development and production stages, then begins again upon publication in anticipation of the next edition.

This process is designed to provide a broad, comprehensive spectrum of feedback for refinement and innovation of our learning tools, for both student and instructor. The 360° Development Process includes market research, content reviews, course- and product-specific symposia, accuracy checks, and art reviews. We appreciate the expertise of the many individuals involved in this process.

Ancillary Authors

Connect Question Bank: Krissy Johnson, Alex James, and Betsy Harris, *Appalachian State University*; Sandy Windelspecht, *Ricochet Creative Productions*; **Test Bank:** Dave Cox, *Lincoln Land Community College*; **Lecture Outlines:** Felicia Scott, *Macomb Community College*; **Instructor's Manual:** Andrea Thomason, *Roxbury Community College*; **Practice Tests:** Deborah Dardis, *Southeastern Louisiana University*; **eBook Quizzes:** Eric Rabitoy, *Citrus College*; **LearnSmart Authors:** Patrick Galliart, *North Iowa Area Community College*; Sylvester Allred, *Northern Arizona University*; Tammy Atchison, *Pitt Community College*; Dena Berg, *Tarrant County College*; Joy Brookshire, *Kennesaw State University*; Jeffrey Isaacson, *Nebraska Wesleyan University*; **LearnSmart Reviewers:** Jill Nugent, *University of North Texas*; Murad Odeh, *South Texas College*

Eleventh Edition Reviewers

Nina Abubakari, *Wayne County Community College District*
LaQuetta B. Anderson, *Grambling State University*
Rachele Arrigoni-Restrepo, *New York City College of Technology*
Dennis Bakewicz, *New York City College of Technology*
Sarah Bales, *Moraine Valley Community College*
Marilyn Banta, *Texas State University–San Marcos*
Isaac Barjis, *New York City College of Technology*
Morgan Benowitz-Fredericks, *Bucknell University*

Gretchen Bernard, *Moraine Valley Community College*
Karen Bledsoe, *Western Oregon University*
Lois Borek, *Georgia State University*
Anthony Botyrius, *York College of Pennsylvania*
Denise Chung, *Long Island University–Brooklyn*
Pamela Anderson Cole, *Shelton State Community College*
David Cox, *Lincoln Land Community College*
Deborah Dardis, *Southeastern Louisiana University*
Diane Day, *Georgia State University*
Lewis Deaton, *University of Louisiana at Lafayette*
Helen Donis-Keller, *Franklin W. Olin College of Engineering*
C. Craig Farquhar, *University of Texas–Austin*
Jennifer Foulk, *Montgomery County Community College*
Cynthia M. Galloway, *Texas A&M University–Kingsville*
Raul Galvan, *South Texas College*
Kristine Garner, *University of Arkansas–Fort Smith*
Michele B. Garrett, *Guilford Technical Community College–Jamestown*
Sandra Gibbons, *Moraine Valley Community College*
Melanie Glasscock, *Wallace State Community College*
Andrew Goliszek, *North Carolina A&T State University*
Lula (Gwen) Gordon, *Wayne County Community College–Downtown*
Susan Michele Green, *Texas State University–San Marcos*
Robert Greene, *Cranbrook Kingswood School*
Bradley L. Griggs, *Piedmont Technical College*
Tray Hamil, *University of South Alabama*
Jerrie Hanible, *Southeastern Louisiana University*
Chris Haynes, *Shelton State Community College*
Jennifer (Wearly) Hooks, *Winthrop University*
Brenda Hunzinger, *Lake Land College*
Felix Ifeanyi, *Grambling State University*
David Jarrell, *Armstrong Atlantic State University*

Ragupathy Kannan, *University of Arkansas–Fort Smith*
Carolyn Lebsack, *Linn-Benton Community College*
Stephen G. Lebsack, *Linn-Benton Community College*
Julian Lee, *University of Miami*
Tammy J. Liles, *Bluegrass Community and Technical College*
Lynne Lohmeier, *Mississippi Gulf Coast Community College*
Chintamani S. Manish, *Midland Lutheran College*
Jessica Mayfield, *Southeastern Louisiana University*
Mark Meade, *Jacksonville State University*
Sandra L. Millward, *The Christ College of Nursing and Health Sciences*
Scott Murdoch, *Moraine Valley Community College*
Joseph Murray, *Blue Ridge Community College*
Necia M. Nicholas, *Calhoun Community College*
Therese Poole, *Georgia State University*
Michelle Priest, *Los Angeles Valley College*
Kirstin Purcell, *Saint Paul College*
Jason Raymond, *University of California–Merced*
Pamela Riddell, *Macomb Community College–Center Campus*
Abraham Saraya, *New York City College of Technology*
Dale Smoak, *Piedmont Technical College*
Phillip Snider, *Gadsden State Community College*
Lisa Strain, *Northeast Lakeview College*
Diane Teter, *South Texas College*
Mark X. VanCura, *Cape Fear Community College*
Van Wheat, *South Texas College*
Leslie Whiteman-Richardson, *Virginia State University*
Ann R. Witham, *University of Cincinnati, Raymond Walters College*
Frank Wray, *University of Cincinnati, Raymond Walters College*

Contents

Preface   iv

1 A View of Life   1
1.1   How to Define Life   2
1.2   Evolution, the Unifying Concept of Biology   6
1.3   How the Biosphere Is Organized   9
1.4   The Process of Science   11

UNIT 1 The Cell   20

2 Basic Chemistry   21
2.1   Chemical Elements   22
2.2   Molecules and Compounds   26
2.3   Chemistry of Water   28
2.4   Acids and Bases   32

3 The Chemistry of Organic Molecules   37
3.1   Organic Molecules   38
3.2   Carbohydrates   41
3.3   Lipids   45
3.4   Proteins   49
3.5   Nucleic Acids   54

4 Cell Structure and Function   60
4.1   Cellular Level of Organization   61
4.2   Prokaryotic Cells   65
4.3   Introducing Eukaryotic Cells   67
4.4   The Nucleus and Ribosomes   70
4.5   The Endomembrane System   72
4.6   Other Vesicles and Vacuoles   75
4.7   The Energy-Related Organelles   76
4.8   The Cytoskeleton   78

5 Membrane Structure and Function   85
5.1   Plasma Membrane Structure and Function   86
5.2   Passive Transport Across a Membrane   91
5.3   Active Transport Across a Membrane   95
5.4   Modification of Cell Surfaces   98

6 Metabolism: Energy and Enzymes   104
6.1   Cells and the Flow of Energy   105
6.2   Metabolic Reactions and Energy Transformations   107
6.3   Metabolic Pathways and Enzymes   109
6.4   Organelles and the Flow of Energy   113

7 Photosynthesis   119
7.1   Photosynthetic Organisms   120
7.2   The Process of Photosynthesis   122
7.3   Plants as Solar Energy Converters   124
7.4   Plants as Carbon Dioxide Fixers   128
7.5   Other Types of Photosynthesis   130

8 Cellular Respiration   135
8.1   Cellular Respiration   136
8.2   Outside the Mitochondria: Glycolysis   138
8.3   Outside the Mitochondria: Fermentation   140
8.4   Inside the Mitochondria   142
8.5   Metabolic Pool   147

UNIT 2 Genetic Basis of Life   152

9 The Cell Cycle and Cellular Reproduction   153
9.1   The Cell Cycle   154
9.2   Mitosis and Cytokinesis   157
9.3   The Cell Cycle and Cancer   163
9.4   Prokaryotic Cell Division   166

10 Meiosis and Sexual Reproduction   171
10.1   Halving the Chromosome Number   172
10.2   Genetic Variation   174
10.3   The Phases of Meiosis   176
10.4   Meiosis Compared to Mitosis   177
10.5   The Cycle of Life   180
10.6   Changes in Chromosome Number and Structure   183

11 Mendelian Patterns of Inheritance   192
11.1   Gregor Mendel   193
11.2   Mendel's Laws   195
11.3   Extending the Range of Mendelian Genetics   205

12 Molecular Biology of the Gene   214
12.1   The Genetic Material   215
12.2   Replication of DNA   220
12.3   The Genetic Code of Life   223
12.4   First Step: Transcription   225
12.5   Second Step: Translation   228
12.6   Structure of the Eukaryotic Chromosome   233

13 Regulation of Gene Expression 237
13.1 Prokaryotic Regulation 238
13.2 Eukaryotic Regulation 241
13.3 Gene Mutations 247

14 Biotechnology and Genomics 254
14.1 DNA Cloning 255
14.2 Biotechnology Products 258
14.3 Gene Therapy 260
14.4 Genomics 261

Appendices
A Answer Key A-1
B Tree of Life A-16

Glossary G-1
Credits C-1
Index I-1

Readings

THEME Evolution

Living with Klinefelter Syndrome   186
Copy Number Variations   266
The Anatomy of Speciation   309
Carboniferous Forests   435
Evolutionary History of Maize   438

Survival Mechanisms of Plants   448
Plants and Their Pollinators   506
Evolution of the Animal Body Plan   524
Sexual Selection in Male Bowerbirds   832
Interactions and Coevolution   867

THEME Biological Systems

The Interconnectedness of Water, Plants, and People   33
How Cells Talk to One Another   90
Tropical Rain Forest Destruction and Climate Change   127
Aspects of DNA Replication   221
Flu Pandemic   370
African Sleeping Sickness   398
Deadly Fungi   411
The Uses of Bryophytes   425
The Uses of Ferns   429
The Uses of Pines   431

The Concept of Water Potential   474
Biocultural Evolution Began with *Homo*   582
AIDS and Opportunistic Infections   638
Drugs of Abuse   710
Preventing Transmission of STDs   789
Preventing and Testing for Birth Defects   807
When a Population Grows Too Large   850
Biomagnification of Mercury   903

THEME Nature of Science

The Benefits and Limitations of Statistical Studies   13
Everyone Needs a Little Fat, Right?   45
Microscopy Today   63
Enzyme Inhibitors Can Spell Death   112
Fermentation Helps Produce Numerous Food Products   141
The G_1 Checkpoint   156
Reproductive and Therapeutic Cloning   162
Testing for Genetic Disorders   204
Alternative mRNA Splicing in Disease   246
DNA Microarray Technology   264
The Tree of Life: 150 Years of Support for the Theory of Evolution by Natural Selection   282
Inbreeding in Populations   300
Genetic Basis of Beak Shape in Darwin's Finches   318
DNA Barcoding of Life   352
The Many Uses of Bamboo   458
Plants Can Clean Up Toxic Messes   470
Arabidopsis Is a Model Organism   492
Vertebrates and Human Medicine   560
A Genomic Comparison of *Homo sapiens* and Chimpanzees   574

Regenerative Medicine   594
New Information About Preventing Cardiovascular Disease   617
How Horseshoe Crabs Save Human Lives   622
Cancer Vaccines: Becoming a Reality   640
New Approaches to Treating Obesity   655
Artificial Lung Technology   676
Misuse of Erythropoietin in Sports   689
An Accidental Experimental Model for Parkinson Disease   706
Artificial Retinas Come into Focus   725
The Accidental Discovery of Botox   746
Identifying Insulin as a Chemical Messenger   766
Preimplantation Genetic Diagnosis   786
Do Animals Have Emotions?   827
Island Biogeography Pertains to Biodiversity   862
Global Climate Change   879
Wildlife Conservation and DNA   889
Overexploitation of Asian Turtles   917
Emiquon Floodplain Restoration   921

The tuatara (*Sphenodon punctatus*).

1

A View of Life

CHAPTER OUTLINE

1.1 How to Define Life 2

1.2 Evolution, the Unifying Concept of Biology 6

1.3 How the Biosphere Is Organized 9

1.4 The Process of Science 11

At first glance, the tuatara of New Zealand appears to be just another lizard. However, recently, scientists have realized that this reptile, which may live as long as 80 years, is something very special. The tuatara represents a living fossil, a remnant of the type of reptiles that lived before the age of the dinosaurs hundreds of millions of years ago. Yet, despite being very old, the tuatara continues to mystify scientists. Some studies suggest that some traits in tuataras are evolving at rates faster than any other vertebrate animal, allowing scientists to use this organism as a test case for how species evolve over long periods of time.

The Earth hosts a wide variety of ecosystems, from which spring a mind-boggling diversity of life, including the tuataras. Even so, all Earth's organisms, regardless of form, are united by a number of common characteristics, such as the need to acquire nutrients, the ability to respond to a changing environment, and to reproduce their own kind. Incredibly, even organisms as diverse as the tuatara and a human being share similar characteristics, including a common chemistry and genetic code. As you read this chapter, reflect on the staggering diversity of life on Earth and on the many ties that bind even the most diverse organisms, from bacteria to the titan arum to humans. It is through these ties that our fates are linked together in the web of life.

As you read through this chapter, think about the following questions

1. What are the general characteristics shared by all living organisms?

2. What is the relationship between evolutionary change and the study of biology?

3. How do scientists use the scientific method to study living organisms?

FOLLOWING *the* THEMES

CHAPTER 1 A VIEW OF LIFE	
Evolution	The study of biology is based on the principles of evolutionary change and the adaptations of species to their environments.
Nature of Science	Scientists make observations, form hypotheses, and conduct experiments in an attempt to understand the principles of life.
Biological Systems	From communities of organisms to individual cells, all life is based on atoms and molecules.

1.1 How to Define Life

Learning Outcomes

Upon completion of this section, you should be able to
1. Distinguish between the levels of biological organization.
2. Identify the basic characteristics of life.

Biology is the scientific study of life. Life on Earth takes on a staggering variety of forms, often functioning and behaving in ways strange to humans. For example, gastric-brooding frogs swallow their embryos and give birth to them later by throwing them up! Some species of puffballs, a type of fungus, are capable of producing trillions of spores when they reproduce. Fetal sand sharks kill and eat their siblings while still inside their mother. Some *Ophrys* orchids look so much like female bees that male bees try to mate with them. Octopuses and squid have remarkable problem-solving abilities despite a small brain. Some bacteria live their entire life in 15 minutes, while bristle-cone pine trees outlive ten generations of humans. Simply put, from the deepest oceanic trenches to the upper reaches of the atmosphere, life is plentiful and diverse.

Figure 1.1 illustrates the major groups of living organisms. From left to right, bacteria are widely distributed, tiny, microscopic organisms with a very simple structure. A *Paramecium* is an example of a microscopic protist. Protists are larger in size and more complex than bacteria. The other organisms in Figure 1.1 are easily seen with the naked eye. They can be distinguished by how they get their food. A morel is a fungus that digests its food externally. A sunflower is a photosynthetic plant that makes its own food, and an octopus is an aquatic animal that ingests its food.

Although life is tremendously diverse, it may be defined by several basic characteristics that are shared by all organisms. Like nonliving things, organisms are composed of chemical elements. Also, organisms obey the same laws of chemistry and physics that govern everything within the universe. The characteristics of life, however, will provide great insight into the unique nature of organisms and will help us distinguish living things from nonliving things.

MP3
Life
Characteristics

Living Things Are Organized

The levels of organization depicted in Figure 1.2 begin with atoms, which are the basic units of matter. Atoms combine with other atoms of the same or different elements to form molecules. The **cell,** which is composed of a variety of molecules working together, is the basic unit of structure and function of all living things. Some cells, such as **unicellular** paramecia, live independently. Other cells, for example, the colonial alga *Volvox*, cluster together in microscopic colonies.

Many living things are **multicellular,** meaning they contain more than one cell. In multicellular organisms, similar cells combine to form a tissue; nerve tissue is a common tissue in animals. Tissues make up organs, as when various tissues combine to form the brain. Organs work together in systems; for example, the brain works with the spinal cord and a network of nerves to form the nervous system. Organ systems are joined together to form a complete living thing, or organism, such as an elephant.

The levels of biological organization extend beyond the individual organism. All the members of one species in a particular area belong to a population. A nearby forest may have a population of gray squirrels and a population of white oaks, for example. The populations of various animals and plants in the forest make up a community. The community of populations interacts with the physical environment (water, land, climate) to form an ecosystem. Collectively, all the Earth's ecosystems make up the biosphere.

Emergent Properties

Each level of biological organization builds upon the previous level and is more complex. Moving up the hierarchy, each level acquires new **emergent properties** that are determined by the interactions between the individual parts. When cells are broken down into bits of membrane and liquids, these parts themselves cannot carry out the business of living. For example, you can take apart a lump of coal, rearrange the pieces in any order, and still have a lump of coal with the same function as the original one. But, if you slice apart a living plant and rearrange the pieces, the plant is no longer functional as a complete plant, because it depends on the exact order of those pieces.

Bacteria   *Paramecium*   Morel   Sunflower   Octopus

Figure 1.1 Diversity of life.   Biology is the scientific study of life. Many diverse forms of life are found on planet Earth.

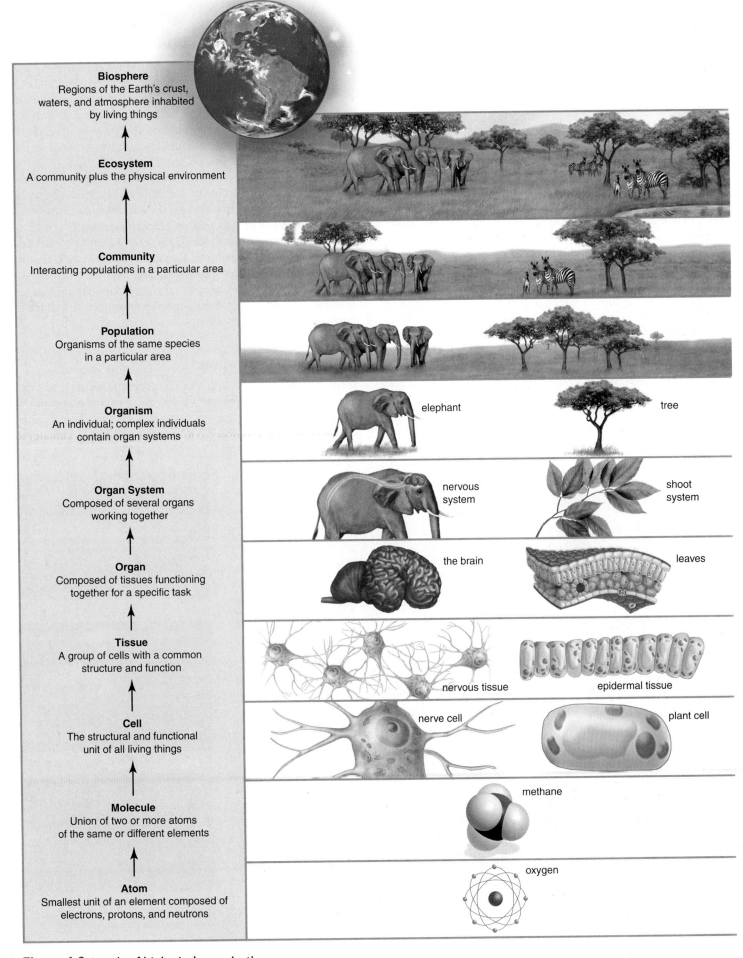

Biosphere
Regions of the Earth's crust, waters, and atmosphere inhabited by living things

Ecosystem
A community plus the physical environment

Community
Interacting populations in a particular area

Population
Organisms of the same species in a particular area

Organism
An individual; complex individuals contain organ systems

elephant

tree

Organ System
Composed of several organs working together

nervous system

shoot system

Organ
Composed of tissues functioning together for a specific task

the brain

leaves

Tissue
A group of cells with a common structure and function

nervous tissue

epidermal tissue

Cell
The structural and functional unit of all living things

nerve cell

plant cell

Molecule
Union of two or more atoms of the same or different elements

methane

Atom
Smallest unit of an element composed of electrons, protons, and neutrons

oxygen

Figure 1.2 Levels of biological organization.

In the living world, the whole is indeed more than the sum of its parts. The emergent properties created by the interactions between levels of biological organization are new, unique characteristics. These properties are governed by the laws of chemistry and physics.

Living Things Acquire Materials and Energy

Living things cannot maintain their organization or carry on life's activities without an outside source of nutrients and energy (Fig. 1.3). Food provides nutrients, which are used as building blocks or for energy. **Energy** is the capacity to do work, and it takes work to maintain the organization of the cell and the organism. When cells use nutrient molecules to make their parts and products, they carry out a sequence of chemical reactions. The term **metabolism** [Gk. *meta*, change] encompasses all the chemical reactions that occur in a cell.

The ultimate source of energy for nearly all life on Earth is the Sun. Plants and certain other organisms are able to capture solar energy and carry on **photosynthesis,** a process that transforms solar energy into the chemical energy of organic nutrient molecules. All life on Earth acquires energy by metabolizing nutrient molecules made by photosynthesizers. This applies even to plants themselves.

Living Things Maintain Homeostasis

To survive, it is imperative that an organism maintain a state of biological balance, or **homeostasis** [Gk. *homoios*, like, and *stasis*, the same]. For life to continue, temperature, moisture level, acidity, and other physiological factors must remain within the tolerance range of the organism. Homeostasis is maintained by systems that monitor internal conditions and make routine and necessary adjustments.

Organisms have intricate feedback and control mechanisms that do not require any conscious activity. These mechanisms may be controlled by one or more tissues themselves, or by the nervous system. When you are studying and forget to eat lunch, your liver releases stored sugar to keep blood sugar levels within normal limits. Many organisms depend on behavior to regulate their internal environment. In animals, these behaviors are controlled by the nervous system, and are usually not consciously controlled. For example, a lizard may raise its internal temperature by basking in the sun, or cool down by moving into the shade.

Living Things Respond

Living things interact with the environment as well as with other living things. Even unicellular organisms can respond to

Figure 1.3 Acquiring nutrients and energy. **a.** An eagle ingesting fish. **b.** A human eating an apple. **c.** A cypress tree capturing sunlight. **d.** An amoeba engulfing food. **e.** A fungus feeding on a tree. **f.** A bison eating grass.

their environment. In some, the beating of microscopic hairs or, in others, the snapping of whiplike tails moves them toward or away from light or chemicals. Multicellular organisms can manage more complex responses. A vulture can detect a carcass a kilometer away and soar toward dinner. A monarch butterfly can sense the approach of Fall and begin its flight south where resources are still abundant.

The ability to respond often results in movement: the leaves of a land plant turn toward the Sun, and animals dart toward safety. Appropriate responses help ensure survival of the organism and allow it to carry on its daily activities. All together, these activities are termed the behavior of the organism. Organisms display a variety of behaviors as they maintain homeostasis and search and compete for energy, nutrients, shelter, and mates. Many organisms display complex communication, hunting, and defense behaviors.

Living Things Reproduce and Develop

Life comes only from life. Every type of living thing can **reproduce,** or make another organism like itself. Bacteria, protists, and other unicellular organisms simply split in two. In most multicellular organisms, the reproductive process begins with the pairing of a sperm from one partner and an egg from the other partner. The union of sperm and egg, followed by many cell divisions, results in an immature stage, which grows and develops through various stages to become the adult.

An embryo develops into a humpback whale or a purple iris because of a blueprint inherited from its parents. The instructions, or blueprint, for an organism's metabolism and organization are encoded in genes. The **genes,** which contain specific information for how the organism is to be ordered, are made of long molecules of DNA (deoxyribonucleic acid). DNA has a shape resembling a spiral staircase with millions of steps. Housed within this spiral staircase is the genetic code that is shared by all living things.

When living things reproduce, their genes are passed on to the next generation. Random combinations of sperm and egg, each of which contains a unique collection of genes, ensure that the new individual has new and different characteristics. The DNA of organisms, over time, also undergoes mutations (changes) that may be passed on to the next generation. These events help to create a staggering diversity of life, even within a group of otherwise identical organisms. Sometimes, organisms inherit characteristics that allow them to be more suited to their way of life.

Living Things Have Adaptations

Adaptations [L. *ad*, toward, and *aptus*, suitable] are modifications that make organisms better able to function in a particular environment. For example, penguins are adapted to an aquatic existence in the Antarctic. An extra layer of downy feathers is covered by short, thick feathers that form a waterproof coat. Layers of blubber also keep the birds warm in cold water. Most birds have forelimbs proportioned for

Figure 1.4 Living Things Have Adaptations.   Penguins have evolved complex behaviors, such as sliding across ice to conserve energy, to adapt to their environment.

flying, but penguins have stubby, flattened wings suitable for swimming. Their feet and tails serve as rudders in the water, but the flat feet also allow them to walk on land. Penguins also have many behavioral adaptations to living in the Antarctic. Penguins often slide on their bellies across the snow in order to conserve energy when moving quickly (Fig. 1.4). Their eggs—one or at most two—are carried on the feet, where they are protected by a pouch of skin. This also allows the birds to huddle together for warmth while standing erect and incubating eggs.

From penguins to fire ants, life on Earth is very diverse because over long periods of time, organisms respond to ever-changing environments by developing new adaptations. These adaptations are unintentional, but they provide the framework for evolutionary change. **Evolution** [L. *evolutio*, an unrolling] includes the way in which populations of organisms change over the course of many generations to become more suited to their environments. All living things have the capacity to evolve, and the process of evolution constantly reshapes every species on the planet, potentially providing a way for organisms to persist, despite a changing environment.

Check Your Progress   1.1

1. Distinguish between an ecosystem and a population in the levels of biological organization.
2. List the common characteristics of all living organisms.
3. Explain how adaptations relate to evolutionary change.

1.2 Evolution, the Unifying Concept of Biology

Learning Outcomes

Upon completion of this section you should be able to

1. Distinguish between the three domains of life.
2. Explain the relationship between the process of natural selection and evolutionary change.

Table 1.1 Levels of Classification

Category	Human	Corn
Domain	Eukarya	Eukarya
Kingdom	Animalia	Plantae
Phylum	Chordata	Anthophyta
Class	Mammalia	Monocotyledones
Order	Primates	Commelinales
Family	Hominidae	Poaceae
Genus	*Homo*	*Zea*
Species*	*H. sapiens*	*Z. mays*

*To specify an organism, you must use the full binomial name, such as Homo sapiens.

Despite diversity in form, function, and lifestyle, organisms share the same basic characteristics. As mentioned, they are all composed of cells organized in a similar manner. Their genes are composed of DNA, and they carry out the same metabolic reactions to acquire energy and maintain their organization. The unity of living things suggests that they are descended from a common ancestor—the first cell or cells.

An evolutionary tree is like a family tree (Fig. 1.5). Just as a family tree shows how a group of people have descended from one couple, an evolutionary tree traces the ancestry of life on Earth to a common ancestor. One couple can have diverse children, and likewise a population can be a common ancestor to several other groups, each adapted to a particular set of environmental conditions. In this way, over time, diverse life-forms have arisen. Evolution may be considered the unifying concept of biology because it explains so many aspects of biology, including how living organisms arose from a single ancestor.

Organizing Diversity

Because life is so diverse, it is helpful to group organisms into categories. **Taxonomy** [Gk. *tasso*, arrange, and *nomos*, usage] is the discipline of identifying and grouping organisms according to certain rules. Taxonomy makes sense out of the bewildering variety of life on Earth and is meant to provide valuable insight into evolution. **Systematics** is the study of the evolutionary relationships between organisms. As systematists learn more about living things, the taxonomy often changes. DNA technology is now widely used

by systematists to revise current information and to discover previously unknown relationships between organisms.

Several of the basic classification categories, or *taxa*, going from least inclusive to most inclusive, are **species, genus, family, order, class, phylum, kingdom,** and **domain** (Table 1.1). The least inclusive category, species [L. *species*, model, kind], is defined as a group of interbreeding individuals. Each successive classification category above species contains more types of organisms than the preceding one. Species placed within one genus share many specific characteristics and are the most closely related, while species placed in the same kingdom share only general characteristics with one another. For example, all species in the genus *Pisum* look

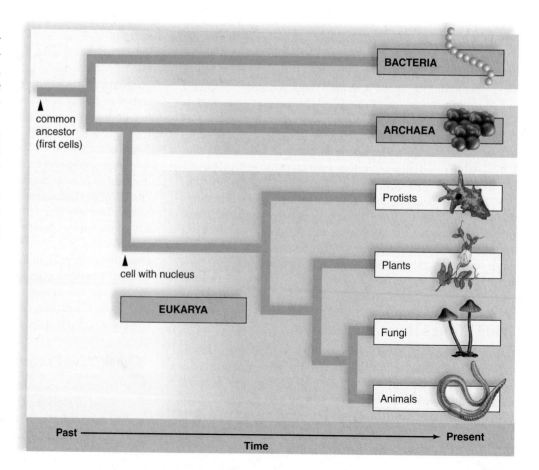

Figure 1.5 Evolutionary tree of life. As existing organisms change over time, they give rise to new species. Evolutionary studies show that all living organisms arose from a common ancestor about 4 billion years ago. Domain Archaea and domain Bacteria include the prokaryotes. Domain Eukarya includes both unicellular and multicellular organisms that possess a membrane-bounded nucleus.

common ancestor (first cells)

cell with nucleus

BACTERIA

ARCHAEA

Protists

Plants

EUKARYA

Fungi

Animals

Past ←——————————————→ Present

Time

pretty much the same—that is, like pea plants—but species in the plant kingdom can be quite varied, as is evident when we compare grasses to trees. Species placed in different domains are the most distantly related.

Domains

Biochemical evidence suggests that there are only three domains: **domain Bacteria, domain Archaea,** and **domain Eukarya.** Figure 1.5 shows how the domains are believed to be related. Both domain Bacteria and domain Archaea may have evolved from the first common ancestor soon after life began. These two domains contain the **prokaryotes,** which lack the membrane-bounded nucleus found in the **eukaryotes** of domain Eukarya. However, archaea organize their DNA differently than bacteria, and their cell walls and membranes are chemically more similar to eukaryotes than to bacteria. So, the conclusion is that eukarya split off from the archaeal line of descent.

▶ **Animation**
Three Domains

Prokaryotes are structurally simple but metabolically complex. Archaea (Fig. 1.6) can live in aquatic environments that lack oxygen or are too salty, too hot, or too acidic for most other organisms. Perhaps these environments are similar to those of the primitive Earth, and archaea (Gk. *archae*, ancient) are the least evolved forms of life, as their name implies. Bacteria (Fig. 1.7) are variously adapted to living almost anywhere—in the water, soil, and atmosphere, as well as on our skin and in our mouths and large intestines.

Taxonomists are in the process of deciding how to categorize archaea and bacteria into kingdoms. Domain Eukarya, on the other hand, contains four major groups of organisms (Fig. 1.8). **Protists,** which now comprise a number of kingdoms, range from unicellular forms to a few multicellular ones. Some are photosynthesizers, and some must acquire their food. Common protists include algae, the protozoans, and the water molds. Figure 1.5 shows that plants, fungi, and animals most likely evolved from

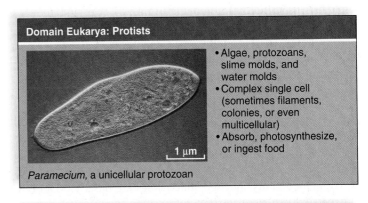

Domain Eukarya: Protists
- Algae, protozoans, slime molds, and water molds
- Complex single cell (sometimes filaments, colonies, or even multicellular)
- Absorb, photosynthesize, or ingest food

1 μm

Paramecium, a unicellular protozoan

Domain Eukarya: Kingdom Fungi
- Molds, mushrooms, yeasts, and ringworms
- Mostly multicellular filaments with specialized, complex cells
- Absorb food

Amanita, a mushroom

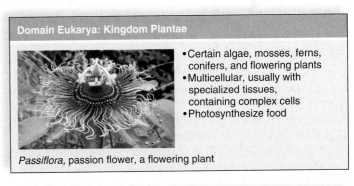

Domain Eukarya: Kingdom Plantae
- Certain algae, mosses, ferns, conifers, and flowering plants
- Multicellular, usually with specialized tissues, containing complex cells
- Photosynthesize food

Passiflora, passion flower, a flowering plant

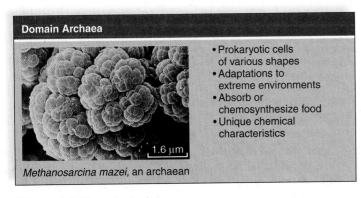

Domain Archaea
- Prokaryotic cells of various shapes
- Adaptations to extreme environments
- Absorb or chemosynthesize food
- Unique chemical characteristics

1.6 μm

Methanosarcina mazei, an archaean

Figure 1.6 Domain Archaea.

Domain Eukarya: Kingdom Animalia
- Sponges, worms, insects, fishes, frogs, turtles, birds, and mammals
- Multicellular with specialized tissues containing complex cells
- Ingest food

Vulpes, a red fox

Figure 1.8 Domain Eukarya.

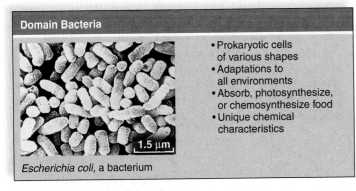

Domain Bacteria
- Prokaryotic cells of various shapes
- Adaptations to all environments
- Absorb, photosynthesize, or chemosynthesize food
- Unique chemical characteristics

1.5 μm

Escherichia coli, a bacterium

Figure 1.7 Domain Bacteria.

protists. **Plants** (kingdom Plantae) are multicellular photosynthetic organisms. Example plants include azaleas, zinnias, and pines. Among the **fungi** (kingdom Fungi) are the familiar molds and mushrooms that, along with bacteria, help decompose dead organisms. **Animals** (kingdom Animalia) are multicellular organisms that must ingest and process their food. Aardvarks, jellyfish, and zebras are representative animals.

Scientific Name

Biologists use **binomial nomenclature** [L. *bi*, two, and *nomen*, name] to assign each living thing a two-part name called a scientific name. For example, the scientific name for mistletoe is *Phoradendron tomentosum*. The first word is the genus, and the second word is the species designation (or *specific epithet*) of each species within a genus. The genus may be abbreviated (e.g., *P. tomentosum*) and if the species has not been determined, it may simply be indicated with a generic abbreviation (e.g., *Phoradendron* sp.). Scientific names are universally used by biologists to avoid confusion. Common names tend to overlap and often differ depending on locality and the language of a particular country. But scientific names are based on Latin, a universally used language that not too long ago was well known by most scholars.

Evolution Is Common Descent with Modification

The phrase "common descent with modification" sums up the process of evolution because it means that as descent occurs from common ancestors, so do modifications that cause organisms to be adapted to their environment. Through many observations and experiments, Charles Darwin came to the conclusion that **natural selection** was the process that made modification—that is, adaptation—possible.

Natural Selection

During the process of natural selection, some aspect of the environment selects which traits are more apt to be passed on to the next generation. The selective agent can be an abiotic agent (part of the physical environment, such as altitude) or it can be a biotic agent (part of the living environment, such as a deer). Figure 1.9 shows how the dietary habits of deer might eventually affect the characteristics of the leaves of a particular land plant.

Mutations fuel natural selection because mutation introduces variations among the members of a population. In Figure 1.9, a plant species generally produces smooth leaves, but a mutation occurs that causes one plant to have leaves that are covered with small extensions or "hairs." The plant with hairy leaves has an advantage because the deer (the selective agent) prefer to eat smooth leaves and not hairy leaves. Therefore, the plant with hairy leaves survives best and produces more seeds than most of its neighbors. As a result, generations later most plants of this species produce hairy leaves.

As with this example, Darwin realized that although all individuals within a population have the potential to reproduce, not all do so with the same success. Prevention of reproduction can run the gamut from an inability to capture resources, as when

Some plants within a population exhibit variation in leaf structure.

Deer prefer a diet of smooth leaves over hairy leaves. Plants with hairy leaves reproduce more than other plants in the population.

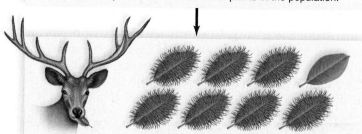

Generations later, most plants within the population have hairy leaves, as smooth leaves are selected against.

Figure 1.9 Natural selection. Natural selection selects for or against new traits introduced into a population by mutations. Over many generations, selective forces such as competition, predation, and the physical environment alter the makeup of a population, favoring those more suited to the environment and lifestyle.

long-necked, but not short-necked, giraffes can reach their food source, to an inability to escape being eaten because long legs, but not short legs, can carry an animal to safety.

Whatever the example, it can be seen that living things with advantageous traits can produce more offspring than those that lack them. In this way, living things change over time, and these changes are passed on from one generation to the next. Over long periods of time, the introduction of newer, more advantageous traits into a population may drastically reshape a species. Natural selection tends to sculpt a species to fit its environment and lifestyle and can create new species from existing ones. The end result is the diversity of life classified into the three domains of life (see Fig. 1.5).

Video Finches—Natural Selection

Check Your Progress 1.2

1. List the levels of taxonomic classification from most inclusive to least inclusive.
2. Describe the differences that might be used to distinguish the various kingdoms of domain Eukarya.
3. Explain how natural selection results in new adaptations within a species.

1.3 How the Biosphere Is Organized

Learning Outcomes

Upon completion of this section you should be able to

1. Distinguish among populations, communities, ecosystems, and the biosphere.
2. Recognize the importance of maintaining biodiversity.

The organization of life extends beyond the individual organism to the **biosphere,** the zone of air, land, and water at the surface of the Earth where organisms exist (see Fig. 1.2). Individual organisms belong to a **population,** which is all the members of a species within a particular area. The populations of a **community** interact among themselves and with the physical environment (e.g., soil, atmosphere, and chemicals), thereby forming an **ecosystem.**

Figure 1.10 depicts a grassland inhabited by populations of rabbits, mice, snakes, hawks, and various types of land plants. These populations exchange gases with and give off heat to the atmosphere. They also take in water from and give off water to the physical environment. In addition, populations interact by forming food chains in which one population feeds on another. Mice feed on plants and seeds, snakes feed on mice, and hawks feed on rabbits and snakes, for example. Interactions between the various food chains make up a food web.

Ecosystems are characterized by chemical cycling and energy flow, both of which begin when photosynthetic plants, aquatic algae, and some bacteria take in solar energy and inorganic nutrients to produce food in the form of organic nutrients. The gray arrows in Figure 1.10 represent chemical cycling—chemicals move from one population to another in a food chain, until with death and decomposition, inorganic nutrients are returned to living plants once again. The yellow to red arrows represent energy flow. Energy flows from the Sun through plants and other members of the food chain as one population feeds on another. With each transfer some energy is lost as heat. Eventually, all the energy taken in by photosynthesizers has dissipated into the atmosphere. Because energy flows and does not cycle, ecosystems could not stay in existence without a constant input of solar energy and the ability of photosynthesizers to absorb it.

Video
Tallgrass Prairie Ecology

The Human Population

Humans possess the unique ability to modify existing ecosystems, which can greatly upset their natural nutrient cycles. When an ecosystem's natural energy flow has been disrupted by eliminating food sources for other animal populations even the human population can eventually suffer harm. Humans clear forests or grasslands to grow crops; later, they build houses on what was once farmland; and finally, they convert small towns into cities. Coastal ecosystems are most vulnerable. As

Figure 1.10 Grassland, a terrestrial ecosystem. In an ecosystem, chemical cycling (gray arrows) and energy flow (yellow to red arrows) begin when plants use solar energy and inorganic nutrients to produce food for themselves and directly or indirectly for all other populations in the ecosystem. As one population feeds on another, chemicals and energy are passed along a food chain. With each transfer, some energy is lost as heat. Eventually, all the energy dissipates. With the death and decomposition of organisms, inorganic nutrients are returned to the environment and eventually may be used by plants.

heat

solar energy

heat

heat

heat

heat

heat

heat

WASTE MATERIAL, DEATH, AND DECOMPOSITION

⇨ Chemical cycling
⇨ Energy flow

they are developed, humans send sediments, sewage, and other pollutants into the sea. Human activities destroy valuable coastal wetlands, which serve as protection against storms and as nurseries for a myriad of invertebrates and vertebrates.

Biodiversity

The two most biologically diverse ecosystems—tropical rain forests and coral reefs—are home to many organisms. These ecosystems are also threatened by human activities. The canopy of the tropical rain forest alone supports a variety of organisms including orchids, insects, and monkeys. Coral reefs, which are found just offshore of the continents and islands of the Southern Hemisphere, are built up from calcium carbonate skeletons of sea animals called corals. Reefs provide a habitat for many animals, including jellyfish, sponges, snails, crabs, lobsters, sea turtles, moray eels, and some of the world's most colorful fishes (Fig. 1.11a). Like tropical rain forests, coral reefs are severely threatened as the human population increases in size. Some reefs are 50 million years old, and yet in just a few decades, human activities have destroyed an estimated 25% of all coral reefs and seriously degraded another 30% (Fig. 1.11b). At this rate, nearly three-quarters could be destroyed within 40 years. Similar statistics are available for tropical rain forests.

Video
Coral Reef Ecosystems

Destruction of healthy ecosystems has many unintended effects. For example, we depend on them for food, medicines, and various raw materials. Draining the natural wetlands of the Mississippi and Ohio rivers and the construction of levees has worsened flooding problems, making once fertile farmland undesirable. The destruction of South American rain forests has killed many species that may have yielded the next miracle drug and has also decreased the availability of many types of lumber.

We are only now beginning to realize that we depend on ecosystems even more for the services they provide. Just as chemical cycling occurs within a single ecosystem, so all ecosystems keep chemicals cycling throughout the entire biosphere. The workings of ecosystems ensure that the environmental conditions of the biosphere are suitable for the continued existence of humans. And several studies show that ecosystems cannot function properly unless they remain biologically diverse.

Biodiversity is the total number and relative abundance of species, the variability of their genes, and the different ecosystems in which they live. The present biodiversity of our planet has been estimated to be as high as 15 million species, and so far, less than 2 million have been identified and named. **Extinction** is the death of a species or larger classification category. It is estimated that presently we are losing as many as 400 species per day due to human activities and that as much as 38% of all species, including most primates, birds, and amphibians, may be in danger of extinction before the end of the century. Many biologists are alarmed about the present rate of extinction and hypothesize it may eventually rival the rates of the five mass extinctions that have occurred during our planet's history. The last mass extinction, about 65 million years ago, caused many plant and animal species, including the dinosaurs, to become extinct.

It would seem that the primary bioethical issue of our time is preservation of ecosystems. Just as a native fisherman who assists in overfishing a reef is doing away with his own food source, so are we as a society contributing to the destruction of our home, the biosphere. If instead we adopt a conservation ethic that preserves the biosphere, we would help ensure the continued existence of our own species.

Check Your Progress   1.3

1. Explain the relationship between a population, a community, and an ecosystem.
2. Describe some unintentional ways in which human activities affect ecosystems.
3. Discuss why ecosystems with high biodiversity might be more vulnerable to destruction by human activities.

a. Healthy coral reef

Figure 1.11 Coral reef, a marine ecosystem.   a. Coral reefs, a type of ecosystem found in tropical seas, contain many diverse forms of life, a few of which are shown here. **b.** Various human activities have caused catastrophic damage to this coral reef off the coast of Florida, as shown over the course of 19 years. Preserving biodiversity is a modern-day challenge of great proportions.

1975 Minimal coral death

1985 Some coral death with no fish present

1995 Coral bleaching with limited chance of recovery

2004 Coral is black from sedimentation; bleaching still evident

b.

1.4 The Process of Science

The process of science pertains to the study of biology. Biology consists of many disciplines and areas of specialty because life has numerous aspects. Some biological disciplines are cytology, the study of cells; anatomy, the study of structure; physiology, the study of function; botany, the study of plants; zoology, the study of animals; genetics, the study of heredity; and ecology, the study of the interrelationships between organisms and their environment.

Religion, aesthetics, ethics, and science are all ways in which human beings seek order in the natural world. Science differs from these other ways of knowing and learning because the scientific process uses the **scientific method,** a standard series of steps used in gaining new knowledge that is widely accepted among scientists. The steps of the scientific method are often applicable to other situations, and begin with observation (Fig. 1.12).

Observation

Scientists believe that nature is orderly and measurable—that natural laws, such as the law of gravity, do not change with time, and that a natural event, or **phenomenon,** can be understood more fully through **observation**—a formal way of "seeing what happens."

Scientists use all of their senses in making observations. The behavior of chimpanzees can be observed through visual means, the disposition of a skunk can be observed through olfactory means, and the warning rattles of a rattlesnake provide auditory information of imminent danger. Scientists also extend the ability of their senses by using instruments; for example, the microscope enables us to see objects that could never be seen by the naked eye. Finally, scientists may expand their understanding even further by taking advantage of the knowledge and experiences of other scientists. For instance, they may look up past studies at the library or on the Internet, or they may write or speak to others who are researching similar topics.

Hypothesis

After making observations and gathering knowledge about a phenomenon, a scientist uses inductive reasoning to formulate a possible explanation. **Inductive reasoning** occurs whenever a person uses creative thinking to combine isolated facts into a cohesive whole. In some cases, chance alone may help a scientist arrive at an idea.

One famous case pertains to the antibiotic penicillin, which was discovered in 1928. While examining a petri dish of bacteria that had become contaminated with the mold *Penicillium*,

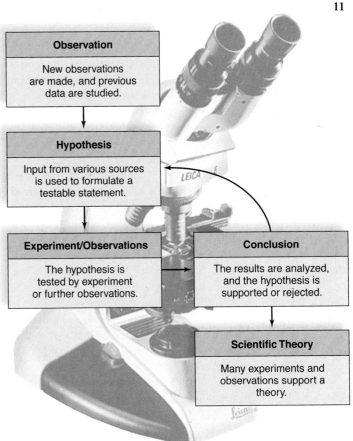

Figure 1.12 Flow diagram for the scientific method. On the basis of new and/or previous observations, a scientist formulates a hypothesis, which is then tested by further observations and/or experiments. Experiments provide data that either support or do not support the hypothesis. The return arrow indicates that a scientist often chooses to retest the same hypothesis or to test a related hypothesis. Conclusions from many different but related experiments may lead to the development of a scientific theory.

Alexander Flemming observed an area that was free of bacteria. Flemming, an early expert on antibacterial substances, reasoned that the mold might be producing an antibacterial compound.

We call such a possible explanation for a natural event a **hypothesis.** A hypothesis is not merely a guess; rather, it is an informed statement that can be tested in a manner suited to the processes of science.

All of a scientist's past experiences, no matter what they might be, have the potential to influence the formation of a hypothesis. But a scientist considers only hypotheses that can be tested. Moral and religious beliefs, while very important in the lives of many people, differ between cultures and through time, and these may not be scientifically testable.

Experiments, Observations, and Data

Scientists often perform an **experiment,** which is a series of procedures, to test a hypothesis. To determine how to test a hypothesis, a scientist uses deductive reasoning. **Deductive reasoning** involves "if, then" logic. In designing the experiment, the scientist may make a **prediction,** or an expected outcome, based on knowledge of the factors in the experiment.

The manner in which a scientist intends to conduct an experiment is called the **experimental design.** A good experimental design ensures that scientists are examining the contribution of a specific variable, called the **experimental variable**, to the observation. To ensure that the results will be meaningful, an experiment contains both test groups and a **control** group. A test group is exposed to the environmental variable, but the control group is not. If the control groups and test groups show the same results, the experimenter knows that the hypothesis predicting a difference between them is not supported.

In some cases, scientists may use a **model** as a representation of the actual object because altering the actual object may be physically impossible, very expensive, or morally questionable. Later in this section, a scientist uses bluebird models because it would have been impossible to get live birds to cooperate. As other examples, computer models are used to decide how human activities may affect climate, because of expense, ethical concerns, and physical limitations. Scientists often use mice instead of humans for medical research because of ethical concerns. Bacteria are used in much genetic research because they are inexpensive to grow and reproduce very quickly. Although these models are usually relevant and give useful information, they are themselves still hypotheses in need of testing to ensure that they are valid representations.

The results of an experiment are referred to as the **data.** Data should be observable and objective, rather than subjective. Mathematical data are often displayed in the form of a graph or table. Often, these results include a **standard deviation**, a statistical analysis that is a measure of how much the data in the experiment varies. Many studies, such as the one discussed in the Nature of Science feature on page 13, rely on statistical data.

An Example

As a hypothetical example, let's say an investigator wants to know if eating onions can prevent women from getting osteoporosis (weak bones). The scientist conducts a survey asking women about their onion-eating habits and then correlates this data with the condition of their bones. Other scientists critiquing this study would want to know: How many women were surveyed? How old were the women? What were their exercise habits? What proportion of the diet consisted of onions? And what criteria were used to determine the condition of their bones?

If the investigators conclude that eating onions does protect a woman from osteoporosis, then other scientists might want to know the statistical probability of error. The probability of error is a mathematical calculation based on the conditions and methods of the experiment. If the results are significant at a 0.30 level, then the probability that the correlation is incorrect is 30% or less. (This would be considered a high probability of error.) The greater the variance in the data, the greater the probability of error.

Even if this study had a low probability of error, it would be considered hypothetical until scientists identified one or more active components in onions that have a direct biochemical or physiological effect on bones. Therefore, scientists must be skeptics who always pressure one another to continue investigating a particular topic.

Conclusion

Scientists must analyze the data in order to reach a **conclusion** as to whether the hypothesis is supported or not (see Fig. 1.12). Because science progresses, the conclusion of one experiment can lead to the hypothesis for another experiment, as represented by the return arrow in Figure 1.12. Results that do not support one hypothesis can often help a scientist formulate another hypothesis to be tested.

Scientists report their findings in scientific journals so that their methodology and data are available to other scientists for critique. Experiments and observations must be repeatable—that is, the reporting scientist and any scientist who repeats the experiment must get the same results, or else the data are suspect.

Scientific Theory

The ultimate goal of science is to understand the natural world in terms of **scientific theories,** which are concepts that join together well-supported and related hypotheses. In ordinary speech, the word *theory* refers to a speculative idea. In contrast, a scientific theory is supported by a broad range of observations, experiments, and data often from a variety of disciplines. Some of the basic theories of biology are:

Theory	Concept
Cell	All organisms are composed of cells, and new cells come only from preexisting cells.
Homeostasis	The internal environment of an organism stays relatively constant—within a range that is protective of life.
Gene	Organisms contain coded information that dictates their form, function, and behavior.
Ecosystem	Organisms are members of populations, which interact with each other and the physical environment within a particular locale.
Evolution	All living things have a common ancestor, but each is adapted to a particular way of life.

As stated earlier, the theory of evolution is the unifying concept of biology because it pertains to many different aspects of living things. For example, the theory of evolution enables scientists to understand the history of living things, and the anatomy, physiology, and embryological development of organisms. Even behavior can be described through evolution, as we shall see in a study discussed later in this chapter.

The theory of evolution has been a fruitful scientific theory, meaning that it has helped scientists generate new hypotheses. Because this theory has been supported by so many observations and experiments for over 100 years, some biologists refer to the **principle** of evolution, a term sometimes used for theories that are generally accepted by an overwhelming number of scientists. The term **law** instead of principle is preferred by some. For instance, in a subsequent chapter concerning energy relationships, we will examine the laws of thermodynamics.

THEME Nature of Science

The Benefits and Limitations of Statistical Studies

Many of the studies published in scientific journals and reported in the news are statistical studies, so it behooves us to be aware of their benefits and limitations. At the start, you should know that a statistical study will gather numerical information from various sources and then try to make sense out of it, for the purpose of coming to a conclusion.

Example of a Statistical Study

Let's take a look at a study that allows us to conclude that babies conceived 18 months to five years after a previous birth are healthier than those conceived at shorter or longer intervals. In other words, spacing children about two to five years apart is a good idea (Fig. 1A). Here is how the authors collected their data and the results they published in the *Journal of the American Medical Association*.[1]

Objective.   To determine whether there is an association between birth spacing and a healthy baby when data are corrected for maternal characteristics or socioeconomic status.

Data.   The authors collected data from studies performed around the world in 1966 through January 2006. The studies were published in various journals, reported on at professional meetings, or were known to the authors by personal contact. The authors gathered a very large pool of data that included over 11 million pregnancies from 67 individual studies. Twenty of the studies were from the United States, with the remaining 47 coming from 61 different countries. The authors attempted to adjust the data (by elimination of certain data) for factors such as mother's age, wealth, access to prenatal care, and breast-feeding. These adjustments allow the findings to be applied to both developed and developing countries.

Conclusion.

1. A pregnancy that begins less than six months after a previous birth has a 77% higher chance of being preterm and a 39% higher chance of lower birth weight.
2. For up to 18 months between pregnancies, the chance of a preterm birth decreases by 2% per month, and the chance of a low-weight birth decreases

Figure 1A Does spacing pregnancies lead to healthier children?   A recent statistical study suggests that it does. If so, which mother, left or right, may have a healthier younger child?

by 3% per month as the 18-month time period is approached.
3. Babies conceived after 59 months have the same risk as those conceived in the less-than-six-months group.
4. The optimum spacing between pregnancies appears to be 18 months to five years after a previous birth.

The study leader, Agustin Conde-Agudelo, said, "Health officials should counsel women who have just given birth to delay their next conception by 18 to 59 months."

Limitations of Experimental Studies

The expression "statistical study" is a bit of a misnomer because most scientists collect quantitative data and use them to come to a conclusion. However, if we compare this study to experimental studies, we can see that the experimental studies include both a control group and test groups. The groups are treated the same except for the experimental variable. Obviously, you wouldn't be able to divide women of the same childbearing age into various groups and tell each group when they will conceive their children for the purpose of deciding the best interval between pregnancies for the health of the newborn. So, what is the next best thing? Do a statistical study utilizing data already available about women who became pregnant at different intervals.

A statistical study is really a correlation study. In our example, the authors studied the correlation between birth spacing and the health of a newborn. The more data collected from more varied sources make a correlation study more reliable. The study by Conde-Agudelo has a very large sample size, which goes a long way to validating the results. Even so, a correlation does not necessarily translate to causation. So, it is not surprising that Dr. Mark A. Klebanoff, director of the National Institute of Child Health and Human Development, commented that many factors will affect birth spacing and that the study is not detailed enough to take all factors into consideration. Is any statistical study detailed enough? Most likely not.

Benefits of Statistical Studies

Before we give up on statistical studies, let's consider that they do provide us with information not attainable otherwise. Regardless of whether we understand the intricacies of statistical analysis, statistical studies do allow scientists to gain information and insights into many problems. True, further study is needed to find out if the observed correlation does mean causation, but science is always a work in progress, with additional findings being published every day.

Questions to Consider

1. Why is a large sample size needed in a statistical study? Why might this be a challenge for scientists?
2. How might both statistical and experimental studies be combined to enhance the validity of a scientific study?

1. Conde-Agudelo, A., Rosas-Bermudez, A., and Kafury-Goeta, A. C. 2006. Birth spacing and risk of adverse perinatal outcomes. Abstract. *JAMA* 295: 1809–23.

Using the Scientific Method

This section demonstrates the use of the scientific method in a controlled study to ensure that the outcome is due to the experimental variable, or independent variable—the component or factor being tested. The result is termed the **responding variable,** or dependent variable, because it is due to the experimental variable:

Experimental Variable (Independent Variable)	Responding Variable (Dependent Variable)
Factor of the experiment being tested	Result or change that occurs due to the experimental variable

Observation

Researchers doing this study knew that in the short run, nitrogen fertilizer enhances yield and increases food supplies. However, excessive nitrogen fertilizer application can cause pollution by adding toxic levels of nitrates to water supplies. Also, applying nitrogen fertilizer year after year may alter soil properties to the point that crop yields may decrease instead of increase. At that point, the only solution is to let the land remain unplanted for several years until the soil recovers naturally.

An alternative to the use of nitrogen fertilizers is the use of legumes, plants such as peas and beans, that increase soil nitrogen. Legumes provide a home for bacteria that convert atmospheric nitrogen to a form usable by the plant. The bacteria live in nodules on the roots (Fig. 1.13). The bacteria supply the plant with nitrogen compounds, and in turn, the plant passes the product of photosyntheis to the nodules.

Numerous legume crops can be rotated (planted every other season) with any number of cereal crops. The nitrogen added to the soil by the legume crop is a natural fertilizer that increases the yield of cereal crops. The particular rotation used by farmers tends to depend on the location, climate, and market demand. In this study, researchers performed an experiment in which method of fertilization is the experimental variable and enhanced yield is the responding variable.

Figure 1.13 Root nodules.   Bacteria that live in nodules on the roots of legumes, such as pea plants, convert nitrogen in the air to a form that land plants can use to make proteins and other nitrogen-containing molecules.

Hypothesis

Researchers doing this study knew that the pigeon pea plant is a legume with a high rate of atmospheric nitrogen conversion. This plant is widely grown as a food crop in India, Kenya, Uganda, Pakistan, and other subtropical countries. Researchers formulated the hypothesis that a pigeon pea/winter wheat rotation would be a reasonable alternative to the use of nitrogen fertilizer to increase the yield of winter wheat.

> HYPOTHESIS: A pigeon pea/winter wheat rotation will cause winter wheat production to increase as well as or better than the use of nitrogen fertilizer.

> PREDICTION: Wheat biomass following the growth of pigeon peas will surpass wheat biomass following nitrogen fertilizer treatment.

Experiment and Data

In this study, the investigators decided on the following experimental design (Fig. 1.14a):

CONTROL POTS
- Winter wheat was planted in pots of soil that received no fertilization treatment—that is, no nitrogen fertilizer and no preplanting of pigeon peas.

TEST POTS
- Winter wheat was grown in clay pots in soil treated with nitrogen fertilizer equivalent to 45 kilograms (kg)/hectare (ha).
- Winter wheat was grown in clay pots in soil treated with nitrogen fertilizer equivalent to 90 kg/ha.
- Pigeon pea plants were grown in clay pots in the summer. The pigeon pea plants were then tilled into the soil and winter wheat was planted in the same pots.

To ensure a controlled experiment, the conditions for the control pots and the test pots were identical; the plants were exposed to the same environmental conditions and watered equally. During the following spring, the wheat plants were dried and weighed to determine wheat biomass production in each of the pots.

After the first year, wheat biomass was higher in certain test pots than in the control pots (Fig. 1.14b). Specifically, test pots with 45 kg/ha of nitrogen fertilizer (orange) had only slightly more wheat biomass production than the control pots, but test pots that received 90 kg/ha treatment (green) demonstrated nearly twice the biomass production of the control pots. To the surprise of investigators, wheat production following summer planting of pigeon peas (brown) did not demonstrate as high a biomass production as the control pots.

Conclusion and Further Investigation

Wheat biomass following the growth of pigeon peas is not as great as that obtained with nitrogen fertilizer treatments, meaning that the data from the experiment did not support the investigators' hypothesis. This is not an uncommon event in scientific investigations. However, the investigators decided to continue the experiment using the same design and the same pots as before, to see if the buildup of residual soil nitrogen from pigeon peas would eventually increase wheat biomass. So they proposed a new hypothesis.

Figure 1.14 **Pigeon pea/winter wheat rotation study.**
a. Experiment involves control pots and test pots of three types: test pots that received 45 kg/ha of nitrogen; test pots that received 90 kg/ha of nitrogen; and test pots in which pigeon peas rotated with winter wheat. **b.** The graph compares wheat biomass for each of three years. Wheat biomass in test pots that received the most nitrogen fertilizer (green) declined while wheat biomass in test pots with pigeon pea/winter wheat rotation (brown) increased dramatically.

HYPOTHESIS: A sustained pigeon pea/winter wheat rotation will eventually cause an increase in winter wheat production.

PREDICTION: Wheat biomass following two years of pigeon pea/winter wheat rotation will surpass wheat biomass following nitrogen fertilizer treatment.

After two years, the yield following 90 kg/ha nitrogen treatment (green) was not as much as it was the first year (Fig. 1.14b). Indeed, wheat biomass following summer planting of pigeon peas (brown) was the highest of all treatments, suggesting that buildup of residual nitrogen from pigeon peas had the potential to provide fertilization for winter wheat growth.

CONCLUSION: The hypothesis is supported. At the end of two years, the yield of winter wheat following a pigeon pea/winter wheat rotation was better than for the other type pots.

The researchers continued their experiment for still another year. After three years, winter wheat biomass production had decreased in the control pots and in the pots treated with nitrogen fertilizer. Pots treated with nitrogen fertilizer still had increased wheat biomass production compared with the control pots, but not nearly as much as pots following summer planting of pigeon peas. Compared to the first year, wheat biomass increased almost fourfold in pots having a pigeon pea/winter wheat rotation (brown, Fig. 1.14b). The researchers suggested that the soil was improved by the organic matter as well as the addition of nitrogen from the pigeon peas. The researchers published their results in a scientific journal.[1]

A Field Study

Researcher David Barash observed the mating behavior of mountain bluebirds (Fig. 1.15a, b) and noted that males perform aggressive behavior during the mating season. He was interested in whether this behavior changed during the events of mating and reproduction.

1 Bidlack, J. E., Rao, S. C., and Demezas, D. H. 2001. Nodulation, nitrogenase activity, and dry weight of chickpea and pigeon pea cultivars using different *Bradyrhizobium* strains. *Journal of Plant Nutrition* 24: 549–60.

Hypothesis

Barash formulated the hypothesis that aggression of the male varies during the reproductive cycle. To test this hypothesis, he reasoned that he should evaluate the intensity of male aggression at three stages: after the nest is built, after the first egg is laid, and after the eggs hatch.

> HYPOTHESIS: Male bluebird aggression varies during the reproductive cycle.
>
> PREDICTION: Aggression intensity will change after the nest is built, after the first egg is laid, and after hatching.

Experiment and Data

For his experiment, Barash decided to measure aggression intensity by recording the number of approaches per minute a male made toward a rival male and his own female mate. To provide a rival, Barash posted a male bluebird model near the nests while resident males were out foraging. The aggressive behavior (approaches) of the resident male was noted and counted during the first 10 minutes of the male's return (Fig. 1.15c).

To give his results validity, Barash included a control group. For his control, Barash posted a male robin model instead of a male bluebird near certain nests.

Resident males of the control group did not exhibit any aggressive behavior, but resident males of the experimental groups did exhibit aggressive behavior. Barash graphed his mathematical data on number of approaches (Fig. 1.15d). By examining the graph, you can see that the resident male was more aggressive toward the rival male model than toward his female mate, and that he was most aggressive while the nest was under construction, less aggressive after the first egg was laid, and least aggressive after the eggs hatched.

Conclusion

The results allowed Barash to conclude that aggression in male bluebirds is related to their reproductive cycle. Therefore, his hypothesis was supported. If male bluebirds were always aggressive, even toward male robin models, his hypothesis would not have been supported.

> CONCLUSION: The hypothesis is supported. Male bluebird aggression does vary during the reproductive cycle.

Barash reported his experiment in *The American Naturalist*.[2] In this article, Barash gave an evolutionary interpretation to his results. It is adaptive, he said, for male bluebirds to be less aggressive after the first egg is laid because by then the male bird is "sure the offspring is his own." It is maladaptive for the male bird to waste energy being aggressive after hatching, because his offspring are already present.

Check Your Progress   1.4

1. Identify the role of the experimental variable in an experiment.
2. Distinguish between the roles of the test group and the control group in an experiment.
3. Describe the process by which a scientist may test a hypothesis about an observation.

2 Barash, D. P. 1976. Male response to apparent female adultery in the mountain bluebird (*Sialia currucoides*): an evolutionary interpretation. *The American Naturalist* 110: 1097–1101.

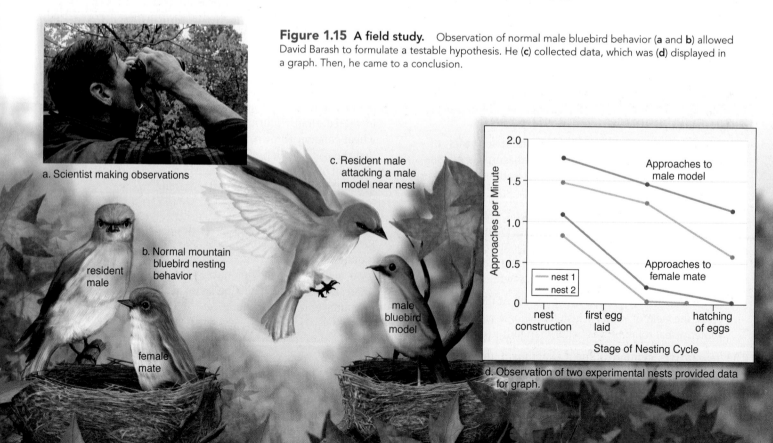

Figure 1.15 A field study.   Observation of normal male bluebird behavior (**a** and **b**) allowed David Barash to formulate a testable hypothesis. He (**c**) collected data, which was (**d**) displayed in a graph. Then, he came to a conclusion.

a. Scientist making observations

b. Normal mountain bluebird nesting behavior

resident male

female mate

c. Resident male attacking a male model near nest

male bluebird model

d. Observation of two experimental nests provided data for graph.

CONNECTING *the* CONCEPTS *with the* THEMES

Evolution

- Evolution is the core concept of biology, and explains how species develop adaptations to an ever-changing environment.
- Natural selection is the mechanism by which evolutionary change occurs.

Nature of Science

- Science is based on the ability to observe the natural world and then formulate hypotheses as potential explanations for these observations.
- Scientists use an ordered series of events, called the scientific method, to construct experiments that explore the structure of the natural world.

Biological Systems

- All life is based on atoms and molecules, which in turn are involved in the formation of cells, the basic unit of all life.
- Members of a species form populations. Populations of different species in a given area are called a community. The interaction of a community with the environment is called an ecosystem.
- Ecosystems are characterized by energy flow and chemical cycling.

Media Study Tools

www.mhhe.com/maderbiology11

Enhance your study of this chapter with study tools and practice tests. Also ask your instructor about the resources available through ConnectPlus, including the media-rich eBook, interactive learning tools, and animations.

Summarize

1.1 How to Define Life

Although living things are diverse, they have certain characteristics in common. Living things (a) are organized, and their levels of organization extend from the cell to ecosystems; (b) need an outside source of materials and energy; (c) maintain homeostasis; (d) respond to external stimuli; (e) reproduce and develop, passing on genes to their offspring; and (f) have adaptations suitable to their way of life in a particular environment. Together, these characteristics unify life on Earth.

1.2 Evolution, the Unifying Concept of Biology

Life on Earth is diverse, but the theory of evolution unifies life and describes how all living organisms evolved from a common ancestor. Taxonomists assign each living thing an italicized binomial name that consists of the genus and the specific epithet. From the least inclusive to the most inclusive category, each species belongs to a genus, family, order, class, phylum, kingdom, and finally domain. Systematists study the evolutionary relationships between species.

The three domains of life are Archaea, Bacteria, and Eukarya. The first two domains contain prokaryotic organisms that are structurally simple but metabolically complex. Domain Eukarya contains the protists, fungi, plants, and animals. Protists range from unicellular to multicellular organisms and include the protozoans and most algae. Among the fungi are the familiar molds and mushrooms. Plants are well known as the multicellular photosynthesizers of the world, while animals are multicellular and ingest their food. An evolutionary tree shows how the domains are related by way of common ancestors.

Natural selection describes the process by which living organisms are descended from a common ancestor. Mutations occur within a population, creating new traits. The agents of natural selection, present in both biological and physical environments, shape species over time and may create new species from existing ones.

1.3 How the Biosphere Is Organized

Within an ecosystem, populations interact with one another and with the physical environment. Nutrients cycle within and between ecosystems, but energy flows unidirectionally and is eventually lost as an unusable form. Adaptations of organisms allow them to play particular roles within an ecosystem.

1.4 The Process of Science

When studying the natural world, scientists use the scientific process. Observations, along with previous data, are used to formulate a hypothesis. New observations and/or experiments are carried out in order to test the hypothesis. A good experimental design includes an experimental variable and a control group. The experimental and observational results are analyzed, and the scientist comes to a conclusion as to whether the results support the hypothesis or do not support the hypothesis.

Several conclusions in a particular area may allow scientists to arrive at a theory, such as the cell theory, the gene theory, or the theory of evolution. The theory of evolution is a unifying concept of biology.

Key Terms

adaptation 5	domain Bacteria 7
animal 8	domain Eukarya 7
binomial nomenclature 8	ecosystem 9
biodiversity 10	emergent property 2
biology 2	energy 4
biosphere 9	eukaryote 7
cell 2	evolution 5
class 6	experiment 11
community 9	experimental design 11
conclusion 12	experimental variable 12
control 12	extinction 10
data 12	family 6
deductive reasoning 11	fungi 8
domain 6	gene 5
domain Archaea 7	genus 6

homeostasis   4
hypothesis   11
inductive reasoning   11
kingdom   6
law   12
metabolism   4
model   12
multicellular   2
natural selection   8
observation   11
order   6
phenomenon   11
photosynthesis   4
phylum   6
plant   8

population   9
prediction   11
principle   12
prokaryote   7
protist   7
reproduce   5
responding variable   14
scientific method   11
scientific theory   12
species   6
standard deviation 12
systematics 6
taxonomy   6
unicellular   2

▮ Assess

Reviewing This Chapter

1. What are the common characteristics of life?   2–5
2. Describe the levels of biological organization.   2
3. Why do living things require an outside source of nutrients and energy? Describe these sources.   4
4. What is passed from generation to generation when organisms reproduce? What has to happen to the hereditary material DNA for evolution to occur?   5
5. How does evolution explain both the unity and the diversity of life?   5–6
6. What are the categories of classification? How does the domain Eukarya differ from domain Bacteria and domain Archaea?   6
7. Explain the scientific name of an organism.   6
8. How does natural selection result in adaptation to the environment?   8
9. What is an ecosystem, and why should human beings preserve ecosystems?   9–10
10. Describe the series of steps involved in the scientific method.   11–12
11. Give an example of a controlled study. Name the experimental variable and the responding variable.   14–15

Testing Yourself

Choose the best answer for each question.

1. Which of these is not a property of all living organisms?
   a. organization
   b. acquisition of materials and energy
   c. care for their offspring
   d. reproduction
   e. responding to the environment
2. Describe an emergent property that might arise when moving from a single neuron (nerve cell) to nervous tissue.
3. The level of organization that includes cells of similar structure and function would be
   a. an organ.
   b. a tissue.
   c. an organ system.
   d. an organism.

4. Which of the following is an example of adaptation?
   a. In a very wet year, some plants grow unusually tall stalks and large leaves.
   b. Over millions of years, the eyes of cave salamanders lose their function.
   c. An escaped dog joins a pack of wild dogs and begins interbreeding with them.
   d. A harsh winter kills many birds within a population, especially the smallest ones.
5. Energy is brought into ecosystems by which of the following?
   a. fungi and other decomposers
   b. cows and other organisms that graze on grass
   c. meat-eating animals
   d. organisms that photosynthesize, such as plants
   e. All of these are correct.
6. Which of the following statements is a hypothesis?
   a. Will increasing my cat's food increase her weight?
   b. Increasing my cat's food consumption will result in a 25% increase in her weight.
   c. I will feed my cat more food.
   d. My cat has gained weight; therefore, she is eating more food.
7. After formulating a hypothesis, a scientist
   a. proves the hypothesis true or false.
   b. tests the hypothesis.
   c. decides how to best avoid having a control.
   d. makes sure environmental conditions are just right.
   e. formulates a scientific theory.
8. The experimental variable in the bluebird experiment (pages 15-16) was the
   a. use of a model male bluebird.
   b. observations of the experimenter.
   c. various behavior of the males.
   d. identification of what bluebirds to study.
   e. All of these are correct.
9. The control group in the pigeon pea/winter wheat experiment (pages 14-15) was the pots that were
   a. planted with pigeon peas.
   b. treated with nitrogen fertilizer.
   c. not treated.
   d. not watered.
   e. Both c and d are correct.
10. Which of the following are agents of natural selection?
    a. changes in the environment
    b. competition among individuals for food and water
    c. predation by another species
    d. competition among members of a population for prime nesting sites
    e. All of these are correct.
11. Which of the following is an example of natural selection?
    a. In a very wet year, some plants grow unusually tall stalks and large leaves.
    b. After several unusually cold winters, squirrels with an extra layer of fat have more offspring.
    c. Squirrels may have long or short tails.
    d. Dogs with longer legs are able to run faster than dogs with shorter legs.

12. Which of the following statements regarding evolution is false?
    a. Adaptations may be physical or behavioral.
    b. Natural selection always results in organisms becoming more adapted to the environment.
    c. A trait selected for, may suddenly become selected against when the environment changes.
    d. Some traits are neither selected for nor against.

For questions 13–15, write a brief answer.

13. Why is it said that all energy used by living organisms originates from the Sun?

14. Carbon dioxide emissions have been blamed for climate change by many scientists. How might excessive amounts of carbon dioxide affect nutrient cycling?

15. Would the accidental introduction of a new species to an ecosystem necessarily have a negative effect on biodiversity? Why or why not?

 Engage

 Virtual Lab
Dependent and Independent Variables

The virtual lab "Dependent and Independent Variables" provides an interactive exploration of how scientists construct scientific experiments.

Thinking Scientifically

1. An investigator spills dye on a culture plate and notices that the bacteria live despite exposure to sunlight. He decides to test if the dye is protective against ultraviolet (UV) light. He exposes one group of culture plates containing bacteria and dye and another group containing only bacteria to UV light. The bacteria on all plates die. Complete the following diagram.

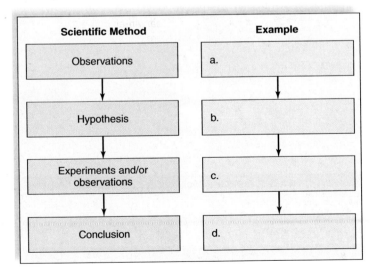

2. You want to grow large tomatoes and notice that a name-brand fertilizer claims to produce larger produce than a generic brand. How would you test this claim?

3. A scientist wishes to test her hypothesis that a commonly used drug causes heart attacks in some individuals. What kind of study should she initiate? What would you expect her experimental and responding variables to be?

Bioethical Issue
Oil Drilling in the Arctic

Established by an act of Congress in 1980, the Arctic National Wildlife Refuge (ANWR) covers a total of 19 million acres of northernmost Alaska far above the Arctic Circle. ANWR is home to a variety of wildlife, such as caribou, migratory birds, grizzly and polar bears, wolves, and musk oxen. But it is also home to substantial oil reserves, which has led to an ongoing contentious debate over its future: Should Congress allow development of ANWR for oil exploration and drilling?

Those who favor oil drilling in ANWR insist that first and foremost, the impact on the land would be minimal. The affected area would be roughly the size of an airport in a total area roughly the size of the state of South Carolina. They contend that the effect would mainly be underground because new techniques allow us to go lower and spread out beneath the surface to get the oil. Waste treatment and disposal methods have also improved. Acquiring the oil, advocates say, would also protect jobs and national security in the United States by lessening dependence on often hostile foreign countries for oil, and would have the added benefit of insulating the U.S. economy from oil price spikes and supply shocks.

Those who do not favor oil drilling in ANWR are eager to point out that at current levels of consumption, the oil coming from ANWR would hardly have a noticeable impact on prices and supply levels. Furthermore, they believe that the best solution to the current energy crunch would be for U.S. citizens to adopt simple energy conservation measures and invest in research on alternative fuels. They suggest that this would save many times the oil that could come from drilling in the Arctic refuge and that, by using a renewable energy resource, the environment in the lower 48 states would be protected, in addition to protecting the wildlife in the Arctic National Wildlife Refuge. Using renewable energy would lessen the need for foreign oil, and would also protect our national security.

Should Congress approve oil drilling in ANWR? Or should Congress invest in alternative and renewable energy forms, and insist that citizens adopt energy conservation measures? Should public tax monies be made available to Congress for oil exploration or for investment in alternative energy sources?

The Cell

We're going to take a fairly long journey through the various levels of biological organization from atoms to ecosystems, as shown in Figure 1.2. Whenever you get ready to go on a trip, you think about what you should bring with you and how to pack your suitcase. Similarly, you can think of the chapters in Unit I as the necessities you are going to bring with you as we take our biological journey.

The chapters in Unit I will teach you principles of biology that will apply to every chapter in the book. Chapters 2 and 3 introduce you to chemistry because all organisms are composed of chemicals, some of them quite unique to living things. In Chapters 4 and 5, we will see how these chemicals are arranged to form the structure of a cell, the basic unit of life. Some organisms are single cells and some are multicellular, but all are made up of cells. Chapters 6, 7, and 8 are about the physiology of cells—how they stay alive.

Your understanding of these chapters will serve you well as you move through the other parts of this text. Just as building a house first requires a solid foundation, your learning begins with the foundation provided in this first unit.

UNIT OUTLINE

Chapter 2 Basic Chemistry   21

Chapter 3 The Chemistry of Organic Molecules   37

Chapter 4 Cell Structure and Function   60

Chapter 5 Membrane Structure and Function   85

Chapter 6 Metabolism: Energy and Enzymes   104

Chapter 7 Photosynthesis   119

Chapter 8 Cellular Respiration   135

UNIT LEARNING OUTCOMES

The learning outcomes for this unit focus on three major themes in the life sciences.

Evolution	Examine how inanimate elements can be combined to produce a living cell.
Nature of Science	Describe how science is used to investigate cellular phenomena.
Biological Systems	Evaluate how cellular components work together in order to function and live.

Bottle-nosed dolphin (*Tursiops truncatus*).

2

Basic Chemistry

A bottle-nosed dolphin, an amazing and intelligent creature, can tolerate a certain salinity, can stay underwater for only so long, and must eat a particular diet to keep its complex organ systems functioning. Chemistry affects every aspect of the dolphin's life, whether it is playing in the Gulf of Mexico or performing at Sea World. Without molecular chemistry, a dolphin wouldn't be able to live at all.

At one time, people believed that organisms contained a "vital force" that allowed them to live. Over time, science has shown us that living and nonliving things are all composed of the same elements. It is true, though, that living and nonliving things differ as to which elements are most common, as we shall see. This chapter reviews inorganic chemistry, which largely pertains to nonliving things, and also explores the composition and chemistry of water, an inorganic substance that is intimately connected to the life of organisms on planet Earth. Our search for water on other planets further emphasizes the essential role of water in all life.

As you read through the chapter, think about the following questions:

1. What unique properties do chemical elements have?
2. How do elements interact with one another?
3. How is it possible for inanimate chemical elements to produce a living organism?

CHAPTER OUTLINE

2.1 Chemical Elements 22
2.2 Molecules and Compounds 26
2.3 Chemistry of Water 28
2.4 Acids and Bases 32

BEFORE YOU BEGIN

Before beginning this chapter, take a few moments to review the following discussions.

Figure 1.2 Why is it important to understand scale when studying biology?

Figures 1.5-1.8 Why do we organize biological concepts into systems?

Section 1.4 How does scientific study help us to understand the natural world?

FOLLOWING *the* THEMES

CHAPTER 2 BASIC CHEMISTRY		
UNIT 1 THE CELL	**Evolution**	Chemicals form the basis of living things, which evolve by changing their chemistry over time.
	Nature of Science	Knowledge of chemicals is used to understand the scientific basis of life.
	Biological Systems	Chemical elements are combined into molecular compounds, which are used to build life systems.

2.1 Chemical Elements

Learning Outcomes

Upon completion of this section, you should be able to

1. Describe how protons, neutrons, and electrons relate to atomic structure.
2. Use the periodic table to evaluate relationships between atomic number and mass number.
3. Describe how variations in an atomic nucleus account for its physical properties.
4. Determine how electrons are configured around a nucleus.

Throw a ball, pat your dog, rake leaves, turn a page; everything we touch—from the water we drink to the air we breathe—is composed of matter. **Matter** refers to anything that takes up space and has mass. Although matter has many diverse forms—anything from molten lava to kidney stones—it only exists in three distinct states: solid, liquid, or gas.

Elements

All matter, both nonliving and living, is composed of certain basic substances called **elements.** An element is a substance that cannot be broken down to simpler substances with different properties (a property is a physical or chemical characteristic, such as density, solubility, melting point, and reactivity) by ordinary chemical means. It is quite remarkable that, in the known universe, there are only 92 naturally occurring elements that serve as the building blocks of matter. Other elements have been artificially constructed by physicists and are not biologically important.

Both the Earth's crust and all organisms are composed of elements, but they differ as to which ones are common. Only six elements—carbon, hydrogen, nitrogen, oxygen, phosphorus, and sulfur—are basic to life and make up about 95% of the body weight of organisms. The acronym CHNOPS helps us remember these six elements. The properties of these elements are essential to the uniqueness of cells and organisms, such as the macaws in Figure 2.1. The macaws have gathered on a salt lick in South America. Salt contains the elements sodium and chlorine and is commonly sought after by many forms of life. Potassium, calcium, iron, and magnesium are still other elements found in living things.

Atoms

In the early 1800s, the English scientist John Dalton (1776-1844) developed the atomic theory, which says that elements consist of tiny particles called **atoms** [Gk. *atomos,* uncut, indivisible]. An atom is the smallest part of an element that displays the properties of the element. An element and its atoms share the same name. One or two letters create the **atomic symbol,** which stands for this name. For example, the symbol H means a hydrogen atom, the symbol Rn stands for radon, and the symbol Na (for *natrium* in Latin) is used for a sodium atom.

Physicists have identified a number of subatomic particles that make up atoms. The three best known subatomic particles include positively charged **protons,** uncharged **neutrons,** and negatively charged **electrons** [Gk. *elektron,* electricity]. Protons and neutrons are located within the nucleus of an atom, and electrons move about the nucleus. Figure 2.2 shows the arrangement of the subatomic particles in a helium atom, which has only two electrons. In Figure 2.2*a,* the stippling shows the

Figure 2.1 Elements that make up the Earth's crust and its organisms. Scarlet macaws gather on a salt lick in South America. The graph inset shows the Earth's crust primarily contains the elements silicon (Si), aluminum (Al) and oxygen (O). Living organisms primarily contain the elements oxygen (O), nitrogen (N), carbon (C), and hydrogen (H). Biological molecules also contain the elements sulfur (S) and phosphorus (P).

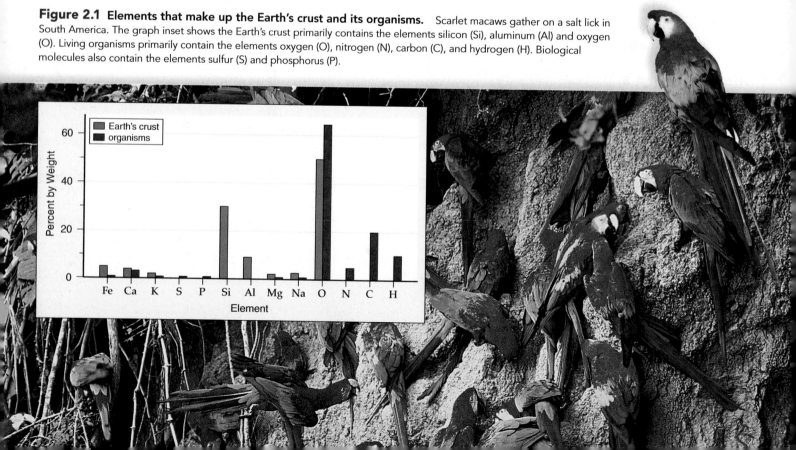

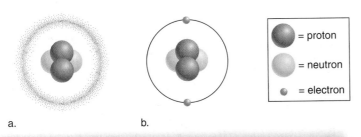

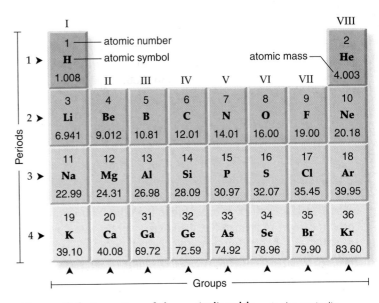

Figure 2.2 Model of helium (He). Atoms contain subatomic particles, which are located as shown. Protons and neutrons are found within the nucleus, and electrons are outside the nucleus. **a.** The stippling shows the probable location of the electrons in the helium atom. **b.** The average location of an electron is sometimes represented by a circle termed an electron shell. **c.** The electric charge and the atomic mass units (AMU) of the subatomic particles vary as shown.

Figure 2.3 A portion of the periodic table. In the periodic table, elements are listed in the order of their atomic numbers, but arranged so each element is placed in a group (vertical column) and period (horizontal row). All the atoms in a particular group have the same number of valence electrons and therefore share common chemical characteristics. Each period shows the number of electron shells for an element. This abbreviated periodic table contains elements most important in biology; the complete periodic table is in Appendix D.

probable location of electrons, and in Figure 2.2b, the circle represents an **electron shell,** the average location of electrons.

The concept of an atom has changed greatly since Dalton's day. If an atom could be drawn the size of a football field, the nucleus would be like a gumball in the center of the field, and the electrons would be tiny specks whirling about in the upper stands. Most of an atom is empty space. We should also realize that we can only indicate where the electrons are expected to be most of the time. In our analogy, the electrons might very well stray outside the stadium at times.

Atomic Number and Mass Number

Atoms not only have an atomic symbol, they also have an atomic number and mass number. All atoms of an element have the same number of protons housed in the nucleus. This is called the **atomic number,** which accounts for the unique properties of this type of atom.

Each atom also has its own mass number dependent on the number of subatomic particles in that atom. Protons and neutrons are assigned one atomic mass unit (AMU) each. Electrons are so small that their AMU is considered zero in most calculations (Fig. 2.2c). Therefore, the **mass number** of an atom is the sum of protons and neutrons in the nucleus.

The term mass is used, and not *weight,* because mass is constant, while weight changes according to the gravitational force of a body. The gravitational force of the Earth is greater than that of the moon; therefore, substances weigh less on the moon, even though their mass has not changed.

By convention, when an atom stands alone (and not in the periodic table, discussed next), the atomic number is written as a subscript to the lower left of the atomic symbol. The mass number is written as a superscript to the upper left of the atomic

symbol. Regardless of position, the smaller number is always the atomic number, as shown here for carbon.

$$\text{mass number} \longrightarrow {}^{12}_{\ 6}\text{C} \longleftarrow \text{atomic symbol}$$
$$\text{atomic number} \longrightarrow$$

The Periodic Table

Once chemists discovered a number of the elements, they began to realize that even though each element consists of a different atom, certain chemical and physical characteristics recur. The periodic table, developed by the Russian chemist Dmitri Mendeleev (1834–1907), was constructed as a way to group the elements, and therefore atoms, according to these characteristics.

Figure 2.3 is a portion of the periodic table, which is shown in total in Appendix D. The atoms shown in the periodic table are assumed to be electrically neutral. Therefore, the atomic number not only tells you the number of protons, it also tells you the number of electrons. The **atomic mass** is the average of the AMU for all the isotopes (discussed next) of that atom. To determine the number of neutrons, subtract the number of protons from the atomic mass, and take the closest whole number.

In the periodic table, every atom is in a particular period (the horizontal rows) and in a particular group (the vertical columns). The atomic number of every atom in a period increases by one if you read from left to right. All the atoms in a group share the same binding characteristics. For example, all the atoms in group VII react with one atom at a time, for reasons we will soon explore. The atoms in group VIII are called the noble gases because they are inert and rarely react with another atom. Notice that helium, neon, argon, and krypton are noble gases.

Isotopes

Isotopes [Gk. *isos*, equal, and *topos*, place] are atoms of the same element that differ in the number of neutrons. Isotopes have the same number of protons, but they have different atomic masses. For example, the element carbon has three common isotopes:

$$^{12}_{6}C \qquad ^{13}_{6}C \qquad ^{14}_{6}C*$$

*radioactive

Carbon 12 has six neutrons, carbon 13 has seven neutrons, and carbon 14 has eight neutrons. Unlike the other two isotopes of carbon, carbon 14 is unstable; it changes over time into nitrogen 14, which is a stable isotope of the element nitrogen. As carbon 14 decays, it releases various types of energy in the form of rays and subatomic particles, and therefore it is termed a radioactive isotope. The radiation given off by radioactive isotopes can be detected in various ways. The Geiger counter is an instrument that is commonly used to detect radiation. In 1860, the French physicist Antoine-Henri Becquerel (1852-1908) discovered that a sample of uranium would produce a bright image on a photographic plate even in the dark, and a similar method of detecting radiation is still in use today. Marie Curie (1867-1934), who worked with Becquerel, coined the term "radioactivity" and contributed much to its study. Today, radiation is used by biologists to date objects from our distant past, create images, and trace the movement of substances in the body.

Animation
Half-Life

Low Levels of Radiation

The chemical behavior of a radioactive isotope is essentially the same as that of the stable isotopes of an element. This means that you can put a small amount of radioactive isotope in a sample and it becomes a **tracer** by which to detect molecular changes. Melvin Calvin and his co-workers used carbon 14 to detect all the various reactions that occur during the process of photosynthesis (see Chapter 7).

The importance of chemistry to medicine is nowhere more evident than in the many medical uses of radioactive isotopes. Specific tracers are used in imaging the body's organs and tissues. For example, after a patient drinks a solution containing a minute amount of ^{131}I, it becomes concentrated in the thyroid—the only organ to take it up. A subsequent image of the thyroid indicates whether it is healthy in structure and function (Fig. 2.4a).

Positron-emission tomography (PET) is a way to determine the comparative activity of tissues. Radioactively labeled glucose, which emits a subatomic particle known as a positron, is injected into the body. The radiation given off is detected by sensors and analyzed by a computer. The result is a color image that shows which tissues took up glucose and are therefore metabolically active. The red areas surrounded by green in Figure 2.4b indicate which areas of the brain are most active. PET scans of the brain are used to evaluate patients who have memory disorders of an undetermined cause or suspected brain tumors or seizure disorders that could possibly benefit from surgery. PET scans, utilizing radioactive thallium, can detect signs of coronary artery disease and low blood flow to the heart.

Video
Nuclear Medicine

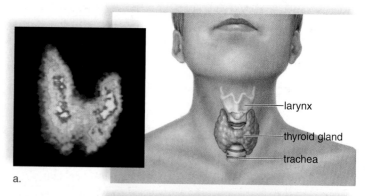

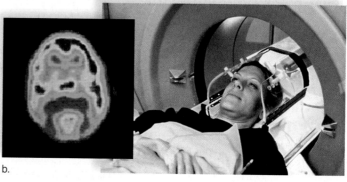

a.

b.

Figure 2.4 Low levels of radiation. **a.** Medical scan of the thyroid gland (colored image) indicates the presence of a tumor that does not take up the radioactive iodine. **b.** A PET (positron-emission tomography) scan reveals which portions of the brain are most active (green and red colors).

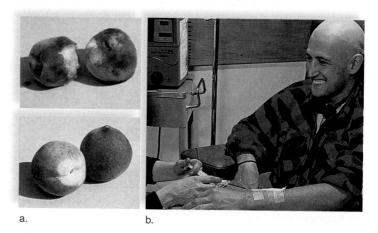

a.   b.

Figure 2.5 High levels of radiation. **a.** Radiation used to kill bacteria and fungi on peaches helps them spoil less quickly and keep for a longer period of time. **b.** Physicians use targeted radiation therapy to kill cancer cells.

High Levels of Radiation

Radioactive substances in the environment can harm cells, damage DNA, and cause cancer. When Marie Curie was studying radiation, its harmful effects were not known, and she and many of her co-workers developed cancer. The release of radioactive particles following a nuclear power plant accident can have far-reaching and long-lasting effects on human health. The harmful effects of radiation can be put to good use, however (Fig. 2.5). Radiation from radioactive isotopes has been used for many years to sterilize medical and dental products. Now it can be used to sterilize the U.S. mail and other packages to free them of possible pathogens, such as anthrax spores. High radiation is often used to kill cancer cells. Targeted radioisotopes can be introduced into the body so that the subatomic particles emitted destroy only cancer cells, with little risk to the rest of the body.

Electrons and Energy

In an electrically neutral atom, the positive charges of the protons in the nucleus are balanced by the negative charges of electrons moving about the nucleus. Various models in years past have attempted to illustrate the precise location of electrons. Figure 2.6 uses the Bohr model, which is named after the physicist Niels Bohr (1885-1962). The Bohr model is useful as a way to visualize electron location, but we need to realize that today's physicists tell us it is not possible to determine the precise location of any individual electron at any given moment.

In the Bohr model, the electron shells about the nucleus also represent energy levels. Because negatively charged electrons are attracted to the positively charged nucleus, it takes energy to push them away and keep them in their own shell. The more distant the shell, the more energy it takes. Therefore, it is more accurate to speak of electrons as being at particular energy levels in relation to the nucleus. When you study photosynthesis, you will learn that when atoms absorb the energy of the Sun, electrons are boosted to a higher energy level. Later, as the electrons return to their original energy level, energy is released and transformed into chemical energy. This chemical energy supports all life on Earth and therefore our very existence is dependent on the energy of electrons.

You will want to learn to draw a Bohr model for each of the elements that occurs in the periodic table shown in Figure 2.3. Let's begin by examining the models depicted in Figure 2.6. Notice that the first shell (closest to the nucleus) can contain two electrons; thereafter, each additional shell can contain eight electrons. Also, each lower level is filled with electrons before the next higher level contains any electrons.

Animation
Atomic Structure

The sulfur atom, with an atomic number of 16, has two electrons in the first shell, eight electrons in the second shell, and six electrons in the third, or outer, shell. Revisit the periodic table (see Fig. 2.3), and note that sulfur is in the third period. In other words, the period tells you how many shells an atom has. Also note that sulfur is in group VI. The group tells you how many electrons an atom has in its outer shell.

Regardless of how many shells an atom has, the outermost shell is called the valence shell. The valence shell is important because it determines many of an atom's chemical properties. If an atom has only one shell, the outermost valence shell is complete when it has two electrons. But if an atom has more than one shell, the **octet rule** holds. This rule states that the outermost shell is most stable when it has eight electrons. As mentioned previously, atoms in group VIII of the periodic table are called the noble gases because they do not ordinarily react. Stability exists because the valence shell is filled with eight electrons and therefore has less energy. In general, lower energy states represent stability, as we will have an opportunity to point out again in Chapter 6.

Just as you sometimes communicate with and react to other people by using your hands, so atoms use the electrons in their valence shells to undergo reactions. Atoms with fewer than eight electrons in the outer shell react with other atoms in such a way that after the reaction, each has a stable outer shell. As we shall see, the number of electrons in an atom's **valence shell** determines whether the atom gives up, accepts, or shares electrons to acquire eight electrons in the outer shell. Each atom in a group within the periodic table has the same number of electrons in its valence shell.

Check Your Progress   2.1

1. Contrast atomic number and mass number.
2. Examine the periods and groups from the periodic table to determine the electron configuration of chlorine.
3. Explain what would happen if you used low radiation to medically treat cancer.

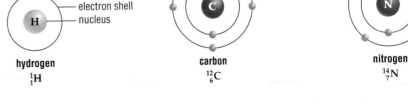

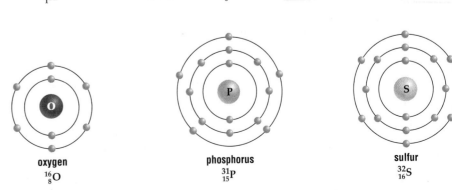

Figure 2.6 Bohr models of atoms.
Electrons orbit the nucleus at particular energy levels (electron shells). The first shell contains up to two electrons, and each shell thereafter can contain up to eight electrons as long as we consider only atoms with an atomic number of 20 or below. Each shell is filled before electrons are placed in the next shell. The outermost, or valence, shell helps determine the atom's chemical properties and how many other elements it can interact with.

2.2 Molecules and Compounds

Learning Outcomes

Upon completion of this section, you should be able to

1. Describe how elements are combined into molecules and compounds.
2. List different types of bonds that occur between elements.
3. Compare the relative strengths of ionic, covalent, and hydrogen bonds.

A **molecule** [L. *moles*, mass] exists when two or more elements bond together, and is the smallest part of a compound that retains its chemical properties. A **compound** is a molecule containing at least two different elements. In practice, these two terms are used interchangeably, but in biology, we usually speak of molecules. Water (H_2O) is a molecule that contains atoms of hydrogen and oxygen. A **formula** tells you the number of each kind of atom in a molecule. For example, in glucose:

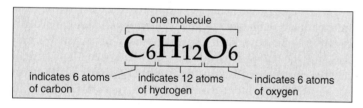

one molecule

$$C_6H_{12}O_6$$

indicates 6 atoms of carbon   indicates 12 atoms of hydrogen   indicates 6 atoms of oxygen

Electrons possess energy, and the bonds that exist between atoms also contain energy. Organisms are directly dependent on chemical-bond energy to maintain their organization. As you may know, organisms routinely break down glucose, the sugar shown to the left, to obtain energy. When a chemical reaction occurs, as when glucose is broken down, electrons shift in their relationship to one another, and energy is released. Spontaneous reactions, which are ones that occur freely, always release energy.

MP3
Chemical Bonding

Ionic Bonding

Sodium (Na), with only one electron in its third shell, tends to be an electron donor (Fig. 2.7a). Once it gives up this electron, the second shell, with eight electrons, becomes its outer shell. Chlorine (Cl), on the other hand, tends to be an electron acceptor. Its outer shell has seven electrons, so if it acquires only one more electron it has a completed outer shell. When a sodium atom and a chlorine atom come together, an electron is transferred from the sodium atom to the chlorine atom. Now both atoms have eight electrons in their outer shells.

This electron transfer, however, causes a charge imbalance in each atom. After giving up an electron, the sodium atom has one more proton than it has electrons; therefore, it has a net charge of +1 (symbolized by Na^+). After accepting an electron, the chlorine atom has one more electron than it has protons; therefore, it has a net charge of −1 (symbolized by Cl^-). Such charged particles are called **ions**. Sodium (Na^+) and chloride (Cl^-) are not the only biologically important ions. Some, such as potassium (K^+), are formed by the transfer of a single electron to another atom; others, such as calcium (Ca^{2+}) and magnesium (Mg^{2+}), are formed by the transfer of two electrons.

Ionic compounds are held together by a strong attraction between negatively and positively charged ions called an **ionic bond**. When sodium reacts with chlorine, an ionic compound called sodium chloride (NaCl) results. Sodium chloride is

Figure 2.7 Formation of sodium chloride (table salt). a. During the formation of sodium chloride, an electron is transferred from the sodium atom to the chlorine atom. At the completion of the reaction, each atom has eight electrons in the outer shell, but each also carries a charge as shown. **b.** In a sodium chloride crystal, ionic bonding between Na^+ and Cl^- causes the atoms to assume a three-dimensional lattice in which each sodium ion is surrounded by six chloride ions, and each chloride ion is surrounded by six sodium ions. The result is crystals of salt as in table salt.

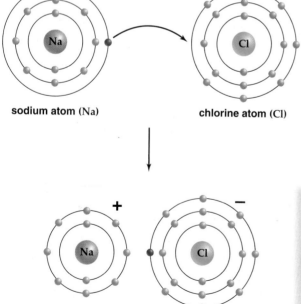

sodium atom (Na)   chlorine atom (Cl)

+   **−**

sodium ion (Na⁺)   chloride ion (Cl⁻)

sodium chloride (NaCl)

a.

Na⁺ Cl⁻

b.

a salt, commonly known as table salt, because it is used to season our food (Fig. 2.7*b*). **Salts** are solid substances that usually separate and exist as individual ions in water, as discussed on page 30.

Animation
Ionic Bonds

Covalent Bonding

A **covalent bond** [L. *co*, together, with, and *valens*, strength] results when two atoms share electrons in such a way that each atom has an octet of electrons in the outer shell (or two electrons, in the case of hydrogen). In a hydrogen atom, the outer shell is complete when it contains two electrons. If hydrogen is in the presence of a strong electron acceptor, it gives up its electron to become a hydrogen ion (H^+). But if this is not possible, hydrogen can share with another atom and thereby have a completed outer shell. For example, one hydrogen atom will share with another hydrogen atom. Their two electron shells overlap and the electrons are shared between them (Fig. 2.8*a*). Because they share the electron pair, each atom has a completed outer shell.

A more common way to symbolize that atoms are sharing electrons is to draw a line between the two atoms, as in the structural formula H—H. Just as a handshake requires two hands, one from each person, a covalent bond between two atoms requires two electrons, one from each atom. In a molecular formula, the line is omitted and the molecule is simply written as H_2.

Sometimes, atoms share more than one pair of electrons to complete their octets. A double covalent bond occurs when two atoms share two pairs of electrons (Fig. 2.8*b*). To show that oxygen gas (O_2) contains a double bond, the molecule can be written as O = O. It is also possible for atoms to form triple covalent bonds, as in nitrogen gas (N_2), which can be written as N≡N. Single covalent bonds between atoms are quite strong, but double and triple bonds are even stronger.

Nonpolar and Polar Covalent Bonds

When the sharing of electrons between two atoms is equal, the covalent bond is said to be a **nonpolar covalent bond.** If one atom is able to attract electrons to a greater degree than the other atom, it is the more electronegative atom. **Electronegativity** is dependent on the number of protons—the greater the number of protons, the greater the electronegativity. When electrons are not shared equally, the covalent bond is a **polar covalent bond.**

Animation
Electronegativity

You can readily see that the bonds in methane (Fig. 2.8*c*) must be polar because carbon has more protons than a hydrogen atom. However, methane is a symmetrical molecule and the polarities cancel each other out—methane is a nonpolar molecule. Not so in water, which has this shape:

Oxygen is partially negative (δ^-)

Hydrogens are partially positive (δ^+)

In water, the oxygen atom is more electronegative than the hydrogen atoms and the bonds are polar. Moreover, because of its

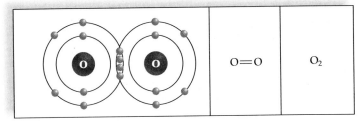
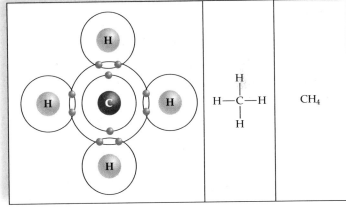

Electron Model	Structural Formula	Molecular Formula
(H—H electron model)	H—H	H_2
a. Hydrogen gas		
(O=O electron model)	O=O	O_2
b. Oxygen gas		
(methane electron model)	H—C—H with H above and below	CH_4
c. Methane		

Figure 2.8 Covalently bonded molecules. In a covalent bond, atoms share electrons, allowing each atom to have a completed outer shell. **a.** A molecule of hydrogen (H_2) contains two hydrogen atoms sharing a pair of electrons. This single covalent bond can be represented in any of the three ways shown. **b.** A molecule of oxygen (O_2) contains two oxygen atoms sharing two pairs of electrons. This results in a double covalent bond. **c.** A molecule of methane (CH_4) contains one carbon atom bonded to four hydrogen atoms.

nonsymmetrical shape, the polar bonds cannot cancel each other, and water is a polar molecule. The more electronegative end of the molecule is designated slightly negative (δ^-), and the hydrogens are designated slightly positive (δ^+).

Water is not the only polar molecule in living things. For example, the amine group (—NH_2) is polar, and this causes amino acids and nucleic acids to exhibit polarity, as we shall see in the next chapter. The polarity of molecules affects how they interact with other molecules.

Animation
Ionic vs. Covalent Bonding

Check Your Progress   2.2

1. Compare and contrast an ionic bond with a covalent bond.
2. Explain why calcium ion carries two positive charges.
3. Describe how the atoms in methane (CH_4) produce a complete outer shell.

2.3 Chemistry of Water

Learning Outcomes

Upon completion of this section, you should be able to

1. Describe how water associates with other molecules in solution.
2. Evaluate which property of water is important for biological life.
3. Analyze how water's solid, liquid, and vapor states allow life to exist on Earth.

Figure 2.9a recaps what we know about the water molecule. The structural formula on the far left shows that when water forms, an oxygen atom is sharing electrons with two hydrogen atoms. The ball-and-stick model in the center shows that the covalent bonds between oxygen and each of the hydrogens are at an angle of 104.5°. Finally, the space-filling molecule gives us the three-dimensional shape of the molecule and indicates its polarity.

The shape of water and of all organic molecules is necessary to the structural and functional roles they play in living things. For example, hormones have specific shapes that allow them to be recognized by the cells in the body. We can stay well only when antibodies recognize the shape of disease-causing agents, like a key fits a lock, and are able to remove them. Similarly, homeostasis is only maintained when enzymes have the proper shape to carry out their particular reactions in cells.

The shape of a water molecule and its polarity make hydrogen bonding possible. A **hydrogen bond** is the attraction of a slightly positive hydrogen to a slightly negative atom in the vicinity. In carbon dioxide, $O = C = O$, a slight difference in polarity between carbon and the oxygens is present, but because carbon dioxide is symmetrical, the opposing charges cancel one another and hydrogen bonding does not occur.

Hydrogen Bonding

The dotted lines in Figure 2.9b indicate that the hydrogen atoms in one water molecule are attracted to the oxygen atoms in other water molecules. Each of these hydrogen bonds is weaker than an ionic or covalent bond. The dotted lines indicate that hydrogen bonds are more easily broken than the other bonds.

Hydrogen bonding is not unique to water. Other biological molecules, such as DNA, have polar covalent bonds involving an electropositive hydrogen and usually an electronegative oxygen or nitrogen. In these instances, a hydrogen bond can occur within the same molecule or between nearby molecules.

Although a single hydrogen bond is more easily broken than a single covalent bond, multiple hydrogen bonds are collectively quite strong. Hydrogen bonds between cellular molecules help maintain their proper structure and function. For example, hydrogen bonds hold the two strands of DNA together.

Figure 2.9 Water molecule. **a.** Three models for the structure of water. The electron model does not indicate the shape of the molecule. The ball-and-stick model shows that the two bonds in a water molecule are angled at 104.5°. The space-filling model also shows the V shape of a water molecule. **b.** Hydrogen bonding between water molecules. Each water molecule can hydrogen bond with up to four other molecules, in three dimensions. When in a liquid state, water is constantly forming and breaking hydrogen bonds.

Electron Model

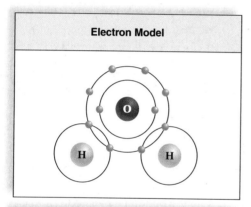

Ball-and-stick Model

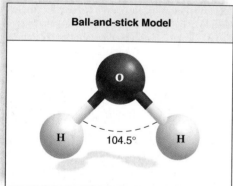

Space-filling Model

Oxygen attracts the shared electrons and is partially negative.

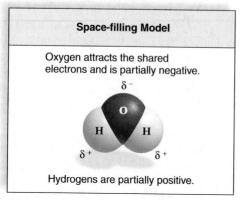

Hydrogens are partially positive.

a. Water (H_2O)

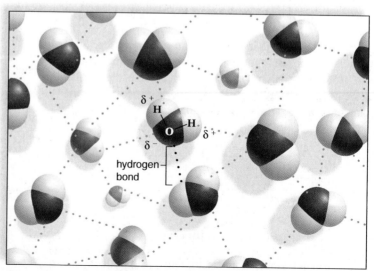

b. Hydrogen bonding between water molecules

When DNA makes a copy of itself, hydrogen bonds easily break, allowing DNA to unzip. But normally, the hydrogen bonds add stability to the DNA molecule. Similarly, the shape of protein molecules is often maintained by hydrogen bonding between different parts of the same molecule. As we shall see, many of the important properties of water are the result of hydrogen bonding.

Properties of Water

The first cell(s) evolved in water, and all living things are 70–90% water. Because of hydrogen bonding, water molecules cling together, and this association gives water its unique chemical properties. Without hydrogen bonding between molecules, water would freeze at –100°C and boil at –91°C, making most of the water on Earth steam, and life unlikely. Hydrogen bonding is responsible for water being a liquid at temperatures typically found on the Earth's surface. It freezes at 0°C and boils at 100°C. These and other unique properties of water make it essential to the existence of life as we know it. When scientists examine other planets with the hope of finding life, they first look for signs of water.

Animation Properties of Water

Water Has a High Heat Capacity. A **calorie** is the amount of heat energy needed to raise the temperature of 1 g of water 1°C. In comparison, other covalently bonded liquids require input of only about half this amount of energy to rise in temperature 1°C. The many hydrogen bonds that link water molecules together help water absorb heat without a great change in temperature. Converting 1 g of the coldest liquid water to ice requires the loss of 80 calories of heat energy (Fig. 2.10a). Water holds onto its heat, and its temperature falls more slowly than that of other liquids. This property of water is important not only for aquatic organisms but also for all living things.

Because the temperature of water rises and falls slowly, organisms are better able to maintain their normal internal temperatures and are protected from rapid temperature changes.

Water Has a High Heat of Evaporation. When water boils, it evaporates—that is, vaporizes into the environment. Converting 1 g of the hottest water to a gas requires an input of 540 calories of energy. Water has a high heat of evaporation because hydrogen bonds must be broken before water boils.

Water's high heat of vaporization gives animals in a hot environment an efficient way to release excess body heat. When an animal sweats, or gets splashed, body heat is used to vaporize water, thus cooling the animal (Fig. 2.10b). Because of water's high heat of vaporization and ability to hold onto its heat, temperatures along the coasts are moderate. During the summer, the ocean absorbs and stores solar heat, and during the winter, the ocean releases it slowly. In contrast, the interior regions of continents experience abrupt changes in temperatures.

Water Is a Solvent. Due to its polarity, water facilitates chemical reactions, both outside and within living systems. As

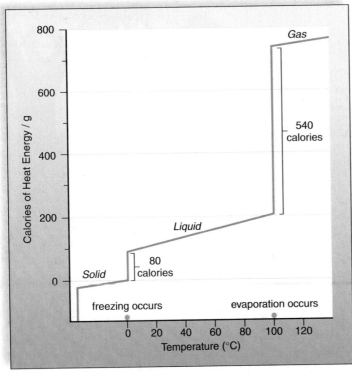

a. Calories lost when 1 g of liquid water freezes and calories required when 1 g of liquid water evaporates.

b. Bodies of organisms cool when their heat is used to evaporate water.

Figure 2.10 Temperature and water. **a.** Water can be a solid, a liquid, or a gas at naturally occurring environmental temperatures. At room temperature and pressure, water is a liquid. When water freezes and becomes a solid (ice), it gives off heat, and this heat can help keep the environmental temperature higher than expected. On the other hand, when water evaporates, it takes up a large amount of heat as it changes from a liquid to a gas. **b.** This means that splashing water on the body will help keep body temperature within a normal range. Can you also see why water's properties help keep the coasts moderate in both winter and summer?

a solvent, it dissolves a great number of substances, especially those that are also polar. A **solution** contains dissolved substances, which are then called **solutes**. When ionic salts—for example, sodium chloride (NaCl)—are put into water, the negative ends of the water molecules are attracted to the sodium ions, and the positive ends of the water molecules are attracted to the chloride ions. This attraction causes the sodium ions and the chloride ions to separate, or dissociate, in water.

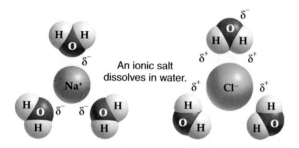

An ionic salt dissolves in water.

Water is also a solvent for larger polar molecules, such as ammonia (NH_3).

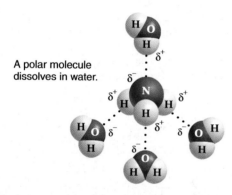

A polar molecule dissolves in water.

Molecules that can attract water are said to be **hydrophilic** [Gk. *hydrias,* of water, and *phileo,* love]. When ions and molecules disperse in water, they move about and collide, allowing reactions to occur. Nonionized and nonpolar molecules that cannot attract water are said to be **hydrophobic** [Gk. *hydrias,* of water, and *phobos,* fear]. Hydrophilic molecules tend to attract other polar molecules; similarly, hydrophobic substances usually associate with other nonpolar molecules. Gasoline contains nonpolar molecules, and therefore does not mix with water and is hydrophobic.

Water Molecules Are Cohesive and Adhesive. Cohesion refers to the ability of water molecules to cling to each other due to hydrogen bonding. At any moment in time, a water molecule can form hydrogen bonds with at most four other water molecules. Because of cohesion, water exists as a liquid under the conditions of temperature and pressure present at the Earth's surface. The strong cohesion of water molecules is apparent because water flows freely, yet water molecules do not separate from each other.

Adhesion refers to the ability of water molecules to cling to other polar surfaces. This is a result of water's polarity. Multicellular animals often contain internal vessels in which water assists the transport of nutrients and wastes because the cohesion and adhesion of water allows blood to fill the tubular

vessels of the cardiovascular system. For example, the liquid portion of our blood, which transports dissolved and suspended substances about the body, is 90% water.

Cohesion and adhesion also contribute to the transport of water in plants. Plants have their roots anchored in the soil, where they absorb water, but the leaves are uplifted and exposed to solar energy. Water evaporating from the leaves is immediately replaced with water molecules from transport vessels that extend from the roots to the leaves (Fig. 2.11). Because water molecules are cohesive, a tension is created that pulls the water column up from the roots. Adhesion of water to the walls of the transport vessels also helps prevent the water column

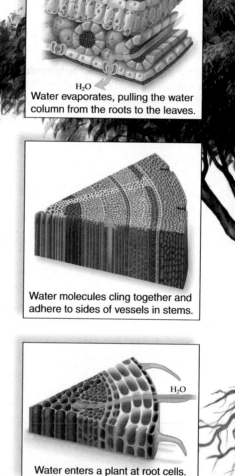

H_2O
Water evaporates, pulling the water column from the roots to the leaves.

Water molecules cling together and adhere to sides of vessels in stems.

H_2O
Water enters a plant at root cells.

Figure 2.11 Water as a transport medium.
How does water rise to the top of tall trees when they have no heart to pump it? Plants have water-filled pipelines that run from the roots to the leaves. When water evaporates from the leaves, the water column is pulled upward due to the cohesion of water molecules to one another and the adhesion of water molecules to the sides of the vessels. This capillary action is critical for plants to function.

from breaking apart. This capillary action is essential to plant life, as will be discussed in chapter 25.

Because water molecules are attracted to each other, they cling together where the liquid surface is exposed to air. The stronger the force between molecules in a liquid, the greater the **surface tension.** Water's high surface tension makes it possible for humans to skip rocks on water. Water striders, a common insect, can even walk on the surface of a pond without breaking the surface.

Frozen Water (Ice) Is Less Dense than Liquid Water.   As liquid water cools, the molecules come closer together. Water is most dense at 4°C, but the water molecules are still moving about (Fig. 2.12). At temperatures below 4°C, only vibrational movement occurs, and hydrogen bonding becomes more rigid but also more open. This means that water expands as it reaches 0°C and freezes, which is why cans of soda burst when placed in a freezer, or why frost heaves make northern roads bumpy in the winter. It also means that ice is less dense than liquid water, and therefore ice floats on liquid water.

If ice did not float on water, it would sink to the bottom, and ponds, lakes, and perhaps even the ocean would freeze solid, making life impossible in the water and also on land. Instead, bodies of water always freeze from the top down. When a body of water freezes on the surface, the ice acts as an insulator to prevent the water below it from freezing. This allows aquatic organisms to survive the winter. As ice melts in the spring, it draws heat from the environment, helping to prevent a sudden change in temperature that might be harmful to life.

Check Your Progress   2.3

1. Explain how water's high heat of vaporization allows coastal cities to have a consistent temperature throughout the year.
2. Analyze which property of water helps children cool off during summertime by playing in a sprinkler.
3. Evaluate what would happen to life if ice sank instead of floating in the winter.

Figure 2.12 A pond in winter.   *Above:* Remarkably, water is more dense at 4°C than at 0°C. Most substances contract when they solidify, but water expands when it freezes because in ice, water molecules form a lattice in which the hydrogen bonds are farther apart than in liquid water. *Below:* The layer of ice that forms at the top of a pond shields the water and protects the protists, plants, and animals so that they can survive the winter. These animals, except for the otter, are ectothermic, which means that they take on the temperature of the outside environment. This might seem disadvantageous until you realize that water remains relatively warm because of its high heat capacity. During the winter, frogs and turtles hibernate and in this way, lower their oxygen needs. Insects survive in air pockets. Fish, as you will learn later in this text, have an efficient means of extracting oxygen from the water, and they need less oxygen than the endothermic otter, which depends on muscle activity to warm its body.

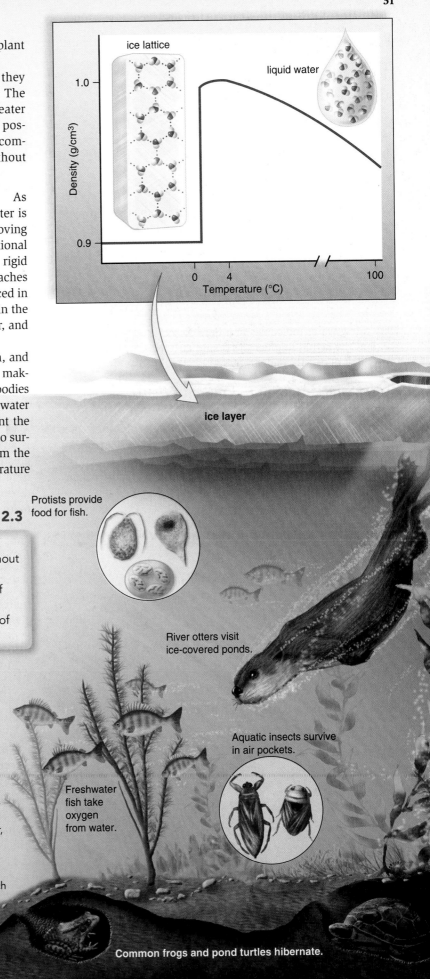

ice lattice

liquid water

Density (g/cm³)

1.0

0.9

0   4   100

Temperature (°C)

ice layer

Protists provide food for fish.

River otters visit ice-covered ponds.

Aquatic insects survive in air pockets.

Freshwater fish take oxygen from water.

Common frogs and pond turtles hibernate.

2.4 Acids and Bases

Learning Outcomes

Upon completion of this section, you should be able to

1. Identify common acidic and basic substances.
2. Determine pH from a known H^+ or OH^- concentration.
3. Analyze how buffers prevent large pH changes in solutions.

When water ionizes, it releases an equal number of **hydrogen ions (H^+)** (also called protons[1]) and **hydroxide ions (OH^-)**:

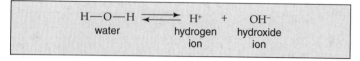

Only a few water molecules at a time dissociate, and the actual number of H^+ and OH^- is very small (1×10^{-7} moles/liter).[2]

MP3
Water and pH

Acidic Solutions (High H⁺ Concentrations)

Lemon juice, vinegar, tomatoes, and coffee are all acidic solutions. What do they have in common? **Acids** are substances that dissociate in water, releasing hydrogen ions (H^+). The acidity of a substance depends on how fully it dissociates in water. For example, hydrochloric acid (HCl) is a strong acid that dissociates almost completely in this manner:

$$HCl \longrightarrow H^+ + Cl^-$$

If hydrochloric acid is added to a beaker of water, the number of hydrogen ions (H^+) increases greatly.

Basic Solutions (Low H⁺ Concentration)

Milk of magnesia and ammonia are common basic solutions familiar to most people. **Bases** are substances that either take up hydrogen ions (H^+) or release hydroxide ions (OH^-). For example, sodium hydroxide (NaOH) is a strong base that dissociates almost completely in this manner:

$$NaOH \longrightarrow Na^+ + OH^-$$

If sodium hydroxide is added to a beaker of water, the number of hydroxide ions increases.

pH Scale

The **pH scale** is used to indicate the acidity or basicity (alkalinity) of a solution.[3] The pH scale (Fig. 2.13) ranges from 0 to 14. A pH of 7 represents a neutral state in which the hydrogen ion and hydroxide ion concentrations are equal. A pH below 7

---

1 A hydrogen atom contains one electron and one proton. A hydrogen ion has only one proton, so it is often simply called a proton.
2 In chemistry, a mole is defined as 6.02×10^{23} of any atom, molecule, or ion. For example, 6.02×10^{23} atoms of 12C would have a mass of exactly 12 g. The same number of glucose molecules (1 mole) would have a mass of 180 g.
3 pH is defined as the negative log of the hydrogen ion concentration [H^+]. A log is the power to which 10 must be raised to produce a given number.

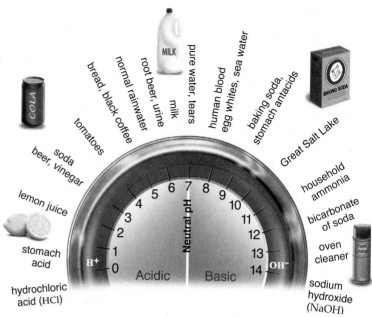

Figure 2.13 The pH scale.   The pH scale ranges from 0 to 14 with 0 being the most acidic and 14 being the most basic. pH 7 (neutral pH) has equal amounts of hydrogen ions (H^+) and hydroxide ions (OH^-). An acidic pH has more H^+ than OH^- and a basic pH has more OH^- than H^+.

is an acidic solution because the hydrogen ion concentration is greater than the hydroxide concentration. A pH above 7 is basic because the [OH^-] is greater than the [H^+]. Further, as we move down the pH scale from pH 14 to pH 0, each unit is 10 times more acidic than the previous unit. As we move up the scale from 0 to 14, each unit is 10 times more basic than the previous unit. Therefore pH 5 is 100 times more acidic than pH 7 and a 100 times more basic than pH 3.

The pH scale was devised to eliminate the use of cumbersome numbers. For example, the possible hydrogen ion concentrations of a solution are on the left of this listing and the pH is on the right:

[H⁺] (moles per liter)		pH
0.000001	$= 1 \times 10^{-6}$	6
0.0000001	$= 1 \times 10^{-7}$	7
0.00000001	$= 1 \times 10^{-8}$	8

To further illustrate the relationship between hydrogen ion concentration and pH, consider the following question. Which of the pH values listed indicates a higher hydrogen ion concentration [H^+] than pH 7, and therefore would be an acidic solution? A number with a smaller negative exponent indicates a greater quantity of hydrogen ions than one with a larger negative exponent. Therefore, pH 6 is an acidic solution.

The Biological Systems feature on page 33 describes detrimental environmental consequences to nonliving and living things as rain and snow have become more acidic. In humans, pH needs to be maintained within a narrow range or there are health consequences. The pH of blood is around 7.4, and blood is buffered in the manner described next to keep the pH within a normal range.

THEME Biological Systems

The Interconnectedness of Water, Plants, and People

Acid Deposition

Normally, rainwater has a pH of about 5.6 because the carbon dioxide in the air combines with water to give a weak solution of carbonic acid. Acid deposition includes rain or snow that has a pH of less than 5, as well as dry acidic particles that fall to Earth from the atmosphere.

When fossil fuels such as coal, oil, and gasoline are burned, sulfur dioxide and nitrogen oxides combine with water to produce sulfuric and nitric acids. These pollutants are generally found eastward of where they originated because of wind patterns. The use of very tall smokestacks causes them to be carried even hundreds of miles away. For example, acid rain in southeastern Canada results from the burning of fossil fuels in factories and power plants in the midwestern United States.

Impact on Lakes

Acid rain adversely affects many aspects of biological systems. Aluminum may leach from the soil of lakes, particularly in areas where the soil is thin and lacks limestone (calcium carbonate, or $CaCO_3$) as a buffer. Acid rain may convert mercury in lake bottom sediments to toxic methyl mercury. Methyl mercury accumulates in fish, which wildlife and people eat. Over time, methyl mercury can accumulate in body tissues and cause serious sensory and muscular health problems. Acid rain in Canada and New England has caused hundreds of lakes to be devoid of fish, and in some cases, any life at all.

Impact on Forests

The leaves of plants damaged by acid rain can no longer carry on photosynthesis as before. When plants are under stress, they become susceptible to diseases and pests of all types. Forests on mountaintops re-

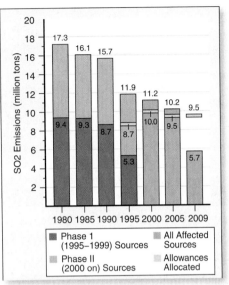
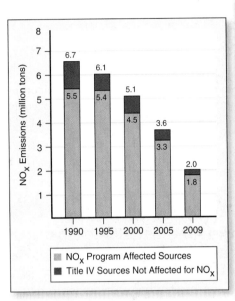

Figure 2A Trends in U.S. acid rain emissions. The burning of fossil fuels in factories, automobiles, and other industrial processes produces chemicals like SO_2 and NO_x that lead to acid deposition and destruction of the environment. Clean air legislation and stricter emission standards over the past 20 years have resulted in steady decreases in SO_2 and NO_x, chemicals that lead to acid rain.

ceive more rain than those at lower levels; therefore, they are more affected by acid rain. Forests are also damaged when toxic chemicals such as aluminum are leached from the soil. These kill soil fungi that assist roots in acquiring the nutrients trees need. In New England, 1.3 million acres of high-elevation forests have been devastated. Sulfur dioxide and nitrogen oxides, the main precursors of acid rain, have been steadily decreasing in the United States due to clean air legislation and strict emission limits (see Figure 2A).

Impact on Humans and Structures

Humans may be affected by acid rain. Inhaling dry sulfate and nitrate particles appears to increase the occurrence of respiratory illnesses, such as asthma. Buildings and monu-

ments made of limestone and marble break down when exposed to acid rain. The paint on homes and automobiles is likewise degraded. However, damage to natural systems and human structures due to acid rain is likely to decrease if we continue efforts to reduce chemicals that contribute to acid rain.

Questions to Consider

1. What acid rain trends are evident from the EPA data?
2. Considering that manufacturing is essential to our national interests, how might we modify industrial processing to reduce sulfur dioxide and nitrogen oxide contamination?
3. How might we prevent methyl mercury from entering biological systems and reduce the amount already present?

Buffers and pH

A **buffer** is a chemical or a combination of chemicals that keeps pH within normal limits. Many commercial products such as shampoos or deodorants are buffered as an added incentive for us to buy them.

In living things, the pH of body fluids is maintained within a narrow range, or else molecules don't function correctly and our

health suffers. The pH of our blood when we are healthy is always about 7.4—that is, just slightly basic (alkaline). If the blood pH drops to about 7, acidosis results. If the blood pH rises to about 7.8, alkalosis results. Both conditions can be life threatening, so the blood pH must be kept around 7.4. Normally, pH stability is possible because the body has built-in mechanisms to prevent pH changes. Buffers are one of these important mechanisms.

Buffers help keep the pH within normal limits because they are chemicals or combinations of chemicals that take up excess hydrogen ions (H^+) or hydroxide ions (OH^-). For example, carbonic acid (H_2CO_3) is a weak acid that minimally dissociates and then re-forms in the following manner:

$$\underset{\text{carbonic acid}}{H_2CO_3} \underset{\underset{\text{re-forms}}{\longleftarrow}}{\overset{\overset{\text{dissociates}}{\longrightarrow}}{}} H^+ + \underset{\text{bicarbonate ion}}{HCO_3^-}$$

Blood always contains a combination of some carbonic acid and some bicarbonate ions. When hydrogen ions (H^+) are added to blood, the following reaction reduces acidity:

$$H^+ + HCO_3^- \longrightarrow H_2CO_3$$

When hydroxide ions (OH^-) are added to blood, this reaction reduces basicity:

$$OH^- + H_2CO_3 \longrightarrow HCO_3^- + H_2O$$

These reactions prevent any significant change in blood pH.

Check Your Progress   2.4

1. Explain the difference in H^+ concentration between an acid and a base.
2. Predict what would happen to plant and animal life where you live if the pH of rain dropped to 6.
3. Interpret what would happen to your blood pH if the amount of buffer decreased by a factor of 10.

CONNECTING *the* CONCEPTS *with the* THEMES

This chapter has explored concepts that integrate with the major themes of life science.

Evolution

- Six of the 92 naturally occurring elements—carbon, hydrogen, nitrogen, oxygen, phosphorus, and sulfur (CHNOPS)—make up 95% of the body mass of organisms on Earth.
- Carbon-containing molecules can be modified in numerous ways, and this accounts for life's diversity. Molecules can undergo evolution (change), and this in turn can account for evolution of species.
- Much biological evolution has occurred due to life's interactions with water. Our search for water on other planets underscores the central role that water plays in living matter.

Nature of Science

- Scientific discoveries about chemistry, water, and carbon help us understand substances that are built from these atoms.
- Our understanding of life continues to change over time as we uncover fundamental truths about chemistry. Items we use every day, including food, plastics, and medicine, are products of ongoing research in chemistry.

Biological Systems

- All of life consists of systems, from the atomic and molecular levels to the ecosystem and planet levels.
- Like all systems, chemistry consists of inputs and outputs, with resulting changes in energy.
- The total of all the chemical reactions in our bodies is called metabolism, which is responsible for regulating life-supporting processes.
- Many elements exist as ions in the body, and their functions depend on their charged nature.
- Cells consist largely of water, a molecule that contains only hydrogen and oxygen atoms. Because of oxygen's strong electronegativity, water is a polar molecule, making hydrogen bonding possible.

Media Study Tools

www.mhhe.com/maderbiology11

Enhance your study of this chapter with study tools and practice tests. Also ask your instructor about the resources available through ConnectPlus, including the media-rich eBook, interactive learning tools, and animations.

Summarize

2.1 Chemical Elements

Both living and nonliving things are composed of matter consisting of elements. The most significant elements (atoms) are found in living things: carbon, hydrogen, nitrogen, oxygen, phosphorus, and sulfur (CHNOPS).

Elements contain atoms, and atoms contain subatomic particles. Protons have positive charges, neutrons are uncharged, and electrons have negative charges. Protons and neutrons in the nucleus determine the mass number of an atom. The atomic number indicates the number of protons and the number of electrons in electrically neutral atoms.

Isotopes are atoms of a single element that differ in their numbers of neutrons. Radioactive isotopes have many uses, including serving as tracers in biological experiments and medical procedures.

Electrons occupy energy levels (electron shells) at discrete distances from the nucleus. The number of electrons in the outer shell determines the reactivity of an atom. The first shell is complete when it is occupied by two electrons. In atoms up through calcium, number 20, every shell beyond the first shell is complete when eight electrons are present. The octet rule states that atoms react with one another in order to have a completed outer shell. Most atoms, including those common to living things, do not have filled outer shells and this causes them to react with one another to form compounds and/or molecules. Following the reaction, the atoms have completed outer shells.

2.2 Molecules and Compounds

Compounds and molecules are formed when elements associate with each other. Ions, which are created when atoms lose or gain one or more electrons to achieve a completed outer shell, form ionic bonds between oppositely charged ions.

Covalent compounds form when atoms share one or more pairs of electrons. There are single, double, and triple covalent bonds.

In polar covalent bonds, the sharing of electrons is not equal. If the molecule is polar, the more electronegative atom carries a slightly negative charge and the other atom carries a slightly positive charge.

2.3 Chemistry of Water

Water is an essential molecule for life. The polarity of water molecules allows hydrogen bonding to occur between water molecules. A hydrogen bond is a weak attraction between a slightly positive hydrogen atom and a slightly negative oxygen or nitrogen atom within the same or a different molecule. Hydrogen bonds help maintain the structure and function of cellular molecules.

Water's polarity and hydrogen bonding account for its unique properties. These features allow living things to exist and carry on cellular activities.

2.4 Acids and Bases

pH is a measure of how acidic or basic a substance is. A small fraction of water molecules dissociate to produce an equal number of hydrogen ions and hydroxide ions. Solutions with equal numbers of H^+ and OH^- are termed neutral.

Acidic solutions contain more hydrogen ions than hydroxide ions; these solutions have a pH less than 7. Basic solutions have more hydroxide ions than hydrogen ions; these solutions have a pH greater than 7. Cells are sensitive to pH changes. Biological systems often contain buffers that help keep the pH within a normal range.

Key Terms

acid 32
atom 22
atomic mass 23
atomic number 23
atomic symbol 22
base 32
buffer 33
calorie 29
compound 26
covalent bond 27
electron 22
electronegativity 27

electron shell 23
element 22
formula 26
hydrogen bond 28
hydrogen ion (H^+) 32
hydrophilic 30
hydrophobic 30
hydroxide ion (OH^-) 32
ion 26
ionic bond 26
isotope 24
mass number 23

matter 22
molecule 26
neutron 22
nonpolar covalent bond 27
octet rule 25
pH scale 32
polar covalent bond 27

proton 22
salt 27
solute 30
solution 30
surface tension 31
valence shell 25

 **Assess**

Reviewing This Chapter

1. Name the kinds of subatomic particles studied. What is their atomic mass unit, charge, and location in an atom? 21–23
2. What is an isotope? A radioactive isotope? Radioactivity is always considered dangerous. Why? 24–26
3. Using the Bohr model, draw an atomic structure for a carbon that has six protons and six neutrons. 26
4. Draw an atomic representation for $MgCl_2$. Using the octet rule, explain the structure of the compound. 27
5. Explain whether CO_2 (O=C=O) is an ionic or a covalent compound. Why does this arrangement satisfy all atoms involved? 27
6. Of what significance is the shape of molecules in organisms? 28
7. Explain why water is a polar molecule. What does the polarity and shape of water have to do with its ability to form hydrogen bonds? 28
8. Name five properties of water, and relate them to the structure of water, including its polarity and hydrogen bonding between molecules. 28–31
9. On the pH scale, which numbers indicate a solution is acidic? Basic? Neutral? 32
10. What are buffers, and why are they important to life? 32–33

Testing Yourself

Choose the best answer for each question.

1. Which of the subatomic particles contributes almost no weight to an atom?
   a. protons in the electron shells
   b. electrons in the nucleus
   c. neutrons in the nucleus
   d. electrons at various energy levels

2. The atomic number tells you the
   a. number of neutrons in the nucleus.
   b. number of protons in the atom.
   c. atomic mass of the atom.
   d. number of its electrons if the atom is neutral.
   e. Both b and d are correct.

3. An atom that has two electrons in the outer shell, such as magnesium, would most likely
   a. share to acquire a completed outer shell.
   b. lose these two electrons and become a negatively charged ion.
   c. lose these two electrons and become a positively charged ion.
   d. bind with carbon by way of hydrogen bonds.
   e. bind with another calcium atom to satisfy its energy needs.

4. Isotopes differ in their
   a. number of protons.
   b. atomic number.
   c. number of neutrons.
   d. number of electrons.

5. When an atom gains electrons, it
   a. forms a negatively charged ion.
   b. forms a positively charged ion.
   c. forms covalent bonds.
   d. forms ionic bonds.
   e. gains atomic mass.

6. A covalent bond is indicated by
   a. plus and minus charges attached to atoms.
   b. dotted lines between hydrogen atoms.
   c. concentric circles about a nucleus.
   d. overlapping electron shells or a straight line between atomic symbols.
   e. the touching of atomic nuclei.

7. The shape of a molecule
   a. is dependent in part on the angle of bonds between its atoms.
   b. influences its biological function.
   c. is dependent on its electronegativity.
   d. is dependent on its place in the periodic table.
   e. Both a and b are correct.

8. In the molecule

$$H-\overset{\displaystyle H}{\underset{\displaystyle H}{C}}-H$$

   a. all atoms have eight electrons in the outer shell.
   b. all atoms are sharing electrons.
   c. carbon could accept more hydrogen atoms.
   d. the bonds point to the corners of a square.
   e. All of these are correct.

9. Which of these properties of water cannot be attributed to hydrogen bonding between water molecules?
   a. Water stabilizes temperature inside and outside the cell.
   b. Water molecules are cohesive.
   c. Water is a solvent for many molecules.
   d. Ice floats on liquid water.
   e. Both b and c are correct.

10. Complete this diagram by placing an O for oxygen or an H for hydrogen on the appropriate atoms. Place partial charges where they belong.

11. H_2CO_3/$NaHCO_3$ is a buffer system in the body. What effect will the addition of an acid have on the pH of a solution that is buffered?
    a. The pH will rise.   c. The pH will not change.
    b. The pH will lower.   d. All of these are correct.

12. Acids
    a. release hydrogen ions in solution.
    b. cause the pH of a solution to rise above 7.
    c. take up hydroxide ions and become neutral.
    d. increase the number of water molecules.
    e. Both a and b are correct.

13. If a chemical accepted H^+ from the surrounding solution, the chemical could be
    a. a base.   d. None of the above are correct.
    b. an acid.   e. Both a and c are correct.
    c. a buffer.

14. The periodic table tells us
    a. the atomic number, symbol, and mass.
    b. how many shells an atom has.
    c. how many electrons are in the outer shell.
    d. whether the atom will react or not.
    e. All of these are correct.

15. Which of these best describes the changes that occur when a solution goes from pH 5 to pH 7?
    a. The solution is now 100 times more acidic.
    b. The solution is now 100 times more basic.
    c. The hydrogen ion concentration decreases by only a factor of 20, as the solution goes from basic to acidic.
    d. The hydrogen ion concentration changes by only a factor of 20, as the solution goes from acidic to basic.

For questions 16–19, match the statements with a property of water in the key.

KEY:
   a. Water flows because it is cohesive.
   b. Water holds its heat.
   c. Water has neutral pH.
   d. Water has a high heat of vaporization.

16. Sweating helps cool us off.

17. Our blood is composed mostly of water and cells.

18. Our blood is just about pH 7.

19. We usually maintain a normal body temperature.

Engage

Thinking Scientifically

1. Natural phenomena often require an explanation. Based on how sodium chloride dissociates in water (see pages 29–30) and Figure 2.12, explain why the oceans don't freeze.

2. Melvin Calvin used radioactive carbon (as a tracer) to discover a series of molecules that form during photosynthesis. Explain why carbon behaves chemically the same, even when radioactive.

Bioethical Issue

The Right to Refuse an IV

When a person gets sick or endures physical stress—as, for example, during childbirth—pH levels may dip or rise too far, endangering that person's life. In most U.S. hospitals, doctors routinely administer IVs, or intravenous infusions, of certain fluids to maintain a patient's pH level. Some people who oppose IVs for philosophical reasons may refuse an IV. That's relatively safe, as long as the person is healthy.

Problems arise when hospital policy dictates an IV, even though a patient does not want one. Should a patient be allowed to refuse an IV? Or does a hospital have the right to insist, for health reasons, that patients accept IV fluids? And what role should doctors play—patient advocates or hospital representatives?

Granddaughter Sylvia with azalea plant.

3

The Chemistry of Organic Molecules

CHAPTER OUTLINE

3.1 Organic Molecules 38
3.2 Carbohydrates 41
3.3 Lipids 45
3.4 Proteins 49
3.5 Nucleic Acids 54

A ll life is interconnected because it uses a common set of chemicals to build larger, more complex molecules that are used as the building blocks of every living thing. In fact, the same organic molecules are used to build a bacterium, a flower, or a little girl. These macromolecules—namely, carbohydrates, lipids, proteins, and nucleic acids—are combined to produce different structures which lead them to have different functions. The similarities in molecules makes it possible for vegetarians to eat only plants and be healthy, as long as they include enough different plants in their diet. When we consume other things, we break down their macromolecules to smaller molecules, and then we use these smaller molecules to build our own types of carbohydrates, lipids, proteins, and nucleic acids. Both the breakdown and building processes are made possible using special catalysts called enzymes.

A bacterium, plant, and human are different because of their genes. All genes are made of DNA, and the way genes function in cells is essentially the same in all organisms. In this chapter, we extend our knowledge of chemistry and consider macromolecules, how their structure and function are related, and how these support life on Earth.

As you read through the chapter, think about the following questions:

1. How can a relatively small number of chemicals be used to build many large, complex, and diverse molecules?
2. Why can one organism use molecules from another organism to build their own?
3. How are organic molecules combined to create the structures and functions necessary to support life?

BEFORE YOU BEGIN

Before beginning this chapter, take a few moments to review the following discussions.

Figures 1.5–1.8 What are the the major kingdoms of life?

Figure 2.3 What chemical elements are most important for producing organic molecules?

Sections 2.2–2.3 What types of bonds can form between elements in an organic molecule?

FOLLOWING *the* THEMES

	CHAPTER 3 THE CHEMISTRY OF ORGANIC MOLECULES	
UNIT 1 THE CELL	**Evolution**	The diversity of biological life is the result of changes in DNA sequences.
	Nature of Science	Investigating relationships between a molecule's structure and its function allows discovery of new and useful substances.
	Biological Systems	Macromolecules form the functional basis for all cellular systems.

3.1 Organic Molecules

Learning Outcomes

Upon completion of this section, you should be able to

1. Explain how the properties of carbon enable it to produce diverse organic molecules.
2. Describe how functional groups affect a carbon molecule's chemical reactivity.
3. Compare what is added and what is produced during biomolecule synthesis and degradation reactions.

Table 3.1 Inorganic Versus Organic Molecules

Inorganic Molecules	Organic Molecules
Usually contain positive and negative ions	Always contain carbon and hydrogen
Usually ionic bonding	Always covalent bonding
Always contain a small number of atoms	Often quite large, with many atoms
Often associated with nonliving matter	Usually associated with living organisms

Chemists of the nineteenth century thought that the molecules of cells must contain a vital force, so they divided chemistry into **organic chemistry,** the chemistry of living organisms, and **inorganic chemistry,** the chemistry of nonliving matter. We still use this terminology, even though many types of organic molecules can now be synthesized in the laboratory. Today, we simply define **organic molecules** as molecules that contain both carbon and hydrogen atoms (Table 3.1).

There are only four classes of organic compounds in any living thing: carbohydrates, lipids, proteins, and nucleic acids. Collectively, these are called the **biomolecules** and despite the limited number of types, their functions in a cell are quite diverse. A bacterial cell contains some 5,000 different organic molecules, and a plant or animal cell has twice that number. The diversity of life is possible because of this diversity of organic molecules (Fig. 3.1). Ultimately, the variety of organic molecules is based on the unique chemical properties of the carbon atom.

The Carbon Atom

What is there about carbon that makes organic molecules the same and also different? Carbon is quite small, with only a total of six electrons: two electrons in the first shell and four electrons in the outer shell. To acquire four electrons to complete its outer shell, a carbon atom almost always shares electrons with—you guessed it—CHNOPS, the elements that make up most of the weight of living things (see Fig. 2.1).

Because carbon needs four electrons to complete its outer shell, it can share with as many as four other elements. This flexibility makes carbon an ideal building block for biomolecules, and makes the diversity of molecules we see in nature possible. But even more significant to the shape, and therefore the function, of biomolecules, is the ability of carbon to share electrons with other carbon atoms. The C—C

Figure 3.1 Carbon and life. Carbon (**a**) is the basis for many compounds in living things, including (**b**) an apple and other foods, (**c**) plants, and (**d**) animals, as well as nonliving things like (**e**) tires, (**f**) diamonds, and (**g**) airplanes.

bond that is formed is quite stable, and allows formation of long carbon chains. The molecules termed hydrocarbons are chains of carbon atoms that have additional bonds exclusively with hydrogen atoms.

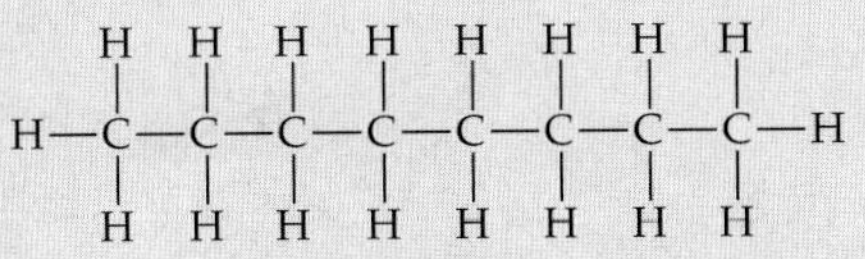

octane

Branching of the chain at any carbon atom is possible, and a hydrocarbon can also turn back on itself to form a ring compound when placed in water:

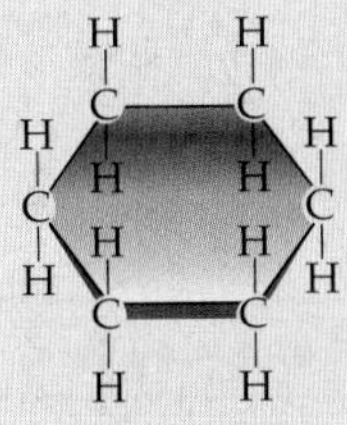

cyclohexane

In addition to forming single bonds, carbon can form double bonds with itself and other atoms. Double bonds aren't as flexible as single bonds, and they restrict the movement of bonded atoms. Double bonds affect a molecule's shape and therefore influence its function. The presence of double bonds is one way to distinguish between saturated and unsaturated fats, which are important to heart health. Carbon is also capable of forming triple bonds with itself, as in acetylene, $H-C\equiv C-H$, a gas used in industrial welding.

The diversity of organic molecules is further enhanced by the presence of particular functional groups, chemical groups attached to the carbon skeleton or backbone, as discussed next. Contrast the structure of cyclohexane, above, with the structure of glucose in Figure 3.6. Notice how the difference in structure can be attributed to the functional groups added to the same number of carbons.

The Carbon Skeleton and Functional Groups

The carbon chain of an organic molecule is called its skeleton or backbone. Just as a skeleton accounts for your body's shape, so does the carbon skeleton of an organic molecule account for its shape. The diversity of vertebrates, species with a backbone, results from the overall shapes of the organisms and the types of appendages (fins, wings, limbs) they have developed. Likewise, the diversity of organic molecules comes from the attachment of different functional groups to the carbon skeleton.

Table 3.2 Functional groups.

Group	Structure	Compound	Significance
Hydroxyl	$R-OH$	Alcohol as in ethanol	Polar, forms hydrogen bond
			Present in sugars, some amino acids
Carbonyl		Aldehyde as in formaldehyde	Polar
			Present in sugars
		Ketone as in acetone	Polar
			Present in sugars
Carboxyl (acidic)		Carboxylic acid as in acetic acid	Polar, acidic
			Present in fatty acids, amino acids
Amino		Amine as in tryptophan	Polar, basic, forms hydrogen bonds
			Present in amino acids
Sulfhydryl	$R-SH$	Thiol as in ethanethiol	Forms disulfide bonds
			Present in some amino acids
Phosphate		Organic phosphate as in phosphorylated molecules	Polar, acidic
			Present in nucleotides, phospholipids

R = remainder of molecule

A **functional group** is a specific combination of bonded atoms that always reacts in the same way, regardless of the particular carbon skeleton. Much of a biomolecule's chemistry can be attributed to its functional groups, rather than to the carbon skeleton to which they are attached. As in Table 3.2, it is even acceptable to use an R to stand for the "remainder" of the molecule, which is the carbon skeleton, because only the functional group is involved in a chemical reaction.

When a particular functional group is added to a carbon skeleton, the molecule becomes a certain type of compound. For example, the addition of an −OH (hydroxyl group) to a carbon skeleton turns that molecule into an alcohol. When an −OH replaces one of the hydrogens in ethane, a 2-carbon hydrocarbon, it becomes ethanol, a type of alcohol that is familiar because humans can consume it. Whereas ethane, like other hydrocarbons, is **hydrophobic** (not soluble in water), ethanol is **hydrophilic** (soluble in water) because the −OH functional group makes the otherwise nonpolar carbon skeleton polar. Because cells are 70–90% water, the ability to interact with and be soluble in water profoundly affects the function of organic molecules in cells.

Organic molecules containing carboxyl (acidic) groups (−COOH) are highly polar. They tend to ionize and release hydrogen ions in solution:

$$-COOH \longrightarrow -COO^- + H^+$$

The attached functional groups determine not only the polarity of an organic molecule, but also the types of reactions it will undergo. You will see that alcohols react with carboxyl groups when a fat forms, and that carboxyl groups react with amino groups during protein formation.

Isomers

Isomers [Gk. *isos*, equal, and *meros*, part, portion] are organic molecules that have identical molecular formulas but a different arrangement of atoms. In essence, isomers are variations in the molecular architecture of a molecule. Isomers are another example of how the chemistry of carbon leads to variations in organic molecules.

The two molecules in Figure 3.2 are isomers of one another; they have the same molecular formula but different functional groups. Therefore, we would expect them to have different properties and react differently in chemical reactions.

The Biomolecules of Cells

You are familiar with the names of biomolecules—carbohydrates, lipids, proteins, and nucleic acids—because certain foods are known to be rich in them, as shown in Figure 3.3. For example, bread is rich in carbohydrates, and meat is rich in proteins. When you digest food, it gets broken down into smaller molecules that are subunits for biomolecules that your body uses. Digestion of bread releases glucose molecules, and digestion of

glyceraldehyde	dihydroxyacetone
H—C—C—C—H with H, H, O double bond at end carbon, OH, OH	H—C—C—C—H with H, O double bond at middle carbon, H, OH, OH

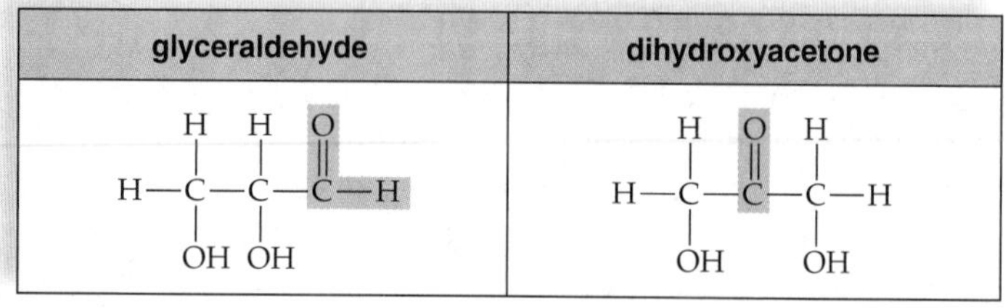

Figure 3.2 Isomers. Isomers have the same molecular formula but different atomic configurations. Both of these compounds have the formula $C_3H_6O_3$. In glyceraldehyde, a colorless crystalline solid, oxygen is double-bonded to an end carbon. In dihydroxyacetone, a white crystalline solid, oxygen is double-bonded to the middle carbon.

Biomolecules		
Category	**Subunit(s)**	**Polymer**
Carbohydrates*	Monosaccharide ⟶	Polysaccharide
Lipids	Glycerol and fatty acids ⟶	Fat
Proteins*	Amino acids ⟶	Polypeptide
Nucleic acids*	Nucleotide ⟶	DNA, RNA

*Polymers

Figure 3.3 Common foods. Carbohydrates in bread and pasta are digested to sugars; lipids such as oils are digested to glycerol and fatty acids; and proteins in meat are digested to amino acids. Cells use these subunit molecules as a source of energy and to build their own biomolecules.

meat releases amino acids. Your body then takes these subunits and builds from them the particular carbohydrates and proteins that make up your cells (Fig. 3.3).

Polymers

The largest of the biomolecules are called **polymers,** and like all biomolecules, polymers are constructed by linking together a large number of the same type of subunit. However, in the case of polymers, the subunits are called **monomers.** A polysaccharide, a protein, and a nucleic acid are all polymers that contain many monomers. Just as a train increases in length when boxcars are hitched together one by one, so a polymer gets longer as monomers bond to one another.

Synthesis and Degradation

A cell uses a condensation reaction to synthesize (build up) any type of biomolecule. It's called a **dehydration reaction** because the equivalent of a water molecule—that is, an −OH (hydroxyl group) and an −H (hydrogen atom), is removed as subunits are

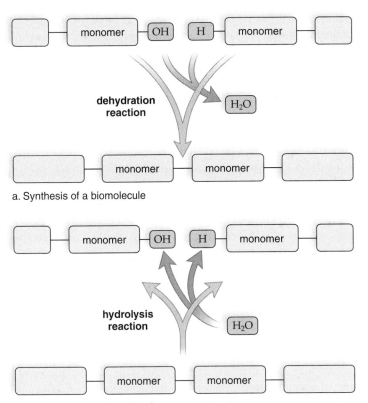

a. Synthesis of a biomolecule

b. Degradation of a biomolecule

Figure 3.4 Synthesis and degradation of biomolecules.
a. In cells, synthesis often occurs when subunits bond during a dehydration reaction (removal of H_2O). **b.** Degradation occurs when the subunits separate during a hydrolysis reaction (the addition of H_2O).

joined. Therefore, water molecules are formed as biomolecules are synthesized (Fig. 3.4*a*).

To break down biomolecules, a cell uses an opposite type of reaction. During a **hydrolysis** [Gk. *hydro*, water, and *lyse*, break] **reaction,** an −OH group from water attaches to one subunit, and an −H from water attaches to the other subunit. In other words, biomolecules are broken down by adding water to them (Fig. 3.4*b*).

Enzymes are required for cells to carry out dehydration and hydrolysis reactions. An **enzyme** is a molecule that speeds a reaction by bringing reactants together and helping them to form new molecules. The enzyme partici- pates in the reaction but is unchanged by it.

MP3
Organic Molecules

Check Your Progress 3.1

1. Describe the properties of a carbon atom that make it ideally suited to produce varied carbon skeletons.
2. Compare solubility in water of a 2-carbon alcohol and a 2-carbon carboxylic acid biomolecule.
3. Discuss what would happen if no water was present during degradation of a biomolecule.

3.2 Carbohydrates

Learning Outcomes

Upon completion of this section, you should be able to

1. List several examples of important monosaccharides and polysaccharides.
2. Compare the energy and structural uses of starch, glycogen, and cellulose.

Carbohydrates are almost universally used as an immediate energy source in living things, but they also play structural roles in a variety of organisms (Fig. 3.5). The majority of carbohy- drates have a carbon to hydrogen to oxygen ratio of 1:2:1. The term *carbohydrate* (literally, carbon-water) includes single sugar molecules and chains of sugars. Chain length varies from a few sugars to hundreds of sugars. The monomer subunits, called monosaccharides, are assembled into long polymer chains called polysaccharides.

b. Shell contains chitin.

a. Cell walls contain cellulose.

c. Cell walls contain peptidoglycan.

Figure 3.5 Carbohydrates as structural materials. **a.** Plants, such as the cactus shown here, have the carbohydrate cellulose in their cell walls. **b.** The shell of a crab contains chitin, a different carbohydrate. **c.** The cell walls of bacteria contain another type of carbohydrate known as peptidoglycan.

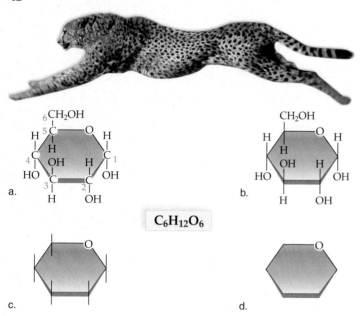

Figure 3.6 Glucose. Glucose provides energy for organisms, such as this cheetah. Each of these structural formulas is glucose. **a.** The carbon skeleton and all attached groups are shown. **b.** The carbon skeleton is omitted. **c.** The carbon skeleton and attached groups are omitted. **d.** Only the ring shape, which includes one oxygen atom, remains.

Monosaccharides: Ready Energy

Monosaccharides [Gk. *monos*, single, and *sacchar*, sugar] consist of only a single sugar molecule and are called simple sugars. A simple sugar can have a carbon backbone of three to seven carbons. The molecular formula for a simple sugar is some multiple of CH_2O, suggesting that every carbon atom is bonded to an $-H$ and an $-OH$. This is not strictly correct, as you can see by examining the structural formula for glucose (Fig. 3.6). Still, sugars do have many hydroxyl groups, and this polar functional group makes them soluble in water.

Glucose, with six carbon atoms, is a **hexose** [Gk. *hex*, six] sugar and has a molecular formula of $C_6H_{12}O_6$. Despite the fact that glucose has several isomers, such as fructose and galactose, we usually think of $C_6H_{12}O_6$ as glucose. Glucose is critical to biological function, and is the major source of cellular fuel for all living things. Glucose is transported in the blood of animals, and

it is the molecule that is broken down and converted into stored chemical energy (ATP) during cellular respiration in nearly all types of organisms.

Ribose and **deoxyribose,** with five carbon atoms, are **pentose** [Gk. *pent,* five] sugars that are significant because they are found respectively in the nucleic acids RNA and DNA. RNA and DNA are discussed later in the chapter.

Disaccharides: Varied Uses

A **disaccharide** contains two monosaccharides that have joined during a dehydration reaction. Figure 3.7 shows how the disaccharide maltose (an ingredient used in brewing) arises when two glucose molecules bond together. Note the position of the bond that results when the $-OH$ groups participating in the reaction project below the ring. When our hydrolytic digestive juices break this bond, the result is two glucose molecules.

Sucrose (the structure shown above) is another disaccharide of special interest because it is sugar we use at home to sweeten our food. Sucrose is also the form in which sugar is transported in plants. We acquire sucrose from plants such as sugarcane and sugar beets. You may also have heard of lactose, a disaccharide found in milk. Lactose is glucose combined with galactose. Individuals that are lactose intolerant cannot break this disaccharide down and have subsequent medical problems. To prevent problems they can buy foods in which lactose has been broken down into its subunit monosaccharides.

Polysaccharides: Energy Storage Molecules

Polysaccharides are polymers of monosaccharides. Some types of polysaccharides function as short-term energy storage molecules. When an organism requires energy, the polysaccharide is broken down to release sugar molecules. The helical shape of the polysaccharides in Figure 3.8 exposes the sugar linkages to the hydrolytic enzymes that can break them down.

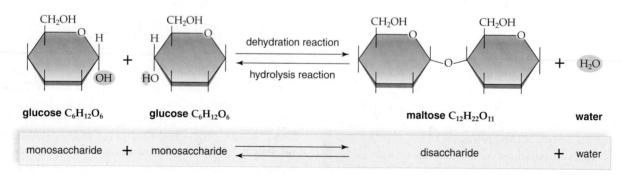

Figure 3.7 Synthesis and degradation of maltose, a disaccharide. Synthesis of maltose occurs following a dehydration reaction when a bond forms between two glucose molecules, and water is removed. Degradation of maltose occurs following a hydrolysis reaction when this bond is broken by the addition of water.

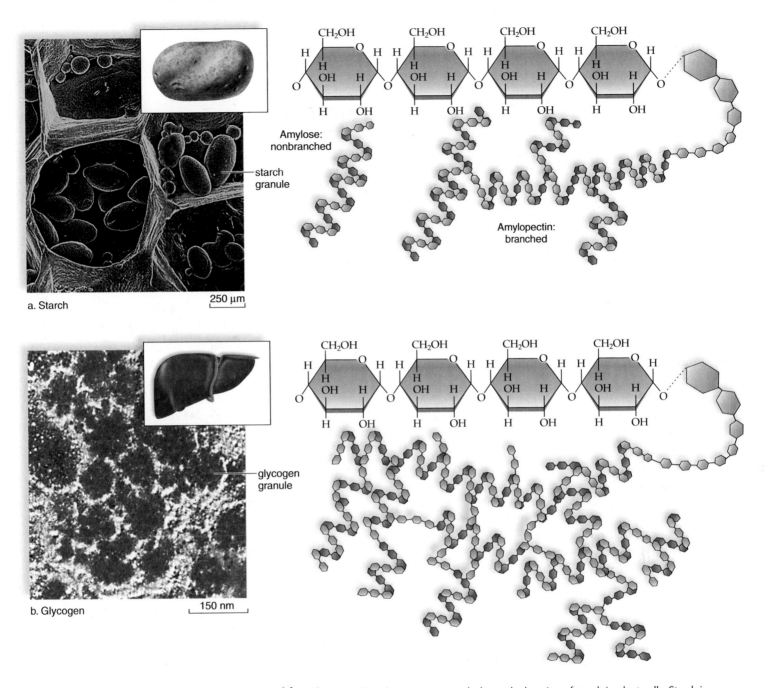

Figure 3.8 Starch and glycogen structure and function. **a.** The electron micrograph shows the location of starch in plant cells. Starch is a chain of glucose molecules that can be branched or unbranched. **b.** The electron micrograph shows glycogen deposits in a portion of a liver cell. Glycogen is a highly branched polymer of glucose molecules.

Plants store glucose as **starch.** The cells of a potato contain granules where starch resides during winter until energy is needed for growth in the spring. Notice in Figure 3.8a that starch exists in two forms: One form (amylose) is nonbranched and the other (amylopectin) is branched. When a polysaccharide is branched, there is no main carbon chain because new chains occur at regular intervals, always at the sixth carbon of the monomer.

Animals store glucose as **glycogen.** In our bodies and those of other vertebrates, liver cells contain granules where glycogen is stored until needed. The storage and release of glucose from liver cells is controlled by hormones. After we eat, the release of the hormone insulin from the pancreas promotes the storage of glucose as glycogen. Notice in Figure 3.8b that glycogen is even more branched than starch.

Polysaccharides serve as storage molecules because they are not as soluble in water, and are much larger than a simple sugar. Therefore, polysaccharides cannot easily pass through the plasma membrane, a sheetlike structure that encloses cells.

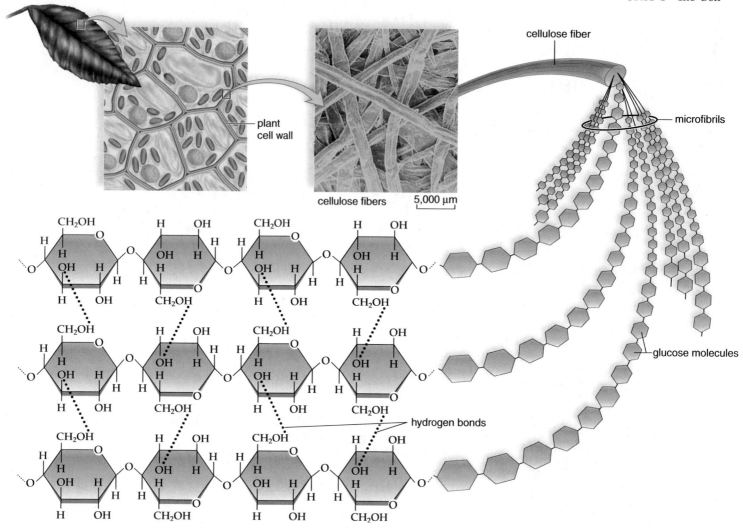

Figure 3.9 Cellulose fibrils. Cellulose fibers criss-cross in plant cell walls for added strength. A cellulose fiber contains several microfibrils, each a polymer of glucose molecules—notice that the linkage bonds differ from those of starch. Every other glucose is flipped, permitting hydrogen bonding and greater strength between the microfibrils.

Polysaccharides: Structural Molecules

Structural polysaccharides include **cellulose** in plants, **chitin** in animals and fungi, and **peptidoglycan** in bacteria (see Fig. 3.5). In all three, monomers are joined by the type of bond shown for cellulose in Figure 3.9. The cellulose monomer is simply glucose, but in chitin, the monomer has an attached amino group. The structure of peptidoglycan is even more complex because each monomer also has an amino acid chain. In both cases, the addition of a functional group to the glucose monomer changes its chemical properties.

Cellulose is the most abundant carbohydrate, and in fact, the most abundant organic molecule on Earth—over 100 billion tons of cellulose is produced by plants each year. Wood, a cellulose plant product, is used for construction, and cotton is used for cloth. Microorganisms, but not animals, are able to digest the bond between glucose monomers in cellulose. The protozoans in the gut of termites enable these insects to digest wood. In cows and other ruminants, microorganisms break down cellulose in a special digestive-tract pouch before the "cud" is returned to the mouth for more chewing and reswallowing. In rabbits, microorganisms digest cellulose in a pouch where it is packaged into pellets. In order to make use of these nutrient pellets, rabbits have to reswallow them as soon as they pass out at the anus. For other animals, including humans, that have no means of digesting cellulose, cellulose serves as dietary fiber, which maintains regularity of fecal elimination.

Chitin [Gk. *chiton*, tunic] is found in fungal cell walls and in the exoskeletons of crabs and related animals, such as lobsters, scorpions, and insects. Chitin, like cellulose, cannot be digested by animals; however, humans have found many other good uses for chitin. Seeds are coated with chitin, and this protects them from attack by soil fungi. Because chitin also has antibacterial and antiviral properties, it is processed and used in medicine as a wound dressing and suture material. Chitin is even useful during the production of cosmetics and various foods.

MP3
Carbohydrates

Check Your Progress   3.2

1. Explain why humans cannot utilize the glucose in cellulose as a nutrient source.
2. Compare and contrast the structure and function of cellulose with chitin.

3.3 Lipids

Learning Outcomes

Upon completion of this section, you should be able to

1. Describe why lipids are essential to living organisms.
2. Explain where fats and oils are produced.
3. Contrast the structures of fats, phospholipids, and steroids.
4. Compare the functions of phospholipids and steroids in cells.

A variety of organic compounds are classified as **lipids** [Gk. *lipos*, fat] (Table 3.3). These compounds are insoluble in water due to their hydrocarbon chains. Hydrogens bonded only to carbon are nonpolar and have no tendency to form hydrogen bonds with water molecules. Fat, a well-known lipid, is used by animals for both insulation and long-term energy storage. Fat below the skin of marine mammals is called blubber; in humans, it is given slang expressions such as "spare tire" and "love handles." Plants use oil instead of fat for long-term energy storage. We are familiar with fats and oils because we use them as foods and for cooking.

Table 3.3 Lipids

Type	Functions	Human Uses
Fats	Long-term energy storage and insulation in animals	Butter, lard
Oils	Long-term energy storage in plants and their seeds	Cooking oils
Phospholipids	Component of plasma membrane	—
Steroids	Component of plasma membrane (cholesterol), sex hormones	Medicines
Waxes	Protection, prevent water loss (cuticle of plant surfaces), beeswax, earwax	Candles, polishes

Phospholipids and steroids are also important lipids found in living things. They serve as major components of the plasma membrane in cells. Steroids are also involved in cell communication. Waxes, which are sticky, not greasy like fats and oils, tend to have a protective function in living things.

THEME Nature of Science

Everyone Needs a Little Fat, Right?

Fats are an essential part of the diet. They provide lots of energy, having more than twice the caloric density of carbohydrates. Fats are needed to build and maintain cell membranes, which are critical to biological life, as well as hormones like testosterone and estrogen, and they provide essential padding for our internal organs. Fats are also a major reason why some foods taste good.

A short time ago, scientists and nutritionists thought that too much fat was bad for you. Now we know that saturated fats, which come from animals and are solid at room temperature, have effects in the body that are different from those of unsaturated fats, which come from plants and are liquid at room temperature. Saturated fats are flat molecules that easily stick together in the blood, and too much saturated fat has been shown by scientists to negatively affect heart health, contributing to clogging of arteries and coronary heart disease (CHD). By comparison, unsaturated fats seem to help prevent CHD because they don't stick together in the blood, and therefore don't clog arteries.

A Food Revolution

Unsaturated fats might be healthier for you, but plant oils can easily go rancid and aren't solid at room temperature, which makes them more difficult to cook with and to use in solid food products. To get around this problem, food manufacturers hydrogenated unsaturated fatty acids by heating the oil and exposing it to hydrogen gas. This treatment made the otherwise liquid plant oils semi-solid at room temperature, and gave foods containing partially hydrogenated oils better shelf life.

An unintended consequence of hydrogenation, however, was the formation of **trans-fats**. Many commercially packaged foods contain trans-fats, which recently have been shown to increase LDL or "bad" cholesterol and lower HDL or "good" cholesterol in the blood. Trans-fat consumption also appears to increase risk of CHD and heart attack.

Scientific Evidence Changes Our Perceptions

Initially, investigators thought that the total amount of lipid in the diet caused coronary and other heart-related diseases. As scientific evidence accumulated showing a distinction between the effects of saturated and unsaturated fats, public perception changed. Until recently, trans-fats were of little concern to the general public, and people readily consumed them without much thought. As science has brought the negative effects of trans-fats to light, perception has changed once again. Public outcry has prompted changes in the food services industry, with clear labeling of trans-fats on all food products and with more restaurants using trans-fat-free oils during cooking.

This example shows how our perceptions change over time based on scientific evidence, and it illustrates the essential role that science plays in the common good. Science constantly refines what we know as new evidence provides greater insights into how we function and live.

Questions to Consider

1. How much trans-fat do you consume daily?
2. What is the chemical structure of a trans-fat compared to a non-trans-fat?
3. How might your new scientific knowledge of fats affect your nutritional decision-making?

Triglycerides: Long-Term Energy Storage

Fats and **oils** contain two types of subunit molecules: fatty acids and glycerol. Each **fatty acid** consists of a long hydrocarbon chain with an even number of carbons and a $-COOH$ (carboxyl) group at one end. Most of the fatty acids in cells contain 16 or 18 carbon atoms per molecule, although smaller ones are also found. Fatty acids are either saturated or unsaturated. **Saturated fatty acids** have no double bonds between the carbon atoms and contain as many hydrogens as they can potentially hold. **Unsaturated fatty acids** have double bonds in the carbon chain, which reduces the number of bonded hydrogen atoms. In addition, double bonds in unsaturated fatty acids may have chemical groups arranged on the same side (termed *cis* configuration) or on opposite sides (termed *trans* configuration) of the double bond. The *cis* or *trans* configuration of an unsaturated fatty acid affects its biological activity.

Glycerol is a 3-carbon compound with three $-OH$ groups. The $-OH$ groups are polar, making glycerol soluble in water. When a fat or oil forms, the $-COOH$ functional groups of three fatty acids react with the $-OH$ groups of glycerol during a dehydration reaction (Fig. 3.10a), resulting in a fat molecule and three molecules of water. Fats and oils are degraded during a hydrolysis reaction. Because three fatty acids are attached to each glycerol molecule, fats and oils are sometimes called **triglycerides.** Notice that triglycerides have many nonpolar $C-H$ bonds; therefore, they do not mix with water. Even though cooking oils and water are both liquid, they do not mix, even after shaking, because the nonpolar oil and polar water are chemically incompatible.

Triglycerides containing fatty acids with unsaturated bonds melt at a lower temperature than those containing only saturated fatty acids. The reason is that a double bond creates a kink in the fatty acid chain that prevents close packing between the hydrocarbon chains (Fig. 3.10a). We can infer that butter, a fat that is solid at room temperature, must contain primarily saturated fatty acids, while corn oil, which is a liquid even when placed in the refrigerator, must contain primarily unsaturated fatty acids (Fig. 3.10b). This difference is useful to living things. For example, the feet of reindeer and penguins contain unsaturated triglycerides, and this helps protect those exposed parts from freezing.

In general, fats, which most often come from animals, are solid at room temperature, whereas oils, which come from plants, are liquid at room temperature. Diets high in animal fat have been associated with circulatory disorders because saturated fats and other molecules can accumulate inside the lining of blood vessels and block blood flow. Health organizations have recommended replacing fat with oils such as olive oil and canola oil in our diet whenever possible.

Nearly all animals use fat rather than glycogen for long-term energy storage. Gram for gram, fat stores more energy than glycogen. The $C-H$ bonds of fatty acids make them a richer source of chemical energy than glycogen, because more bonds with stored energy are present in fatty acids; in contrast, glycogen has many $C-OH$ bonds, which are less energetic bonds. Also, fat droplets do not contain water because they are nonpolar. Small birds, like the broad-tailed hummingbird, store a great deal of fat before they start their long spring and fall migratory flights. About 0.15 g of fat per gram of body weight is accumulated each day. If the same amount of energy were stored as glycogen, a bird would be so heavy it would not be able to fly.

Phospholipids: Membrane Components

Phospholipids [Gk. *phos*, light, and *lipos*, fat], as implied by their name, contain a phosphate group. Essentially, a phospholipid is constructed like a fat, except that in place of the third fatty acid attached to glycerol, there is a polar phosphate group. The phosphate group is usually bonded to another organic group, indicated by *R* in Figure 3.11a. This portion of the molecule becomes the polar head, while the hydrocarbon chains of the fatty acids become the nonpolar tails. Notice that a double bond causes a tail to kink.

Phospholipids have hydrophilic heads and hydrophobic tails. When exposed to water, phospholipids tend to arrange themselves so that the polar heads are oriented toward water, and the nonpolar fatty acid tails are oriented away from water. In living things, which are made mostly of water, phospholipids tend to become a bilayer (double layer) because the polar heads prefer to interact with other polar molecules like water. Conversely, the nonpolar tails associate together and stay away from polar water molecules. So, phospholipids arrange themselves like a "sandwich," with the polar heads facing to the the outside (the bread slices) and the fatty acid tails on the inside (the filling). This phospholipid bilayer is a key component used to keep cells and the biological compartments within cells separate.

The plasma membrane that surrounds cells consists primarily of a phospholipid bilayer (Fig. 3.11b). The presence of kinks in the tails causes the plasma membrane to be fluid across a range of temperatures found in nature. A plasma membrane is absolutely essential to the structure and function of a cell, and this signifies the importance of phospholipids to living things.

Steroids: Four Fused Rings

Steroids are lipids that have entirely different structures from those of fats. Steroid molecules have skeletons of four fused carbon rings (Fig. 3.12a). Each type of steroid differs primarily by the types of functional groups attached to the carbon skeleton.

Cholesterol is an essential component of an animal cell's plasma membrane, where it provides physical stability. Cholesterol is the precursor of several other steroids, such as the sex hormones testosterone and estrogen (Fig. 3.12b, c). The male sex hormone, testosterone, is formed primarily in the testes, and the female sex hormone, estrogen, is formed primarily in

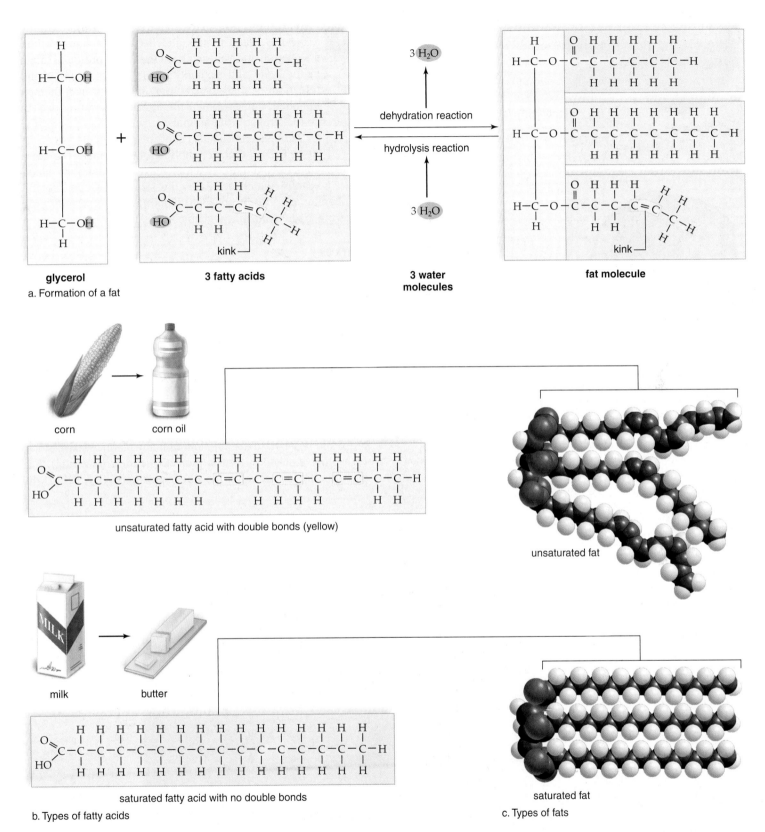

a. Formation of a fat

glycerol 3 fatty acids 3 water molecules fat molecule

unsaturated fatty acid with double bonds (yellow)

corn → corn oil

unsaturated fat

milk → butter

saturated fatty acid with no double bonds

saturated fat

b. Types of fatty acids

c. Types of fats

Figure 3.10 Fat and fatty acids. **a.** Following a dehydration reaction, glycerol is bonded to three fatty acid molecules as fat forms and water is given off. Following a hydrolysis reaction, the bonds are broken due to the addition of water. **b.** A fatty acid has a carboxyl group attached to a long hydrocarbon chain. If there are double bonds between some of the carbons in the chain, the fatty acid is unsaturated and a kink occurs in the chain. If there are no double bonds, the fatty acid is saturated. **c.** Space-filling models of an unsaturated fat and a saturated fat.

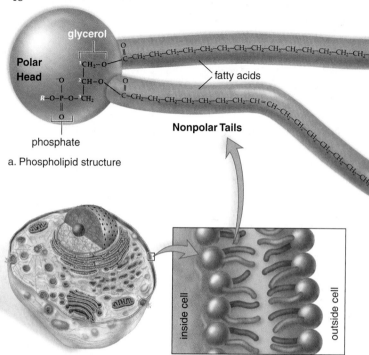

Figure 3.11 Phospholipids form membranes. **a.** Phospholipids are constructed like fats, except that in place of the third fatty acid, they have a polar phosphate group. The hydrophilic (polar) head is soluble in water, whereas the two hydrophobic (nonpolar) tails are not. A tail has a kink wherever there is an unsaturated bond. **b.** Because of their structure, phospholipids form a bilayer that serves as the major component of a cell's plasma membrane. The fluidity of the plasma membrane is affected by kinks in the phospholipids' tails.

the ovaries. Testosterone and estrogen differ only by the functional groups attached to the same carbon skeleton, and yet each have their own profound effect on the body and sexuality of an animal. Human and plant estrogen are similar in structure, and if estrogen therapy is recommended, some women prefer taking soy products in preference to estrogen from animals.

Cholesterol can also contribute to circulatory disorders. The presence of cholesterol encourages the accumulation of fatty material inside the lining of blood vessels, which decreases the size of the opening and thereby can result in high blood pressure. Cholesterol-lowering medications are available.

Waxes

In **waxes,** long-chain fatty acids bond with long-chain alcohols:

long-chain fatty acid

$$O=C-CH_2-CH_2-CH_2-CH_2-CH_2-CH_2-CH_2-CH_2-CH_2-CH_3$$

$$C-CH_2-CH_2-CH_2-CH_2-CH_2-CH_2-CH_2-CH_2-CH_3$$

long-chain alcohol

Waxes are solid at normal temperatures because they have a high melting point. Being hydrophobic, they are also waterproof and resistant to degradation. In many plants, waxes, along with other molecules, form a protective cuticle (covering) that prevents the loss of water for all exposed parts (Fig. 3.13*a*). In

Figure 3.12 Steroid diversity. **a.** Built like cholesterol, (**b**) testosterone and (**c**) estrogen have different effects on the body due to different functional groups attached to the same carbon skeleton. Testosterone is the male sex hormone active in peacocks (*left*), and estrogen is the female sex hormone active in peahens (*right*). These hormones are present in many living creatures.

a.

b.

Figure 3.13 Waxes. Waxes are a type of lipid. **a.** Fruits are protected by a waxy coating that is visible on these plums. **b.** Bees secrete the wax that allows them to build a comb where they store honey. This bee has collected pollen (yellow) to feed growing larvae.

many animals, waxes are involved in skin and fur maintenance. In humans, wax is produced by glands in the outer ear canal. Earwax contains cerumin, an organic compound that at the very least repels insects, and in some cases even kills them. It also traps dust and dirt, preventing these contaminants from reaching the eardrum.

A honeybee produces beeswax in glands on the underside of its abdomen. Beeswax is used to make the six-sided cells of the comb where honey is stored (Fig. 3.13*b*). Honey contains the sugars fructose and glucose, breakdown products of the sugar sucrose.

Humans have found a myriad of uses for waxes, from making candles to polishing cars, furniture, and floors.

 MP3
Lipids

Check Your Progress 3.3

1. Evaluate why lipids and water do not mix.
2. Contrast a saturated fatty acid with an unsaturated fatty acid. Which of these is preferred in the diet, and why?
3. Explain why phospholipids form a bilayer in water.

3.4 Proteins

Learning Outcomes

Upon completion of this section, you should be able to

1. Describe functions of proteins in cells.
2. Explain how a polypeptide is constructed from amino acids.
3. Compare the four levels of protein structure.
4. Analyze the factors that affect protein structure and function.

Proteins [Gk. *proteios,* first place], as their Greek derivation implies, are of primary importance to the structure and function of cells. As much as 50% of the dry weight of most cells consists of proteins. Presently, several hundred thousand proteins have been identified. Here are some of their many functions in animals:

Metabolism Enzyme proteins bring reactants together and thereby speed chemical reactions in cells. They are specific for one particular type of reaction and function best at specific body temperatures and pH.

Support Some proteins have a structural function. For example, keratin makes up hair and nails, while collagen gives strength to ligaments, tendons, and skin.

Transport Channel and carrier proteins in the plasma membrane regulate what substances enter and exit cells. Other proteins transport molecules in the blood of animals; **hemoglobin** is a complex protein that transports oxygen to tissues and cells.

Defense Antibodies are proteins of our immune system that combine with foreign substances, called antigens. Antibodies bind and prevent antigens from destroying cells and upsetting homeostasis.

Regulation Some hormones are proteins that regulate how cells behave. They serve as intercellular messengers that influence cell metabolism. The hormone insulin regulates how much glucose is in the blood and in cells; the presence of growth hormone during childhood and adolescence determines the height of an individual.

Motion The contractile proteins actin and myosin allow parts of cells to move and cause muscles to contract. Muscle contraction allows animals to travel from place to place. All cells contain proteins that move cell components to different internal locations. Without such proteins, cells would not be able to function.

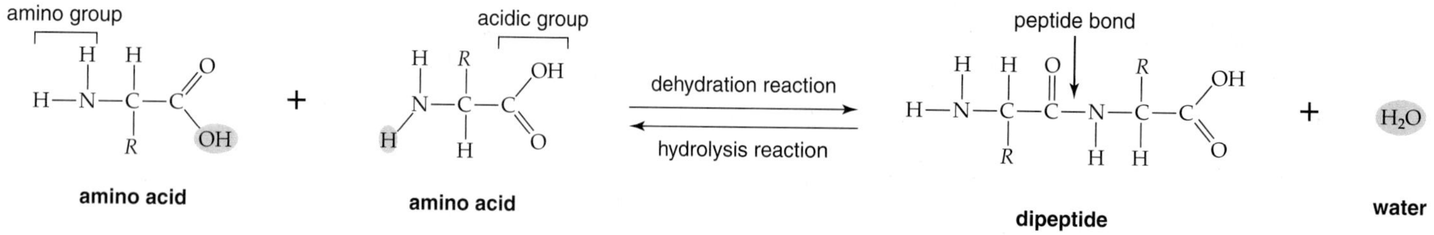

Figure 3.14 Synthesis and degradation of a peptide. Following a dehydration reaction, a peptide bond joins two amino acids and a water molecule is released. Following a hydrolysis reaction, the bond is broken due to the addition of water.

Proteins are such a major part of living organisms that tissues and cells of the body can sometimes be characterized by the proteins they contain or produce. For example, muscle cells contain large amounts of actin and myosin for contraction; red blood cells are filled with hemoglobin for oxygen transport; and support tissues, such as ligaments and tendons, contain the protein collagen, which is composed of tough fibers.

Peptides

Proteins are polymers constructed from amino acid monomers. Figure 3.14 shows how a dehydration reaction joins the carboxyl group of one amino acid to the amino group of another amino acid. The resulting covalent bond between two amino acids is called a **peptide bond.** The atoms associated with the peptide bond share the electrons unevenly because oxygen is more electronegative than nitrogen. Therefore, the hydrogen attached to the nitrogen has a slightly positive charge, while the oxygen has a slightly negative charge:

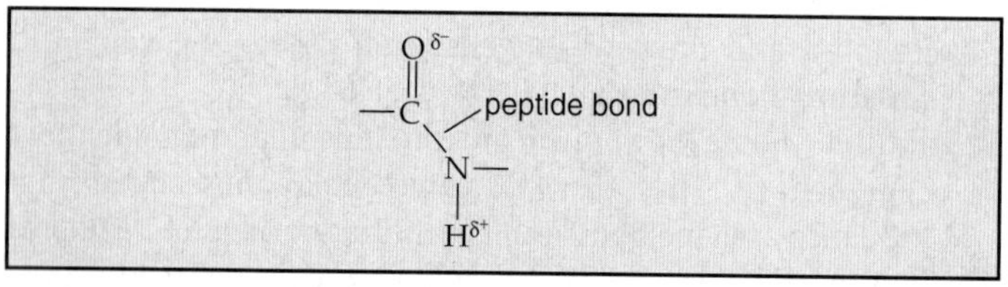

The polarity of the peptide bond means that hydrogen bonding is possible between the −CO of one amino acid and the −NH of another amino acid in a polypeptide. This hydrogen bonding influences the structure, or shape, of a protein.

A **peptide** is two or more amino acids bonded together, and a **polypeptide** is a chain of many amino acids joined by peptide bonds. A protein is a polypeptide that has been folded into a particular shape and has function. Some proteins may consist of more than one polypeptide chain, making it possible for some proteins to have a very large number of amino acids.

In 1953, Frederick Sanger developed a method to determine the sequence of amino acids in a polypeptide. Now that we know the sequences of many thousands of polypeptides found in nature, it is clear that the amino acid sequence greatly influences the final three-dimensional shape and function of a protein. Proteins that have an abnormal sequence often have a three-dimensional shape that causes them to function improperly. From an evolutionary perspective, we also know that, for

a particular protein, the sequences of amino acids are highly similar within a species and are different across species.

Amino Acids: Protein Monomers

The name **amino acid** is appropriate because one of these groups is an −NH$_2$ (amino group) and another is a −COOH (an acid group). The third group is called an *R* group for an amino acid:

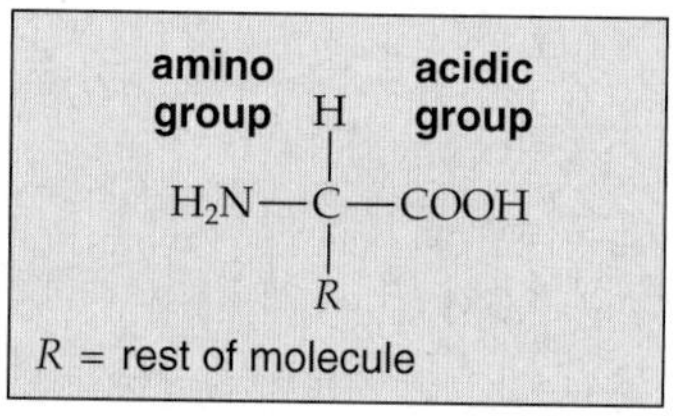

Note that the central carbon atom in an amino acid bonds to a hydrogen atom and also to three other groups of atoms, one of which is the *R* group (Fig. 3.14). Amino acids differ according to their particular *R* group (Fig. 3.15). The *R* groups range in complexity from a single hydrogen atom to complicated ring compounds. Some *R* groups are polar and associate with water, whereas others are nonpolar and do not. Also, the amino acid cysteine has an *R* group that ends with an −SH (sulfide) group, which often serves to covalently connect one chain of amino acids to another by a disulfide bond, −S−S−. Several other amino acids commonly found in cells are shown in Figure 3.15.

Each protein has a sequence of amino acids that is defined by information contained within a gene. This amino acid sequence forms the basis for all levels of protein structure, which directly affect protein function.

Shape of Proteins

A protein can have up to four levels of structure, termed primary, secondary, tertiary, and quaternary; however, not all proteins have all four levels.

Primary Structure

The primary structure of a protein is the sequence of amino acids defined by a gene. Just as millions of different words can be constructed from just 26 letters in the English alphabet, so too can hundreds of thousands of different polypeptides be built from just 20 amino acids. To make a new word in English, all

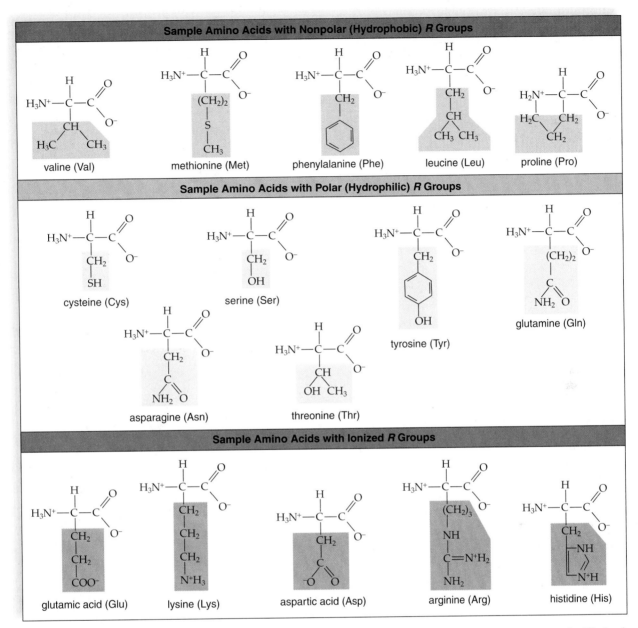

Figure 3.15 Amino acids. Polypeptides contain 20 different kinds of amino acids, some of which are shown here. Amino acids differ by the particular R group (blue) attached to the central carbon. Some R groups are nonpolar and hydrophobic (red), some are polar and hydrophilic (light blue), and some are ionized and hydrophilic (dark blue). The amino acids are shown in ionized form.

that is required is to vary the number and sequence of a few letters. Likewise, changing the sequence of 20 amino acids in a polypeptide can produce a huge array of different proteins.

Secondary Structure

The secondary structure of a protein occurs when the polypeptide coils or folds in a particular way (Fig. 3.16).

Linus Pauling and Robert Corey, who began studying the structure of amino acids in the late 1930s, concluded that a coiling they called an α (alpha) helix and a pleated sheet they called the β (beta) sheet were two basic patterns of structure amino acids assumed within a polypeptide. The names came from the

fact that the α helix was the first, and the β sheet the second, pattern they discovered. Each polypeptide can have multiple α helices and β pleated sheets.

The spiral shape of α helices is formed by hydrogen bonding between every fourth amino acid within the polypeptide chain, whereas β sheets are formed when the polypeptide turns back upon itself, allowing hydrogen bonding to occur between extended lengths of the polypeptide. **Fibrous proteins,** which are structural proteins, exist only as helices or pleated sheets that hydrogen-bond to each other. Examples are keratin, a protein in hair, and silk, a protein that forms spider webs. Both of these proteins have only a secondary structure (Fig. 3.17).

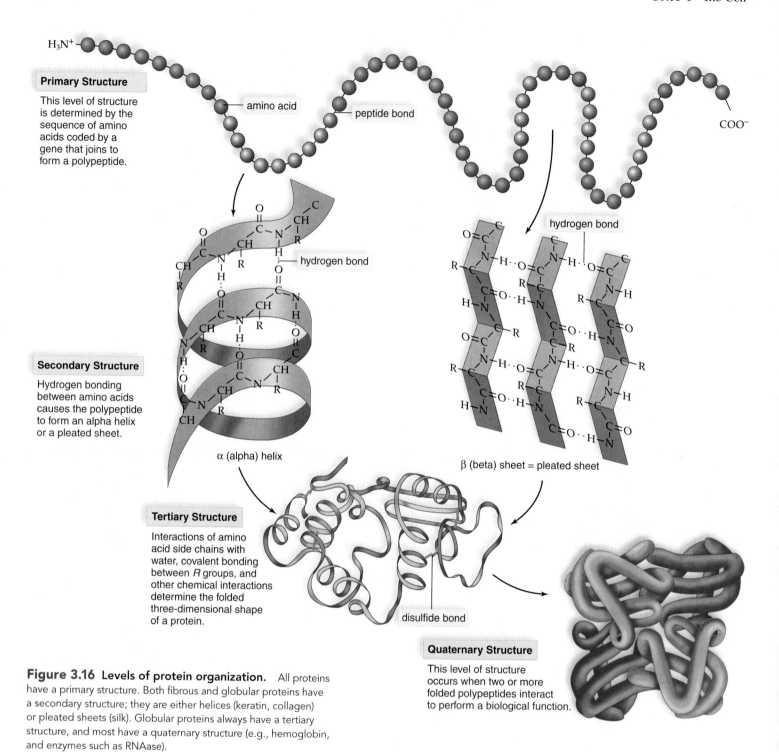

Primary Structure

This level of structure is determined by the sequence of amino acids coded by a gene that joins to form a polypeptide.

H_3N^+

amino acid

peptide bond

COO^-

hydrogen bond

Secondary Structure

Hydrogen bonding between amino acids causes the polypeptide to form an alpha helix or a pleated sheet.

α (alpha) helix

β (beta) sheet = pleated sheet

hydrogen bond

Tertiary Structure

Interactions of amino acid side chains with water, covalent bonding between R groups, and other chemical interactions determine the folded three-dimensional shape of a protein.

disulfide bond

Quaternary Structure

This level of structure occurs when two or more folded polypeptides interact to perform a biological function.

Figure 3.16 Levels of protein organization. All proteins have a primary structure. Both fibrous and globular proteins have a secondary structure; they are either helices (keratin, collagen) or pleated sheets (silk). Globular proteins always have a tertiary structure, and most have a quaternary structure (e.g., hemoglobin, and enzymes such as RNAase).

Tertiary Structure

A tertiary structure is the folding that results in the final three-dimensional shape of a polypeptide. **Globular proteins,** which tend to ball up into rounded shapes, have tertiary structure.

The interaction of hydrophobic amino acids in the polypeptide chain with the surrounding water is a major factor in how proteins fold into, and maintain, their final shape. These nonpolar amino acids tend to group together in the interior of a protein, to be as far away from water as possible. In contrast, the polar hydrophilic and ionic amino acids interact well with water, and tend to orient themselves on the protein's surface. These chemical interactions, along with hydrogen

Figure 3.17 Fibrous proteins. Fibrous proteins are structural proteins. **a.** Keratin—found, for example, in hair, horns, and hoofs—exemplifies fibrous proteins that are helical for most of their length. Keratin is a hydrogen-bonded triple helix. In this photo, Drew Barrymore has straight hair. **b.** In order to give her curly hair, water was used to disrupt the hydrogen bonds, and when the hair dried, new hydrogen bonding allowed it to take on the shape of a curler. A permanent-wave lotion induces new covalent bonds within the helix. **c.** Silk made by spiders and silkworms exemplifies fibrous proteins that are pleated sheets for most of their length. Hydrogen bonding between parts of the molecule occurs as the pleated sheet doubles back on itself.

a. b. c.

bonds, ionic bonds, and covalent bonds between *R* groups, all contribute to the tertiary structure of a protein. Strong disulfide linkages ($-S-S-$) in particular help maintain the tertiary shape.

Enzymes are globular proteins. Enzymes work best at body temperature, and each one also has an optimal pH at which the rate of the reaction is highest. At this temperature and pH, the enzyme can maintain its normal shape. A high temperature and change in pH can disrupt the interactions that maintain the shape of the enzyme. When a protein loses its natural shape, it is said to be **denatured.** An organism can die if too many proteins become denatured because it can no longer maintain the metabolic processes necessary for life.

Animation
Protein Denaturation

Quaternary Structure

Some proteins have a quaternary structure because they consist of more than one polypeptide. Hemoglobin is a much-studied globular protein that consists of four polypeptides, and therefore it has a quaternary structure. Each polypeptide in hemoglobin has a primary, secondary, and tertiary structure. However, a protein can have only two polypeptides and still have quaternary structure.

MP3
Proteins

Protein-Folding Diseases

Proteins cannot function properly unless they fold into their correct shape. In recent years investigators have found that the cell contains **chaperone proteins,** which help new proteins fold into their normal shape. At first it seemed as if chaperone proteins ensured that proteins folded properly, but now it appears that they might correct any misfolding of a new protein. These new findings serve as an example of how scientific research helps correct previous misunderstandings about how life works.

In any case, without fully functioning chaperone proteins, a cell's proteins may not be functional because they have misfolded. Several diseases in humans, such as cystic fibrosis and Alzheimer disease, are associated with misshapen proteins. The possibility exists that the diseases are due to missing or malfunctioning chaperone proteins.

Other diseases in humans are due to misfolded proteins, but the cause may be different. For years, investigators have been studying fatal brain diseases, known as TSEs,[1] that have no cure because no infective agent can be found. Mad cow disease is a well-known example of a TSE disease. Now it appears that TSE diseases could be due to misfolded proteins, called **prions,** that cause other proteins of the same type to fold the wrong way too. A possible relationship between prions and the functioning of chaperone proteins is now under investigation.

Animation
How Prions Arise

Check Your Progress 3.4

1. Explain where the information that specifies amino acid sequence in a polypeptide comes from.
2. Examine which types of amino acids are most likely to be found in the interior of a protein and why.
3. Evaluate which factors are most important to protein folding.

---

1 TSEs: transmissible spongiform encephalopathies.

3.5 Nucleic Acids

Each cell has a storehouse of information that specifies how a cell should behave, respond to the environment, and divide to make new cells. **Nucleic acids,** which are polymers of nucleotides, store information, include instructions for life, and conduct chemical reactions. **DNA (deoxyribonucleic acid)** is one type of nucleic acid that not only stores information about how to copy, or replicate, itself, but also specifies the order in which amino acids are to be joined to make a protein.

RNA (ribonucleic acid) is another diverse type of nucleic acid that has multiple uses. Messenger RNA (mRNA) is a temporary copy of a gene in the DNA that specifies what the amino acid sequence will be during the process of protein synthesis. Transfer RNA (tRNA) is also necessary in synthesizing proteins, and helps to translate the sequence of nucleic acids in a gene into the correct sequence of amino acid during protein synthesis. Ribosomal RNA (rRNA) works as an enzyme to form the peptide bonds between amino acids in a polypeptide. A wide range of other RNA molecules also perform important functions within the cell.

Not all nucleotides are made into DNA or RNA polymers. Some nucleotides are directly involved in metabolic functions in cells. For example, some are components of **coenzymes,** nonprotein organic molecules that help regulate enzymatic reactions. **ATP (adenosine triphosphate)** is a special nucleotide that stores large amounts of energy needed for synthetic reactions and for various other energy-requiring processes in cells.

Structure of DNA and RNA

Every **nucleotide** is comprised of three types of molecules: a pentose sugar, a phosphate (phosphoric acid), and a nitrogen-containing base (Fig. 3.18a). In DNA, the pentose sugar is deoxyribose, and in RNA the pentose sugar is ribose. A difference in the structure of these 5-carbon sugars accounts for their respective names because, as you might guess, deoxyribose lacks an oxygen atom found in ribose (Fig. 3.18b).

Both DNA and RNA contain combinations of four nucleotides, but these differ somewhat between the two nucleic acids (Fig. 3.18c). Nucleotides that have a base with a single ring are called pyrimidines, and nucleotides with a double ring are called purines. In DNA, the pyrimidine bases are cytosine and thymine; in RNA, the pyrimidine bases are cytosine and uracil. Both DNA and RNA contain the purine bases adenine and guanine. These molecules are called bases because their presence raises the pH of a solution.

Nucleotides are joined into a DNA or RNA polymer by a series of dehydration reactions. The resulting polymer is a linear molecule called a strand, in which the backbone is made up of an alternating series of sugar-phosphate-sugar-phosphate molecules. The bases project to one side of the backbone. Nucleotides are joined in an order specified by the strand they are copied from. DNA is double-stranded, and RNA is single-stranded (Fig. 3.19).

The two strands in double-stranded DNA usually twist around each other to form a double helix (Fig. 3.20a, b). The

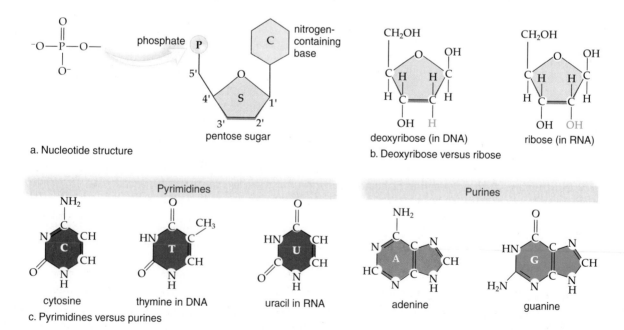

a. Nucleotide structure

b. Deoxyribose versus ribose

c. Pyrimidines versus purines

Figure 3.18 Nucleotides. **a.** A nucleotide consists of a pentose sugar, a phosphate molecule, and a nitrogen-containing base. **b.** DNA contains the sugar deoxyribose, and RNA contains the sugar ribose. **c.** DNA contains the pyrimidines C and T and the purines A and G. RNA contains the pyrimidines C and U and the purines A and G.

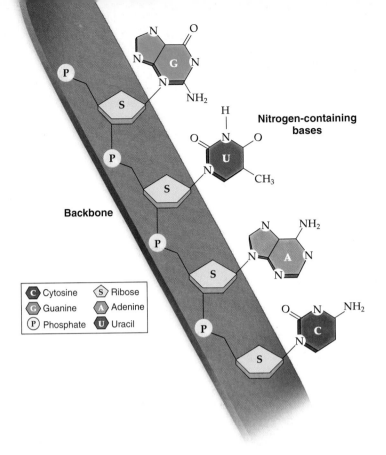

Figure 3.19 RNA structure. RNA is a single-stranded polymer of nucleotides. When the nucleotides join, the phosphate group of one is bonded to the sugar of the next. The bases project out to the side of the resulting sugar-phosphate backbone.

two strands are held together by hydrogen bonds between pyrimidine and purine base pairs. The bases can be in any order within a strand, but between strands, thymine (T) is always paired with adenine (A), and guanine (G) is always paired with cytosine (C). This is called **complementary base pairing.** Therefore, regardless of the order or the quantity of any particular base pair, the number of purine bases (A + G) always equals the number of pyrimidine bases (T + C) (Fig. 3.20c).

Animation
DNA Structure

Table 3.4 summarizes the differences between DNA and RNA.

ATP (Adenosine Triphosphate)

ATP is a special nucleotide comprised of adenine and ribose (adenosine) and three phosphates (triphosphate). The three phosphate groups are attached together and to ribose, the pentose sugar (Fig. 3.21).

Table 3.4 DNA Structure Compared to RNA Structure

	DNA	RNA
Sugar	Deoxyribose	Ribose
Bases	Adenine, guanine, thymine, cytosine	Adenine, guanine, uracil, cytosine
Strands	Double stranded with base pairing	Single stranded
Helix	Yes	No

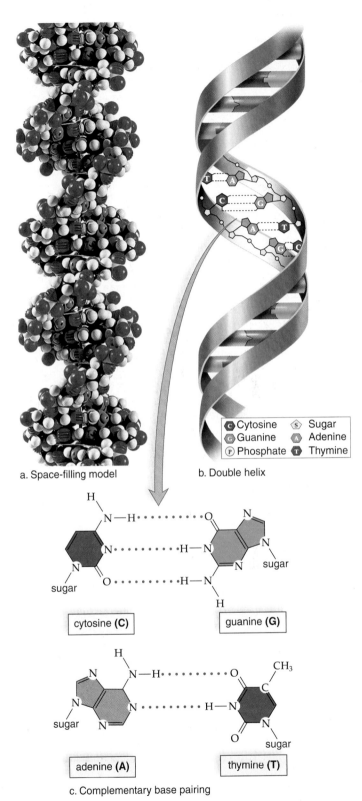

a. Space-filling model

b. Double helix

cytosine (C)   guanine (G)

adenine (A)   thymine (T)

c. Complementary base pairing

Figure 3.20 DNA structure. **a.** Space-filling model of DNA. **b.** DNA is a double helix in which the two polynucleotide strands twist about each other. **c.** Hydrogen bonds (dotted lines) occur between the complementarily paired bases: C is always paired with G, and A is always paired with T.

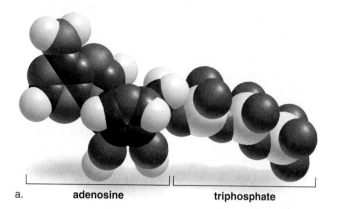

a. **adenosine**   **triphosphate**

c.

Figure 3.21 ATP. ATP, the universal energy currency of cells, is composed of adenosine and three phosphate groups. **a.** Space-filling model of ATP. **b.** When cells require energy, ATP becomes ADP + Ⓟ, and energy is released. **c.** The breakdown of ATP provides the energy that an animal, such as a chipmunk, uses to acquire food and make more ATP.

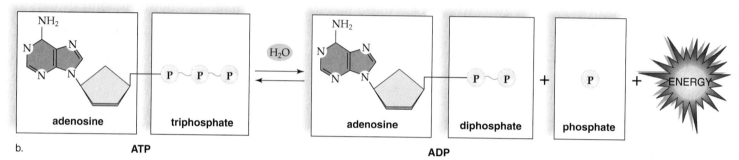

b.   **ATP**   **ADP**

ATP is a high-energy molecule because the last two phosphate bonds are unstable and are easily broken. In cells, hydrolysis of the terminal phosphate bond produces the molecule **ADP (adenosine diphosphate),** a phosphate molecule Ⓟ, and lots of energy to do cellular work.

The energy that is released by ATP hydrolysis is used to power many cellular processes, including enzyme reactions, cell communication, and cell division. ATP hydrolysis is chemically favored because ADP and Ⓟ are more stable than the original ATP molecule. Even though the third phosphate bond is broken, it is the whole molecule that releases energy.

In many cases, the hydrolysis of the ATP nucleotide is coupled to chemically unfavorable reactions in cells to allow these reactions to proceed. For example, key steps in the synthesis of macromolecules, such as carbohydrates and proteins, are able to proceed because the energy from ATP breakdown is used to pay the energy costs of the chemical reaction. ATP also supplies the energy for muscle contraction and nerve impulse conduction. Just as you spend money when you pay for a product or a service, cells "spend" ATP when they need something. That's why ATP is called the energy currency of cells.

MP3
Nucleic Acids

Check Your Progress   3.5

1. Examine how a nucleic acid stores information.
2. Describe the three components of a nucleotide.
3. Evaluate the properties of ATP that make it an ideal carrier of energy.

CONNECTING *the* CONCEPTS *with the* THEMES

Evolution

- Living cells are built from carbohydrates, lipids, proteins, and nucleic acids.
- DNA in genes specify the amino acid sequences found in all proteins. DNA sequence changes can affect secondary, tertiary, and sometimes quaternary protein structures and therefore function.
- The diversity of life on Earth is partly expained by differences in DNA and protein sequences. Closely related species tend to have similar sequences for many genes, whereas distantly related species show less similarity.
- Mutations are changes in an organism's normal DNA or protein sequences, and may increase, decrease, or have no effect on its biological functions.

Nature of Science

- The term *organic* can refer to food products that have been grown without the use of chemicals or been minimally processed, to molecules that contain carbon and hydrogen, to living things, or to anything that has been previously alive, such as the plants and animals that make up fossil fuels.
- When burned, organic molecules release carbon dioxide into the atmosphere just as we do when we breathe.
- Fossil fuel infrastructure is slowly changing as other energy alternatives are developed. Science plays a key role in this transition.

Biological Systems

- Carbon is central to the chemistry of life. The intake and synthesis of biomolecules is necessary to maintain cellular and life systems.
- Most biomolecules are simply polymers of small organic molecules. Monomers of sugars, amino acids, and nucleotides undergo dehydration reactions to become carbohydrates, proteins, and nucleic acids, respectively. Fats are composed of fatty acids and glycerol.

Media Study Tools

Summarize

3.1 Organic Molecules

The chemistry of carbon accounts for the diversity of organic molecules found in living things. Carbon can bond with as many as four other atoms. It can also bond with itself to form both chains and rings. Differences in the carbon skeleton and attached functional groups cause organic molecules to have different chemical properties. The chemical properties of a molecule determine how it interacts with other molecules and its role in the cell. Some functional groups are hydrophobic and others are hydrophilic.

There are four classes of biomolecules in cells: carbohydrates, lipids, proteins, and nucleic acids. Polysaccharides, the largest of the carbohydrates, are polymers of simple sugars called monosaccharides. Lipids are diverse hydrophobic molecules made of long chains or ring carbon structures. The polypeptides of proteins are polymers of amino acids, and nucleic acids are polymers of nucleotides. Polymers are formed by the joining together of monomers. For each bond formed during a dehydration reaction, a molecule of water is removed, and for each bond broken during a hydrolysis reaction, a molecule of water is added.

3.2 Carbohydrates

Monosaccharides, disaccharides, and polysaccharides are all carbohydrates. Therefore, the term *carbohydrate* includes both the monomers (e.g., glucose) and the polymers (e.g., starch, glycogen, and cellulose). Glucose is the immediate energy source of cells. Polysaccharides such as starch, glycogen, and cellulose are all polymers of glucose that have different types of chemical bonds. Starch in plants and glycogen in animals are used to store energy, whereas cellulose in plants and chitin in crabs and related animals, as well as fungi, provides structure.

3.3 Lipids

Lipids include a wide variety of compounds that are insoluble in water. Fats and oils, which allow long-term energy storage, contain one glycerol and three fatty acids. Both glycerol and fatty acids have polar groups, but fats and oils are nonpolar, and this accounts for their insolubility in water. Fats tend to contain saturated fatty acids, and oils tend to contain unsaturated fatty acids. Saturated fatty acids do not have carbon–carbon double bonds, but unsaturated fatty acids do have double bonds in their hydrocarbon chain. The double bond causes a kink in the molecule that accounts for the liquid nature of oils at room temperature.

A phospholipid replaces one of the fatty acids with a phosphate group. In water, phospholipids form a bilayer because the head of each molecule is hydrophilic and the tails are hydrophobic. Steroids have the same four-ring structure as cholesterol, but each differs by the attached functional groups. Waxes are composed of a fatty acid with a long hydrocarbon chain bonded to an alcohol.

3.4 Proteins

Proteins carry out many diverse functions in cells and organisms, including support, metabolism, transport, defense, regulation, and motion. Proteins are polymers of amino acids.

A polypeptide is a long chain of amino acids joined by peptide bonds. There are 20 different amino acids in cells, and they differ only by their *R* groups. Whether or not the *R* groups are hydrophilic or hydrophobic helps determine the structure, and therefore the function, of the protein. A polypeptide has up to four levels of structure: The primary level is the linear sequence of the amino acids, which is determined by the DNA; the secondary level contains α helices and β (pleated) sheets held in place by hydrogen bonding between amino acids along the polypeptide chain; and the tertiary level is the final folded polypeptide, which is held in place by internal bonding and hydrophobic interactions between *R* groups. Proteins that contain more than one polypeptide have a quaternary level of structure as well.

Some proteins serve as enzymes, which regulate and carry out body functions. As with other proteins, the shape of an enzyme is important to its function. Both high temperatures and drastic pH change can cause proteins to denature, lose their shape, and decrease their function.

3.5 Nucleic Acids

The nucleic acids DNA and RNA are linear polymers of nucleotides. Nucleotides can be sequenced in any order. Changes in nucleotide sequence produce the diversity of life seen on Earth. Each nucleotide has three components: a 5-carbon sugar, a phosphate (phosphoric acid), and a nitrogen-containing base.

DNA, which contains the sugar deoxyribose, phosphate, and nitrogen-containing bases, is the genetic material that stores information for its own replication and specifies the order in which amino acids are sequenced in proteins. DNA uses mRNA to direct protein synthesis. DNA is a double-stranded helix in which A pairs with T and C pairs with G through hydrogen bonding. RNA is single stranded, contains the sugar ribose and phosphate, and has the same bases as DNA except for uracil. There are many different types of RNA.

ATP is a special nucleotide that, with its unstable phosphate bonds, stores energy to do cellular work. Hydrolysis of ATP to ADP + Ⓟ releases energy needed by the cell to make a product or conduct metabolism.

Key Terms

ADP (adenosine diphosphate) 56	DNA (deoxyribonucleic acid) 54
amino acid 50	enzyme 41
ATP (adenosine triphosphate) 54	fat 46
biomolecule 38	fatty acid 46
carbohydrate 41	fibrous protein 51
cellulose 44	functional group 39
chaperone protein 53	globular protein 52
chitin 44	glucose 42
coenzyme 54	glycerol 46
complementary base pairing 55	glycogen 43
	hemoglobin 49
dehydration reaction 40	hexose 42
denatured 53	hydrolysis reaction 41
deoxyribose 42	hydrophilic 40
disaccharide 42	hydrophobic 40
	inorganic chemistry 38

isomer   40
lipid   45
monomer   40
monosaccharide   42
nucleic acid   54
nucleotide   54
oil   46
organic chemistry   38
organic molecule   38
pentose   42
peptide   50
peptide bond   50
peptidoglycan   44
phospholipid   46
polymer   40

polypeptide   50
polysaccharide   42
prion   53
protein   49
ribose   42
RNA (ribonucleic acid)   54
saturated fatty acid   46
starch   43
steroid   46
trans-fat   45
triglyceride   46
unsaturated fatty acid   46
wax   48

Assess

Reviewing This Chapter

1. How do the chemical characteristics of carbon affect the structure of organic molecules?   38–39
2. Give examples of functional groups, and discuss the importance of these groups being hydrophobic or hydrophilic.   39–40
3. What biomolecules are monomers of the polymers studied in this chapter? How do monomers join to produce polymers, and how are polymers broken down to monomers?   40
4. Name several monosaccharides, disaccharides, and polysaccharides, and give a function of each. How are these molecules structurally distinguishable?   42–44
5. What is the difference between a saturated and an unsaturated fatty acid? Explain the structure of a fat molecule by stating its components and how they join together.   46
6. How does the structure of a phospholipid differ from that of a fat? How do phospholipids form a bilayer in the presence of water?   46
7. Describe the structure of a generalized steroid. How does one steroid differ from another?   46–48
8. Draw the structure of an amino acid and a peptide, pointing out the peptide bond.   50
9. Discuss the four possible levels of protein structure, and relate each level to particular bonding patterns.   50–53
10. How do nucleotides bond to form nucleic acids? State and explain several differences between the structure of DNA and that of RNA.   54–55
11. Discuss the structure and function of ATP.   55–56

Testing Yourself

Choose the best answer for each question.

1. Which of these is not a characteristic of carbon?
   a. forms four covalent bonds
   b. bonds with other carbon atoms
   c. is sometimes ionic
   d. can form long chains
   e. sometimes shares two pairs of electrons with another atom
2. A hydrophilic group is
   a. attracted to water.
   b. a polar and/or ionized group.
   c. found at the end of fatty acids.
   d. the opposite of a hydrophobic group.
   e. All of these are correct.

3. Which of these is an example of a hydrolysis reaction?
   a. amino acid + amino acid $\longrightarrow$ dipeptide + H_2O
   b. dipeptide + H_2O $\longrightarrow$ amino acid + amino acid
   c. denaturation of a polypeptide
   d. Both a and b are correct.
   e. Both b and c are correct.
4. Which of these makes cellulose nondigestible in humans?
   a. a polymer of glucose subunits
   b. a fibrous protein
   c. the linkage between the glucose molecules
   d. the peptide linkage between the amino acid molecules
   e. the carboxyl groups ionize
5. A fatty acid is unsaturated if it
   a. contains hydrogen.
   b. contains carbon–carbon double bonds.
   c. contains a carboxyl (acidic) group.
   d. bonds to glycogen.
   e. bonds to a nucleotide.
6. The difference between one amino acid and another is found in the
   a. amino group.
   b. carboxyl group.
   c. R group.
   d. peptide bond.
   e. carbon atoms.
7. The shape of a polypeptide is
   a. maintained by bonding between parts of the polypeptide.
   b. ultimately dependent on the primary structure.
   c. necessary to its function.
   d. All of these are correct.
8. Nucleotides
   a. contain a sugar, a nitrogen-containing base, and a phosphate group.
   b. are the monomers of fats and polysaccharides.
   c. join together by covalent bonding between the bases.
   d. are present in both DNA and RNA.
   e. Both a and d are correct.
9. ATP
   a. is an amino acid.
   b. has a helical structure.
   c. is a high-energy molecule that can break down to ADP and phosphate.
   d. provides enzymes for metabolism.
   e. is most energetic when in the ADP state.
10. Label the following diagram using the terms H_2O, monomer, hydrolysis reaction, dehydration reaction, and polymer. Terms can be used more than once and a term need not be used.

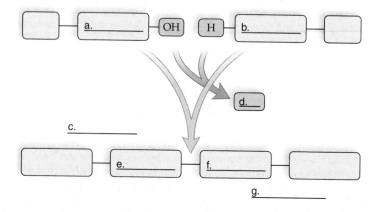

11. The monomer of a carbohydrate is
    a. an amino acid.
    b. a nucleic acid.
    c. a monosaccharide.
    d. a fatty acid.

12. The joining of two adjacent amino acids is called
    a. a peptide bond.
    b. a dehydration reaction.
    c. a covalent bond.
    d. All of these are correct.

13. The shape of a polypeptide
    a. is maintained by bonding between parts of the polypeptide.
    b. is ultimately dependent on the primary structure.
    c. involves hydrogen bonding.
    d. All of these are correct.

14. Which of the following pertains to an RNA nucleotide and not to a DNA nucleotide?
    a. contains the sugar ribose
    b. contains a nitrogen-containing base
    c. contains a phosphate molecule
    d. becomes bonded to other nucleotides following a dehydration reaction

For questions 15–18, match the items to those in the key. Some answers are used more than once.

KEY:
    a. carbohydrate
    b. fats and oils
    c. protein
    d. nucleic acid

15. the 6-carbon sugar, glucose

16. polymer of amino acids

17. glycerol and fatty acids

18. genes

19. Which is a correct statement about carbohydrates?
    a. All polysaccharides serve as energy storage molecules.
    b. Glucose is broken down for immediate energy.
    c. Glucose is not a carbohydrate, only polysaccharides are.
    d. Starch, glycogen, and cellulose have different monomers.
    e. Both a and c are correct.

20. In phospholipids,
    a. heads are polar.
    b. tails are nonpolar.
    c. heads contain phosphate.
    d. All of these are correct.

Engage

Thinking Scientifically

1. The seeds of temperate plants tend to contain unsaturated fatty acids, while the seeds of tropical plants tend to have saturated fatty acids. **a.** How would you test your hypothesis. **b.** Assuming your hypothesis is supported, give an explanation.

2. Chemical analysis reveals that an abnormal form of an enzyme contains a polar amino acid at the location where the normal form has a nonpolar amino acid. Formulate a testable hypothesis concerning the abnormal enzyme.

Bioethical Issue

Organic Pollutants

Organic compounds include the carbohydrates, proteins, lipids, and nucleic acids that make up our bodies. Modern industry also uses all sorts of organic compounds that are synthetically produced. Indeed, our modern way of life wouldn't be possible without synthetic organic compounds.

Pesticides, herbicides, disinfectants, plastics, and textiles contain organic substances that are termed pollutants when they enter the natural environment and cause harm to living things. Global use of pesticides has increased dramatically since the 1950s, and modern pesticides are ten times more toxic than those of the 1950s. The Centers for Disease Control and Prevention in Atlanta reports that 40% of children working in agricultural fields now show signs of pesticide poisoning. The U.S. Geological Survey estimates that 32 million people in urban areas and 10 million people in rural areas are using groundwater that contains organic pollutants. J. Charles Fox, an official of the Environmental Protection Agency, says that "over the life of a person, ingestion of these chemicals has been shown to have adverse health effects such as cancer, reproductive problems, and developmental effects."

At one time, people failed to realize that everything in the environment is connected to everything else. In other words, they didn't know that an organic chemical can wander far from the site of its entry into the environment and that eventually these chemicals can enter our own bodies and cause harm. Now that we are aware of this outcome, we have to decide as a society how to proceed. We might decide to do nothing if the percentage of people dying from exposure to organic pollutants is small. Or we might decide to regulate the use of industrial compounds more strictly than has been done in the past. We could also decide that we need better ways of purifying public and private water supplies so that they do not contain organic pollutants.

Cell Structure and Function

CHAPTER OUTLINE

4.1 Cellular Level of Organization 61

4.2 Prokaryotic Cells 65

4.3 Introducing Eukaryotic Cells 67

4.4 The Nucleus and Ribosomes 70

4.5 The Endomembrane System 72

4.6 Other Vesicles and Vacuoles 75

4.7 The Energy-Related Organelles 76

4.8 The Cytoskeleton 78

BEFORE YOU BEGIN

Before beginning this chapter, take a few moments to review the following discussions.

Figures 3.1 and 3.2 What role do carbon and functional groups serve in biological molecules?

Sections 3.2 to 3.5 What macromolecules are needed to construct a cell?

Figures 3.8, 3.12, 3.17, and 3.21 How does the structure of a macromolecule affect its function?

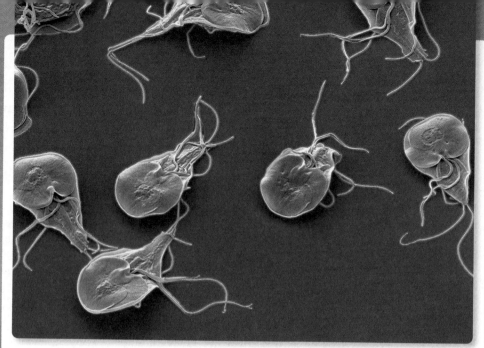

Electron micrograph of *Giardia lamblia*, a cause of diarrhea.

The Dutch shopkeeper Antonie van Leeuwenhoek (1632–1723) may have been the first person to see living cells. Using a microscope he built himself, he looked at everything possible, including his own stool. He wrote, "I have usually of a morning a well-formed stool. But, hitherto, I have had sometimes a looseness of bowels, so I went to stool some twice, thrice, or four times a day. My excrement being so thin, I was at diverse times constrained to examine it. Wherein I have sometimes seen animalcules a moving prettily. Their bodies were somewhat longer than broad, and the belly, which was flat-lie, furnished with sundry little paws. . . ." [November 9, 1681]

In this way, Antonie van Leeuwenhoek reported seeing the parasite *Giardia lamblia* in his feces. *Giardia* are unicellular organisms, while humans are multicellular organisms. In this chapter, you will see that cells are the fundamental building blocks of organisms, organized to carry out basic metabolic functions and adapt to changing environmental conditions. The presentation concentrates on the generalized bacterial, animal, or plant cell; however, all cells are specialized in particular ways.

As you read through the chapter, think about the following questions:

1. How is a cell more than simply the sum of its macromolecular parts?

2. What characteristics enable cells to be alive and allow them to self-replicate?

3. How are cells able to metabolize and respond to environmental changes so quickly?

FOLLOWING *the* THEMES

CHAPTER 4 CELL STRUCTURE AND FUNCTION

UNIT 1 THE CELL		
	Evolution	All cells are produced from existing cells, creating an unbroken lineage back to cells from early Earth.
	Nature of Science	Understanding how cells function allows us to discover ways to treat cell-based diseases.
	Biological Systems	Cells metabolize and adapt to changing environmental conditions.

4.1 Cellular Level of Organization

Cells are the basic units of life. All of the chemistry and biomolecules we have discussed to this point are necessary but insufficient on their own to support life. It is only when these components are brought together and organized into a cell that life is possible.

All organisms are made up of cells. When we observe plants, animals, and other organisms, it is important to realize that what we are seeing is a collection of cells that work together in a highly organized, regulated manner, and thus conduct the business of life. Figure 4.1 shows the connection between whole organisms and their component cells. Although the cellular basis of life is clear to us now, scientists were unaware of this fact as recently as two hundred years ago. The link between cells and life became clear to microscopists during the 1830s.

The **cell** is the smallest unit of living matter. The collective work of the 19th century scientists Robert Brown (1773-1858), Matthais Schleiden (1804-1881), and Theodor Schwann (1810-1882) helped determine that plants and animals are composed of cells. Further work by the German physician Rudolph Virchow (1821-1902) showed that cells self-reproduce and "every cell comes from a preexisting cell." Today, we know that various illnesses of the body, such as diabetes and prostate cancer, are due to cellular malfunction. Countless scientific investigations since that time verify these initial findings. From these results, we can infer that all life on Earth today came from cells in ancient times, and that all cells are related in some way. In reality, a continuity of cells has been present from generation to generation, even back to the very first cell (or cells) in the history of life.

Today, some life-forms exist as single cells, whereas others are complex, interconnected systems of cells. When unicellular organisms reproduce, a single cell divides and becomes two new organisms. When multicellular organisms grow, many cells divide. The presence of many cells allows some to specialize to do particular jobs within the multicellular organism, including the cells that create genetic variation through sexual reproduction.

The work of Schleiden, Schwann, and Virchow helped created the **cell theory.** It states that:

1. all organisms are composed of cells,
2. cells are the basic units of structure and function in organisms, and
3. cells come only from preexisting cells because cells are self-reproducing.

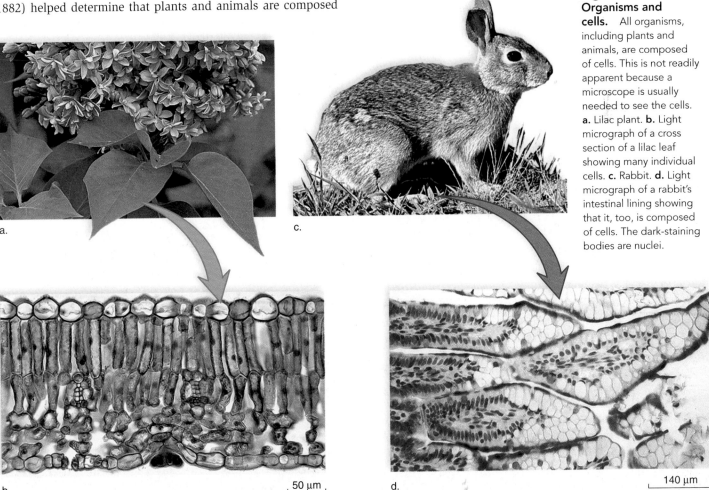

**Figure 4.1
Organisms and cells.** All organisms, including plants and animals, are composed of cells. This is not readily apparent because a microscope is usually needed to see the cells. **a.** Lilac plant. **b.** Light micrograph of a cross section of a lilac leaf showing many individual cells. **c.** Rabbit. **d.** Light micrograph of a rabbit's intestinal lining showing that it, too, is composed of cells. The dark-staining bodies are nuclei.

a.

c.

b.   50 μm

d.   140 μm

Cell Size

Although they range in size, cells are generally quite small. A frog's egg, at about 1 millimeter (mm) in diameter, is large enough to be seen by the human eye. But most cells are far smaller than 1 mm; some are even as small as 1 micrometer (μm)—one thousandth of a millimeter. Cell inclusions and macromolecules are smaller than a micrometer and are measured in terms of nanometers (nm).

Because of their size, very small biological structures can only be viewed with microscopes, which magnify a visual image. Figure 4.2 shows the visual range of the eye, light microscope, and electron microscope; the discussion of microscopy in the Nature of Science feature on pages 63–64 explains why the electron microscope allows us to see so much more detail than the light microscope does.

Why are cells so small? To answer this question, consider that a cell is a system by itself, and as such needs a surface area large enough to allow adequate nutrients to enter and for wastes to be eliminated. Small cells, not large cells, are likely to have an adequate surface area for exchanging wastes for nutrients. As cells increase in size, the surface area becomes inadequate to exchange the materials that the volume of the cell requires.

Figure 4.3 visually demonstrates this relationship; dividing a large cube into smaller cubes provides a lot more surface area per volume. Calculations show that a 1-cm cube has a **surface-area-to-volume ratio** of 6:1, whereas a 4-cm cube has a surface-area-to-volume ratio of 1.5:1. The former ratio allows sufficient transport in and out of the cell to support life; the latter ratio does not.

A mental image might help you visualize the importance of surface-area-to-volume-ratios and why this relationship favors smaller cell size. Imagine a small room and a large room filled with people. The small room, which holds 20 people, has only two doors, and the large room, which holds 80 people, has four doors. If a fire occurred in both rooms, it would be faster to

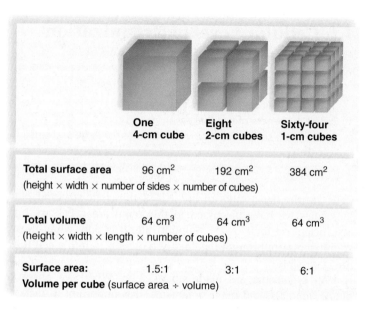

	One 4-cm cube	Eight 2-cm cubes	Sixty-four 1-cm cubes
Total surface area (height × width × number of sides × number of cubes)	96 cm²	192 cm²	384 cm²
Total volume (height × width × length × number of cubes)	64 cm³	64 cm³	64 cm³
Surface area: **Volume per cube** (surface area ÷ volume)	1.5:1	3:1	6:1

Figure 4.3 Surface-area-to-volume relationships. As cell size decreases from 4 cm³ to 1 cm³, the surface-area-to-volume ratio increases.

get the people out of the smaller room because it has the more favorable ratio of doors to people. Similarly, a small cell size is more advantageous for exchanging molecules because of its greater surface-area-to-volume ratio.

Check Your Progress   4.1

1. Describe the major components of cell theory.
2. Evaluate why a cell and a whole organism are both examples of biological systems.
3. Explain why a large surface-area-to-volume ratio is needed for the proper functioning of cells.

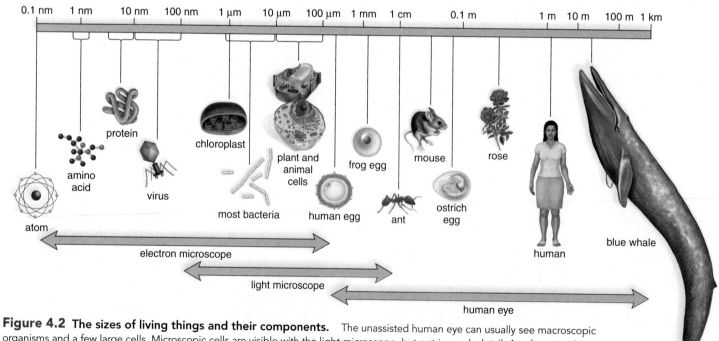

Figure 4.2 The sizes of living things and their components. The unassisted human eye can usually see macroscopic organisms and a few large cells. Microscopic cells are visible with the light microscope, but not in much detail. An electron microscope is necessary to see organelles in detail and to observe viruses and molecules. In the metric system (see back endsheet), each higher unit is ten times greater than the preceding unit. (1 meter = 10^2 cm = 10^3 mm = 10^6 μm = 10^9 nm)

THEME Nature of Science

Microscopy Today

Since cells are the basic unit of life, the more we learn about cells, the more we understand life. Cells were not discovered until the seventeenth century, when the microscope was invented. Since that time, various types of microscopes have been developed for studying cells and their components.

Many times when scientists don't have suitable tools to investigate natural phenomena, they invent them. Microscopes have given scientists a deeper look into how life works than is possible with the naked eye. Today, there are many types of microscopes. A *compound light microscope* uses a set of glass lenses to focus light rays passing through a specimen to produce an image that is viewed by the human eye. A *transmission electron microscope (TEM)* uses a set of electromagnetic lenses to focus electrons passing through a specimen to produce an image that is projected onto a fluorescent screen or photographic film. A *scanning electron microscope (SEM)* uses a narrow beam of electrons to scan over the surface of a specimen that is coated with a thin metal layer. Secondary electrons given off by the metal are detected and used to produce a three-dimensional image on a television screen. Figure 4A shows these three types of microscopic images.

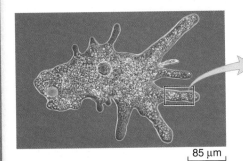

85 μm

amoeba, light micrograph

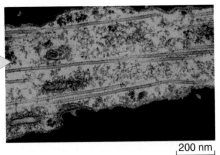

200 nm

pseudopod segment, transmission electron micrograph

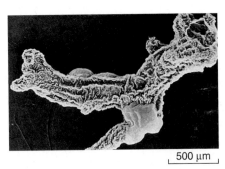

500 μm

amoeba, scanning electron micrograph

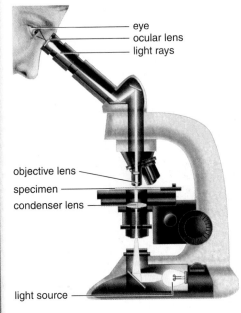

eye
ocular lens
light rays

objective lens
specimen
condenser lens

light source

a. Compound light microscope

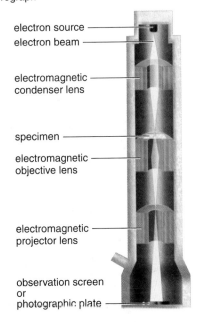

electron source
electron beam

electromagnetic condenser lens

specimen
electromagnetic objective lens

electromagnetic projector lens

observation screen or photographic plate

b. Transmission electron microscope

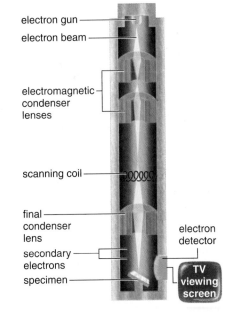

electron gun
electron beam

electromagnetic condenser lenses

scanning coil

final condenser lens

secondary electrons
specimen

electron detector

TV viewing screen

c. Scanning electron microscope

Figure 4A Diagram of microscopes with accompanying micrographs of *Amoeba proteus*. **a.** The compound light microscope and **(b)** the transmission electron microscope provide an internal view of an organism. **c.** The scanning electron microscope provides an external view of an organism.

Magnification, Resolution, and Contrast

Magnification is the ratio between the size of an image and its actual size. Electron microscopes magnify to a greater extent than do compound light microscopes. A light microscope can magnify objects about a thousand times, but an electron microscope can magnify them hundreds of thousands of times. The difference lies in the means of illumination. The path of light rays and electrons moving through space is wavelike, but the wavelength of electrons is much shorter than the wavelength of light. This difference in wavelength accounts for the electron microscope's greater magnifying capability and its greater ability to distinguish between two points (resolving power).

Resolution is the minimum distance between two objects that allows them to be seen as two separate objects. A microscope with poor resolution might enable a student to see only one cellular granule, while the microscope with the better resolution would show two granules next to each other. The greater the resolving power, the greater the detail seen.

If oil is placed between the sample and the objective lens of the compound light microscope, the resolving power is increased, and if ultraviolet light is used instead of visible light, it is also increased. But typically, a light microscope can resolve down to 0.2 µm, while the transmission electron microscope can resolve down to 0.0002 µm. If the resolving power of the average human eye is set at 1.0, then the typical compound light microscope is about 500, and the transmission electron microscope is 100,000 (Fig. 4A*b*).

The ability to make out, or resolve, a particular object can depend on *contrast*, a difference in the shading of an object compared to its background. Higher contrast is often achieved by staining cells with colored dyes (light microscopy) or with electron-dense metals (electron microscopy), which make them easier to see. Optical methods such as phase contrast and differential interference contrast (Fig. 4B) can also be used to improve contrast. Using fluorescently tagged antibodies can also help us visualize subcellular components like specific proteins (see Fig. 4.18).

Illumination, Viewing, and Recording

Light rays can be bent (refracted) and brought to focus as they pass through glass lenses, but electrons do not pass through glass. Electrons have a charge that allows them to be brought into focus by electromagnetic lenses. The human eye uses light to see an object but cannot use electrons for the same purpose. Therefore, electrons leaving the specimen in the electron microscope are directed toward a screen or a photographic plate that is sensitive to their presence. Humans can view the image on the screen or photograph.

A major advancement in illumination has been the introduction of *confocal microscopy*, which uses a laser beam scanned across the specimen to focus on a single shallow plane within the cell. The microscopist can "optically section" the specimen by focusing up and down, and a series of optical sections can be combined in a computer to create a three-dimensional image, which can be displayed and rotated on the computer screen.

An image from a microscope may be recorded by placing a television camera where the eye would view the image. The television camera converts the light image into an electronic image, which can be entered into a computer. In *video-enhanced contrast microscopy*, the computer makes the darkest areas of the original image much darker and the lightest areas of the original much lighter. The result is a high-contrast image with deep blacks and bright whites. Even more contrast can be introduced by the computer if shades of gray are replaced by colors.

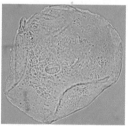 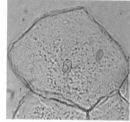 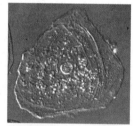 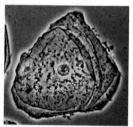 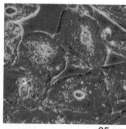

30 µm | 30 µm | 25 µm | 25 µm | 25 µm

Bright-field. Light passing through the specimen is brought directly into focus. Usually, the low level of contrast within the specimen interferes with viewing all but its largest components.

Bright-field (stained). Dyes are used to stain the specimen. Certain components take up the dye more than other components, and therefore contrast is enhanced.

Differential interference contrast. Optical methods are used to enhance density differences within the specimen so that certain regions appear brighter than others. This technique is used to view living cells, chromosomes, and organelle masses.

Phase contrast. Density differences in the specimen cause light rays to come out of "phase." The microscope enhances these phase differences so that some regions of the specimen appear brighter or darker than others. The technique is widely used to observe living cells and organelles.

Dark-field. Light is passed through the specimen at an oblique angle so that the objective lens receives only light diffracted and scattered by the object. This technique is used to view organelles, which appear quite bright against a dark field.

Figure 4B Photomicrographs of cheek cells. Bright-field microscopy is the most common form used with a compound light microscope. Other types of microscopy include differential interference contrast, phase contrast, and dark-field.

4.2 Prokaryotic Cells

Learning Outcomes

Upon completion of this section, you should be able to

1. Examine the evolutionary relatedness of prokaryotes, eukaryotes, and archaeans.

2. Describe the fundamental components of a bacterial cell.

Fundamentally, three different types of cells exist in nature. **Prokaryotic cells** [Gk. *pro*, before, and *karyon*, kernel, nucleus] are so named because they lack a membrane-enclosed nucleus. Another type of cell, called a **eukaryotic cell** [Gk. *eu*, true, and *karyon*, kernel, nucleus], has a nucleus (see Figs. 4.6 and 4.7). A third group of cells, called **archaeans** [Gk. *arkhaios*, ancient], possess qualities of both prokaryotes and eukaryotes. Prokaryotic cells and archaeans were once thought to be closely related because of their similar size and shape. Comparisons of DNA and RNA sequences now show archaeans to be biochemically distinct from prokaryotes and eukaryotes. Although we have learned more about archaeans than was previously known, we have studied prokaryotes and eukaryotes in much greater detail.

Prokaryotes as a group are one of the most abundant and diverse life-forms on Earth, and they are present in great numbers in the air, water, and soil, as well as living in and on other organisms. Although they are structurally less complicated than eukaryotes, their metabolic capabilities as a group far exceed those of eukaryotes. Prokaryotes are an extremely successful group of organisms whose evolutionary history dates back to the first cells on Earth.

Bacteria are well known because they cause some serious diseases, such as tuberculosis, anthrax, tetanus, throat infections, and gonorrhea. But many species of bacteria are important to the environment because they decompose the remains of dead organisms and contribute to ecological cycles. Bacteria also assist humans in still another way—we use them to manufacture all sorts of products, from industrial chemicals to foodstuffs and drugs. For example, today we know how to place human genes in certain cultured bacteria so that they can produce human insulin, a necessary hormone for the treatment of diabetes.

 Video *E. coli* Wars

The Structure of Prokaryotes

Prokaryotes are quite small; an average size is 1.1–1.5 µm wide and 2.0–6.0 µm long. While other prokaryote shapes have been identified, three basic shapes are most common:

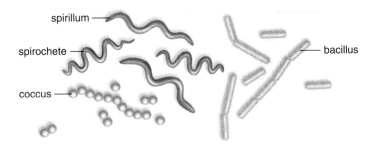

A rod-shaped bacterium is called a **bacillus,** while a spherical-shaped bacterium is a **coccus.** Both of these can occur

as pairs or chains, and in addition, cocci can occur as clusters. Some long rods are twisted into spirals, in which case they are **spirilla** if they are rigid or **spirochetes** if they are flexible.

 Animation Prokaryotic Cell Shapes

Figure 4.4 shows the generalized structure of a bacterium. "Generalized" means that not all bacteria have all the structures depicted, and some have more than one of each. Also, for the sake of discussion, we divide the organization of bacteria into the cell envelope, the cytoplasm, and the appendages.

Cell Envelope

In bacteria, the **cell envelope** includes the plasma membrane, the cell wall, and the glycocalyx. The **plasma membrane** is a phospholipid bilayer with embedded proteins:

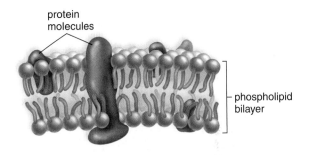

The plasma membrane has the important function of regulating the entrance and exit of substances into and out of the cytoplasm. Regulating the flow of materials in and out of the cytoplasm is necessary in order to maintain its normal composition.

In prokaryotes, the plasma membrane can form internal pouches called mesosomes. **Mesosomes** most likely increase the internal surface area for the attachment of enzymes that are carrying on metabolic activities.

The **cell wall,** when present, maintains the shape of the cell, even if the cytoplasm should happen to take up an abundance of water. You may recall that the cell wall of a plant cell is strengthened by cellulose; in contrast, the cell wall of a bacterium contains peptidoglycan, a complex molecule containing a unique amino disaccharide and peptide fragments.

Animation Cell Wall Antibiotics

The **glycocalyx** is a layer of polysaccharides that lies outside the cell wall in some bacteria. When the layer is well organized and not easily washed off, it is called a **capsule.** A slime layer, on the other hand, is not well organized and is easily removed. The glycocalyx aids against drying out and helps bacteria resist a host's immune system. It also helps bacteria attach to almost any surface.

Cytoplasm

The **cytoplasm** is a semifluid solution composed of water and inorganic and organic molecules encased by a plasma membrane. Among the organic molecules are a variety of enzymes, which speed the many types of chemical reactions involved in metabolism.

The DNA of a prokaryote is found in a single, coiled chromosome that is located in a region called the **nucleoid.** Many bacteria also have extrachromosomal pieces of circular DNA called **plasmids.** Plasmids are routinely used in biotechnology

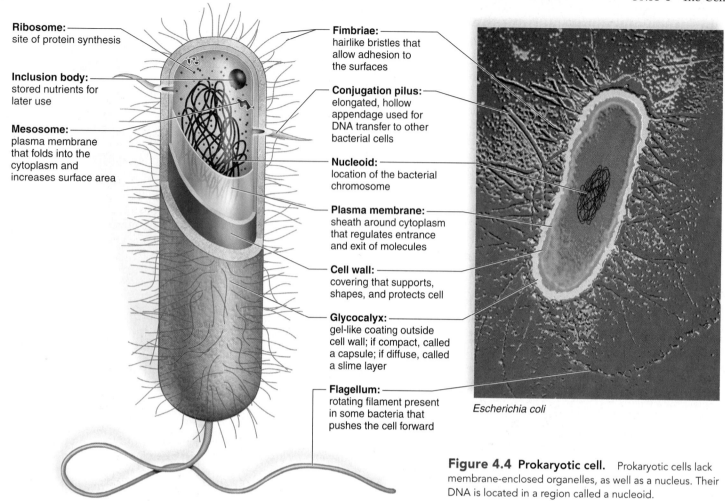

Ribosome:
site of protein synthesis

Inclusion body:
stored nutrients for
later use

Mesosome:
plasma membrane
that folds into the
cytoplasm and
increases surface area

Fimbriae:
hairlike bristles that
allow adhesion to
the surfaces

Conjugation pilus:
elongated, hollow
appendage used for
DNA transfer to other
bacterial cells

Nucleoid:
location of the bacterial
chromosome

Plasma membrane:
sheath around cytoplasm
that regulates entrance
and exit of molecules

Cell wall:
covering that supports,
shapes, and protects cell

Glycocalyx:
gel-like coating outside
cell wall; if compact, called
a capsule; if diffuse, called
a slime layer

Flagellum:
rotating filament present
in some bacteria that
pushes the cell forward

Escherichia coli

Figure 4.4 Prokaryotic cell. Prokaryotic cells lack
membrane-enclosed organelles, as well as a nucleus. Their
DNA is located in a region called a nucleoid.

laboratories as a molecular vehicle, also called a **vector**, to
transport DNA from different organisms, including humans, into
a bacterium. This technique is possible because all life on Earth
is constructed from the same four DNA nucleotides: A, G, C,
and T. The ability to combine genes from different life-forms is
important in the production of new medicines and many com-
merical products we use every day.

The many proteins encoded by the bacterial DNA are synthesized on tiny structures called **ribosomes.** A bacterial cell
contains thousands of ribosomes that are similar in shape and
function, but are smaller than eukaryotic ribosomes. Like their
eukaryotic counterparts, bacterial ribosomes still contain RNA
and protein in two subunits.

Most bacteria carry out metabolism in the same manner
as animals, but the **cyanobacteria** are bacteria that are capable
of photosynthesis in the same manner as plants. These organisms live in water, in ditches, on buildings, and on the bark of
trees. Their cytoplasm contains extensive internal membranes
called **thylakoids** [Gk. *thylakon,* small sac], where chlorophyll
and other pigments absorb solar energy for the production of
carbohydrates. Cyanobacteria are called the blue-green bacteria
because some have a pigment that adds a shade of blue to the
cell, in addition to the green color of chlorophyll. The cyanobacteria release oxygen as a by-product of photosynthesis, which
is one reason why scientists think that ancestral cyanobacteria
were the earliest photosynthesizers on Earth. Many sources of
evidence show that the composition of the early Earth's atmosphere was changed by addition of oxygen.

Appendages

The appendages of a bacterium, namely the flagella, fimbriae, and
conjugation pili, are made of protein. Motile bacteria can propel
themselves in water by the means of appendages called **flagella**
(usually 20 nm in diameter and 1–70 nm long). The bacterial flagellum is one of the great wonders of nature, and it consists of a
filament, a hook, and a basal body. The basal body is a series of
rings anchored in the cell wall and membrane. The hook rotates
360° within the basal body, and this rotation propels bacteria—the
bacterial flagellum does not move back and forth like a whip.
Sometimes flagella occur only at the two ends of a cell, and sometimes they are dispersed randomly over the surface. The number
and location of flagella can be used to help distinguish different types of bacteria.

Animation
Bacterial
Locomotion

Fimbriae are small, bristlelike fibers that sprout from the
cell surface. They are not involved in locomotion; instead, fimbriae attach bacteria to a surface. **Conjugation pili** are rigid
tubular structures used by bacteria to pass DNA from cell to
cell. Bacteria reproduce asexually by binary fission, but they
can exchange DNA by way of the conjugation pili. They can also
take up DNA from the external medium or by way of viruses.

Check Your Progress   4.2

1. Explain the major differences between a prokaryotic and
   eukaryotic cell.
2. Describe the functions of the bacterial cell envelope,
   cytoplasm, and appendages.

4.3 Introducing Eukaryotic Cells

Learning Outcomes

Upon completion of this section, you should be able to

1. Explain how membranes compartmentalize a cell.
2. Examine how organelles divide cellular work.
3. Apply the endosymbiosis theory to eukaryotic cell structure.

Eukaryotic cells, like prokaryotic cells and archaeans, have a plasma membrane that separates the contents of the cell from the environment and regulates the passage of molecules into and out of the cytoplasm. The plasma membrane is a phospholipid bilayer with embedded proteins. Some scientists have suggested that the nucleus evolved as the result of the invagination, or pocketing, of the plasma membrane (Fig. 4.5). The resulting compartment may have allowed specific functions to occur in the nucleus, freeing up cellular resources in the cytoplasm for other work. An increased ability to metabolize would have given the new cell a comparative advantage over other cells.

Origin of the Eukaryotic Cell

Much scientific evidence also shows that mitochondria and chloroplasts, the two energy-related organelles, arose when a large eukaryotic cell engulfed independent prokaryotes. This relationship is referred to as the **endosymbiotic theory**. This theory explains why mitochondria and chloroplasts are bounded by a double membrane and contain their own genetic material separate from that of the nucleus.

Figure 4.5 shows conceptually how endosymbiosis is thought to have occurred. Figures 4.6 and 4.7 show general features of fully evolved, present day animal and plant cells. Specialized cells, as opposed to generalized cells, do not necessarily contain all the structures depicted and may have more or fewer copies of any particular organelle, depending on their particular function. These generalized depictions of plant and animal cells are useful for study purposes. A baseline understanding of cell structure and function will be helpful when you study the function of specialized cells later in this text.

Structure of a Eukaryotic Cell

As shown in Figures 4.6 and 4.7, eukaryotic cells are compartmentalized. Membranes create internal spaces that divide the labor necessary to conduct life functions. The compartments of a eukaryotic cell, typically called **organelles,** carry out specialized functions that together allow the cell to be more efficient and successful. Nearly all organelles are surrounded by a membrane with embedded proteins, many of which are enzymes. These enzymes make products specific to that organelle, but their action benefits the whole cell system. The cell can be seen as a system of interconnected organelles that work together to metabolize, regulate, and conduct life processes. For example, the nucleus is a compartment that houses the genetic material within eukaryotic chromosomes and contains hereditary information. The nucleus communicates with ribosomes in the cytoplasm, and the organelles of the endomembrane system—notably the endoplasmic reticulum and the Golgi apparatus—communicate with one another.

Production of specific molecules takes place inside or on the surface of organelles. As mentioned, enzymes embedded in the organelles' membranes make these molecules. These products are then transported around the cell by transport **vesicles,** membranous sacs that enclose the molecules and keep them separate from the cytoplasm. For example, the endoplasmic reticulum communicates with the Golgi apparatus by means of transport vesicles. Communication with the energy-related organelles—mitochondria and chloroplasts—is less obvious, but it does occur because they import particular molecules from the cytoplasm.

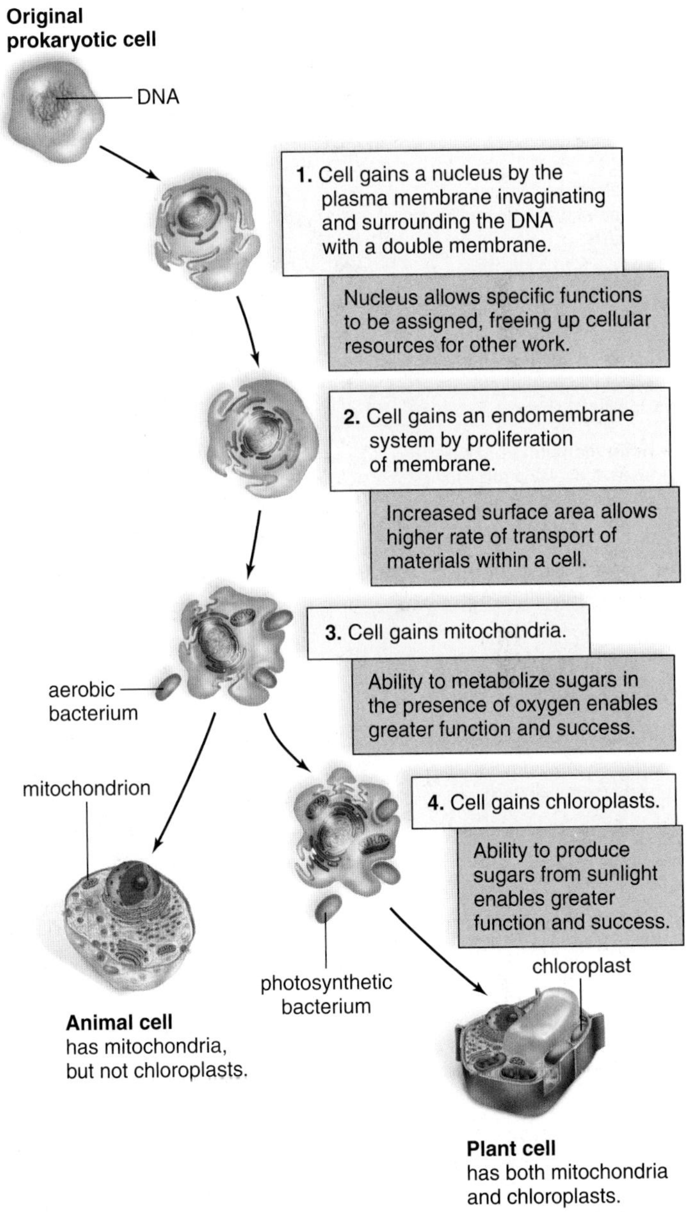

Figure 4.5 Origin of organelles. Invagination of the plasma membrane could have created the nuclear envelope and an endomembrane system that involves several organelles. The endosymbiotic theory states that mitochondria and chloroplasts were independent prokaryotes that took up residence in a eukaryotic cell. Endosymbiosis was a first step toward the origin of the eukaryotic cell during the evolutionary history of life.

Figure 4.6 Animal cell anatomy. Micrograph of an insect cell (*right*) and drawing of a generalized animal cell (*below*).

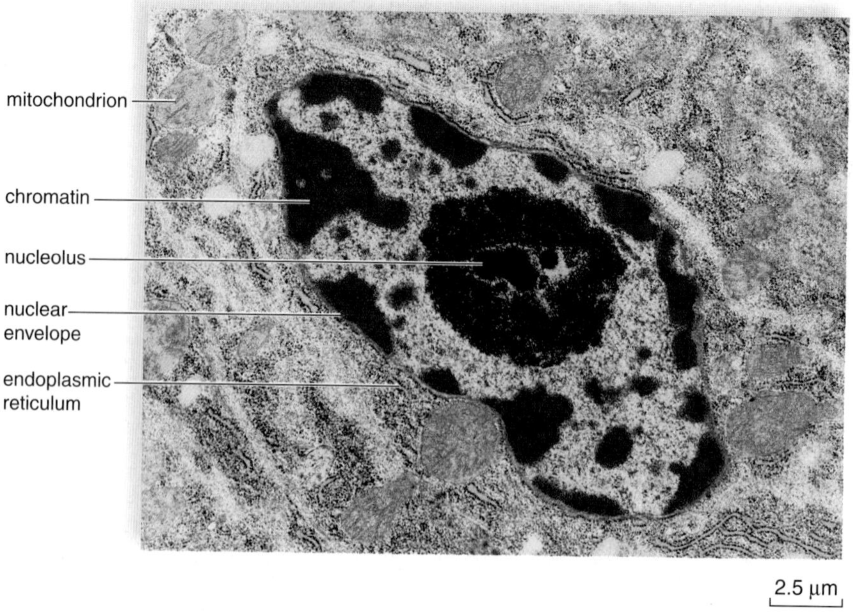

mitochondrion

chromatin

nucleolus

nuclear envelope

endoplasmic reticulum

2.5 μm

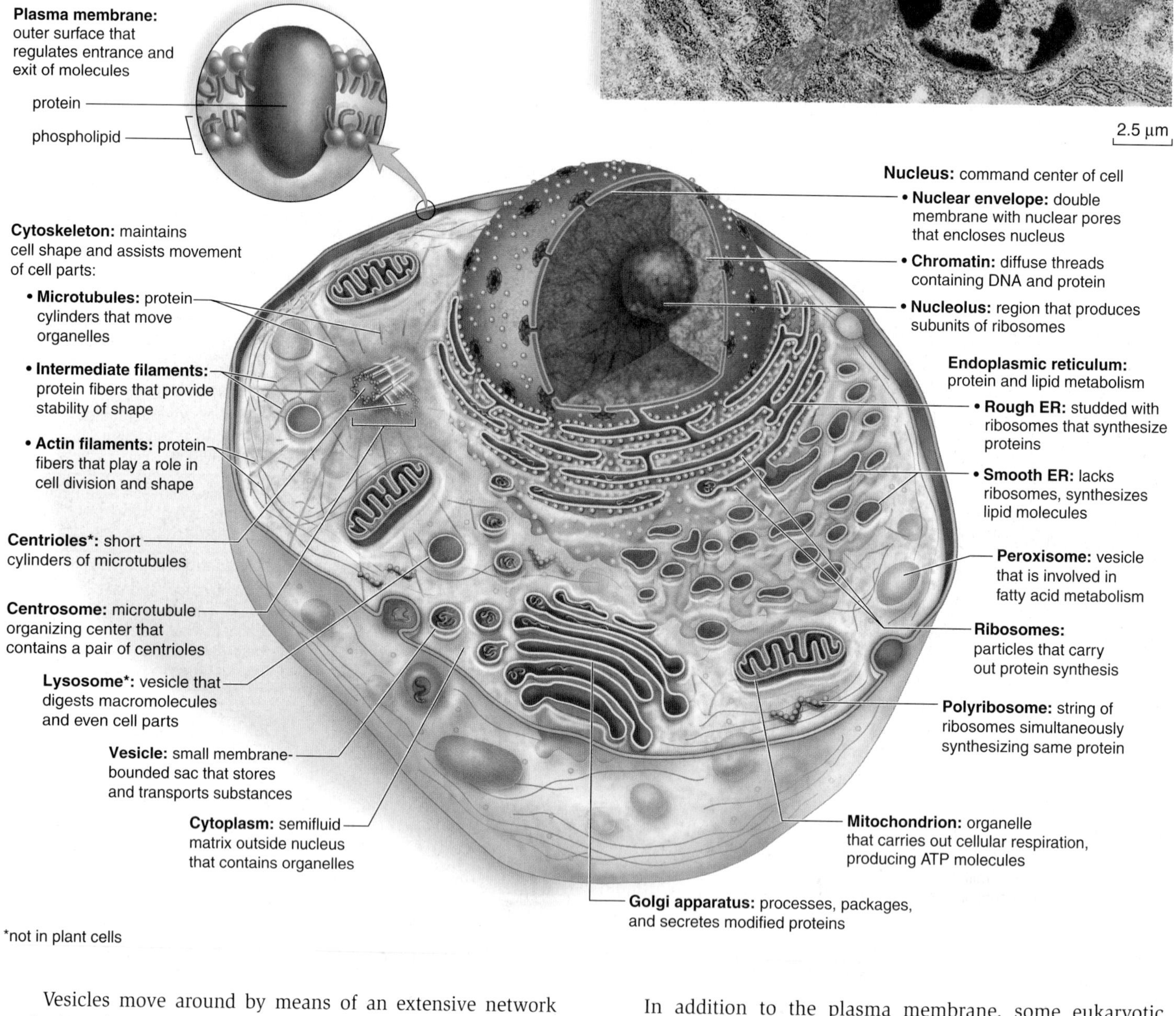

Plasma membrane: outer surface that regulates entrance and exit of molecules

protein

phospholipid

Cytoskeleton: maintains cell shape and assists movement of cell parts:

- **Microtubules:** protein cylinders that move organelles

- **Intermediate filaments:** protein fibers that provide stability of shape

- **Actin filaments:** protein fibers that play a role in cell division and shape

Centrioles*: short cylinders of microtubules

Centrosome: microtubule organizing center that contains a pair of centrioles

Lysosome*: vesicle that digests macromolecules and even cell parts

Vesicle: small membrane-bounded sac that stores and transports substances

Cytoplasm: semifluid matrix outside nucleus that contains organelles

*not in plant cells

Nucleus: command center of cell

- **Nuclear envelope:** double membrane with nuclear pores that encloses nucleus

- **Chromatin:** diffuse threads containing DNA and protein

- **Nucleolus:** region that produces subunits of ribosomes

Endoplasmic reticulum: protein and lipid metabolism

- **Rough ER:** studded with ribosomes that synthesize proteins

- **Smooth ER:** lacks ribosomes, synthesizes lipid molecules

- **Peroxisome:** vesicle that is involved in fatty acid metabolism

- **Ribosomes:** particles that carry out protein synthesis

- **Polyribosome:** string of ribosomes simultaneously synthesizing same protein

- **Mitochondrion:** organelle that carries out cellular respiration, producing ATP molecules

Golgi apparatus: processes, packages, and secretes modified proteins

Vesicles move around by means of an extensive network or lattice of protein fibers called the **cytoskeleton,** which also maintains cell shape and assists with cell movement. The protein fibers serve as tracks for the transport vesicles that are taking molecules from one organelle to another. Organelles are also moved from place to place using this transport system. Think of the cytoskeleton as a three-dimensional road system inside cells used to transport important cargo from place to place. The cytoskeleton is discussed in detail later in this chapter.

In addition to the plasma membrane, some eukaryotic cells, notably plant cells and those of fungi and many protists, have a cell wall. A plant cell wall contains cellulose fibrils and, therefore, has a different composition from the bacterial cell wall.

Cells can vary the proportion of organelles they have, depending on the specialized function of the cell. For example, a liver cell whose function is partly to detoxify drugs and other ingested compounds contains a greater proportion of smooth

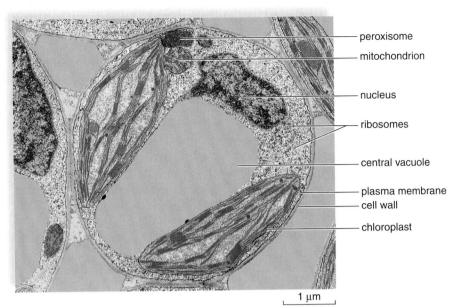

peroxisome
mitochondrion
nucleus
ribosomes
central vacuole
plasma membrane
cell wall
chloroplast

1 μm

Figure 4.7 Plant cell anatomy. False-colored micrograph of a young plant cell (*left*) and drawing of a generalized plant cell (*below*).

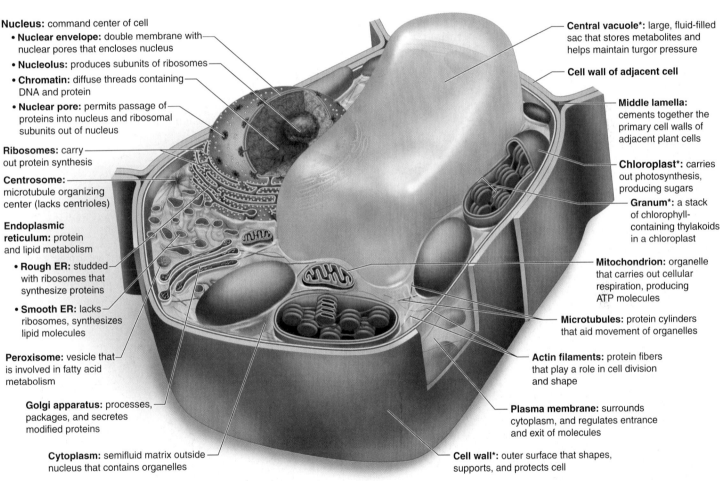

Nucleus: command center of cell
- **Nuclear envelope:** double membrane with nuclear pores that encloses nucleus
- **Nucleolus:** produces subunits of ribosomes
- **Chromatin:** diffuse threads containing DNA and protein
- **Nuclear pore:** permits passage of proteins into nucleus and ribosomal subunits out of nucleus

Ribosomes: carry out protein synthesis

Centrosome: microtubule organizing center (lacks centrioles)

Endoplasmic reticulum: protein and lipid metabolism
- **Rough ER:** studded with ribosomes that synthesize proteins
- **Smooth ER:** lacks ribosomes, synthesizes lipid molecules

Peroxisome: vesicle that is involved in fatty acid metabolism

Golgi apparatus: processes, packages, and secretes modified proteins

Cytoplasm: semifluid matrix outside nucleus that contains organelles

Central vacuole*: large, fluid-filled sac that stores metabolites and helps maintain turgor pressure

Cell wall of adjacent cell

Middle lamella: cements together the primary cell walls of adjacent plant cells

Chloroplast*: carries out photosynthesis, producing sugars

Granum*: a stack of chlorophyll-containing thylakoids in a chloroplast

Mitochondrion: organelle that carries out cellular respiration, producing ATP molecules

Microtubules: protein cylinders that aid movement of organelles

Actin filaments: protein fibers that play a role in cell division and shape

Plasma membrane: surrounds cytoplasm, and regulates entrance and exit of molecules

Cell wall*: outer surface that shapes, supports, and protects cell

*not in animal cells

endoplasmic reticulum, the organelle that accomplishes that task. A nerve cell, whose job is to conduct electrical signals across long distances, contains more plasma membrane relative to other cells. Other cells may specialize so extensively that they completely lose an organelle, like a red blood cell that ejects its nucleus to increase the surface area needed to carry oxygen in the blood. The Nature of Science feature describes the process by which investigators were able to discover the structure and function of various organelles.

Check Your Progress   4.3

1. Describe three benefits of compartmentalization found in cells.
2. Examine why organelles increase cell efficiency and function.
3. Infer how the proportion of organelles might differ between a muscle cell and a nerve cell.

4.4 The Nucleus and Ribosomes

The nucleus is essential to the life of a cell. It contains the genetic information that is passed on from cell to cell and from generation to generation. It specifies the information that ribosomes use to carry out protein synthesis. It also contains instructions for copying itself.

The Nucleus

The nucleus, which has a diameter of about 5 μm, is a prominent structure in the eukaryotic cell (Fig. 4.8). It generally appears as an oval structure located near the center of most cells. Some cells, such as skeletal muscle cells, can have more than one nucleus. The nucleus contains **chromatin** [Gk. *chroma*, color,

and *teino*, stretch] in a semifluid matrix called the **nucleoplasm.** Chromatin looks grainy, but actually it is a network of strands that condenses and undergoes coiling into rodlike structures called **chromosomes** [Gk. *chroma*, color, and *soma*, body], just before the cell divides. All the cells of an individual contain the same number of chromosomes, and the mechanics of nuclear division ensure that each daughter cell receives the normal number of chromosomes, except for the egg and sperm, which usually have half this number. This alone suggested to early investigators that the chromosomes are the carriers of genetic information and that the nucleus is the command center of the cell.

Chromatin, and therefore chromosomes, contains DNA, protein, and some RNA (ribonucleic acid). **Genes,** composed of DNA, are units of heredity located on the chromosomes.

Three types of RNA are produced in the nucleus: *ribosomal RNA (rRNA), messenger RNA (mRNA),* and *transfer RNA (tRNA).* Ribosomal RNA is produced in the **nucleolus,** a dark region of chromatin where rRNA joins with proteins to form the subunits of ribosomes. Ribosomes are small bodies in the cytoplasm that facilitate protein synthesis. Messenger RNA, a mobile molecule, acts as an intermediary for DNA, a sedentary molecule, which specifies the sequence of amino acids in a protein. Transfer RNA participates in the assembly of amino acids into a polypeptide by recognizing both mRNA and amino acids during protein synthesis.

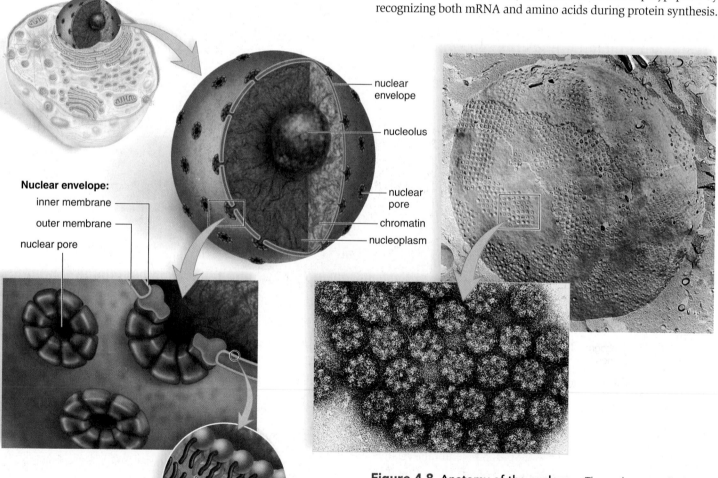

Nuclear envelope:
inner membrane
outer membrane
nuclear pore

nuclear envelope
nucleolus
nuclear pore
chromatin
nucleoplasm

phospholipid

Figure 4.8 Anatomy of the nucleus. The nucleus contains chromatin. The nucleolus is a region of chromatin where ribosomal RNA is produced, and ribosomal subunits are assembled. The nuclear envelope contains pores, as shown in the larger micrograph of a freeze-fractured nuclear envelope. Each pore is lined by a complex of eight proteins, as shown in the smaller micrograph and drawing. Nuclear pore complexes serve as passageways for substances to pass into and out of the nucleus.

The nucleus is important to cell structure and function because it specifies the code to make proteins. Although the nucleus is physically separated from the cytoplasm by a double membrane known as the **nuclear envelope,** it is still able to communicate with the cytoplasm through nuclear pores. **Nuclear pores** are of sufficient size (100 nm) to permit the passage of ribosomal subunits and mRNA out of the nucleus into the cytoplasm, and the passage of proteins from the cytoplasm into the nucleus. High-resolution electron micrographs show that nonmembrane components associated with the pores form a nuclear pore complex. Nuclear pore complexes act like gatekeepers to regulate what comes in and goes out of a nucleus.

Ribosomes

Ribosomes are particles where protein synthesis occurs. A large and small ribosomal subunit, each comprised of a mix of proteins and rRNA, are necessary components of a functional ribosome. In eukaryotes, ribosomes are 20 nm by 30 nm, and in prokaryotes they are slightly smaller. The number of ribosomes in a cell varies depending on its functions; for example, pancreatic cells and those of other glands have many ribosomes because they produce secretions that contain proteins.

In eukaryotic cells, some ribosomes occur freely within the cytoplasm, either singly or in groups called **polyribosomes,** whereas others are attached to the endoplasmic reticulum (ER), a membranous system of flattened saccules (small sacs) and tubules,

which is discussed more fully in the next section. In the nucleus, a gene is copied into mRNA, which is exported through a nuclear pore complex into the cytoplasm. Ribosomes receive the mRNA, which carries a coded message from DNA indicating the correct sequence of amino acids in a particular protein. Proteins synthesized by cytoplasmic ribosomes are used in the cytoplasm, and those synthesized by attached ribosomes end up in the ER.

What causes a ribosome to bind to the endoplasmic reticulum? Binding occurs only if the protein being synthesized by a ribosome begins with a sequence of amino acids called a **signal peptide.** The signal peptide binds a particle (signal recognition particle, SRP), which then binds to a receptor on the ER. Once the protein enters the ER, an enzyme cleaves off the signal peptide, and the protein ends up within the lumen (interior) of the ER, where it folds into its final shape (Fig. 4.9).

The sequence of DNA being transcribed into mRNA, and this in turn being translated into a protein, occurs in all living cells, at least during some point in their lifespan. Because of its universality, the DNA—mRNA—protein sequence of events is termed the *central dogma of molecular biology.*

Check Your Progress   4.4

1. Explain the importance of nuclear pore complexes.
2. Describe the sequence of events from a gene to a functional protein.

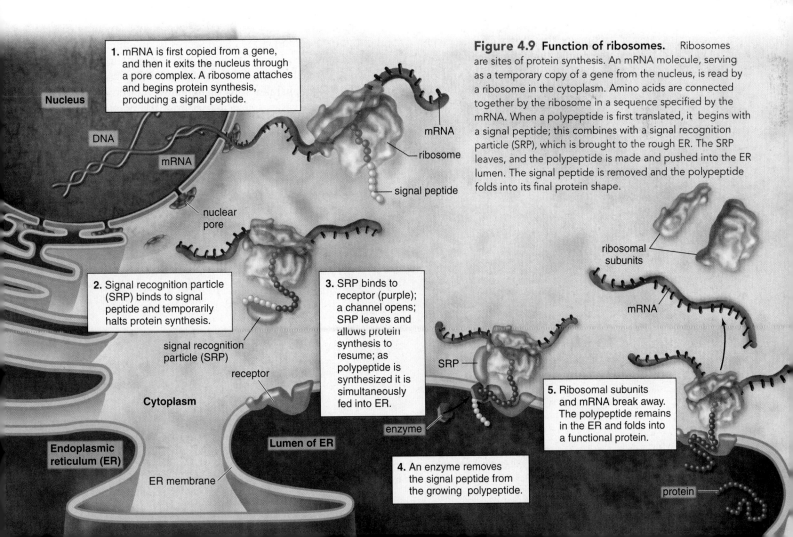

1. mRNA is first copied from a gene, and then it exits the nucleus through a pore complex. A ribosome attaches and begins protein synthesis, producing a signal peptide.

Nucleus

DNA

mRNA

nuclear pore

2. Signal recognition particle (SRP) binds to signal peptide and temporarily halts protein synthesis.

signal recognition particle (SRP)

receptor

Cytoplasm

Endoplasmic reticulum (ER)

ER membrane

3. SRP binds to receptor (purple); a channel opens; SRP leaves and allows protein synthesis to resume; as polypeptide is synthesized it is simultaneously fed into ER.

Lumen of ER

enzyme

4. An enzyme removes the signal peptide from the growing polypeptide.

mRNA

ribosome

signal peptide

ribosomal subunits

mRNA

SRP

5. Ribosomal subunits and mRNA break away. The polypeptide remains in the ER and folds into a functional protein.

protein

Figure 4.9 Function of ribosomes. Ribosomes are sites of protein synthesis. An mRNA molecule, serving as a temporary copy of a gene from the nucleus, is read by a ribosome in the cytoplasm. Amino acids are connected together by the ribosome in a sequence specified by the mRNA. When a polypeptide is first translated, it begins with a signal peptide; this combines with a signal recognition particle (SRP), which is brought to the rough ER. The SRP leaves, and the polypeptide is made and pushed into the ER lumen. The signal peptide is removed and the polypeptide folds into its final protein shape.

4.5 The Endomembrane System

Learning Outcomes

Upon completion of this section, you should be able to

1. Explain the importance of the endomembrane system in cellular function.
2. Examine how ER, Golgi, and lysosome membranes differ from one another.
3. Describe how endomembrane vesicles are able to fuse with organelles.

The **endomembrane system** consists of the nuclear envelope, the membranes of the endoplasmic reticulum, the Golgi apparatus, and several types of vesicles. This system compartmentalizes the cell so that particular enzymatic reactions are restricted to specific regions and overall cell efficiency is increased. The vesicles transport molecules from one part of the system to another.

Endoplasmic Reticulum

The **endoplasmic reticulum (ER)** [Gk. *endon,* within; *plasma,* something molded; L. *reticulum,* net], consisting of a complicated system of membranous channels and saccules (flattened vesicles), is physically continuous with the nuclear envelope (Fig. 4.10). The ER consists of rough ER and smooth ER, which have different structures and functions.

Rough ER is studded with ribosomes on the side of the membrane that faces the cytoplasm, giving it the capacity to produce proteins. Inside its lumen, the rough ER allows proteins to fold and take on their final three-dimensional shape. The rough ER also contains enzymes that can add carbohydrate (sugar) chains to proteins, forming glycoproteins, that are important in many cell functions.

Smooth ER, which is continuous with the nuclear envelope and the rough ER, does not have attached ribosomes. Certain organs contain cells with an abundance of smooth ER, depending on the organ's function. In some organs, increased smooth ER helps produce more lipids. For example, in the testes, smooth ER produces testosterone, a steroid hormone. In the liver, smooth ER helps detoxify drugs. The smooth ER of the liver increases in quantity when a person consumes alcohol or takes barbiturates on a regular basis. Regardless of functional differences, both rough and smooth ER form vesicles that transport molecules to other parts of the cell, notably the Golgi apparatus.

The Golgi Apparatus

The **Golgi apparatus** is named for Camillo Golgi (1843-1926), who discovered its presence in cells in 1898. The Golgi apparatus typically consists of a stack of three to twenty slightly curved, flattened saccules whose appearance can be compared to a stack of pancakes (Fig. 4.11). In animal cells, one side of the stack (the *cis* or inner face) is directed toward the ER, and the other side of the stack (the *trans* or outer face) is directed toward the plasma membrane. Vesicles can frequently be seen at the edges of the saccules.

Protein-filled vesicles that bud from the rough ER and lipid-filled vesicles that bud from the smooth ER are received by the Golgi apparatus at its inner face. These substances are altered as they move through the saccules. For example, the Golgi apparatus contains enzymes that modify the carbohydrate chains first attached to proteins in the rough ER. It can change or modify one sugar into another sugar on glycoproteins. In some cases, the modified carbohydrate chain serves as a signal molecule or molecular address label that determines the protein's final destination in the cell.

The Golgi apparatus sorts the modified molecules and packages them into vesicles that depart from the outer face. These vesicles may be transported to various locations within the cell,

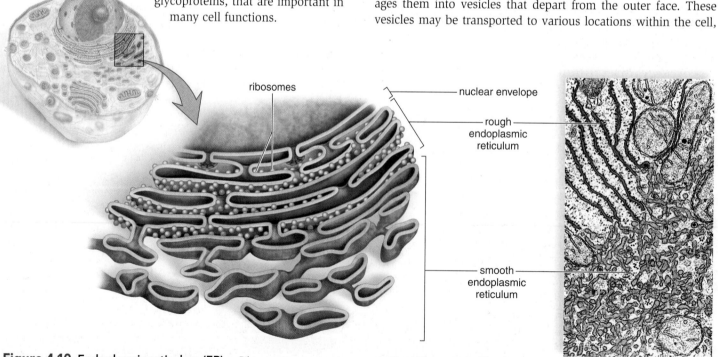

ribosomes

nuclear envelope

rough endoplasmic reticulum

smooth endoplasmic reticulum

0.08 µm

Figure 4.10 Endoplasmic reticulum (ER).   Ribosomes are present on rough ER, which consists of flattened saccules, but not on smooth ER, which is more tubular. Proteins are synthesized by rough ER. Smooth ER is involved in lipid synthesis, detoxification reactions, and several other possible functions.

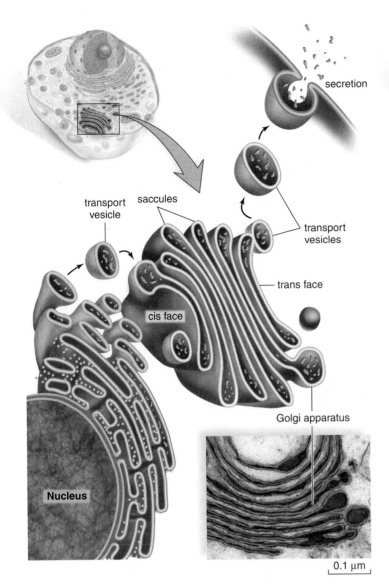

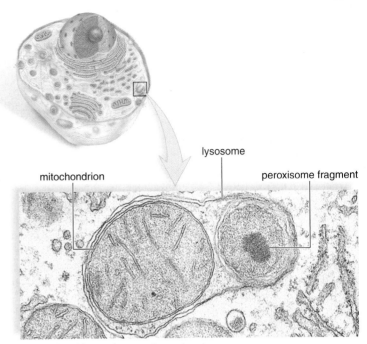

a. Mitochondrion and a peroxisome in a lysosome

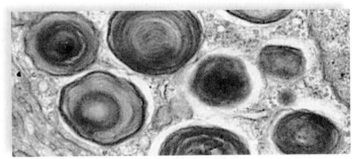

b. Storage bodies in a cell with defective lysosomes

Figure 4.11 Golgi apparatus. The Golgi apparatus is a stack of flattened, curved saccules. It processes proteins and lipids and packages them in transport vesicles that distribute these molecules to various locations within the cell, or secrete them externally.

Figure 4.12 Lysosomes. **a.** Lysosomes, which bud off the Golgi apparatus in cells, are filled with hydrolytic enzymes that digest molecules and parts of the cell. Here a lysosome digests a worn mitochondrion and a peroxisome. **b.** The nerve cells of a person with Tay-Sachs disease are filled with membranous cytoplasmic bodies storing a fat that lysosomes are unable to digest.

depending on their molecular address label. In animal cells, some of these vesicles are lysosomes, which are discussed next. Other vesicles may return to the ER or proceed to the plasma membrane, where they merge and discharge their contents to the outside of the cell during **secretion.** Secretion is termed exocytosis because the substance exits the cytoplasm.

Lysosomes

Lysosomes [Gk. *lyo,* loose, and *soma,* body] are membrane-bounded vesicles produced by the Golgi apparatus. They have a very low pH and store powerful hydrolytic-digestive enzymes in an inactive state. Lysosomes act much like your stomach in that they assist in digesting material taken into the cell. They also destroy nonfunctional organelles and portions of cytoplasm (Fig. 4.12).

Materials can be brought into a cell by vesicle or vacuole formation at the plasma membrane. When a lysosome fuses with either, the lysosomal enzymes are activated and digest the material into simpler subunits that are exported into the cytoplasm

and recycled by other cell processes. White blood cells, specialized to protect the body from foreign entities, are well known for engulfing pathogens (e.g., disease-causing viruses and bacteria) that are then broken down in lysosomes. White blood cells have a greater proportion of lysosomes than other cells because their specialized function is digestion of foreign bodies.

A number of human lysosomal storage diseases are due to a missing lysosomal enzyme. In Tay-Sachs disease, the missing enzyme digests a fatty substance that helps insulate nerve cells and increases their efficiency. The fatty substance accumulates in so many storage bodies that nerve cells die off. Affected individuals appear normal at birth but begin to develop neurological problems at four to six months of age. Eventually, the child suffers cerebral degeneration, slow paralysis, blindness, and loss of motor function. Children with Tay-Sachs disease live only about three to four years. In the future, it may be possible to provide the missing enzyme and, in that way, prevent lysosomal storage diseases.

Animation
Lysosomes

Endomembrane System Summary

You have seen that the endomembrane system is a series of membranous organelles that work together and communicate by means of transport vesicles. The endoplasmic reticulum (ER) and the Golgi apparatus are essentially flattened saccules, and lysosomes are specialized vesicles.

Organelles within the endomembrane system can interact because their membranes readily fuse together, and because membrane-associated proteins enable communication and specialized functions. Figure 4.13 shows how the components of the endomembrane system work together. Products of both rough ER and smooth ER are carried in transport vesicles to the Golgi apparatus, where they are further modified. Using signaling sequences and molecular address labels, the Golgi apparatus sorts these products and packages them into vesicles that transport them to various cellular destinations. Secretory vesicles take the proteins

to the plasma membrane, where they exit the cell by exocytosis. For example, secretion into ducts occurs when the mammary glands produce milk or the pancreas produces digestive enzymes.

In animal cells, the Golgi apparatus also produces lysosomes that contain stored hydrolytic enzymes. Lysosomes fuse with incoming vesicles from the plasma membrane and digest macromolecules brought into a cell.

Check Your Progress 4.5

1. Contrast the structure and functions of rough and smooth endoplasmic reticulum.
2. Describe the relationship between the components of the endomembrane system.
3. Examine how cellular function would be affected if the Golgi apparatus ceased to function.

Figure 4.13
Endomembrane system.
The organelles in the endomembrane system work together to carry out the functions noted. Plant cells do not have lysosomes, nor do they have incoming and outgoing (secretory) vesicles.

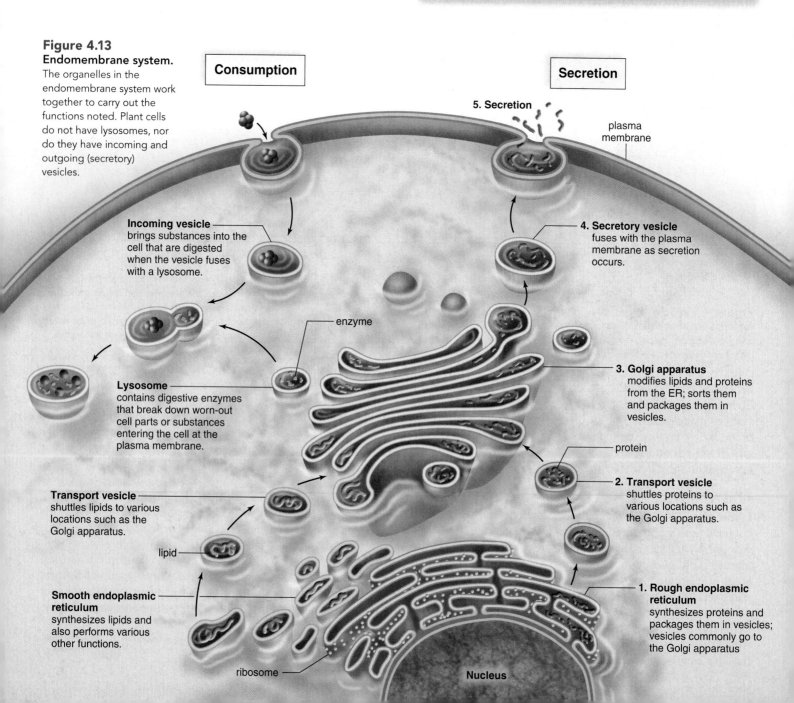

Consumption

Secretion

5. **Secretion**

plasma membrane

Incoming vesicle brings substances into the cell that are digested when the vesicle fuses with a lysosome.

4. **Secretory vesicle** fuses with the plasma membrane as secretion occurs.

enzyme

Lysosome contains digestive enzymes that break down worn-out cell parts or substances entering the cell at the plasma membrane.

3. **Golgi apparatus** modifies lipids and proteins from the ER; sorts them and packages them in vesicles.

protein

Transport vesicle shuttles lipids to various locations such as the Golgi apparatus.

2. **Transport vesicle** shuttles proteins to various locations such as the Golgi apparatus.

lipid

Smooth endoplasmic reticulum synthesizes lipids and also performs various other functions.

1. **Rough endoplasmic reticulum** synthesizes proteins and packages them in vesicles; vesicles commonly go to the Golgi apparatus

ribosome

Nucleus

4.6 Other Vesicles and Vacuoles

Learning Outcomes

Upon completion of this section, you should be able to

1. Describe the role of peroxisomes and vacuoles in cell function.
2. Contrast peroxisomes and vacuoles with endomembrane organelles.

Peroxisomes and the vacuoles of cells do not communicate with the organelles of the endomembrane system, and therefore are not part of it.

Peroxisomes

Peroxisomes, similar to lysosomes, are membrane-bounded vesicles that enclose enzymes. However, the enzymes in peroxisomes are synthesized by free ribosomes and transported into a peroxisome from the cytoplasm. All peroxisomes contain enzymes whose actions result in hydrogen peroxide (H_2O_2):

$$RH_2 + O_2 \longrightarrow R + H_2O_2$$

Hydrogen peroxide, a toxic molecule, is immediately broken down to water and oxygen by another peroxisomal enzyme called catalase. When hydrogen peroxide is applied to a wound, bubbling occurs as catalase breaks it down.

Peroxisomes are metabolic assistants to the other organelles. They have varied functions but are especially prevalent in cells that synthesize and break down lipids. In the liver, some peroxisomes produce bile salts from cholesterol, and others break down fats. The 1992 film *Lorenzo's Oil* is based on a medical case of a boy with defective peroxisomes. Lorenzo Odone's peroxisomes lacked a membrane protein

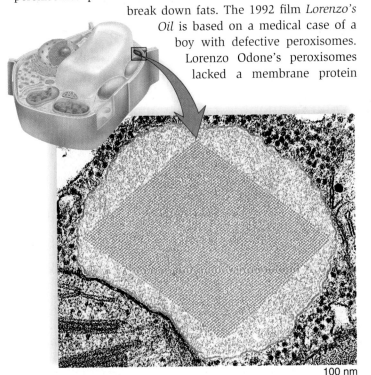

Figure 4.14 Peroxisomes. Peroxisomes contain one or more enzymes that can oxidize various organic substances.

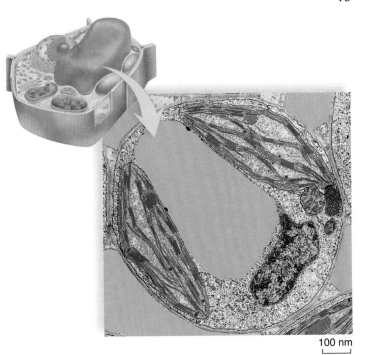

Figure 4.15 Plant cell central vacuole. The large central vacuole of plant cells has numerous functions, from storing molecules to helping the cell increase in size.

needed to import a specific enzyme and/or long chain fatty acids from the cytoplasm. As a result, long-chain fatty acids accumulated in his brain, and he suffered neurological damage. This disorder is known as adrenoleukodystrophy (ALD).

Plant cells also have peroxisomes (Fig. 4.14). In germinating seeds, they oxidize fatty acids into molecules that can be converted to sugars needed by the growing plant. In leaves, peroxisomes can carry out a reaction that is opposite to photosynthesis—the reaction uses up oxygen and releases carbon dioxide.

Vacuoles

Like vesicles, **vacuoles** are membranous sacs, but vacuoles are larger than vesicles. The vacuoles of some protists are quite specialized, including contractile vacuoles for ridding the cell of excess water and digestive vacuoles for breaking down nutrients. Vacuoles usually store substances. In general, few animal cells contain vacuoles; however, fat cells contain a very large lipid-engorged vacuole that takes up nearly two-thirds of the volume of the cell!

Vacuoles are essential to plant function. Plant vacuoles contain not only water, sugars, and salts but also water-soluble pigments and toxic molecules. The pigments are responsible for many of the red, blue, or purple colors of flowers and some leaves. The toxic substances help protect a land plant from herbivorous animals.

Plant Cell Central Vacuole

Typically, plant cells have a large **central vacuole** that may take up to 90% of the volume of the cell. The vacuole is filled with a watery fluid called cell sap that gives added support to the cell (Fig. 4.15). The central vacuole maintains hydrostatic pressure or turgor pressure in plant cells, which provides structural support. A plant cell can rapidly increase in size by enlarging its vacuole. Eventually, a plant cell also produces more cytoplasm.

The central vacuole functions in storage of both nutrients and waste products. Metabolic waste products are pumped across the vacuole membrane and stored permanently in the central vacuole. As organelles age and become nonfunctional, they fuse with the vacuole, where digestive enzymes break them down. This is an analogous function to that carried out by lysosomes in animal cells.

Check Your Progress 4.6

1. Compare the structure and functions of a peroxisome with a lysosome.
2. Distinguish between where peroxisome and lysosome proteins are produced.

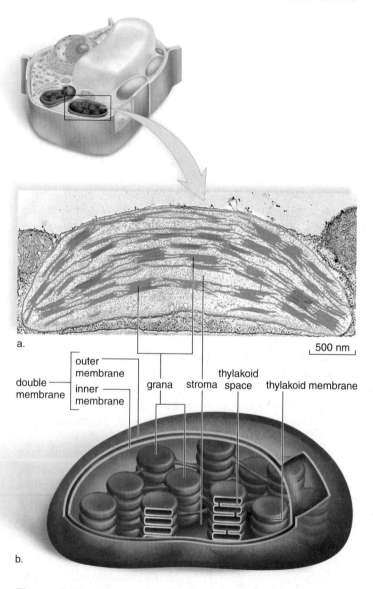

a.

500 nm

double membrane
outer membrane
inner membrane
grana
stroma
thylakoid space
thylakoid membrane

b.

Figure 4.16 Chloroplast structure. Chloroplasts carry out photosynthesis. **a.** Electron micrograph of a longitudinal section of a chloroplast. **b.** Generalized drawing of a chloroplast in which the outer and inner membranes have been cut away to reveal the grana, each of which is a stack of membranous sacs called thylakoids. In some grana, but not all, thylakoid spaces are interconnected.

4.7 The Energy-Related Organelles

Learning Outcomes

Upon completion of this section, you should be able to

1. Compare the energy management of cellular respiration versus photosynthesis.
2. Describe the evidence that suggests chloroplasts and mitochondria are derived from ancient bacteria and endosymbiosis.
3. Explain why increased membrane surface area is necessary for chloroplast and mitochondrial function.

Life is possible only because a constant input of energy maintains the structure of cells. Chloroplasts and mitochondria are the two eukaryotic membranous organelles that specialize in converting energy to a form that can be used by the cell. Although animal cells contain only mitochodria, plant cells contain both mitochondria and chloroplasts.

During photosynthesis, **chloroplasts** [Gk. *chloros*, green, and *plastos*, formed, molded] use solar energy to synthesize carbohydrates, which serve as organic nutrient molecules for plants and all living things on Earth. *Photosynthesis* can be represented by this equation:

solar energy + carbon dioxide + water → carbohydrate + oxygen

Plants, algae, and cyanobacteria are capable of conducting photosynthesis in this manner, but only plants and algae have chloroplasts because they are eukaryotes.

In cellular respiration, **mitochondria** (sing., mitochondrion) break down carbohydrate-derived products to produce ATP (adenosine triphosphate). *Cellular respiration* can be represented by this equation:

carbohydrate + oxygen → carbon dioxide + water + energy

Here the word *energy* stands for ATP molecules. When a cell needs energy, ATP supplies it. The energy of ATP is used to drive synthetic reactions, active transport, and all energy-requiring processes in cells.

Chloroplasts

Some algal cells have only one chloroplast, while some plant cells have as many as a hundred. Chloroplasts can be quite large, being twice as wide and as much as five times the length of a mitochondrion.

Chloroplasts have a three-membrane system (Fig. 4.16). They are bounded by a double membrane, which includes an outer membrane and an inner membrane. The double membrane encloses the semifluid **stroma,** which contains enzymes and **thylakoids,** disk-like sacs formed from a third chloroplast membrane. A stack of thylakoids is a **granum.** The lumens of the thylakoids are believed to form a large internal compartment called the thylakoid space. Chlorophyll and the other pigments that capture solar energy are located in the thylakoid membrane, and the enzymes that synthesize carbohydrates are located outside the thylakoid in the fluid of the stroma.

The endosymbiotic theory holds that chloroplasts are derived from a photosynthetic bacterium that was engulfed by a eukaryotic cell. This certainly explains why a chloroplast is bounded by a double membrane—one membrane is derived from the vesicle that brought the prokaryote into the cell, while the inner membrane is derived from the prokaryote. The endosymbiotic theory is also supported by the finding that chloroplasts have their own prokaryotic-type chromosome and ribosomes, and they produce some of their own enzymes even today.

Other Types of Plastids

A chloroplast is a type of plastid. **Plastids** are plant organelles that are surrounded by a double membrane and have varied functions. **Chromoplasts** contain pigments that result in a yellow, orange, or red color. Chromoplasts are responsible for the color of autumn leaves, fruits, carrots, and some flowers. **Leucoplasts** are generally colorless plastids that synthesize and store starches and oils. A microscopic examination of potato tissue reveals a number of leucoplasts.

Mitochondria

Nearly all eukaryotic cells, and certainly all plant and algal cells in addition to animal cells, contain mitochondria. Even though mitochondria are smaller than chloroplasts, they can usually be seen using a light microscope. The number of mitochondria can vary depending on the metabolic activities and energy needed within a cell. Some cells, such as liver cells, may have as many as 1,000 mitochondria.

We think of mitochondria as having a shape like that shown in Figure 4.17, but actually they often change shape to be longer and thinner or shorter and broader. Mitochondria can form long, moving chains, or they can remain fixed in one location—typically where energy is most needed. For example, they are packed between the contractile elements of cardiac cells and wrapped around the interior of a sperm's flagellum. In contrast, fat cells contain few mitochondria—they function in fat storage, which does not require energy.

Mitochondria have two membranes, the outer membrane and the inner membrane. The inner membrane is highly convoluted into folds called **cristae** that project into the matrix. These cristae increase the surface area of the inner membrane so much that in a liver cell they account for about one-third the total membrane in the cell. The inner membrane encloses a semifluid **matrix,** which contains mitochondrial DNA and ribosomes. Again, the presence of a double membrane and mitochondrial genes is consistent with the endosymbiotic theory regarding the origin of mitochondria, which was illustrated in Figure 4.5.

Mitochondria are often called the powerhouses of the cell because they produce most of the ATP utilized by the cell. The procedure described in the Nature of Science feature on page 63 allowed investigators to separate the inner membrane, the outer membrane, and the matrix from each other. Then they discovered that the matrix is a highly concentrated mixture of enzymes that break down carbohydrates and other nutrient molecules. These reactions supply the chemical energy needed for a chain of proteins on the inner membrane to create the conditions that allow ATP synthesis to take place. The entire process, which also involves the cytoplasm, is called cellular respiration because oxygen is used and carbon dioxide is given off, as shown at the beginning of this section.

Animation Endosymbiosis

Figure 4.17
Mitochondrion structure. Mitochondria are involved in cellular respiration. **a.** Electron micrograph of a longitudinal section of a mitochondrion. **b.** Generalized drawing in which the outer membrane and portions of the inner membrane have been cut away to reveal the cristae.

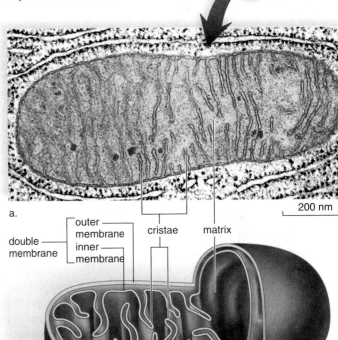

a.

double membrane — outer membrane, inner membrane   cristae   matrix   200 nm

b.

Mitochondrial Diseases

So far, more than 40 different mitochondrial diseases that affect the brain, muscles, kidneys, heart, liver, eyes, ears, or pancreas have been identified. The common factor among these genetic diseases is that the patient's mitochondria are unable to completely metabolize organic molecules to produce ATP. As a result, toxins accumulate inside the mitochondria and the body. The toxins can be free radicals (substances that readily form harmful compounds when they react with other molecules), and these compounds damage mitochondria over time. In the United States, between 1,000 and 4,000 children per year are born with a mitochondrial disease. In addition, it is possible that many diseases of aging are due to malfunctioning mitochondria.

Video Aging Secret

Check Your Progress   4.7

1. Discuss the evidence that chloroplasts and mitochondria are derived from ancient bacteria.
2. Explain the role of ATP in photosynthesis and cellular respiration.

4.8 The Cytoskeleton

Learning Outcomes

Upon completion of this section, you should be able to

1. Compare the structure and function of actin filaments, intermediate filaments, and microtubules.
2. Describe how motor molecules interact with cytoskeletal elements to produce movement.
3. Explain the diverse roles of microtubules within the cell.

Cells are exposed to many physical forces. Cell shape, movement, and internal transport all require structural support provided by the cytoskeleton. The protein components of the cytoskeleton [Gk. *kytos,* cell, and *skeleton,* dried body] interconnect and extend from the nucleus to the plasma membrane in eukaryotic cells. Prior to the 1970s, it was believed that the cytoplasm was an unorganized mixture of organic molecules. Then, high-voltage electron microscopes, which can penetrate thicker specimens, showed instead that the cytoplasm was highly organized. The technique of immunofluorescence microscopy identified the makeup of the protein components within the cytoskeletal network (Fig. 4.18).

The cytoskeleton contains actin filaments, intermediate filaments, and microtubules, which maintain cell shape and allow the cell and its organelles to move. Therefore, the cytoskeleton is often compared to the bones and muscles of an animal. However, the cytoskeleton is dynamic, and can rearrange its protein components as necessary in response to changes in internal and external environments. A number of different mechanisms appear to regulate this process, including protein phosphatases, which remove phosphates from proteins and bring about assembly, and protein kinases, which phosphorylate proteins and lead to disassembly.

Actin Filaments

Actin filaments (formerly called microfilaments) are long, extremely thin, flexible fibers (about 7 nm in diameter) that occur in bundles or meshlike networks. Each actin filament contains two chains of globular actin monomers twisted about one another in a helical manner.

Actin filaments provide structural support as a dense, complex web just under the plasma membrane, to which they are anchored by special proteins. Sometimes, actin filaments can dynamically rearrange themselves and facilitate cellular movement, such as when an amoeba moves over a surface with pseudopods [L. *pseudo,* false, and *pod,* feet], or when intestinal cell microvilli lengthen and shorten into the gut lumen (the space where ingested food is processed). In plant cells, actin filaments form the tracks along which chloroplasts circulate in a particular direction in a process called cytoplasmic streaming.

Actin filaments move the cell and its organelles by interacting with **motor molecules,** which are proteins that can attach, detach, and reattach farther along an actin filament. The motor molecule myosin uses ATP to pull actin filaments along in this way. Myosin has both a head and a tail. In muscle cells, the tails of several myosin molecules are joined to form a thick filament. In non-muscle cells, cytoplasmic myosin tails are bound to membranes, but the heads still interact with actin:

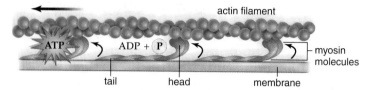

During animal cell division, the two new cells form when actin, in conjunction with myosin, pinches off the cells from one another.

Intermediate Filaments

Intermediate filaments (8–11 nm in diameter) are so named because they are intermediate in size between actin filaments and microtubules. They form a ropelike assembly of fibrous polypeptides, but the specific filament type varies according to the tissue. Some intermediate filaments support the nuclear envelope, whereas others support the plasma membrane and take part in the formation of cell-to-cell junctions. In the skin, intermediate filaments made of the protein keratin give great mechanical strength to skin cells. Like other cytoskeletal components, intermediate filaments are highly dynamic and disassemble when phosphate is added to them by a kinase.

Microtubules

Microtubules [Gk. *mikros,* small, little; L. *tubus,* tube] are small, hollow cylinders about 25 nm in diameter and from 0.2 to 25 μm in length.

Microtubules are made of a globular protein called tubulin, which is of two types called α and β. Alpha tubulin has a slightly different amino acid sequence than β tubulin. When assembly occurs, α and β tubulin molecules come together as dimers, and the dimers arrange themselves in rows. Microtubules have 13 rows of tubulin dimers, surrounding what appears in electron micrographs to be an empty central core.

Microtubule assembly is under the regulatory control of a microtubule organizing center (MTOC). In most eukaryotic cells, the main MTOC is in the **centrosome** [Gk. *centrum,* center, and *soma,* body], which lies near the nucleus. Microtubules radiate from the centrosome, helping to maintain the shape of the cell and acting as tracks along which organelles can be moved. Whereas the motor molecule myosin is associated with actin filaments, the motor molecules kinesin and dynein are associated with microtubules:

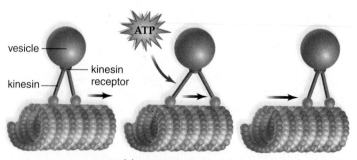

vesicle moves, not microtubule

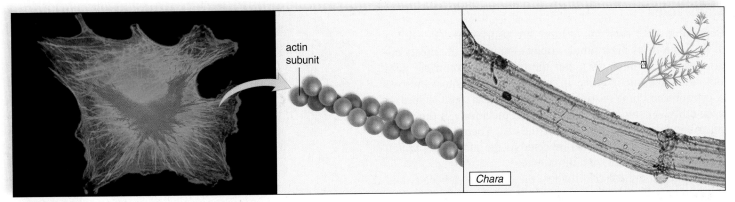

a. Actin filaments

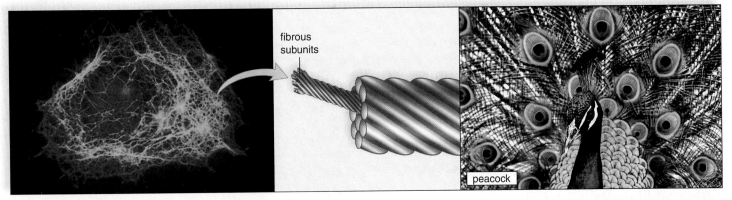

b. Intermediate filaments

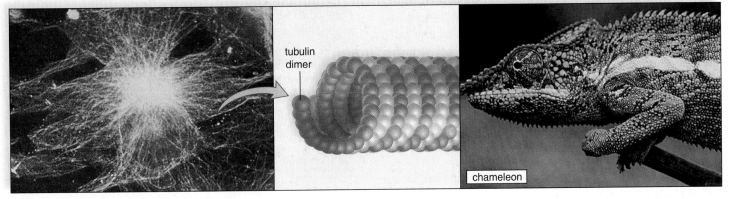

c. Microtubules

Figure 4.18 The cytoskeleton. The cytoskeleton maintains a cell's shape and allows its parts to move. Three types of protein components make up the cytoskeleton. They can be detected in cells by using labeling and fluorescence microscopy. **a.** *Left to right:* Animal cells showing a twisted double chain of actin filaments (green fibers). The giant cells of the green alga *Chara* use actin filaments to move organelles within the cell. **b.** *Left to right:* Animal cells showing fibrous, ropelike intermediate filaments (blue fibers). A peacock's colorful feathers are strengthened by intermediate filaments. **c.** *Left to right:* Animal cells showing hollow microtubules made of tubulin dimers (orange fibers). A chameleon's skin cells use microtubules to move pigment granules around so that they take on the color of their environment.

There are different types of kinesin proteins, each specialized to move one kind of vesicle or cellular organelle. Kinesin moves vesicles or organelles in an opposite direction from dynein. Cytoplasmic dynein is closely related to the molecule dynein found in flagella.

Before a cell divides, microtubules disassemble and then reassemble into a structure called a spindle that distributes chromosomes in an orderly manner. At the end of cell division, the spindle disassembles, and microtubules reassemble once again into their former array. In the "arms race" between plants and herbivores, plants have evolved various types of poisons that prevent them from being eaten. Colchicine is a plant poison that binds tubulin and blocks the assembly of microtubules.

Centrioles

Centrioles [Gk. *centrum,* center] are short cylinders with a 9 + 0 pattern of microtubule triplets—nine sets of triplets are arranged in an outer ring, but the center of a centriole does not contain a microtubule. In animal cells and most protists, a centrosome contains two centrioles lying at right angles to each other. A centrosome, as mentioned previously, is the major microtubule-organizing center for the cell. Therefore, it is possible that centrioles are also involved in the process by which microtubules assemble and disassemble.

Before an animal cell divides, the centrioles replicate, and the members of each pair are at right angles to one another (Fig. 4.19). Then each pair becomes part of a separate centrosome. During cell division, the centrosomes move apart and most likely function to organize the mitotic spindle. In any case, each new cell has its own centrosome and pair of centrioles. Plant and fungal cells have the equivalent of a centrosome, but this structure does not contain centrioles, suggesting that centrioles are not necessary to the assembly of cytoplasmic microtubules.

A **basal body** is an organelle that lies at the base of cilia and flagella and may direct the organization of microtubules within these structures. In other words, a basal body may do for a cilium or flagellum what the centrosome does for the cell. In cells with cilia and flagella, centrioles are believed to give rise to basal bodies.

Cilia and Flagella

Cilia [L. *cilium,* eyelash, hair] and **flagella** [L. *flagello,* whip] are hairlike projections that can move either in an undulating fashion, like a whip, or stiffly, like an oar. In free cells, cilia (or flagella) move the cell through liquid. For example, unicellular paramecia are organisms that move by means of cilia, whereas sperm cells move by means of flagella. If the cell is attached to other cells, cilia (or flagella) are capable of moving liquid over the cell. The cells that line our upper respiratory tract have cilia that sweep debris trapped within mucus back up into the throat, where it can be swallowed or expelled. This action helps keep the lungs clean.

In eukaryotic cells, cilia are much shorter than flagella, but they have a similar construction. Both are membrane-bounded cylinders enclosing a matrix area. In the matrix are nine microtubule doublets arranged in a circle around two central microtubules; this is called the 9 + 2 pattern of microtubules (Fig. 4.20). Cilia and flagella move when the microtubule doublets slide past one another using motor molecules.

As mentioned, each cilium and flagellum has a basal body lying in the cytoplasm at its base. Basal bodies have the same circular arrangement of microtubule triplets as centrioles and are believed to be derived from them. It is possible that basal bodies organize the microtubules within cilia and flagella, but this idea is not supported by the observation that cilia and flagella grow by the addition of tubulin dimers to their tips.

empty center of centriole

one microtubule triplet

one centrosome: one pair of centrioles

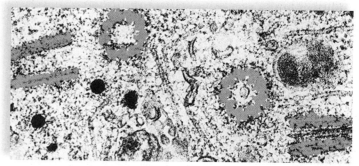

two centrosomes: two pairs of centrioles   200 nm

Figure 4.19 Centrioles. In a nondividing animal cell, a single pair of centrioles is present in the centrosome located just outside the nucleus. Just before a cell divides, the centrioles replicate, producing two centrosomes. During cell division, the centrosomes separate so that each new cell has one centrosome containing one pair of centrioles.

Check Your Progress   4.8

1. Differentiate between the components of the cytoskeleton and how they provide support to the cell.
2. Explain how ATP is used to produce movement in a cell.
3. Describe the role of motor molecules in cilia and flagella.

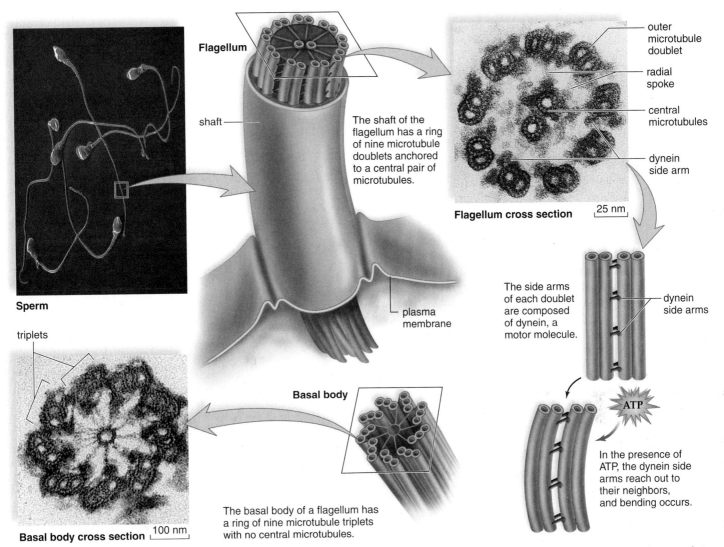

Flagellum

shaft

The shaft of the flagellum has a ring of nine microtubule doublets anchored to a central pair of microtubules.

Sperm

triplets

plasma membrane

Basal body

Basal body cross section ⌊ 100 nm ⌋

The basal body of a flagellum has a ring of nine microtubule triplets with no central microtubules.

outer microtubule doublet

radial spoke

central microtubules

dynein side arm

Flagellum cross section ⌊ 25 nm ⌋

The side arms of each doublet are composed of dynein, a motor molecule.

dynein side arms

ATP

In the presence of ATP, the dynein side arms reach out to their neighbors, and bending occurs.

Figure 4.20 Structure of a flagellum. *Below, left:* The basal body of a flagellum has a 9 + 0 pattern of microtubule triplets. Notice the ring of nine triplets, with no central microtubules. *Above, left:* In sperm, the shaft of the flagellum has a 9 + 2 pattern (a ring of nine microtubule doublets surrounds a central pair of microtubules). *Middle, right:* In place of the triplets seen in a basal body, a flagellum's outer doublets have side arms of dynein, a motor molecule. *Below, right:* In the presence of ATP, the dynein side arms reach out and attempt to move along their neighboring doublet. Because of the radial spokes connecting the doublets to the central microtubules and motor molecules, bending occurs.

CONNECTING *the* CONCEPTS *with the* THEMES

Evolution

- Cells self-replicate. All modern day cells are descendants of the first cells on Earth.
- Endosymbiosis gave previously separate prokaryotic cells a metabolic advantage, which allowed them to become more numerous.
- Over time, specialized functions became associated with separate, membrane-enclosed spaces within the cell. This compartmentalization allowed previously incompatible chemical reactions to occur simultaneously, making cells more efficient.

Nature of Science

- Our knowledge of cell anatomy has been gathered by studying micrographs of cells. Cytologists (biologists who study cells) have arrived at a picture of generalized cells, such as those depicted for the animal and plant cells in Figures 4.6 and 4.7.
- The Nature of Science feature on page 63-64 describes tools used for studying the function of cells and organelles. Many other techniques have provided additional detail and insight into cell structure and function.

Biological Systems

- Cells are integrated systems of assembled macromolecules that collectively support life. Organelles are assemblies that carry out specialized functions within the cell.
- All cellular systems must function normally to maintain the metabolic activity necessary for life. Cellular systems must also be able to adapt to rapidly changing environmental conditions.

Media Study Tools

www.mhhe.com/maderbiology11

Enhance your study of this chapter with study tools and practice tests. Also ask your instructor about the resources available through ConnectPlus, including the media-rich eBook, interactive learning tools, and animations.

Summarize

4.1 Cellular Level of Organization

All organisms are composed of cells, the smallest units of living matter. Cells self-reproduce, and existing cells come only from preexisting cells. Cells are very small (measured in micrometers) and must remain small in order to have an adequate surface area to volume ratio. The plasma membrane regulates exchange of materials between the cell interior and the external environment.

4.2 Prokaryotic Cells

Prokaryotic cells lack the nucleus of eukaryotic cells. The cell envelope of bacteria includes a plasma membrane, a cell wall, and an outer glycocalyx. The cytoplasm contains ribosomes, inclusion bodies, and a nucleoid without a nuclear envelope. The cytoplasm of cyanobacteria also includes thylakoids. The appendages of a bacterium are flagella, fimbriae, and conjugation pili.

4.3 Introducing Eukaryotic Cells

Eukaryotic cells are much larger than prokaryotic cells, and contain compartmentalized structures called organelles that each have a specific structure and function (Table 4.1) that increases cell efficiency. Endosymbiont theory helps explain the evolutionary origins of many membrane-enclosed organelles. Most membranous organelles are in constant communication.

4.4 The Nucleus and Ribosomes

The nucleus of eukaryotic cells is bounded by a nuclear envelope containing pores that regulate transport between the cytoplasm and the nucleoplasm. The nucleus contains DNA that is organized into chromosomes.

Ribosomes are organelles that function in protein synthesis. In order to make a protein, mRNA is copied exactly from the DNA, processed, and exits the nucleus through a nuclear pore. After a ribosome attaches to an mRNA, most of the time this assembly goes to the rough ER to make a protein.

4.5 The Endomembrane System

The endomembrane system includes the ER (both rough and smooth), the Golgi apparatus, the lysosomes (in animal cells), and transport vesicles. Newly produced proteins made in the rough ER are modified before they are packaged in transport vesicles, many of which go to the Golgi apparatus. The smooth ER has various metabolic functions, depending on the cell type, but it generally makes lipids that are carried by vesicles to different locations, particularly the Golgi apparatus. The Golgi apparatus modifies, sorts, and repackages proteins and also processes lipids. Some proteins are tagged for transport to different cellular destinations; others are secreted from the cell.

Table 4.1 Comparison of Prokaryotic Cells and Eukaryotic Cells

	Prokaryotic Cells (1–20 μm in diameter)	Eukaryotic Cells (10–100 μm in diameter)	
		Animal	Plant
Cell wall	Usually (peptidoglycan)	No	Yes (cellulose)
Plasma membrane	Yes	Yes	Yes
Nucleus	No	Yes	Yes
Nucleolus	No	Yes	Yes
Ribosomes	Yes (smaller)	Yes	Yes
Endoplasmic reticulum	No	Yes	Yes
Golgi apparatus	No	Yes	Yes
Lysosomes	No	Yes	No
Mitochondria	No	Yes	Yes
Chloroplasts	No	No	Yes
Peroxisomes	No	Usually	Usually
Cytoskeleton	No	Yes	Yes
Centrioles	No	Yes	No
9 + 2 cilia or flagella	No	Often	No (in flowering plants) Yes (sperm of bryophytes, ferns, and cycads)

4.6 Other Vesicles and Vacuoles

Cells contain numerous vesicles and vacuoles, some of which, such as lysosomes, have already been discussed. Peroxisomes are vesicles that are involved in the metabolism of long chain fatty acids. The large central vacuole in plant cells functions in storage and also in the breakdown of molecules and cell parts.

4.7 The Energy-Related Organelles

Cells require a constant input of energy to maintain their structure. Chloroplasts capture the energy of the sun and conduct photosynthesis, which produces carbohydrates. Carbohydrate-derived products are broken down in mitochondria in the presence of oxygen via cellular respiration, and ATP is produced as a result.

4.8 The Cytoskeleton

The cytoskeleton contains actin filaments, intermediate filaments, and microtubules. These maintain cell shape and help transport orgenelles from place to place within the cell. Actin, the thinnest filaments, interact with motor proteins to allow a range of functions from muscular contraction to cellular division. Intermediate filaments support the nuclear and plasma membranes and participate in the cell-to-cell junctions that produce tissues. Microtubules radiate out from the centrosome and are present in centrioles, cilia, and flagella. They serve as an internal transport system along which vesicles and other organelles move.

Key Terms

actin filament   78
archaean   65
bacillus   65
basal body   80
capsule   65
cell   61
cell envelope 65
cell theory   61
cell wall   65
central vacuole   75
centriole   79
centrosome   78
chloroplast   76
chromatin   70
chromoplast   77
chromosome   70
cilium   80
coccus   65
conjugation pili   66
cristae   77
cyanobacteria   66
cytoplasm   65
cytoskeleton   68
endomembrane system   72
endoplasmic reticulum (ER)   72
endosymbiotic theory   67
eukaryotic cell   65
fimbriae   66
flagellum (pl., flagella)   66, 80
gene   70
glycocalyx   65
Golgi apparatus   72
granum   76
intermediate filament   78

leucoplast   77
lysosome   73
matrix   77
mesosome   65
microtubule   78
mitochondrion   76
motor molecule   78
nuclear envelope   71
nuclear pore   71
nucleoid   65
nucleolus   70
nucleoplasm   70
organelle   67
peroxisome   75
plasma membrane   65
plasmid   65
plastid   77
polyribosome   71
prokaryotic cell   65
ribosome   66, 71
rough ER   72
secretion   73
signal peptide   71
smooth ER   72
spirillum   65
spirochete   65
stroma   76
surface-area-to-volume ratio   62
thylakoid   66, 76
vector 66
vacuole   75
vesicle   67

Assess

Reviewing This Chapter

1. What are the three basic principles of the cell theory?   60
2. Why is it advantageous for cells to be small?   61
3. Roughly sketch a bacterial (prokaryotic) cell, label its parts, and state a function for each of these.   65
4. How do eukaryotic and prokaryotic cells differ?   66
5. Describe how the nucleus, the chloroplast, and the mitochondrion may have become a part of the eukaryotic cell.   66
6. What does it mean to say that the eukaryotic cell is compartmentalized?   66–67
7. Describe the structure and the function of the nuclear envelope and the nuclear pores.   70–71
8. Distinguish between the nucleolus, rRNA, and ribosomes.   70–71
9. Name organelles that are a part of the endomembrane system and explain the term.   72
10. Trace the path of a protein from rough ER to the plasma membrane.   74
11. Give the overall equations for photosynthesis and cellular respiration, contrast the two, and tell how they are related.   76
12. Describe the structure and function of chloroplasts and mitochondria. How are these two organelles related to one another?   76–77
13. What are the three components of the cytoskeleton? What are their structures and functions?   78–79
14. Relate the structure of flagella (and cilia) to centrioles, and discuss the function of both.   80

Testing Yourself

Choose the best answer for each question.

1. The small size of cells best correlates with
   a. the fact that they are self-reproducing.
   b. their prokaryotic versus eukaryotic nature.
   c. an adequate surface area for exchange of materials.
   d. the fact that they come in multiple sizes.
   e. All of these are correct.
2. Which of these is not a true comparison of the compound light microscope and the transmission electron microscope?

	LIGHT	ELECTRON
a.	Uses light to "view" object	Uses electrons to "view" object
b.	Uses glass lenses for focusing	Uses magnetic lenses for focusing
c.	Specimen must be killed and stained	Specimen may be alive and nonstained
d.	Magnification is not as great	Magnification is greater
e.	Resolution is not as great	Resolution is greater

3. Which of these best distinguishes a prokaryotic cell from a eukaryotic cell?
   a. Prokaryotic cells have a cell wall, but eukaryotic cells never do.
   b. Prokaryotic cells are much larger than eukaryotic cells.
   c. Prokaryotic cells have flagella, but eukaryotic cells do not.
   d. Prokaryotic cells do not have a membrane-bounded nucleus, but eukaryotic cells do have such a nucleus.
   e. Prokaryotic cells have ribosomes, but eukaryotic cells do not have ribosomes.

4. Which of these is not found in the nucleus?
   a. functioning ribosomes
   b. chromatin that condenses to chromosomes
   c. nucleolus that produces rRNA
   d. nucleoplasm instead of cytoplasm
   e. all forms of RNA

5. Vesicles from the ER most likely are on their way to
   a. the rough ER.
   b. the lysosomes.
   c. the Golgi apparatus.
   d. the plant cell vacuole only.
   e. the location suitable to their size.

6. Lysosomes function in
   a. protein synthesis.   d. lipid synthesis.
   b. processing and packaging.   e. production of hydrogen
   c. intracellular digestion.   peroxide.

7. Mitochondria
   a. are involved in cellular respiration.
   b. break down ATP to release energy for cells.
   c. contain grana and cristae.
   d. are present in animal cells but not plant cells.
   e. All of these are correct.

8. Which organelle releases oxygen?
   a. ribosome   c. chloroplast
   b. Golgi apparatus   d. smooth ER

9. Which of these is not true?
   a. Actin filaments are found in muscle cells.
   b. Microtubules radiate out from the ER.
   c. Intermediate filaments sometimes contain keratin.
   d. Motor molecules use microtubules as tracks.

10. Cilia and flagella
    a. have a 9 + 0 pattern of microtubules, same as basal bodies.
    b. contain myosin that pulls on actin filaments.
    c. are organized by basal bodies derived from centrioles.
    d. are constructed similarly in prokaryotes and eukaryotes.
    e. Both a and c are correct.

11. Which of the following organelles contains its (their) own DNA, suggesting they were once independent prokaryotes?
    a. Golgi apparatus   d. ribosomes
    b. mitochondria   e. Both b and c are correct.
    c. chloroplasts

12. Which organelle most likely originated by invagination of the plasma membrane?
    a. mitochondria   d. chloroplasts
    b. flagella   e. All of these are correct.
    c. nucleus

13. Which structures are found in a prokaryotic cell?
    a. cell wall, ribosomes, thylakoids, chromosome
    b. cell wall, plasma membrane, nucleus, flagellum
    c. nucleoid, ribosomes, chloroplasts, capsule
    d. plasmid, ribosomes, enzymes, DNA, mitochondria
    e. chlorophyll, enzymes, Golgi apparatus, plasmids

14. Study the example given in (a) below. Then for each other organelle listed, state another that is structurally and functionally related. Tell why you paired these two organelles.
    a. The nucleus can be paired with nucleoli because nucleoli are found in the nucleus. Nucleoli occur where chromatin is producing rRNA.
    b. mitochondria
    c. centrioles
    d. ER

Engage

Thinking Scientifically

1. The protists that cause malaria contribute to infections associated with AIDS. Scientists have discovered that an antibiotic that inhibits prokaryotic enzymes will kill the parasite because it is effective against the plastids in the protist. What can you conclude about the origin of the plastids?

2. For your cytology study, you have decided to label and, thereby, detect the presence of the base uracil in an animal cell. In what parts of the cell do you expect to find your radioactive tracer?

Bioethical Issue
Stem Cells

A stem cell is an immature cell capable of producing many different types of differentiated mature cells. Stem cells exist in the various organs of the human body; however, they are difficult to obtain, except for those that reside in red bone marrow and produce all types of blood cells. A rich source of stem cells is an umbilical cord; another, less controversial source is adult stem cells from, say, skin. Since the nucleus contains the genetic information, it is possible to take a 2n adult nucleus, manipulate it genetically, and put it in an enucleated egg cell. Under the right conditions, the new cells can be grown and used to make neurological tissues that could possibly cure Alzheimer or Parkinson disease or any other type of neurological disorder. However, if development were to continue, a clone of the human that donated the 2n nucleus could possibly result.

   Is it bioethical to continue investigating such research? Especially when you consider that the "embryo" that provided the stem cells was not produced by the normal method of having a sperm fertilize an egg? Or, is it wrong to produce an embryo only to serve as a source of stem cells?

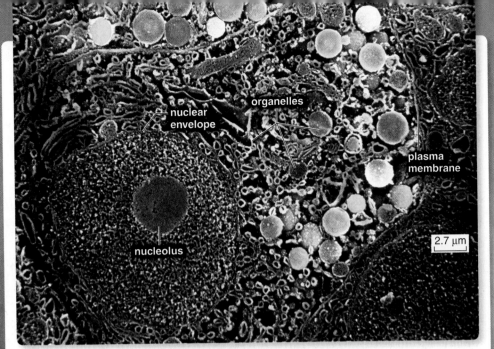

nuclear envelope

organelles

plasma membrane

nucleolus

2.7 µm

A eukaryotic cell is surrounded by a plasma membrane, and membrane also compartmentalizes the cell into various organelles with diverse functions.

An overweight diabetic, an African pygmy, and a young child with cystic fibrosis all suffer from a defect in their cells' plasma membrane. The diabetic's plasma membrane does not respond properly to insulin, growth hormone does not bind to the pygmy's membrane, and the child's membrane does not transport chloride from the cells.

Every living cell is enclosed by a plasma membrane, which creates a dynamic barrier that allows life functions to occur separate from the external environment. The plasma membrane regulates what goes into and out of the cell and enables cells to communicate with one another. Internal cellular membranes create compartments such as organelles, which together with membrane-associated enzymes, allow many, sometimes incompatible chemical processes to occur simultaneously within the cell. This "division of labor" is an essential cell feature that has undergone many evolutionary adaptations, including giving rise to the distinctions between plant and animal cells. This chapter describes the plasma membrane and its core functions. It also discusses various ways cells communicate so that the activities of tissues and organs are coordinated.

As you read through the chapter, think about the following questions:

1. Why is creating compartments with membranes necessary for cellular life?
2. How does compartmentalization increase cell efficiency and use of energy?
3. In what ways have membranes enabled cells to specialize within an organism?

5

Membrane Structure and Function

CHAPTER OUTLINE

5.1 Plasma Membrane Structure and Function 86

5.2 Passive Transport Across a Membrane 91

5.3 Active Transport Across a Membrane 95

5.4 Modification of Cell Surfaces 98

BEFORE YOU BEGIN

Before beginning this chapter, take a few moments to review the following discussions.

Figures 4.6 and 4.7 What are the key features of animal and plant cells?

Figure 4.13 How do membranes work together in cellular systems?

Figure 4.18 How is the cytoskeleton related to cellular membranes?

FOLLOWING *the* THEMES

CHAPTER 5   MEMBRANE STRUCTURE AND FUNCTION

UNIT 1 THE CELL		
	Evolution	Membrane compartments have evolved to support specialized functions for cells.
	Nature of Science	Research in membranes and associated proteins leads to new discoveries in medicine and disease treatment.
	Biological Systems	Membranes play an important role in cellular communication and response to environmental stimuli.

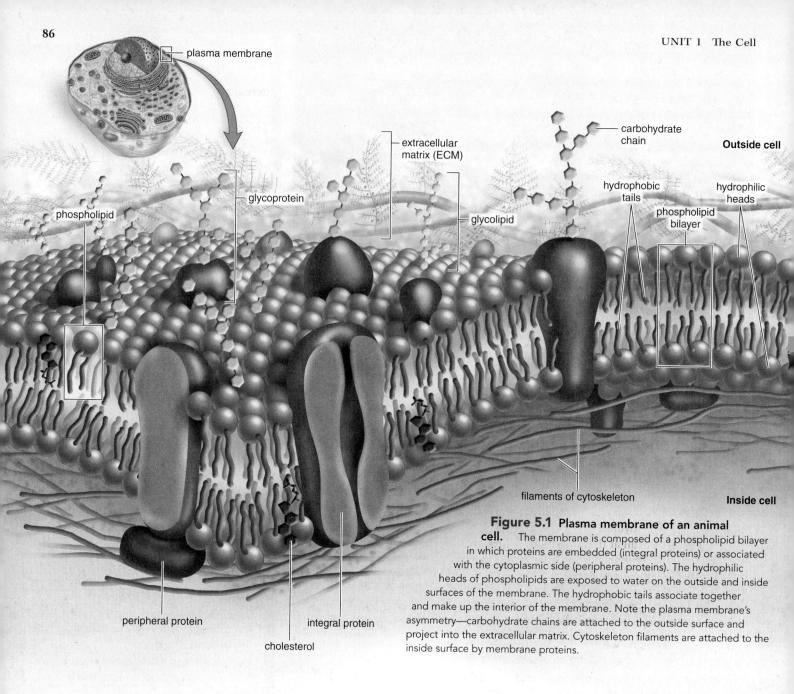

Figure 5.1 Plasma membrane of an animal cell.   The membrane is composed of a phospholipid bilayer in which proteins are embedded (integral proteins) or associated with the cytoplasmic side (peripheral proteins). The hydrophilic heads of phospholipids are exposed to water on the outside and inside surfaces of the membrane. The hydrophobic tails associate together and make up the interior of the membrane. Note the plasma membrane's asymmetry—carbohydrate chains are attached to the outside surface and project into the extracellular matrix. Cytoskeleton filaments are attached to the inside surface by membrane proteins.

5.1 Plasma Membrane Structure and Function

Learning Outcomes

Upon completion of this section, you should be able to

1. Distinguish between the different structural components of membranes.
2. Explain the functional benefits of using membrane-bound cellular compartments.
3. Describe the diverse role of proteins in membranes.
4. Compare membrane permeability for polar and nonpolar molecules.

The ability to create compartments is a key feature of cells. Membranes, made of a phospholipid bilayer, create separation between the cell and the external environment as well as compartments within the cell itself. Having separate spaces allows multiple, sometimes incompatible, chemical processes to occur simultaneously. This "division of labor" allows cells to operate more efficiently and respond to changing environmental conditions.

Components of the Plasma Membrane

The structure of an animal cell's plasma membrane is depicted in Figure 5.1. In addition to the phospholipid bilayer, membrane components include protein molecules that are either partially or wholly embedded in the bilayer. **Cholesterol** is another lipid found in the animal plasma membrane; related steroids are found in the plasma membrane of plants. As discussed later in this chapter, cholesterol helps modify the fluidity of the membrane over a range of temperatures.

Recall that a phospholipid is an *amphipathic molecule*, meaning that it has both a hydrophilic (water-loving) region and a hydrophobic (water-fearing) region. The amphipathic nature of phospholipids largely explains why they form a bilayer in water.

Because similar substances associate with one another, the hydrophilic polar heads of the phospholipid molecules naturally associate with the polar water molecules found on the outside and inside of the cell. Likewise, the hydrophobic nonpolar tails associate with each other because they want to "get away" from the polar water.

Cell membranes are highly similar in the types of molecules they contain, which makes them interchageable and allows them to fuse together fairly easily. What makes one membrane different from another are the types of proteins integrated into the membrane. As shown in Figure 5.1, proteins are scattered throughout the membrane in an irregular pattern, and this pattern can vary from membrane to membrane.

Electron micrographs verify the embedded nature of many membrane proteins. A research method called freeze-fracture first freezes, and then splits, the membrane so that the upper and lower layers separate. The proteins remain intact and go with one layer or the other. The embedded proteins are termed integral proteins, whereas the proteins that occur only on the cytoplasmic side of the membrane are termed peripheral proteins.

Some integral proteins protrude from only one surface of the bilayer, but most span the membrane, with a hydrophobic core region that associates with the nonpolar core of the membrane. Hydrophilic ends of integral proteins protrude from both surfaces of the bilayer, interacting with polar water molecules. Integral proteins can be held in place by attachments to protein fibers of the cytoskeleton (inside) and fibers of the extracellular matrix (outside). Only animal cells have an **extracellular matrix (ECM),** which contains various protein fibers and very large, complex carbohydrate molecules. The ECM, which is discussed in greater detail at the end of the chapter, has a number of functions, from lending external support to the plasma membrane to assisting in communication between cells.

bilayer is fluid. The fluidity of the membrane also prevents it from solidifying as external temperatures drop.

The lipid content of the membrane is responsible for its fluidity. At body temperature, the phospholipid bilayer of the plasma membrane has the consistency of olive oil. The greater the concentration of unsaturated fatty acid residues, the more fluid the bilayer. In each monolayer, the fatty acid tails jostle around, and an entire phospholipid molecule can move sideways at a rate averaging about 2 μm—the length of a prokaryotic cell—per second. Although it is possible for phospholipid molecules to flip-flop from one monolayer to the other, they rarely do so because this would require the hydrophilic head to move through the hydrophobic center of the membrane. However, at times special proteins help the phospholipids flip.

The presence of cholesterol molecules prevents the plasma membrane from becoming too fluid at higher temperatures and too solid at lower temperatures. At higher temperatures, cholesterol stiffens the membrane and makes it less fluid than it would otherwise be. At lower temperatures, cholesterol helps prevent the membrane from freezing by not allowing contact between certain phospholipid tails.

A plasma membrane is considered a mosaic because of the presence of many proteins. The number and kinds of proteins can vary in the plasma membrane and in the membranes of the various organelles. The position of these proteins can shift over time, unless they are anchored to another structure, such as the cytoskeleton. Figure 5.2 describes an experiment in which the proteins were tagged prior to allowing mouse and human cells to fuse. An hour after fusion, the proteins were completely

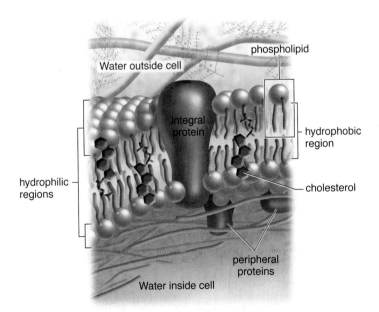

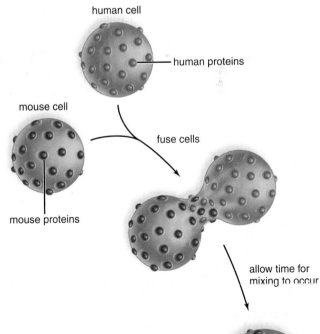

Figure 5.2 Drifting of plasma membrane proteins. After human and mouse cells fuse, the plasma membrane proteins of the mouse (purple circles) and human cell (orange circles) mix within a short time.

intermixed membrane proteins

Fluid-Mosaic Model

Membranes are not rigid, but rather are flexible structures. One model used to describe the plasma membrane is called the **fluid-mosaic model.** Cells are pliable because the phospholipid mixed, suggesting that at least some proteins are able to move sideways in the membrane.

Scientists once thought that all membrane proteins could freely move sideways within the fluid bilayer. Today, however, we know that membrane proteins are often associated with the ECM, the cytoskeleton, or both. These connections hold a protein in place and serve to partially anchor the otherwise fluid phospholipid bilayer.

3D Animation Lipid Bilayer   **MP3** Membrane Structure

Carbohydrate Chains

Phospholipids and proteins that have attached carbohydrate (sugar) chains are called **glycolipids** and **glycoproteins,** respectively. Because the carbohydrate chains occur only on the outside surface, and peripheral proteins occur on one surface or the other, the two sides of the membrane are not identical, and the membrane is said to be asymmetrical.

In animal cells, the carbohydrate chains attached to proteins give the cell a "sugar coat," more properly called the glycocalyx. The glycocalyx protects the cell and has various other functions, including cell-to-cell adhesion, reception of signaling molecules, and cell-to-cell recognition.

The carbohydrate (sugar) chains on a cell's exterior can be highly diverse. The chains can vary in the number (15 is usual, but there can be several hundred) and sequence of sugars, and in whether the chain is branched. Each cell within an individual has its own particular "fingerprint" because of these chains.

As you probably know, transplanted tissues are often rejected by the recipient. Rejection occurs because the immune system is able to detect that the foreign tissue's cells do not have the appropriate carbohydrate chains to be recognized as self. In humans, carbohydrate chains are also the basis for the A, B, and O blood groups.

The Functions of the Proteins

Although the protein components of cell membranes differ depending on the type of cell and the processes it is undergoing, several types of proteins are likely to be routinely present:

Channel proteins   Channel proteins are involved in passing molecules through the membrane. They form a channel that allows a substance to simply move from one side to the other (Fig. 5.3a). For example, a channel protein allows hydrogen ions to flow across the inner mitochondrial membrane. Without this movement of hydrogen ions, ATP would never be produced.

Animation Receptors Linked to a Channel Protein

Carrier proteins   Carrier proteins are also involved in passing molecules through the membrane. They receive a substance and change their shape, and this change serves to move the substance across the membrane (Fig. 5.3b). A carrier protein transports sodium and potassium ions across the plasma membrane of a nerve cell. Without this carrier protein, nerve impulse conduction would be impossible.

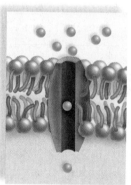

Channel Protein: Allows a particular molecule or ion to cross the plasma membrane freely. Cystic fibrosis, an inherited disorder, is caused by a faulty chloride (Cl⁻) channel; a thick mucus collects in airways and in pancreatic and liver ducts.

a.

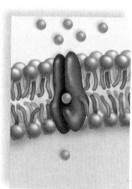

Carrier Protein: Selectively interacts with a specific molecule or ion so that it can cross the plasma membrane. The inability of some persons to use energy for sodium-potassium (Na^+-K^+) transport has been suggested as the cause of their obesity.

b.

Cell Recognition Protein: The MHC (major histocompatibility complex) glycoproteins are different for each person, so organ transplants are difficult to achieve. Cells with foreign MHC glycoproteins are attacked by white blood cells responsible for immunity.

c.

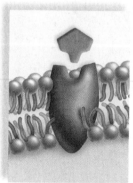

Receptor Protein: Is shaped in such a way that a specific molecule can bind to it. Pygmies are short, not because they do not produce enough growth hormone, but because their plasma membrane growth hormone receptors are faulty and cannot interact with growth hormone.

d.

Enzymatic Protein: Catalyzes a specific reaction. The membrane protein, adenylate cyclase, is involved in ATP metabolism. Cholera bacteria release a toxin that interferes with the proper functioning of adenylate cyclase; sodium (Na^+) and water leave intestinal cells, and the individual may die from severe diarrhea.

e.

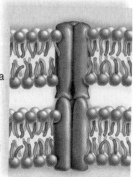

Junction Proteins: Tight junctions join cells so that a tissue can fulfill a function, as when a tissue pinches off the neural tube during development. Without this cooperation between cells, an animal embryo would have no nervous system.

f.

Figure 5.3 Membrane protein diversity.   These are some of the functions performed by proteins found in the plasma membrane.

Table 5.1 Passage of Molecules into and out of the Cell

Name	Direction	Requirement	Examples
Diffusion	Toward lower concentration	Concentration gradient	Lipid-soluble molecules, and gases
Facilitated transport	Toward lower concentration	Channels or carrier and concentration gradient	Some sugars, and amino acids
Active transport	Toward higher concentration	Carrier plus energy	Sugars, amino acids, and ions
Bulk transport	Toward outside or inside	Vesicle utilization	Macromolecules

Cell recognition proteins Cell recognition proteins are glyco-proteins (Fig. 5.3c). Among other functions, these proteins help the body recognize when it is being invaded by pathogens so that an immune response can occur. Without this recognition, pathogens would be able to freely invade the body and hinder its function.

Receptor proteins Receptor proteins have a shape that allows only a specific molecule to bind to it (Fig. 5.3d). The binding of this molecule causes the protein to change its shape and thereby bring about a cellular response. The coordination of the body's organs is totally dependent on such signaling molecules. For example, the liver stores glucose after it is signaled to do so by insulin.

Enzymatic proteins Some plasma membrane proteins are enzymes that carry out metabolic reactions directly (Fig. 5.3e). Without these enzymes, some of which are attached to the various membranes of the cell, a cell would never be able to perform the chemical reactions needed to maintain its metabolism.

Junction proteins As discussed on page 88, proteins are involved in forming various types of junctions between animal cells (Fig. 5.3f). Signaling molecules that pass through gap junctions allow the cilia of cells that line your respiratory tract to beat in unison.

Permeability of the Plasma Membrane

The plasma membrane regulates the passage of molecules into and out of the cell. This function is critical because the cell must maintain its normal composition under changing environmental conditions. The plasma membrane is essential because it is **selectively permeable,** allowing only certain substances into the cell while keeping others out.

Molecules that can freely cross a membrane generally require no energy to do so. Substances that are hydrophobic and therefore similar to the phospholipid center of the membrane are able to diffuse across membranes at no energy cost. Polar molecules, however, are chemically incompatible with the center of the membrane, and so require an expenditure of energy to drive their transport.

Table 5.1 lists, and Figure 5.4 illustrates, which types of molecules can passively cross a membrane (no energy required), and which may require transport by a carrier protein and/or an expenditure of energy. In general, small, noncharged molecules, such as carbon dioxide, oxygen, glycerol, and alcohol, can freely cross the membrane. They are able to slip between the hydrophilic heads of the phospholipids and pass through the hydrophobic tails of the membrane because they are similarly nonpolar.

These molecules follow their **concentration gradient** as they move from an area where their concentration is high, to an area where their concentration is low. Consider that a cell is always using oxygen when it carries on cellular respiration. The internal consumption of oxygen results in a low cellular concentration. Because oxygen concentration is higher outside than inside the cell, oxygen tends to move across the membrane into the cell. The concentration of carbon dioxide, on the other hand, is highest inside the cell because it is produced during cellular respiration. Therefore, carbon dioxide tends to move with its concentration gradient from inside to outside the cell.

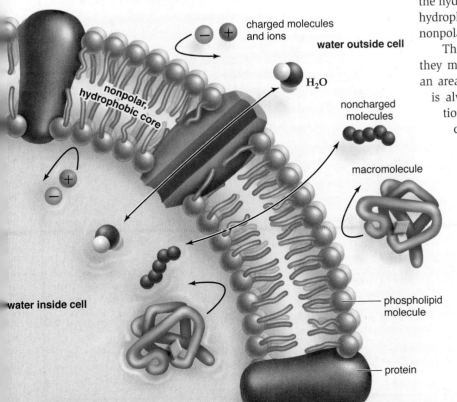

charged molecules and ions

water outside cell

H_2O

noncharged molecules

macromolecule

nonpolar, hydrophobic core

water inside cell

phospholipid molecule

protein

Figure 5.4 How molecules cross the plasma membrane. The curved arrows indicate that these substances cannot passively cross the plasma membrane, and the long back-and-forth arrows indicate that these substances can diffuse across the plasma membrane.

THEME   Biological Systems

How Cells Talk to One Another

All organisms are comprised of cells that are able to sense and respond to specific signals in their environment. A bacterium that lives in your body responds to signaling molecules when it finds food and escapes immune cells in order to stay alive. Signaling helps the bread mold that grows on stale bread detect an opposite mating strain to begin its sexual life cycle. Similarly, the cells of a developing embryo respond to signaling molecules as they move to specific locations and become specific tissues (Fig. 5Aa).

In newborn animals, internal signals like hormones are essential to ensure specific tissues develop when and how they should. In plants, external signals, such as a change in the amount of light, tells them when it is time to resume growth or flower. Internal signaling molecules enable animals and plants to coordinate their cellular activities, to metabolize, and better respond in a changing environment. The ability of cells to communicate with one another is an essential part of all biological systems.

Cell Signaling

The cells of a multicellular organism "talk" to one another by using signaling molecules, sometimes called chemical messengers. Some messengers are produced in one location and, in animals, are carried by the circulatory system to various target sites around the body. For example, the pancreas releases a hormone called insulin, which is transported in blood vessels to the liver, and this signal causes the liver to store glucose as glycogen. Failure of the liver to respond appropriately results in a medical condition called diabetes.

In Chapter 9, we are particularly interested in growth factors, which act locally as signaling molecules and cause cells to divide. Overproduction of growth factors can disrupt the balance in cellular systems. If left uncorrected, uncontrolled cell growth and formation of a tumor can result. The importance of cell signaling in regulating cell systems is the focus of much research in cell biology.

Cells respond to only certain signaling molecules. Why? Because they must bind to a receptor protein, and only cells that possess matching receptors can respond to certain signaling molecules. Each cell has a mix of receptors, which gives them the ability to respond differently to a variety of external and internal stimuli. Each cell is also able to balance the relative strength of incoming signals in order to change cellular structure or function. If a minimum level of signaling is not met, the cell dies.

Signaling molecules interacting with their receptor is only the beginning of a complex process of communication that tells the cell how to respond. Once a signaling molecule and receptor interact, a cascade of events occurs that increase, decrease, or otherwise change the signal to elicit a cellular response. This process is called a signal transduction pathway. This pathway is analogous to television transmission: a TV camera (the receptor) views a scene, converts the picture into electrical signals (transduction pathway) that are understood by the TV receiver in your house, which converts these signals to a picture on your screen (the response). The process in cells is more complicated because each member of the pathway can activate a number of other proteins. As shown in Figure 5Ab, the cell response to a transduction pathway can be a change in the shape or movement of a cell, the activation of a particular enzyme, or the activation of a specific gene.

Questions to Consider

1. If your cells needed to rapidly respond to a changing environment, would you want their effect to be short- or long-lived?
2. Given the essential role of signaling in cellular and organismal health, how might diseases arise from signaling errors?

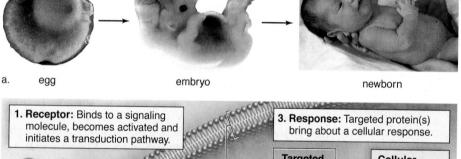

a.   egg   embryo   newborn

Figure 5A   Cell signaling.   a. The process of signaling helps account for the transformation of an egg into an embryo and then an embryo into a newborn. **b.** The process of signaling involves three steps: binding of the signaling molecule, transduction of the signal, and response of the cell depending on what type protein is targeted.

1. Receptor: Binds to a signaling molecule, becomes activated and initiates a transduction pathway.

signaling molecule

plasma membrane

receptor activation

2. Transduction pathway: Series of relay proteins that ends when a protein is activated.

unactivated receptor protein

nuclear envelope

Cytoplasm

Nucleus

3. Response: Targeted protein(s) bring about a cellular response.

Targeted protein:

structural protein

enzyme

gene regulatory protein

Cellular response:

Altered shape or movement of cell

Altered metabolism or cellular function

Altered gene expression and the types and amount of proteins produced

b.

Water, a polar molecule, would not be expected to readily cross the primarily nonpolar membrane. However, scientists have discovered that some, perhaps all, cells have channel proteins called **aquaporins** that allow water to cross a membrane more quickly than expected. Aquaporins also allow cells to equalize water pressure differences between their interior and exterior environments so their membranes don't burst from environmental pressure changes.

Ions and polar molecules, such as glucose and amino acids, can slowly cross a membrane. To move as quickly as is necessary, they are often assisted across the plasma membrane by carrier proteins. Each carrier protein recognizes particular shapes of molecules, and must combine with an ion, such as sodium (Na^+), or a molecule, such as glucose, before changing its shape and transporting the molecule across the membrane. Therefore, carrier proteins are specific for the substances they transport across the plasma membrane.

Bulk transport is a way that large particles can exit or enter a cell. During exocytosis, fusion of a vesicle with the plasma membrane moves a particle to outside the membrane. During endocytosis, vesicle formation moves a particle to inside the plasma membrane. Vesicle formation is reserved for movement of macromolecules or even for something larger, such as a virus. As with many other processes, a cell is selective about what enters by endocytosis.

Check Your Progress 5.1

1. Examine the effect of reducing cholesterol in cellular membranes.
2. Explain the role of proteins in the fluid mosaic model.
3. Compare how cells transport polar and nonpolar molecules across a membrane.

5.2 Passive Transport Across a Membrane

Learning Outcomes

Upon completion of this section, you should be able to
1. Describe how molecules move from high to low concentration.
2. Compare diffusion and osmosis across a membrane.
3. Differentiate between hypotonic, isotonic, and hypertonic solutions for animal and plant cells.

Diffusion is the movement of molecules from a higher to a lower concentration—that is, down their concentration gradient—until equilibrium is achieved and the molecules are distributed equally. Diffusion is a physical process that results from random molecular motion that can be observed with any type of molecule. For example, when a crystal of dye is placed in water (Fig. 5.5), the dye and water molecules move in various directions, but their net movement, which is the sum of their motion, is toward the region of lower concentration. Eventually, the dye is dissolved evenly in the water, resulting in equilibrium and a uniform colored solution.

A **solution** contains both a solute, usually a solid, and a solvent, usually a liquid. In this case, the **solute** is the dye and the **solvent** is the water molecules. Once the solute and solvent are evenly distributed, they continue to move about, but there is no net movement of either one in any direction.

The chemical and physical properties of the plasma membrane allow only a few types of molecules to enter and exit a cell simply by diffusion. Gases can freely diffuse through the lipid bilayer because they are small and nonpolar; this is the

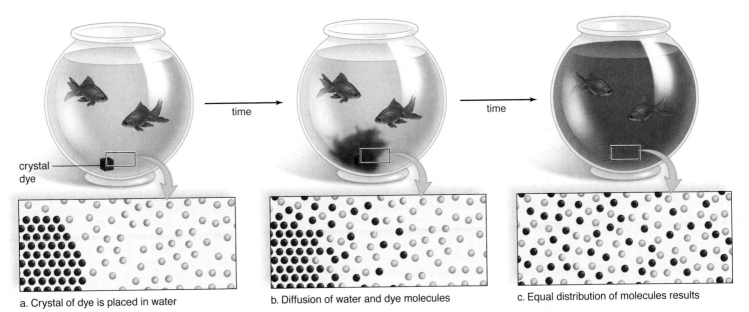

a. Crystal of dye is placed in water b. Diffusion of water and dye molecules c. Equal distribution of molecules results

Figure 5.5 Process of diffusion. Diffusion is spontaneous, and no chemical energy is required to bring it about. **a.** When a dye crystal is placed in water, it is concentrated in one area. **b.** The dye dissolves in the water, and over time a net movement of dye molecules from a higher to a lower concentration occurs. There is also a net movement of water molecules from a higher to a lower concentration. **c.** Eventually, the water and the dye molecules are equally distributed throughout the container.

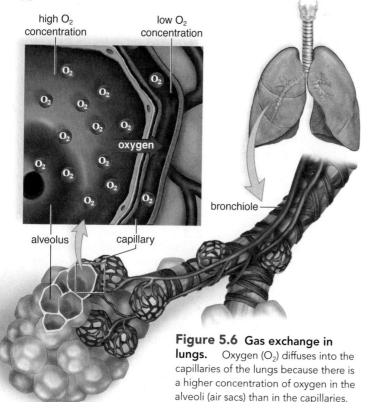

high O₂ concentration

low O₂ concentration

oxygen

bronchiole

alveolus   capillary

Figure 5.6 Gas exchange in lungs. Oxygen (O₂) diffuses into the capillaries of the lungs because there is a higher concentration of oxygen in the alveoli (air sacs) than in the capillaries.

mechanism by which oxygen enters cells and carbon dioxide exits cells. This is also how oxygen diffuses from the alveoli (air sacs) of the lungs into the blood in the lung capillaries (Fig. 5.6). After inhalation (breathing in), the concentration of oxygen in the alveoli is higher than that in the blood; therefore, oxygen diffuses into the blood along its concentration gradient.

Several factors influence the rate of diffusion, including temperature, pressure, electrical currents, and molecular size. For example, as temperature increases, the rate of diffusion increases. The movement of fishes in the tank would also speed the rate of diffusion (Fig. 5.5).

3D Animation
Diffusion

MP3
Diffusion

Animation
How Diffusion Works

Osmosis

The diffusion of water across a selectively permeable membrane from high to low concentration is called **osmosis.** To illustrate osmosis, a thistle tube containing a 10% solute solution[1] is covered at one end by a selectively permeable membrane and then placed in a beaker containing a 5% solute solution (Fig. 5.7a). The beaker has a higher concentration of water molecules (lower percentage of solute), and the thistle tube has a lower concentration of water molecules (higher percentage of solute). Diffusion

---
1 Percent solutions are grams of solute per 100 mL of solvent. Therefore, a 10% solution is 10 g of sugar with water added to make 100 mL of solution.

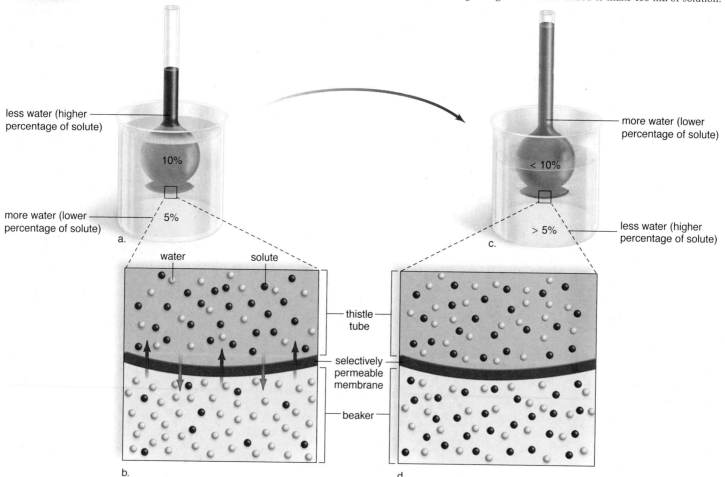

less water (higher percentage of solute)

more water (lower percentage of solute)

10%

5%

a.

more water (lower percentage of solute)

< 10%

> 5%

c.

less water (higher percentage of solute)

water   solute

thistle tube

selectively permeable membrane

beaker

b.

d.

Figure 5.7 Osmosis demonstration. **a.** A thistle tube, covered at the broad end by a selectively permeable membrane, contains a 10% solute solution. The beaker contains a 5% solute solution. **b.** The solute (purple circles) is unable to pass through the membrane, but the water (blue circles) passes through in both directions. There is a net movement of water toward the inside of the thistle tube, where there is a lower percentage of water molecules. **c.** Due to the incoming water molecules, the level of the solution rises in the thistle tube. **d.** Eventually, the concentration of water across the membrane equalizes.

always occurs from higher to lower concentration. Therefore, a net movement of water takes place, moving across the membrane from the beaker to the inside of the thistle tube (Fig. 5.7*b*).

MP3
Osmosis

The solute does not diffuse out of the thistle tube. Why not? Because the membrane is not permeable to the solute. As water enters and the solute does not exit, the level of the solution within the thistle tube rises (Fig. 5.7*c*). In the end, the concentration of solute in the thistle tube is less than 10%. Why? Because there is now less solute per unit volume. And the concentration of solute in the beaker is greater than 5%. Why? Because there is now more solute per unit volume.

Water enters the thistle tube due to the osmotic pressure of the solution within the thistle tube until it reaches equilibrium (Fig 5.7*d*). **Osmotic pressure** is the pressure that develops in a system due to osmosis.[2] In other words, the greater the possible osmotic pressure, the more likely it is that water will diffuse in that direction. Due to osmotic pressure, water is absorbed by the kidneys and taken up by capillaries in the tissues. Osmosis also occurs across the plasma membrane, as we'll see next (Fig. 5.8).

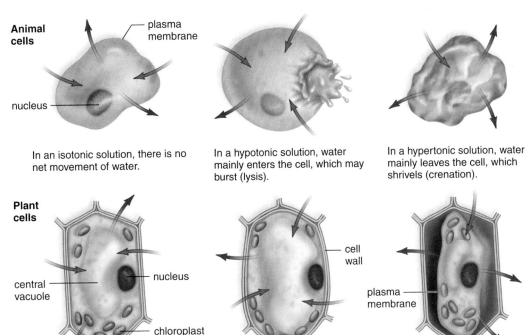

Figure 5.8 Osmosis in animal and plant cells. The arrows indicate the net movement of water molecules. To determine the net movement of water, compare the number of blue arrows that are taking water molecules into the cell versus the number of red arrows that are taking water out of the cell. In an isotonic solution, a cell neither gains nor loses water; in a hypotonic solution, a cell gains water; and in a hypertonic solution, a cell loses water.

Isotonic Solution

In the laboratory, cells are normally placed in **isotonic solutions**—that is, the solute concentration and the water concentration both inside and outside the cell are equal, and therefore there is no net gain or loss of water. The prefix *iso* means "the same as," and the term **tonicity** refers to the strength of the solution. A 0.9% solution of the salt sodium chloride (NaCl) is known to be isotonic to red blood cells. Therefore, intravenous solutions medically administered usually have this tonicity. Terrestrial animals can usually take in either water or salt as needed to maintain the tonicity of their internal environment. Many animals living in an estuary, such as oysters, blue crabs, and some fishes, are able to cope with changes in the salinity (salt concentrations) of their environment using specialized kidneys, gills, and other structures.

Hypotonic Solution

Solutions that cause cells to swell, or even to burst, due to an intake of water are said to be **hypotonic solutions.** The prefix *hypo* means "less than" and refers to a solution with a lower concentration of solute (higher concentration of water) than inside the cell. If a cell is placed in a hypotonic solution, water enters the cell because the lower cellular concentration of water prompts a net movement of water from the outside to the inside of the cell.

Any concentration of a salt solution lower than 0.9% is hypotonic to red blood cells. Animal cells placed in such a solution expand and sometimes burst because of the buildup of pressure. The term *cytolysis* is used to refer to disrupted cells; hemolysis, then, is disrupted red blood cells.

The swelling of a plant cell in a hypotonic solution creates **turgor pressure.** When a plant cell is placed in a hypotonic solution, the cytoplasm expands because the large central vacuole gains water and the plasma membrane pushes against the rigid cell wall. Unlike animal cells that have no cell wall, the plant cell does not burst because the cell wall does not give way. Turgor pressure in plant cells is extremely important to the maintenance of the plant's erect position. If you forget to water your plants, they wilt due to decreased turgor pressure.

Organisms that live in fresh water have to avoid taking in too much water. Many protozoans, such as paramecia, have contractile vacuoles that rid the body of excess water. Freshwater fishes have well-developed kidneys that excrete a large volume of dilute urine. These fish still have to take in salts through their gills. Even though freshwater fishes are good osmoregulators, they would not be able to survive in either distilled water or a salty marine environment.

Video
Contractile
Vacuoles

2 Osmotic pressure is measured by placing a solution in an osmometer and then immersing the osmometer in pure water. The pressure that develops is the osmotic pressure of a solution.

Hypertonic Solution

Solutions that cause cells to shrink or shrivel due to loss of water are said to be **hypertonic solutions.** The prefix *hyper* means "more than" and refers to a solution with a higher percentage of solute (lower concentration of water) outside of the cell. If a cell is placed in a hypertonic solution, water leaves the cell; the net movement of water is from the inside to the outside of the cell.

Any concentration of a salt solution higher than 0.9% is hypertonic to red blood cells. If animal cells are placed in this solution, they shrink. The term **crenation** refers to red blood cells in this condition. Meats are sometimes preserved by salting them. The bacteria are not killed by the salt but by the lack of water in the meat.

When a plant cell is placed in a hypertonic solution, the plasma membrane pulls away from the cell wall as the large central vacuole loses water. This is an example of **plasmolysis,** a shrinking of the cytoplasm due to osmosis. The dead plants you may see along a salted roadside died because they were exposed to a hypertonic solution during the winter. Also, when salt water invades coastal marshes due to storms and human activities, coastal plants die. Without roots to hold the soil, it washes into the sea, doing away with many acres of valuable wetlands.

Marine animals cope with their hypertonic environment in various ways that prevent them from losing excess water to the environment. Sharks increase or decrease urea in their blood until their blood is isotonic with the environment, and in this way do not lose too much water. Marine fishes and other types of animals drink no water but excrete salts across their gills. Have you ever seen a marine turtle cry? It is ridding its body of salt by means of glands near the eye.

3D Animation Osmosis

Animation Plasmolysis

Animation Hemolysis and Crenation

Facilitated Transport

The plasma membrane impedes the passage of all but a few substances. Yet, biologically useful molecules are able to rapidly enter and exit the cell either by way of a channel protein or because of carrier proteins in the membrane. These transport proteins are specific; each can transport only a certain type of molecule or ion across the membrane. How carrier proteins function is not completely understood, but after a carrier combines with a molecule, the carrier is believed to undergo a conformational change in shape that moves the molecule across the membrane. Carrier proteins are utilized for both facilitated transport (movement with concentration gradient; requires no energy) and active transport (movement against concentration gradient; requires energy)(see Table 5.1).

Facilitated transport explains how molecules such as glucose and amino acids are rapidly transported across the plasma membrane. Whereas water moves through a channel protein, the passage of glucose and amino acids is facilitated by their reversible combination with carrier proteins, which transport them through the plasma membrane. These carrier proteins are specific. For example, various sugar molecules of identical size might be present inside or outside the cell, but glucose can cross the membrane hundreds of times faster than the other sugars. As stated earlier, this is the reason the membrane can be called selectively permeable.

A model for facilitated transport (Fig. 5.9) shows that after a carrier has assisted the movement of a molecule to the other side of the membrane, it is free to assist the passage of other solute molecules. Neither diffusion nor facilitated transport requires an expenditure of energy because the molecules are moving down their concentration gradient.

Animation How Facilitated Diffusion Works

Check Your Progress 5.2

1. Explain how polar water can rapidly move across the nonpolar plasma membrane.
2. Contrast diffusion with facilitated transport.

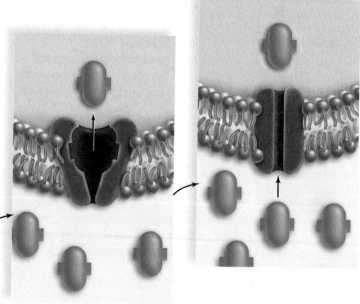

Figure 5.9 Facilitated transport. Facilitated transport by a carrier protein. A carrier protein can speed the rate at which a solute crosses the plasma membrane toward a lower concentration. Note that the carrier protein undergoes a change in shape as it moves a solute across the membrane.

Inside

plasma membrane

carrier protein

solute

Outside

5.3 Active Transport Across a Membrane

Learning Outcomes

Upon completion of this section, you should be able to

1. Explain how active transport moves substances across a membrane.
2. Compare the energy requirements of passive and active transport.
3. Contrast the active transport of large and small substances into a cell.

At times, a cell may need to further increase a concentration gradient across a membrane in order to do more work. As you might imagine, transporting a molecule against its concentration gradient, also called **active transport**, requires energy. During active transport, molecules or ions move through the plasma membrane, accumulating either inside or outside the cell. For example, iodine collects in the cells of the thyroid gland; glucose is completely absorbed from the gut by the cells lining the digestive tract; and sodium can be almost completely withdrawn from urine by cells lining the kidney tubules. In each of these instances, molecules have moved from a lower to a higher concentration, exactly opposite to the process of diffusion.

Carrier proteins and an expenditure of energy are both needed to transport molecules against their concentration gradient. In this case, chemical energy (ATP molecules usually) is required for the carrier to combine with the substance to be transported. Therefore, it is not surprising that cells involved primarily in active transport, such as kidney cells, have a large number of mitochondria near membranes where active transport is occurring.

Proteins involved in active transport often are called pumps because, just as a water pump uses energy to move water against the force of gravity, proteins use energy to move a substance against its concentration gradient. One type of pump that is active in all animal cells, but is especially associated with nerve and muscle cells, moves sodium ions (Na^+) to the outside of the cell and potassium ions (K^+) to the inside of the cell. The transport of sodium and potassium are linked together through the same carrier protein, called a **sodium-potassium pump.**

The sodium-potassium carrier protein has an initial shape that allows it to bind three sodium ions. Phosphate from an ATP molecule is added to the carrier protein, and it changes shape; this shape change moves sodium across the membrane. The new shape is no longer compatible with binding to the sodium, which falls away.

The new shape, however, is compatible with picking up two potassium ions, which bind to their sites. As the phosphate that was added from ATP in an earlier step leaves, the carrier protein assumes its original shape, and the two potassium ions are released inside the cell (Fig. 5.10). This bidirectional transport of three sodium and two potassium creates a solute gradient and electrical gradient across the plasma membrane.

Animation
How the Sodium-Potassium Pump Works

3D Animation
Active Transport

The passage of salt (NaCl) across a plasma membrane is of primary importance to most cells. The chloride ion (Cl^-) usually crosses the plasma membrane because it is attracted by positively charged sodium ions (Na^+). First sodium ions are pumped across a membrane, and then chloride ions simply diffuse through channels that allow their passage.

Animation
Cotransport

As noted in Figure 5.3a, the genetic disorder cystic fibrosis results from a faulty chloride channel protein. When chloride is unable to exit a cell, water stays behind. The lack of water outside the cells causes abnormally thick mucus in the bronchial tubes and pancreatic ducts, thus interfering with the function of the lungs and pancreas.

Video
Good Poison

Bulk Transport

How do large molecules such as proteins, polysaccharides, or nucleic acids enter and exit a cell? These molecules are too large to be transported by carrier proteins, so they are instead transported into and out of the cell by vesicles. Membrane vesicles formed around macromolecules require an expenditure of cellular energy, but the cost is worth it because each vesicle keeps its cargo from mixing with molecules within the cytoplasm that could alter the cell's function. Generally, substances can exit a cell through exocytosis, and enter a cell through endocytosis.

Exocytosis

During **exocytosis,** an intracellular vesicle fuses with the plasma membrane as secretion occurs (Fig. 5.11). Hormones, neurotransmitters, and digestive enzymes are secreted from cells in this manner. The Golgi body often produces the vesicles that carry these cell products to the membrane. During exocytosis, the membrane of the vesicle becomes a part of the plasma membrane, because both are nonpolar. Adding additional vesicle membrane to the plasma membrane can enlarge the cell, and is a part of growth in some cells. The proteins released from the vesicle may adhere to the cell surface or become incorporated into an extracellular matrix.

Cells of particular organs are specialized to produce and export molecules. For example, pancreatic cells produce digestive enzymes or insulin, and anterior pituitary cells produce growth hormone, among other hormones. In these cells, secretory vesicles accumulate near the plasma membrane, and the vesicles release their contents only when the cell is stimulated by a signal received at the plasma membrane. A rise in blood sugar, for example, signals pancreatic cells to release the hormone insulin. This is called regulated secretion, because vesicles fuse with the plasma membrane only when the needs of the body trigger it to do so.

Figure 5.10 The sodium-potassium pump. The same carrier protein transports sodium ions (Na⁺) to the outside of the cell and potassium ions (K⁺) to the inside of the cell because it undergoes an ATP-dependent change in shape. Three sodium ions are carried outward for every two potassium ions carried inward; therefore, the inside of the cell is less positively charged compared to the outside.

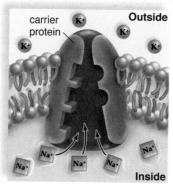

1. Carrier has a shape that allows it to take up 3 Na⁺.

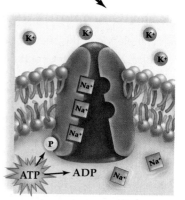

2. ATP is split, and phosphate group attaches to carrier.

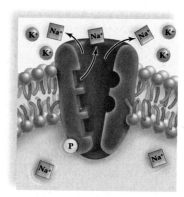

3. Change in shape results and causes carrier to release 3 Na⁺ outside the cell.

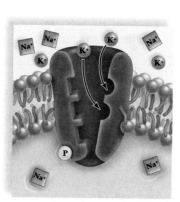

4. Carrier has a shape that allows it to take up 2 K⁺.

5. Phosphate group is released from carrier.

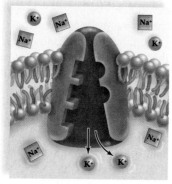

6. Change in shape results and causes carrier to release 2 K⁺ inside the cell.

Figure 5.11 Exocytosis. Exocytosis secretes or deposits substances on the outside of the cell.

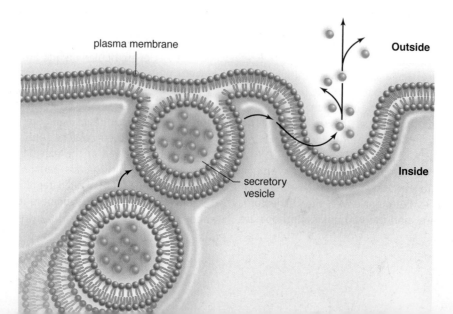

plasma membrane

secretory vesicle

Outside

Inside

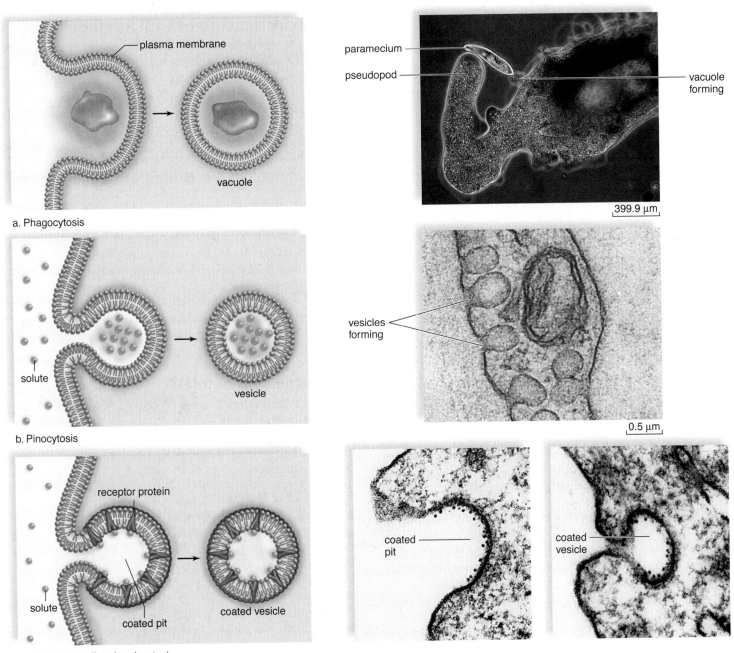

a. Phagocytosis

b. Pinocytosis

c. Receptor-mediated endocytosis

Figure 5.12 Three methods of endocytosis. **a.** Phagocytosis occurs when the substance to be transported into the cell is large; amoebas ingest by phagocytosis. Digestion occurs when the resulting vacuole fuses with a lysosome. **b.** Pinocytosis occurs when a macromolecule such as a polypeptide is transported into the cell. The result is a vesicle (small vacuole). **c.** Receptor-mediated endocytosis is a form of pinocytosis. Molecules first bind to specific receptor proteins, which migrate to or are already in a coated pit. The coated vesicle that forms contains the molecules and their receptors.

Endocytosis

During **endocytosis,** cells take in substances by forming vesicles around the material. A portion of the plasma membrane invaginates to envelop the substance, and then the membrane pinches off to form an intracellular vesicle. Endocytosis occurs in one of three ways, as illustrated in Figure 5.12. Phagocytosis transports large substances, such as a virus, and pinocytosis transports small substances, such as a macromolecule, into a cell. Receptor-mediated endocytosis is a special form of pinocytosis.

Phagocytosis.   When the material taken in by endocytosis is large, such as a food particle or another cell, the process is called **phagocytosis** [Gk. *phagein,* to eat]. Phagocytosis is common in unicellular organisms such as amoebas (Fig. 5.12*a*). It

Animation
Endocytosis and
Exocytosis

also occurs in humans. Certain types of human white blood cells are amoeboid—that is, they are mobile like an amoeba, and they can engulf debris such as worn-out red blood cells or viruses. When an endocytic vesicle fuses with a lysosome, digestion occurs. Later in this text you will see that this process is a necessary and preliminary step toward the development of our immunity to bacterial diseases.

Pinocytosis. **Pinocytosis** [Gk. *pinein*, to drink] occurs when vesicles form around a liquid or around very small particles (Fig. 5.12*b*). Blood cells, cells that line the kidney tubules or the intestinal wall, and plant root cells all use pinocytosis to ingest substances.

Whereas phagocytosis can be seen with the light microscope, the electron microscope must be used to observe pinocytic vesicles, which are no larger than 0.1–0.2 μm. Still, pinocytosis involves a significant amount of the plasma membrane because it occurs continuously. Cells do not shrink in size because the loss of plasma membrane due to pinocytosis is balanced by the occurrence of exocytosis.

Receptor-Mediated Endocytosis. **Receptor-mediated endocytosis** is a form of pinocytosis that is quite specific because it uses a receptor protein to recognize compatible molecules and bring them into the cell. Molecules such as vitamins, peptide hormones, or lipoproteins can bind to specific receptors, found in special locations in the plasma membrane (Fig. 5.12*c*). This location is called a coated pit because there is a layer of protein on the cytoplasmic side of the pit. Once formed, the vesicle is uncoated and may fuse with a lysosome. When empty, a used vesicle fuses with the plasma membrane, and the receptors return to their former location.

Receptor-mediated endocytosis is selective and much more efficient than ordinary pinocytosis. It is involved in uptake and also in the transfer and exchange of substances between cells. Such exchanges take place when substances move from maternal blood into fetal blood at the placenta, for example.

The importance of receptor-mediated endocytosis is demonstrated by a genetic disorder called familial hypercholesterolemia. Cholesterol is transported in blood by a complex of lipids and proteins called low-density lipoprotein (LDL). Ordinarily, body cells take up LDL when LDL receptors gather in a coated pit. But in some individuals, the LDL receptor is unable to properly bind to the coated pit, and the cells are unable to take up cholesterol. Instead, cholesterol accumulates in the walls of arterial blood vessels, leading to high blood pressure, occluded (blocked) arteries, and heart attacks.

Check Your Progress   5.3

1. Compare facilitated transport with active transport.
2. Examine how exocytosis and endocytosis change membrane surface area.

5.4 Modification of Cell Surfaces

Learning Outcomes

Upon completion of this section, you should be able to

1. Explain the role of the extracellular matrix in animal cell behavior.
2. Compare the structure and function of adhesion, tight, and gap junctions in animals.
3. Contrast cell-to-cell junctions between animals and plants.

Most cells do not live isolated from other cells. Rather, they live and interact within an external environment that can dramatically affect cell structure and function. This extracellular environment is made of large molecules produced by nearby cells and secreted from their membranes. In plants, prokaryotes, fungi, and most algae, the extracellular environment is a fairly rigid cell wall, which is consistent with a somewhat sedentary lifestyle. Animals, which tend to be more active, have a more varied extracellular environment that can change depending on the tissue type.

Cell Surfaces in Animals

We consider two different types of animal cell surface features: (1) the extracellular matrix (ECM) that is observed outside cells, and (2) junctions that occur between some types of cells. Both of these can connect to the cytoskeleton and contribute to communication between cells, and therefore tissue formation.

Extracellular Matrix

A protective extracellular matrix is a meshwork of proteins and polysaccharides in close association with the cell that produced them (Fig. 5.13). Collagen and elastin fibers are two well-known structural proteins in the ECM; collagen resists stretching and elastin gives the ECM resilience. Fibronectin is an adhesive protein, colored green in Figure 5.13, that binds to a protein in the plasma membrane called integrin. Integrins are integral membrane proteins that connect to fibronectin externally and to the actin cytoskeleton internally. Through its connections with both the ECM and the cytoskeleton, integrin plays a role in cell signaling, permitting the ECM to influence the activities of the cytoskeleton and, therefore, the shape and activities of the cell.

Amino sugars in the ECM form multiple polysaccharides that attach to a protein and are, therefore, called proteoglycans. Proteoglycans, in turn, attach to a very long, centrally placed polysaccharide. The entire structure, which looks like an enormous bottle brush, resists compression of the extracellular matrix. Proteoglycans assist cell signaling when they regulate the passage of molecules through the ECM to the plasma membrane, where receptors are located. During development, they help bring about differentiation by guiding cell migration along collagen fibers to specific locations. Thus, the ECM has a dynamic role in all aspects of a cell's behavior.

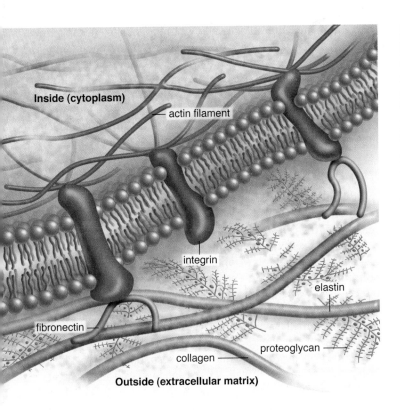

Inside (cytoplasm)

actin filament

integrin

elastin

fibronectin

proteoglycan

collagen

Outside (extracellular matrix)

Figure 5.13 Animal cell extracellular matrix. In the extracellular matrix, collagen and elastin have a support function, while fibronectins bind to integrin, and in this way, assist communication between ECM and the cytoskeleton.

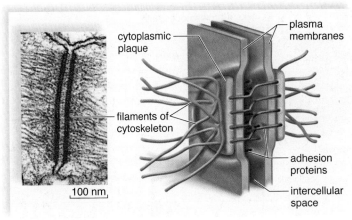

cytoplasmic plaque

plasma membranes

filaments of cytoskeleton

100 nm

adhesion proteins

intercellular space

a. Adhesion junction

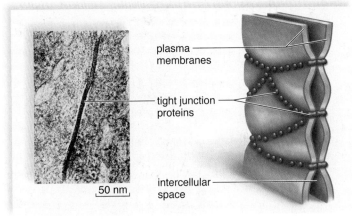

plasma membranes

tight junction proteins

50 nm

intercellular space

b. Tight junction

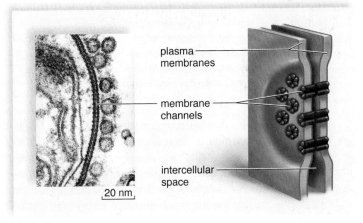

plasma membranes

membrane channels

20 nm

intercellular space

c. Gap junction

Figure 5.14 Junctions between cells of the intestinal wall.
a. In adhesion junctions such as a desmosome, adhesive proteins connect two cells. **b.** Tight junctions between cells form an impermeable barrier because their adjacent plasma membranes are joined and don't allow molecules to pass. **c.** Gap junctions allow communication between two cells because adjacent plasma membrane channels are joined.

Later on, in the discussion of tissues, you'll see that the extracellular matrix varies in quantity and in consistency from being quite flexible, as in loose connective tissue; semiflexible, as in cartilage; and rock solid, as in bone. The extracellular matrix of bone is hard because, in addition to the components mentioned, mineral salts, notably calcium salts, are deposited outside the cell.

The proportion of cells to ECM also varies. In the small intestine, for example, epithelial cells comprise the majority of the tissue, and the ECM is a thin sheet beneath the cells. In bone, the ECM makes up most of the tissue, with comparatively fewer cells.

Junctions Between Cells

Certain tissues of vertebrate animals are known to have junctions between their cells that allow them to behave in a coordinated manner. Three types of junctions are shown in Figure 5.14.

Adhesion junctions serve to mechanically attach adjacent cells. Two types of adhesion junctions are described here. In **desmosomes,** internal cytoplasmic plaques, firmly attached to the intermediate filament cytoskeleton within each cell, are joined by integral membrane proteins called cadherins between cells. The result is a sturdy but flexible sheet of cells. In some organs—such as the heart, stomach, and bladder, where tissues get stretched—desmosomes hold the cells together. At a *hemidesmosome*, the intermediate filaments of the cytoskeleton are attached to the ECM through integrin proteins. Adhesion junctions are the most common type of intercellular junction between skin cells.

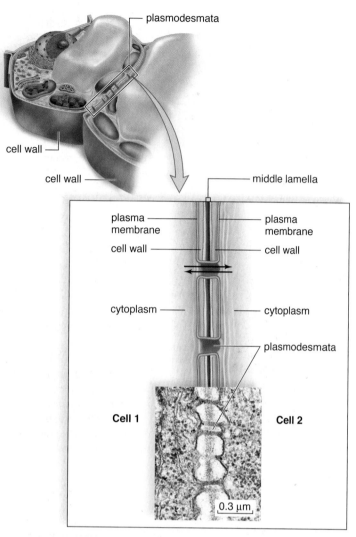

Figure 5.15 Plasmodesmata. Plant cells are joined by membrane-lined channels that contain cytoplasm. Water and small molecules can pass from cell to cell.

Another type of adhesion junction between adjacent cells are **tight junctions,** which bring cells even closer than desmosomes. Tight junction proteins actually connect plasma membranes between adjacent cells together, producing a zipperlike fastening. Tissues that serve as barriers are held together by tight junctions; in the intestine, the digestive juices stay out of the rest of the body, and in the kidneys the urine stays within kidney tubules, because the cells are joined by tight junctions.

A **gap junction** allows cells to communicate. A gap junction is formed when two identical plasma membrane channels join. The channel of each cell is lined by six plasma membrane proteins. A gap junction lends strength to the cells, but it also allows small molecules and ions to pass between them. Gap junctions are important in heart muscle and smooth muscle because they permit a flow of ions that is required for the cells to contract as a unit.

Plant Cell Walls

In addition to a plasma membrane, plant cells are surrounded by a porous **cell wall** that varies in thickness, depending on the function of the cell.

All plant cells have a primary cell wall. The primary cell wall contains cellulose fibrils in which microfibrils are held together by noncellulose substances. Pectins allow the wall to stretch when the cell is growing, and noncellulose polysaccharides harden the wall when the cell is mature. Pectins are especially abundant in the middle lamella, which is a layer of adhesive substances that holds the cells together.

Some cells in woody plants have a secondary wall that forms inside the primary cell wall. The secondary wall has a greater quantity of cellulose fibrils than the primary wall, and layers of cellulose fibrils are laid down at right angles to one another. Lignin, a substance that adds strength, is a common ingredient of secondary cell walls in woody plants.

In a plant, the cytoplasm of living cells is connected by **plasmodesmata** (sing., plasmodesma), numerous narrow, membrane-lined channels that pass through the cell wall (Fig. 5.15). Cytoplasmic strands within these channels allow direct exchange of some materials between adjacent plant cells and eventually connect all the cells within a plant. The plasmodesmata allow only water and small solutes to pass freely from cell to cell. This limitation means that plant cells can maintain their own concentrations of larger substances and differentiate into particular cell types.

Check Your Progress   5.4

1. Describe the molecular composition of the extracellular matrix of an animal cell.
2. Contrast a plant's primary cell wall with its secondary cell wall.
3. Compare the size of molecules allowed passage in a gap junction vs. plasmodesmata.

CONNECTING *the* CONCEPTS *with the* THEMES

Evolution

- The plasma membrane is appropriately called the gatekeeper of the cell because it maintains the integrity of the cell and stands guard over what enters and leaves.
- Over many generations, membranes have enabled cells to become specialized in their functions because they allow incompatible processes to occur simultaneously. This leads to greater biological fitness within particular environments.
- Glycoproteins present in membranes have also evolved over time, allowing a number of important cellular functions to arise, such as immunity.

Nature of Science

- The progression in our knowledge about the plasma membrane illustrates how science works. The knowledge we have today will be amended and expanded by new investigations.
- Basic science and membrane research is applied to treating disease and promoting health. To know that the plasma membrane is malfunctioning in a person who has diabetes or cystic fibrosis is a first step toward treating or curing these conditions.
- Cancer is sometimes due to membrane receptor proteins that signal the cell to divide even when it should not. Identification and treatment of cancer can target these receptors.

Biological Systems

- Our ability to understand the functioning of the plasma membrane is dependent on a working knowledge of the molecules that make up the cell and how they interact.
- Membranes that surround various organelles in the cell interact in a coordinated fashion, bringing greater efficiency to the entire cell system.

Media Study Tools

www.mhhe.com/maderbiology11

Enhance your study of this chapter with study tools and practice tests. Also ask your instructor about the resources available through ConnectPlus, including the media-rich eBook, interactive learning tools, and animations.

3D Animation
Membrane Transport

For a detailed examination of the processes involved in the movement of molecules across the plasma membrane, watch McGraw-Hill's new 3D animation "Membrane Transport."

Summarize

5.1 Plasma Membrane Structure and Function

Two components of the plasma membrane are lipids and proteins. In the lipid bilayer, phospholipids are arranged with their hydrophilic (polar) heads adjacent to water and their hydrophobic (nonpolar) tails buried in the interior. The lipid bilayer has the consistency of oil but acts as a barrier to the entrance and exit of most biological molecules. Membrane glycolipids and glycoproteins are involved in marking the cell as belonging to a particular individual and tissue.

The hydrophobic portion of an integral protein lies in the lipid bilayer of the plasma membrane, and the hydrophilic portion lies at the surfaces. Proteins act as receptors, carry on enzymatic reactions, join cells together, form channels, or act as carriers to move substances across the membrane. Some of these proteins make contact with the extracellular matrix (ECM) outside and with the cytoskeleton inside. Thus, the ECM can influence the happenings inside the cell.

5.2 Passive Transport Across a Membrane

The plasma membrane is selectively permeable. Some molecules (lipid-soluble compounds, water, and gases) simply diffuse across the membrane from the area of higher concentration to the area of lower concentration. No metabolic energy is required for diffusion to occur.

The diffusion of water across a selectively permeable membrane is called osmosis. Water moves across the membrane into the area of higher solute (less water) content per volume. When cells are in an isotonic solution, they neither gain nor lose water. When cells are in a hypotonic solution, they gain water, and when they are in a hypertonic solution, they lose water (Table 5.2).

Other molecules are transported across the membrane either by a channel protein or by carrier proteins that span the membrane. During facilitated transport, a substance moves down its concentration gradient. No energy is required.

Table 5.2 Effect of Osmosis on a Cell

Tonicity of Solution	Concentrations		Net Movement of Water	Effect on Cell
	Solute	Water		
Isotonic	Same as cell	Same as cell	None	None
Hypotonic	Less than cell	More than cell	Cell gains water	Swells, turgor pressure
Hypertonic	More than cell	Less than cell	Cell loses water	Shrinks, plasmolysis

5.3 Active Transport Across a Membrane

During active transport, a carrier protein acts as a pump that causes a substance to move against its concentration gradient. One example is the sodium-potassium pump that carries Na$^+$ to the outside of the cell and K$^+$ to the inside of the cell. Energy in the form of ATP molecules is required for active transport to occur.

Larger substances can enter and exit a membrane by exocytosis and endocytosis. Exocytosis involves secretion. Endocytosis includes phagocytosis, pinocytosis, and receptor-mediated endocytosis. Receptor-mediated endocytosis makes use of receptor proteins in the plasma membrane. Once a specific solute binds to receptors, a coated pit becomes a coated vesicle. After losing the coat, the vesicle can join with the lysosome, or after discharging the substance, the receptor-containing vesicle can fuse with the plasma membrane.

5.4 Modification of Cell Surfaces

Animal cells have an extracellular matrix (ECM) that influences their shape and behavior. The amount and character of the ECM varies by tissue type. Some animal cells have junction proteins that join them to other cells of the same tissue. Adhesion junctions and tight junctions help hold cells together; gap junctions allow passage of small molecules between cells.

Plant cells have a freely permeable cell wall, with cellulose as its main component. Also, plant cells are joined by narrow, membrane-lined channels called plasmodesmata that span the cell wall and contain strands of cytoplasm that allow materials to pass from one cell to another.

Key Terms

active transport   95
adhesion junction   99
aquaporin   91
bulk transport   91
carrier protein   88
cell recognition protein   89
cell wall   100
channel protein   88
cholesterol   86
concentration gradient   89
crenation   94
desmosome   99
diffusion   91
endocytosis   97
enzymatic protein   89
exocytosis   95
extracellular matrix (ECM)   87
facilitated transport   94
fluid-mosaic model   87
gap junction   100
glycolipid   88
glycoprotein   88

hypertonic solution   94
hypotonic solution   93
isotonic solution   93
junction protein   89
osmosis   92
osmotic pressure   93
phagocytosis   97
pinocytosis   98
plasmodesmata   100
plasmolysis   94
receptor-mediated
   endocytosis   98
receptor protein   89
selectively permeable   89
sodium-potassium pump   95
solute   91
solution   91
solvent   91
tight junction   100
tonicity   93
turgor pressure   93

▨ **Assess**

Reviewing This Chapter

1. Describe the fluid-mosaic model of membrane structure.   87–88
2. Tell how the phospholipids are arranged in the plasma membrane. What other lipid is present in the membrane, and what functions does it serve?   86–87
3. Describe the possible functions of proteins in the plasma membrane.   86–88

4. What is cell signaling and how does it occur?   90
5. Define diffusion. What factors can influence the rate of diffusion? What substances can diffuse through a differentially permeable membrane?   91–92
6. Define osmosis. Describe verbally and with drawings what happens to an animal cell and a plant cell when placed in isotonic, hypotonic, and hypertonic solutions.   92–94
7. Why do most substances have to be assisted through the plasma membrane? Contrast movement by facilitated transport with movement by active transport.   94–95
8. Draw and explain a diagram that shows how the sodium-potassium pump works.   95–96
9. Describe and contrast three methods of endocytosis.   97
10. Describe the structure and function of animal and plant cell modifications.   98–100

Testing Yourself

Choose the best answer for each question.

1. Write hypotonic solution or hypertonic solution beneath each cell. Justify your conclusions.

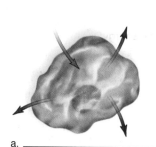 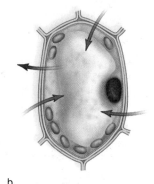

a. _____   b. _____

2. Electron micrographs following freeze-fracture of the plasma membrane indicate that
   a. the membrane is a phospholipid bilayer.
   b. some proteins span the membrane.
   c. protein is found only on the surfaces of the membrane.
   d. glycolipids and glycoproteins are antigenic.
   e. there are receptors in the membrane.

3. A phospholipid molecule has a head and two tails. The tails are found
   a. at the surfaces of the membrane.
   b. in the interior of the membrane.
   c. spanning the membrane.
   d. where the environment is hydrophilic.
   e. Both a and b are correct.

4. During diffusion,
   a. solvents move from the area of higher to lower concentration, but solutes do not.
   b. there is a net movement of molecules from the area of higher to lower concentration.
   c. a cell must be present for any movement of molecules to occur.
   d. molecules move against their concentration gradient if they are small and charged.
   e. All of these are correct.

5. When a cell is placed in a hypotonic solution,
   a. solute exits the cell to equalize the concentration on both sides of the membrane.

b.   water exits the cell toward the area of lower solute concentration.

c.   water enters the cell toward the area of higher solute concentration.

d.   solute exits and water enters the cell.

e.   Both c and d are correct.

6. When a cell is placed in a hypertonic solution,
   a.   solute exits the cell to equalize the concentration on both sides of the membrane.
   b.   water exits the cell toward the area of lower solute concentration.
   c.   water exits the cell toward the area of higher solute concentration.
   d.   solute exits and water enters the cell.
   e.   Both a and c are correct.

7. Active transport
   a.   requires a carrier protein.
   b.   moves a molecule against its concentration gradient.
   c.   requires a supply of chemical energy.
   d.   does not occur during facilitated transport.
   e.   All of these are correct.

8. The sodium-potassium pump
   a.   helps establish an electrochemical gradient across the membrane.
   b.   concentrates sodium on the outside of the membrane.
   c.   uses a carrier protein and chemical energy.
   d.   is present in the plasma membrane.
   e.   All of these are correct.

9. Receptor-mediated endocytosis
   a.   is no different from phagocytosis.
   b.   brings specific solutes into the cell.
   c.   helps concentrate proteins in vesicles.
   d.   results in high osmotic pressure.
   e.   All of these are correct.

10. Plant cells
   a.   always have a secondary cell wall, even though the primary one may disappear.
   b.   have channels between cells that allow strands of cytoplasm to pass from cell to cell.
   c.   develop turgor pressure when water enters the nucleus.
   d.   do not have cell-to-cell junctions like animal cells.
   e.   All of these are correct.

11. Label this diagram of the plasma membrane.

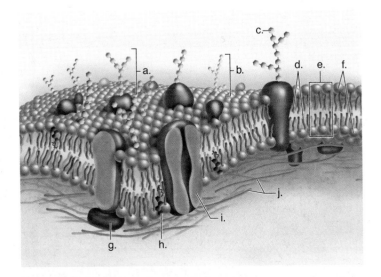

12. The fluid-mosaic model of membrane structure refers to
   a.   the fluidity of proteins and the pattern of phospholipids in the membrane.
   b.   the fluidity of phospholipids and the pattern of proteins in the membrane.
   c.   the fluidity of cholesterol and the pattern of carbohydrate chains outside the membrane.
   d.   the lack of fluidity of internal membranes compared to the plasma membrane, and the ability of the proteins to move laterally in the membrane.
   e.   the fluidity of hydrophobic regions, proteins, and the mosaic pattern of hydrophilic regions.

13. Which of the following is not a function of proteins present in the plasma membrane? Proteins
   a.   assist the passage of materials into the cell.
   b.   interact and recognize other cells.
   c.   bind with specific hormones.
   d.   carry out specific metabolic reactions.
   e.   produce lipid molecules.

14. The carbohydrate chains projecting from the plasma membrane are involved in
   a.   adhesion between cells.
   b.   reception of molecules.
   c.   cell-to-cell recognition.
   d.   All of these are correct.

15. Plants wilt on a hot summer day because of a decrease in
   a.   turgor pressure.
   b.   evaporation.
   c.   condensation.
   d.   diffusion.

16. The extracellular matrix
   a.   assists in the movement of substances across the plasma membrane.
   b.   prevents the loss of water when cells are placed in a hypertonic solution.
   c.   has numerous functions that affect the shape and activities of the cell that produced it.
   d.   contains the junctions that sometimes occur between cells.
   e.   All of these are correct.

Engage

Thinking Scientifically

1. The mucus in bronchial tubes must be thin enough for cilia to move bacteria and viruses up into the throat away from the lungs. Which way would Cl⁻ normally cross the plasma membrane of bronchial tube cells in order for mucus to be thin (see Fig. 5.3a)? Use the concept of osmosis to explain your answer.

2. Winter wheat is planted in the early fall, grows over the winter when the weather is colder, and is harvested in the spring. As the temperature drops, the makeup of the plasma membrane of winter wheat changes. Unsaturated fatty acids replace saturated fatty acids in the phospholipids of the membrane. Why is this a suitable adaptation?

6

Metabolism: Energy and Enzymes

CHAPTER OUTLINE

6.1 Cells and the Flow of Energy 105

6.2 Metabolic Reactions and Energy Transformations 107

6.3 Metabolic Pathways and Enzymes 109

6.4 Organelles and the Flow of Energy 113

BEFORE YOU BEGIN

Before beginning this chapter, take a few moments to review the following discussions.

Figures 5.1 and 5.3 How are proteins embedded in biological membranes important to cellular function?

Figure 5.4 What membrane characteristics allow some biological molecules to freely pass and not others?

Section 5.3 What is necessary to move molecules against their concentration gradient?

The cheetah, and more directly the impala, depend on solar energy captured by photosynthesizers.

Photosynthesizing grasses on an African plain provide impalas with organic building blocks and the energy they need to evade being caught by a cheetah. Eating impalas provides cheetahs with food and the energy they need to be quick enough to catch impalas.

All life on Earth depends on the flow of energy coming from the Sun. You, like the cheetah, consume plants and animals that get their energy either directly or indirectly from the Sun. Solar energy is concentrated enough to allow plants to photosynthesize and make biological molecules that, in turn, provide a continual supply of food for you and other creatures within the biosphere.

As you digest food and break the bonds in vegetables and meat, some of the energy is used for work, and some energy escapes into the environment as heat. Energy is critical to metabolism and enzymatic reactions, so it is the first topic we consider in this chapter. Without enzymes, you and the cheetah would not be able to use energy to maintain your bodies, nor to carry on any type of activity.

As you read through the chapter, think about the following questions:
1. What forms of energy are used by a cell?
2. How is energy used to drive biological processes within cells?
3. What might happen if insufficient energy is available for cells to function?

FOLLOWING *the* THEMES

CHAPTER 6 METABOLISM: ENERGY AND ENZYMES	
UNIT 1 THE CELL	
Evolution	All cells have evolved to metabolize energy in order to support the basic characteristics of life.
Nature of Science	Understanding how energy works allows scientists to design products that benefit our lives every day.
Biological Systems	Energy flows through all biological systems, creating the ability to do work, although eventually all energy is lost as heat.

6.1 Cells and the Flow of Energy

Learning Outcomes

Upon completion of this section, you should be able to

1. Compare potential and kinetic energy.
2. Describe the first and second laws of thermodynamics.
3. Examine how organization and structure of living things is related to heat and entropy.

To maintain their structural organization and carry out metabolic activities, cells—and organisms comprised of cells—need a constant supply of energy. **Energy,** defined as the ability to do work or bring about a change, allows living things to carry on the processes of life, including growth, development, metabolism, and reproduction.

Organic nutrients, made by photosynthesizing producers (algae, plants, and some bacteria), directly provide organisms with energy by capturing energy from sunlight. Considering that producers use light energy to produce organic nutrients, the majority of life on Earth is ultimately dependent on solar energy.

Forms of Energy

Energy occurs in two forms: kinetic and potential energy. **Kinetic energy** is the energy of motion, as when water flows over a waterfall, a ball rolls down a hill, or a moose walks through grass. **Potential energy** is stored energy whose capacity to accomplish work is not being used at the moment. The food we eat has potential energy because the energy stored in chemical bonds can be converted into various types of kinetic energy. Food is specifically called **chemical energy** because it is composed of organic molecules such as carbohydrates, proteins, and fat. When a moose walks, it converts chemical energy into a type of kinetic energy called **mechanical energy** (Fig. 6.1).

> **Animation**
> Energy
> Conversion

Two Laws of Thermodynamics

In nature, energy flows in biological systems. Figure 6.1 illustrates the flow of energy in a terrestrial ecosystem. Plants capture only a small portion of solar energy, and much of it dissipates as **heat.** When plants photosynthesize and then make use of the food they produce, more heat results. Even with this considerable heat loss, there is enough remaining to sustain a moose and the other organisms in an ecosystem. As they metabolize nutrient molecules, all the captured solar energy eventually dissipates as heat. Therefore, energy flows and does not cycle.

Two **laws of thermodynamics,** formulated by early energy researchers, explain why energy flows through ecosystems and through cells:

> The first law of thermodynamics—the law of conservation of energy—states energy cannot be created or destroyed, but it can be changed from one form to another.

When leaf cells photosynthesize, they use solar energy to form carbohydrate molecules from carbon dioxide gas and water. (Carbohydrates are energy-rich molecules because they have many bonds that store energy; carbon dioxide and water are energy-poor molecules because of the relative lack of bonds.) Not all of the captured solar energy becomes carbohydrates; some becomes heat:

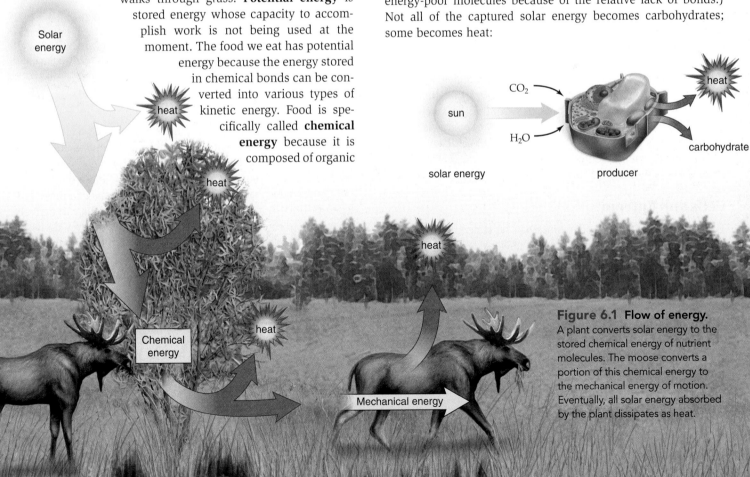

Figure 6.1 **Flow of energy.**
A plant converts solar energy to the stored chemical energy of nutrient molecules. The moose converts a portion of this chemical energy to the mechanical energy of motion. Eventually, all solar energy absorbed by the plant dissipates as heat.

Obviously, plant cells do not create the energy they use to produce carbohydrate molecules; that energy comes from the Sun. Is any energy destroyed? No, because the heat they give off is also a form of energy. Similarly, as a moose walks, it uses the potential energy stored in carbohydrates to kinetically power its muscles. As its cells use this energy, none is destroyed, but each energy exchange produces some heat, which dissipates into the environment:

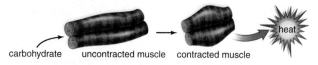

carbohydrate   uncontracted muscle   contracted muscle

The second law of thermodynamics therefore applies to living systems:

> The second law of thermodynamics states energy cannot be changed from one form to another without a loss of usable energy.

In our example, this law is upheld because some of the solar energy taken in by the plant and some of the chemical energy within the nutrient molecules taken in by the moose become heat. When heat dissipates into the environment, it is no longer usable—that is, it is not available to do work. Each energy transformation moves us closer to a condition where all usable forms of energy become heat that is lost to the environment. Heat that dissipates into the environment cannot be captured and converted to one of the other forms of energy.

As a result of the second law of thermodynamics, no process requiring a conversion of energy is ever 100% efficient. Much of the energy is lost in the form of heat. In automobiles, the internal combustion engine is between 20% and 30% efficient in converting chemical energy stored in gasoline into mechanical energy used to drive the wheels. The majority of energy is lost as dissipated heat. Cells are capable of about 40% efficiency, with the remaining energy being given off to the surrounding environment as heat.

MP3
Laws of
Thermodynamics

Cells and Entropy

The second law of thermodynamics can be stated another way: Every energy transformation makes the universe less organized, or structured, and more disordered, or chaotic. The term **entropy** [Gk. *entrope*, a turning inward] is used to indicate the relative amount of disorganization. Because the processes that occur in cells are energy transformations, the second law means that every process that occurs in cells always does so in a way that increases the total entropy of the universe. The second law means that each cellular process makes less energy available to do useful work in the future.

Figure 6.2 shows two processes that occur in cells. The second law of thermodynamics tells us that glucose tends to break apart into carbon dioxide and water over time. Why? Because glucose is more organized and structured, and therefore less stable, than its breakdown products. Also, hydrogen ions on one side of a membrane tend to move to the other side unless they are prevented from doing so. Why? Because when they are distributed randomly, entropy has increased. As an analogy, you know from

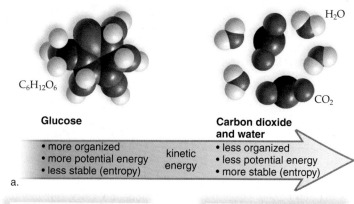

$C_6H_{12}O_6$

Glucose

H_2O

CO_2

Carbon dioxide and water

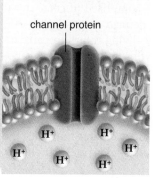

- more organized
- more potential energy
- less stable (entropy)

kinetic energy

- less organized
- less potential energy
- more stable (entropy)

a.

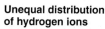

channel protein

Unequal distribution of hydrogen ions
- more organized
- more potential energy
- less stable (entropy)

H⁺

Equal distribution of hydrogen ions
- less organized
- less potential energy
- more stable (entropy)

b.

Figure 6.2 Cells and entropy.   The second law of thermodynamics tells us that (**a**) glucose, which is more organized, tends to break down to carbon dioxide and water, which are less organized. **b.** Similarly, hydrogen ions (H⁺) on one side of a membrane tend to move to the other side so that the ions are randomly distributed. Both processes result in an increase in entropy.

experience that a neat room is more organized but less stable than a messy room, which is disorganized but more stable. How do you know a neat room is less stable than a messy room? Consider that a neat room always tends to become more messy.

On the other hand, you know that some cells can make glucose out of carbon dioxide and water, and all cells can actively move ions to one side of the membrane. How do they do it? By the input of energy from an outside source. Photosynthesizing producers use energy from sunlight to create organized structure in biological molecules. Organisms that consume producers are then able to use this potential energy to kinetically drive their own metabolic processes. Thus, living things depend on a constant supply of energy ultimately provided by the Sun. The ultimate fate of all solar energy in the biosphere is to become randomized in the universe as heat. A living cell can function because it serves as a temporary repository of order, purchased at the cost of a constant flow of energy.

Check Your Progress   6.1

1. Discuss where glucose stores its potential energy.
2. Appraise how the second law of thermodynamics and entropy may be related to room cleanliness.

6.2 Metabolic Reactions and Energy Transformations

Learning Outcomes

Upon completion of this section, you should be able to

1. Compare the energy associated with endergonic and exergonic reactions.
2. Describe how energy is stored in a molecule of ATP.
3. Examine how cells use ATP to drive energetically unfavorable reactions.

All living things maintain their structure and function through chemical reactions. **Metabolism** is the sum of all the chemical reactions that occur in a cell. **Reactants** are substances that participate in a reaction, while **products** are substances that form as a result of a reaction. In the reaction A + B ⟶ C + D, A and B are the reactants while C and D are the products. Whether a reaction occurs spontaneously—that is, without an input of energy—depends on how much energy is left over after the reaction. Using the concept of entropy or disorder, a reaction occurs spontaneously if it increases the entropy of the universe.

In cell biology, which occurs on a small scale, we are less concerned about the entire universe, which is vast. In such specific instances, cell biologists use the concept of free energy instead of entropy. **Free energy** is the amount of energy left to do work after a chemical reaction has occurred. The change in free energy (also called "delta G," or ΔG) after a reaction occurs is determined by subtracting the free energy content of the reactants from that of the products. A negative result ($-\Delta G$) means that the products have less free energy than the reactants, and the reaction will occur spontaneously. In our reaction, if C and D have less free energy than A and B, then the reaction occurs without additional input of energy.

Metabolism includes both spontaneous reactions and energy-requiring reactions. **Exergonic reactions** are spontaneous and release energy, while **endergonic reactions** require an input of energy to occur. In the body, many reactions, such as protein synthesis, nerve conduction, or muscle contraction, are endergonic. For these nonspontaneous reactions to occur during metabolism, they must be coupled with exergonic reactions, such that a net spontaneous reaction results. Many biological processes use ATP as an energy carrier between exergonic and endergonic reactions.

ATP: Energy for Cells

ATP (adenosine triphosphate) is the common energy currency of cells; when cells require energy, they use ATP. A sedentary oak tree, a flying bat, and a human being require vast amounts of ATP. The more active the organism, the greater the demand for ATP. However, the amount on hand at any one moment is minimal because ATP is constantly being generated from **ADP (adenosine diphosphate)** and a molecule of inorganic phosphate, Ⓟ (Fig. 6.3). A cell is constantly creating a supply of ATP from breakdown of glucose and other biomolecules during cellular respiration. Of all the free energy stored in the bonds of glucose, only 39% of it is transformed to ATP; the rest is lost as heat.

There are many biological advantages to the use of ATP as an energy carrier in living systems. ATP provides a common and universal energy currency because it can be used in many different types of reactions. Also, when ATP is converted to energy, ADP, and Ⓟ, the amount of energy released is sufficient to drive particular biological functions with little waste of energy. In addition, ATP breakdown can be coupled to endergonic reactions in such a way that it minimizes energy loss.

Structure of ATP

ATP is a nucleotide composed of the nitrogen-containing base adenine and the 5-carbon sugar ribose (together called adenosine) and three phosphate groups. The three phosphates of ATP repel each other, creating instability and potential energy (Fig. 6.3). ATP is called a "high-energy" molecule because a phosphate group can be easily removed. Under cellular conditions, the amount of energy released when ATP is hydrolyzed to ADP + Ⓟ is about 7.3 kcal per **mole** (a unit of measurement in chemistry—equal to the molecular weight of a molecule expressed in grams).

MP3 ATP

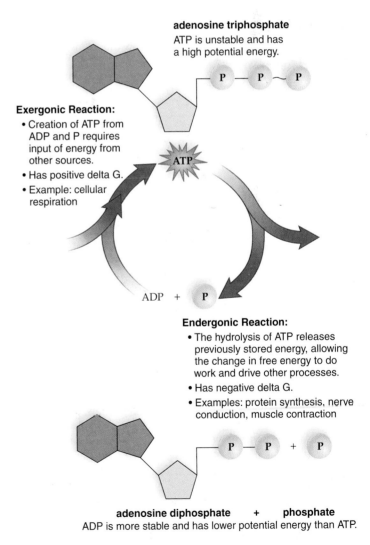

adenosine triphosphate
ATP is unstable and has a high potential energy.

Exergonic Reaction:
- Creation of ATP from ADP and P requires input of energy from other sources.
- Has positive delta G.
- Example: cellular respiration

ATP

ADP + P

Endergonic Reaction:
- The hydrolysis of ATP releases previously stored energy, allowing the change in free energy to do work and drive other processes.
- Has negative delta G.
- Examples: protein synthesis, nerve conduction, muscle contraction

adenosine diphosphate + phosphate
ADP is more stable and has lower potential energy than ATP.

Figure 6.3 The ATP cycle. In cells, ATP carries energy between exergonic reactions and endergonic reactions. When a phosphate group is removed by hydrolysis, ATP releases the appropriate amount of energy for most metabolic reactions.

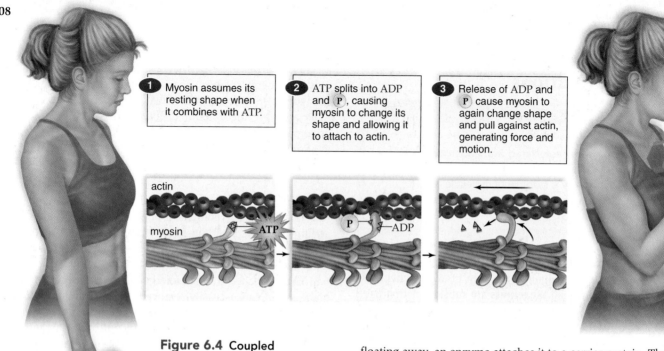

1 Myosin assumes its resting shape when it combines with ATP.

2 ATP splits into ADP and P, causing myosin to change its shape and allowing it to attach to actin.

3 Release of ADP and P cause myosin to again change shape and pull against actin, generating force and motion.

actin

myosin

Figure 6.4 Coupled reactions. Muscle contraction occurs only when it is coupled to ATP breakdown.

Coupled Reactions

How can the energy released by ATP hydrolysis be transferred to an endergonic reaction that requires energy and therefore would not ordinarily occur? In other words, how does ATP act as a carrier of chemical energy? How can that energy be transferred efficiently to an energetically unfavorable reaction?

The answer is that ATP breakdown is *coupled* to the energy-requiring reaction, such that both the energetically favorable and unfavorable reactions occur in the same place, at the same time. Usually the energy-releasing reaction is the hydrolysis of ATP. Because the cleavage of ATP's phosphate groups releases more energy than the amount consumed by the energy-requiring reaction, the net reaction is exergonic, entropy increases, and both reactions proceed. The simplest way to represent a coupled reaction is like this:

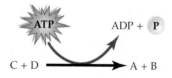

This reaction tells you that coupling occurs, but it does not show how coupling is achieved. A cell has two main ways to couple ATP hydrolysis to an energy-requiring reaction: ATP is used to energize a reactant, or ATP is used to change the shape of a reactant. Both can be achieved by transferring a phosphate group to the reactant so that the product is *phosphorylated*.

For example, when a polar ion moves across the nonpolar plasma membrane of a cell, it requires a carrier protein. In order to make the carrier protein assume a shape conducive to the ion, ATP is hydrolyzed, and then, instead of the last phosphate group

floating away, an enzyme attaches it to a carrier protein. The negatively charged phosphate causes the protein to undergo a change in shape that allows it to interact with and move the ion across the membrane. Another example of a coupled reaction is when a polypeptide is synthesized at a ribosome. There, an enzyme transfers a phosphate group from ATP to each amino acid in turn, and this transfer supplies the energy needed to overcome the energy cost associated with bonding one amino acid to another.

Figure 6.4 shows how ATP hydrolysis provides the necessary energy for muscle contraction. During muscle contraction, myosin filaments pull actin filaments to the center of the cell, and the muscle shortens. 1 A myosin head combines with ATP (three connected green triangles) and takes on its resting shape. 2 ATP breaks down to ADP (two connected green triangles) plus P (one green triangle). A resulting change in shape allows myosin to attach to actin. 3 The release of ADP and P from the myosin head causes it to change its shape again and pull on the actin filament. The cycle begins again at 1, when the myosin head combines with ATP and takes on its resting shape. During this cycle, chemical energy has been transformed to mechanical energy, and entropy has increased.

Through coupled reactions, ATP drives forward energetically unfavorable processes that must occur to create the high degree of order and structure essential for life. Macromolecules must be made and organized to form cells and tissues; the internal composition of the cell and the organism must be maintained; and movement of cellular organelles and the organism must occur if life is to continue.

Animation
Breakdown of ATP and Cross-Bridge Movement During Muscle Contraction

Check Your Progress 6.2

1. Explain why ATP is an effective short-term energy storage molecule.
2. Examine how transferring a phosphate from ATP changes a molecule's structure and function.

6.3 Metabolic Pathways and Enzymes

Learning Outcomes

Upon completion of this section, you should be able to

1. Explain the purpose of a metabolic pathway and how enzymes help to regulate it.
2. Examine how enzymes lower activation energy and increase reaction rate.
3. Distinguish between conditions and factors that affect an enzyme's rate of reaction.

The chemical reactions that comprise metabolism would not easily occur without the use of organic catalysts called enzymes. An **enzyme** is a protein molecule that functions to speed a chemical reaction without itself being affected by the reaction. Enzymes allow reactions to occur under mild conditions, and they regulate metabolism, partly by eliminating nonspecific side reactions.

Not all enzymes are proteins. **Ribozymes,** which are made of RNA instead of proteins, can also serve as biological catalysts. Ribozymes are involved in the synthesis of RNA and the synthesis of proteins at ribosomes.

Chemical reactions do not occur haphazardly in healthy cells; they are usually part of a **metabolic pathway,** a series of linked reactions. Metabolic pathways begin with a particular reactant and end with a final product. Many specific steps can be involved in a metabolic pathway, and each step is a chemical reaction catalyzed by an enzyme. The reactants for the first reaction are converted into products, and those products then serve as the reactants for the next enzyme-catalyzed reaction. One reaction leads to the next reaction in an organized, highly regulated manner.

This arrangement makes it possible for one pathway to interact with several others, because different pathways may have several molecules in common. Also, metabolic pathways are useful for releasing and capturing small increments of molecular energy rather than releasing it all at once. Ultimately, enzymes in metabolic pathways enable cells to regulate and respond to changing environmental conditions. **Animation Biochemical Pathways**

A metabolic pathway can be represented by the following diagram:

$$A \xrightarrow{E_1} B \xrightarrow{E_2} C \xrightarrow{E_3} D \xrightarrow{E_4} E \xrightarrow{E_5} F \xrightarrow{E_6} G$$

In this diagram, reactant A is converted by enzyme E_1 to product B. Product B then becomes the reactant for enzyme E_2 and is converted to product C. Any one of the molecules (A–G) in this metabolic pathway could also be a reactant in another pathway. A diagram showing all the possibilities would be highly branched.

Each step in the metabolic chain can be regulated because each step requires an enzyme. This gives our cells fine control over how they respond in a changing environment, and helps maximize cell efficiency.

Energy of Activation

Molecules frequently do not react with one another unless they are activated in some way. In the lab, for example, in the absence of an enzyme, molecules may be heated in order to increase the number of effective collisions. The energy that must be added to cause molecules to react with one another is called the **energy of activation (E_a).** Activation energy is essential to keep molecules from spontaneously degrading within the cell. Figure 6.5 shows that an enzyme effectively lowers E_a, thus reducing the energy needed for a chemical reaction to begin. The enzyme has no effect on the energy content of the product; rather, only the reactants are affected. **Animation Energy of Activation**

Enzymes allow reactions to occur under mild conditions by bringing reactants into contact with one another in such a way that the chemistry occurs more readily than it otherwise would have.

Enzyme-Substrate Complex

The reactants in an enzymatic reaction are called the **substrates** for that enzyme. Considering the metabolic pathway shown previously, A is the substrate for E_1, and B is the product. Now B becomes the substrate for E_2, and C is the product. This process continues until the final product G forms.

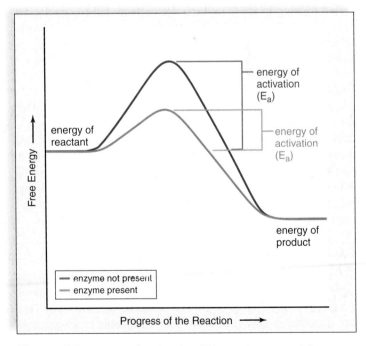

Figure 6.5 Energy of activation (E_a). Enzymes speed the rate of reactions because they lower the amount of energy required for the reactants to activate. Even spontaneous reactions like this one, in which the energy of the product is less than the energy of the reactant, speed up when an enzyme is present.

The following equation, which is illustrated in Figure 6.6, is often used to indicate that an enzyme forms a complex with its substrate:

$$\text{E} \ + \ \text{S} \ \longrightarrow \ \text{ES} \ \longrightarrow \ \text{E} \ + \ \text{P}$$

| enzyme | substrate | enzyme-substrate complex | enzyme | product |

In most instances, only one small part of the enzyme, called the **active site,** associates directly with the substrate(s). In the active site, the enzyme and substrate are positioned in such a way that they more easily fit together, seemingly like a key fits a lock. However, an active site differs from a lock and key because it undergoes a slight change in shape to accommodate the substrate(s). This is called the **induced fit model** because the enzyme is induced to undergo a slight alteration to achieve optimum fit for the substrates.

 Animation How Enzymes Work

The change in shape of the active site facilitates the reaction that now occurs. After the reaction has been completed, the product(s) is released, and the active site returns to its original state, ready to bind to another substrate molecule. Only a small amount of enzyme is actually needed in a cell because enzymes are not used up by the reaction; they merely enable it to happen more quickly.

Some enzymes do more than simply form a complex with their substrate(s); they participate in the reaction. Trypsin digests protein by breaking peptide bonds. The active site of trypsin contains three amino acids with *R* groups that actually interact with members of the peptide bond—first to break the bond and then to introduce the components of water. This illustrates that the formation of the enzyme-substrate complex is very important in speeding the reaction. Because enzymes bind only with their substrates, they are sometimes named for their substrates, and usually end in *-ase*. For example, lipase is involved in hydrolyzing lipids.

MP3 Enzymes

Regulation of Metabolism

The specificity of enzymes allows regulation of metabolism. The presence of particular enzymes helps determine which metabolic pathways are operative. In addition, some reactants can produce more than one type of product, depending upon which pathway is open to them. Therefore, which enzyme is present determines which product is produced as well as determining the direction of metabolism, without several alternative pathways being activated.

Factors Affecting Enzymatic Speed

Generally, enzymes work quickly, and in some instances they can increase the reaction rate more than 10 million times. The rate of a reaction is the amount of product produced per unit time. This rate depends on how much substrate is available to associate at the active sites of enzymes. Therefore, increasing the amount of substrate and also the amount of enzyme can increase the rate of the reaction. Any factor that alters the shape of the active site, such as pH or temperature or an inhibitor, can decrease the rate of a reaction. Thus, enzymes require specific conditions to be met in order to be fully operational. In fact, some enzymes require

additional molecules called cofactors that help speed the rate of the reaction because they help bind the substrate to the active site, or they participate in the reaction at the active site.

Substrate Concentration

Molecules must collide to react. Generally, enzyme activity increases as substrate concentration increases because there are more collisions between substrate molecules and the enzyme. As more substrate molecules fill active sites, more product results per unit time. But when the active sites are filled almost continuously with substrate, the rate of the reaction can no longer increase. Maximum rate has been reached.

Just as the amount of substrate can increase or limit the rate of an enzymatic reaction, so the amount of active enzyme can also increase or limit the rate of an enzymatic reaction. Therefore, sufficient concentrations of substrate and enzymes are necessary to achieve maximum reaction rate.

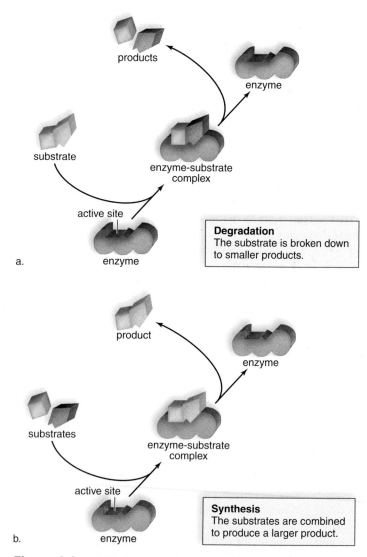

Figure 6.6 Enzymatic actions. Enzymes have an active site where the substrate(s) specifically fit together so the reaction will occur. Following the reaction, the product(s) is released, and the enzyme is free to act again. Certain enzymes carry out (**a**) degradation and others carry out (**b**) synthesis.

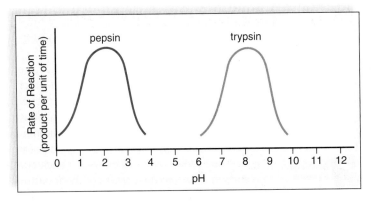

Figure 6.7 The effect of pH on rate of reaction. The optimal pH for pepsin, an enzyme that acts in the stomach, is about 2, while the optimal pH for trypsin, an enzyme that acts in the small intestine, is about 8. Enzyme shape is best maintained at the optimal pH, which allows it to best function and bind with its substrates.

Optimal pH

Each enzyme also has an optimal pH at which the reaction rate is highest. Figure 6.7 shows the optimal pH for the enzymes pepsin and trypsin. At their respective pH values, each enzyme can maintain its normal structural configuration, which enables optimum function. The globular structure of an enzyme is dependent on interactions, such as hydrogen bonding, between *R* groups. A change in pH can alter the ionization of these side chains and disrupt normal interactions, and under extreme conditions of pH, the enzyme loses its structure and becomes inactive. Inactivity occurs because the enzyme has an altered shape and is then unable to combine efficiently with its substrate.

Temperature

Typically, as temperature rises, enzyme activity increases (Fig. 6.8*a*). This occurs because warmer temperatures cause more effective collisions between enzyme and substrate. The body temperature of an animal seems to affect whether it is normally active or inactive (Fig. 6.8*b*, *c*). It has been suggested that mammals are more prevalent today than reptiles because they maintain a warm internal temperature that allows their enzymes to work at a rapid rate.

In the laboratory and in your body, if the temperature rises beyond a certain point, enzyme activity eventually levels out and then declines rapidly because the enzyme is **denatured.** An enzyme's shape changes during denaturation, and then it can no longer bind its substrate(s) efficiently.

Exceptions to this generalization do occur. For example, some prokaryotes can live in hot springs because their enzymes do not denature. These organisms are responsible for the brilliant colors of the hot springs. Another exception involves the coat color of animals. Siamese cats have inherited a mutation that causes an enzyme to be active only at cooler body temperatures. The enzyme's activity causes the cooler regions of the body—the face, ears, legs, and tail—to be dark in color (Fig. 6.9). The coat color pattern in several other animals can be explained similarly.

Figure 6.9 The effect of temperature on enzymes. Siamese cats have inherited a mutation that causes an enzyme to be active only at cooler body temperatures. Therefore, only certain regions of the body are dark in color.

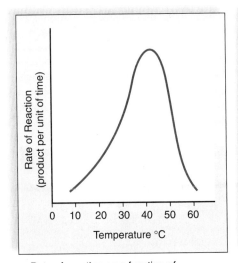

a. Rate of reaction as a function of temperature

b. Body temperature of ectothermic animals often limits rates of reactions.

c. Body temperature of endothermic animals promotes rates of reactions.

Figure 6.8 The effect of temperature on rate of reaction. **a.** Usually, the rate of an enzymatic reaction doubles with every 10°C rise in temperature. This enzymatic reaction is maximum at about 40°C; then it decreases until the reaction stops altogether, because the enzyme has become denatured. **b.** The body temperature of ectothermic animals, such as an iguana, which take on the temperature of their environment, often limits rates of reactions. **c.** The body temperature of endothermic animals, such as a polar bear, promotes rates of reaction.

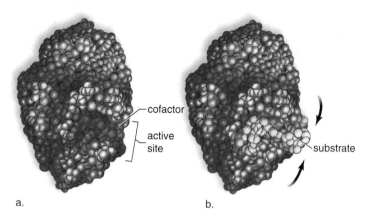

Figure 6.10 Cofactors at active site. **a.** Cofactors, including inorganic ions and organic coenzymes, may participate in the reaction at the active site (**b**).

Enzyme Cofactors

Many enzymes require the presence of an inorganic ion or non-protein organic molecule at the active site in order to work properly; these necessary ions or molecules are called **cofactors** (Fig. 6.10). The inorganic ions include metals such as copper, zinc, or iron. The nonprotein organic molecules are called **coenzymes.** These cofactors participate in the reaction and may even accept or contribute atoms to the reactions. In the next section, we discuss two coenzymes that play significant roles in photosynthesis and cellular respiration, respectively.

Vitamins are relatively small organic molecules that are required in trace amounts in our diet and in the diets of other animals for synthesis of coenzymes. The vitamin becomes part of a coenzyme's molecular structure. If a vitamin is not available, enzymatic activity will decrease, and the result will be a vitamin-deficiency disorder: Niacin deficiency results in a skin disease called pellagra, and riboflavin deficiency results in cracks at the corners of the mouth.

Animation
B Vitamins

Enzyme Inhibition

Sometimes it is necessary to limit enzyme activity. **Enzyme inhibition** occurs when a molecule (the inhibitor) binds to an enzyme and decreases its activity. **1** In Figure 6.11, F is the end product of a metabolic pathway that can act as an inhibitor. This type of inhibition is beneficial because once sufficient end product is present, inhibiting further production can conserve raw materials and energy.

2 Figure 6.11 also illustrates **noncompetitive inhibition** because the inhibitor (F, the end product) binds to the enzyme E_1 at a location other than the active site. The site is called an **allosteric site.** When an inhibitor is at the allosteric site, the active site of the enzyme changes shape, which in turn changes its function.

THEME Nature of Science

Enzyme Inhibitors Can Spell Death

Cyanide gas was formerly used to execute people. How did it work? Cyanide can be fatal because it binds to a mitochondrial enzyme necessary for the production of ATP. MPTP (1-methyl-4-phenyl-1,2,3.6-tetrahydropyridine) is another enzyme inhibitor that stops mitochondria from producing ATP. The toxic nature of MPTP was discovered in the early 1980s, when a group of intravenous drug users in California suddenly developed symptoms of Parkinson disease, including uncontrollable tremors and rigidity. All of the drug users had injected a synthetic form of heroin that was contaminated with MPTP. Parkinson disease is characterized by the death of brain cells, the very ones that are also destroyed by MPTP.

Sarin is a chemical that inhibits an enzyme at neuromuscular junctions, where nerves stimulate muscles. When the enzyme is inhibited, the signal for muscle contraction cannot be turned off, so the muscles are unable to relax and become paralyzed. Sarin can be fatal if the muscles needed for breathing become paralyzed. In 1995, terrorists released sarin gas on a subway in Japan (Fig. 6A). Although many people developed symptoms, only 17 died.

A fungus that contaminates and causes spoilage of sweet clover produces a chemical called warfarin. Cattle that eat the spoiled feed die from internal bleeding because warfarin inhibits a crucial enzyme for blood clotting. Today, warfarin is widely used as a rat poison. Unfortunately, it is not uncommon for warfarin to be mistakenly eaten by pets and even very small children, with tragic results.

Many people are prescribed a medicine called Coumadin to prevent inappropriate blood clotting. For example, those who have received an artificial heart valve need such a medication. Coumadin contains a nonlethal dose of warfarin.

These examples all show how our understanding of science can have positive or negative consequences, and emphasize the role of ethics in scientific investigation.

Questions to Consider

1. Do you feel it is ethical to use dangerous chemicals to treat diseases?
2. Under what conditions do you think they should be used?

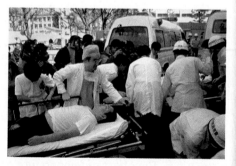

Figure 6A Sarin gas. The aftermath when sarin, a nerve gas that results in the inability to breathe, was released by terrorists in a Japanese subway in 1995.

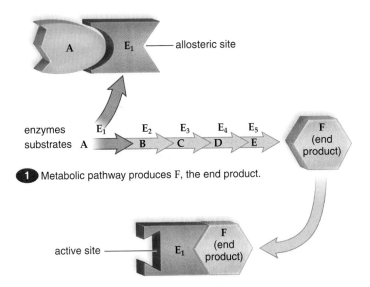

① Metabolic pathway produces F, the end product.

② F binds to allosteric site and the active site of E_1 changes shape.

③ A cannot bind to E_1; the enzyme has been inhibited by F.

Figure 6.11 Noncompetitive inhibition of an enzyme.
In the pathway, A–E are substrates, E_1–E_5 are enzymes, and F is the end product of the pathway that inhibits enzyme E_1. This negative feedback is useful because it prevents wasteful production of product F when it is not needed.

③ The enzyme E_1 is inhibited because it is unable to bind to A, its substrate. The inhibition of E_1 means that the metabolic pathway is inhibited and no more end product is produced, until conditions change and more end product is needed.

In contrast to noncompetitive inhibition, **competitive inhibition** occurs when an inhibitor and the substrate compete for the active site of an enzyme. Product forms only when the substrate, not the inhibitor, is at the active site. In this way, the amount of product is regulated.

Normally, enzyme inhibition is reversible, and the enzyme is not damaged by being inhibited. When enzyme inhibition is irreversible, the inhibitor permanently inactivates or destroys an enzyme.

Animation
Feedback Inhibition
of Biochemical
Pathways

Check Your Progress 6.3

1. Explain how enzymes maintain specificity in metabolic pathways.
2. Evaluate the usefulness of cofactors in enzyme regulation.

6.4 Organelles and the Flow of Energy

Learning Outcomes

Upon completion of this section, you should be able to
1. Compare the role of carbon dioxide, water, and oxygen in photosynthesis and cellular respiration.
2. Describe how high energy electrons are captured by NAD^+ and used to do work.
3. Explain how electrochemical gradients are used to produce ATP.

Two organelles are particularly involved in the flow of energy from the Sun through all living things. Photosynthesis, a process that captures solar energy to produce carbohydrates, takes place in chloroplasts. Cellular respiration, which breaks down carbohydrates and produces chemical energy, takes place in mitochondria.

Photosynthesis

The overall reaction for photosynthesis can be written like this:

$$6\,CO_2 + 6\,H_2O + energy \longrightarrow C_6H_{12}O_6 + 6\,O_2$$
carbon dioxide   water   glucose   oxygen

This equation shows that hydrogen atoms ($H^+ + e^-$) are transferred from water to carbon dioxide, when glucose is formed. This transfer of electrons from one molecule to another is called an **oxidation-reduction reaction**. **Oxidation** is defined as the loss of electrons and **reduction** is the gain of electrons. Therefore, water has been oxidized and carbon dioxide has been reduced. This reaction is also referred to as a **redox reaction.**

Animation Redox

The creation of a glucose molecule requires input of a lot of energy. Chloroplasts are able to capture solar energy and convert it by way of an electron transport chain (discussed on next page) to the chemical energy of ATP molecules. ATP is then used along with hydrogen atoms to reduce carbon dioxide to glucose.

Glucose production also requires a high-energy electron-carrier molecule, or coenzyme, of oxidation-reduction called **$NADP^+$ (nicotinamide adenine dinucleotide phosphate)**. This molecule carries a positive charge, and therefore is written as $NADP^+$. During photosynthesis, $NADP^+$ accepts electrons plus a hydrogen ion derived from water, and it later passes them along by way of a metabolic pathway to reduce carbon dioxide and form glucose. The reaction that reduces $NADP^+$ is:

$$NADP^+ + 2\,e^- + H^+ \longrightarrow NADPH$$

Cellular Respiration

The overall equation for cellular respiration is opposite to that for photosynthesis:

$$C_6H_{12}O_6 \ + \ 6\,O_2 \ \longrightarrow \ 6\,CO_2 \ + \ 6\,H_2O \ + \ \text{energy}$$
glucose   oxygen   carbon   water
                            dioxide

In this reaction, glucose has lost hydrogen atoms (been oxidized), and oxygen has gained hydrogen atoms (been reduced). The hydrogen atoms that were formerly bonded to carbon are now bonded to oxygen. Glucose is a high-energy molecule, whereas its breakdown products, carbon dioxide and water, are low-energy molecules; therefore, energy is released. Mitochondria use the energy released from glucose breakdown to build ATP molecules by way of an electron transport chain, as depicted in Figure 6.12.

In metabolic pathways, most oxidations such as those that occur during cellular respiration involve a coenzyme called **NAD⁺ (nicotinamide adenine dinucleotide)**. This molecule carries a positive charge, and therefore is represented as NAD^+. During oxidation reactions, NAD^+ accepts two electrons but only one hydrogen ion. The reaction that reduces NAD^+ is:

Animation
How NAD⁺ Works

$$NAD^+ \ + \ 2\,e^- \ + \ H^+ \ \longrightarrow \ NADH$$

Electron Transport Chain

As previously mentioned, chloroplasts use solar energy to generate ATP, and mitochondria use energy stored in glucose and other biomolecules to generate ATP by way of an electron

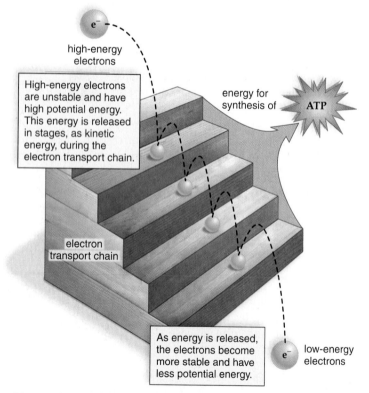

Figure 6.12 Electron transport chain. With each redox step, high energy electrons release energy that is used for ATP production.

transport chain. An **electron transport chain (ETC)** is a series of membrane-bound carriers that pass electrons from one carrier to another via redox reactions. High-energy electrons are delivered to the chain, and low-energy electrons leave it. As an analogy, if a hot potato is passed from one person to another, it loses heat with each transfer. In the same manner, each time electrons are transferred to a new carrier, energy is released. However, unlike in the hot potato transfer example, the cell is able to capture the released energy and use it to produce ATP molecules (Fig. 6.12).

In certain redox reactions, the result is release of energy, and in others, energy is required. In an ETC, each carrier is reduced and then oxidized in turn. The overall effect of oxidation-reduction as electrons are passed from carrier to carrier of the electron transport chain is the release of energy that is ultimately used for ATP production.

Animation
Electron Transport Chain and ATP Synthesis

ATP Production

For many years, scientists knew that ATP synthesis was somehow coupled to the ETC, but the exact mechanism could not be determined. Peter Mitchell, a British biochemist, received a Nobel Prize in 1978 for his theory of ATP production in both mitochondria and chloroplasts.

In chloroplasts and mitochondria, the proteins and other molecules of the ETC are located within a membrane: thylakoid membranes in chloroplasts, and cristae in mitochondria. Hydrogen ions (H^+), which are often referred to as protons in this context, are in low concentration on one side of the membrane and are pumped to the other side of the membrane. This process requires energy because certain carriers of the electron transport chain move these protons against their diffusion gradient. This establishes a larger electrochemical gradient across the membrane, and the potential energy of this gradient can then be used to do work, becoming kinetic energy for ATP production. Protons can move back across the membrane by interacting with other enzyme complexes in the membrane called **ATP synthases.** Each ATP synthase contains a channel that allows hydrogen ions to flow down their electrochemical gradient. The flow of hydrogen ions through the channel provides the kinetic energy for the ATP synthase enzyme to produce ATP from ADP + Ⓟ (Fig. 6.13). The production of ATP due to a hydrogen ion gradient across a membrane is called **chemiosmosis** [Gk. *osmos*, push].

Consider this analogy to understand chemiosmosis: The Sun's rays evaporate water from the seas and help create the winds that blow clouds to the mountains, where water falls in the form of rain and snow. The water in a mountain reservoir has a higher potential energy than water in the ocean. The potential energy is converted to electrical energy when water is released and used to turn turbines in an electrochemical dam before it makes its way to the ocean. The continual release of water results in a continual production of electricity.

Likewise, during photosynthesis, the solar energy collected by chloroplasts leads to continuous ATP production. Energized electrons lead to the pumping of hydrogen ions across a thylakoid membrane, which acts like a dam to retain them. The

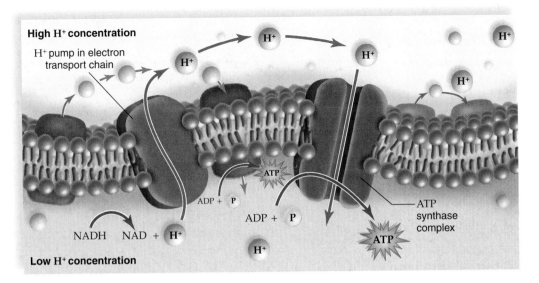

Figure 6.13 Chemiosmosis.
Carriers in the electron transport chain use energy from redox reactions to pump hydrogen ions (H⁺) across a membrane, creating greater potential energy. When the hydrogen ions flow back across the membrane through an ATP synthase complex, ATP is synthesized. This gradient-based chemiosmosis occurs in chloroplasts and mitochondria.

hydrogen ions flow through the channel of an ATP synthase complex. This complex couples the flow of hydrogen ions to the formation of ATP, just as the turbines in a hydroelectric dam system couple the flow of water to the production of electricity.

Similarly during cellular respiration, glucose breakdown provides the energy to establish a hydrogen ion gradient across the cristae of mitochondria. And again, hydrogen ions flow through the channel within an ATP synthase complex that couples the flow of hydrogen ions to the production of ATP.

Check Your Progress 6.4

1. Compare the role of carbon dioxide in photosynthesis and cellular respiration.
2. Distinguish how energy from electrons is used to establish an electrochemical gradient in chloroplasts and mitochondria.

CONNECTING *the* CONCEPTS *with the* THEMES

Evolution

- Almost all life-forms have evolved to use ATP as an energy source to drive metabolic reactions. ATP is called the universal energy "currency" of life. This is an apt analogy—before we can spend currency (e.g., money), we must first make some money. Similarly, before the cell can spend ATP molecules, it must make them.
- Cellular respiration in mitochondria transforms the chemical energy of carbohydrates into that of ATP molecules. ATP is spent when it is hydrolyzed, and the resulting energy is coupled to an endergonic reaction.
- All cells are continually making and breaking down ATP. If ATP is lacking, the organism dies.

Nature of Science

- What is the ultimate source of energy for ATP production? In Chapter 7, you will see that, except for a few deep ocean vents and certain cave communities, the answer is the Sun. Photosynthesis inside chloroplasts transforms solar energy into the chemical energy of carbohydrates.
- In Chapter 8 we discuss how carbohydrate products are broken down in mitochondria as ATP is built up. Chloroplasts and mitochondria are the cellular organelles that permit a flow of energy from the Sun through all living things.
- For many years, scientists believed there was little life in the deep ocean and around volcanic vents. Advanced technology has allowed us to investigate these previously unknown areas. New studies show a tremendous diversity of life exists within biological communities that have never been exposed to sunlight.

Biological Systems

- All cells use energy. Energy is the ability to do work, to bring about change, and to make things happen, whether it's a leaf growing or a human running. The metabolic pathways inside cells use the chemical energy of ATP to synthesize molecules, cause muscle contraction, and even allow you to read these words.
- A metabolic pathway consists of a series of individual chemical reactions, each with its own enzyme. The cell can regulate the activity of the many hundreds of different enzymes taking part in cellular metabolism.
- Enzymes are proteins, and as such they are sensitive to environmental conditions, including pH, temperature, and even certain pollutants, as will be discussed in later chapters.

Media Study Tools

www.mhhe.com/maderbiology11

Enhance your study of this chapter with study tools and practice tests. Also ask your instructor about the resources available through ConnectPlus, including the media-rich eBook, interactive learning tools, and animations.

Summarize

6.1 Cells and the Flow of Energy

Two energy laws are basic to understanding patterns of energy throughout biology. The first law of thermodynamics states that energy cannot be created or destroyed, but can only be transferred or transformed. The second law of thermodynamics states that one usable form of energy cannot be completely converted into another usable form. As a result of these laws, we know that the entropy of the universe is increasing and that only a flow of energy from the Sun maintains the organization of living things.

6.2 Metabolic Reactions and Energy Transformations

The term *metabolism* encompasses all the chemical reactions occurring in a cell. Considering individual reactions, only those that result in a negative free-energy difference—that is, the products have less usable energy than the reactants—occur spontaneously. Such reactions, called exergonic reactions, release energy.

An endergonic reaction, which requires an input of energy, occurs only when coupled with an exergonic process. The energy released from the exergonic reaction must exceed the net energy cost of the endergonic reaction in order for the overall reaction to proceed. Hydrolysis of ATP, an exergonic reaction, is commonly used to drive energetically unfavorable metabolic reactions.

6.3 Metabolic Pathways and Enzymes

A metabolic pathway is a series of reactions that proceed in an orderly, step-by-step manner. Enzymes speed reactions by lowering the energy of activation when they form a complex with their substrates. Enzymes regulate metabolism because, in general, no reaction occurs unless its enzyme is present. Which enzymes are present determine which metabolic pathways will be utilized.

Generally, enzyme activity increases as substrate concentration increases; once all active sites are filled, maximum reaction rate has been achieved. Environmental factors such as temperature or pH can affect the shape of an enzyme, and therefore its function. Many enzymes need cofactors or coenzymes to carry out their reactions. The activity of most metabolic pathways is regulated by feedback inhibition.

6.4 Organelles and the Flow of Energy

A flow of energy occurs through organisms because (1) photosynthesis in chloroplasts captures solar energy and produces carbohydrates, and (2) cellular respiration in mitochondria breaks down these carbohydrates to produce ATP molecules, which (3) provide energy

for metabolic reactions. The overall equation for photosynthesis is opposite that for cellular respiration.

Both processes use an electron transport chain in which electrons are transferred from one carrier to the next. Each transfer releases energy that is ultimately used to produce ATP molecules. Chemiosmosis explains how the electron transport chain produces ATP. The carriers of this system actively pump hydrogen ions (H$^+$) from one side of a membrane to the other, thereby creating a larger gradient. This larger electrochemical gradient pushes hydrogen ions through an ATP synthase complex, which makes ATP from ADP and Ⓟ.

Key Terms

active site   110
ADP (adenosine
   diphosphate)   107
allosteric site   112
ATP (adenosine
   triphosphate)   107
ATP synthases   114
chemical energy   105
chemiosmosis   114
coenzyme   112
cofactor   112
competitive inhibition   113
denatured   111
electron transport chain
   (ETC)   114
endergonic reaction   107
energy   105
energy of activation   109
entropy   106
enzyme   109
enzyme inhibition   112
exergonic reaction   107
free energy   107
heat   105
induced fit model   110

kinetic energy   105
laws of thermodynamics   105
mechanical energy   105
metabolic pathway   109
metabolism   107
mole   107
NAD$^+$ (nicotinamide adenine
   dinucleotide)   114
NADP$^+$ (nicotinamide
   adenine dinucleotide
   phosphate)   113
noncompetitive inhibition   112
oxidation   113
oxidation-reduction reaction
   113
potential energy   105
product   107
reactant   107
redox reaction   113
reduction   113
ribozyme   109
substrate   109
vitamin   112

Assess

Reviewing This Chapter

1. State the first law of thermodynamics, and give an example.   105
2. State the second law of thermodynamics, and give an example.   106
3. Explain why the entropy of the universe is always increasing and why an organized system such as an organism requires a constant input of useful energy.   106
4. What is the difference between exergonic reactions and endergonic reactions? Why can exergonic but not endergonic reactions occur spontaneously?   107
5. Why is ATP called the energy currency of cells? What is the ATP cycle?   107
6. Define coupling, and write an equation that shows an endergonic reaction being coupled to ATP breakdown.   108
7. Diagram a metabolic pathway. Label the reactants, products, and enzymes. Explain how enzymes regulate metabolism.   109–10

8. Why is less energy needed for a reaction to occur when an enzyme is present?   109
9. Why are enzymes specific, and why can't each one speed many different reactions?   110
10. Name and explain the manner in which at least three environmental factors can influence the speed of an enzymatic reaction. How do cells regulate the activity of enzymes?   111–12
11. What are cofactors and coenzymes?   112
12. Compare and contrast competitive and noncompetitive inhibition.   112–113
13. How do chloroplasts and mitochondria permit a flow of energy through all organisms. What role is played by oxidation and reduction?   113–14
14. Describe an electron transport chain.   114
15. Tell how cells form ATP during chemiosmosis.   114–15

Testing Yourself

Choose the best answer for each question.

1. A form of potential energy is
   a. a boulder at the top of a hill.
   b. the bonds of a glucose molecule.
   c. a starch molecule.
   d. stored fat tissue.
   e. All of these are correct.

2. Consider this reaction: A + B ⟶ C + D + energy.
   a. This reaction is exergonic.
   b. An enzyme could still speed the reaction.
   c. ATP is not needed to make the reaction go.
   d. A and B are reactants; C and D are products.
   e. All of these are correct.

3. The active site of an enzyme
   a. is similar to that of any other enzyme.
   b. is the part of the enzyme where its substrate can fit.
   c. can be used over and over again.
   d. is not affected by environmental factors, such as pH and temperature.
   e. Both b and c are correct.

4. If you want to increase the amount of product per unit time of an enzymatic reaction, do not increase the
   a. amount of substrate.
   b. amount of enzyme.
   c. temperature somewhat.
   d. pH.
   e. All of these are correct.

5. An allosteric site on an enzyme is
   a. the same as the active site.
   b. nonprotein in nature.
   c. where ATP attaches and gives up its energy.
   d. often involved in feedback inhibition.
   e. All of these are correct.

6. During photosynthesis, carbon dioxide
   a. is oxidized to oxygen.
   b. is reduced to glucose.
   c. gives up water to the environment.
   d. is a coenzyme of oxidation-reduction.
   e. All of these are correct.

7. Use these terms to label the following diagram: substrates, enzyme (used twice), active site, product, and enzyme-substrate complex. Explain the importance of an enzyme's shape to its activity.

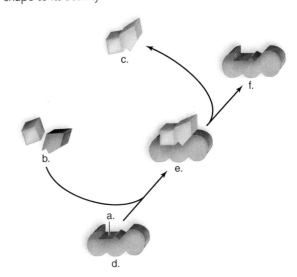

8. Coenzymes
   a. have specific functions in reactions.
   b. have an active site just as enzymes do.
   c. can be carriers for proteins.
   d. always have a phosphate group.
   e. are used in photosynthesis, but not in cellular respiration.

For questions 9–14 match each description to a process in the key.

KEY:

   a. photosynthesis
   b. cellular respiration
   c. Both
   d. Neither

9. captures solar energy
10. requires enzymes and coenzymes
11. releases CO_2 and H_2O
12. utilizes an electron transport chain
13. transforms one form of energy into another form with the release of heat
14. creates energy for the living world

15. Oxidation
   a. is the opposite of reduction.
   b. sometimes uses NAD^+.
   c. is involved in cellular respiration.
   d. occurs when ATP goes to ADP + Ⓟ.
   e. All of these but d are correct.

16. NAD^+ is the _____ form, and when it later becomes NADH, it is said to be _____.
   a. reduced, oxidized
   b. neutral, a coenzyme
   c. oxidized, reduced
   d. active, denatured

17. Electron transport chains
    a. are found in both mitochondria and chloroplasts.
    b. release energy as electrons are transferred.
    c. are involved in the production of ATP.
    d. are located in a membrane.
    e. All of these are correct.

18. Chemiosmosis is dependent on
    a. the diffusion of water across a differentially permeable membrane.
    b. an outside supply of phosphate and other chemicals.
    c. the establishment of an electrochemical hydrogen ion (H^+) gradient.
    d. the ability of ADP to join with ⓟ even in the absence of a supply of energy.
    e. All of these are correct.

19. The difference between NAD^+ and $NADP^+$ is that
    a. only NAD^+ production requires niacin in the diet.
    b. one is an organic molecule, and the other is inorganic because it contains phosphate.
    c. one carries electrons to the electron transport chain, and the other carries them to synthetic reactions.
    d. one is involved in cellular respiration, and the other is involved in photosynthesis.
    e. Both c and d are correct.

20. Label this diagram describing chemiosmosis.

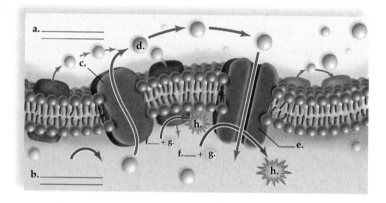

Engage

Virtual Lab
Enzyme Controlled Reactions

The virtual lab "Enzyme Controlled Reactions" provides an interactive examination of many of the factors that regulate enzymatic activity.

Thinking Scientifically

1. A flower generates heat in order to attract pollinating insects. Why might the flower break down a sugar and not ATP to produce heat?

2. You decide to calculate how much energy is released when sucrose is broken down by a flower and run into complications because you have to first heat the sucrose before it breaks down. Explain why this complication is not a problem for the flower.

Plants appear green because chlorophyll reflects green light (*left*). Otherwise, plants would be black (*right*).

7

Photosynthesis

Sunlight, the kind that shines down on us every day, contains many different colors, from violet to green, yellow, orange, and red. Plants use all the colors of light, except green, when they photosynthesize—that's why most plants are green! They are reflecting the green light back to our eyes. Does this mean that if plants used green light, in addition to all the other colors, they would appear black to us? In fact, yes. As a result natural areas like the one pictured above would be black, as shown on the right.

How did it happen that plants do not use green light for photosynthesis? When the ancestors of plants evolved in the ocean, green light was already being absorbed by other photosynthesizers, so natural selection favored the evolution of a pigment such as chlorophyll, which does not absorb green light. When plants moved onto land, chlorophyll remained as the primary pigment, but because there is plentiful sunlight on land, the selective pressure relaxed, allowing for the evolution of additional pigments.

Photosynthesis, as discussed in this chapter, consists of two interconnected pathways that allow chloroplasts to produce carbohydrate while releasing oxygen. This remarkable process is the basis for much life on Earth.

As you read through the chapter, think about the following questions:

1. Why are plants so important to most life on Earth?
2. What relationships do heterotrophs have with the photosynthesizing autotrophs?
3. How might the increased destruction of plants affect our environment, climate, and lives in the future?

CHAPTER OUTLINE

7.1 Photosynthetic Organisms 120

7.2 The Process of Photosynthesis 122

7.3 Plants as Solar Energy Converters 124

7.4 Plants as Carbon Dioxide Fixers 128

7.5 Other Types of Photosynthesis 130

BEFORE YOU BEGIN

Before beginning this chapter, take a few moments to review the following discussions.

Figure 6.1 How does energy flow in biological systems?

Section 6.3 What role do enzymes play in regulating metabolic processes?

Section 6.4 How are redox reactions and membranes used to conduct cellular work?

FOLLOWING *the* THEMES

CHAPTER 7 PHOTOSYNTHESIS		
UNIT 1 THE CELL	**Evolution**	Plants have adapted and spread to nearly every environment and climate on Earth.
	Nature of Science	Researchers have created new plant varieties that produce more food and commercially useful products.
	Biological Systems	Most ecosystems on Earth depend on photosynthesizing autotrophs as the basis of their food webs.

7.1 Photosynthetic Organisms

Learning Outcomes

Upon completion of this section, you should be able to

1. Explain how autotrophs are able to produce their own food.
2. Describe the components of a chloroplast.
3. Compare the role of carbon dioxide in autotrophs and heterotrophs.

Photosynthesis converts solar energy into the chemical energy of a carbohydrate. Photosynthetic organisms, including land plants, algae, and cyanobacteria, are called **autotrophs** because they produce their own food (Fig. 7.1). Globally, photosynthesis produces an enormous amount of carbohydrate—so much that, if it were instantly converted to coal and the coal were loaded into standard railroad cars (each car holding about 50 tons), the photosynthesizers of the biosphere would fill more than 100 cars per second with coal.

No wonder photosynthetic organisms are able to sustain themselves and all other living things on Earth. With few exceptions, it is possible to trace any food chain back to plants and algae. In other words, producers, which have the ability to synthesize carbohydrates, feed not only themselves but also consumers, which must take in preformed organic molecules. Collectively, consumers are called **heterotrophs.** Both autotrophs and heterotrophs use organic molecules produced by photosynthesis as a source of building blocks for growth and repair and as a source of chemical energy for cellular work.

Photosynthesizers also produce copious amounts of oxygen gas (O_2) as a by-product. Oxygen, which is required by organisms when they carry on cellular respiration, rises high into the atmosphere, where it forms an ozone shield that filters out ultraviolet radiation and makes terrestrial life possible.

Our analogy about photosynthetic products becoming coal is apt because the bodies of many ancient plants did become the coal we burn today, usually to produce electricity. Coal formation happened several hundred million years ago, and that is why coal is called a fossil fuel. Today's trees are also commonly used as fuel. Fermentation of plant materials produces ethanol, which can be used to fuel automobiles directly or as a gasoline additive.

The products of photosynthesis are critical to humankind in a number of other ways. They serve as a source of building materials, fabrics, paper, and pharmaceuticals. Of course, we also appreciate green plants for the simple beauty of a magnolia blossom, the scent of a rose, or the majesty of the Earth's forests.

Figure 7.1 Photosynthetic organisms. Photosynthetic organisms include plants, such as trees, garden plants, and mosses, which typically live on land; photosynthetic protists, such as *Euglena*, diatoms, and kelp, which typically live in water; and cyanobacteria, a type of bacterium that lives in water, damp soil, and rocks.

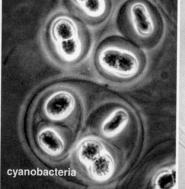

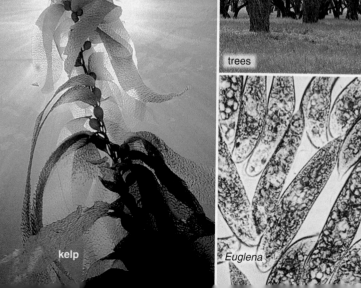

Flowering Plants as Photosynthesizers

Photosynthesis takes place in the green portions of plants. The leaves of a flowering plant contain mesophyll tissue in which cells are specialized for photosynthesis (Fig. 7.2). The raw materials for photosynthesis are water and carbon dioxide. The roots of a plant absorb water, which then moves in vascular tissue up the stem to a leaf by way of the leaf veins. Carbon dioxide in the air enters a leaf through small openings called **stomata** (sing., stoma). After entering a leaf, carbon dioxide and water diffuse into **chloroplasts** [Gk. *chloros*, green, and *plastos*, formed, molded], the organelles that carry on photosynthesis.

A double membrane surrounds a chloroplast, and its semi-fluid interior called the **stroma** [Gk. *stroma*, bed, mattress]. A different membrane system within the stroma forms flattened sacs called **thylakoids** [Gk. *thylakos*, sack, and *eides*, like, resembling], which in some places are stacked to form **grana** (sing., granum), so called because they looked like piles of seeds to early microscopists. The space of each thylakoid is thought to be connected to the space of every other thylakoid within a chloroplast, thereby forming an inner compartment within chloroplasts called the thylakoid space. Overall, chloroplast membranes provide tremendous surface area for photosynthesis to occur.

3D Animation
Structure of Chloroplasts

The thylakoid membrane contains **chlorophyll** and other pigments that are capable of absorbing solar energy, the type of energy that drives photosynthesis. The stroma contains an enzyme-rich solution where carbon dioxide is first attached to an organic compound and is then reduced to a carbohydrate.

Therefore, it is proper to associate the absorption of solar energy with the thylakoid membranes making up the grana and to associate the reduction of carbon dioxide to a carbohydrate with the stroma of a chloroplast.

Human beings, and indeed nearly all organisms, release carbon dioxide into the air when they respire. Some of these same carbon dioxide molecules enter a leaf through the stoma and are converted to carbohydrate. Carbohydrate, in the form of glucose, is the chief source of chemical energy for most organisms. Thus, an interdependent relationship exists between organisms that make their own food (autotrophs) and those that consume their food (heterotrophs).

Check Your Progress   7.1

1. Describe three major groups of photosynthetic organisms.
2. Distinguish the part of a chloroplast that absorbs solar energy from the part that forms a carbohydrate.

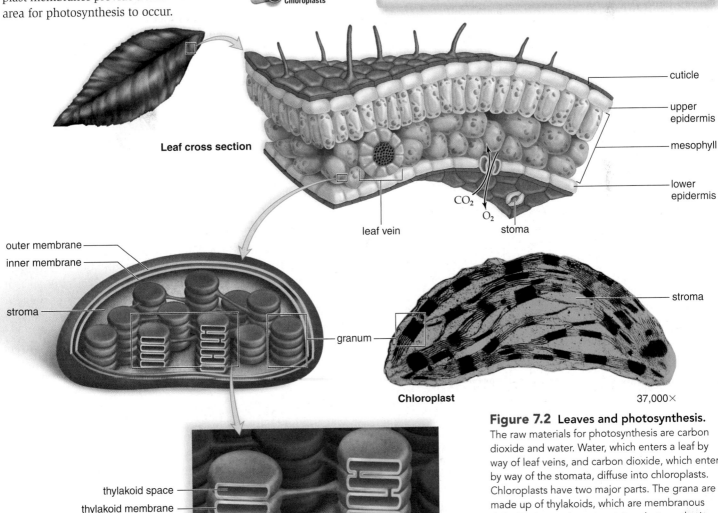

Leaf cross section

cuticle

upper epidermis

mesophyll

lower epidermis

CO_2

O_2

leaf vein

stoma

outer membrane

inner membrane

stroma

stroma

granum

Chloroplast   37,000×

thylakoid space

thylakoid membrane

independent thylakoid in a granum

overlapping thylakoid in a granum

Grana

Figure 7.2 Leaves and photosynthesis.
The raw materials for photosynthesis are carbon dioxide and water. Water, which enters a leaf by way of leaf veins, and carbon dioxide, which enters by way of the stomata, diffuse into chloroplasts. Chloroplasts have two major parts. The grana are made up of thylakoids, which are membranous disks. Their membrane contains photosynthetic pigments such as chlorophylls *a* and *b*. These pigments absorb solar energy. The stroma is a semifluid interior where carbon dioxide is enzymatically reduced to a carbohydrate.

7.2 The Process of Photosynthesis

Learning Outcomes

Upon completion of this section, you should be able to:

1. Describe the overall process of photosynthesis.
2. Compare energy input and output of the light reaction.
3. Compare carbon input and output of the Calvin cycle reaction.

The overall process of photosynthesis can be represented by an equation:

$$6CO_2 + 12H_2O \xrightarrow{\text{solar energy}} 6(CH_2O) + 6H_2O + 6O_2$$

In this equation, (CH_2O) represents carbohydrate. If the equation were multiplied by six, the carbohydrate would be $C_6H_{12}O_6$, or glucose.

The overall equation implies that photosynthesis involves oxidation-reduction (redox) and the movement of electrons from one molecule to another. Recall that oxidation is the loss of electrons, and reduction is the gain of electrons. In living things, as discussed in Chapter 6, the electrons are very often accompanied by hydrogen ions so that oxidation is the loss of hydrogen atoms $(H^+ + e^-)$, and reduction is the gain of hydrogen atoms. This simplified rewrite of the above equation makes it clear that carbon dioxide has been reduced, and water has been oxidized:

$$\overbrace{CO_2 + H_2O \xrightarrow{\text{solar energy}} (CH_2O) + O_2}^{\text{Reduction}}_{\text{Oxidation}}$$

It takes hydrogen atoms and a lot of energy to reduce carbon dioxide. From your study of energy and enzymes in Chapter 6, you probably expect that solar energy is not used directly during photosynthesis; rather, it is converted to ATP molecules. ATP is the energy currency of cells and, when cells need something, they spend ATP. In this case, solar energy is used to generate the ATP needed to reduce carbon dioxide to a carbohydrate. Of course, we always want to keep in mind that this carbohydrate represents the food produced by land plants, algae, and cyanobacteria that feeds the biosphere.

The Role of NADP⁺/NADPH

A review of Section 6.4 will also lead you to suspect that the electrons needed to reduce carbon dioxide are carried by a coenzyme. $NADP^+$ is the coenzyme of oxidation-reduction (redox coenzyme) active during photosynthesis. When $NADP^+$ is reduced, it has accepted two electrons and one hydrogen atom, and when NADPH is oxidized, it gives up its electrons:

$$NADP^+ + 2\,e^- + H^+ \longrightarrow NADPH$$

Figure 7.3 Photosynthesis releases oxygen. Bubbling indicates that the aquatic plant *Elodea* releases O_2 gas when it photosynthesizes.

What molecule supplies the electrons that reduce $NADP^+$ during photosynthesis? Put a sprig of *Elodea* in a beaker, and supply it with light, and you will observe a bubbling (Fig. 7.3). The bubbling occurs because the plant is releasing oxygen as it photosynthesizes.

A very famous experiment performed by C. B. van Niel of Stanford University found that the oxygen given off by photosynthesizers comes from water. Van Niel performed two separate experiments. When an isotope of oxygen, ^{18}O, was a part of water, the O_2 given off by the plant contained ^{18}O. When ^{18}O was a part of carbon dioxide supplied to a plant, the O_2 given off by a plant did not contain the ^{18}O. Why not? Because the oxygen in carbon dioxide doesn't come from water, it comes from the air. This was the first step toward discovering that water splits during photosynthesis. When water splits, oxygen is released, and the hydrogen atoms $(H^+ + e^-)$ are taken up by $NADP^+$. Later, NADPH reduces carbon dioxide to a carbohydrate.

Two Sets of Reactions

Many investigators have contributed to our understanding of the overall equation of photosynthesis and to our current realization that photosynthesis consists of two separate sets of reactions. F. F. Blackman (1866-1947) was the first to suggest, in 1905, that enzymes must be involved in the reduction of carbon dioxide to a carbohydrate and that the process must consist of two separate sets of reactions. We call the two sets of reactions the light reactions and the Calvin cycle reactions.

Light Reactions

The **light reactions** are so named because they only occur when solar energy is available (during daylight hours). The overall equation for photosynthesis gives no hint that the green pigment chlorophyll, present in thylakoid membranes, is largely responsible for absorbing the solar energy that drives photosynthesis.

During the light reactions, solar energy energizes electrons that move down an electron transport chain (see Fig. 6.12). As the electrons move down the chain, energy is released and captured to produce ATP molecules. Energized electrons are also taken up by $NADP^+$, which is reduced and becomes NADPH. This equation can be used to summarize the light reactions because, during the light reactions, solar energy is converted to chemical energy:

$$\text{solar energy} \longrightarrow \text{chemical energy}$$
$$\text{(ATP, NADPH)}$$

Calvin Cycle Reactions

The **Calvin cycle reactions** are named for Melvin Calvin, who received a Nobel Prize for discovering the enzymatic reactions that reduce carbon dioxide to a carbohydrate in the stroma of chloroplasts (Fig. 7.4). The enzymes that speed the reduction of carbon dioxide during both day and night are located in the semifluid substance of the chloroplast stroma.

During the Calvin cycle reactions, CO_2 is taken up and then reduced to a carbohydrate that can later be converted to glucose. This equation can be used to summarize the Calvin cycle reactions because during these reactions, the ATP and NADPH formed during the light reactions are used to reduce carbon dioxide:

$$\text{chemical energy} \longrightarrow \text{chemical energy}$$
$$\text{(ATP, NADPH)} \qquad \text{(carbohydrate)}$$

Summary

Figure 7.5 summarizes our discussion so far and shows that during the light reactions, (1) solar energy is absorbed, (2) water is split so that oxygen is released, and (3) ATP and NADPH are produced.

During the Calvin cycle reactions, (1) CO_2 is absorbed and (2) reduced to a carbohydrate (CH_2O) by utilizing ATP and

**Figure 7.4
Melvin Calvin in the laboratory.**
Melvin Calvin used tracers to discover the cycle of reactions that reduce CO_2 to a carbohydrate.

NADPH from the light reactions (see bottom set of red arrows). The top set of red arrows takes ADP + Ⓟ and $NADP^+$ back to light reactions, where they become ATP and NADPH once more so that carbohydrate production can continue.

Check Your Progress   7.2

1. Explain how redox reactions are used in photosynthesis.
2. Describe the role of enzymes during photosynthesis.

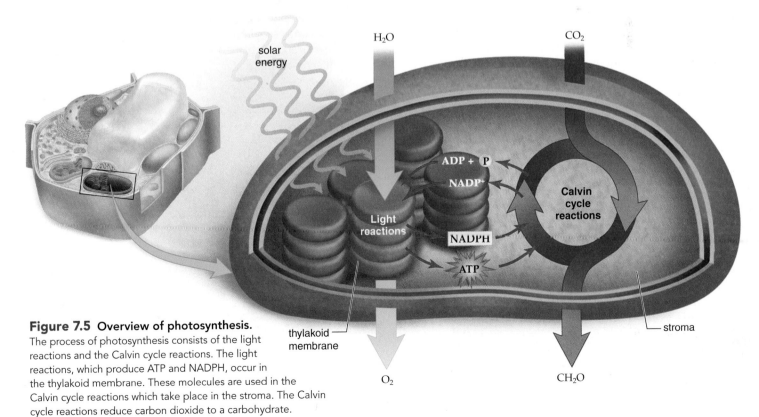

Figure 7.5 Overview of photosynthesis.
The process of photosynthesis consists of the light reactions and the Calvin cycle reactions. The light reactions, which produce ATP and NADPH, occur in the thylakoid membrane. These molecules are used in the Calvin cycle reactions which take place in the stroma. The Calvin cycle reactions reduce carbon dioxide to a carbohydrate.

7.3 Plants as Solar Energy Converters

Learning Outcomes

Upon completion of this section, you should be able to

1. Describe the relationship between wavelength and energy in the electromagnetic spectrum.
2. Explain the role of photosynthetic pigments in harnessing solar energy.
3. Examine how ATP and NADPH are produced from redox reactions and membrane gradients.

Solar energy can be described in terms of its wavelength and its energy content. Figure 7.6a lists the different types of radiant energy from the shortest wavelength, gamma rays, to the longest, radio waves. Most of the radiation reaching the Earth is within the visible-light range. Higher-energy wavelengths are screened out by the ozone layer in the atmosphere, and lower-energy wavelengths are screened out by water vapor and carbon dioxide, before they reach the Earth's surface. Because visible light is the most prevalent in the environment, we can conclude that organic molecules and processes within organisms, such as vision and photosynthesis, are chemically adapted to the radiation associated with visible light (Fig. 7.6a).

 3D Animation Properties of Light

Pigments and Photosystems

Pigment molecules absorb wavelengths of light. Most pigments absorb only some wavelengths; they reflect or transmit the other wavelengths. The pigments found in chloroplasts are capable of absorbing various portions of visible light. This is called their **absorption spectrum.**

Photosynthetic organisms differ in the type of chlorophyll they contain. In plants, chlorophyll *a* and chlorophyll *b* play prominent roles in photosynthesis. **Carotenoids** play an accessory role. Both chlorophylls *a* and *b* absorb violet, blue, and red light better than the light of other colors. Because green light is transmitted and reflected by chlorophyll, plant leaves appear green to us. The carotenoids, which are shades of yellow and orange, are able to absorb light in the violet-blue-green range. These pigments become noticeable in the fall when chlorophyll breaks down.

 Animation Absorption of Light

How do you determine the absorption spectrum of pigments? To identify the absorption spectrum of a particular pigment, a purified sample is exposed to different wavelengths of light inside an instrument called a spectrophotometer. A spectrophotometer measures the amount of light that passes through the sample, and from this it is possible to calculate how much was absorbed. The amount of light absorbed at each wavelength is plotted on a graph, and the result is a record of the pigment's absorption spectrum (Fig. 7.6b).

A **photosystem** consists of a pigment complex (molecules of chlorophyll *a*, chlorophyll *b*, and the carotenoids) and electron acceptor molecules within the thylakoid membrane. The pigment complex serves as an "antenna" for gathering solar energy.

The Electron Flow in the Light Reactions

The light reactions utilize two photosystems, called photosystem I (PS I) and photosystem II (PS II). The photosystems are named for the order in which they were discovered, not for the order in which they occur in the thylakoid membrane or participate in the photosynthetic process.

During the light reactions, electrons usually, but not always, follow a **noncyclic pathway** that begins with photosystem II (Fig. 7.7). The pigment complex absorbs solar energy, which is then passed from one pigment to the other until it is concentrated in a particular pair of chlorophyll *a* molecules, called the *reaction center.* Electrons (e⁻) in the reaction center become so energized that they escape from the reaction center and move to nearby electron acceptor molecules.

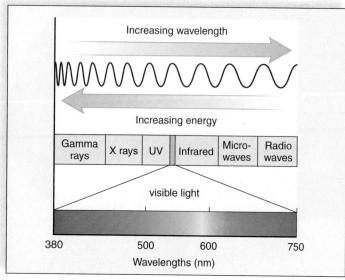

a. The electromagnetic spectrum includes visible light.

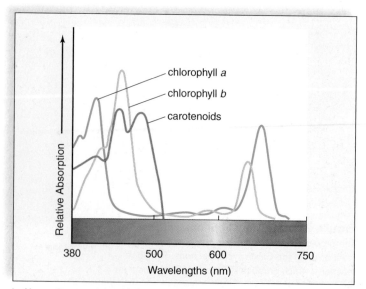

b. Absorption spectrum of photosynthetic pigments.

Figure 7.6 Photosynthetic pigments and photosynthesis. **a.** The wavelengths in visible light differ according to energy content and color. **b.** The photosynthetic pigments in chlorophylls *a* and *b* and the carotenoids absorb certain wavelengths within visible light. This is their absorption spectrum.

PS II would disintegrate without replacement electrons, and these are removed from water, which splits, releasing oxygen to the atmosphere. Notice that with the loss of electrons, water has been oxidized, and that indeed, the oxygen released during photosynthesis does come from water. Many organisms, including plants themselves and human beings, use this oxygen within their mitochondria to make ATP. The hydrogen ions (H^+) stay in the thylakoid space and contribute to the formation of a hydrogen ion gradient.

An electron acceptor sends energized electrons, received from the reaction center, down an **electron transport chain (ETC)**, a series of carriers that pass electrons from one to the other (see Fig. 6.13). As the electrons pass from one carrier to the next, energy is captured and stored in the form of a hydrogen ion (H^+) gradient. When these hydrogen ions flow down their electrochemical gradient through ATP synthase complexes, ATP production occurs (see Fig. 7.8). Notice that this ATP is then used by the Calvin cycle reactions in the stroma to reduce carbon dioxide to a carbohydrate.

When the PS I pigment complex absorbs solar energy, energized electrons leave its reaction center and are captured by electron acceptors. (Low-energy electrons from the *electron transport chain* adjacent to PS II replace those lost by PS I.) The electron acceptors in PS I pass their electrons to $NADP^+$ molecules. Each $NADP^+$ accepts two electrons and an H^+ to become reduced and forms NADPH. This NADPH is then used by the Calvin cycle reactions in the stroma along with ATP in the reduction of carbon dioxide to a carbohydrate.

3D Animation
Light-Dependent Reactions

ATP and NADPH are not made in equal amounts during the light reactions, and more ATP than NADPH is required during the Calvin cycle. Where does this extra ATP come from? Every so often, an electron moving down the noncyclic pathway is rerouted back to an earlier point in the electron transport chain. This cyclic pathway enables electrons to participate in additional redox reactions, moving more H^+ across the thylakoid membrane and through ATP synthase, and ultimately producing more ATP.

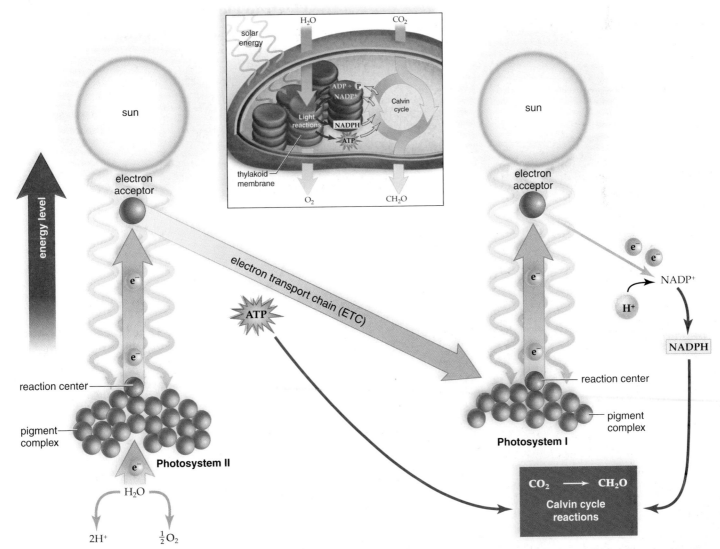

Figure 7.7 Noncyclic pathway: Electrons move from water to $NADP^+$. Energized electrons (replaced from water, which splits, releasing oxygen) leave photosystem II and pass down an electron transport chain, leading to the formation of ATP. Energized electrons (replaced by photosystem II by way of the ETC) leave photosystem I and pass to $NADP^+$, which then combines with H^+, becoming NADPH.

The Organization of the Thylakoid Membrane

As we have discussed, the following molecular complexes are present in the thylakoid membrane (Fig. 7.8):

PS II, which consists of a pigment complex and electron-acceptor molecules, receives electrons from water as water splits, releasing oxygen.

The electron transport chain (ETC), consisting of Pq (plastoquinone) and cytochrome complexes, carries electrons from PS II to PS I via redox reactions. Pq also pumps H^+ from the stroma into the thylakoid space.

PS I, which also consists of a pigment complex and electron-acceptor molecules, is adjacent to NADP reductase, which reduces $NADP^+$ to NADPH.

The **ATP synthase** complex, which has a channel and a protruding ATP synthase, is an enzyme that joins ADP + Ⓟ.

Animation
Photosynthetic
Electron and ATP
Synthesis

ATP Production

The thylakoid space acts as a reservoir for many hydrogen ions (H^+). First, each time water is oxidized, two H^+ remain in the thylakoid space. Second, as the electrons move from carrier to carrier via redox reactions along the electron transport chain, the electrons give up energy, which is used to pump H^+ from the stroma into the thylakoid space. Therefore, there are more H^+ in the thylakoid space than in the stroma. This difference and the resulting flow of H^+ (often referred to as protons in this context) from high to low concentration provides kinetic energy that allows an ATP synthase complex enzyme to enzymatically produce ATP from ADP + Ⓟ. This method of producing ATP is called **chemiosmosis** because ATP production is tied to the establishment of an H^+ gradient (see Fig. 6.13).

Animation
Proton Pump

Video
Spinach Battery

Check Your Progress   7.3

1. Distinguish visible light from the electromagnetic spectrum.
2. Evaluate the energy level of molecules that go in and come out of the light reaction.

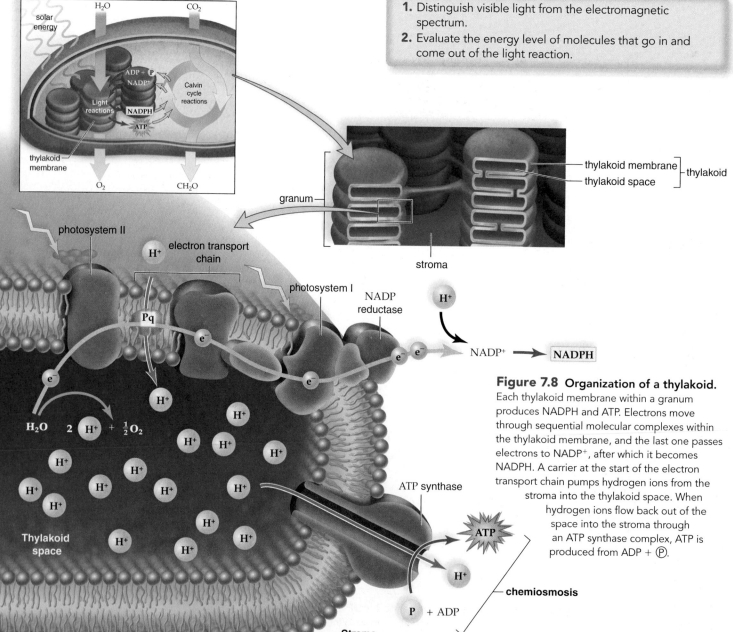

Figure 7.8 Organization of a thylakoid. Each thylakoid membrane within a granum produces NADPH and ATP. Electrons move through sequential molecular complexes within the thylakoid membrane, and the last one passes electrons to $NADP^+$, after which it becomes NADPH. A carrier at the start of the electron transport chain pumps hydrogen ions from the stroma into the thylakoid space. When hydrogen ions flow back out of the space into the stroma through an ATP synthase complex, ATP is produced from ADP + Ⓟ.

THEME Biological Systems

Tropical Rain Forest Destruction and Climate Change

Al Gore, former presidential candidate, won the 2007 Nobel Peace Prize for raising public awareness concerning climate change. The Nobel Committee said that "global warming could induce large-scale migrations and lead to greater competition for the Earth's resources. As such, it may increase the danger of violent conflicts and wars, within and between countries."

Climate change refers to an expected rise in the average global temperature during the twenty-first century due to the introduction of certain gases into the atmosphere. For at least a thousand years prior to 1850, atmospheric carbon dioxide (CO_2) levels remained fairly constant at 0.028%. Since the 1850s, when industrialization began, the amount of CO_2 in the atmosphere has increased to 0.038% (Fig. 7A).

Role of Carbon Dioxide

In much the same way as the panes of a greenhouse, CO_2 and other gases in our atmosphere trap radiant heat from the Sun. Therefore, these gases are called greenhouse gases. Without any greenhouse gases, the Earth's temperature would be about 33°C cooler than it is now. Likewise, increasing the concentration of greenhouse gases is predicted to affect climate change.

Certainly, the burning of fossil fuels adds CO_2 to the atmosphere. But another factor that contributes to an increase in atmospheric CO_2 is tropical rain forest destruction.

Role of Tropical Rain Forests

Tropical rain forests are considered by many scientists to be the "lungs" of the Earth. Between 10 and 30 million hectares of rain forests are lost every year to ranching, logging, mining, and otherwise developing areas of the forest for human needs.

Each year, deforestation in tropical rain forests accounts for 20–30% of all CO_2 in the atmosphere. With your body, if you lose lung capacity, you lose body function. Similarly, the consequence of losing forests is greater trouble for climate change because burning a forest adds CO_2 to the atmosphere and removes trees that would ordinarily absorb CO_2.

The Earth Is a System

Carbon dioxide is removed from the air via photosynthesis, which takes place in forests, oceans, and other terrestrial and marine ecosystems. In fact, photosynthesis produces organic matter that is 300 to 600 times the mass of people currently living on Earth this year. Thus, these environments act as a sink for CO_2, preventing too much from accumulating in the atmosphere where CO_2 can affect global temperatures and bring about climate change.

Despite their reduction in size from an original 14% to 6% of land surface today, tropical rain forests make a substantial contribution to global CO_2 removal. They are a critical element of the Earth's systems, and, like any biological system, are essential for normal, healthy function. Tropical rain forests contribute greatly to the uptake of CO_2 and the productivity of photosynthesis because they are the most efficient of all terrestrial ecosystems.

Tropical rain forests occur near the equator. They can exist wherever temperatures are above 26°C and rainfall is heavy (from 100–200 cm) and regular. Huge trees with buttressed trunks and broad, undivided, dark-green leaves predominate. Nearly all land plants in a tropical rain forest are woody, and woody vines are also abundant.

It might be hypothesized that an increased amount of CO_2 in the atmosphere would cause photosynthesis to increase in the remaining portion of the forest. To study this possibility, investigators measured atmospheric CO_2 levels, daily temperature levels, and tree girth in La Selva, Costa Rica, for 16 years. The results demonstrated relatively lower forest productivity at higher temperatures. These findings suggest that, as temperatures rise, tropical rain forests may add to ongoing atmospheric CO_2 accumulation and accelerated climate change rather than the reverse.

These and other studies show that, as with any biological system, equilibrium and balance are necessary for healthy function. As a biological system, the Earth is sensitive to environmental change. Learning how to properly balance human activity with the needs of the biosphere requires that people become educated about how the Earth functions.

Questions to Consider

1. Are you concerned about climate change?
2. What actions can a person take to learn more about the facts of climate change?

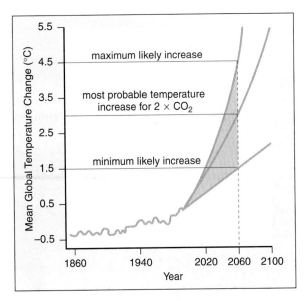

Figure 7A Climate change. Mean global temperature change is expected to rise due to the introduction of greenhouse gases into the atmosphere.

7.4 Plants as Carbon Dioxide Fixers

The Calvin cycle is a series of reactions that occur after the light reactions. The Calvin cycle produces carbohydrate before returning to its starting point, ready to accept more carbon dioxide (CO_2) (Fig. 7.9). The cycle is named for Melvin Calvin, who, with colleagues, used the radioactive isotope ^{14}C as a tracer to discover the reactions making up the cycle.

This series of reactions uses carbon dioxide from the atmosphere to produce carbohydrate. How does carbon dioxide get into the atmosphere? We and most other organisms take in oxygen from the atmosphere and release carbon dioxide to the atmosphere. The Calvin cycle includes (1) carbon dioxide fixation, (2) carbon dioxide reduction, and (3) regeneration of RuBP (pronounced "ruby-P"; described shortly).

3D Animation
Calvin Cycle

Fixation of Carbon Dioxide

Carbon dioxide fixation is the first step of the Calvin cycle. During this reaction, a molecule of carbon dioxide from the atmosphere is attached to RuBP (ribulose-1,5-bisphosphate), a 5-carbon molecule. The result is one 6-carbon molecule, which splits into two 3-carbon molecules.

The enzyme that speeds this reaction, called **RuBP carboxylase**, is a protein that makes up about 20–50% of the protein content in chloroplasts. The reason for its abundance may be

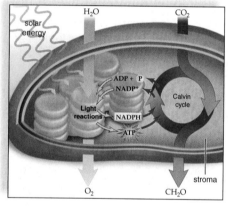

Figure 7.9 The Calvin cycle reactions. The Calvin cycle is divided into three portions: CO_2 fixation, CO_2 reduction, and regeneration of RuBP. Because five G3P are needed to re-form three RuBP, it takes three turns of the cycle to have a net gain of one G3P. Two G3P molecules are needed to form glucose.

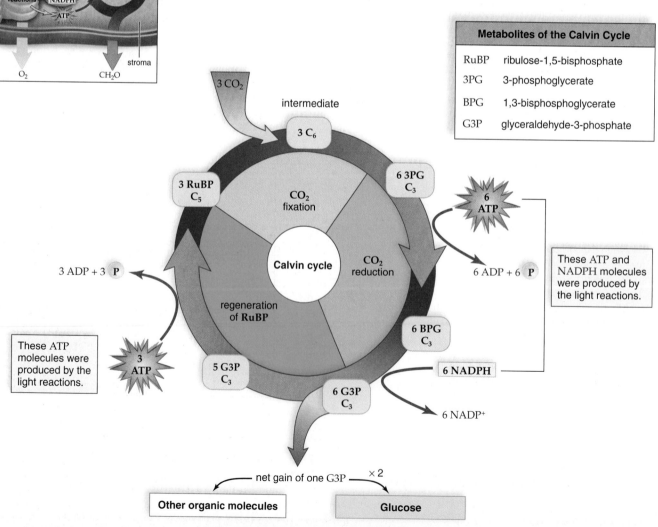

Metabolites of the Calvin Cycle	
RuBP	ribulose-1,5-bisphosphate
3PG	3-phosphoglycerate
BPG	1,3-bisphosphoglycerate
G3P	glyceraldehyde-3-phosphate

that it is unusually slow—it processes only a few molecules of substrate per second compared to thousands per second for a typical enzyme—and so there has to be a lot of it to keep the Calvin cycle going.

Reduction of Carbon Dioxide

The first 3-carbon molecule in the Calvin cycle is called 3PG (3-phosphoglycerate). Each of two 3PG molecules undergoes reduction to G3P (glyceraldehyde-3-phosphate) in two steps:

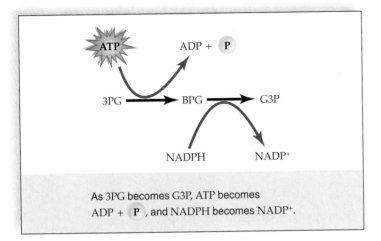

As 3PG becomes G3P, ATP becomes ADP + P , and NADPH becomes NADP$^+$.

This is the sequence of reactions that uses some ATP and NADPH from the light reactions. This sequence signifies the reduction of carbon dioxide to a carbohydrate because R—CO_2 has become R—CH_2O. Energy and electrons are needed for this reduction reaction, and these are supplied by ATP and NADPH.

Regeneration of RuBP

Notice that the Calvin cycle reactions in Figure 7.9 are multiplied by three because it takes three turns of the Calvin cycle to allow one G3P to exit. Why? Because, for every three turns of the Calvin cycle, five molecules of G3P are used to re-form three molecules of RuBP, and the cycle continues. Notice that 5×3 (carbons in G3P) = 3×5 (carbons in RuBP):

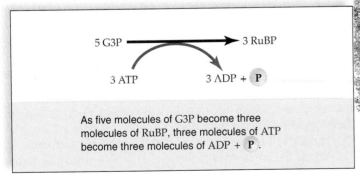

As five molecules of G3P become three molecules of RuBP, three molecules of ATP become three molecules of ADP + P .

This reaction also uses some of the ATP pro- **Animation** duced by the light reactions. **How the Calvin Cycle Works**

The Importance of the Calvin Cycle

G3P is the product of the Calvin cycle that can be converted to other molecules a plant needs. Notice that glucose phosphate is

among the organic molecules that result from G3P metabolism (Fig. 7.10). This is of interest to us because glucose is the molecule that plants and animals most often metabolize to produce the ATP molecules they require for their energy needs.

Glucose phosphate can be combined with fructose (and the phosphate removed) to form sucrose, the molecule that plants use to transport carbohydrates from one part of the plant to the other.

Glucose phosphate is also the starting point for the synthesis of starch and cellulose. Starch is the storage form of glucose. Some starch is stored in chloroplasts, but most starch is stored in amyloplasts in roots. Cellulose is a structural component of plant cell walls and becomes fiber in our diet because we are unable to digest it.

A plant can use the hydrocarbon skeleton of G3P to form fatty acids and glycerol, which are combined in plant oils. We are all familiar with corn oil, sunflower oil, or olive oil used in cooking. Also, when nitrogen is added to the hydrocarbon skeleton derived from G3P, amino acids are formed, allowing the plant to produce protein.

Check Your Progress 7.4

1. Describe the three major steps of the Calvin cycle.
2. Illustrate why it takes 3 turns of the Calvin cycle to produce 1 G3P.

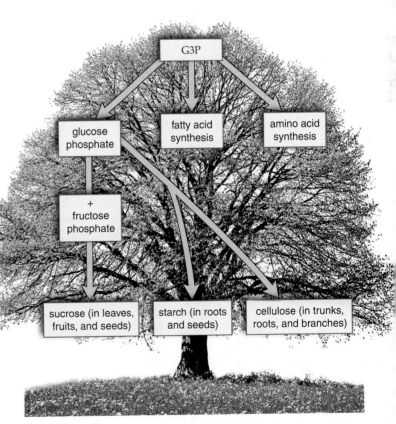

Figure 7.10 Fate of G3P. G3P is the first reactant in a number of plant cell metabolic pathways. Two G3Ps are needed to form glucose phosphate; glucose is often considered the end product of photosynthesis. Sucrose is the transport sugar in plants; starch is the storage form of glucose; and cellulose is a major constituent of plant cell walls.

7.5 Other Types of Photosynthesis

The majority of land plants, such as azaleas, maples, and tulips, carry on photosynthesis as described and are called **C_3 plants** (Fig. 7.11a). C_3 plants use the enzyme RuBP carboxylase to fix CO_2 to RuBP in mesophyll cells. The first detected molecule following fixation is the 3-carbon molecule 3PG:

$$RuBP + CO_2 \xrightarrow{\text{RuBP carboxylase}} 2\ 3PG$$

As shown in Figure 7.2, leaves have small openings called stomata through which water can leave and carbon dioxide (CO_2) can enter. If the weather is hot and dry, the stomata close, conserving water. (Water loss might cause the plant to wilt and die.) Now the concentration of CO_2 decreases in leaves, while O_2, a by-product of photosynthesis, increases. When O_2 rises in C_3 plants, RuBP carboxylase combines it with RuBP instead of CO_2. The result is one molecule of 3PG and the eventual release of CO_2. This is called **photorespiration** because in the presence of light (*photo*), oxygen is taken up and CO_2 is released (*respiration*).

An adaptation called C_4 photosynthesis enables some plants to avoid photorespiration.

C_4 Photosynthesis

In a C_3 plant, the mesophyll cells contain well-formed chloroplasts and are arranged in parallel layers. In a C_4 leaf, the bundle sheath cells, as well as the mesophyll cells, contain chloroplasts. Further, the mesophyll cells are arranged concentrically around the bundle sheath cells:

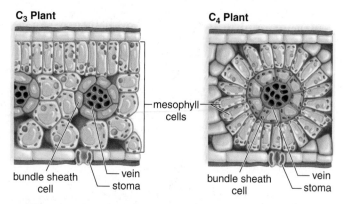

C_4 plants fix CO_2 to PEP (phosphoenolpyruvate, a C_3 molecule) using the enzyme PEP carboxylase (PEPCase). The result is oxaloacetate, a C_4 molecule:

$$PEP + CO_2 \xrightarrow{\text{PEPCase}} oxaloacetate$$

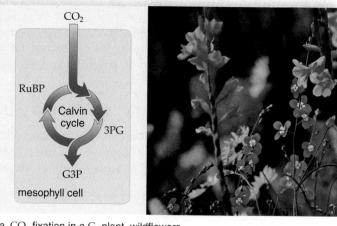

a. CO_2 fixation in a C_3 plant, wildflowers

b. CO_2 fixation in a C_4 plant, corn, *Zea mays*

Figure 7.11 Carbon dioxide fixation in C_3 and C_4 plants.
a. In C_3 plants, CO_2 is taken up by the Calvin cycle directly in mesophyll cells. **b.** C_4 plants form a C_4 molecule in mesophyll cells prior to releasing CO_2 to the Calvin cycle in bundle sheath cells.

In a C_4 plant, CO_2 is taken up in mesophyll cells, and then malate, a reduced form of oxaloacetate, is pumped into the bundle sheath cells (Fig. 7.11b). Here, and only here, does CO_2 enter the Calvin cycle.

Because it takes energy to pump molecules, you would think that the C_4 pathway would be disadvantageous. Yet in hot, dry climates, the net photosynthetic rate of C_4 plants, such as sugarcane, corn, and Bermuda grass, is about two to three times that of C_3 plants (e.g., wheat, rice, and oats). Why do C_4 plants enjoy such an advantage? The answer is that they can avoid photorespiration, discussed previously. Photorespiration is wasteful because it is not part of the Calvin cycle. Photorespiration does not occur in C_4 leaves because PEPCase, unlike RuBP carboxylase, does not combine with O_2. Even when stomata are closed, CO_2 is delivered to the Calvin cycle in the bundle sheath cells.

When the weather is moderate, C_3 plants ordinarily have the advantage, but when the weather becomes hot and dry, C_4 plants have the advantage, and we can expect them to predominate. In the early summer, C_3 plants such as Kentucky bluegrass and creeping bent grass predominate in lawns in the cooler parts of the United States, but by midsummer, crabgrass, a C_4 plant, begins to take over.

CO₂ fixation in a CAM plant, pineapple, *Ananas comosus*

Figure 7.12 Carbon dioxide fixation in a CAM plant. CAM plants, such as pineapple, fix CO_2 at night, forming a C_4 molecule that is released to the Calvin cycle during the day.

CAM Photosynthesis

CAM stands for crassulacean-acid metabolism; the Crassulaceae is a family of flowering succulent (water-containing) plants that live in warm, dry regions of the world. CAM was first discovered in these plants, but now it is known to be prevalent among other groups of plants.

Whereas a C_4 plant represents partitioning in space—carbon dioxide fixation occurs in mesophyll cells while the Calvin cycle occurs in bundle sheath cells—CAM is partitioning by the use of time. During the night, CAM plants use PEPCase to fix some CO_2, forming C_4 molecules, which are stored in large vacuoles in mesophyll cells. During the day, C_4 molecules (malate) release CO_2 to the Calvin cycle when NADPH and ATP are available from the light reactions (Fig. 7.12). The primary

advantage for this partitioning again has to do with the conservation of water. CAM plants open their stomata only at night, and therefore only at that time does atmospheric CO_2 enter the plant. During the day, the stomata close; this conserves water, but CO_2 cannot enter the plant.

Photosynthesis in a CAM plant is minimal because a limited amount of CO_2 is fixed at night, but it does allow CAM plants to live under stressful conditions.

Photosynthesis and Adaptation to the Environment

The different types of photosynthesis give us an opportunity to consider that organisms are metabolically adapted to their environment. Each method of photosynthesis has its advantages and disadvantages, depending on the climate.

C_4 plants most likely evolved in, and are adapted to, areas of high light intensities, high temperatures, and limited rainfall. C_4 plants, however, are more sensitive to cold, and C_3 plants do better than C_4 plants below 25°C. CAM plants, on the other hand, compete well with either type of plant when the environment is extremely arid. Surprisingly, CAM is quite widespread and has evolved in 23 families of flowering plants, including some lilies and orchids! And it is found among nonflowering plants, including some ferns and cone-bearing trees.

Check Your Progress 7.5

1. Describe some plants that use a method of photosynthesis other than C_3 photosynthesis.
2. Explain why C_4 photosynthesis is advantageous in hot, dry conditions.

CONNECTING *the* CONCEPTS *with the* THEMES

Evolution

- Plants have evolved to capture solar energy and store it in carbon-based organic nutrients. These are passed on to organisms that have evolved to feed on plants, and in turn to organisms that have evolved to feed on the plant-eaters, and so on in a food web.
- Plants are called autotrophs because they make their own organic food. Heterotrophs are organisms that take in organic food made by other organisms.

Nature of Science

- The amount of carbon dioxide in the atmosphere is increasing steadily, in part because of burning fossil fuels. This buildup of carbon dioxide can contribute to climate change.
- We can use the tools of science to understand the scope of global climate change, learn about our atmosphere and how to keep it healthy, and make informed choices about how best to maintain the Earth.

Biological Systems

- Autotrophs take in carbon dioxide when they photosynthesize. Carbon dioxide is returned to the atmosphere when autotrophs and heterotrophs carry on cellular respiration. In this way, carbon atoms cycle through living things.
- Energy does not cycle, and therefore all life is dependent on the ability of plants to capture solar energy and produce carbohydrate molecules from CO_2.

Media Study Tools

www.mhhe.com/maderbiology11

Enhance your study of this chapter with study tools and practice tests. Also ask your instructor about the resources available through

ConnectPlus, including the media-rich eBook, interactive learning tools, and animations.

3D Animation For a detailed examination of the process of photosynthesis, including a description of the properties of light, watch McGraw-Hill's new 3D animation "Photosynthesis."

Summarize

7.1 Photosynthetic Organisms

Photosynthesis produces carbohydrates and releases oxygen, both of which are used by the majority of living things. Cyanobacteria, algae, and land plants carry on photosynthesis. In plants, photosynthesis takes place in chloroplasts. A chloroplast is bounded by a double membrane and contains two main components: the semifluid stroma and the membranous grana made up of thylakoids.

7.2 The Process of Photosynthesis

The overall equation for photosynthesis shows that it is a redox reaction. Carbon dioxide is reduced, and water is oxidized. During photosynthesis, the light reactions take place in the thylakoid membranes, and the Calvin cycle reactions take place in the stroma.

7.3 Plants as Solar Energy Converters

Photosynthesis uses solar energy in the visible-light range. Specifically, chlorophylls a and b absorb violet, blue, and red wavelengths best and reflect green light, whereas the carotenoids absorb violet-blue-green light and reflect yellow-to-orange light.

In the light reactions, noncyclic electron flow begins when solar energy enters PS II and energizes chlorophyll a electrons. The oxidation (splitting) of water replaces these electrons in the reaction-center chlorophyll a molecules. Oxygen is released to the atmosphere, and hydrogen ions (H^+) remain in the thylakoid space. Electrons are ultimately passed to PS I via an electron transport chain, which pumps hydrogen ions across the thylakoid membrane and contributes to the chemiosmotic gradient used to make ATP via ATP synthetase. Light-energized electrons from PS I are captured by $NADP^+$, which combines with H^+ from the stroma to become NADPH. Cyclic electron flow in the light reactions pumps additional hydrogen ions and also contributes to ATP production.

7.4 Plants as Carbon Dioxide Fixers

The energy yield of the light reactions is stored in ATP and NADPH. These molecules are used by the Calvin cycle reactions to reduce CO_2 to carbohydrate, namely G3P, which is then converted to all the organic molecules a plant needs.

During the first stage of the Calvin cycle, the enzyme RuBP carboxylase fixes CO_2 to RuBP, producing a 6-carbon molecule that immediately breaks down to two C_3 molecules. During the second stage, CO_2 (incorporated into an organic molecule) is reduced to carbohydrate (CH_2O). This step requires the NADPH and some of the ATP from the light reactions. For every three turns of the Calvin cycle, the net gain is one G3P molecule; the other five G3P molecules are used to re-form three molecules of RuBP, which also requires ATP. It takes two G3P molecules to make one glucose molecule.

7.5 Other Types of Photosynthesis

Plants have adapted ways other than the C3 process just described to photosynthesize in various environments. In C_4 plants, carbon dioxide is first fixed in mesophyll cells via PEPCase, is transported to a different location in bundle sheath cells, and then released to the Calvin cycle. PEPCase has an advantage over RuBP carboxylase because it doesn't participate in photorespiration. C_4 plants avoid the photores-

piration complication by dividing where carbon fixation occurs from where the Calvin cycle occurs.

CAM plants, which live in hot, dry environments, cannot leave their stomata open during the day, or they will die from loss of water. CAM plants fix carbon only at night, conserving water. Stores of CO_2 are released to the Calvin cycle during the day, when photosynthesis is possible. CAM plants avoid drying out by dividing when they bring in carbon dioxide from when they release it to the Calvin cycle.

Key Terms

absorption spectrum 124	chloroplast 121
ATP synthase 126	electron transport chain 125
autotroph 120	grana (sing., granum) 121
C_3 plant 130	heterotroph 120
C_4 plant 130	light reactions 122
Calvin cycle reactions 123	noncyclic pathway 124
CAM 131	photorespiration 130
carbon dioxide (CO_2)	photosynthesis 120
fixation 128	photosystem 124
carotenoid 124	RuBP carboxylase 128
chemiosmosis 126	stomata 121
climate change 127	stroma 121
chlorophyll 121	thylakoid 121

Assess

Reviewing This Chapter

1. Why is it proper to say that almost all living things are dependent on solar energy?   120
2. Name the two major components of chloroplasts, and associate each with one of two sets of reactions that occur during photosynthesis. How are the two sets of reactions related?   121–23
3. Write the overall equation of photosynthesis and associate each participant with either the light reactions or the Calvin cycle reactions.   122–23
4. Discuss the electromagnetic spectrum and the combined absorption spectrum of chlorophylls a and b and the carotenoids. Why is chlorophyll a green pigment, and the carotenoids a yellow-orange pigment?   124
5. Trace the noncyclic electron pathway, naming and explaining all the events that occur as the electrons move from water to $NADP^+$.   124–25
6. How is the thylakoid membrane organized? Name the main complexes in the membrane. Give a function for each.   126
7. Explain what is meant by chemiosmosis, and relate this process to the electron transport chain present in the thylakoid membrane.   126
8. Describe the three stages of the Calvin cycle. Which stage uses the ATP and NADPH from the light reactions?   128–29
9. Compare C_3 and C_4 photosynthesis, contrasting the actions of RuBP carboxylase and PEPCase.   130
10. Explain CAM photosynthesis, contrasting it to C_4 photosynthesis in terms of partitioning a pathway.   131

Testing Yourself

Choose the best answer for each question.

1. The absorption spectrum of chlorophyll
   a. is not the same as that of carotenoids.
   b. approximates the action spectrum of photosynthesis.
   c. explains why chlorophyll is a green pigment.
   d. shows that some colors of light are absorbed more than others.
   e. All of these are correct.

2. The final acceptor of electrons during the noncyclic electron pathway is
   a. PS I.
   b. PS II.
   c. ATP.
   d. $NADP^+$.
   e. water.

3. A photosystem contains
   a. pigments, a reaction center, and electron acceptors.
   b. ADP, Ⓟ, and hydrogen ions (H^+).
   c. protons, photons, and pigments.
   d. cytochromes only.
   e. Both b and c are correct.

For questions 4–8, match each item to those in the key. Use an answer more than once, if possible.

KEY:
   a. solar energy
   b. chlorophyll
   c. chemiosmosis
   d. Calvin cycle

4. light energy

5. ATP synthase

6. thylakoid membrane

7. green pigment

8. RuBP

For questions 9–11, indicate whether the statement is true (T) or false (F).

9. RuBP carboxylase is the enzyme that fixes carbon dioxide to RuBP in the Calvin cycle. _____

10. When 3PG becomes G3P during the light reactions, carbon dioxide is reduced to carbohydrate. _____

11. NADPH and ATP cycle between the Calvin cycle and the light reactions constantly. _____

12. The NADPH and ATP from the light reactions are used to
    a. split water.
    b. cause RuBP carboxylase to fix CO_2.
    c. re-form the photosystems.
    d. cause electrons to move along their pathways.
    e. convert 3PG to G3P.

13. Chemiosmosis
    a. depends on complexes in the thylakoid membrane.
    b. depends on an electrochemical gradient.
    c. depends on a difference in H^+ concentration between the thylakoid space and the stroma.
    d. results in ATP formation.
    e. All of these are correct.

14. The function of the light reactions is to
    a. obtain CO_2.
    b. make carbohydrate.
    c. convert light energy into a usable form of chemical energy.
    d. regenerate RuBP.

15. Label the following diagram of a chloroplast:

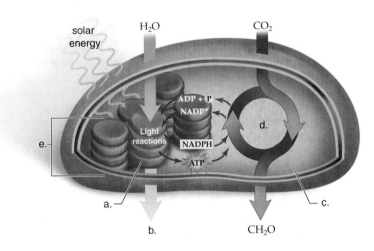

   f. The light reactions occur in which part of a chloroplast?
   g. The Calvin cycle reactions occur in which part of a chloroplast?

16. The oxygen given off by photosynthesis comes from
    a. H_2O.
    b. CO_2.
    c. glucose.
    d. RuBP.

17. The glucose formed by photosynthesis can be used by plants to make
    a. starch.
    b. cellulose.
    c. lipids and oils.
    d. proteins.
    e. All of these are correct.

18. The Calvin cycle reactions
    a. produce carbohydrate.
    b. convert one form of chemical energy into a different form of chemical energy.
    c. regenerate more RuBP.
    d. use the products of the light reactions.
    e. All of these are correct.

19. CAM photosynthesis
    a. is the same as C_4 photosynthesis.
    b. is an adaptation to cold environments in the Southern Hemisphere.
    c. is prevalent in desert plants that close their stomata during the day.
    d. occurs in plants that live in marshy areas.
    e. stands for chloroplasts and mitochondria.

20. C_4 photosynthesis
    a. is the same as C_3 photosynthesis because it takes place in chloroplasts.
    b. occurs in plants whose bundle sheath cells contain chloroplasts.
    c. takes place in plants such as wheat, rice, and oats.
    d. is an advantage when the weather is hot and dry.
    e. Both b and d are correct.

Engage

Thinking Scientifically

1. In 1882, T. W. Engelmann carried out an ingenious experiment to demostrate that chlorophyll absorbs light in the blue and red portions of the spectrum. He placed a single filament of a green alga in a drop of water on a microscope slide. Then he passed light through a prism and onto the string of algal cells. The slide also contained aerobic bacterial cells. After some time, he peered into the microscope and saw the bacteria clustered around the regions of the algal filament that were receiving blue light and red light, as shown in the illustration. Why do you suppose the bacterial cells were clustered in this manner?

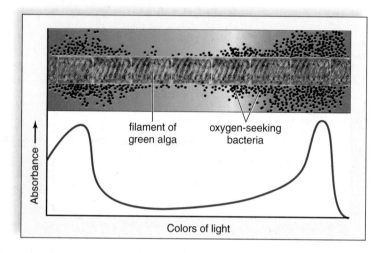

filament of green alga

oxygen-seeking bacteria

Absorbance

Colors of light

2. In the fall of the year, the leaves of many trees change from green to red or yellow. Two hypotheses can explain this color change: (a) In the fall, chlorophyll degenerates, and red or yellow pigments that were earlier masked by chlorophyll become apparent. (b) In the fall, red or yellow pigments are synthesized, and they mask the color of chlorophyll. How could you test these two hypotheses?

Bioethical Issue

The World's Food Supply

The Food and Agriculture Organization of the United Nations warns that the world's food supply is dwindling rapidly and food prices are soaring to historic levels. They estimate that approximately 1 billion people currently live in hunger. Their records show that the reserves of cereals are severely depleted, and presently only 12 weeks of the world's total consumption is stored, which is much less than the average of 18 weeks consumption in storage during the years 2000-2005. Only 8 weeks of corn are in storage compared to 11 weeks during this same time period. Various reasons are offered for a possible calamitous shortfall in the world's grain supplies in the near future. Possible causes are an ever larger world population, water shortages, climate change, and the growing costs of fertilizer. Also of concern is the converting of corn into ethanol as a fuel source, although this is becoming less of a concern as better fuel crops are developed. There are apparently no quick fixes to boost supplies. In years past, newly-developed hybrid crops led to enormous increases in yield per acre, but they also caused pollution problems that degrade the environment. Even if the promised biotech advances in drought, cold, and disease resistant crops are made, they will not immediately boost food supplies. Recent weather fluctuations, including widespread flooding and regional temperature fluctuations, are adding pressure to an already compressed food production situation. Possible solutions have been offered. Rather than exporting food to needy countries, it may be better to improve their ability to grow their own food, especially when you consider that transportation costs are soaring. Also, it would be beneficial to achieve zero population growth as quickly as possible and use renewable energy supplies other than converting corn to ethanol. The use of ethanol only contributes to climate change, which is expected to be a contributing factor to producing less grain. What do you think should be done to solve the expected shortage in the world's food supply, and how should your solution be brought about?

Triathlete racing past photosynthesizing trees and vegetation.

8

Cellular Respiration

CHAPTER OUTLINE

8.1 Cellular Respiration 136

8.2 Outside the Mitochondria: Glycolysis 138

8.3 Outside the Mitochondria: Fermentation 140

8.4 Inside the Mitochondria 142

8.5 Metabolic Pool 147

BEFORE YOU BEGIN

Before beginning this chapter, take a few moments to review the following discussions.

Figure 6.3 How does an ATP molecule store energy?

Figure 7.5 Where does the glucose that we metabolize come from?

Section 6.4 How are high energy electrons used to make energy for cellular work?

A triathlete racing a bike, a bacterium with undulating flagella, an ocelot climbing a tree, or a snail moving slowly to hide under a rock—each, including the tree, are making and using ATP. ATP is an ancient "molecular fossil." Its molecular structure, plus its presence in the first cell or cells that arose on planet Earth, accounts for its being the universal energy currency of cells.

ATP is unique among the cell's storehouse of chemicals; amino acids join to make a protein, and nucleotides join to make DNA or RNA, but ATP is singular and works alone. Whether you go skiing, take an aerobics class, or just hang out, ATP molecules provide the energy needed for nerve conduction, muscle contraction, and any other cellular process that requires energy. Cellular respiration, by which cells harvest the energy of organic compounds and convert it to ATP molecules, is the topic of this chapter. It's a process that requires many steps and involves the cytoplasm and the mitochondria, the powerhouses of the cell.

As you read through the chapter, think about the following questions:

1. How does the ATP molecule store chemical energy needed to run biological processes?
2. How are enzymes involved in regulating energy metabolism?
3. If nearly all life on Earth uses ATP, what does that indicate about its origins and biological importance?

FOLLOWING *the* THEMES

CHAPTER 8 CELLULAR RESPIRATION		
UNIT 1 THE CELL	**Evolution**	The majority of life on Earth uses cellular respiration, indicating an ancient biological lineage.
	Nature of Science	Athletes and trainers are constantly looking for ways to improve performance by boosting cellular respiration.
	Biological Systems	As an interconnected system of enzymatic processes, cellular respiration is only as fast as its slowest steps.

8.1 Cellular Respiration

Learning Outcomes

Upon completion of this section, you should be able to

1. Describe the overall reaction for glucose breakdown and show that it is a redox reaction.
2. Examine the role of NADH and FADH₂ redox reactions in cellular respiration.
3. Evaluate where each carbon molecule goes during cellular respiration for a 6-carbon glucose molecule.

Cellular respiration is the process by which cells acquire energy by breaking down nutrient molecules produced by photosynthesizers. Cellular respiration requires oxygen (O_2) and gives off carbon dioxide (CO_2), which, in effect, is the opposite of photosynthesis. In fact, it is the reason any animal, such as an ocelot or human, breathes (Fig. 8.1) and why plants also require a supply of oxygen. This chemical interaction between animals and plants is important because animals, like humans, breathe the oxygen made by photosynthesizers. Most often, cellular respiration involves the complete breakdown of glucose to carbon dioxide and water (H_2O):

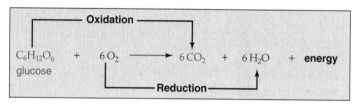

This equation shows that cellular respiration is an oxidation-reduction reaction. Recall that oxidation is the loss of electrons, and reduction is the gain of electrons; therefore, glucose has been oxidized and O_2 has been reduced. Also remember that a hydrogen atom consists of a hydrogen ion plus an electron ($H^+ + e^-$). Therefore, when hydrogen atoms are removed from glucose, so are electrons, and similarly, when hydrogen atoms are added to oxygen, so are electrons.

Glucose is a high-energy molecule, and its breakdown products, CO_2 and H_2O, are low-energy molecules. Therefore, as the equation shows, energy is released. This is the energy that will be used to produce ATP molecules. The cell carries out cellular respiration in order to build up ATP molecules.

The pathways of cellular respiration allow the energy within a glucose molecule to be released slowly so that ATP can be produced gradually. Cells would lose a tremendous amount of energy if glucose breakdown occurred all at once—most of the energy would become nonusable heat. The step-by-step breakdown of glucose to CO_2 and H_2O usually makes a maximum yield of 36 or 38 ATP molecules, dependent on conditions to be discussed later. The energy in these ATP molecules is equivalent to about 39% of the energy that was available in glucose. Even though it might seem less efficient, this conversion is more efficient than many others; for example, only between 20% and 30% of the energy within gasoline is converted to the motion of a car.

NAD⁺ and FAD

Cellular respiration involves many individual metabolic reactions, each one catalyzed by its own enzyme. Enzymes of particular significance are those that use **NAD⁺**, a coenzyme of oxidation-reduction (sometimes called a redox coenzyme). When a metabolite is oxidized, NAD⁺ accepts two electrons plus a hydrogen ion (H^+), and NADH results. The electrons received by NAD⁺ are high-energy electrons that are usually carried to the electron transport chain (see Fig. 6.12):

$$NAD^+ + 2\,e^- + H^+ \longrightarrow NADH$$

NAD⁺ can oxidize a metabolite by accepting electrons and can reduce a metabolite by giving up electrons. Only a small amount of NAD⁺ needs to be present in a cell, because each NAD⁺ molecule is used over and over again. **FAD,** another coenzyme of oxidation-reduction, is sometimes used instead of NAD⁺. FAD

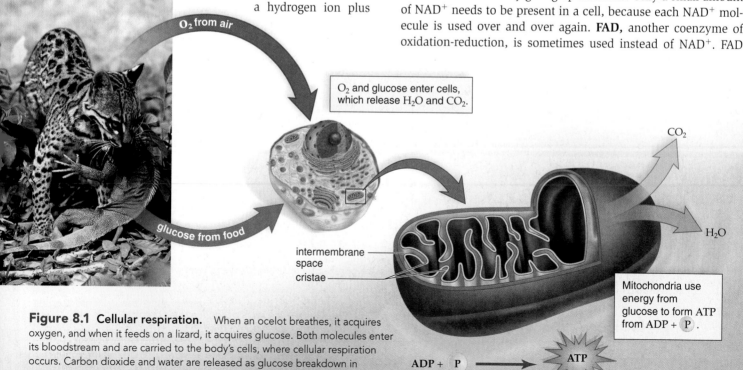

Figure 8.1 Cellular respiration. When an ocelot breathes, it acquires oxygen, and when it feeds on a lizard, it acquires glucose. Both molecules enter its bloodstream and are carried to the body's cells, where cellular respiration occurs. Carbon dioxide and water are released as glucose breakdown in mitochondria provides the energy for ATP production.

accepts two electrons and two hydrogen ions (H^+) to become $FADH_2$.

 Animation
How the
NAD⁺Works

Phases of Cellular Respiration

Cellular respiration involves four phases: glycolysis, the preparatory reaction, the citric acid cycle, and the electron transport chain (Fig. 8.2). Glycolysis takes place outside the mitochondria and does not require the presence of oxygen. Therefore, glycolysis is **anaerobic.** The other phases of cellular respiration take place inside the mitochondria, where oxygen is the final acceptor of electrons. Because they require oxygen, these phases are called **aerobic.**

During these phases, notice where CO_2 and H_2O, the end products of cellular respiration, and ATP, the main outcome of respiration, are produced.

- **Glycolysis** [Gk. *glycos*, sugar, and *lysis*, splitting] is the breakdown of glucose (a 6-carbon molecule) to two molecules of pyruvate (two 3-carbon molecules). Oxidation results in NADH and provides enough energy for the net gain of two ATP molecules.
- The **preparatory (prep) reaction** takes place in the matrix of the mitochondrion. Pyruvate is broken down from a 3-carbon (C_3) to a 2-carbon (C_2) acetyl group, and a 1-carbon CO_2 molecule is released. Since glycolysis ends with two molecules of pyruvate, the prep reaction occurs twice per glucose molecule.

- The **citric acid cycle** also takes place in the matrix of the mitochondrion. Each 2-carbon acetyl group matches up with a 4-carbon molecule, forming two 6-carbon citrate molecules. As citrate bonds are broken and oxidation occurs, NADH and $FADH_2$ are formed, and two CO_2 per citrate are released. The citric acid cycle is able to produce one ATP per turn. Because two acetyl groups enter the cycle per glucose molecule, the cycle turns twice.
- The **electron transport chain (ETC)** is a series of carriers on the cristae of the mitochondria. NADH and $FADH_2$ give up their high-energy electrons to the chain. Energy is released and captured as the electrons move from a higher-energy to a lower-energy state during each redox reaction. Later, this energy is used for the production of ATP by chemiosmosis. After oxygen receives electrons at the end of the chain, it combines with hydrogen ions (H^+) and becomes water (H_2O).

Pyruvate, the end product of glycolysis, is a pivotal metabolite; its further treatment depends on whether oxygen is available. If oxygen is available, pyruvate enters a mitochondrion and is broken down completely to CO_2 and H_2O as shown in the cellular respiration equation (p. 136). If oxygen is not available, pyruvate is further metabolized in the cytoplasm by an anaerobic process called **fermentation.** Fermentation results in a net gain of only two ATP per glucose molecule.

MP3
Cellular
Respiration

Check Your Progress   8.1

1. Explain the benefit of slow glucose breakdown rather than rapid breakdown during cellular respiration.
2. Describe the four phases of complete glucose breakdown, including which release CO_2 and which produce H_2O.

Figure 8.2 The four phases of complete glucose breakdown. The complete breakdown of glucose consists of four phases. Glycolysis in the cytoplasm produces pyruvate, which enters mitochondria if oxygen is available. The conversion reaction and the citric acid cycle that follow occur inside the mitochondria. Also, inside mitochondria, the electron transport chain receives the electrons that were removed from glucose breakdown products. Each stage generates electrons (e^-) from chemical breakdown and oxidation reactions. The theoretical yield per glucose is 36 to 38 ATP, depending on the particular cell.

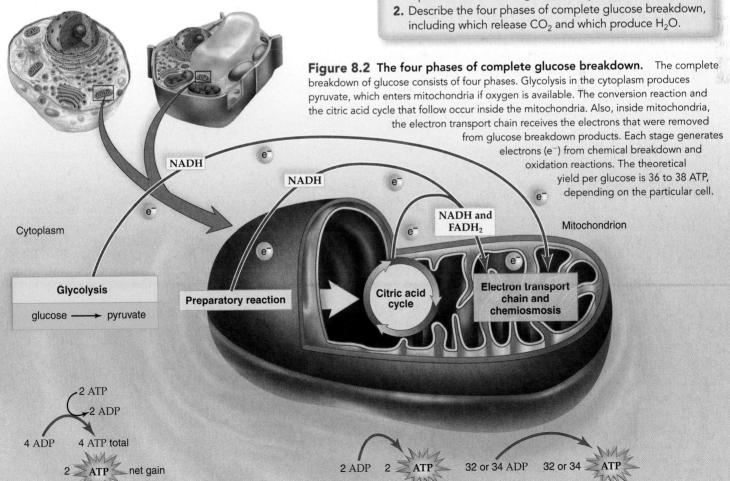

Cytoplasm

Mitochondrion

NADH

NADH

NADH and $FADH_2$

Glycolysis

glucose ⟶ pyruvate

Preparatory reaction

Citric acid cycle

Electron transport chain and chemiosmosis

2 ATP

2 ADP

4 ADP   4 ATP total

2 **ATP** net gain

2 ADP   2 **ATP**   32 or 34 ADP   32 or 34 **ATP**

8.2 Outside the Mitochondria: Glycolysis

Glycolysis, which takes place within the cytoplasm outside the mitochondria, is the breakdown of C_6 (6-carbon) glucose to two C_3 (3-carbon) pyruvate molecules. Since glycolysis occurs universally in organisms, it most likely evolved before the citric acid cycle and the electron transport chain. This may be why glycolysis occurs in the cytoplasm and does not require oxygen. There was no free oxygen in the early atmosphere of the Earth.

Glycolysis is series of ten reactions, and just as you would expect for a metabolic pathway, each step has its own enzyme. The pathway can be conveniently divided into the energy-investment step and the energy-harvesting steps. During the energy-investment step, ATP is used to "jump-start" glycolysis. During the energy-harvesting steps, four total ATP are made, producing 2 net ATP overall.

Energy-Investment Step

As glycolysis begins, two ATP are used to activate glucose by adding phosphate. Glucose eventually splits into two C_3 molecules known as G3P, the same molecule produced during photosynthesis. Each G3P has a phosphate group, each of which is acquired from an ATP molecule. From this point on, each C_3 molecule undergoes the same series of reactions.

Energy-Harvesting Step

Oxidation of G3P now occurs by the removal of electrons accompanied by hydrogen ions. In duplicate reactions, electrons are picked up by coenzyme NAD^+, which becomes

$$\text{NADH: } 2\ NAD^+ + 4\ e^- + 2\ H^+ \longrightarrow 2\ NADH$$

When O_2 is available, each NADH molecule carries two high-energy electrons to the electron transport chain and becomes NAD^+ again. In this way, NAD^+ is recycled and used again.

The addition of inorganic phosphate results in a high-energy phosphate group on each C_3 molecule. These phosphate groups are used to directly synthesize two ATP in the later steps of glycolysis. This is called **substrate-level ATP synthesis** (sometimes called substrate-level phosphorylation) because an enzyme passes a high-energy phosphate to ADP, and ATP results (Fig. 8.3). Notice that this is an example of coupling: An energy-releasing reaction is driving forward an energy-requiring reaction on the surface of the enzyme.

Oxidation occurs again, but by the removal of H_2O. Substrate-level ATP synthesis occurs again per each C_3, and two molecules

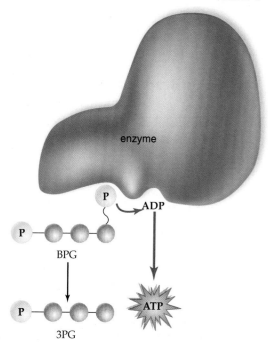

Figure 8.3 Substrate-level ATP synthesis. Substrates participating in the reaction are oriented on the enzyme. A phosphate group is transferred to ADP, producing one ATP molecule. During glycolysis (see Fig. 8.4), BPG is a C_3 substrate (each gray ball is a carbon atom) that gives up a phosphate group to ADP. This reaction occurs twice per glucose molecule.

of pyruvate result. Subtracting the two ATP that were used to get started, and the four ATP produced overall, there is a net gain of two ATP from glycolysis (Fig. 8.4).

Animation
How Glycolysis Works

Inputs and Outputs of Glycolysis

All together, the inputs and outputs of glycolysis are as follows:

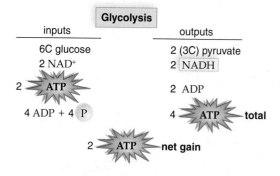

Notice that, so far, we have accounted for only two of the 36 to 38 ATP molecules that are theoretically possible when glucose is completely broken down to CO_2 and H_2O. When O_2 is available, the end product of glycolysis, pyruvate, enters the mitochondria, where it is metabolized. If O_2 is not available, fermentation, which is discussed next, occurs.

3D Animation
Glycolysis

Check Your Progress   8.2

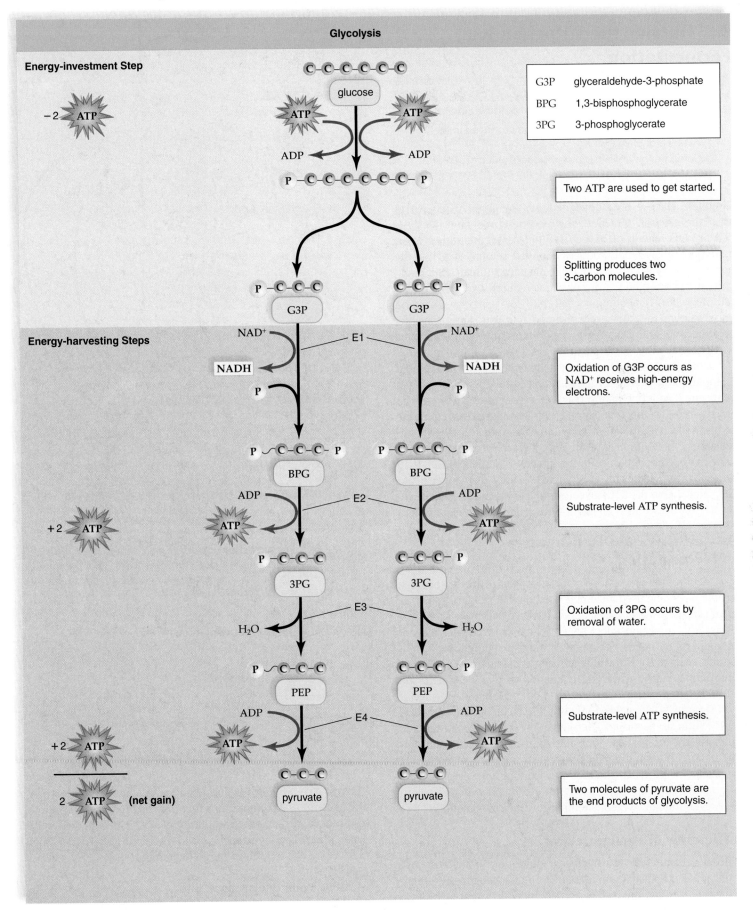

Figure 8.4 Glycolysis. This metabolic pathway begins with C₆ glucose (each gray ball is a carbon atom) and ends with two C₃ pyruvate molecules. Net gain of two ATP molecules can be calculated by subtracting those expended during the energy-investment step from those produced during the energy-harvesting steps. Each step is catalyzed by a specialized enzyme (E).

8.3 Outside the Mitochondria: Fermentation

Complete glucose breakdown requires an input of oxygen to keep the electron transport chain working. So how does the cell produce energy if oxygen is limited? **Fermentation** is an anaerobic process that produces a limited amount of ATP in the absence of oxygen. In animal cells, including human cells, pyruvate, the end product of glycolysis, is reduced by NADH to lactate (Fig. 8.5). Depending on their particular enzymes, bacteria vary as to whether they produce an organic acid, such as lactate, or an alcohol and CO_2. Yeasts are good examples of organisms that generate ethyl alcohol and CO_2 as a result of fermentation.

Why is it beneficial for pyruvate to be reduced when oxygen is not available? Because the cell still needs energy when oxygen is absent. The fermentation reaction regenerates NAD^+, which is required for the first step in the energy-harvesting phase of glycolyis. This NAD^+ is now "free" to return to the earlier reaction (see return arrow in Fig. 8.5) and become reduced once more. Although this process generates much less ATP than when oxygen is present and glucose is fully metabolized into CO_2 and H_2O in the ETC, glycolysis and substrate-level ATP synthesis produce enough energy for the cell to continue working.

Advantages and Disadvantages of Fermentation

As discussed in the Nature of Science feature in this chapter, people have long used anaerobic bacteria that produce lactate to create cheese, yogurt, and sauerkraut—even before we knew that bacteria were responsible! Other bacteria produce chemicals of industrial importance, including isopropanol, butyric acid, propionic acid, and acetic acid when they ferment. Yeasts, of course, are used to make breads rise. In addition, alcoholic fermentation is utilized to produce wine, beer, and other alcoholic beverages.

Despite its low yield of only two ATP made by substrate-level ATP synthesis, lactic acid fermentation is essential to certain animals and/or tissues. Typically, animals use lactic acid fermentation for a rapid burst of energy, such as a cheetah chasing a gazelle. Also, when muscles are working vigorously over a short period of time, lactic acid fermentation provides them with ATP, even though oxygen is temporarily in limited supply.

Efficiency of Fermentation

The two ATP produced per glucose during alcoholic fermentation and lactic acid fermentation are equivalent to 14.6 kcal. Complete glucose breakdown to CO_2 and H_2O represents a possible energy yield of 686 kcal per molecule. Therefore, the efficiency of fermentation is only 14.6 kcal/686 kcal × 100, or 2.1%

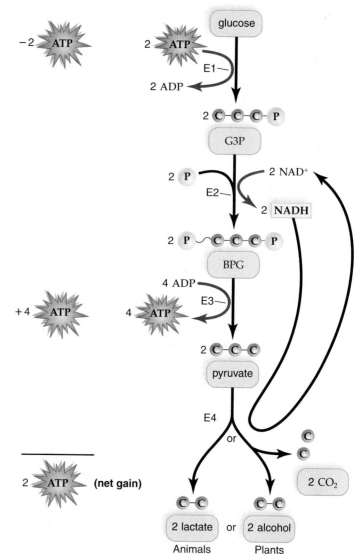

Figure 8.5 Fermentation. Fermentation consists of glycolysis followed by a reduction of pyruvate. This "frees" NAD^+ and it returns to the glycolytic pathway to pick up more electrons. As with glycolysis, each step is catalyzed by a specialized enzyme (E).

of the total possible for the complete breakdown of glucose. The inputs and outputs of fermentation are shown here:

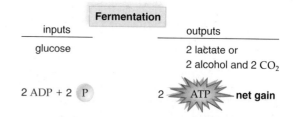

The two ATP produced by fermentation fall far short of the theoretical 36 or 38 ATP molecules that may be produced by cellular respiration. To achieve this number of ATP per glucose molecule, it is necessary to move on to the reactions and pathways that occur with oxygen in the mitochondria.

Check Your Progress 8.3

1. Describe the role of NADH in fermentation.

THEME Nature of Science

Fermentation Helps Produce Numerous Food Products

At the grocery store, you will find such items as bread, yogurt, soy sauce, pickles, and maybe even beer or wine (**Fig. 8A**). These are just a few of the many foods that are produced when microorganisms ferment (break down sugar in the absence of oxygen). Foods produced by fermentation last longer because the fermenting organisms have removed many of the nutrients that would attract other organisms. The products of fermentation can even be dangerous to the very organisms that produced them, as when yeasts are killed by the alcohol they produce.

Yeast Fermentation

Baker's yeast, *Saccharomyces cerevisiae*, is added to bread for the purpose of leavening—the dough rises when the yeasts give off CO_2. The ethyl alcohol produced by the fermenting yeast evaporates during baking. The many different varieties of sourdough breads obtain their leavening from a starter

composed of fermenting yeasts along with bacteria from the environment. Depending on the community of microorganisms in the starter, the flavor of the bread may range from sour and tangy, as in San Francisco–style sourdough, to a milder taste, such as that produced by most Amish friendship bread recipes.

Ethyl alcohol in beer and wine is produced when yeasts ferment carbohydrates. When yeasts ferment fruit carbohydrates, the end result is wine. If they ferment grain, beer results. A few specialized varieties of beer, such as traditional wheat beers, have a distinctive sour taste because they are produced with the assistance of lactic acid–producing bacteria, such as those of the genus *Lactobacillus*. Stronger alcoholic drinks (e.g., whiskey and vodka) require distillation to concentrate the alcohol content.

Bacteria that produce acetic acid, including *Acetobacter aceti*, spoil wine. These bacteria convert the alcohol in wine or cider to acetic acid (vinegar). Until the renowned nineteenth-century scientist Louis Pasteur invented the process of pasteurization, acetic acid bacteria commonly caused wine to spoil. Although today we generally associate the process of pasteurization with making milk safe to drink, it was originally developed to reduce bacterial contamination in wine so that limited acetic acid would be produced. The discovery of pasteurization is another example of how the pursuit of scientific knowledge can positively affect our lives.

Bacterial Fermentation

Yogurt, sour cream, and cheese are produced through the action of various lactic acid bacteria that cause milk to sour. Milk contains lactose, which these bacteria use as a carbohydrate source for fermentation. Yogurt, for example, is made by adding lactic acid bacteria, such as *Streptococcus thermophilus* and *Lactobacillus bulgaricus*, to milk and then incubating it to encourage the bacteria to convert the lactose. During the production of cheese, an enzyme called rennin must also be added to the milk to cause it to coagulate and become solid.

Old-fashioned brine cucumber pickles, sauerkraut, and kimchi are pickled vegetables produced by the action of acid-producing, fermenting bacteria that can survive in high-salt environments. Salt is used to draw liquid out of the vegetables and aid in their preservation. The bacteria need not be added to the vegetables, because they are already present on the surfaces of the plants.

Soy Sauce Production

Soy sauce is traditionally made by adding a mold, *Aspergillus*, and a combination of yeasts and fermenting bacteria to soybeans and wheat. The mold breaks down starch, supplying the fermenting microorganisms with sugar they can use to produce alcohol and organic acids.

As you can see from each of these examples, fermentation is a biologically and economically important process that scientists use for the betterment of our lives.

Questions to Consider:

1. How many products of fermentation do you consume daily?
2. What might everyday life be like without fermentation?

Figure 8A Products from fermentation. *Fermentation of different carbohydrates by microorganisms like bacteria and yeast helps produce the products shown.*

8.4 Inside the Mitochondria

Learning Outcomes

Upon completion of this section, you should be able to

1. Explain the fate of each carbon during the complete aerobic metabolism of glucose.
2. Contrast substrate-level phosphorylation and chemiosmosis as methods of ATP synthesis.
3. Describe how electron energy from redox reactions is used to create a proton gradient.

The preparatory (prep) reaction, the citric acid cycle, and the electron transport chain, which are needed for the complete breakdown of glucose, take place within the mitochondria. A **mitochondrion** has a double membrane with an intermembrane space (between the outer and inner membrane). Cristae are folds of inner membrane that jut out into the matrix, the innermost compartment, which is filled with a gel-like fluid (Fig. 8.6). Like a chloroplast, a mitochondrion is highly structured, and as such we would expect reactions to be located in particular parts of this organelle.

The enzymes that speed the prep reaction and the citric acid cycle are arranged in the matrix, and the electron transport chain is located in the cristae in a very organized manner.

Most of the ATP from cellular respiration is produced in mitochondria; therefore, mitochondria are often called the powerhouses of the cell.

The Preparatory Reaction

The **preparatory (prep) reaction** is so called because it converts products from glycolysis into products that enter the citric acid cycle. In this reaction, the C_3 pyruvate is converted to a C_2 acetyl group and CO_2 is given off. This is an oxidation-reaction in which electrons are removed from pyruvate by NAD^+, and NADH is formed. One prep reaction occurs per pyruvate, so altogether, the prep reaction occurs twice per glucose molecule:

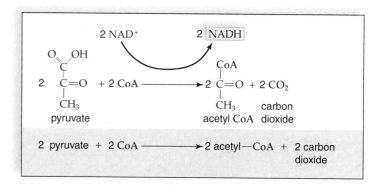

$$2 \text{ pyruvate } + 2 \text{ CoA} \longrightarrow 2 \text{ acetyl—CoA } + 2 \text{ carbon dioxide}$$

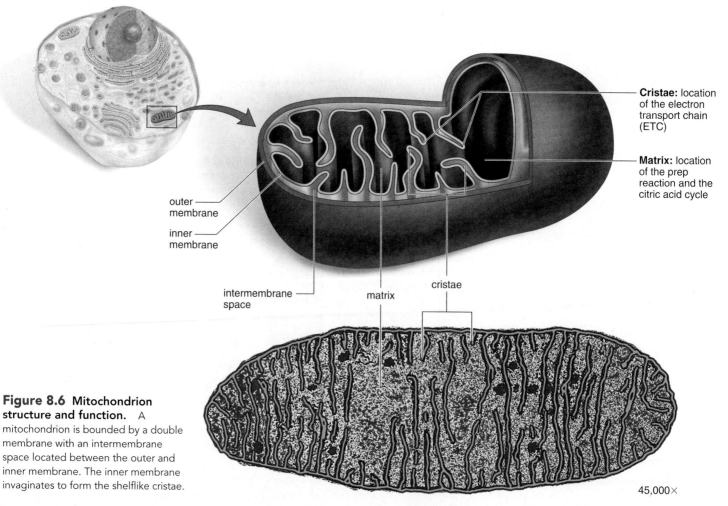

Figure 8.6 Mitochondrion structure and function. A mitochondrion is bounded by a double membrane with an intermembrane space located between the outer and inner membrane. The inner membrane invaginates to form the shelflike cristae.

outer membrane

inner membrane

intermembrane space

matrix

cristae

Cristae: location of the electron transport chain (ETC)

Matrix: location of the prep reaction and the citric acid cycle

45,000×

The C_2 acetyl group is combined with a molecule known as CoA. CoA will carry the acetyl group to the citric acid cycle in the mitochondrial matrix. The two NADH carry electrons to the electron transport chain. What about the CO_2? In vertebrates, such as ourselves, CO_2 freely diffuses out of cells into the blood, which transports it to the lungs where it is exhaled.

Citric Acid Cycle

The **citric acid cycle** is a cyclical metabolic pathway located in the matrix of mitochondria (Fig. 8.7). The citric acid cycle is also known as the Krebs cycle, after Hans Krebs, the chemist who worked out the fundamentals of the process in the 1930s.

Animation
How the Krebs Cycle Works

At the start of the citric acid cycle, the (C_2) acetyl group carried by CoA joins with a C_4 molecule, and a C_6 citrate molecule results. During the cycle, oxidation occurs when electrons are accepted by NAD^+ in three instances and by FAD in one instance. Therefore, three NADH and one $FADH_2$ are formed as a result of one turn of the citric acid cycle. Also, the acetyl group received from the prep reaction is oxidized to two CO_2 molecules. Substrate-level ATP synthesis is also an important event of the citric acid cycle. In substrate-level ATP synthesis, you will recall, an enzyme passes a high-energy phosphate to ADP, and ATP results.

Because the citric acid cycle turns twice for each original glucose molecule, the inputs and outputs of the citric acid cycle per glucose molecule are as follows:

Citric acid cycle	
inputs	outputs
2 (2C) acetyl groups	4 CO_2
6 NAD^+	6 NADH
2 FAD	2 $FADH_2$
2 ADP + 2 P	2 ATP

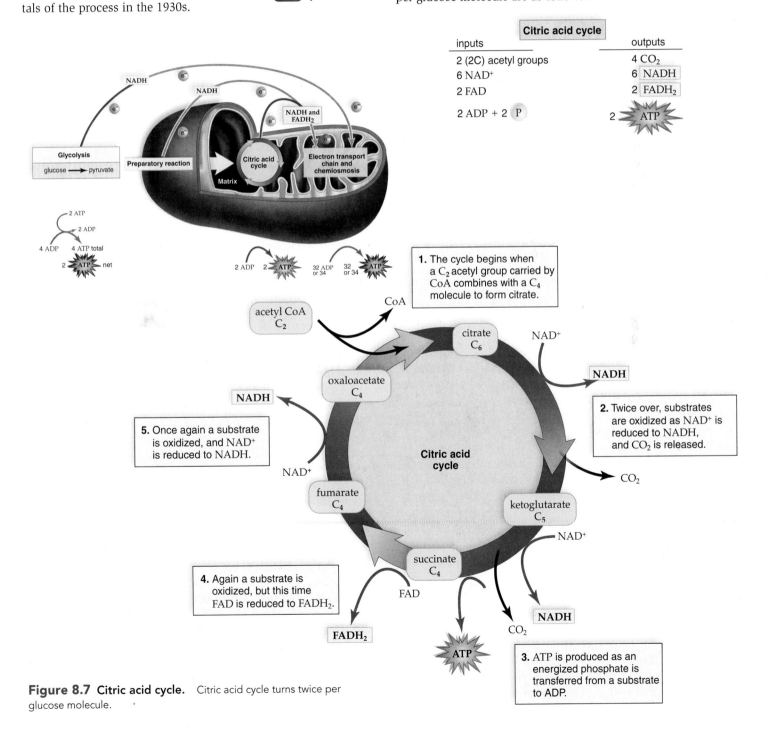

Figure 8.7 Citric acid cycle. Citric acid cycle turns twice per glucose molecule.

Production of CO₂

The six carbon atoms originally located in a glucose molecule have now become CO_2. The prep reaction produces the first two CO_2, and the citric acid cycle produces the last four CO_2 per glucose molecule. We have already mentioned that this is the CO_2 humans and other animals breathe out.

3D Animation
The Citric Acid Cycle

Thus far, we have broken down glucose to CO_2 and hydrogen atoms. Recall that, as bonds are broken and glucose gets converted to CO_2, energy in the form of high energy electrons is released. NADH and $FADH_2$ capture those high-energy electrons and carry them to the electron transport chain, as discussed next.

Electron Transport Chain

The **electron transport chain (ETC),** located in the cristae of the mitochondria and the plasma membrane of aerobic prokaryotes, is a series of carriers that pass electrons from one to the other. The high-energy electrons that enter the electron transport chain are carried by NADH and $FADH_2$. Figure 8.8 is arranged to show that high-energy electrons enter the chain, and low-energy electrons leave the chain.

Members of the Chain

When NADH gives up its electrons, it becomes oxidized to NAD^+, and when $FADH_2$ gives up its electrons, it becomes oxidized to FAD. The next carrier gains the electrons and is reduced. This oxidation-reduction reaction starts the process, and each of the carriers, in turn, becomes reduced and then oxidized as the electrons move down the chain.

Many of the redox carriers are cytochrome molecules. A **cytochrome** is a protein that has a tightly bound heme group with a central atom of iron, the same as hemoglobin does. When the iron accepts electrons, it becomes reduced, and when iron gives them up, it becomes oxidized. As the pair of electrons is passed from carrier to carrier, energy is captured and eventually used to form ATP molecules. A number of poisons, such as cyanide, cause death by binding to and blocking the function of cytochromes.

Animation
Electron Transport System and ATP Synthesis

What is the role of oxygen in cellular respiration and the reason we breathe to take in oxygen? Oxygen is the final acceptor of electrons from the electron transport chain. Oxygen receives the energy-spent electrons from the last of the carriers (i.e., cytochrome oxidase). After receiving electrons, oxygen combines with hydrogen ions, and water forms:

$$\tfrac{1}{2}O_2 + 2\,e^- + 2\,H^+ \longrightarrow H_2O$$

The critical role of oxygen as the final acceptor of electrons during cellular respiration is exemplified by noting that if oxygen is not present, the chain does not function, and no ATP is produced by mitochondria. The limited capacity of the body to form ATP in a way that does not involve the electron transport chain means that death eventually results if oxygen is not available.

Cycling of Carriers

When NADH delivers high energy electrons to the first carrier of the electron transport chain, enough energy is captured by the time the electrons are received by O_2 to permit the production of three ATP molecules. When $FADH_2$ delivers high-energy electrons to the electron transport chain, two ATP are produced.

Once NADH has delivered electrons to the electron transport chain and becomes NAD^+, it is able to return and pick up more hydrogen atoms. The reuse of coenzymes increases cellular efficiency because the cell does not have to constantly make new NAD^+; it simply recycles what is already there.

The Cristae of a Mitochondrion and Chemiosmosis

The carriers of the electron transport chain and the proteins involved with ATP synthesis are spatially arranged on the cristae of mitochondria. Their sequential arrangement on the cristae allows the production of ATP to occur.

The ETC Pumps Hydrogen Ions.   Essentially, the electron transport chain consists of three protein complexes and two carriers. The three protein complexes include NADH-Q reductase complex, the cytochrome reductase complex, and cytochrome oxidase complex. The two other carriers that transport electrons between the complexes are coenzyme Q and cytochrome c (Fig. 8.8).

Animation
Proton Pump

We have already seen that the members of the electron transport chain accept electrons, which they pass from one to the other via redox reactions. So what happens to the hydrogen ions (H^+) carried by NADH and $FADH_2$? The complexes of the electron transport chain use the energy released during redox reactions to pump these hydrogen ions from the matrix into the intermembrane space of a mitochondrion.

The vertical arrows in Figure 8.8 show that the protein complexes of the electron transport chain all pump H^+ into the intermembrane space. Energy obtained from electron passage is needed because H^+ ions are pumped and actively transported against their gradient. This means the few H^+ ions in the matrix will be moved to the intermembrane space, where there are already many H^+ ions. Just as the walls of a dam hold back water, allowing it to collect, so do cristae hold back hydrogen ions. Eventually, a strong electrochemical gradient develops; about ten times as many H^+ are found in the intermembrane space as are present in the matrix.

Animation
Electron Transport System and ATP Synthesis

The ATP Synthase Complex Produces ATP.   The ATP synthase complex can be likened to the gates of a dam. When the gates of a hydroelectric dam are opened, water rushes through, and electricity (energy) is produced. Similarly, when H^+ flows down a gradient from the intermembrane space into the matrix, the enzyme ATP synthase synthesizes ATP from ADP $+$ Ⓟ. This process

3D Animation
Electron Transport Chain

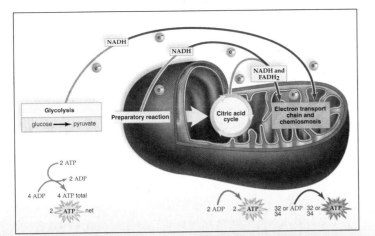

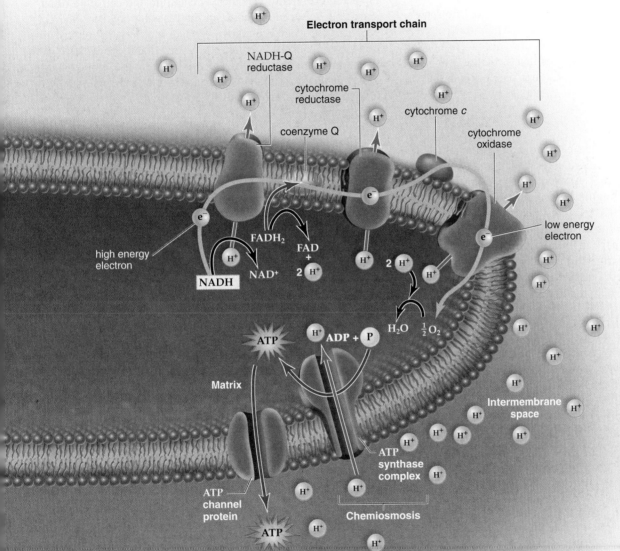

Figure 8.8 Organization and function of the electron transport chain. The electron transport chain is located in the mitochondrial cristae. NADH and FADH₂ bring electrons to the electron transport chain. As electrons move from one protein complex to the other via redox reactions, energy is used to pump hydrogen ions (H⁺) from the matrix into the intermembrane space. As hydrogen ions flow down a concentration gradient from the intermembrane space into the mitochondrial matrix, ATP is synthesized by the enzyme ATP synthase. For every pair of electrons that enters by way of NADH, three ATP result. For every pair of electrons that enters by way of FADH₂, two ATP result. Oxygen, the final acceptor of the electrons, becomes a part of water. ATP leaves the matrix by way of a channel protein.

is called **chemiosmosis** because ATP production is tied to the establishment of an H⁺ gradient.

Once formed, ATP moves out of mitochondria and is used to perform cellular work, during which it breaks down to ADP and Ⓟ. These molecules are then returned to mitochondria for recycling. At any given time, the amount of ATP in a human would sustain life for only about a minute; therefore, ATP synthase must constantly produce ATP. It is estimated that mitochondria produce our body weight in ATP every day.

Active Tissues Contain More Mitochondria. Active tissues, such as muscles, require greater amounts of ATP and have more mitochondria than less active cells. When a burst of energy is required, however, muscles still utilize fermentation.

As an example of the relative amounts of ATP, consider that the dark meat of chickens, namely the thigh meat, contains more mitochondria than the white meat of the breast. This suggests that chickens mainly walk or run, rather than fly, about the barnyard.

Energy Yield from Glucose Metabolism

Figure 8.9 calculates the theoretical ATP yield for the complete breakdown of glucose to CO_2 and H_2O during cellular respiration. Notice that the diagram includes the number of ATP produced directly by glycolysis and the citric acid cycle (to the left), as well as the number produced as a result of electrons passing down the electron transport chain (to the right). A maximum of between 32 to 34 ATP molecules may be produced by the electron transport chain.

Substrate-Level ATP Synthesis

Per glucose molecule, there is a net gain of two ATP from glycolysis, which takes place in the cytoplasm. The citric acid cycle, which occurs in the matrix of mitochondria, accounts for two ATP per glucose molecule. This means that a total of four ATP are formed by substrate-level ATP synthesis outside the electron transport chain.

ETC and Chemiosmosis

Most ATP is produced by the electron transport chain and chemiosmosis. Per glucose molecule, ten NADH and two $FADH_2$ take electrons to the electron transport chain. For each NADH formed *inside* the mitochondria by the citric acid cycle, three ATP result, but for each $FADH_2$, only two ATP are produced. Figure 8.8 explains the reason for this difference: $FADH_2$ delivers its electrons to the transport chain after NADH, and therefore these electrons do not participate in as many redox reactions and don't pump as many H^+ as NADH. Therefore, $FADH_2$ cannot account for as much ATP production.

What about the ATP yield per NADH generated *outside* the mitochondria by the glycolytic pathway? In some cells, NADH cannot cross mitochondrial membranes, but a "shuttle" mechanism allows its electrons to be delivered to the electron transport chain inside the mitochondria. The cost to the cell is one ATP for each NADH that is shuttled to the ETC. This reduces the overall count of ATP produced as a result of glycolysis, in some cells, to four instead of six ATP.

Efficiency of Cellular Respiration

It is interesting to calculate how much of the energy in a glucose molecule eventually becomes available to the cell. The difference in energy content between the reactants (glucose and O_2) and the products (CO_2 and H_2O) is 686 kcal. An ATP phosphate bond has an energy content of 7.3 kcal, and 36 of these are potentially produced during glucose breakdown; 36 phosphates are equivalent to a total of 263 kcal. Therefore, 263/686, or 39%, of the available energy is usually transferred from glucose to ATP. The rest of the energy is lost in the form of heat.

3D Animation Summary of Cellular Respiration

In the next section, we consider how cellular respiration fits into metabolism as a whole.

Check Your Progress 8.4

1. Explain when carbon is converted from glucose into carbon dioxide during cellular respiration.
2. Examine which processes during glucose breakdown produce the most ATP.
3. Compare the function of the mitochondrial inner membrane to a hydroelectric dam.

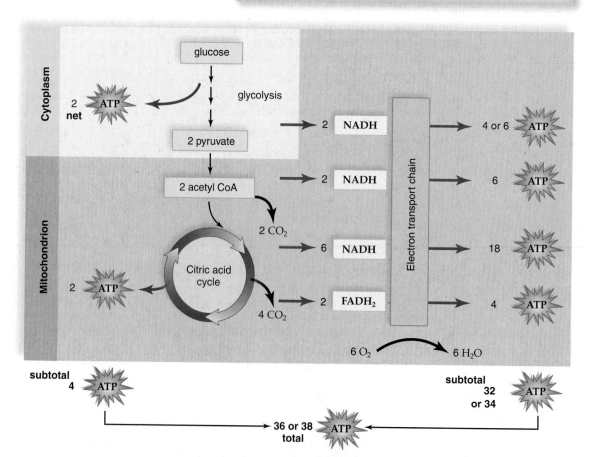

Figure 8.9 Accounting of energy yield per glucose molecule breakdown. Substrate-level ATP synthesis during glycolysis and the citric acid cycle accounts for 4 ATP. The electron transport chain accounts for 32 or 34 ATP, making the theoretical grand total of ATP between 36 and 38 ATP. Other factors may reduce the efficiency of cellular respiration. For example, cells differ as to the delivery of the electrons from NADH generated outside the mitochondria. If they are delivered by a shuttle mechanism to the start of the electron transport chain, 6 ATP result; otherwise, 4 ATP result.

8.5 Metabolic Pool

Learning Outcomes

Upon completion of this section, you should be able to

1. Compare the pathways of carbohydrate, fat, and protein catabolism.
2. Explain how the structure of mitochondria and chloroplasts enable a flow of energy through living things.

Key metabolic pathways routinely draw from pools of particular substrates needed to synthesize or degrade larger molecules. Substrates like the end product of glycolysis, pyruvate, exist as a pool that is continuously affected by changes in cellular and environmental conditions (Fig. 8.10). Degradative reactions, termed **catabolism**, that break down molecules must be dynamically balanced with constructive reactions, or **anabolism**. For example, catabolic breakdown of fats will occur when insufficient carbodydrate is present; this breakdown adds to the **metabolic pool** of pyruvate. When energy needs to be stored as fat, pyruvate is taken from the pool. This dynamic balance of catabolism and anabolism is essential to optimal cellular function.

Catabolism

We already know that glucose is broken down during cellular respiration. However, other molecules like fats and proteins can also be broken down as necessary. When a fat is used as an energy source, it breaks down to glycerol and three fatty acids. As Figure 8.10 indicates, glycerol can be converted to pyruvate and enter glycolysis. The fatty acids are converted to 2-carbon acetyl CoA that enters the citric acid cycle. An 18-carbon fatty acid results in nine acetyl CoA molecules. Calculation shows that respiration of these can produce a total of 108 ATP molecules. This is why fats are an efficient form of stored energy—the three long fatty acid chains per fat molecule can produce considerable ATP when needed.

Proteins are less frequently used as an energy source, but are available as necessary. The carbon skeleton of amino acids can enter glycolysis, be converted to acetyl groups, or enter the citric acid cycle at some other juncture. The carbon skeleton is produced in the liver when an amino acid undergoes **deamination**, or the removal of the amino group. The amino group becomes ammonia (NH_3), which enters the urea cycle and becomes part of urea, the primary excretory product of humans. Just where the carbon skeleton begins degradation depends on the length of the *R* group, since this determines the number of carbons left after deamination.

Anabolism

We have already mentioned that the building of new molecules requires ATP produced during breakdown of molecules. These catabolic reactions also provide the basic components used to build new molecules. For example, excessive carbohydrate intake can result in the formation of fat. Extra G3P from glycolysis can be converted to glycerol, and acetyl groups from

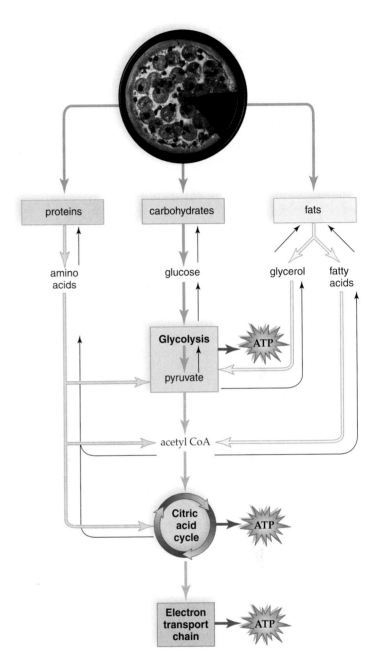

Figure 8.10 The metabolic pool concept. Carbohydrates, fats, and proteins can be used as energy sources, and their monomers (carbohydrates and proteins) or subunits (fats) enter degradative pathways at specific points. Catabolism produces molecules that can also be used for anabolism of other compounds.

glycolysis can be joined to form fatty acids, which in turn are used to synthesize fat. This explains why you gain weight from eating too much candy, ice cream, or cake.

Some substrates of the citric acid cycle can be converted to amino acids through transamination—the transfer of an amino group to an organic acid, forming a different amino acid. Plants are able to synthesize all of the amino acids they need. Animals, however, lack some of the enzymes necessary for synthesis of all amino acids. Adult humans, for example, can synthesize 11 of the common amino acids, but they cannot synthesize the other 9. The amino acids that cannot be synthesized must be supplied by the diet; they are called the essential amino acids. (The amino acids that can be synthesized are called nonessential.) It is quite possible for animals to suffer from protein deficiency if their diets do not contain adequate quantities of all the essential amino acids.

The Energy Organelles Revisited

The equation for photosynthesis in a chloroplast is opposite to that of cellular respiration in a mitochondrion (Fig. 8.11):

$$\text{energy} + 6\,CO_2 + 6\,H_2O \underset{\text{cellular respiration}}{\overset{\text{photosynthesis}}{\rightleftharpoons}} C_6H_{12}O_6 + 6\,O_2$$

While you were studying photosynthesis and cellular respiration, you may have noticed a remarkable similarity in the structural organization of chloroplasts and mitochondria. Through evolution, all organisms are related, and the similar organization of these organelles suggests that they may be related also. The two organelles carry out related but opposite processes:

1. *Use of membrane.* In a chloroplast, an inner membrane forms the thylakoids of the grana. In a mitochondrion, an inner membrane forms the convoluted cristae.
2. *Electron transport chain (ETC).* An ETC is located on the thylakoid membrane of chloroplasts and the cristae of mitochondria. In chloroplasts, the electrons passed down the ETC have been energized by the Sun; in mitochondria, energized electrons have been removed from glucose and glucose products. In both, the ETC establishes an electrochemical gradient of H^+ with subsequent ATP production by chemiosmosis.
3. *Enzymes.* In a chloroplast, the stroma contains the enzymes of the Calvin cycle and in mitochondria, the matrix contains the enzymes of the citric acid cycle. In the Calvin cycle, NADPH and ATP are used to reduce carbon dioxide to a carbohydrate. In the citric acid cycle, the oxidation of glucose products produces NADH and ATP.

Flow of Energy

The ultimate source of energy for producing a carbohydrate in chloroplasts is the Sun; the ultimate goal of cellular respiration in a mitochondrion is the conversion of carbohydrate energy into that of ATP molecules. Therefore, energy flows from the Sun, through chloroplasts to carbohydrates, and then through mitochondria to ATP molecules.

This flow of energy maintains biological organization at all levels from molecules, organisms, and ultimately the biosphere. In keeping with the energy laws, some energy is lost with each chemical transformation, and eventually, the solar energy captured by plants is lost in the form of heat. Therefore, living things depend on a continual input of solar energy.

Although energy flows through organisms, chemicals cycle within natural systems. Aerobic organisms utilize the carbohydrate and oxygen produced by chloroplasts to generate energy

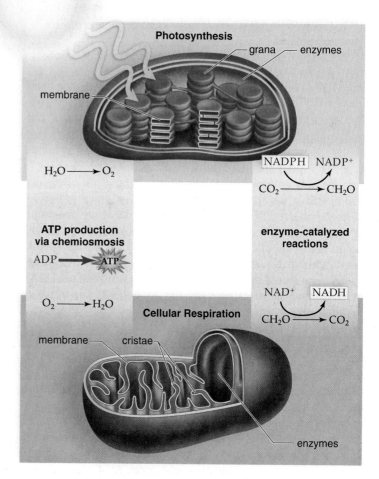

Figure 8.11 Photosynthesis versus cellular respiration.
In photosynthesis (top), water is oxidized and oxygen is released; in cellular respiration (bottom), oxygen is reduced to water. Both processes have an electron transport chain located within membranes (the grana of chloroplasts and the cristae of mitochondria), where ATP is produced by chemiosmosis. Both have enzyme-catalyzed reactions within the semifluid interior. In photosynthesis, CO_2 is reduced to a carbohydrate; in cellular respiration, a carbohydrate is oxidized to CO_2.

within the mitochondria to sustain life. Likewise, the carbon dioxide produced by mitochondria returns to chloroplasts to be used in the manufacture of carbohydrates, producing oxygen as a byproduct. Therefore, chloroplasts and mitochondria are instrumental in not only allowing a flow of energy through living things, but also permitting a cycling of chemicals.

Check Your Progress   8.5

1. Evaluate how catabolism and anabolism are balanced within a cell.
2. Compare the structure and function of chloroplasts and mitochondria.

CONNECTING *the* CONCEPTS *with the* THEMES

Evolution

- "Structure equals function" is a concept exemplified by chloroplasts and mitochondria. Their membranous structure has evolved over millions of years and is well suited to the isolation of enzymatic reactions in the interior from complexes located on the membrane.
- As high-energy electrons make energy available, these complexes pump H^+ ions into the thylakoid space of chloroplasts and the intermembrane space of mitochondria.
- When H^+ flows down its concentration gradient through ATP synthase complexes, ATP synthesis results.
- ATP production in mitochondria is traceable back to the ability of chloroplasts to capture solar energy.

Nature of Science

- Scientists who research athletic performance may focus their investigations on ways to manipulate energy metabolism.
- Understanding energy metabolism like respiration may have positive effects, such as helping people with chronic fatigue, or negative effects, such as overconsumption of substances like energy drinks.
- Ongoing research in cellular respiration may produce new medicines that help patients better cope with the negative side effects of diseases like cancer.

Biological Systems

- Chloroplasts and mitochondria play a significant role in metabolism and their enzyme-requiring pathways permit a flow of energy through all living things.
- The energy transformations that take place in these organelles results in a loss of energy in the form of heat. Therefore, all organisms are in need of a constant supply of energy, which they get from their food.
- Food is ultimately produced by plants, which have the ability to capture solar energy. Photosynthesizing organisms form the basis of most food chains on Earth.

Media Study Tools

www.mhhe.com/maderbiology11

Enhance your study of this chapter with study tools and practice tests. Also ask your instructor about the resources available through ConnectPlus, including the media-rich eBook, interactive learning tools, and animations.

3D Animation
Cellular
Respiration

For an interactive exploration of the processes of cellular respiration, take a moment to watch McGraw-Hill's new 3D animation on cellular respiration.

Summarize

8.1 Cellular Respiration

Cellular respiration, during which glucose is completely broken down to CO_2 and H_2O, consists of four phases: glycolysis, the prep reaction, the citric acid cycle, and the passage of electrons along the electron transport chain. Oxidation of substrates involves the removal of hydrogen atoms ($H^+ + e^-$), usually by redox coenzymes. NAD^+ becomes NADH, and FAD becomes $FADH_2$.

8.2 Outside the Mitochondria: Glycolysis

Glycolysis, the breakdown of glucose to two molecules of pyruvate, is a series of enzymatic reactions that occurs in the cytoplasm and is anaerobic. Breakdown releases enough energy to immediately give a net gain of two ATP by substrate-level ATP synthesis and the production of 2 NADH.

8.3 Outside the Mitochondria: Fermentation

Fermentation involves glycolysis followed by the reduction of pyruvate by NADH either to lactate (animals) or to alcohol (yeast) and carbon dioxide (CO_2). The reduction process "frees" NAD^+ so that it can accept more hydrogen atoms from glycolysis.

Although fermentation results in only two ATP molecules, it still serves a purpose. Many of the products of fermentation are used in the baking and brewing industries. In vertebrates, it provides a quick burst of ATP energy for short-term, strenuous muscular activity. The accumulation of lactate puts the individual in oxygen debt because oxygen is needed when lactate is completely metabolized to CO_2 and H_2O.

8.4 Inside the Mitochondria

When oxygen is available, pyruvate from glycolysis enters the mitochondrion, where the prep reaction takes place. During this reaction, oxidation occurs as CO_2 is removed from pyruvate. NAD^+ is reduced, and CoA receives the C_2 acetyl group that remains. Because the reaction must take place twice per glucose molecule, two NADH result.

The acetyl group enters the citric acid cycle, a cyclical series of reactions located in the mitochondrial matrix. Complete oxidation follows, as two CO_2 molecules, three NADH molecules, and one $FADH_2$ molecule are formed. The cycle also produces one ATP molecule. The entire cycle must turn twice per glucose molecule.

The final stage of glucose breakdown involves the electron transport chain located in the cristae of the mitochondria. The electrons received from NADH and $FADH_2$ are passed down a chain of carriers until they are finally received by oxygen, which combines with H^+ to produce water. As the electrons pass down the chain, energy is captured and stored for ATP production.

The cristae of mitochondria contain complexes of the electron transport chain that not only pass electrons from one to the other but also pump H$^+$ into the intermembrane space, setting up an electrochemical gradient. When H$^+$ flows down this gradient through an ATP synthase complex, energy is captured and used to form ATP molecules from ADP and $\textcircled{P}$. This is ATP synthesis by chemiosmosis.

Of the 36 or 38 ATP formed by complete glucose breakdown, four are the result of substrate-level ATP synthesis and the rest are produced as a result of the electron transport chain. For most NADH molecules that donate electrons to the electron transport chain, three ATP molecules are produced. However, in some cells, each NADH formed in the cytoplasm results in only two ATP molecules because a shuttle, rather than NADH, takes electrons through the mitochondrial membrane. FADH$_2$ results in the formation of only two ATP because its electrons enter the electron transport chain at a lower energy level.

8.5 Metabolic Pool

Carbohydrate, protein, and fat can be metabolized by entering the degradative pathways at different locations. These pathways also provide metabolites needed for the anabolism of various important substances. Therefore, catabolism and anabolism both use the same pools of metabolites.

Similar to the metabolic pool concept, photosynthesis and cellular respiration can be compared. For example, both utilize an ETC and chemiosmosis. As a result of the ETC in chloroplasts, water is split, while in mitochondria, water is formed. The enzymatic reactions in chloroplasts reduce CO$_2$ to a carbohydrate, while the enzymatic reactions in mitochondria oxidize carbohydrate with the release of CO$_2$.

Key Terms

aerobic 137	FAD 136
anabolism 147	fermentation 137, 140
anaerobic 137	glycolysis 137, 138
catabolism 147	metabolic pool 147
cellular respiration 136	mitochondrion 142
chemiosmosis 145	NAD$^+$ 136
citric acid cycle 137, 143	preparatory (prep)
cytochrome 144	reaction 137, 142
deamination 147	substrate-level
electron transport chain	ATP synthesis 138
(ETC) 137, 144	

Assess

Reviewing This Chapter

1. What is the overall chemical equation for the complete breakdown of glucose to CO$_2$ and H$_2$O? Explain how this is an oxidation-reduction reaction.   136
2. What are NAD$^+$ and FAD? What are their functions?   136–37
3. Briefly describe the four phases of cellular respiration.   137
4. What are the main events of glycolysis? How is ATP formed?   138–39
5. What is fermentation, and how does it differ from glycolysis? Mention the benefit of pyruvate reduction during fermentation. What types of organisms carry out lactic acid fermentation, and what types carry out alcoholic fermentation?   140–41
6. Give the substrates and products of the prep reaction. Where does it take place?   142–43
7. What are the main events of the citric acid cycle?   143
8. What is the electron transport chain, and what are its functions?   144–46
9. Describe the organization of protein complexes within the cristae. Explain how the complexes are involved in ATP production.   145
10. Calculate the theoretical energy yield of glycolysis and complete glucose breakdown. Compare the yields from substrate-level ATP synthesis and from the electron transport chain.   146
11. Give examples to support the concept of the metabolic pool.   147
12. Compare the structure and function of chloroplasts and mitochondria. Explain the flow of energy concept.   148

Testing Yourself

Choose the best answer for each question.

For questions 1–8, identify the pathway involved by matching each description to the terms in the key.

KEY:
  a. glycolysis
  b. citric acid cycle
  c. electron transport chain

1. carbon dioxide (CO$_2$) given off
2. water (H$_2$O) formed
3. G3P
4. NADH becomes NAD$^+$
5. pump H$^+$
6. cytochrome carriers
7. pyruvate
8. FAD becomes FADH$_2$
9. The prep reaction
    a. connects glycolysis to the citric acid cycle.
    b. gives off CO$_2$.
    c. uses NAD$^+$.
    d. results in an acetyl group.
    e. All of these are correct.
10. The greatest contributor of electrons to the electron transport chain is
    a. oxygen.
    b. glycolysis.
    c. the citric acid cycle.
    d. the prep reaction.
    e. fermentation.
11. Substrate-level ATP synthesis takes place in
    a. glycolysis and the citric acid cycle.
    b. the electron transport chain and the prep reaction.
    c. glycolysis and the electron transport chain.
    d. the citric acid cycle and the prep reaction.
    e. Both b and d are correct.
12. Which of these is not true of fermentation?
    a. net gain of only two ATP
    b. occurs in cytoplasm
    c. NADH donates electrons to electron transport chain
    d. begins with glucose
    e. carried on by yeast

13. Fatty acids are broken down to
    a. pyruvate molecules, which take electrons to the electron transport chain.
    b. acetyl groups, which enter the citric acid cycle.
    c. amino acids, which excrete ammonia.
    d. glycerol, which is found in fats.
    e. All of these are correct.

14. How many ATP molecules are usually produced per NADH?
    a. 1
    b. 3
    c. 36
    d. 10

15. How many NADH molecules are produced during the complete breakdown of one molecule of glucose?
    a. 5
    b. 30
    c. 10
    d. 6

16. What is the name of the process that adds the third phosphate to an ADP molecule using the flow of hydrogen ions?
    a. substrate-level ATP synthesis
    b. fermentation
    c. reduction
    d. chemiosmosis

17. The metabolic process that produces the most ATP molecules is
    a. glycolysis.
    b. citric acid cycle.
    c. electron transport chain.
    d. fermentation.

18. Which of these is not true of the citric acid cycle? The citric acid cycle
    a. includes the prep reaction.
    b. produces ATP by substrate-level ATP synthesis.
    c. occurs in the mitochondria.
    d. is a metabolic pathway, as is glycolysis.

19. Which of these is not true of the electron transport chain? The electron transport chain
    a. is located on the cristae.
    b. produces more NADH than any metabolic pathway.
    c. contains cytochrome molecules.
    d. ends when oxygen accepts electrons.

20. The oxygen required by cellular respiration is reduced and becomes part of which molecule?
    a. ATP
    b. H_2O
    c. pyruvate
    d. CO_2

Engage

Thinking Scientifically

1. You are able to extract mitochondria from the cell and remove the outer membrane. You want to show that the mitochondria can still produce ATP if placed in the right solution. The solution should be isotonic, but at what pH? Why?

2. You are working with acetyl CoA molecules that contain only radioactive carbon. They are incubated with all the components of the citric acid cycle long enough for one turn of the cycle. Examine Figure 8.7 and explain why the carbon dioxide given off is radioactive.

Bioethical Issue

Alternative Medicine

Feeling tired and run-down? Want to jump-start your mitochondria? If you seem to have no specific ailment, you might be tempted to turn to what is now called alternative medicine. Alternative medicine includes such nonconventional therapies as herbal supplements, acupuncture, chiropractic therapy, homeopathy, osteopathy, and therapeutic touch (e.g., laying on of hands).

Advocates of alternative medicine have made some headway in having alternative medicine practices accepted by almost anyone. For example, Congress has established the National Center for Complementary and Alternative Medicine. It has also passed the Dietary Supplement Health and Education Act, which allows vitamins, minerals, and herbs to be marketed without first being approved by the Food and Drug Administration (FDA).

But is this a mistake? Many physicians believe controlled studies are needed to test the efficacy of alternative medications and practices. Do you agree? Should every food supplement or approach to health be subject to scientific testing, or are there other ways to evaluate successful treatment? Explain your reasoning.

Genetic Basis of Life

This unit provides an opportunity to become acquainted with the basics of cellular reproduction and Mendelian and molecular genetics. Cellular reproduction is one of the basic characteristics of life: the processes of mitosis and meiosis allow organisms to reproduce, grow, and repair damaged tissues. An understanding of cellular reproduction has led to the study of stem cells, which have the potential to offer treatments for many human diseases.

Mendelian genetics explains the patterns of inheritance that are founded in the process of meiosis. Among the many applications of knowledge of these patterns is the ability to predict the chances of having a child with a specific genetic disorder. An understanding of molecular genetics has led to the development of DNA technologies that have the potential to cure genetic diseases and produce crops to feed an ever-increasing human population.

The field of genetics is making progress in other areas too. We are beginning to understand how cell division is regulated by numerous genes, and how a failure of these regulatory mechanisms may lead to cancer. Many other human diseases are the result of mutations in genes as well. Thus, at every turn, it is clear that you can't fully appreciate the happenings of the twenty-first century without a knowledge of genetics, and this is your chance to become a part of the action.

UNIT OUTLINE

Chapter 9 The Cell Cycle and Cellular Reproduction   153

Chapter 10 Meiosis and Sexual Reproduction   171

Chapter 11 Mendelian Patterns of Inheritance   192

Chapter 12 Molecular Biology of the Gene   214

Chapter 13 Regulation of Gene Activity   237

Chapter 14 Biotechnology and Genomics   254

UNIT LEARNING OUTCOMES

The learning outcomes for this unit focus on three major themes in the life sciences.

Evolution	Explain how the process of meiosis introduces the variation necessary for evolutionary change.
Nature of Science	Discuss how an understanding of cellular reproduction and molecular biology can be used to treat human disease.
Biological Systems	Evaluate how the information contained with the DNA is responsible for the physical characteristics of an organism.

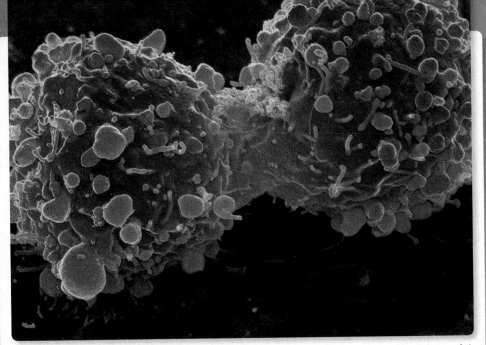

A cell may become cancerous when regulation of cell division fails.

9

The Cell Cycle and Cellular Reproduction

The process of cell division is highly regulated. In humans, life begins as a single cell, yet in a very short period of time the process of cell division produces trillions of cells, each specialized for a special function. Over 200 different types of cells are found in the human body, and although each is specialized, they all work together in harmony.

But what happens when the regulation of cell division fails? In the United States this year, over 68,000 individuals will be diagnosed with melanoma, a form of skin cancer, and around 8,000 people will die from this disease. In many instances of melanoma, exposure to ultraviolet radiation (UV) from the Sun has caused a mutation in the regulatory mechanisms of the cell cycle. Without proper regulation, cell division occurs continuously, a characteristic of cancer. For melanoma, this loss of cell cycle control results from a mutation in a gene known as *CDKN2A*. This gene is an example of a tumor suppressor gene, one of the key regulatory mechanisms of the cell cycle. In this chapter we describe the process of cell division, how it is regulated, and how cancer may develop when regulatory mechanisms malfunction.

As you read through the chapter, think about the following questions:

1. What is the normal sequence of events in the process of cellular reproduction?
2. What are the roles of the checkpoints in a cell cycle?
3. How do tumor suppressor genes regulate the cell cycle?

CHAPTER OUTLINE

9.1 The Cell Cycle 154

9.2 Mitosis and Cytokinesis 157

9.3 The Cell Cycle and Cancer 163

9.4 Prokaryotic Cell Division 166

BEFORE YOU BEGIN

Before beginning this chapter, take a few moments to review the following discussions.

Section 3.5 What is the role of the DNA in a cell?

Sections 4.2 and 4.3 What are the major differences between prokaryotic and eukaryotic cells?

Section 4.8 What is the role of the cytoskeleton in a eukaryotic cell?

FOLLOWING *the* THEMES

CHAPTER 9 THE CELL CYCLE AND CELLULAR REPRODUCTION

UNIT 2 GENETIC BASIS OF LIFE		
	Evolution	As eukaryotic cells became increasingly complex, a similarly complex series of events evolved to separate their multiple chromosomes, located within a membrane-bound nucleus, into new daughter cells.
	Nature of Science	By studying the regulatory mechanisms of the cell cycle, scientists are able to gather a deeper understanding of why cancer occurs.
	Biological Systems	For unicellular organisms, cell division results in the formation of two new organisms, while in multicellular organisms, cell division is the basis of growth and tissue repair.

9.1 The Cell Cycle

Learning Outcomes

Upon completion of this section, you should be able to

1. List the four stages of interphase, and describe the major events that occur during each stage in preparation for cell division.
2. Describe the difference between mitosis and cytokinesis.
3. List the checkpoints that regulate the progression of cells through the cell cycle.
4. Explain the mechanisms within the G_1 cell cycle checkpoint that evaluate growth signals, determine nutrient availability, and assess DNA integrity.

The **cell cycle** is an orderly set of stages that take place between the time a eukaryotic cell divides and the time the resulting daughter cells also divide. When a cell is going to divide, it grows larger, the number of organelles doubles, and the amount of DNA doubles as DNA replication occurs. The two portions of the cell cycle are interphase, which includes a number of stages, and the mitotic stage when mitosis and cytokinesis occur.

Animation
Overview of Cell Division

Interphase

As Figure 9.1 shows, most of the cell cycle is spent in **interphase.** This is the time when a cell performs its usual functions, depending on its location in the body. The amount of time the cell takes for interphase varies widely. Embryonic cells complete the entire cell cycle in just a few hours. For adult mammalian cells, interphase lasts for about 20 hours, which is 90% of the cell cycle. In the past, interphase was known as the resting stage. However, today it is known that interphase is very busy, and that preparations are being made for mitosis. Interphase consists of three stages, referred to as G_1, S, and G_2.

3D Animation
Interphase

G_1 Stage

Cell biologists named the stage before DNA replication G_1, and they named the stage after DNA replication G_2. G stood for "gap," but now that we know how metabolically active the cell is, it is better to think of G as standing for "growth." During G_1, the cell recovers from the previous division. The cell grows in size, increases the number of organelles (such as mitochondria and ribosomes), and accumulates materials that will be used for DNA synthesis. Otherwise, cells are constantly performing their normal daily functions during G_1, including communicating with other cells, secreting substances, and carrying out cellular respiration.

Some cells, such as nerve and muscle cells, typically do not complete the cell cycle and are permanently arrested. These cells exit interphase and enter a stage called G_0. While in the G_0 stage, the cells continue to perform normal everyday processes, but no preparations are being made for cell division. Cells may not leave the G_0 stage without proper signals from other cells and other parts of the body. Thus, completion of the cell cycle is very tightly controlled.

S Stage

Following G_1, the cell enters the S stage, when DNA synthesis or replication occurs. At the beginning of the S stage, each chromosome is composed of one DNA double helix. Following DNA replication, each chromosome is composed of two identical DNA double helix molecules. Each double helix is called a **chromatid,** and the two identical chromatids are referred to as **sister chromatids.** The sister chromatids remain attached until they are separated during mitosis.

G_2 Stage

Following the S stage, G_2 is the stage from the completion of DNA replication to the onset of mitosis. During this stage, the cell synthesizes proteins that will assist cell division. For example, it makes the proteins that form microtubules. Microtubules are used during the mitotic stage to form the mitotic spindle that is critical during M stage.

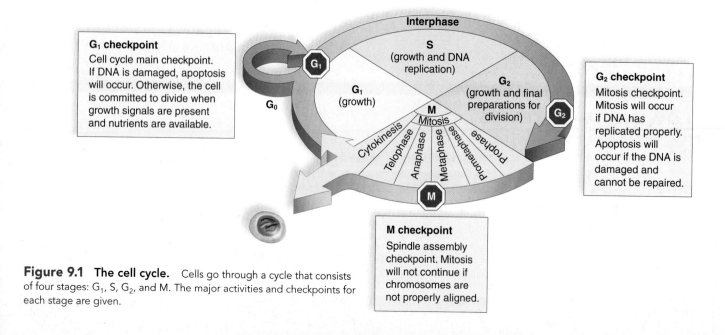

G_1 checkpoint

Cell cycle main checkpoint. If DNA is damaged, apoptosis will occur. Otherwise, the cell is committed to divide when growth signals are present and nutrients are available.

G_2 checkpoint

Mitosis checkpoint. Mitosis will occur if DNA has replicated properly. Apoptosis will occur if the DNA is damaged and cannot be repaired.

M checkpoint

Spindle assembly checkpoint. Mitosis will not continue if chromosomes are not properly aligned.

Interphase

S
(growth and DNA replication)

G_2
(growth and final preparations for division)

G_1
(growth)

G_0

M

Mitosis

Cytokinesis
Telophase
Anaphase
Metaphase
Prometaphase
Prophase

Figure 9.1   The cell cycle.   Cells go through a cycle that consists of four stages: G_1, S, G_2, and M. The major activities and checkpoints for each stage are given.

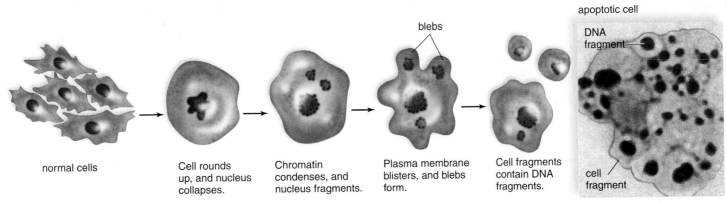

Figure 9.2 Apoptosis. Apoptosis is a sequence of events that results in a fragmented cell. The fragments are phagocytized (engulfed) by white blood cells and neighboring tissue cells.

Labels below figure: normal cells | Cell rounds up, and nucleus collapses. | Chromatin condenses, and nucleus fragments. | Plasma membrane blisters, and blebs form. | Cell fragments contain DNA fragments.

Labels on figure: blebs | apoptotic cell | DNA fragment | cell fragment

M (Mitotic) Stage

Following interphase, the cell enters the M (for mitotic) stage. This cell division stage includes **mitosis** (nuclear division) and **cytokinesis** (division of the cytoplasm). During mitosis, daughter chromosomes are distributed by the **mitotic spindle** to two daughter nuclei. When division of the cytoplasm is complete, two daughter cells are present.

Control of the Cell Cycle

A **signal** is an agent that influences the activities of a cell. **Growth factors** are signaling proteins received at the plasma membrane. Even cells arrested in G_0 will finish the cell cycle if stimulated to do so by growth factors. In general, signals ensure that the cell cycle stages follow one another in the normal sequence.

Animation Cell Proliferation Signaling Pathway

Cell Cycle Checkpoints

The red barriers in Figure 9.1 represent three checkpoints at which the cell cycle either stops or continues on, depending on the internal signals received. Researchers have identified a family of internal signaling proteins called **cyclins** that increase and decrease as the cell cycle continues. Specific cyclins must be present for the cell to proceed from the G_1 stage to the S stage and from the G_2 stage to the M stage.

3D Animation Checkpoints

As discussed in the Nature of Science feature "The G_1 Checkpoint," the primary checkpoint of the cell cycle is the G_1 checkpoint. In mammalian cells, the signaling protein **p53** stops the cycle at the G_1 checkpoint when DNA is damaged. (In the name p53, p stands for *protein* and 53 represents its molecular weight in kilodaltons.) First, p53 attempts to initiate DNA repair, but rising levels of p53 can bring about **apoptosis,** which is programmed cell death (Fig. 9.2). Another protein, called **RB,** is responsible for interpreting growth signals and also nutrient availability signals. RB stands for *retino*blastoma, a cancer of the retina that occurs when the *RB* gene undergoes a mutation.

The cell cycle may also stop at the G_2 checkpoint if DNA has not finished replicating. This checkpoint prevents the initiation of the M stage before completion of the S stage. If DNA is physically damaged, such as from exposure to solar radiation or X-rays, the G_2 checkpoint also offers the opportunity for DNA to be repaired.

Another cell cycle checkpoint occurs during the mitotic stage. The cycle stops if the chromosomes are not properly attached to the mitotic spindle. Normally, the mitotic spindle ensures that the chromosomes are distributed accurately to the daughter cells.

Animation Control of the Cell Cycle

Apoptosis

Apoptosis is often defined as programmed cell death because the cell progresses through a typical series of events that bring about its destruction (Fig. 9.2). The cell rounds up, causing it to lose contact with its neighbors. The nucleus fragments, and the plasma membrane develops blisters. Finally, the cell fragments are engulfed by white blood cells and/or neighboring cells.

A remarkable finding of the past few years is that the enzymes that bring about apoptosis, called *caspases,* are always present in the cell. The enzymes are ordinarily held in check by inhibitors, but they can be unleashed by either internal or external signals.

Apoptosis and Cell Division. In living systems, opposing events keep the body in balance and maintain homeostasis. cell division and apoptosis are two opposing processes that keep the number of cells in the body at an appropriate level. Cell division increases and apoptosis decreases the number of **somatic** (body) **cells.** Both are normal parts of growth and development. An organism begins as a single cell that repeatedly divides to produce many cells, but eventually some cells must die for the organism to take shape. For example, when a tadpole becomes a frog, the tail disappears as apoptosis occurs. In a human embryo, the fingers and toes are at first webbed, but then they are usually freed from one another as a result of apoptosis.

Cell division occurs during your entire life. Even now, your body is producing thousands of new red blood cells, skin cells, and cells that line your respiratory and digestive tracts. Also, if you suffer a cut, cell division repairs the injury. Apoptosis occurs all the time too, particularly if an abnormal cell that could become cancerous appears, or a cell becomes infected with a virus. Death through apoptosis prevents a tumor from developing and helps to limit the spread of viruses.

Check Your Progress 9.1

1. List, in order, the four stages of the cell cycle and briefly summarize what is happening at each stage.
2. Explain what conditions might cause a cell to halt the cell cycle.
3. Discuss how apoptosis represents a regulatory event of the cell cycle.

The G₁ Checkpoint

Cell division is very tightly regulated so that only certain cells in an adult body are actively dividing. After cell division occurs, cells enter the G₁ stage. Upon completing G₁, they will divide again, but before this happens they have to pass through the G₁ checkpoint.

The G₁ checkpoint ensures that conditions are right for making the commitment to divide by evaluating the meaning of growth signals, determining the availability of nutrients, and assessing the integrity of DNA. Failure to meet any one of these criteria results in a cell's halting the cell cycle and entering G₀ stage, or undergoing apoptosis if the problems are severe.

Evaluating Growth Signals

Multicellular organisms tightly control cell division so that it occurs only when needed. Signaling molecules, such as hormones, may be sent from nearby cells or distant tissues to encourage or discourage cells from entering the cell cycle. Such signals may cause a cell to enter a G₀ stage, or complete G₁ and enter the S stage. Growth signals that promote cell division cause a cyclin-dependent-kinase (CDK) to add a phosphate group to the RB protein, a major regulator of the G₁ checkpoint.

Ordinarily, a protein called E2F is bound to RB, but when RB is phosphorylated, its shape changes and it releases E2F. Now, E2F binds to DNA, activating certain genes whose products are needed to complete the cell cycle (Fig. 9Aa). Likewise, growth signals prompt cells that are in G₀ stage to reenter the G₁ stage, complete it, and enter the S stage. If growth signals are sufficient, a cell passes through the G₁ checkpoint and cell division occurs.

Determining Nutrient Availability

Just as experienced hikers ensure that they have sufficient food for their journey, a cell ensures that nutrient levels are adequate before committing to cell division.   For example, scientists know that starving cells in culture enter G₀. At that time, phosphate groups are removed from RB (see reverse arrows in Figure 9Aa); RB does not release E2F; and the proteins needed to complete the cell cycle are not produced. When nutrients become available, CDKs bring about the phosphorylation of RB, which then

releases E2F (see forward arrows in Figure 9Aa). After E2F binds to DNA, proteins needed to complete the cell cycle are produced. Therefore, you can see that cells do not commit to divide until conditions are conducive for them to do so.

Assessing DNA Integrity

For cell division to occur, DNA must be free of errors and damage. The p53 protein is involved in this quality control function. Ordinarily, p53 is broken down because it has no job to do. In response to DNA damage, CDK phosphorylates p53 (Fig. 9Ab). Now, the molecule is not broken down as usual, and instead its level in the nucleus begins to rise. Phosphorylated p53 binds to DNA; certain genes are activated; and DNA repair proteins are produced. If the DNA damage cannot be repaired, p53 levels continue to rise, and apoptosis is triggered. If the damage is successfully repaired, p53 levels fall, and the cell is

allowed to complete G₁ stage—as long as growth signals and nutrients are present, for example.

Actually, many criteria must be met for a cell to commit to cell division, and the failure to meet any one of them may cause the cell cycle to be halted and/or apoptosis to be initiated. The G₁ checkpoint is currently an area of intense research because understanding it holds the key to possibly curing cancer, and for unleashing the power of normal, healthy cells to regenerate tissues, which could be used to cure many other human conditions.

Questions to Consider

1. What potentially could be the effect of an abnormally high level of a growth hormone on the regulation of the cell cycle?
2. Why might some cancers be associated with a mutation in the gene encoding the p53 protein?

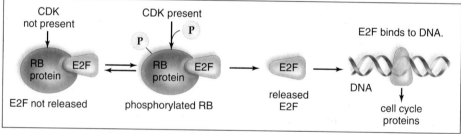

a.

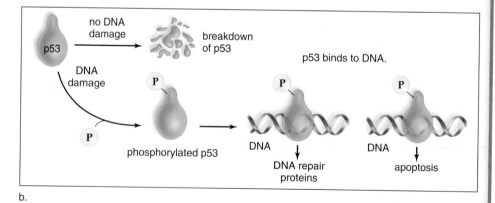

b.

Figure 9A Regulation of the G1 checkpoint.   a. When CDK (cyclin-dependent-kinase) is not present, RB retains E2F. When CDK is present, a phosphorylated RB releases E2F, and after it binds to DNA, proteins necessary to completing cell division are produced. **b.** If DNA is damaged, p53 is not broken down, and instead is involved in the production of DNA repair enzymes and in triggering apoptosis when repair is impossible.

9.2 Mitosis and Cytokinesis

Learning Outcomes

Upon completion of this section you should be able to

1. Explain how the cell prepares the chromosomes and centrosomes prior to nuclear division.
2. Summarize the major events that occur during mitosis and cytokinesis.
3. Discuss why human stem cells continuously conduct mitosis.

Table 9.1 Diploid Chromosome Numbers of Some Eukaryotes

Type of Organism	Name of Chromosome	Chromosome Number
Fungi	*Saccharomyces cerevisiae* (yeast)	32
Plants	*Pisum sativum* (garden pea)	14
	Solanum tuberosum (potato)	48
	Ophioglossum vulgatum (Southern adder's tongue fern)	1,320
Animals	*Drosophila melanogaster* (fruit fly)	8
	Homo sapiens (human)	46
	Carassius auratus (goldfish)	94

As mentioned, cell division in eukaryotes involves mitosis, which is nuclear division, and cytokinesis, which is division of the cytoplasm. During mitosis, the sister chromatids are separated and distributed to two daughter cells.

Eukaryotic Chromosomes

The DNA in the chromosomes of eukaryotes is associated with various proteins, including **histones** that are especially involved in organizing chromosomes. When a eukaryotic cell is not undergoing division, the DNA (and associated proteins) are located within **chromatin,** which has the appearance of a tangled mass of thin threads. Before mitosis begins, chromatin becomes highly coiled and condensed, and it is easy to see the individual chromosomes.

When the chromosomes are visible, it is possible to photograph and count them. Each species has a characteristic chromosome number (Table 9.1). This is the full or **diploid (2n)** number [Gk. *diplos*, twofold, and *-eides*, like] of chromosomes that is found in all cells of the individual. The diploid number includes two chromosomes of each kind. Half the diploid number, called the **haploid (n)** number [Gk. *haplos*, single, and *-eides*, like] of chromosomes, contains only one chromosome of each kind. Typically, only sperm and eggs have the haploid number of chromosomes in the life cycle of animals.

Preparations for Mitosis

During interphase, a cell must make preparations for cell division. These arrangements include replicating the chromosomes and duplicating most cellular organelles, including the centrosome, which will organize the spindle apparatus necessary for movement of chromosomes.

Chromosome Duplication

During mitosis, a 2n nucleus divides to produce daughter nuclei that are also 2n. The dividing cell is called the *parent cell,* and the resulting cells are called *daughter cells.* Before nuclear division takes place, DNA replicates, duplicating the chromosomes in the parent cell. This occurs during the S stage of interphase. Now each chromosome has two identical double helical molecules. Each double helix is a *chromatid,* and the two identical chromatids are called *sister chromatids* (Fig. 9.3). Sister chromatids are constricted and attached to each other at a region called the **centromere.** Protein complexes called **kinetochores** develop on either side of the centromere during cell division.

During nuclear division, the two sister chromatids separate at the centromere, and in this way each duplicated chromosome gives rise to two daughter chromosomes. Each daughter chromosome has only one double helix molecule. The daughter chromosomes are distributed equally to the daughter cells. In this way, each daughter nucleus gets a copy of each chromosome that was in the parent cell.

Division of the Centrosome

The **centrosome** [Gk. *centrum*, center, and *soma*, body], the main microtubule-organizing center of the cell, also divides before mitosis begins. Each centrosome in an animal cell contains a pair

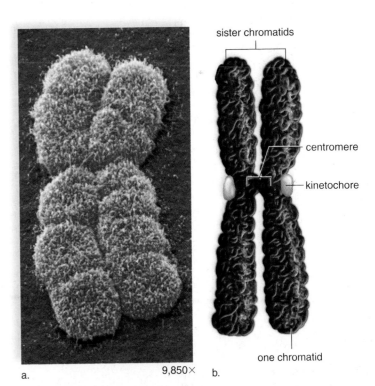

a.   9,850×   b.

Figure 9.3 Duplicated chromosomes. A duplicated chromosome contains two sister chromatids, each with a copy of the same genes. **a.** Electron micrograph of a highly coiled and condensed chromosome, typical of a nucleus about to divide. **b.** Diagrammatic drawing of a condensed chromosome. The chromatids are held together at a region called the centromere.

of barrel-shaped organelles called **centrioles.** Centrioles are not found in plant cells.

The centrosomes organize the mitotic spindle, which contains many fibers, each of which is composed of a bundle of microtubules. Microtubules are hollow cylinders made up of the protein tubulin. They assemble when tubulin subunits join, and when they disassemble, tubulin subunits become free once more. The microtubules of the cytoskeleton disassemble when spindle fibers begin forming. Most likely, this provides tubulin for the formation of the spindle fibers, or it may allow the cell to change shape as needed for cell division.

Figure 9.4 Phases of mitosis in animal and plant cells. The blue chromosomes were inherited from one parent and the red from the other parent.

Phases of Mitosis

Mitosis is a continuous process that is arbitrarily divided into five phases for convenience of description: prophase, prometaphase, metaphase, anaphase, and telophase (Fig. 9.4).

Prophase

It is apparent during **prophase** that nuclear division is about to occur because chromatin has condensed and the chromosomes are visible. Recall that DNA replication occurred during interphase, and therefore the *parental chromosomes are already duplicated and composed of two sister chromatids held together at a centromere.* Counting the number of centromeres in diagrammatic drawings gives the number of chromosomes for the cell depicted.

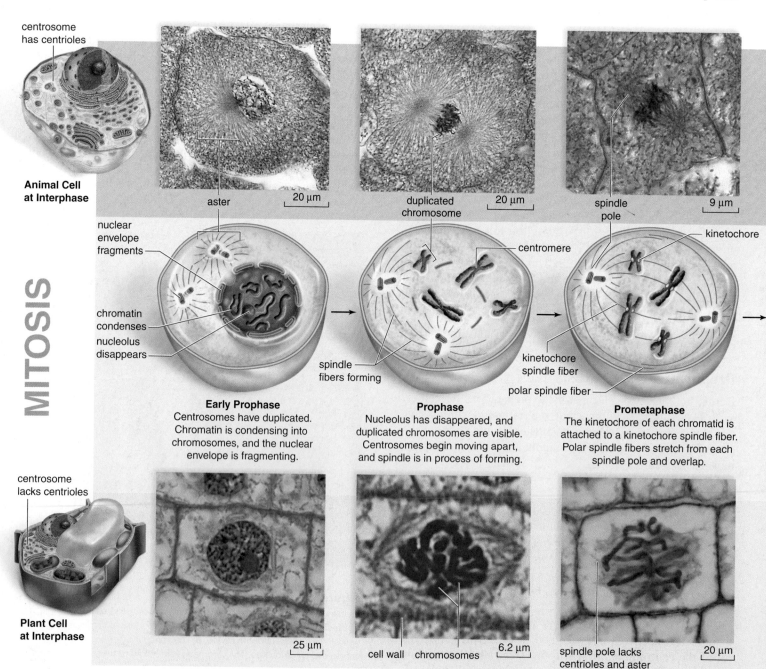

MITOSIS

Animal Cell at Interphase
centrosome has centrioles

aster   20 μm

duplicated chromosome   20 μm

spindle pole   9 μm

nuclear envelope fragments

chromatin condenses

nucleolus disappears

spindle fibers forming

Early Prophase
Centrosomes have duplicated. Chromatin is condensing into chromosomes, and the nuclear envelope is fragmenting.

centromere

Prophase
Nucleolus has disappeared, and duplicated chromosomes are visible. Centrosomes begin moving apart, and spindle is in process of forming.

kinetochore

kinetochore spindle fiber

polar spindle fiber

Prometaphase
The kinetochore of each chromatid is attached to a kinetochore spindle fiber. Polar spindle fibers stretch from each spindle pole and overlap.

Plant Cell at Interphase
centrosome lacks centrioles

25 μm

cell wall   chromosomes   6.2 μm

spindle pole lacks centrioles and aster   20 μm

During prophase, the nucleolus disappears and the nuclear envelope fragments. The spindle begins to assemble as the two centrosomes migrate away from one another. In animal cells, an array of microtubules radiates toward the plasma membrane from the centrosomes. These structures are called **asters.** It is thought that asters serve to brace the centrioles during later stages of cell division. Notice that the chromosomes have no particular orientation because the spindle has not yet formed.

Prometaphase (Late Prophase)

During **prometaphase,** preparations for sister chromatid separation are evident. Kinetochores appear on each side of the centromere, and these attach sister chromatids to the *kinetochore spindle fibers*. These fibers extend from the poles to the chromosomes, which will soon be located at the center of the spindle.

The kinetochore fibers attach the sister chromatids to opposite poles of the spindle, and the chromosomes are pulled first toward one pole and then toward the other before the chromosomes come into alignment. Notice that even though the chromosomes are attached to the spindle fibers in prometaphase, they are still not in alignment.

Metaphase

During **metaphase,** the centromeres of chromosomes are now in alignment on a single plane at the center of the cell. The chromosomes usually appear as a straight line across the middle of the cell when viewed under a light microscope. An imaginary plane that is perpendicular and passes through this circle is called the **metaphase plate.** It indicates the future axis of cell division.

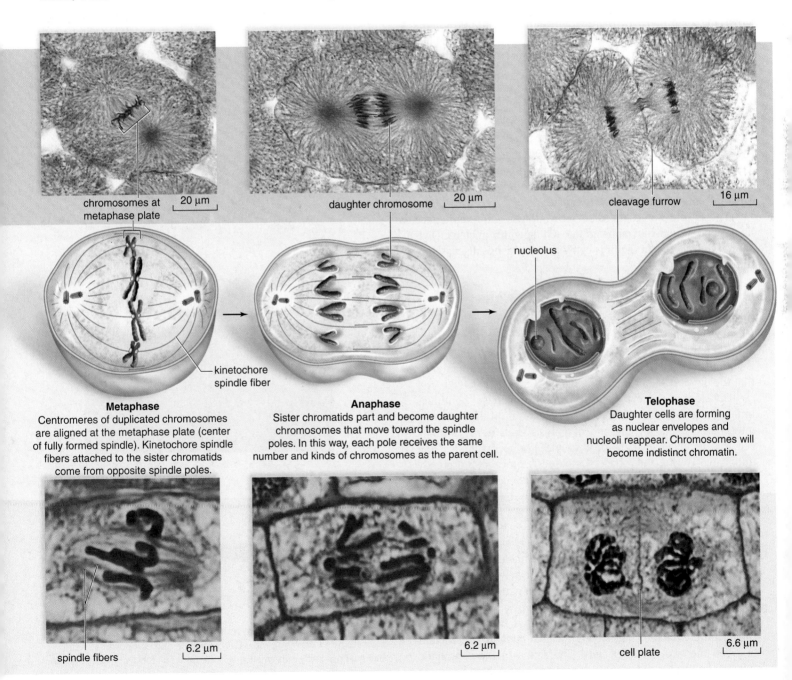

chromosomes at metaphase plate   20 µm

daughter chromosome   20 µm

cleavage furrow   16 µm

nucleolus

kinetochore spindle fiber

Metaphase
Centromeres of duplicated chromosomes are aligned at the metaphase plate (center of fully formed spindle). Kinetochore spindle fibers attached to the sister chromatids come from opposite spindle poles.

Anaphase
Sister chromatids part and become daughter chromosomes that move toward the spindle poles. In this way, each pole receives the same number and kinds of chromosomes as the parent cell.

Telophase
Daughter cells are forming as nuclear envelopes and nucleoli reappear. Chromosomes will become indistinct chromatin.

spindle fibers   6.2 µm

6.2 µm

cell plate   6.6 µm

Several nonattached spindle fibers called *polar spindle fibers* reach beyond the metaphase plate and overlap. A cell cycle checkpoint, the M checkpoint, delays the start of anaphase until the kinetochores of each chromosome are attached properly to spindle fibers and the chromosomes are properly aligned along the metaphase plate.

Anaphase

At the start of **anaphase,** the two sister chromatids of each duplicated chromosome separate at the centromere, giving rise to two daughter chromosomes. Daughter chromosomes, each with a centromere and single chromatid composed of a single double helix, appear to move toward opposite poles. Actually, the daughter chromosomes are being pulled to the opposite poles as the kinetochore spindle fibers disassemble at the region of the kinetochores.

Even as the daughter chromosomes move toward the spindle poles, the poles themselves are moving farther apart because the polar spindle fibers are sliding past one another. Microtubule-associated proteins such as the motor molecules kinesin and dynein are involved in the sliding process. Anaphase is the shortest phase of mitosis.

Telophase

During **telophase,** the spindle disappears as new nuclear envelopes form around the daughter chromosomes. Each daughter nucleus contains the same number and kinds of chromosomes as the original parent cell. Remnants of the polar spindle fibers are still visible between the two nuclei.

The chromosomes become more diffuse chromatin once again, and a nucleolus appears in each daughter nucleus. Division of the cytoplasm requires cytokinesis, which is discussed in the next section.

Cytokinesis in Animal and Plant Cells

As mentioned previously, cytokinesis is division of the cytoplasm. Cytokinesis accompanies mitosis in most cells but not all. When mitosis occurs but cytokinesis doesn't occur, the result is a multinucleated cell. For example, you will see in Chapter 27 that the embryo sac in flowering plants is multinucleated.

Division of the cytoplasm begins in anaphase, continues in telophase, but does not reach completion until the following interphase begins. By the end of mitosis each newly forming cell has received a share of the cytoplasmic organelles that duplicated during interphase. Cytokinesis proceeds differently in plant and animal cells because of differences in cell structure.

Animation
Cytokinesis

Cytokinesis in Animal Cells

In animal cells a **cleavage furrow,** which is an indentation of the membrane between the two daughter nuclei, forms just as anaphase draws to a close. By that time, the newly forming cells have received a share of the cytoplasmic organelles that duplicated during the previous interphase.

The cleavage furrow deepens when a band of actin filaments, called the contractile ring, slowly forms a circular constriction between the two daughter cells. The action of the contractile ring can be likened to pulling a drawstring ever tighter about the

middle of a balloon. As the drawstring is pulled tight, the balloon constricts in the middle as the material on either side of the constriction gathers in folds. These folds are represented by the longitudinal lines in Figure 9.5.

A narrow bridge between the two cells can be seen during telophase, and then the contractile ring continues to separate the cytoplasm until there are two independent daughter cells (Fig. 9.5).

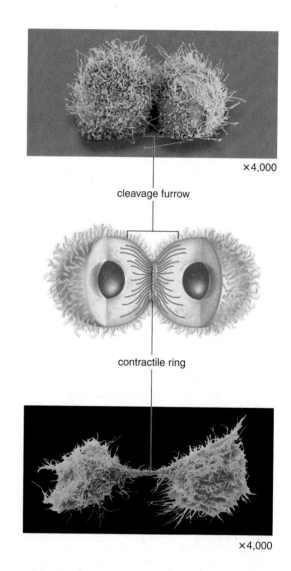

×4,000

cleavage furrow

contractile ring

×4,000

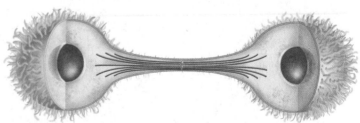

Figure 9.5 Cytokinesis in animal cells. A single cell becomes two cells by a furrowing process. A contractile ring composed of actin filaments gradually gets smaller, and the cleavage furrow pinches the cell into two cells.

Cytokinesis in Plant Cells

Cytokinesis in plant cells occurs by a process different from that seen in animal cells (Fig. 9.6). The rigid cell wall that surrounds plant cells does not permit cytokinesis by furrowing. Instead, cytokinesis in plant cells involves the building of new cell walls between the daughter cells.

Cytokinesis is apparent when a small, flattened disk appears between the two daughter plant cells near the site where the metaphase plate once was. In electron micrographs, it is possible to see that the disk is at right angles to a set of microtubules that radiate outward from the forming nuclei. The Golgi apparatus produces vesicles, which move along the microtubules to the region of the disk. As more vesicles arrive and fuse, a cell plate can be seen. The **cell plate** is simply newly formed plasma membrane that expands outward until it reaches the old plasma membrane and fuses with this membrane.

The new membrane releases molecules that form the new plant cell walls. These cell walls, known as primary cell walls, are later strengthened by the addition of cellulose fibrils. The space between the daughter cells becomes filled with middle lamella, which cements the primary cell walls together.

3D Animation Cytokinesis

The Functions of Mitosis

Mitosis permits growth and repair. In both plants and animals, mitosis is required during development as a single cell develops into an individual. In plants, the individual could be a fern or daisy, while in animals, the individual could be a grasshopper or a human being.

In flowering plants, meristematic tissue retains the ability to divide throughout the life of a plant. Meristematic tissue at the shoot tip accounts for an increase in the height of a plant for as long as it lives. Then, too, lateral meristem accounts for the ability of trees to increase their girth each growing season.

In human beings and other mammals, mitosis is necessary as a fertilized egg becomes an embryo and as the embryo becomes a fetus. Mitosis also occurs after birth as a child becomes an adult. Throughout life, mitosis allows a cut to heal or a broken bone to mend.

Video Mitosis

Stem Cells

Earlier, you learned that the cell cycle is tightly controlled, and that most cells of the body at adulthood are permanently arrested in the G_0 stage. However, mitosis is needed to repair injuries, such as a cut or a broken bone. Many mammalian organs contain stem cells (often called adult stem cells) that retain the ability to divide. As one example, red bone marrow stem cells repeatedly divide to produce millions of cells that go on to become various types of blood cells.

Researchers are learning to manipulate the production of various types of tissues from adult stem cells in the laboratory. If successful, these tissues could be used to cure illnesses. As discussed in the Nature of Science feature "Reproductive and Therapeutic Cloning," **therapeutic cloning,** which is used to produce human tissues, can begin with either adult stem cells or embryonic stem cells. Embryonic stem cells can also be used for **reproductive cloning,** the production of a new individual.

Video Heart Stem Cells

Video Stem Cells

Check Your Progress   9.2

1. Describe the major events that occur during each phase of mitosis.
2. Summarize the differences between cytokinesis in animal and plant cells and explain why the differences are necessary.
3. Discuss the importance of stem cells in the human body.

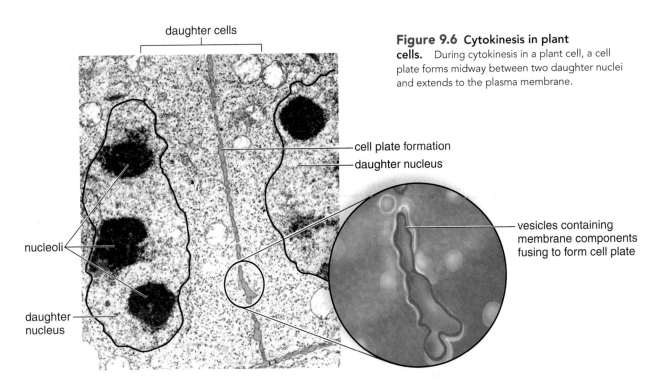

daughter cells

nucleoli

daughter nucleus

cell plate formation
daughter nucleus

vesicles containing membrane components fusing to form cell plate

Figure 9.6 Cytokinesis in plant cells. During cytokinesis in a plant cell, a cell plate forms midway between two daughter nuclei and extends to the plasma membrane.

THEME   Nature of Science

Reproductive and Therapeutic Cloning

Our knowledge of how the cell cycle is controlled has yielded major technological breakthroughs, including reproductive cloning—the ability to clone an adult animal from a normal body cell, and therapeutic cloning, which allows the rapid production of mature cells of a specific type. Both types of cloning are a direct result of recent discoveries about how the cell cycle is controlled.

Reproductive cloning, or the cloning of adult animals, was once thought to be impossible because investigators found it difficult to have the nucleus of an adult cell "start over" with the cell cycle, even when it was placed in an egg cell that had its own nucleus removed.

In 1997, Dolly the sheep demonstrated that reproductive cloning is indeed possible. The donor cells were starved before the cell's nucleus was placed in an enucleated egg. This caused them to stop dividing and go into a G_0 (resting) stage, and this made the nuclei amenable to cytoplasmic signals for initiation of development (Fig. 9Ba). This advance has made it possible to clone all sorts of farm animals that have desirable traits and even to clone rare animals that might otherwise become extinct. Despite the encouraging results, however, there are still obstacles to be overcome, and a ban on the use of federal funds in experiments to clone human beings remains firmly in place.

In therapeutic cloning, however, the objective is to produce mature cells of various cell types rather than an individual organism. The purpose of therapeutic cloning is (1) to learn more about how specialization of cells occurs and (2) to provide cells and tissues that could be used to treat human illnesses, such as diabetes, or major injuries like strokes or spinal cord injuries.

There are two possible ways to carry out therapeutic cloning. The first way is to use the exact same procedure as reproductive cloning, except that *embryonic stem cells (ESCs)* are separated and each is subjected to a treatment that causes it to develop into a particular type of cell, such as red blood cells, muscle cells, or nerve cells (Fig. 9Bb). Some have ethical concerns about this type of therapeutic cloning, which is still experimental, because if the embryo were allowed to continue development, it would become an individual.

The second way to carry out therapeutic cloning is to use *adult stem cells.* Stem cells are found in many organs of the adult's body; for example, the bone marrow has stem cells that produce new blood cells. However, adult stem cells are limited in the possible number of cell types that they may become. Nevertheless, scientists are beginning to overcome this obstacle. In 2006, by adding just four genes to adult skin stem cells, Japanese scientists were able to coax the cells, called fibroblasts, into becoming induced pluripotent stem cells (iPS), a type of stem cell that is similar to an ESC. The researchers were then able to create heart and brain cells from the adult stem cells. Other researchers have used this technique to reverse Parkinson-like symptoms in rats.

Although questions exist on the benefits of iPS cells, these advances demonstrate that scientists are actively investigating methods of overcoming the current limitations and ethical concerns of using embryonic stem cells.

Questions to Consider

1. How might the study of therapeutic cloning benefit scientific studies of reproductive cloning?
2. What types of diseases might not be treatable using therapeutic cloning?

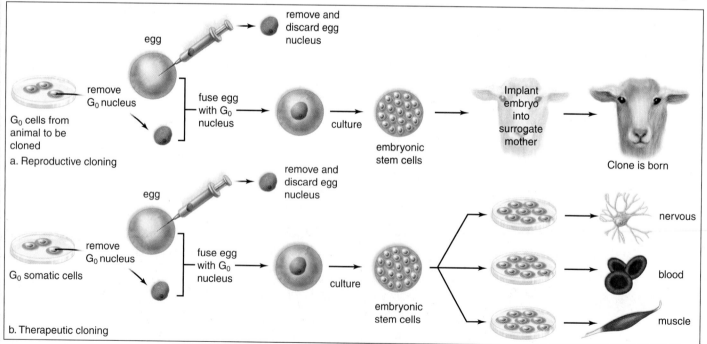

Figure 9B Two types of cloning.   a. The purpose of somatic cell cloning is to produce an individual that is genetically identical to the one that donated a nucleus. The nucleus is placed in an enucleated egg, and, after several mitotic divisions, the embryo is implanted into a surrogate mother for further development. **b.** The purpose of therapeutic cloning is to produce specialized tissue cells. A nucleus is placed in an enucleated egg, and, after several mitotic divisions, the embryonic cells (called embryonic stem cells) are separated and treated to become specialized cells.

9.3 The Cell Cycle and Cancer

Learning Outcomes

Upon completion of this section, you should be able to

1. Describe the basic characteristics of cancer cells.
2. Distinguish between the roles of the tumor-suppressor genes and proto-oncogenes in the regulation of the cell cycle.

Cancer is a cellular growth disorder that occurs when cells divide uncontrollably. Although causes widely differ, most cancers are the result of accumulating mutations that ultimately cause a loss of control of the cell cycle.

Although cancers vary greatly, they usually follow a common multi-step progression (Fig. 9.7). Most cancers begin as an abnormal cell growth that is **benign,** or not cancerous, and usually does not grow larger. However, additional mutations may occur, causing the abnormal cells to fail to respond to inhibiting signals that control the cell cycle. When this occurs, the growth becomes **malignant,** meaning that it is cancerous and possesses the ability to spread.

Characteristics of Cancer Cells

The development of cancer is gradual. A mutation in a cell may cause it to become precancerous, but many other regulatory processes within the body prevent it from becoming cancerous. In fact, it may be decades before a cell possesses most or all of the characteristics of a cancer cell (Table 9.2 and Fig. 9.7). Although cancers vary greatly, cells that possess the following characteristics are generally recognized as cancerous:

Cancer cells lack differentiation. Cancer cells are not specialized and do not contribute to the functioning of a tissue. Although cancer cells may still possess many of the characteristics of surrounding normal cells, they usually look distinctly abnormal. Normal cells can enter the cell cycle about 50 times before they are incapable of dividing again. Cancer cells can enter the cell cycle an indefinite number of times, and in this way seem immortal.

Cancer cells have abnormal nuclei. The nuclei of cancer cells are enlarged and may contain an abnormal number of chromosomes. Often, extra copies of one or more chromosomes may be present. Often, there are also duplicated portions of some chromosomes present, which causes gene amplification,

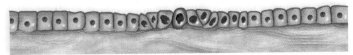

New mutations arise, and one cell (brown) has the ability to start a tumor.

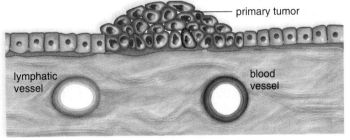

Cancer in situ. The tumor is at its place of origin. One cell (purple) mutates further.

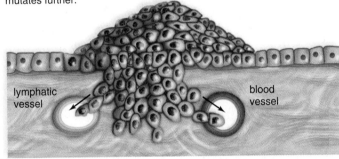

Cancer cells now have the ability to invade lymphatic and blood vessels and travel throughout the body.

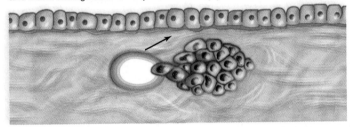

New metastatic tumors are found some distance from the primary tumor.

Figure 9.7 Progression of cancer. The development of cancer requires a series of mutations leading first to a localized tumor and then to metastatic tumors. With each successive step toward cancer, the most genetically altered and aggressive cell becomes the dominant type of tumor. The cells take on characteristics of embryonic cells; they are not differentiated, they can divide uncontrollably; and they are able to metastasize and spread to other tissues.

or extra copies of specific genes. Some chromosomes may also possess deleted portions.

Cancer cells do not undergo apoptosis. Ordinarily, cells with damaged DNA undergo apoptosis, or programmed cell death. The immune system can also recognize abnormal cells and trigger apoptosis, which normally prevents tumors from developing. Cancer cells fail to undergo apoptosis even though they are abnormal cells.

Cancer cells form tumors. Normal cells anchor themselves to a substratum and/or adhere to their neighbors. They exhibit contact inhibition—in other words, when they come in contact with a neighbor, they stop dividing. Cancer cells have lost all restraint and do not exhibit contact inhibition. The abnormal cancer cells pile on top of one another and grow in multiple

Table 9.2 Cancer Cells Versus Normal Cells

Cancer Cells	Normal Cells
Nondifferentiated cells	Differentiated cells
Abnormal nuclei	Normal nuclei
Do not undergo apoptosis	Undergo apoptosis
No contact inhibition	Contact inhibition
Disorganized, multilayered	One organized layer
Undergo metastasis	

layers, forming a **tumor.** During carcinogenesis, the most aggressive cell becomes the dominant cell of the tumor.

Cancer cells undergo metastasis and angiogenesis. Additional mutations may cause a benign tumor, which is usually contained within a capsule and cannot invade adjacent tissue, to become malignant, and spread throughout the body, forming new tumors distant from the primary tumor. These cells now produce enzymes that they normally do not express, allowing tumor cells to invade underlying tissues. Then, they travel through the blood and lymph, to start tumors elsewhere in the body. This process is known as **metastasis.**

> **Video**
> Melanoma Marker

Tumors that are actively growing soon encounter another obstacle—the blood vessels supplying nutrients to the tumor cells become insufficient to support the rapid growth of the tumor. In order to grow further, the cells of the tumor must receive additional nutrition. Thus, the formation of new blood vessels is required to bring nutrients and oxygen to support further growth. Additional mutations occurring in tumor cells allow them to direct the growth of new blood vessels into the tumor in a process called **angiogenesis.** Some modes of cancer treatment are aimed at preventing angiogenesis from occurring.

Origin of Cancer

Normal growth and maintenance of body tissues depend on a balance between signals that promote and inhibit cell division. When this balance is upset, conditions such as cancer may occur. Thus, cancer is usually caused by mutations affecting genes that directly or indirectly affect this balance, such as those shown in Figure 9.8. These two types of genes are usually affected:

1. **Proto-oncogenes** code for proteins that promote the cell cycle and prevent apoptosis. They are often likened to the gas pedal of a car because they cause the cell cycle to speed up.
2. **Tumor suppressor genes** code for proteins that inhibit the cell cycle and promote apoptosis. They are often likened to the brakes of a car because they cause the cell cycle to go more slowly or even stop.

Proto-oncogenes Become Oncogenes

Proto-oncogenes are normal genes that promote progression through the cell cycle. They are often at the end of a *stimulatory pathway* extending from the plasma membrane to the nucleus. A stimulus, such as an injury, results in the release of a growth factor that binds to a receptor protein in the plasma membrane. This sets in motion a whole series of enzymatic reactions leading to the activation of genes that promote the cell cycle, both directly and indirectly. Proto-oncogenes include the receptors and signal molecules that make up these pathways.

When mutations occur in proto-oncogenes, they become **oncogenes,** or cancer-causing genes. Oncogenes are under constant stimulation and keep on promoting the cell cycle regardless of circumstances. For example, an oncogene may code for a faulty receptor in the stimulatory pathway such that the cell cycle is stimulated, even when no growth factor is present! Or, an oncogene may specify either an abnormal protein product or

produce abnormally high levels of a normal product that stimulate the cell cycle to begin or to go to completion. As a result, uncontrolled cell division may occur.

Researchers have identified perhaps 100 oncogenes that can cause increased growth and lead to tumors. The oncogenes most frequently involved in human cancers belong to the *ras* gene family. Mutant forms of the *BRCA1* oncogene (breast cancer predisposition gene 1) are associated with certain hereditary forms of breast and ovarian cancer.

Tumor Suppressor Genes Become Inactive

Tumor suppressor genes, on the other hand, directly or indirectly inhibit the cell cycle and prevent cells from dividing uncontrollably. Some tumor suppressor genes prevent progression of the cell cycle when DNA is damaged. Other tumor suppressor genes may promote apoptosis as a last resort.

A mutation in a tumor suppressor gene is much like brake failure in a car; when the mechanism that slows down and stops cell division does not function, the cell cycle accelerates and does not halt. Researchers have identified about a half-dozen tumor suppressor genes. Among these are the *RB* and *p53* genes that code for the RB and p53 proteins. The Nature of Science feature "The G_1 Checkpoint" discusses the function of these proteins in controlling the cell cycle. The *RB* tumor suppressor gene was discovered when the inherited condition retinoblastoma was being studied, but malfunctions of this gene have now been identified in many other cancers as well, including breast, prostate, and bladder cancers. The *p53* gene turns on the expression of other genes that inhibit the cell cycle. The p53 protein can also stimulate apoptosis. It is estimated that over half of human cancers involve an abnormal or deleted *p53* gene.

> **Animation**
> How Tumor Suppressor
> Genes Block Cell Division

Other Causes of Cancer

As mentioned previously, cancer develops when the delicate balance between promotion and inhibition of cell division is tilted toward uncontrolled cell division. Other mutations may occur within a cell that affect this balance. For example, while a mutation affecting the cell's DNA repair system will not immediately cause cancer, it leads to a much greater chance of a mutation occurring within a proto-oncogene or tumor suppressor gene. And in some cancer cells, mutation of the telomerase enzyme that regulates the length of **telomeres,** or the ends of chromosomes, causes the telomeres to remain at a constant length. Because cells with shortened telomeres normally stop dividing, keeping the telomeres at a constant length allows the cancer cells to continue dividing over and over again.

> **Animation**
> Telomerase
> Function

Check Your Progress   9.3

> 1. List the major characteristics of cancer cells that distinguish them from normal cells.
> 2. Distinguish between a malignant and benign tumor.
> 3. Compare and contrast the effect on the cell cycle of **(a)** a mutation in a proto-oncogene; **(b)** a mutation in a tumor suppressor gene.

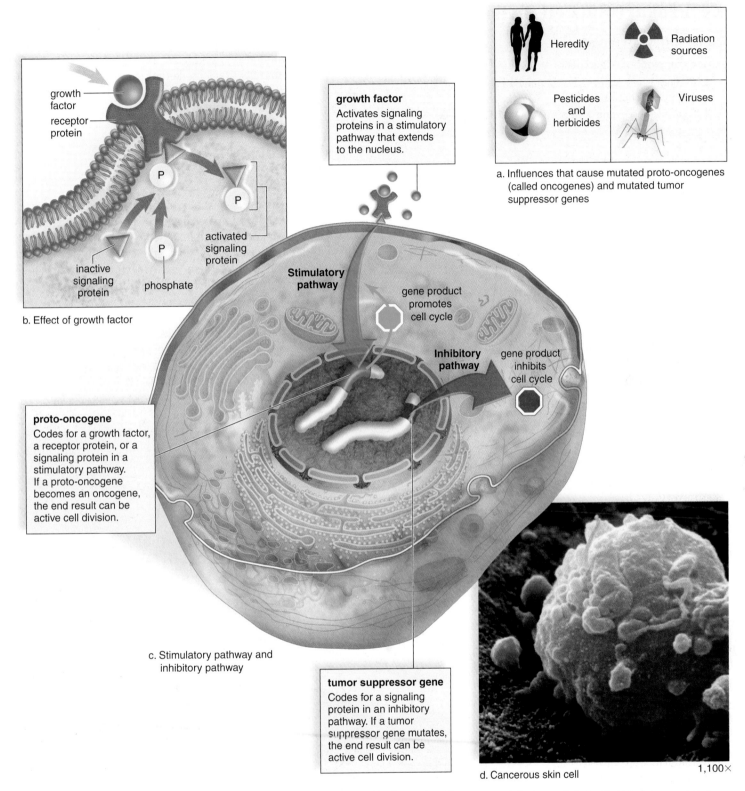

growth factor

receptor protein

P

inactive signaling protein

phosphate

P

activated signaling protein

b. Effect of growth factor

growth factor
Activates signaling proteins in a stimulatory pathway that extends to the nucleus.

Heredity

Radiation sources

Pesticides and herbicides

Viruses

a. Influences that cause mutated proto-oncogenes (called oncogenes) and mutated tumor suppressor genes

Stimulatory pathway

gene product promotes cell cycle

Inhibitory pathway

gene product inhibits cell cycle

proto-oncogene
Codes for a growth factor, a receptor protein, or a signaling protein in a stimulatory pathway. If a proto-oncogene becomes an oncogene, the end result can be active cell division.

c. Stimulatory pathway and inhibitory pathway

tumor suppressor gene
Codes for a signaling protein in an inhibitory pathway. If a tumor suppressor gene mutates, the end result can be active cell division.

d. Cancerous skin cell

1,100×

Figure 9.8 Causes of cancer. **a.** Mutated genes that cause cancer can be due to the influences noted. **b.** A growth factor that binds to a receptor protein initiates a reaction that triggers a stimulatory pathway. **c.** A stimulatory pathway that begins at the plasma membrane turns on proto-oncogenes. The products of these genes promote the cell cycle and double back to become part of the stimulatory pathway. When proto-oncogenes become oncogenes, they are turned on all the time. An inhibitory pathway begins with tumor suppressor genes whose products inhibit the cell cycle. When tumor suppressor genes mutate, the cell cycle is no longer inhibited. **d.** Cancerous skin cell.

9.4 Prokaryotic Cell Division

Learning Outcomes

Upon completion of this section you should be able to

1. Distinguish between the structure of a prokaryotic and eukaryotic chromosome.
2. Describe the events that occur during binary fission.

Cell division in unicellular organisms, such as prokaryotes, produces two new individuals. This is **asexual reproduction** in which the offspring are genetically identical to the parent. In prokaryotes, reproduction consists of duplicating the single chromosome and distributing a copy to each of the daughter cells. Unless a mutation has occurred, the daughter cells are genetically identical to the parent cell.

The Prokaryotic Chromosome

Prokaryotes (bacteria and archaea) lack a nucleus and other membranous organelles found in eukaryotic cells. Still, they do have a chromosome, which is composed of DNA and a limited number of associated proteins. The single chromosome of prokaryotes contains just a few proteins and is organized differently from eukaryotic chromosomes. A eukaryotic chromosome has many more associated proteins than does a prokaryotic chromosome.

In electron micrographs, the bacterial chromosome appears as an electron-dense, irregularly shaped region called the **nucleoid** [L. *nucleus,* nucleus, kernel; Gk. *-eides,* like], which is not enclosed by membrane. When stretched out, the chromosome is seen to be a circular loop with a length that is up to about a thousand times the length of the cell. Special enzymes and proteins help coil the chromosome so that it will fit within the prokaryotic cell.

 Animation Bacterial Chromosome Compaction

Binary Fission

Prokaryotes reproduce asexually by binary fission. The process is termed **binary fission** because division (fission) produces two (binary) daughter cells that are identical to the original parent cell. Before division takes place, the cell enlarges, and after DNA replication occurs, there are two chromosomes. These chromosomes attach to a special plasma membrane site and separate by an elongation of the cell that pulls them apart. During this period, new plasma membrane and cell wall develop and grow inward to divide the cell. When the cell is approximately twice its original length, the new cell wall and plasma membrane for each cell are complete (Fig. 9.9).

Animation Binary Fission

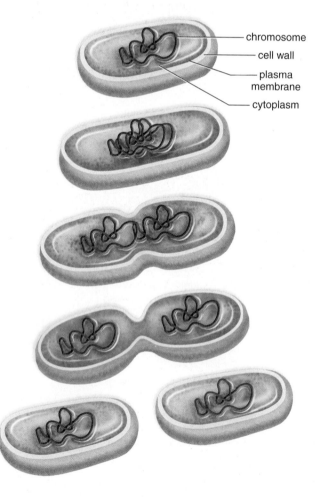

1. Attachment of chromosome to a special plasma membrane site indicates that this bacterium is about to divide.

chromosome
cell wall
plasma membrane
cytoplasm

2. The cell is preparing for binary fission by enlarging its cell wall, plasma membrane, and overall volume.

3. DNA replication has produced two identical chromosomes. Cell wall and plasma membrane begin to grow inward.

4. As the cell elongates, the chromosomes are pulled apart. Cytoplasm is being distributed evenly.

5. New cell wall and plasma membrane has divided the daughter cells.

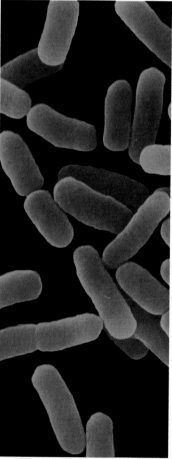

SEM 2,345×

Figure 9.9 Binary fission.   First, DNA replicates, and as the cell lengthens, the two chromosomes separate, and the cells become divided. The two resulting bacteria are identical.

Escherichia coli, which lives in our intestines, has a generation time (the time it takes the cell to divide) of about 20 minutes under favorable conditions. In about seven hours, a single cell can increase to over 1 million cells! The division rate of other bacteria varies depending on the species and conditions.

Comparing Prokaryotes and Eukaryotes

Both binary fission and mitosis ensure that each daughter cell is genetically identical to the parent cell. The genes are portions of DNA found in the chromosomes. Prokaryotes (bacteria and archaea), protists (many algae and protozoans), and some fungi (yeasts) are unicellular. Cell division in unicellular organisms produces two new individuals:

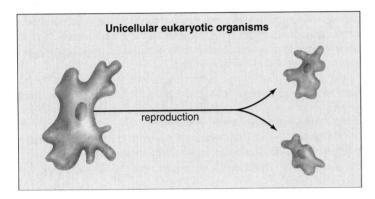

This is a form of asexual reproduction because one parent has produced identical offspring (Table 9.3).

Table 9.3 Functions of Cell Division

Type of Organism	Cell Division	Function
Prokaryotes		
Bacteria and archaea	Binary fission	Asexual reproduction
Eukaryotes		
Protists, and some fungi (yeast)	Mitosis and cytokinesis	Asexual reproduction
Other fungi, plants, and animals	Mitosis and cytokinesis	Development, growth, and repair

In multicellular fungi (molds and mushrooms), plants, and animals, cell division is part of the growth process. It produces the multicellular form we recognize as the mature organism. Cell division is also important in multicellular forms for renewal and repair:

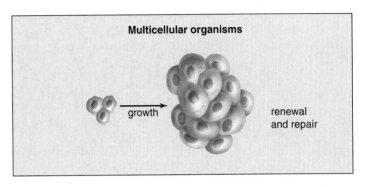

The chromosomes of eukaryotic cells are composed of DNA and many associated proteins. The histone proteins organize a chromosome, allowing it to extend as chromatin during interphase and to coil and condense just prior to mitosis. Each species of multicellular eukaryotes has a characteristic number of chromosomes in the nuclei. As a result of mitosis, each daughter cell receives the same number and kinds of chromosomes as the parent cell. The spindle, which appears during mitosis, is involved in distributing the daughter chromosomes to the daughter nuclei. Cytokinesis, either by the formation of a cell plate (plant cells) or by furrowing (animal cells), is division of the cytoplasm.

In prokaryotes, the single chromosome consists largely of DNA with a few associated proteins. During binary fission, this chromosome duplicates, and each daughter cell receives one copy as the parent cell elongates, and a new cell wall and plasma membrane form between the daughter cells. No spindle is involved in binary fission.

Check Your Progress 9.4

1. Explain how binary fission in prokaryotes differs from mitosis and cytokinesis in eukaryotes.
2. Distinguish between the structure of a prokaryotic and eukaryotic chromosome.

CONNECTING *the* CONCEPTS *with the* THEMES

Evolution

- Eukaryotic cells have evolved the process of mitosis to sort chromosomes into daughter cells.
- The stages of mitosis are the same for all eukaryotic cells, suggesting a common evolutionary lineage.
- Plants and animals have evolved different strategies for cytokinesis that compensates for the presence or lack of a cell wall.

Nature of Science

- An understanding of the regulatory mechanisms of the cell cycle has led to insight into the causes of cancer.
- The advances in stem cell technologies, specifically reproductive and therapeutic cloning, have been made possible by research on the cell cycle.

Biological Systems

- In prokaryotic organisms and unicellular eukaryotes, binary fission provides for cellular reproduction and the formation of new individuals.
- In eukaryotic organisms, mitosis provides for growth of tissues and the repair of damage.

Media Study Tools

3D Animation
Cell Cycle and Mitosis

For an interactive exploration of the cell cycle and mitosis, take a moment to watch McGraw-Hill's new 3D animation.

Summarize

9.1 The Cell Cycle

The cell cycle of a eukaryotic cell includes (1) interphase and (2) a mitotic stage that consists of mitosis and cytokinesis. Interphase, in turn, is composed of three stages: G_1 (growth as certain organelles double), S (the synthesis stage, where the chromosomes are duplicated), and G_2 (growth as the cell prepares to divide). Cells of the body that are no longer dividing are said to be arrested in a G_0 state. During the mitotic stage (M), the chromosomes are sorted into two daughter cells so that each receives a full complement of chromosomes.

The cell cycle is regulated by three well-known checkpoints—the G_1 checkpoint, the G_2 checkpoint prior to the M stage, and the M stage checkpoint, or spindle assembly checkpoint, immediately before anaphase. The G_1 checkpoint ensures that conditions are favorable and that the proper signals are present, and also checks the DNA for damage. If the DNA is damaged beyond repair, apoptosis may occur. Cell division and apoptosis are two opposing processes that keep the number of healthy cells in balance.

9.2 Mitosis and Cytokinesis

Interphase represents the portion of the cell cycle between nuclear divisions, and during this time, preparations are made for cell division. These preparations include duplication of most cellular contents, including the centrosome, which organizes the mitotic spindle. The DNA is duplicated during S stage, at which time the chromosomes, which consisted of a single chromatid each, are duplicated. The G_2 checkpoint ensures that DNA has replicated properly. This results in a nucleus containing the same number of chromosomes, with each now consisting of two chromatids attached at the centromere. During interphase, the chromosomes are not distinct and are collectively called chromatin. Each eukaryotic species has a characteristic number of chromosomes. The total number is called the diploid number, and half this number is the haploid number.

Among eukaryotes, cell division involves both mitosis (nuclear division) and division of the cytoplasm (cytokinesis). As a result of mitosis, the chromosome number stays constant because each chromosome is duplicated and gives rise to two daughter chromosomes that consist of a single chromatid each.

Mitosis consists of five phases:

Prophase—The nucleolus disappears, the nuclear envelope fragments, and the spindle forms between centrosomes. The chromosomes condense and become visible under a light microscope. In animal cells, asters radiate from the centrioles within the centrosomes. Plant cells lack centrioles and, therefore, asters. Even so, the mitotic spindle forms.

Prometaphase (late prophase)—The kinetochores of sister chromatids attach to kinetochore spindle fibers extending from opposite poles. The chromosomes move back and forth until they are aligned at the metaphase plate.

Metaphase—The spindle is fully formed, and the duplicated chromosomes are aligned at the metaphase plate. The spindle consists of polar spindle fibers that overlap at the metaphase plate and kinetochore spindle fibers that are attached to chromosomes. The M stage checkpoint, or spindle assembly checkpoint, must be satisfied before progressing to the next phase.

Anaphase—Sister chromatids separate, becoming daughter chromosomes that move toward the poles. The polar spindle fibers slide past one another, and the kinetochore spindle fibers disassemble. Cytokinesis by furrowing begins.

Telophase—Nuclear envelopes re-form, chromosomes begin changing back to chromatin, the nucleoli reappear, and the spindle disappears. Cytokinesis continues, and is complete by the end of telophase.

Cytokinesis in animal cells is a furrowing process that divides the cytoplasm. Cytokinesis in plant cells involves the formation of a cell plate from which the plasma membrane and cell wall are completed.

9.3 The Cell Cycle and Cancer

The development of cancer is primarily due to the mutation of genes involved in control of the cell cycle. Cancer cells lack differentiation, have abnormal nuclei, do not undergo apoptosis, form tumors, and undergo metastasis and angiogenesis. Cancer often follows a progression in which mutations accumulate, gradually causing uncontrolled growth and the development of a tumor.

Proto-oncogenes stimulate the cell cycle after they are turned on by environmental signals such as growth factors. Oncogenes are mutated proto-oncogenes that stimulate the cell cycle without need of environmental signals. Tumor suppressor genes inhibit the cell cycle. Mutated tumor suppressor genes no longer inhibit the cell cycle, allowing unchecked cell division.

9.4 Prokaryotic Cell Division

Binary fission (in prokaryotes) and mitosis (in unicellular eukaryotic protists and fungi) allow organisms to reproduce asexually. Mitosis in multicellular eukaryotes is primarily for the purpose of development, growth, and repair of tissues.

The prokaryotic chromosome has a few proteins and a single, long loop of DNA. When binary fission occurs, the chromosome attaches to the inside of the plasma membrane and replicates. As the cell elongates, the chromosomes are pulled apart. Inward growth of the plasma membrane and formation of new cell wall material divide the cell in two.

Key Terms

anaphase 160	kinetochore 157
angiogenesis 164	malignant 163
apoptosis 155	metaphase 159
asexual reproduction 166	metaphase plate 159
aster 159	metastasis 164
benign 163	mitosis 155
binary fission 166	mitotic spindle 155
cancer 163	nucleoid 166
cell cycle 154	oncogene 164
cell plate 161	p53 155
centriole 158	prometaphase 159
centromere 157	prophase 158
centrosome 157	proto-oncogene 164
chromatid 154	RB 155
chromatin 157	reproductive cloning 161
cleavage furrow 160	signal 155
cyclin 155	sister chromatids 154
cytokinesis 155	somatic cell 155
diploid (2n) 157	telomere 164
growth factor 155	telophase 160
haploid (n) 157	therapeutic cloning 161
histone 157	tumor 164
interphase 154	tumor suppressor gene 164

Assess

Reviewing This Chapter

1. Describe the cell cycle, including its different stages.   154–55
2. Describe three checkpoints of the cell cycle.   155
3. What is apoptosis, and what are its functions?   155
4. Distinguish between chromosome, chromatin, chromatid, centromere, and kinetochore.   154–57
5. Describe the events that occur during the phases of mitosis.   158–60
6. Contrast cytokinesis in animal cells and plant cells.   160–61
7. List and discuss characteristics of cancer cells that distinguish them from normal cells.   163–64
8. Compare and contrast the functions of proto-oncogenes and tumor suppressor genes in controlling the cell cycle.   164–65
9. Describe the prokaryotic chromosome and the process of binary fission.   166
10. Contrast the function of cell division in prokaryotic and eukaryotic cells.   167

Testing Yourself

Choose the best answer for each question.

1. In contrast to a eukaryotic chromosome, a prokaryotic chromosome
   a. is shorter and fatter.
   b. has a single loop of DNA.
   c. never replicates.
   d. contains many histones.
   e. All of these are correct.

2. The diploid number of chromosomes
   a. is the 2n number.
   b. is in a parent cell and therefore in the two daughter cells following mitosis.
   c. varies according to the particular organism.
   d. is in every somatic cell.
   e. All of these are correct.

For questions 3–5, match the descriptions that follow to the terms in the key.

KEY:
   a. centrosome
   b. chromosome
   c. centromere
   d. cyclin

3. Point of attachment for sister chromatids
4. Found at a spindle pole in the center of an aster
5. Coiled and condensed chromatin
6. If a parent cell has 14 chromosomes prior to mitosis, how many chromosomes will each daughter cell have?
   a. 28 because each chromatid is a chromosome
   b. 14 because the chromatids separate
   c. only 7 after mitosis is finished
   d. any number between 7 and 28
   e. 7 in the nucleus and 7 in the cytoplasm, for a total of 14
7. In which phase of mitosis are the kinetochores of the chromosomes being attached to spindle fibers?
   a. prophase
   b. prometaphase
   c. metaphase
   d. anaphase
   e. telophase
8. Interphase
   a. is the same as prophase, metaphase, anaphase, and telophase.
   b. is composed of G_1, S, and G_2 stages.
   c. requires the use of polar spindle fibers and kinetochore spindle fibers.
   d. is the majority of the cell cycle.
   e. Both b and d are correct.
9. At the metaphase plate during metaphase of mitosis, there are
   a. single chromosomes.
   b. duplicated chromosomes.
   c. G_1 stage chromosomes.
   d. always 23 chromosomes.
10. During which mitotic phases are duplicated chromosomes present?
    a. all but telophase
    b. prophase and anaphase
    c. all but anaphase and telophase
    d. only during metaphase at the metaphase plate
    e. Both a and b are correct.
11. Which of these is paired incorrectly?
    a. prometaphase—the kinetochores become attached to spindle fibers
    b. anaphase—daughter chromosomes are located at the spindle poles
    c. prophase—the nucleolus disappears and the nuclear envelope disintegrates
    d. metaphase—the chromosomes are aligned in the metaphase plate
    e. telophase—a resting phase between cell division cycles
12. When cancer occurs,
    a. cells cannot pass the G_1 checkpoint.
    b. control of the cell cycle is impaired.
    c. apoptosis has occurred.
    d. the cells can no longer enter the cell cycle.
    e. All of these are correct.

13. Which of the following is not characteristic of cancer cells?
    a. Cancer cells often undergo angiogenesis.
    b. Cancer cells tend to be nonspecialized.
    c. Cancer cells undergo apoptosis.
    d. Cancer cells often have abnormal nuclei.
    e. Cancer cells can metastasize.

14. Which of the following statements is true?
    a. Proto-oncogenes cause a loss of control of the cell cycle.
    b. The products of oncogenes may inhibit the cell cycle.
    c. Tumor-suppressor-gene products inhibit the cell cycle.
    d. A mutation in a tumor suppressor gene may inhibit the cell cycle.
    e. A mutation in a proto-oncogene may convert it into a tumor suppressor gene.

For questions 15–18, match the descriptions to a stage in the key.

KEY:
    a. G_1 stage
    b. S stage
    c. G_2 stage
    d. M (mitotic) stage

15. At the end of this stage, each chromosome consists of two attached chromatids.

16. During this stage, daughter chromosomes are distributed to two daughter nuclei.

17. The cell doubles its organelles and accumulates the materials needed for DNA synthesis.

18. The cell synthesizes the proteins needed for cell division.

19. Which is not true of the cell cycle?
    a. The cell cycle is controlled by internal/external signals.
    b. Cyclin is a signaling molcule that increases and decreases as the cycle continues.
    c. DNA damage can stop the cell cycle at the G_1 checkpoint.
    d. Apoptosis occurs frequently during the cell cycle.

20. Label this diagram. What phase of mitosis does it represent?

a. _____
b. _____
c. _____
d. _____

Engage

Virtual Lab
Cell Reproduction

The virtual lab "Cell Reproduction" provides an interactive examination of the cell cycle and provides for a comparison of normal and cancer cells.

Thinking Scientifically

1. After DNA is duplicated in eukaryotes, it must be bound to histones. This requires the synthesis of hundreds of millions of new protein molecules. With reference to Figure 9.1, when in the cell cycle would histones be made?

2. The survivors of the atomic bombs that were dropped on Hiroshima and Nagasaki have been the subjects of long-term studies of the effects of ionizing radiation on cancer incidence. The frequencies of different types of cancer in these individuals varied across the decades. In the 1950s, high levels of leukemia and cancers of the lung and thyroid gland were observed. The 1960s and 1970s brought high levels of breast and salivary gland cancers. In the 1980s, rates of colon cancer were especially high. Why do you suppose the rates of different types of cancer varied across time?

Bioethical Issue
Paying for Cancer Treatment

The risk factors for developing cancer are generally well known. Many lifestyle factors, such as smoking, poor dietary habits, obesity, physical inactivity, risky sexual behavior, and alcohol abuse, among others, have all been linked to higher risks of developing cancer. The greatly increasing rates of cancer over the past few decades have been decried as a public health epidemic. But aside from the cost in human life, the rising tide of cancer is causing a major crisis in today's society—how to pay for it all.

Despite increasing cure rates, effective new drugs, and novel treatments for various types of cancer, the costs of treatment continue to skyrocket. Nowhere is this more apparent than in the pharmaceutical industry. For example, new cancer drugs, while effective, are extremely expensive. Drug companies claim that it costs them between $500 million and $1 billion to bring a single new medicine to market. This cost may seem overblown, especially when you consider that the National Cancer Institute funds basic research into cancer biology and that drug companies often benefit indirectly from the findings. But the drug companies tell us that they need one successful drug to pay for the many drugs they try to develop that do not pay off.

Still, it does seem as if successful drug companies try to keep lower-cost competitors out of the market. The question of how much drug companies can charge for drugs and who should pay for them is a thorny one. If drug companies don't show a profit, they may go out of business and there will be no new drugs. The same is true for insurance companies if they can't raise the cost of insurance to pay for expensive drugs. If the government buys drugs for Medicare patients, taxes may go up dramatically.

But how should the cost of treatment be met? Cancer is an illness that can be the direct result of poor lifestyle choices, but it can also occur in otherwise healthy individuals who make proper choices. And with increasing life spans, the incidence of cancer can only be expected to increase in future years. Should people who develop cancer due to poor lifestyle choices be held fully or partly responsible for paying for treatment? And if so, how? And how should the cost of developing new drugs and treatments be borne? There are no easy answers for any of these questions, but as cancer continues to extract a high toll in both human life and financial resources, future generations may face some difficult choices.

Nanu Ram Jogi, one of the world's oldest fathers.

10

Meiosis and Sexual Reproduction

Nanu Ram Jogi, at 90 years old, recently became a new father. As he hoisted his newborn daughter into the air amid a throng of cameras, microphones, and reporters, he boasted that he plans to continue fathering children with his wife, Saburi, now 50, until he is 100. He cannot even recall how many children he has fathered over the many years of his life, but it is estimated that he has at least twelve sons, nine daughters, and twenty grandchildren. Ramjit Raghavanu, at 94 years old, is now thought to be the world's oldest new father. Nadya Suleman, the so-called Octo-mom, gave birth to 8 babies in 2009. Extreme cases such as these remind us of the huge reproductive potential of most species.

This chapter discusses meiosis, the process that occurs during sexual reproduction and ensures that offspring will have a different combination of genes than their parents. This genetic diversity is essential for survival of a species, but occasionally, offspring inherit a detrimental combination of genes and chromosomes. Such events do not detract from the success of a species overall because they allow a species to evolve and become adapted to an ever-changing environment.

As you read through the chapter, think about the following questions:

1. What is the role of meiosis in introducing new variation?
2. Why is genetic variation necessary for species survival?
3. What effects are seen when different combinations of chromosomes are produced?

CHAPTER OUTLINE

10.1 Halving the Chromosome Number 172

10.2 Genetic Variation 174

10.3 The Phases of Meiosis 176

10.4 Meiosis Compared to Mitosis 177

10.5 The Cycle of Life 180

10.6 Changes in Chromosome Number and Structure 183

BEFORE YOU BEGIN

Before beginning this chapter, take a few moments to review the following discussions.

Figures 3.19 and 3.20 How is genetic information stored in nucleic acids?

Section 4.8 What are microtubules and how do they interact with chromosomes?

Section 9.2 How are eukaryotic chromosomes organized and replicated prior to cell division?

FOLLOWING *the* THEMES

CHAPTER 10 MEIOSIS AND SEXUAL REPRODUCTION

UNIT 2 GENETIC BASIS OF LIFE		
	Evolution	Variation introduced during meiosis can produce permanent changes in a species over time.
	Nature of Science	Research in reproductive technology enables couples who can't conceive to have children.
	Biological Systems	The cells of reproductive systems undergo meiosis, which functions to mix versions of genes and increase genetic diversity.

10.1 Halving the Chromosome Number

Learning Outcomes

Upon completion of this section, you should be able to

1. Contrast haploid and diploid chromosome numbers.
2. Explain what is meant by homologous chromosomes.
3. Describe the central concept of meiosis.

In sexually reproducing organisms, **meiosis** [Gk. *mio*, less, and *-sis*, act or process of] is the type of nuclear division that reduces the chromosome number from the diploid (2n) number [Gk. *diplos*, twofold, and *-eides*, like] to the haploid (n) number [Gk. *haplos*, single, and *-eides*, like]. The **diploid (2n) number** refers to the total number of chromosomes, which exists in two sets. The **haploid (n) number** of chromosomes is half the diploid number, or a single set of chromosomes. In humans, the diploid number of 46 is reduced to the haploid number of 23.

Gametes, or reproductive cells, (often the sperm and egg) usually have the haploid number of chromosomes. In **sexual reproduction**, haploid gametes are produced during meiosis that subsequently merge into a diploid cell called a **zygote.** In plants and animals, the zygote undergoes development to become an adult organism.

Meiosis is necessary in sexually reproducing organisms because the diploid number of chromosomes has to be reduced by half in each of the parents in order to produce diploid off-spring. Otherwise, the number of chromosomes would double with each new generation. Within a few generations, the cells of an animal would be nothing but chromosomes! For example, in humans with a diploid number of 46 chromosomes, in five generations the chromosome number would increase to 1,472 chromosomes (46×2^5). In 10 generations this number would increase to a staggering 47,104 chromosomes (46×2^{10}). The early cytologists (biologists who study cells) realized this, and Pierre-Joseph van Beneden (1809-1894), a Belgian, was gratified to find in 1883 that the sperm and the egg of the roundworm *Ascaris* each contain only two chromosomes, while the zygote and subsequent embryonic cells always have four chromosomes.

Homologous Pairs of Chromosomes

In diploid body cells, the chromosomes occur in pairs. Figure 10.1*a*, a pictorial display of human chromosomes called a karyotype, shows the chromosomes arranged according to pairs. The members of each pair are called homologous chromosomes. **Homologous chromosomes** or **homologues** [Gk. *homologos*, agreeing, corresponding] look alike; they have the same length and centromere position. When stained, homologues have a similar banding pattern because they contain genes for the same traits in the same order in the same locations on both chromosomes in the homologous pair. But while homologous chromosomes have genes for the same traits, such as finger length, the DNA (deoxyribonucleic acid) sequence for the gene on one homologue may code for short fingers and the gene at the same

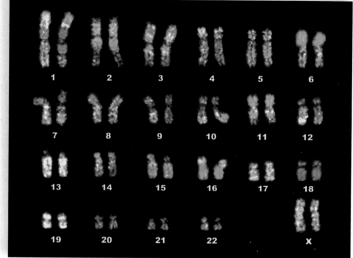

a.

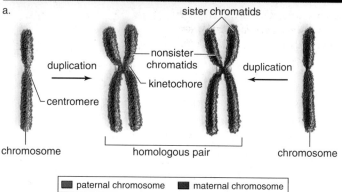

b.

Figure 10.1 Homologous chromosomes. In diploid body cells, the chromosomes occur in pairs called homologous chromosomes. **a.** In this micrograph of stained chromosomes from a human cell, the pairs have been numbered 1–23. Note that chromosome pairs 1–22 are autosomes, coding for non-sex traits, whereas pair 23 include the sex chromosomes, and help determine human gender. **b.** These chromosomes are duplicated, and each chromosome in the homologous pair is composed of two chromatids. The sister chromatids contain the exact same genes; the nonsister chromatids contain genes for the same traits (e.g., type of hair, color of eyes), but they may differ in that one could have DNA that codes for trait variations, such as dark hair versus light hair.

location on the other homologue may code for long fingers. Alternate forms of a gene (as for long fingers and short fingers) are called **alleles.** The DNA sequences of alleles are highly similar, but different enough to produce alternative physical traits like long or short fingers.

To properly produce a haploid number of chromsomes in gametes, you first have to double the amount of DNA. The chromosomes in Figure 10.1*a* are duplicated as they would be just before nuclear division. Recall that during the S stage of the cell cycle, DNA replicates and the chromosomes become duplicated. The results of the duplication process are depicted in Figure 10.1*b*. When duplicated, a chromosome is composed of two identical parts called sister chromatids, each containing one DNA double helix molecule. The sister chromatids are held together at a common region called the centromere.

Why does the zygote have paired chromosomes? One member of a homologous pair was inherited from the male parent, and the other was inherited from the female parent when the haploid sperm and egg fused together. In Figure 10.1*b* and throughout this chapter, the paternal chromosome is colored blue, and the maternal chromosome is colored red. *However, this is simply a conventional distinction. Geneticists generally use chromosome length and centromere location, not color, to recognize homologues.* You will see shortly how meiosis reduces the chromosome number. Whereas the zygote and body cells have homologous pairs of chromosomes, the gametes have only one chromosome of each kind—derived from either the paternal or maternal homologue.

Overview of Meiosis

The central purpose of meiosis is to reduce the chromosome number from 2n to n. Meiosis requires two nuclear divisions and produces four haploid daughter cells, each having one of each kind of chromosome. The process begins by replicating the chrosomosomes, then splitting the matched homologous pairs to go from 2n to n chromosomes during the first division. The second division reduces the amount of DNA in n chromosomes to an amount appropriate for each gamete. Once the DNA has been replicated and chromosomes become a pair, they may exchange genes, creating a genetic mixture different from the parent. The first nuclear division separates each homologous pair, reducing the chromosome number from 2n to n. Even though each daughter cell now has n chromosomes, each chromosome still has a sister chromatid, making a second nuclear division necessary. The end result of meiosis is four gametes with n chromosomes.

Figure 10.2 presents an overview of meiosis, indicating the two nuclear divisions, meiosis I and meiosis II. Prior to meiosis I, DNA replication has occurred; therefore, each chromosome has two sister chromatids. During meiosis I, something new happens that does not occur in mitosis. The homologous chromosomes come together and line up side by side, forming a **synaptonemal complex.** This process is called **synapsis** [Gk. *synaptos*, united, joined together] and results in a **bivalent** [L. *bis*, two, and *valens*, strength]—that is, two homologous chromosomes that stay in close association during the first two phases of meiosis I. Sometimes the term tetrad [Gk. *tetra*, four] is used instead of bivalent because, as you can see, a bivalent contains four chromatids. Chromosomes may recombine or exchange genetic information during this association (see Section 10.2).

Following synapsis, homologous pairs align at the metaphase plate, and then the members of each pair separate. This separation means that only one duplicated chromosome from each homologous pair reaches a daughter nucleus, reducing the chromosome number from 2n to n. It is important for each daughter nucleus to have a member from each pair of homologous chromosomes because only in that way can there be a copy of each *kind* of chromosome in the daughter nuclei. Notice in Figure 10.2 that two possible combinations of chromosomes in the daughter cells are shown: short red with long blue and short blue with long red. Knowing that all daughter cells have to have one short chromosome and one long chromosome, what are the other two possible combinations of chromosomes for these particular cells?

Notice that DNA replication occurs only once during meiosis; no replication is needed between meiosis I and meiosis II because the chromosomes are already duplicated; they already

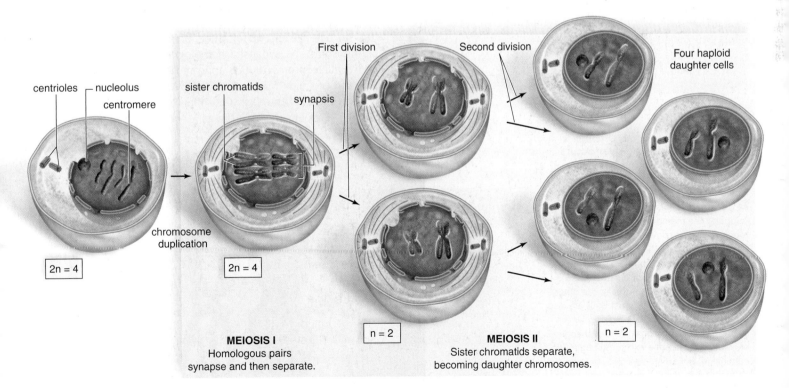

Figure 10.2 Overview of meiosis. Following DNA replication, each chromosome is duplicated and consists of two chromatids. During meiosis I, homologous chromosomes pair and separate. During meiosis II, the sister chromatids of each duplicated chromosome separate. At the completion of meiosis, there are four haploid daughter cells. Each daughter cell has one of each kind of chromosome.

have two sister chromatids. During meiosis II, the sister chromatids separate, becoming daughter chromosomes that move to opposite poles. The chromosomes in each of the four daughter cells now contain only one DNA double helix molecule in the form of a haploid chromosome.

The number of centromeres can be counted to verify that the parent cell has the diploid number of chromosomes. At the end of meiosis I, the chromosome number has been reduced because there are half as many centromeres present, even though each chromosome still consists of two chromatids each. Each daughter cell that forms has the haploid number of chromosomes. At the end of meiosis II, sister chromatids separate, and each daughter cell that forms still contains the haploid number of chromosomes, each consisting of a single chromatid.

Animation
How Meiosis Works

MP3
Meiosis

Fate of Daughter Cells

In the plant life cycle, the daughter cells become haploid spores that germinate to become a haploid generation. This generation produces the gametes by mitosis. The plant life cycle is studied in Chapter 27. In the animal life cycle, the daughter cells become the gametes, either sperm or eggs. The body cells of an animal normally contain the diploid number of chromosomes due to the fusion of sperm and egg during fertilization. If meiotic events go wrong, the gametes can contain the wrong number of chromosomes or altered chromosomes. This possibility and its consequences are discussed in Section 10.6.

Check Your Progress   10.1

1. Describe what is meant by a homologous pair of chromosomes.
2. Examine how chromosome number changes during meiosis I and meiosis II.
3. Explain the purpose of a bivalent in chromosome pairing.

10.2 Genetic Variation

Learning Outcomes

Upon completion of this section, you should be able to
1. Contrast the effects of asexual and sexual reproduction on genetic variation.
2. Explain how crossing-over contributes to genetic variation.
3. Examine how independent assortment contributes to genetic variation in the offspring.

We have seen that meiosis provides a way to keep the chromosome number constant generation after generation. Without meiosis, the chromosome number of the next generation would continually increase. The events of meiosis also help ensure that genetic variation occurs with each generation.

Genetic variation is essential for a species to be able to evolve and adapt in a changing environment. Asexually reproducing organisms, such as the prokaryotes, depend primarily on mutations to generate variation among offspring. This is sufficient for their survival because they produce great numbers of offspring very quickly. Although mutations also occur among sexually reproducing organisms, the reshuffling of genetic material during sexual reproduction ensures that offspring will have a different combination of genes from their parents. Meiosis brings about genetic variation in two key ways: crossing-over and independent assortment of homologous chromosomes.

Genetic Recombination

Crossing-over is an exchange of genetic material between non-sister chromatids of a bivalent during meiosis I. It is estimated that an average of two or three crossovers occur per human chromosome. At synapsis, homologues line up side by side, and a nucleoprotein lattice appears between them (Fig. 10.3). This lattice holds the bivalent together in such a way that the DNA of the duplicated chromosomes of each homologue pair is aligned. This ensures that the genes contained on the nonsister

Figure 10.3 Crossing-over occurs during meiosis I. **a.** The homologous chromosomes pair up, and a nucleoprotein lattice develops between them. This is an electron micrograph of the lattice. It "zippers" the members of the bivalent together so that corresponding genes on paired chromosomes are in alignment. **b.** This visual representation shows only two places where nonsister chromatids 1 and 3 have come into contact. Actually, the other two nonsister chromatids most likely are also crossing-over. **c.** Chiasmata indicate where crossing-over has occurred. The exchange of color represents the exchange of genetic material. **d.** Following meiosis II, daughter chromosomes have a new combination of genetic material due to crossing-over, which occurred between nonsister chromatids during meiosis I.

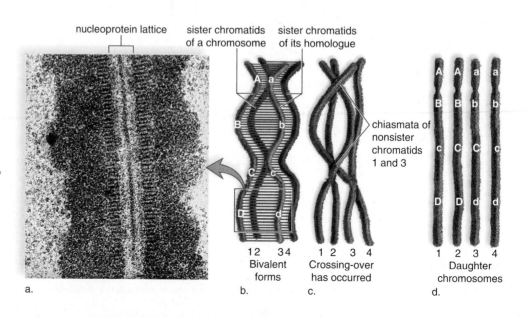

nucleoprotein lattice   sister chromatids   sister chromatids
                             of a chromosome   of its homologue

chiasmata of nonsister chromatids 1 and 3

12   34   1 2   3 4   1   2   3   4
Bivalent   Crossing-over   Daughter
forms   has occurred   chromosomes

a.   b.   c.   d.

chromatids are directly aligned. Now crossing-over may occur. As the lattice breaks down, homologues are temporarily held together by *chiasmata* (sing., chiasma), regions where the non-sister chromatids are attached due to DNA strand exchange and crossing-over. After exchange of genetic information between the mother's and father's chromosomes, the homologues separate and are distributed to different daughter cells.

Crossing-over has been shown to be essential for the normal segregation of chromosomes during meiosis. For example, reduced levels of crossing-over have been linked to Down syndrome, which is caused by an extra copy of chromosome 21.

To appreciate the significance of crossing-over, keep in mind that the members of a homologous pair can carry slightly different instructions for the same genetic traits. In the end, due to a swapping of genetic material during crossing-over, the chromatids held together by a centromere are no longer identical. Therefore, when the chromatids separate during meiosis II, some of the daughter cells receive daughter chromosomes with recombined alleles. Due to **genetic recombination,** the offspring have a different set of alleles, and therefore genes, than their parents. This increases the genetic variation of the offspring.

> **Animation**
> Meiosis with Crossing-Over

Independent Assortment of Homologous Chromosomes

During **independent assortment,** the homologous chromosome pairs separate independently, or in a random manner. When homologues align at the metaphase plate, the maternal or paternal homologue may be oriented toward either pole. Figure 10.4 shows the possible chromosome orientations for a cell that contains only three pairs of homologous chromosomes. Once all possible alignments of independent assortment are considered for these three pairs, the result will be 2^3, or eight, combinations of maternal and paternal chromosomes in the resulting gametes from this cell, simply due to independent assortment of homologues.

> **Animation**
> Random Orientation of Chromosomes During Meiosis

Significance of Genetic Variation

In humans, who have 23 pairs of chromosomes, the possible chromosomal combinations in the gametes is a staggering 2^{23}, or 8,388,608. The variation that results from meiosis is enhanced by **fertilization,** the union of the male and female gametes. The chromosomes donated by the parents are combined, and in humans, this means that there are $(2^{23})^2$, or 70,368,744,000,000, chromosomally different zygotes possible, even assuming no crossing-over. If crossing-over occurs once, then $(4^{23})^2$, or 4,951,760,200,000,000,000,000,000,000, genetically different zygotes are possible for every couple. Keep in mind that crossing-over can occur several times in each chromosome!

> **Animation**
> Genetic Diversity

The staggering amount of genetic variation achieved through meiosis is particularly important to the long-term survival of a species because it increases genetic variation within a population. (Asexual reproduction passes on exactly the same combination of chromosomes and genes.) The process of sexual reproduction brings about genetic recombinations among members of a population.

If a parent is already successful in a particular environment, is asexual reproduction advantageous? It would seem so as long as the environment remains unchanged. However, if the environment changes, genetic variability among offspring introduced by sexual reproduction may be advantageous. Under the new conditions, some offspring may have a better chance of survival and reproductive success than others in a population. For example, suppose the ambient temperature were to rise due to climate change. Perhaps a dog with genes for the least amount of fur may have an advantage over other dogs of its generation.

In a changing environment, sexual reproduction, with its reshuffling of genes due to meiosis and fertilization, might give a few offspring a better chance to survive and reproduce, thereby increasing the possibility of passing on their genes to the next generation.

Check Your Progress   10.2

1. Describe the two main ways in which meiosis contributes to genetic variation.
2. Examine how many combinations of chromosomes are possible in the gametes in a cell with four pairs of homologous chromosomes.
3. Evaluate why meiosis and sexual reproduction are important in responding to the changing environment.

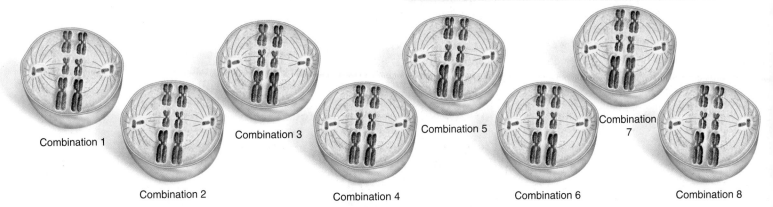

Combination 1
Combination 2
Combination 3
Combination 4
Combination 5
Combination 6
Combination 7
Combination 8

Figure 10.4 Independent assortment. When a parent cell has three pairs of homologous chromosomes, there are 2^3, or 8, possible chromosome alignments at the metaphase plate due to independent assortment. Among the 16 daughter nuclei resulting from these alignments, there are 8 different combinations of chromosomes. Each possible combination is shown, one in each cell.

10.3 The Phases of Meiosis

Learning Outcomes

Upon completion of this section, you should be able to

1. Describe the phases of meiosis and the major events that occur during each phase.
2. Identify the phase of meiosis where chromosome number is reduced from diploid to haploid.

Meiosis consists of two unique, consecutive cell divisions, meiosis I and meiosis II. DNA is replicated in S phase of the cell cycle prior to meiosis I but not meiosis II. Both meiosis I and meiosis II each contain a prophase, metaphase, anaphase, and telophase.

Animation Stages of Meiosis

Prophase I

It is apparent during prophase I that nuclear division is about to occur because a spindle forms as the centrosomes migrate away from one another. The nuclear envelope fragments, and the nucleolus disappears.

The homologous chromosomes, each having replicated during S phase of the cell cycle, consist of two sister chromatids. The homologous chromsomes undergo synapsis to form bivalents. At this time crossing-over may occur between the nonsister chromatids (Fig. 10.3). As described earlier, crossing-over increases the genetic diversity of the daughter cells, because after crossing-over, the sister chromatids are no longer identical.

Throughout prophase I, the homologous chromosomes have been condensing so that by now they have the appearance of compacted metaphase chromosomes.

Metaphase I

During metaphase I, the bivalents held together by chiasmata (see Fig. 10.3) have moved toward the metaphase plate (equator of the spindle). Metaphase I is characterized by a fully formed spindle and alignment of the bivalents at the metaphase plate. As in mitosis, kinetochores are seen, but the two kinetochores of a duplicated chromosome are attached to the same kinetochore spindle fiber.

Bivalents independently align themselves at the metaphase plate of the spindle. Either the maternal or paternal homologue of each bivalent may be oriented toward either pole of the cell. The orientation of one bivalent is not dependent on the orientation of the other bivalents. This independent assortment of chromosomes contributes to the genetic variability of the daughter cells because all possible combinations of chromosomes can occur in the daughter cells.

Anaphase I

During anaphase I, the homologues of each bivalent separate and move to opposite poles, but sister chromatids do not separate. This splitting of the homologous pair reduces the chromosome number from 2n to n. However, each chromosome still has two chromatids (see Fig. 10.5).

Telophase I

Completion of telophase I is not necessary during meiosis. That is, the spindle disappears, but new nuclear envelopes need not form before the daughter cells proceed to meiosis II. Also, this phase may or may not be accompanied by cytokinesis, which is separation of the cytoplasm. Figure 10.5 shows only two of the four possible combinations of haploid chromosomes when the parent cell has two homologous pairs of chromosomes. Can you determine what the other two possible combinations of chromosomes are?

Animation Meiosis I

Interkinesis

Following telophase, the cells enter interkinesis, a short rest period prior to beginning the second nuclear division, meiosis II. The process of **interkinesis** is similar to interphase between mitotic divisions except that DNA replication does not occur because the chromosomes are already duplicated.

Meiosis II and Gamete Formation

At the beginning of meiosis II, the two daughter cells contain the haploid number of chromosomes, or one chromosome from each homologous pair. Note that these chromosomes still consist of duplicated sister chromatids at this point. During metaphase II, the chromosomes align at the metaphase plate, but do not align in homologous pairs as in meiosis I because only one chromosome of each homologous pair is present (see Fig. 10.5). Thus, the alignment of the chromosomes at the metaphase plate is similar to what is observed during mitosis.

During anaphase II, the sister chromatids separate, becoming daughter chromosomes that are not duplicated. These daughter chromosomes move toward the poles. At the end of telophase II and cytokinesis, there are four haploid cells. Because of crossing-over of chromatids during meiosis I, each gamete most likely contains chromosomes with a mixture of maternal and paternal genes.

Animation Meiosis II

As mentioned, following meiosis II, the haploid cells become gametes in animals (see Section 10.5). In plants, they become **spores,** reproductive cells that develop into new multicellular structures without the need to fuse with another reproductive cell. The multicellular structure is the haploid generation, which produces gametes. The resulting zygote develops into a diploid generation. Therefore, plants have both haploid and diploid phases in their life cycle, and plants are said to exhibit an **alternation of generations.** In most fungi and algae, the zygote undergoes meiosis, and the daughter cells develop into new individuals. Therefore, the organism is always haploid.

Check Your Progress   10.3

1. Explain what would cause daughter cells following meiosis II to contain identical chromosomes or nonidentical chromosomes.
2. Examine what might happen if homologous chromosomes lined up top to bottom instead of side by side during meiosis I.

10.4 Meiosis Compared to Mitosis

Learning Outcomes

Upon completion of this section, you should be able to

1. Contrast changes in chromosome number, genetic variability, and number of daughter cells between meiosis and mitosis.
2. Distinguish the events that occur during prophase I of meiosis that do not occur during prophase of mitosis.
3. Compare chromosome alignment during meiosis I to mitosis.

Figure 10.6 graphically compares meiosis and mitosis. Several of the fundamental differences between the two processes include:

- Meiosis requires two nuclear divisions, but mitosis requires only one nuclear division.
- Meiosis produces four daughter nuclei. Following cytokinesis there are four daughter cells. Mitosis followed by cytokinesis results in two daughter cells.
- Following meiosis, the four daughter cells are haploid and have half the chromosome number as the diploid parent cell. Following mitosis, the daughter cells have the same chromosome number as the parent cell.
- Following meiosis, the daughter cells are neither genetically identical to each other nor to the parent cell. Following mitosis, the daughter cells are genetically identical to each other and to the parent cell.

In addition to the fundamental differences between meiosis and mitosis, two specific differences between the two types of nuclear divisions can be categorized. These differences involve occurrence and process.

Occurrence

Meiosis occurs only at certain times in the life cycle of sexually reproducing organisms. In humans, meiosis occurs only in the reproductive organs and produces the gametes. Mitosis is more common because it occurs in all tissues during growth and repair.

Animation Comparison of Meiosis and Mitosis

Process

We now compare the processes of both meiosis I and meiosis II to mitosis.

Meiosis I Compared to Mitosis

Notice that these events distinguish meiosis I from mitosis:

- During prophase I, bivalents form and crossing-over occurs. These events do not occur during mitosis.
- During metaphase I of meiosis, bivalents independently align at the metaphase plate. The paired chromosomes have a total of four chromatids each. During metaphase in mitosis, individual chromosomes align at the metaphase plate. They each have two chromatids.

Table 10.1 Meiosis I Compared to Mitosis

Meiosis I	Mitosis
Prophase I	**Prophase**
Pairing of homologous chromosomes	No pairing of chromosomes
Metaphase I	**Metaphase**
Bivalents at metaphase plate	Duplicated chromosomes at metaphase plate
Anaphase I	**Anaphase**
Homologues of each bivalent separate and duplicated chromosomes move to poles	Sister chromatids separate, becoming daughter chromosomes that move to the poles
Telophase I	**Telophase**
Two haploid daughter cells, not identical to the parent cell	Two diploid daughter cells, identical to the parent cell

Table 10.2 Meiosis II Compared to Mitosis

Meiosis II	Mitosis
Prophase II	**Prophase**
No pairing of chromosomes	No pairing of chromosomes
Metaphase II	**Metaphase**
Haploid number of duplicated chromosomes at metaphase plate	Diploid number of duplicated chromosomes at metaphase plate
Anaphase II	**Anaphase**
Sister chromatids separate, becoming daughter chromosomes that move to the poles	Sister chromatids separate, becoming daughter chromosomes that move to the poles
Telophase II	**Telophase**
Four haploid daughter cells, not genetically identical	Two diploid daughter cells, identical to the parent cell

- During anaphase I of meiosis, homologues of each bivalent separate and duplicated chromosomes (with centromeres intact) move to opposite poles. During anaphase of mitosis, sister chromatids separate, becoming daughter chromosomes that move to opposite poles.

Meiosis II Compared to Mitosis

The events of meiosis II are similar to those of mitosis except that in meiosis II, the nuclei contain the haploid number of chromosomes. In mitosis, the original number of chromosomes is maintained. Meiosis II produces two daughter cells from each parent cell that completes meiosis I, for a total of four daughter cells. These daughter cells contain the same number of chromosomes as they did at the end of meiosis I. Tables 10.1 and 10.2 compare meiosis I and II to mitosis.

Check Your Progress 10.4

1. Compare chromosome alignment between metaphase I of meiosis and metaphase of mitosis.
2. Explain how meiosis II is more similar to mitosis than to meiosis I.

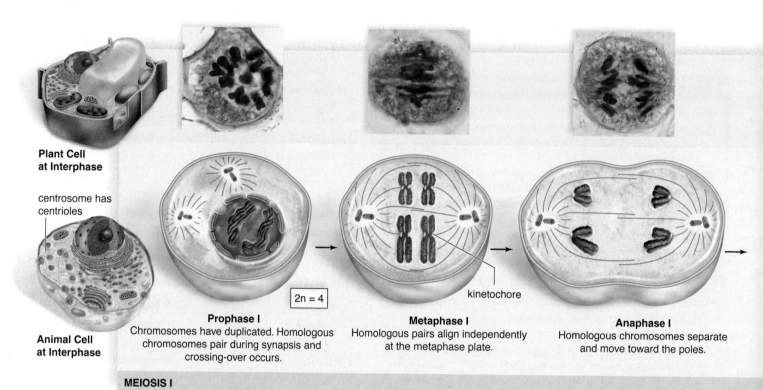

Plant Cell at Interphase

centrosome has centrioles

Animal Cell at Interphase

2n = 4

kinetochore

Prophase I
Chromosomes have duplicated. Homologous chromosomes pair during synapsis and crossing-over occurs.

Metaphase I
Homologous pairs align independently at the metaphase plate.

Anaphase I
Homologous chromosomes separate and move toward the poles.

MEIOSIS I

Figure 10.5 Meiosis I and II in plant cell micrographs and animal cell drawings. When diploid homologous chromosomes pair during meiosis I, crossing-over occurs as represented by the exchange of color. Pairs of homologous chromosomes separate during meiosis I, and chromatids separate, becoming haploid daughter chromosomes with two copies of each during meiosis II. Following meiosis II and the separation of sister chromatids, four haploid daughter cells are produced.

n = 2

n = 2

Prophase II
Cells have one chromosome from each homologous pair.

Metaphase II
Chromosomes align at the metaphase plate.

Anaphase II
Sister chromatids separate and become daughter chromosomes.

MEIOSIS II

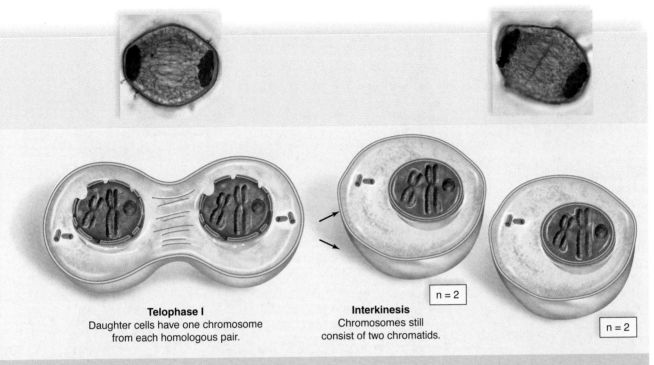

Telophase I
Daughter cells have one chromosome
from each homologous pair.

Interkinesis
Chromosomes still
consist of two chromatids.

n = 2

n = 2

MEIOSIS I cont'd

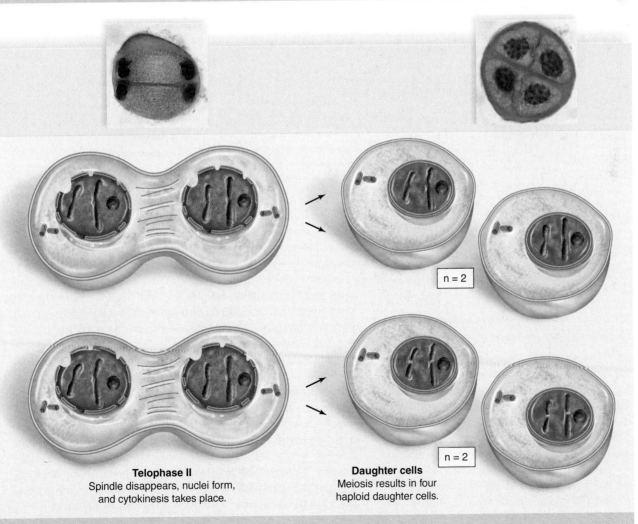

n = 2

Telophase II
Spindle disappears, nuclei form,
and cytokinesis takes place.

Daughter cells
Meiosis results in four
haploid daughter cells.

n = 2

MEIOSIS II cont'd

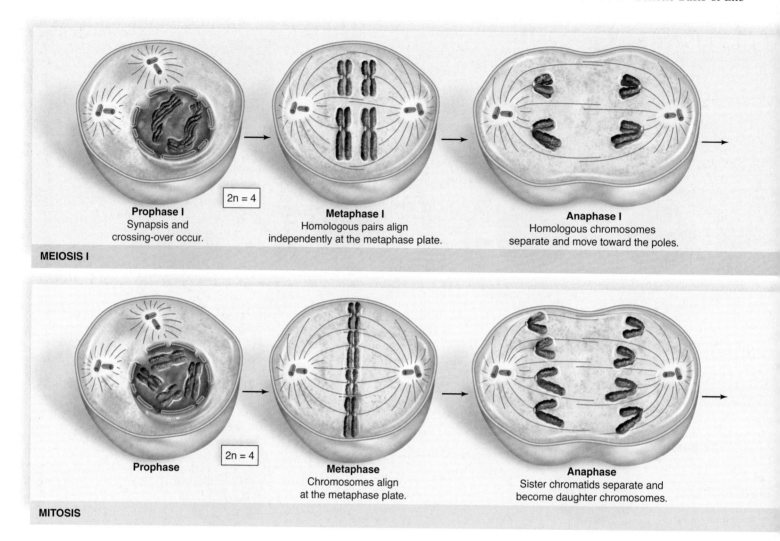

MEIOSIS I

Prophase I
Synapsis and
crossing-over occur.

2n = 4

Metaphase I
Homologous pairs align
independently at the metaphase plate.

Anaphase I
Homologous chromosomes
separate and move toward the poles.

MITOSIS

Prophase

2n = 4

Metaphase
Chromosomes align
at the metaphase plate.

Anaphase
Sister chromatids separate and
become daughter chromosomes.

10.5 The Cycle of Life

Learning Outcomes

Upon completion of this section, you should be able to

1. Contrast the life cycle of plants with the life cycle of animals.
2. Describe spermatogenesis and oogenesis in humans.

The term **life cycle** refers to all the reproductive events that occur from one generation to the next similar generation. In animals, including humans, the individual is always diploid, and meiosis produces the gametes, the only haploid phase of the life cycle (Fig. 10.7). In contrast, plants have a haploid phase that alternates with a diploid phase. The haploid generation, known as the **gametophyte,** may be larger or smaller than the diploid generation, called the **sporophyte.**

Mosses growing on bare rocks and forest floors are the haploid generation, and the diploid generation is short-lived.

In most fungi and algae, the zygote is the only diploid portion of the life cycle, and it undergoes meiosis. Therefore, the black mold that grows on bread and the green scum that floats on a pond are haploid.

The majority of plant species, including pine, corn, and sycamore, are usually diploid, and the haploid generation is short-lived. In plants, algae, and fungi, the haploid phase of the life cycle produces gamete nuclei without the need for meiosis because it has occurred earlier.

Animals are diploid, and meiosis occurs during the production of gametes (**gametogenesis**). In males, meiosis is a part of **spermatogenesis** [Gk. *sperma*, seed; L. *genitus*, producing], which occurs in the testes and produces sperm. In females, meiosis is a part of **oogenesis** [Gk. *oon*, egg; L. *genitus*, producing], which occurs in the ovaries and produces eggs. A sperm and egg join at fertilization, restoring the diploid chromosome number. The resulting zygote undergoes mitosis during development of the fetus. After birth, mitosis is involved in the continued growth of the child and repair of tissues at any time.

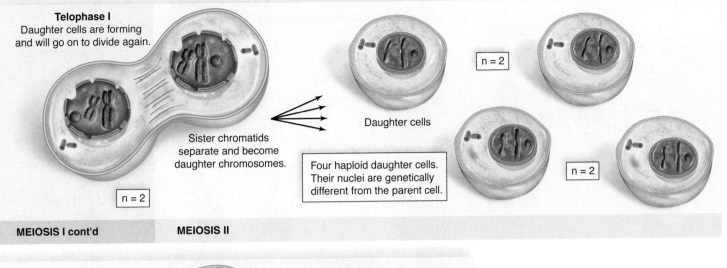

Telophase I
Daughter cells are forming
and will go on to divide again.

Sister chromatids
separate and become
daughter chromosomes.

Daughter cells

n = 2

n = 2

Four haploid daughter cells.
Their nuclei are genetically
different from the parent cell.

n = 2

MEIOSIS I cont'd   MEIOSIS II

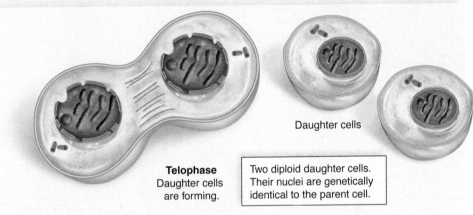

Daughter cells

Telophase
Daughter cells
are forming.

Two diploid daughter cells.
Their nuclei are genetically
identical to the parent cell.

MITOSIS cont'd

Figure 10.6 Meiosis compared to mitosis. Why does meiosis produce daughter cells with half the number of chromosomes, while mitosis produces daughter cells with the same number of chromosomes as the parent cell? Compare metaphase I of meiosis to metaphase of mitosis. Only in metaphase I of meiosis are the homologous chromosomes paired at the metaphase plate. Members of homologous chromosome pairs separate during anaphase I, and therefore the daughter cells are haploid. The exchange of color between nonsister chromatids represents the crossing-over that occurred during meiosis I. The blue chromosomes were inherited from the paternal parent, and the red chromosomes were inherited from the maternal parent.

Spermatogenesis and Oogenesis in Humans

In human males, spermatogenesis occurs within the testes, and in females, oogenesis occurs within the ovaries.

Spermatogenesis

The testes contain stem cells called spermatogonia, and these cells keep the testes supplied with primary spermatocytes that undergo spermatogenesis as described in Figure 10.8, *top.* Primary spermatocytes with 46 chromosomes undergo meiosis I to form two secondary spermatocytes, each with 23 duplicated chromosomes. Secondary spermatocytes undergo meiosis II to produce four spermatids with 23 daughter chromosomes. Spermatids then differentiate into viable sperm (spermatozoa). Upon sexual arousal, the sperm enter ducts and exit the penis upon ejaculation.

Animation
Spermatogenesis

Oogenesis

The ovaries contain stem cells called oogonia that produce many primary oocytes with 46 chromosomes during fetal development.

They even begin oogenesis, but only a few continue when a female has become sexually mature. The result of meiosis I is two haploid cells with 23 chromosomes each (Fig. 10.8, *bottom*). One of these cells, termed the **secondary oocyte** [Gk, *oon*, egg, and *kytos*, cell], receives almost all the cytoplasm. The other is a **polar body** that may either disintegrate or divide again.

The secondary oocyte begins meiosis II but stops at metaphase II. Then the secondary oocyte leaves the ovary and enters an oviduct, where sperm may be present. If no sperm are in the oviduct, or if a sperm does not enter the secondary oocyte, it eventually disintegrates without completing meiosis. If a sperm does enter the oocyte, some of its contents trigger the completion of meiosis II in the secondary oocyte, and another polar body forms.

At the completion of oogenesis, following entrance of a sperm, there is one egg and two to three polar bodies. The polar bodies are a way to "dispose" of chromosomes while retaining much of the cytoplasm in the egg. Cytoplasmic molecules and organelles are needed by a developing embryo following

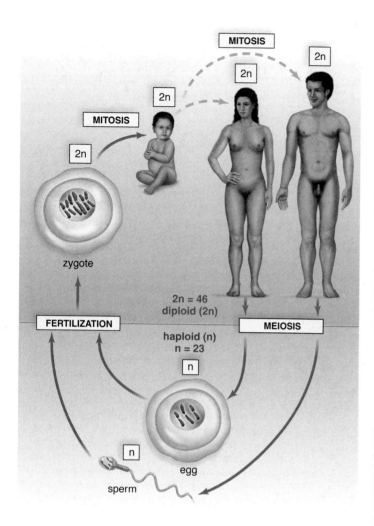

Figure 10.7 Life cycle of humans.   Meiosis in males is a part of sperm production, and meiosis in females is a part of egg production. When a haploid sperm fertilizes a haploid egg, the zygote is diploid. The zygote undergoes mitosis as it develops into a newborn child. Mitosis continues throughout life during growth and repair.

fertilization. Some zygote components, such as the centrosome, are contributed by the sperm.

The mature egg has 23 chromosomes, but the zygote formed when the sperm and egg nuclei fuse has 46 chromosomes. Therefore, fertilization restores the diploid number of chromosomes. The production of haploid gametes and subsequent fusion of those gametes into a diploid zygote completes a human life cycle.

Check Your Progress   10.5

1. Describe where cells that undergo meiosis are located in humans.
2. Compare the number of gametes produced during oogenesis and spermatogenesis in humans.

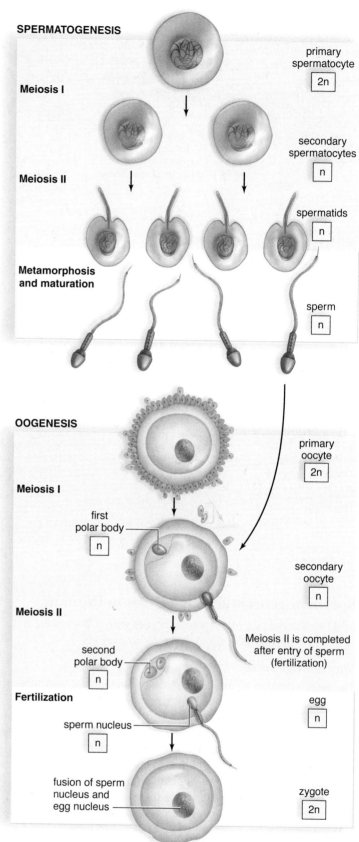

Figure 10.8 Spermatogenesis and oogenesis in mammals.
Spermatogenesis produces four viable sperm, whereas oogenesis produces one egg and at least two polar bodies. In humans, both sperm and egg have 23 chromosomes each; therefore, following fertilization, the zygote has 46 chromosomes.

10.6 Changes in Chromosome Number and Structure

We have seen that crossing-over creates variation within a population and is essential for the normal separation of chromosomes during meiosis. Furthermore, the proper separation of homologous chromosomes during meiosis I and the separation of sister chromatids during meiosis II are essential for the maintenance of normal chromosome numbers in living organisms. Although meiosis almost always proceeds normally, failure of chromosomes to separate, or **nondisjunction,** may occur, resulting in gain or loss of chromosomes. Errors in crossing-over may result in extra or missing parts of chromosomes.

Aneuploidy

The correct number of chromosomes in a species is known as **euploidy.** A change in the chromosome number resulting from nondisjunction during meiosis is called **aneuploidy.** Aneuploidy is seen in both plants and animals. Monosomy and trisomy are two aneuploid states.

Monosomy $(2n - 1)$ occurs when an individual has only one of a particular type of chromosome when they should have two, and **trisomy** $(2n + 1)$ occurs when an individual has three of a particular type of chromosome when they should have two. Both monosomy and trisomy are the result of nondisjunction during mitosis or meiosis. *Primary nondisjunction* occurs during meiosis I when both members of a homologous pair go into the same daughter cell (Fig. 10.9*a*). *Secondary nondisjunction* occurs during meiosis II when the sister chromatids fail to separate and both daughter chromosomes go into the same gamete (Fig. 10.9*b*).

Notice that when secondary nondisjunction occurs, there are two normal gametes and two aneuploid gametes. In contrast, when primary nondisjunction occurs, no normal gametes are produced. Therefore, primary nondisjunction tends to have more deleterious effects than secondary nondisjunction.

In animals, monosomies and trisomies of non-sex, or autosomal, chromosomes are generally lethal, but a trisomic individual is more likely to survive than a monosomic one. In humans,

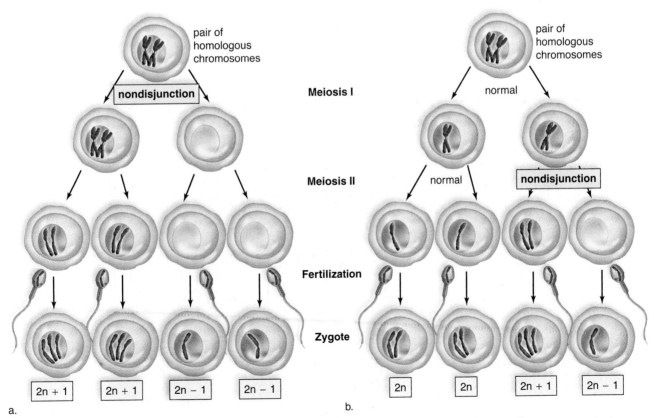

Figure 10.9 Nondisjunction of chromosomes during oogenesis, followed by fertilization with normal sperm. **a.** Nondisjunction can occur during meiosis I (primary nondisjunction) and results in abnormal eggs that also have one more or one less than the normal number of chromosomes. Fertilization of these abnormal eggs with normal sperm results in a zygote with abnormal chromosome numbers. 2n = diploid number of chromosomes. **b.** Nondisjunction can also occur during meiosis II (secondary nondisjunction) if the sister chromatids separate but the resulting daughter chromosomes go into the same daughter cell. Then the egg will have one more or one less than the usual number of chromosomes. Fertilization of these abnormal eggs with normal sperm produces a zygote with abnormal chromosome numbers.

only three autosomal trisomic conditions are known to be viable beyond birth: trisomy 13, 18, and 21. Only trisomy 21 is viable beyond early childhood, and is characterized by a distinctive set of physical and mental abnormalities. In comparison, sex chromosome aneuploids are better tolerated in animals and have a better chance of producing survivors.

Trisomy 21

The most common autosomal trisomy seen among humans is trisomy 21, also called Down syndrome. This syndrome is easily recognized by these characteristics: short stature; an eyelid fold; a flat face; stubby fingers; a wide gap between the first and second toes; a large, fissured tongue; a round head; a distinctive palm crease; heart problems; and some degree of mental retardation, which can sometimes be severe. Individuals with Down syndrome also have a greatly increased risk of developing leukemia and tend to age rapidly, resulting in a shortened life expectancy. In addition, these individuals have an increased chance of developing Alzheimer disease later in life.

Many scientists agree that the symptoms of Down syndrome are caused by gene dosage effects resulting from the presence of the extra chromosome. Recent studies indicate that not all of the genes on the chromosome are expressed at a level of 150%, challenging this theory; however, scientists have identified several genes that have been linked to increased risk of leukemia, cataracts, aging, and mental retardation.

The chances of a woman having a child with Down syndrome increase rapidly with age. In women ages 20 to 30, the incidence of trisomy 21 is 1 in 1,400 births, and in women 30 to 35, the incidence is about 1 in 750 births. It is thought that the longer the oocytes are stored in the female, the greater the chances of nondisjunction occurring. However, even though an older woman is more likely to have a Down syndrome child, most babies with Down syndrome are born to women younger than age 40 because this is the age group having the most babies. Furthermore, some recent research also indicate that in 23% of the cases studied, the sperm contributed the extra chromosome. A **karyotype,** a visual display of the chromosomes arranged by size, shape, and banding pattern, may be performed to identify babies with Down syndrome and other aneuploid conditions (Fig. 10.10).

Changes in Sex Chromosome Number

An abnormal sex chromosome number is the result of inheriting too many or too few X or Y chromosomes. Nondisjunction during oogenesis or spermatogenesis can result in gametes with an abnormal number of sex chromosomes. However, extra copies of the sex chromosomes are much more easily tolerated in humans than are extra copies of autosomes.

A person with Turner syndrome (XO) is a female, and a person with Klinefelter syndrome (XXY) is a male. However, deletion of the *SRY* gene on the short arm of the Y chromosome results in Swyer syndrome, or an "XY female." Individuals with Swyer syndrome lack a hormone called testis-determining factor, which plays a critical role in the development of male genitals. Furthermore, movement of this same gene onto the X chromosome may result in de la Chapelle syndrome, or an "XX male." Men with de la Chapelle syndrome exhibit undersized testes, sterility, and rudimentary breast development. Together, these observations suggest that in humans, the presence of the *SRY* gene, not the number of X chromosomes, determines maleness. In its absence, a person develops as a female.

a.

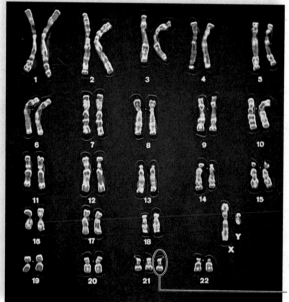

b.

extra chromosome 21

Figure 10.10 Trisomy 21.   Persons with Down syndrome, or trisomy 21, have an extra chromosome 21. **a.** Common characteristics of the syndrome include a wide, rounded face and a fold on the upper eyelids. Mental disabilities, along with an enlarged tongue, may make it difficult for a person with Down syndrome to speak distinctly. **b.** The karyotype of an individual with Down syndrome shows three copies of chromosome 21. Therefore, the individual has three copies instead of two copies of each gene on chromosome 21. Researchers are using new techniques to discover which genes on chromosome 21 are causing the syndrome's disabilities.

Why are newborns with an abnormal sex chromosome number more likely to survive than those with an abnormal autosome number? Because females have two X chromosomes and males have only one, we might expect females to produce twice the amount of each gene from this chromosome, but both males and females produce roughly the same amount. In reality, both males and females only have one functioning X chromosome. In females, and in males with extra X chromosomes, any additional X chromosomes become an inactive mass called a **Barr body,** named after Murray Barr, the person who discovered it. This inactivation provides a natural method for gene dosage compensation of the sex chromosomes and explains why extra sex chromosomes are more easily tolerated than extra autosomes.

Turner Syndrome. From birth, an XO individual with Turner syndrome has only one sex chromosome, an X; the O signifies the absence of a second sex chromosome (Fig. 10.11a). Therefore, the nucleus does not contain a Barr body. The approximate incidence is 1 in 10,000 females.

Turner females are short, with a broad chest and widely spaced nipples. These individuals also have a low posterior hairline and neck webbing. The ovaries, oviducts, and uterus are very small and underdeveloped. Turner females do not undergo puberty or menstruate, and their breasts do not develop. However, some have given birth following in vitro fertilization using donor eggs. They usually are of normal intelligence and can lead fairly normal lives if they receive hormone supplements.

Klinefelter Syndrome. A male with Klinefelter syndrome has two or more X chromosomes in addition to a Y chromosome (Fig. 10.11b). The extra X chromosomes become Barr bodies. The approximate incidence for Klinefelter syndrome is 1 in 500 to 1,000 males.

In Klinefelter males, the testes and prostate gland are underdeveloped and facial hair is lacking. They may exhibit some breast development. Affected individuals have large hands and feet and very long arms and legs. They are usually slow to learn but not mentally retarded unless they inherit more than two X chromosomes. No matter how many X chromosomes there are, an individual with a Y chromosome is a male.

While males with Klinefelter syndrome exhibit no other major health abnormalities, they have an increased risk of some disorders, including breast cancer, osteoporosis, and lupus, which disproportionately affect females. Although men with

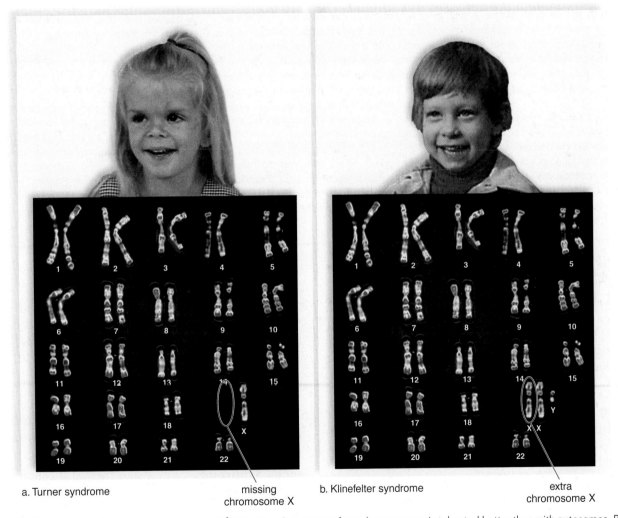

a. Turner syndrome   missing chromosome X   b. Klinefelter syndrome   extra chromosome X

Figure 10.11 Abnormal sex chromosome number. Nondisjunction of sex chromosomes is tolerated better than with autosomes. People with (**a**) Turner syndrome, who have only one X chromosome, as shown, and (**b**) Klinefelter syndrome, who have more than one X chromosome plus a Y chromosome, as shown, can look relatively normal (especially as children) and can lead relatively normal lives.

THEME Evolution

Living with Klinefelter Syndrome

In 1996, at the age of 25, I was diagnosed with Klinefelter syndrome (KS). Being diagnosed has changed my life for the better.

I was a happy baby, but when I was still very young, my parents began to believe that there was something wrong with me. I knew something was different about me, too, as early on as five years old. I was very shy and had trouble making friends. One minute I'd be well behaved, and the next I'd be picking fights and flying into a rage. Many psychologists, therapists, and doctors tested me because of school and social problems and severe mood changes. Their only diagnosis was "learning disabilities" in such areas as reading comprehension, abstract thinking, word retrieval, and auditory processing.

No one could figure out what the real problem was, and I hated the tutoring sessions I had. In the seventh grade, a psychologist told me that I was stupid and lazy, I would probably live at home for the rest of my life, and I would never amount to anything. For the next five years, he was basically right, and I barely graduated from high school.

I believe, though, that I have succeeded because I was told that I would fail. I quit the tutoring sessions when I enrolled at a community college; I decided I could figure things out on my own. I received an associate degree there, then transferred to a small liberal arts college. I never told anyone about my learning disabilities and never sought special help. However, I never had a semester below a 3.0, and I graduated with two B.S. degrees. I was accepted into a graduate program but decided instead to accept a job as a software engineer even though I did not have an educational background in this field. As I later learned, many KS'ers excel in computer skills. I had been using a computer for many years and had learned everything I needed to know on my own, through trial and error.

Around the time I started the computer job, I went to my physician for a physical. He sent me for blood tests because he noticed that my testes were smaller than usual. The results were conclusive: Klinefelter syndrome with sex chromosomes XXY. I initially felt denial, depression, and anger, even though I now had an explanation for many of the problems I had experienced all my life. But then I decided to learn as much as I could about the condition and treatments available. I now give myself a testosterone injection once every two weeks, and it has made me a different person, with improved learning abilities and stronger thought processes in addition to a more outgoing personality.

I found, though, that the best possible path I could take was to help others live with the condition. I attended my first support group meeting four months after I was diagnosed. By spring 1997, I had developed an interest in KS that was more than just a part-time hobby. I wanted to be able to work with this condition and help people forever. I have been very involved in KS conferences and have helped to start support groups in the United States, Spain, and Australia.

Since my diagnosis, it has been my dream to have a son with KS, although when I was diagnosed, I found out it was unlikely that I could have biological children. Through my work with KS, I had the opportunity to meet my wife, Chris. She has two wonderful children: a daughter, and a son who has the same condition that I do. There are a lot of similarities between my stepson and me, and I am happy I will be able to help him get the head start in coping with KS that I never had. I also look forward to many more years of helping other people seek diagnosis and live a good life with Klinefelter syndrome.

—Stefan Schwarz

Questions to Consider

1. If you discovered you had a genetic disease, how would you deal with it?
2. Why have genetic diseases persisted over time in the human population?
3. With scientific advances like the Human Genome Project, what treatments might be available to treat genetic diseases?

Klinefelter syndrome typically do not need medical treatment, some have found that testosterone therapy may help increase muscle strength, sex drive, and concentration ability. Testosterone treatment, however, does not reverse the sterility associated with Klinefelter syndrome due to the incomplete testicle development.

The Evolution feature in this chapter describes the personal experiences of a person with Klinefelter syndrome. The essay suggests that it is best for parents to know right away that they have a child with this abnormality because much can be done to help the child lead a normal life.

Poly-X Females. A poly-X female, sometimes called a superfemale, has more than two X chromosomes and, therefore, extra Barr bodies in the nucleus. Females with three X chromosomes have no distinctive phenotype aside from a tendency to be tall and thin. Although some have delayed motor and language development, as well as learning problems, most poly-X females are not mentally retarded. Some may have menstrual difficulties, but many menstruate regularly and are fertile. Children usually have a normal karyotype. The incidence for poly-X females is about 1 in 1,500 females.

Females with more than three X chromosomes occur rarely. Unlike XXX females, XXXX females are usually tall and severely mentally retarded. Various physical abnormalities are seen, but they may menstruate normally.

Jacobs Syndrome. XYY males, termed Jacobs syndrome, can result only from nondisjunction during spermatogenesis. These individuals are sometimes called supermales. Among all live male births, the frequency of the XYY karyotype is about 1 in 1,000. Affected males are usually taller than average, suffer from persistent acne, and tend to have speech and reading problems, but are fertile and may have children. Based upon the number of XYY individuals in prisons and mental facilities, it was suggested at one time that these men were likely to be criminally aggressive, but it has since been shown that the incidence of such behavior among them may be no greater than among XY males.

Changes in Chromosome Structure

Changes in chromosome structure are another type of chromosomal mutation. Some, but not all, changes in chromosome structure can be detected microscopically. Various agents in the environment, such as radiation, certain organic chemicals, or even viruses, can cause chromosomes to break. Ordinarily, when breaks occur in chromosomes, the two broken ends reunite to give the same sequence of genes. Sometimes, however, the broken ends of one or more chromosomes do not rejoin in the same pattern as before, and the result is various types of chromosomal mutations.

Changes in chromosome structure include deletions, duplications, translocations, and inversions of chromosome segments. A **deletion** occurs when an end of a chromosome breaks off or when two simultaneous breaks lead to the loss of an internal segment (Fig. 10.12a). Even when only one member of a pair of chromosomes is affected, a deletion often causes abnormalities.

Animation
Changes in Chromosome Structure

A **duplication** is the presence of a chromosomal segment more than once in the same chromosome (Fig. 10.12b). Duplications may or may not cause visible abnormalities, depending on the size of the duplicated region. An **inversion** has occurred when a segment of a chromosome is turned around 180° (Fig. 10.12c). Most individuals with inversions exhibit no abnormalities, but this reversed sequence of genes can result in duplications or deletions being passed on to their children, as described in Figure 10.13.

A **translocation** is the movement of a chromosome segment from one chromosome to another, nonhomologous chromosome. The translocation shown in Figure 10.12d is *balanced*, meaning that there is a reciprocal swap of one piece of the chromosome

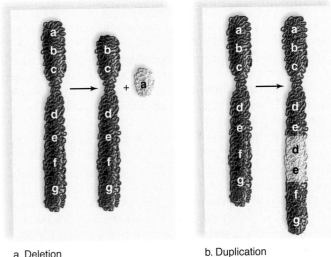

a. Deletion
b. Duplication

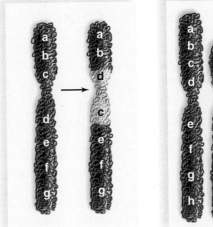
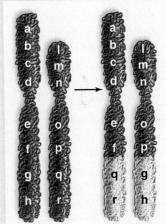

c. Inversion
d. Translocation

Figure 10.12 Types of chromosomal mutations. **a.** Deletion is the loss of a chromosome piece. **b.** Duplication occurs when the same piece is repeated within the chromosome. **c.** Inversion occurs when a piece of chromosome breaks loose and then rejoins in the reversed direction. **d.** Translocation is the exchange of chromosome pieces between nonhomologous pairs.

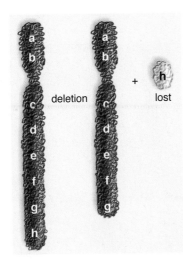

deletion
lost

Figure 10.13 Deletion.

a. When chromosome 7 loses an end piece, the result is Williams syndrome. **b.** These children, although unrelated, have the same appearance, health, and behavioral problems.

a.

b.

for the other. Often, there are no visible effects of the swap, but if the individual has children, they receive one normal copy of the chromosome from the normal parent, and one of the abnormal chromosomes. The translocation is now *unbalanced*, with extra material from one chromosome and missing material from another chromosome. Embryos with unbalanced translocations usually result in miscarriage, but those individuals who are born often have severe symptoms.

Some Down syndrome cases are caused by an unbalanced translocation between chromosomes 21 and 14. In other words, because a portion of chromosome 21 is now attached to a portion of chromosome 14, the individual has three copies of the genes that bring about Down syndrome when they are present in triplet copy. In these cases, Down syndrome is not caused by nondisjunction during meiosis, but is passed on normally like any other genetic trait as described in Chapter 11.

Human Syndromes

Changes in chromosome structure occur in humans and lead to various syndromes, many of which are just now being discovered. Sometimes changes in chromosome structure can be detected in humans by doing a karyotype. They may also be discovered by studying the inheritance pattern of a disorder in a particular family.

Deletion Syndromes. Williams syndrome occurs when chromosome 7 loses a tiny end piece (Fig. 10.13). Children who have this syndrome look like pixies, with turned-up noses, wide mouths, a small chin, and large ears. Although their academic skills are poor, they exhibit excellent verbal and musical abilities. The gene that governs the production of the protein elastin is missing, and this affects the health of the cardiovascular system and causes their skin to age prematurely. Such individuals are very friendly but need an ordered life, perhaps because of the loss of a gene for a protein that is normally active in the brain.

Cri du chat (cat's cry) syndrome is seen when chromosome 5 is missing an end piece. The affected individual has a small head, is mentally retarded, and has facial abnormalities. Abnormal development of the glottis and larynx results in the most characteristic symptom—the infant's cry resembles that of a cat.

Translocation Syndromes. A person who has both of the chromosomes involved in a translocation has the normal amount of genetic material and is healthy, unless the chromosome exchange breaks an allele into two pieces. The person who inherits only one of the translocated chromosomes no doubt has only one copy of certain alleles and three copies of certain other alleles. A genetic counselor begins to suspect a translocation has occurred when spontaneous abortions are commonplace and family members suffer from various syndromes. A special microscopic technique allows a technician to determine that a translocation has occurred.

Figure 10.14 shows a person who has a translocation between chromosomes 2 and 20. Although they have the normal amount of genetic material, they have the distinctive face, abnormalities of the eyes and internal organs, and severe itching characteristic of Alagille syndrome. People with this syndrome ordinarily have a deletion on chromosome 20 (Fig. 10.14a), which can lead to a congenital heart condition called Tetralogy of Fallot that produces digital clubbing of the fingers (Fig. 10.14b). The symptoms of Alagille syndrome range from mild to severe, so some people may not be aware they have the syndrome until after they've had children

Translocations can also be responsible for a variety of other disorders including certain types of cancer. In the 1970s, new staining techniques identified that a translocation from a portion of chromosome 22 to chromosome 9 was responsible for many cases of chronic myelogenous leukemia. This translocated chromosome was called Philadelphia chromosome. In Burkitt lymphoma, a cancer common in children in equatorial Africa, a large tumor develops from lymph glands in the region of the jaw. This disorder involves a translocation from a portion of chromosome 8 to chromosome 14.

Check Your Progress   10.6

1. Explain the kinds of changes in chromosome number that can be caused by nondisjunction in meiosis.
2. Examine why sex chromosome aneuploidy is more common than autosome aneuploidy.
3. Compare structural changes between an inversion and a translocation.

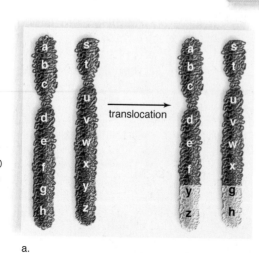

Figure 10.14
Translocation.

a. When chromosomes 2 and 20 exchange segments, (**b**) Alagille syndrome, with distinctive body features, sometimes results because of organ malfunction caused by the chromosome 20 translocation.

translocation

a.

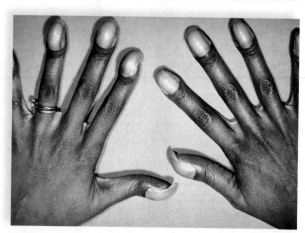

b.

CONNECTING *the* CONCEPTS *with the* THEMES

Evolution

- Meiosis is a key process in sexual reproduction, with both evolutionary costs and benefits.
- Although mutations during meiosis can produce faulty gametes, greater genetic diversity is also possible, and this diversity can benefit the species.
- Understanding chromosomal behavior during meiosis is critical to understanding how genes segregate during gamete formation and how this contributes to patterns of inheritance.

Nature of Science

- Researching meoisis provides a deeper understanding of chromosome transmission, leading to the possiblity of treating genetic diseases like Down syndrome prior to birth.
- Greater understanding of how chromosomes match up and exchange genetic information during meiosis can help us understand one of the foundations of genetic diversity.

Biological Systems

- Meiosis and mitosis use similar processes to separate chromosomes.
- Like the cell cycle and mitosis, meiosis is tightly controlled. Regulatory mechanisms ensure that homologous chromosomes first pair and then separate during the first division, and that sister chromatids do not separate until the second division.
- Meiosis occurs only in certain types of cells during a restricted period of an organism's life span.

Media Study Tools

www.mhhe.com/maderbiology11

Enhance your study of this chapter with study tools and practice tests. Also ask your instructor about the resources available through ConnectPlus, including the media-rich eBook, interactive learning tools, and animations.

Summarize

10.1 Halving the Chromosome Number

Meiosis ensures that the chromosome number in offspring stays constant generation after generation. The nucleus contains pairs of chromosomes, called homologous chromosomes (homologues).

Meiosis requires two cell divisions and results in four daughter cells. Replication of DNA takes place before meiosis begins. During meiosis I, the homologues undergo synapsis (resulting in a bivalent) and align independently at the metaphase plate. The daughter cells receive one member of each pair of homologous chromosomes. There is no replication of DNA during interkinesis, the pause between meiosis I and II. During meiosis II, the sister chromatids separate, becoming daughter chromosomes that move to opposite poles as they do in mitosis. The four daughter cells contain the haploid number of chromosomes and only one of each kind.

10.2 Genetic Variation

Sexual reproduction ensures that the offspring have a different genetic makeup than the parents, and increases the ability of a species to survive. Meiosis contributes to genetic variability in two ways: crossing-over and independent assortment of the homologous chromosomes. When homologous chromosomes lie side by side during synapsis, nonsister chromatids may exchange genetic material. Due to crossing-over, the chromatids that separate during meiosis II have a different combination of genes.

When the homologous chromosomes align at the metaphase plate during metaphase I, either the maternal or the paternal chromosome can be facing either pole. Therefore, there will be all possible combinations of chromosomes in the gametes.

10.3 The Phases of Meiosis

Meiosis I, which splits pairs of homologous chromosomes and reduces the chromosome number from 2n to n, is divided into four phases:

Prophase I—Bivalents form, and crossing-over occurs as chromosomes condense; the nuclear envelope fragments.

Metaphase I—Bivalents independently align at the metaphase plate.

Anaphase I—Homologous chromosomes separate, and duplicated chromosomes move to poles.

Telophase I—Nuclei become haploid, having received one duplicated chromosome from each homologous pair.

Meiosis II, which reduces the amount of DNA in half from previously replicated 1n chromosomes, is divided into four phases:

Prophase II—Chromosomes condense, and the nuclear envelope fragments.

Metaphase II—The haploid number of still duplicated chromosomes align at the metaphase plate.

Anaphase II—Sister chromatids separate, becoming daughter chromosomes that move to the poles.

Telophase II—Four haploid daughter cells are genetically different from the parent cell.

10.4 Meiosis Compared to Mitosis

Mitosis and meiosis can be compared in this manner:

Meiosis I	Mitosis
Prophase	
Pairing of homologous chromosomes	No pairing of chromosomes
Metaphase	
Bivalents at metaphase plate	Duplicated chromosomes at metaphase plate
Anaphase	
Homologous chromosomes separate and move to poles	Sister chromatids separate, becoming daughter chromosomes that move to the poles
Telophase	
Daughter nuclei have the haploid number of chromosomes	Daughter nuclei have the parent cell chromosome number

Meiosis II is like mitosis except the nuclei are haploid.

10.5 The Cycle of Life

Meiosis occurs in any life cycle that involves sexual reproduction. In the animal life cycle, only the gametes are haploid; in plants, meiosis produces spores that develop into a multicellular haploid adult that produces the gametes. In unicellular protists and fungi, the zygote undergoes meiosis, and spores become a haploid adult that gives rise to gametes.

During the life cycle of humans and other animals, meiosis is involved in spermatogenesis and oogenesis. Whereas spermatogenesis produces four sperm per meiosis, oogenesis produces one egg and two to three nonfunctional polar bodies. Spermatogenesis occurs in males, and oogenesis occurs in females. When a sperm fertilizes an egg, the zygote has the diploid number of chromosomes. Mitosis, which is involved in growth and repair, also occurs during the life cycle of all animals.

10.6 Changes in Chromosome Number and Structure

Nondisjunction during meiosis I or meiosis II may result in aneuploidy (extra or missing copies of chromosomes). Monosomy occurs when an individual has only one of a particular type of chromosome $(2n - 1)$ and is usually lethal; trisomy occurs when an individual has three of a particular type of chromosome $(2n + 1)$. Down syndrome is a well-known trisomy in human beings resulting from an extra copy of chromosome 21.

Aneuploidy of the sex chromosomes is tolerated more easily than aneuploidy of the autosomes. Turner syndrome, Klinefelter syndrome, poly-X females, and Jacobs syndrome are examples of sex chromosome aneuploidy.

Abnormalities in crossing-over may result in deletions, duplications, inversions, and translocations within chromosomes. Many human syndromes, including Williams syndrome, cri du chat syndrome, and Alagille syndrome, result from changes in chromosome structure.

Key Terms

allele 172	interkinesis 176
alternation of generations 176	inversion 187
aneuploidy 183	karyotype 184
Barr body 185	life cycle 180
bivalent 173	meiosis 172
crossing-over 174	monosomy 183
deletion 187	nondisjunction 183
diploid (2n) number 172	oogenesis 180
duplication 187	polar body 181
euploidy 183	secondary oocyte 181
fertilization 175	sexual reproduction 172
gamete 172	spermatogenesis 180
gametogenesis 180	spore 176
gametophyte 180	sporophyte 180
genetic recombination 175	synapsis 173
haploid (n) number 172	synaptonemal complex 173
homologous	translocation 187
chromosome 172	trisomy 183
homologue 172	zygote 172
independent assortment 175	

Assess

Reviewing This Chapter

1. Why did early investigators predict that there must be a reduction division in the sexual reproduction process?   172
2. What are homologous chromosomes? Contrast the genetic makeup of sister chromatids with that of nonsister chromatids.   172–74
3. Draw and explain a diagram that illustrates crossing-over and another that shows all possible results from independent assortment of homologous pairs. How do these events ensure genetic variation among the gametes?   174–75
4. Draw and explain a series of diagrams that illustrate the stages of meiosis I and meiosis II.   177–81
5. What accounts for **(a)** the genetic similarity between daughter cells and the parent cell following mitosis, and **(b)** the genetic dissimilarity between daughter cells and the parent cell following meiosis?   180–81
6. Explain the human (animal) life cycle and the roles of meiosis and mitosis.   180–81
7. Compare spermatogenesis in males to oogenesis in females.   181
8. How does aneuploidy occur? Why is sex chromosome aneuploidy more common than autosomal aneuploidy? What are some human syndromes associated with aneuploidy?   183–87
9. Name and explain four types of changes in chromosome structure.   187–88
10. Name some syndromes that occur in humans due to changes in chromosome structure.   188

Testing Yourself

Choose the best answer for each question.

1. A bivalent is
   a. a homologous chromosome.
   b. the paired homologous chromosomes.
   c. a duplicated chromosome composed of sister chromatids.
   d. the two daughter cells after meiosis I.
   e. the two centrioles in a centrosome.

2. If a parent cell has 16 chromosomes, then each of the daughter cells following meiosis will have
   a. 48 chromosomes.   c. 16 chromosomes.
   b. 32 chromosomes.   d. 8 chromosomes.

3. At the metaphase plate during metaphase I of meiosis, there are
   a. chromosomes consisting of one chromatid.
   b. unpaired duplicated chromosomes.
   c. bivalents.
   d. homologous pairs of chromosomes.
   e. Both c and d are correct.

4. At the metaphase plate during metaphase II of meiosis, there are
   a. chromosomes consisting of one chromatid.
   b. unpaired duplicated chromosomes.
   c. bivalents.
   d. homologous pairs of chromosomes.
   e. Both c and d are correct.

5. Crossing-over occurs between
   a. sister chromatids of the same chromosome.
   b. two different kinds of bivalents.
   c. two different kinds of chromosomes.
   d. nonsister chromatids of a bivalent.
   e. two daughter nuclei.

6. During which phase of meiosis do homologous chromosomes separate?
   a. prophase I   c. anaphase I
   b. telophase I   d. anaphase II

7. Nondisjunction during meiosis I of oogenesis will result in eggs that have
   a. the normal number of chromosomes.
   b. one too many chromosomes.
   c. one less than the normal number of chromosomes.
   d. Both b and c are correct.

8. Which two of these chromosomal mutations are most likely to occur when an inverted chromosome is undergoing synapsis?
   a. deletion and translocation
   b. deletion and duplication
   c. duplication and translocation
   d. inversion and duplication

9. A male with underdeveloped testes and some breast development most likely has
   a. Down syndrome.   c. Turner syndrome.
   b. Jacobs syndrome.   d. Klinefelter syndrome.

For questions 10–13, fill in the blanks.

10. If the parent cell has 24 chromosomes, the daughter cells following mitosis will have _____ chromosomes and following meiosis will have _____ chromosomes.

11. Meiosis in males is a part of _____, and meiosis in females is a part of _____.

12. Oogenesis will not go to completion unless _____ occurs.

13. During oogenesis, the primary oocyte has the _____ and the secondary oocyte has the _____ number of chromosomes.

For questions 14–19, match the statements that follow to the items in the key. Answers may be used more than once, and more than one answer may be used.

KEY:
   a. mitosis
   b. meiosis I
   c. meiosis II
   d. Both meiosis I and meiosis II are correct.
   e. All of these are correct.

14. A parent cell with ten duplicated chromosomes will produce daughter cells with five duplicated chromosomes each.

15. Involves pairing of duplicated homologous chromosomes.

16. A parent cell with five duplicated chromosomes will produce daughter cells with five chromosomes consisting of one chromatid each.

17. Nondisjunction may occur, causing abnormal gametes to form.

18. A parent cell with ten duplicated chromosomes will produce daughter cells with ten chromosomes consisting of one chromatid each.

19. Involved in growth and repair of tissues.

Engage

Thinking Scientifically

1. Why is the first meiotic division considered to be the reduction division for chromosome number?

2. Recall that during interphase, the G_2 checkpoint ensures that the DNA has been faithfully replicated before the cell is allowed to divide by mitosis. Would you expect this checkpoint to be active during interkinesis? How might you set up an experiment to test your hypothesis?

3. A man has a balanced translocation between chromosome 2 and 6. If he reproduces with a normal woman could the child have the same translocation? Why or why not?

Bioethical Issue

The Risks of Advanced Maternal Age

In today's society, it is commonplace for women to embark on careers and pursue higher education, delaying marriage and childbirth until later years. Between 1991 and 2001, the birthrate among women aged 35 to 39 increased over 30%, while the birthrate among women aged 40 to 44 leaped by almost 70%. The U.S. Census Bureau indicates the average age at which a woman first gives birth is now 25.1 years, as compared to 21.1 years in 1970. These increases have occurred as society has changed, spurred by the elimination of the social stigmas, better prenatal care, and new medical technologies that can overcome the decline in fertility associated with age and treat at-risk children.

The decision to delay childbirth does carry risks. Although the reasons are not well understood, the risk of many disorders associated with meiotic nondisjunction, such as Down syndrome, increase greatly with age, rising from nearly 1 in 900 at age 30 to 1 in 109 by age 40. The risk of complications to the mother, such as gestational diabetes, are also much higher in women over 30. Thus, the medical community has embarked on a campaign to ensure that women who are pregnant and over age 35 are offered more intensive prenatal care. Many people are concerned about the ultimate cost to society, through increased insurance premiums and increased costs to governments to pay for it.

Although definite risks are associated with advanced maternal age, some people contend that having children later in life provides many advantages. Women over age 35 are usually at a later stage in their careers and have higher salaries, lessening the need for many social welfare programs. Furthermore, women over 35 often have a more stable living situation, are less likely to experience unplanned pregnancy, and are often able to devote more time to the child than are younger women. Therefore, while older mothers may require more medical attention, the overall costs to society are lower.

Considering both the benefits and the disadvantages, are we as a society obligated to fund intense screening and prenatal care for women of advanced maternal age, and to pay for treating the maladies associated with it? As birthrates among women over age 30 continue to soar, the debate over advanced maternal age is not likely to abate any time soon.

11

Mendelian Patterns of Inheritance

CHAPTER OUTLINE

11.1 Gregor Mendel 193

11.2 Mendel's Laws 195

11.3 Extending the Range of Mendelian Genetics 205

BEFORE YOU BEGIN

Before beginning this chapter, take a few moments to review the following discussions.

Figure 10.1 How is DNA-based genotype related to protein-based phenotype?

Section 10.3 How are chromosomes segregated during meiosis I and II?

Figure 10.9 What genetic changes are possible in gametes when chromosomes fail to segregate properly?

Trimethylaminuria is a genetic disorder that produces a fishy body odor.

Camille was painfully aware of her foul body odor because children teased her relentlessly, calling her "Miss Fishy" and other nasty names. She had no idea that she suffers from trimethylaminuria, or "fish odor syndrome," an extremely rare genetic disorder she shares with only 1 in 10,000 people. People with this syndrome have a defective gene that makes a nonfunctional protein unable to break down the smelly chemical trimethylamine, which accumulates in the body and ends up in their urine, sweat, and sometimes even in their breath.

Like the rest of us, you are the product of your family tree. The DNA you inherit from your parents directly affects the proteins that enable your body to function properly. Rare genetic disorders like Camille's pique our curiosity about how traits are inherited from one generation to the next. In this chapter, you will learn that the process of meiosis can be used to predict the inheritance of a trait, and that the genetic diversity produced through meiosis can sometimes create cases like Camille's. Through patterns of inheritance discovered by Mendel, you will also learn that certain traits, such as trimethylaminuria, are recessive and it takes two nonfunctional copies of that gene before you are affected. This chapter will introduce you to observable patterns of inheritance, including human genetic disorders that are linked to specific genes on the chromosomes.

As you read through the chapter, think about the following questions:

1. How does the collection of chromosomes we inherit from our parents affect our body's appearance and function?

2. What patterns of inheritance can be observed across generations?

3. How does meiosis help predict the probability of producing gametes and inheriting a trait?

FOLLOWING *the* THEMES

CHAPTER 11 MENDELIAN PATTERNS OF INHERITANCE

UNIT 2 GENETIC BASIS OF LIFE		
	Evolution	Inheritance of genes within a population is a cornerstone of a species' ability to change over time.
	Nature of Science	Researchers now have the technology to permanently change inheritance patterns and potentially cure genetic diseases.
	Biological Systems	Inheriting abnormal genes can affect many aspects of body function.

11.1 Gregor Mendel

Learning Outcomes

Upon completion of this section you should be able to

1. Describe how Mendel's scientific approach enabled his genetic experiments to be successful.

2. Contrast blending and the particulate concept of inheritance.

The science of genetics explains the stability of inheritance (why you are human, as are your parents) and also variations between offspring from one generation to the next (why you have a different combination of traits than your parents). Virtually every culture in history has attempted to explain observed inheritance patterns. An understanding of these patterns has always been important to agriculture, animal husbandry (the science of breeding animals), and medicine.

The Blending Concept of Inheritance

Until the late nineteenth century, most plant and animal breeders believed that traits were inherited by the blending concept of inheritance, which stated that an offspring's genetic makeup was intermediate to that of its parents. While they acknowledged that both sexes contribute equally to a new individual, they believed that parents of contrasting appearance always produce offspring of intermediate appearance.

If the blending concept were true, a cross between plants with red flowers and plants with white flowers would yield only plants with pink flowers. However, scientists who supported the blending theory could not explain, for example, why pink flowers were able to produce offspring with red and white flowers in later generations. The breeders mistakenly attributed this to instability of the genetic material.

The blending concept of inheritance offered little help to Charles Darwin, the father of evolution, whose treatise on natural selection lacked a strong genetic basis. If populations contained only intermediate individuals and normally lacked variations, how could diverse forms evolve?

Mendel's Particulate Theory of Inheritance

Gregor Mendel was an Austrian monk who developed a particulate theory of inheritance after performing a series of ingenious experiments in the 1860s (Fig. 11.1). Mendel studied science and mathematics at the University of Vienna, and at the time of his research in genetics, he was a substitute natural science teacher at a local high school.

Mendel was a successful scientist for several reasons. First, he was one of the first scientists to apply mathematics to biology. Most likely his background in mathematics prompted him to apply statistical methods and the laws of probability to his breeding experiments. He was also a careful, deliberate scientist who followed the scientific method very closely and kept

Figure 11.1 Gregor Mendel, 1822–84. Mendel grew and tended the pea plants he used for his experiments. For each experiment, he observed as many offspring as possible. For a cross that required him to calculate the ratio of round seeds to wrinkled seeds, he observed and counted a total of 7,324 peas!

very detailed, accurate records. He prepared for his experiments carefully and conducted many preliminary studies with various animals and plants.

Mendel's theory of inheritance is called a particulate theory because it is based on the existence of minute particles or hereditary units we now call genes. Inheritance involves the reshuffling of the same genes from generation to generation. The two laws he proposed, the law of segregation and the law of independent assortment, which we will discuss shortly, describe the behavior of these particulate units of heredity as they are passed from one generation to the next. Much of modern genetics is based upon Mendel's theories, which have withstood the test of time and have been supported by innumerable experiments.

Mendel Worked with the Garden Pea

Mendel's preliminary experiments prompted him to choose the garden pea, *Pisum sativum* (Fig. 11.2a), as his experimental organism. The garden pea was a good choice for many reasons. The plants were easy to cultivate and had a short generation time. Although peas normally self-pollinate (pollen only goes to the same flower), they could be cross-pollinated by hand by

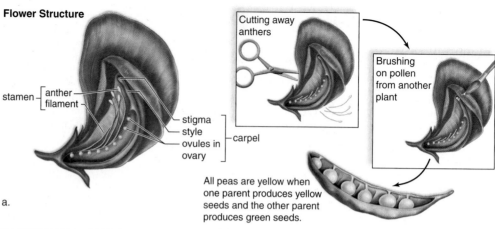

Flower Structure

stamen — [anther / filament]

stigma / style / ovules in ovary — carpel

Cutting away anthers

Brushing on pollen from another plant

All peas are yellow when one parent produces yellow seeds and the other parent produces green seeds.

a.

Trait	Characteristics		
	Dominant		**Recessive**
Stem length	Tall		Short
Pod shape	Inflated		Constricted
Seed shape	Round		Wrinkled
Seed color	Yellow		Green
Flower position	Axial		Terminal
Flower color	Purple		White
Pod color	Green		Yellow

b.

Figure 11.2 Garden pea anatomy and a few traits. **a.** In the garden pea, *Pisum sativum*, pollen grains produced in the anther contain sperm, and ovules in the ovary contain eggs. When Mendel performed crosses, he brushed pollen from one plant onto the stigma of another plant. This cross-pollination allowed sperm to fertilize eggs, and ovules to develop into seeds (peas). The open pod shows the seed color trait that resulted from a cross between plants with yellow seeds and plants with green seeds. **b.** Mendel selected traits to study that were one form or another, and not a blend of two traits. In his research, Mendel observed a dominant, or more prevalent form, as well as a recessive or less prevalent form, in the pea's physical appearance. The text and Figure 11.3 explain the approach Mendel used and how he interpreted his results to discover basic patterns of inheritance.

transferring pollen from the anther (male part of a flower) to the stigma (female part of a flower).

Many varieties of peas were available, and Mendel chose 22 for his experiments. When these varieties self-pollinated, over generations they became *true-breeding*—meaning that all the offspring were the same and exactly like the parent plants. Unlike his predecessors, Mendel studied the inheritance of relatively simple and discrete traits that were not subjective and were easy to observe, such as seed shape, seed color, and flower

color. In his crosses, Mendel observed either dominant or recessive characteristics but no intermediate ones (Fig. 11.2*b*).

Check Your Progress   11.1

1. Describe Gregor Mendel's scientific approach and how it helped make his experiments successful.
2. Explain why the garden pea was a good choice for Mendel's experiments.

11.2 Mendel's Laws

After ensuring that his pea plants were true-breeding—for example, that his tall plants always had tall offspring and his short plants always had short offspring—Mendel was ready to perform cross-pollination experiments (see Fig. 11.2*a*). These crosses allowed Mendel to formulate his law of segregation.

Law of Segregation

For these initial experiments, Mendel chose varieties that differed in only one trait (e.g. plant height). If the blending theory of inheritance were correct, the cross should yield plants with an intermediate appearance of medium height compared to the parents that were all tall or all short.

Mendel's Experimental Design and Results

Mendel called the original, true-breeding all tall or all short parents the *P generation*. The first generation of offspring were called the *F₁*, or *filial* [L. *filius*, sons and daughters] *generation* (Fig. 11.3). He performed *reciprocal crosses*: First he dusted the pollen of tall plants onto the stigmas of short plants, and then he dusted the pollen of short plants onto the stigmas of tall plants. In both cases, all F₁ offspring resembled the tall parent.

Certainly, these results were contrary to those predicted by the blending theory of inheritance. Rather than being intermediate, the F₁ plants were all tall and resembled only one parent. Did these results mean that the other characteristic (i.e., shortness) had disappeared permanently? Apparently not, because when Mendel allowed the F₁ plants to self-pollinate, ³⁄₄ of the next generation of offspring, or *F₂ generation*, were tall and ¼ were short, a 3:1 ratio (Fig. 11.3).

Mendel inferred that the F₁ plants were able to pass on a factor for shortness—it didn't disappear, it just skipped a generation. Because the F₁ plants were tall but clearly still contained the shortness characteristic, Mendel deduced that tallness was dominant to shortness (Fig 11.2*b* and 11.3).

Mendel counted many plants in his plant height and other experiments. When he allowed the F₁ pea plants (which were all tall but carried the characteristic for shortness) to self-fertilize and produce offspring, he counted a total of 1,064 plants, of which 787 were tall and 277 were short. This type of experiment is called a **monohybrid cross** [L. *mono*, single, and *hybrida*, mixture] because it is a cross of a single trait (i.e., plant height)

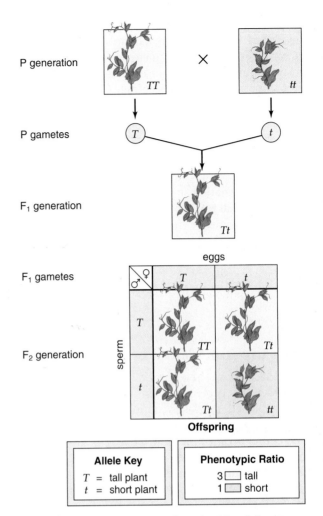

Figure 11.3 Monohybrid cross done by Mendel. The P generation pea plants differ in only one trait—length of the stem. The F₁ generation plants are all tall, but the factor for short has not disappeared because ¼ of the F₂ generation plants are short. The 3:1 ratio allowed Mendel to deduce that individuals have two discrete and separate genetic factors for each trait.

with organisms that are a hybrid (i.e., tall and short characteristics). In fact, in all monohybrid crosses that he performed for the traits shown in Figure 11.2*b*, he found a 3:1 ratio in the F₂ generation. The characteristic for shortness that had disappeared in the F₁ generation reappeared in ¼ of the F₂ offspring. *Today, we know that the expected phenotypic results of a monohybrid cross are always 3:1.*

Mendel's Conclusion

Mendel's mathematical approach led him to interpret his results differently from previous breeders. He knew that the same ratio was obtained among the F₂ generation time and time again when he did a monohybrid cross involving one of the seven traits he was studying. Eventually Mendel arrived at this explanation: A 3:1 ratio among the F₂ offspring was possible if (1) the

F₁ parents contained two separate copies of each hereditary factor, one of these being dominant and the other recessive; (2) the factors separated when the gametes were formed, and each gamete carried only one copy of each factor; and (3) random fusion of all possible gametes occurred upon fertilization. Only in this way could shortness reoccur in the F₂ generation. Thinking this, Mendel arrived at the first of his laws of inheritance—the law of segregation. The law of segregation is a cornerstone of his particulate theory of inheritance.

The **law of segregation** states the following:
- Each individual has two factors for each trait.
- The factors segregate (separate) during the formation of the gametes.
- Each gamete contains only one factor from each pair of factors.
- Fertilization gives each new individual two factors for each trait.

Mendel's Cross as Viewed by Classical Genetics

Figure 11.3 also shows how classical scientists interpreted the results of Mendel's experiments on inheritance of stem length in peas. Stem length in peas is controlled by a single gene. This gene occurs on a homologous pair of chromosomes at a particular location that is called the gene **locus** (Fig. 11.4). Alternative versions of a gene are called **alleles** [Gk. *allelon*, reciprocal, parallel]. The **dominant allele** is so named because the DNA sequence that comprises that gene makes a fully functional protein. The **recessive allele** contains a slightly different DNA sequence and produces a protein with little or no function.

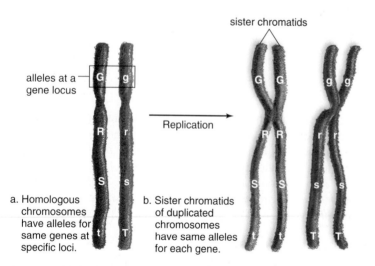

Figure 11.4 Classical view of homologous chromosomes.
a. The letters represent alleles; that is, alternative forms of a gene. Each allelic pair, such as *Gg* or *Tt*, is located on homologous chromosomes at a particular physical location called a gene locus. **b.** Sister chromatids carry the same alleles in the same order. Proteins made from each allele determine the observable traits.

When dominant and recessive alleles for a gene are present in a cell, the resulting mixture of functional and nonfunctional protein allows the dominant physical trait to be shown and the recessive trait to be masked. The dominant allele is identified by a capital letter, and the recessive allele by the same letter but lowercase. Usually, the first letter designating a trait is chosen to identify the allele. Using the plant height example, there is an allele for tallness (*T*) and an allele for shortness (*t*).

As described in the preceding chapter, meiosis is the type of cell division that reduces the chromosome number from diploid (2n) to haploid (n). During meiosis I, the members of bivalents (homologous chromosomes each having sister chromatids) separate. This means that the two alleles for each gene separate from each other during meiosis (see Fig. 11.7). Therefore, the process of meiosis gives an explanation for Mendel's law of segregation, and why only one allele for each trait is in a gamete.

In Mendel's cross, the original parents (P generation) were true-breeding; therefore, the tall plants had two alleles for tallness (*TT*), and the short plants had two alleles for shortness (*tt*). When an organism has two identical alleles, as these had, we say it is **homozygous** [Gk. *homo*, same, and *zygos*, balance, yoke]. Because the parents were homozygous, all gametes produced by the tall plant contained the allele for tallness (*T*), and all gametes produced by the short plant contained an allele for shortness (*t*).

After cross-pollination between different pea plants, all the individuals of the resulting F₁ generation had one allele for tallness and one for shortness (*Tt*). When an organism has two different alleles at a gene locus, we say that it is **heterozygous** [Gk. *hetero*, different, and *zygos*, balance, yoke]. Although the plants of the F₁ generation had one of each type of allele, they were all tall. The allele that is expressed in a heterozygous individual is the dominant allele. The allele that is not expressed in a heterozygote is the recessive allele. This explains why shortness, the recessive trait, skipped a generation in Mendel's experiment.

Continuing with the discussion of Mendel's cross (see Fig. 11.3), the F₁ plants produce gametes in which 50% have the dominant allele *T* and 50% have the recessive allele *t*. During the process of fertilization, we assume that all types of sperm (i.e., *T* or *t*) have an equal chance to fertilize all types of eggs (i.e., *T* or *t*). When this occurs, such a monohybrid cross always produces a 3:1 (dominant to recessive) ratio among the offspring. Figure 11.5 gives Mendel's results for several monohybrid crosses, and you can see that the results were always close to 3:1.

Genotype Versus Phenotype

It is obvious from our discussion that two organisms with different allelic combinations for a trait can have the same outward appearance. (That is, *TT* and *Tt* pea plants are both tall.) For this reason, it is necessary to distinguish between the alleles present in an organism and the appearance of that organism.

The word **genotype** [Gk. *genos*, birth, origin, race, and *typos*, image, shape] refers to the alleles an individual receives

Trait	Characteristics			F₂ Results		
	Dominant		Recessive	Dominant	Recessive	Ratio
Stem length	Tall	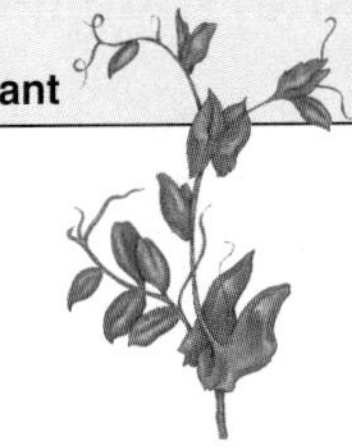	Short	 787	277	2.84:1
Pod shape	Inflated	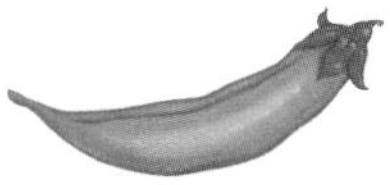	Constricted	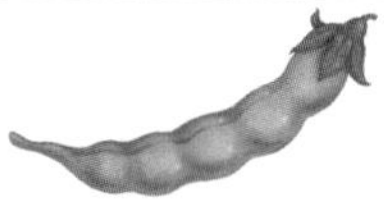 882	299	2.95:1
Seed shape	Round	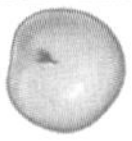	Wrinkled	 5,474	1,850	2.96:1
Seed color	Yellow	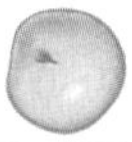	Green	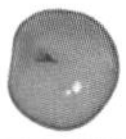 6,022	2,001	3.01:1
Flower position	Axial		Terminal	 651	207	3.14:1
Flower color	Purple	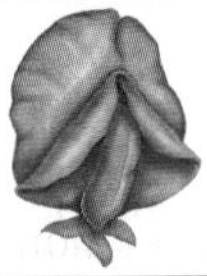	White	 705	224	3.15:1
Pod color	Green	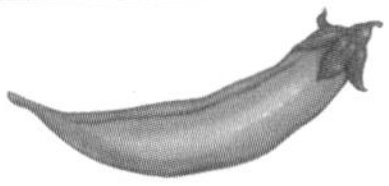	Yellow	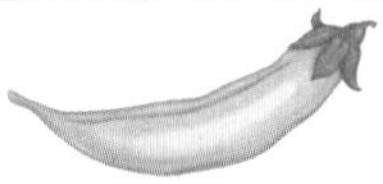 428	152	2.82:1
			Totals:	14,949	5,010	2.98:1

Figure 11.5 Relationship between observed phenotype and F₂ offspring. Mendel was fortunate in choosing the pea plant because the traits he observed were quite distinct and easily classified. After crossing F₁ hybrids and counting hundreds of F₂ pea plants for each trait, Mendel discovered that each showed a 3:1 ratio.

at fertilization. Genotype may be indicated by letters or by short, descriptive phrases, and represents the DNA sequence for a particular gene. Genotype TT is called homozygous dominant, and genotype tt is called homozygous recessive. Genotype Tt is called heterozygous. These refer to the different ways that alleles can be combined in a cell.

The word **phenotype** [Gk. *phaino*, appear, and *typos*, image, shape] refers to the physical appearance of the individual, which is made from the proteins produced by the corresponding alleles. The homozygous dominant (TT) individual and the heterozygous (Tt) individual both show the dominant phenotype and are tall because they make fully functional proteins that build the tall trait, while the homozygous recessive individual that shows the recessive phenotype and makes less or nonfunctional protein for that trait is short. Thus, the DNA

that makes up the genotype produces the proteins that make up the phenotype.

Check Your Progress 11.2A

1. State all possible gametes, noting the proportion of each for the individual, for these genotypes: **a.** WW **b.** Ww **c.** Tt **d.** TT
2. Interpret which of these genotypes (Bb, BB, bb) a white rabbit would have if B = black and b = white.
3. What would be the expected phenotypic ratio of the offspring if two heterozygous rabbits mate? If they produced 20 offspring, how many would you expect to be white?

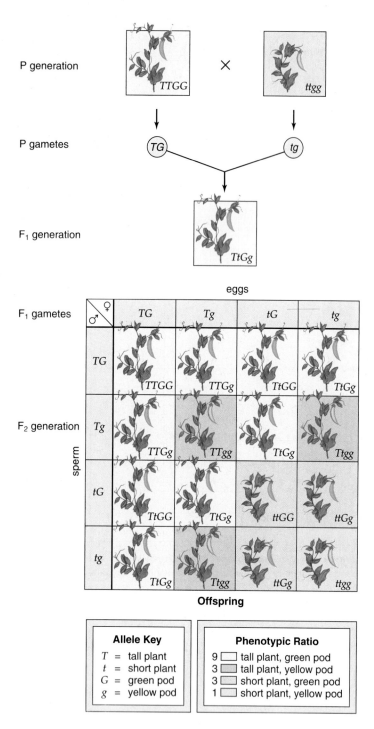

Figure 11.6 Dihybrid cross done by Mendel. P generation plants differ in two traits: —length of the stem, and color of the pod. The F₁ generation shows only the dominant traits, but all possible phenotypes appear among the F₂ generation because the F₁ parents are hybrids. The 9:3:3:1 ratio allowed Mendel to deduce that factors segregate into gametes independently of other factors.

Mendel's Law of Independent Assortment

Mendel performed a second series of crosses in which true-breeding pea plants differed in two traits. For example, he crossed tall plants having green pods with short plants having yellow pods (Fig. 11.6). The F₁ plants showed both dominant characteristics. As before, Mendel then allowed the F₁ plants to self-pollinate. This F₁ cross is known as a **dihybrid cross** [L. *di*, two, and *hybrida*, mixture] because the plants are hybrid in two ways. Two possible results could occur in the F₂ generation:

1. If the dominant factors (*TG*) always segregate into the F₁ gametes together, and the recessive factors (*tg*) always stay together, then there would be two phenotypes among the F₂ plants—tall plants with green pods and short plants with yellow pods.
2. If the four factors segregate into the F₁ gametes independently, then there would be four phenotypes among the F₂ plants—tall plants with green pods, tall plants with yellow pods, short plants with green pods, and short plants with yellow pods.

Figure 11.6 shows that Mendel observed four phenotypes among the F₂ plants, supporting the second hypothesis. This is how Mendel formulated his second law of heredity—the law of independent assortment.

> The **law of independent assortment** states the following:
> - Each pair of factors segregates (assorts) independently of the other pairs.
> - All possible combinations of factors can occur in the gametes.

The law of independent assortment applies only to alleles on different chromosomes. Each chromosome carries a large number of alleles.

We know that the process of meiosis explains why the F₁ plants produced every possible type of gamete and, therefore, four phenotypes appear among the F₂ generation of plants. Figure 11.7 shows a parent cell with two homologous pairs of chromosomes, with alleles *A*, *a* on one pair and *B*, *b* on the other pair. Following duplication of the chromosomes during interphase, the parent cell undergoes meiosis I. At metaphase I, the homologous pairs line up independently of one another, such that the chromosomes with *A* alleles have an equal chance of lining up with the *B* alleles or the *b* alleles. The subsequent segregation of the homologous pairs during anaphase I reduces the chromosome number from 2n to n. Because *A* alleles can be sorted with *B* or *b*, and so can the *a* allele, it is possible to create gametes with *AB*, *Ab*, *aB*, and *ab* allele combinations with equal probability.

Animation
Random Orientation of Chromosomes During Meiosis

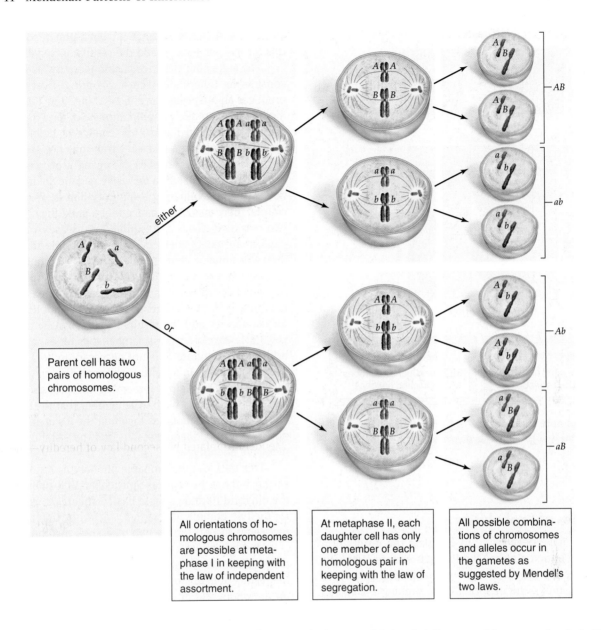

All orientations of homologous chromosomes are possible at metaphase I in keeping with the law of independent assortment.

At metaphase II, each daughter cell has only one member of each homologous pair in keeping with the law of segregation.

All possible combinations of chromosomes and alleles occur in the gametes as suggested by Mendel's two laws.

Parent cell has two pairs of homologous chromosomes.

Figure 11.7 Independent assortment and segregation during meiosis. Mendel's laws hold because of the events of meiosis. The homologous pairs of chromosomes line up randomly at the metaphase plate during meiosis I. It doesn't matter which member of a homologous pair faces which spindle pole. In this example, A alleles can segregate with B or with b alleles. Likewise, a alleles can segregate with B or with b alleles. Therefore, the homologous chromosomes, and alleles they carry, segregate independently during gamete formation. All possible combinations of chromosomes and alleles, that is, AB, Ab, aB, and ab, occur in the gametes.

The same rule of independent assortment applies for the pea plant example in Figure 11.6. In that case, the possible gametes are the two dominants (such as *TG*), the two recessives (such as *tg*), and the ones that have a dominant and a recessive (such as *Tg* and *tG*). Regardless of whether we are using the A and B chromosome or the T and G chromosome examples, when all possible sperm have an opportunity to fertilize all possible eggs, *the expected phenotypic ratio of a dihybrid cross is always 9:3:3:1.*

Check Your Progress   11.2B

1. Identify all possible gametes for a heterozygote in fruit flies where *L* = long wings and *l* = short wings; *G* = gray body and *g* = black body.
2. Describe the expected phenotypic ratio when two heterozygous dihybrids reproduce.

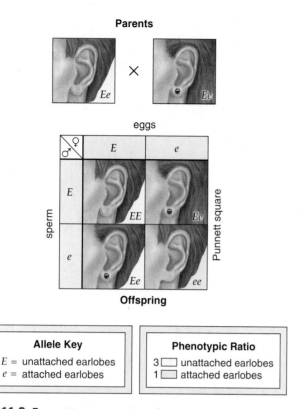

Figure 11.8   Punnett square.   Use of Punnett square to calculate probable results; in this case, a 3 : 1 phenotypic ratio.

Mendel's Laws of Probability

The diagram we have been using to calculate the results of a cross is called a Punnett square. The **Punnett square** allows us to easily calculate the chances, or the probability, of genotypes and phenotypes among the offspring. Like flipping a coin, an offspring of the cross illustrated in the Punnett square in Figure 11.8 has a 50% (or ½) chance of receiving an *E* for unattached earlobe or an *e* for attached earlobe from each parent:

The chance of $E = \frac{1}{2}$
The chance of $e = \frac{1}{2}$

How likely is it that an offspring will inherit a specific set of two alleles, one from each parent? The *product rule* of probability tells us that we have to multiply the chances of independent events to get the answer:

1. The chance of *EE* $= \frac{1}{2} \times \frac{1}{2} = \frac{1}{4}$
2. The chance of *Ee* $= \frac{1}{2} \times \frac{1}{2} = \frac{1}{4}$
3. The chance of *eE* $= \frac{1}{2} \times \frac{1}{2} = \frac{1}{4}$
4. The chance of *ee* $= \frac{1}{2} \times \frac{1}{2} = \frac{1}{4}$

The Punnett square does this for us because we can easily see that each of these is ¼ of the total number of squares.

How do we get the phenotypic results? The *sum rule* of probability tells us that when the same event can occur in more than one way, we can add the results. Because 1, 2, and 3 all result in unattached earlobes, we add them up to know that the chance of unattached earlobes is ¾, or 75%. The chance of

attached earlobes is ¼, or 25%. The Punnett square doesn't do this for us—we have to add the results ourselves.

The statement "Chance has no memory" is important when considering inheritance across offspring. Every time a couple produces an offspring, the child has the same chances of inheriting the different allele combinations. So, for a heterozygous (*Ee*) couple, each child has a 25% chance of having attached (*ee*) earlobes. Inheriting a recessive trait may not seem significant if we are considering earlobes. However, it becomes quite significant when we consider a recessive genetic disorder such as cystic fibrosis, a debilitating respiratory illness. For a heterozygous couple, there is a 25% chance that a child they have will inherit two recessive alleles and exhibit the disease. And because each child is an independent event, it is possible that all their children—or none of them—could exhibit cystic fibrosis.

We can use the product rule and the sum rule of probability to predict the results of a dihybrid cross, such as the one shown in Figure 11.6. The Punnett square carries out the multiplication for us, and we add the results to find that the phenotypic ratio is 9:3:3:1. We expect these same results for each and every dihybrid cross. Therefore, it is not necessary to do a Punnett square over and over again for either a monohybrid or a dihybrid cross. Instead, we can simply remember the probable results of 3:1 and 9:3:3:1. But we have to remember that the 9 represents the two dominant phenotypes together, the 3's are a dominant phenotype with a hidden recessive, and the 1 stands for the double recessive phenotype.

This tells you the probable phenotypic ratio among the offspring, but not the chances for each possible phenotype. Because the dihybrid Punnett square has 16 squares, the chances are $\frac{9}{16}$ for the two dominants together, $\frac{3}{16}$ for the dominants with each recessive, and $\frac{1}{16}$ for the two recessives together.

Mendel counted the results of many similar crosses to get the probable results, and in the laboratory, we too have to count the results of many individual crosses to get the probable results for a monohybrid or a dihybrid cross. Why? Consider that each time you toss a coin, you have a 50% chance of getting heads or tails. If you tossed the coin only a couple of times, you might very well have heads or tails both times. However, if you toss the coin many times, your results are more likely to approach 50% heads and 50% tails.

Testcrosses

To confirm that the F_1 plants of his one-trait crosses were in fact heterozygous, Mendel crossed his F_1 generation tall pea plants with true-breeding short (homozygous recessive) plants; such a mating is termed a **testcross.** These crosses provided Mendel with further support for his law of segregation.

For the cross in Figure 11.9, Mendel reasoned that half the offspring should be tall and half should be short, producing a 1:1 phenotypic ratio. His results supported the hypothesis that alleles segregate when gametes are formed. In Figure 11.9*a*, the homozygous recessive parent can produce only one type of gamete—*t*—and so the Punnett square has only one column. The use of one column signifies that all the gametes carry a *t*. *The expected phenotypic ratio for this type of one-trait cross (heterozygous × recessive) is always 1:1.*

One-Trait Testcross

Today, a one-trait testcross is used to determine if an individual with the dominant phenotype is homozygous dominant (e.g., *TT*) or heterozygous (e.g., *Tt*). Because both of these genotypes produce the dominant phenotype, it is not possible to determine the genotype by observation. Figure 11.9*b* shows that if the individual is homozygous dominant, all the offspring will be tall. Each parent has only one type of gamete and, therefore, a Punnett square is not required to determine the results.

Two-Trait Testcross

When doing a two-trait testcross, an individual with the dominant phenotype is crossed with one having the recessive phenotype. Suppose you are working with fruit flies in which:

L = long wings	*G* = gray bodies
l = vestigial (short) wings	*g* = black bodies

You wouldn't know by examination whether the fly on the left was homozygous or heterozygous for wing and body color. To find out the genotype of the test fly, you cross it with the one on the right. You know by examination that this vestigial-winged and black-bodied fly is homozygous recessive for both traits.

If the test fly is homozygous dominant for both traits with the genotype *LLGG*, it will form only one gamete: *LG*. Therefore, all the offspring from the proposed cross would have long wings and a gray body.

However, if the test fly is heterozygous for both traits with the genotype *LlGg*, it will form four different types of gametes:

Gametes: *LG Lg lG lg*

and could have four different offspring:

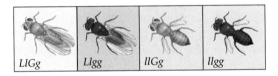

LlGg	*Llgg*	*llGg*	*llgg*

The presence of the offspring with vestigial wings and a black body shows that the test fly is heterozygous for both traits and has the genotype *LlGg*. Otherwise, it could not produce this offspring. In general, you want to remember that *the expected phenotypic ratio for this type of two-trait cross (heterozygous for two traits × recessive for both traits) is always 1:1:1:1.*

Check Your Progress   11.2C

1. State the percentage of pea plants that would have
   a. yellow seeds, and **b.** green seeds in a cross of two heterozygous plants where yellow seed color is dominant over green seed color.
2. State the chances of producing offspring with long wings and a black body from a testcross of a heterozygous (*LlGg*) fruit fly and a homozygous recessive (*llgg*) fruit fly.
3. State the genotype of all the horses if trotter (*T*) is dominant over pacer (*t*), and a pacer is produced when a trotter is mated to a pacer.

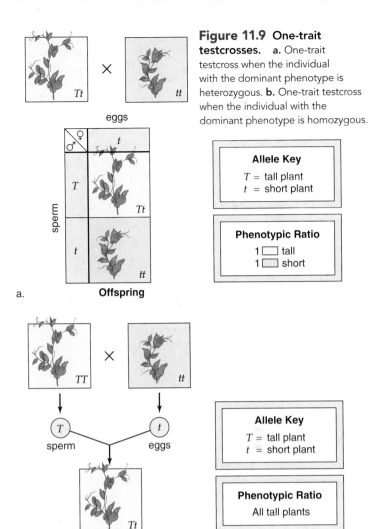

Figure 11.9 One-trait testcrosses. a. One-trait testcross when the individual with the dominant phenotype is heterozygous. **b.** One-trait testcross when the individual with the dominant phenotype is homozygous.

Allele Key
T = tall plant
t = short plant

Phenotypic Ratio
1 ☐ tall
1 ☐ short

Allele Key
T = tall plant
t = short plant

Phenotypic Ratio
All tall plants

Mendel's Laws and Human Genetic Disorders

Many traits and disorders in humans, and other organisms also, are genetic in origin and follow Mendel's laws. These traits are controlled by a single pair of alleles on the autosomal chromosomes. An **autosome** is any chromosome other than a sex (X or Y) chromosome.

Autosomal Patterns of Inheritance

When a genetic disorder is autosomal dominant, the normal allele (*a*) is recessive, and an individual with the alleles *AA* or *Aa* has the disorder. When a genetic disorder is autosomal recessive, the normal allele (*A*) is dominant, and only individuals with the alleles *aa* have the disorder. A pedigree shows the pattern of inheritance for a particular condition and can be used by genetic counselors to determine whether a condition is dominant or recessive. Consider these two possible patterns of inheritance:

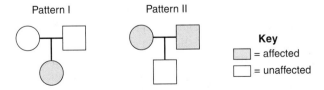

Pattern I   Pattern II

Key
☐ = affected
☐ = unaffected

In a pedigree, males are designated by squares and females by circles. Shaded circles and squares are the affected individuals. The shaded boxes do not indicate whether the condition is

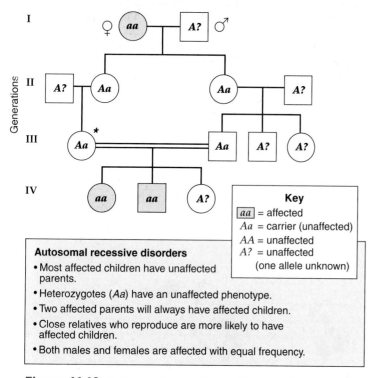

Figure 11.10 Autosomal recessive pedigree. The list gives ways to recognize an autosomal recessive disorder. How would you know the individual at the asterisk is heterozygous? (See Appendix A for answer.)

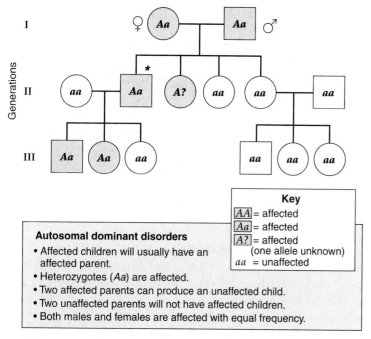

Figure 11.11 Autosomal dominant pedigree. The list gives ways to recognize an autosomal dominant disorder. How would you know the individual at the asterisk is heterozygous? (See Appendix A for answer.)

dominant or recessive, only that the individual exhibits the trait. A line between a square and a circle represents a union. In the patterns on page 201, a vertical line going downward leads to a single child. (If there are more children, they are lined up horizontally.) From page 201, which pattern of inheritance (I or II) do you suppose represents an autosomal dominant characteristic, and which represents an autosomal recessive characteristic?

In pattern I, the child is affected, but neither parent is; this can happen if the condition is recessive and both parents are *Aa*.

Notice that the parents are **carriers** because they appear normal (do not express the trait) but are capable of having a child with the genetic disorder. In pattern II, the child is unaffected, but the parents are affected. This can happen if the condition is dominant and the parents are *Aa*.

Figure 11.10 shows other ways to recognize an autosomal recessive pattern of inheritance, and Figure 11.11 shows other ways to recognize an autosomal dominant pattern of inheritance. In these pedigrees, generations are indicated by Roman numerals placed on the left side. Notice in the third generation of Figure 11.10 that two closely related individuals have produced three children, two of which have the affected phenotype. In this case, a double line denotes consanguineous reproduction, or inbreeding, which is reproduction between two closely related individuals. This illustrates that inbreeding significantly increases the chances of children inheriting two copies of a potentially harmful recessive allele.

Autosomal Recessive Disorders

In humans, a number of autosomal recessive disorders have been identified. Here, we discuss methemoglobinemia and cystic fibrosis.

Methemoglobinemia

Methemoglobinemia is a relatively harmless disorder that results from an accumulation of methemoglobin in the blood. This disorder has been documented for centuries, but the exact cause and genetic link had remained mysterious. Although rarely mentioned, hemoglobin, the main oxygen-carrying protein in the blood, is usually converted at a slow rate to an alternate form called methemoglobin. Unlike hemoglobin, which is bright red when carrying oxygen, methemoglobin has a bluish color, similar to that of oxygen-poor blood. Although this process is harmless, individuals with methemoglobinemia are unable to clear the abnormal blue protein from their blood, causing their skin to appear bluish-purple in color (Fig. 11.12).

A persistent and determined physician finally solved the age-old mystery of what causes methemoglobinemia by doing blood tests and pedigree analysis involving a family known as the "blue Fugates" of Troublesome Creek, Kentucky. Enzyme tests indicated that the blue Fugates lacked the enzyme diaphorase, coded for by a gene on chromosome 22. The enzyme normally converts methemoglobin back to hemoglobin.

The physician treated the disorder in a simple, but rather unconventional manner. He injected the Fugates with a dye called methylene blue! This unusual dye can donate electrons to other compounds, successfully converting the excess methemoglobin back into normal hemoglobin. The results were striking but immediate—the patient's skin quickly turned pink after treatment.

A pedigree analysis of the Fugate family indicated that the trait is common in the family because so many members carried the recessive allele.

Cystic Fibrosis

Cystic fibrosis (CF) is the most common lethal genetic disease among Caucasians in the United States (Fig. 11.13). About 1 in 20 Caucasians is a carrier, and about 1 in 2,000 newborns has the disorder. CF patients exhibit a number of characteristic symptoms, the most obvious being extremely salty sweat. In

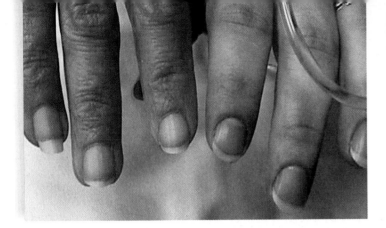

Figure 11.12 Methemoglobinemia. The hands of the woman on the right appear blue due to chemically induced methemoglobinemia.

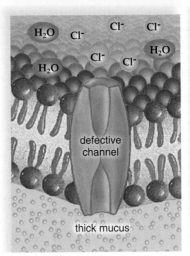

Figure 11.13 Cystic fibrosis. Cystic fibrosis is due to a faulty protein that is supposed to regulate the flow of chloride ions into and out of cells through a channel protein.

children with CF, the mucus in the bronchial tubes and pancreatic ducts is particularly thick and viscous, interfering with the function of the lungs and pancreas. To ease breathing, the thick mucus in the lungs has to be loosened periodically, but still the lungs frequently become infected. The clogged pancreatic ducts prevent digestive enzymes from reaching the small intestine, and to improve digestion, patients take digestive enzymes mixed with applesauce before every meal.

Cystic fibrosis is caused by a defective chloride ion channel that is encoded by the *CFTR* allele on chromosome 7. Research has demonstrated that chloride ions (Cl^-) fail to pass through the defective version of the CFTR chloride ion channel, which is located on the plasma membrane. Ordinarily, after chloride ions have passed through the channel to the other side of the membrane, sodium ions (Na^+) and water follow. It is believed that lack of water is the cause of the abnormally thick mucus in the bronchial tubes and pancreatic ducts.

In the past few years, new treatments have raised the average life expectancy for CF patients to as much as 35 years of age. It is hoped that other novel treatments, such as gene therapy, may be able to correct the defect by replacing a faulty copy of the gene with a normal one. Some scientists have suggested that the mutated *CFTR* allele has persisted in the human population as a means of surviving potentially fatal diseases, such as cholera.

Autosomal Dominant Disorders

A number of autosomal dominant disorders have been identified in humans. Two relatively well-known autosomal dominant disorders include osteogenesis imperfecta and hereditary spherocytosis.

Osteogenesis Imperfecta

Osteogenesis [L. *os*, bone, and *genesis*, origin] imperfecta is an autosomal dominant genetic disorder that results in weakened, brittle bones. Although at least nine types of the disorder are known, most are linked to mutations in two genes necessary to the synthesis of a type I collagen—one of the most abundant proteins in the human body. Collagen has many roles, including providing strength and rigidity to bone and forming the framework for most of the body's tissues. Osteogenesis imperfecta leads to a defective collagen I that causes the bones to be brittle and weak. Because the mutant collagen can cause structural defects even when combined with normal collagen I, osteogenesis imperfecta is generally considered to be dominant.

Osteogenesis imperfecta, which has an incidence of approximately 1 in 5,000 live births, affects all racial groups similarly

and has been documented as long as 300 years ago. Some historians think that the Viking chieftain Ivar Ragnarsson, who was known as Ivar the Boneless and was often carried into battle on a shield, had this condition. In most cases, the diagnosis is made in young children who visit the emergency room frequently due to broken bones. Some children with the disorder have an unusual blue tint in the sclera, the white portion of the eye; reduced skin elasticity; weakened teeth; and occasionally heart valve abnormalities. Currently, the disorder is treatable with a number of drugs that help to increase bone mass, but these drugs must be taken long-term.

Hereditary Spherocytosis

Hereditary spherocytosis is an autosomal dominant genetic blood disorder that results from a defective copy of the ankyrin-1 gene found on chromosome 8. The protein encoded by this gene serves as a structural component of red blood cells, and is responsible for maintaining their disklike shape. The abnormal spherocytosis protein is unable to perform its usual function, causing the affected person's red blood cells to adopt a spherical rather than disklike shape. As a result, the abnormal cells are fragile and burst easily, especially under osmotic stress. Enlargement of the spleen is also commonly seen in people with the disorder.

With an incidence of approximately 1 in 5,000, hereditary spherocytosis is one of the most common hereditary blood disorders. Roughly one-fourth of these cases result from new mutations and are not inherited from either parent. Hereditary spherocytosis exhibits incomplete penetrance, so not all individuals who inherit the mutant allele will actually show the trait. The cause of incomplete penetrance in these cases and others remains poorly understood.

Check Your Progress 11.2D

1. State the genotype of the child in Figure 11.13 and the genotypes of his parents if neither parent has cystic fibrosis. (Use this key: C = normal; c = cystic fibrosis)
2. Identify the chance that the parents in the above problem will have a child with cystic fibrosis.
3. Construct a pedigree of Ivar Ragnarsson's family tree assuming that his mother, and both her parents, were normal and that Ivar's father's father had osteogenesis imperfecta (mother was normal).

Testing for Genetic Disorders

Many human genetic disorders such as Huntington disease and cystic fibrosis are the result of inheriting faulty genes. Huntington disease is a devastating neurological disease caused by the inheritance of a single dominant allele; in contrast, cystic fibrosis, being a recessive disorder, requires the inheritance of two recessive alleles. In each case, mutated sequences in these genes that have been inherited lead to defective proteins, which disrupt normal biological function.

Genetic tests have been developed that can detect a particular sequence of bases for all your genes, and these sequences tell whether you have a particular genetic disorder. When researchers set out to develop a test for Huntington disease, they first obtained multiple **family pedigrees,** such as the one shown in Figure 11A. This pedigree meets the requirements for a dominant allele and autosomal inheritance: Every individual who is affected (shaded box or circle) has a parent who is also affected, heterozygotes are affected, and both males and females are affected in equal numbers. Each offspring of an affected individual has a 50% chance of having received the faulty gene and developing Huntington disease, which doesn't appear until later in life. Thus, a person could already have produced children before they know about the disease.

The letters under the square or circle mean the individual has undergone a blood test that resulted in an analysis of their DNA. A computer analysis of these individuals' DNA found that a large number of them had a sequence designated as J, K, or L. Only the sequence of bases designated as L appears in all the individuals with Huntington disease. A closer look at the pedigree indicates that sequence L is not in the gene for Huntington because at least one individual has the sequence but does not have Huntington disease.

When genes occur on the same chromosome in close proximity, their alleles are said to be linked. The closer linked alleles are on a chromosome, the greater the chance that they will be inherited together. This is the reason that alleles must be on separate chromosomes for the law of independent assortment to hold. Still, even genes that are closely linked can undergo crossing-over and become unlinked on occasion. Testable sequences that are closely linked to that of the faulty gene are called genetic markers, and these may be used as indicators of genetic disorders, such as Huntington disease. Association studies are another way for researchers to find possible sequences that indicate someone has a genetic disorder. During an association study, the DNA of a diverse sample of the general population is tested to find similar DNA sequences. The use of genetic markers and association studies has made it possible to successfully identify many genes involved in human disease.

The mapping of disorders to genes within the human genome has yielded much valuable information to the scientific and medical communities. The information has a variety of uses including prenatal genetic testing, diagnosis of disorders in individuals before symptoms occur, carrier testing of recessive disorders, and to further understand the origin, progression, and pathology of a disorder. This may lead to the development of novel treatment methods. New techniques and technologies have greatly accelerated this process, but the tried and true methods of family pedigrees and association studies are still the primary techniques used by geneticists in pursuing the cure for many human genetic ailments.

Questions to Consider

1. Considering how quickly cell and molecular technology is emerging, what implications does this have for curing genetic diseases?
2. If you or someone you knew suffered from a genetic disease, would you choose to use emerging technologies to treat the disease?

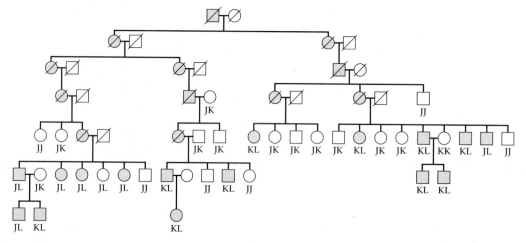

Figure 11A Blood sample testing and pedigree analysis. In individuals with Huntingon disease, a particular sequence of DNA bases (L) is always present. The pedigree chart shows that the L sequence is not present unless an ancestor exhibited Huntington disease. A slash indicates that the ancestor is deceased.

11.3 Extending the Range of Mendelian Genetics

Learning Outcomes

Upon completion of this section you should be able to

1. Explain the inheritance pattern of traits where more than two alleles for the trait exist.
2. Contrast incomplete dominance and incomplete penetrance.
3. Describe the effects of pleiotropy on phenotypic traits.
4. Distinguish the inheritance of polygenic traits.
5. Examine X-linked inheritance and its gender-based effects.

Mendelian genetics can also be applied to complex patterns of inheritance, such as multiple alleles, incomplete dominance, pleiotropy, and polygenic inheritance.

Multiple Allelic Traits

When a trait is controlled by **multiple alleles,** the gene exists in several allelic forms within a population. For example, although a person's ABO blood type is controlled by a single gene pair, there are three possible alleles within the human population that determine the blood type. Each person receives two of these alleles (one from each parent) to determine the presence or absence of antigens on their red blood cells.

I^A = A antigen on red blood cells
I^B = B antigen on red blood cells
i = Neither A nor B antigen on red blood cells

The possible phenotypes and genotypes for blood type are as follows:

Phenotype	Genotype
A	$I^A I^A$, $I^A i$
B	$I^B I^B$, $I^B i$
AB	$I^A I^B$
O	ii

The inheritance of the ABO blood group in humans is also an example of **codominance** because both I^A and I^B are fully expressed in the presence of the other. A person who inherits chromosomes with I^A and I^B alleles will make fully functional A and B protein, and because these alleles are codominant, the resulting mixture of AB protein will give the red blood cell an AB phenotype. On the other hand, both I^A and I^B are dominant over i. Therefore, two genotypes are possible for type A blood, and two genotypes are possible for type B blood.

Use a Punnett square to confirm that reproduction between a heterozygote with type A blood and a heterozygote with type B blood can result in any one of the four blood types. Such a cross makes it clear that an offspring can have a different blood type from either parent, and for this reason, DNA fingerprinting is now used to identify the parents of an individual, instead of blood type.

Incomplete Dominance and Incomplete Penetrance

Incomplete dominance is exhibited when the heterozygote has an intermediate phenotype between that of either homozygote. In a cross between a true-breeding, red-flowered four-o'clock plant strain and a true-breeding, white-flowered strain, the offspring have pink flowers. Although this outcome might appear to be an example of the blending theory of inheritance, it is not. Here's why. When the pink plants self-pollinate, the offspring plants have a phenotypic ratio of 1 red-flowered : 2 pink-flowered : 1 white-flowered. The reappearance of the three phenotypes in this generation makes it clear that we are still dealing with a single pair of alleles (Fig. 11.14).

Incomplete dominance in four-o'clocks actually has more to do with the amount of pigment protein produced in the plant cells: A double dose of pigment results in red flowers; a single dose of pigment results in pink flowers; and a lack of any pigment produces white flowers.

Human Examples of Incomplete Dominance

In humans, familial hypercholesterolemia (FH) is an example of incomplete dominance. An individual with two alleles for this disorder develops fatty deposits in the skin and tendons and may have a heart attack as a child. An individual with one normal allele and one *FH* allele may suffer a heart attack as a young adult, and an individual with two normal alleles does not have the disorder.

Perhaps the inheritance pattern of other human disorders should be considered one of incomplete dominance. To detect the carriers of cystic fibrosis, for example, it is customary to determine the amount of cellular activity of the gene. When the activity is one-half that of the dominant homozygote, the individual is a carrier, even though the individual does not exhibit the genetic disease. In other words, at the level of gene

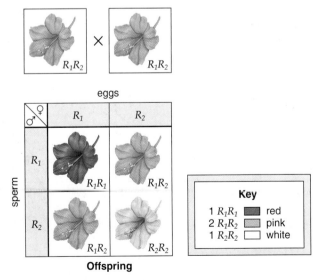

Figure 11.14 Incomplete dominance. When pink four-o'clocks self-pollinate, the results show three phenotypes. This is only possible if the pink parents had an allele for red pigment (R_1) and an allele for no pigment (R_2). Note that alleles involved in incomplete dominance are both given a capital letter.

expression, the homozygotes and heterozygotes do differ in the same manner as four-o'clock plants.

In some cases, a dominant allele may not always lead to the dominant phenotype in a heterozygote, even when the alleles show a true dominant/recessive relationship. The dominant allele in this case does not always determine the phenotype of the individual, so we describe these traits as showing **incomplete penetrance.** In other words, just because a person inherits a dominant allele doesn't mean they will fully express the gene or show the dominant phenotype. Many dominant alleles exhibit varying degrees of penetrance.

The best-known example of incomplete penetrance is polydactyly, the presence of one or more extra digits on hands, feet, or both. Polydactyly is inherited in an autosomal dominant manner; however, not all individuals who inherit the dominant allele exhibit the trait. The reasons for this are not clear, but expression of polydactyly may require additional environmental factors or be influenced by other genes, as discussed later.

Pleiotropic Effects

Pleiotropy occurs when a single mutant gene affects two or more distinct and seemingly unrelated traits. For example, persons with Marfan syndrome have disproportionately long arms, legs, hands, and feet; a weakened aorta; poor eyesight; and other characteristics (Fig. 11.15). All of these characteristics are due to the production of abnormal connective tissue.

Marfan syndrome has been linked to a mutated gene (*FBN1*) on chromosome 15 that ordinarily specifies a functional protein called fibrillin. Fibrillin is essential for the formation of elastic fibers in connective tissue. Without the structural support of normal connective tissue, the aorta can burst, particularly if the person is engaged in a strenuous sport, such as volleyball or basketball. Flo Hyman may have been the best American woman volleyball player ever, but she fell to the floor and died at the age of only 31 because her aorta gave way during a game. Now that coaches are aware of Marfan syndrome, they are on the lookout for it among very tall basketball players. Chris Weisheit, whose career was cut short after he was diagnosed with Marfan syndrome, said, "I don't want to die playing basketball."

Many other disorders, including porphyria and sickle-cell disease, are examples of pleiotropic traits. Porphyria is caused by a chemical insufficiency in the production of hemoglobin, the pigment that makes red blood cells red. The symptoms of porphyria are photosensitivity, strong abdominal pain, port-wine-colored urine, and paralysis in the arms and legs. Many members of the British royal family in the late 1700s and early 1800s suffered from this disorder, which can lead to epileptic convulsions, bizarre behavior, and coma.

In a person suffering from sickle-cell disease (Hb^SHb^S), the cells are sickle-shaped. The underlying mutation is in a gene that codes for a type of polypeptide chain in hemoglobin. Of 146 amino acids, the gene mutation changes only one amino acid, but the result is a less soluble polypeptide chain that stacks up and causes

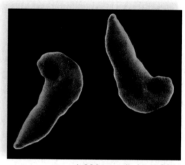

1,600×, colorized SEM

Sickled red blood cell

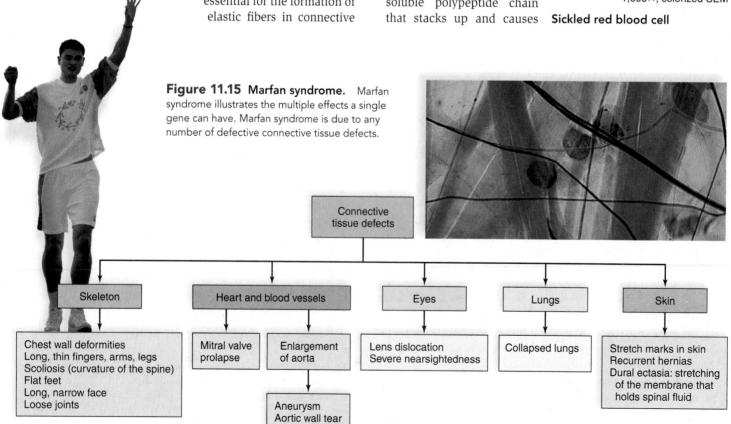

Figure 11.15 Marfan syndrome. Marfan syndrome illustrates the multiple effects a single gene can have. Marfan syndrome is due to any number of defective connective tissue defects.

Connective tissue defects

Skeleton | Heart and blood vessels | Eyes | Lungs | Skin

Chest wall deformities
Long, thin fingers, arms, legs
Scoliosis (curvature of the spine)
Flat feet
Long, narrow face
Loose joints

Mitral valve prolapse

Enlargement of aorta

Aneurysm
Aortic wall tear

Lens dislocation
Severe nearsightedness

Collapsed lungs

Stretch marks in skin
Recurrent hernias
Dural ectasia: stretching of the membrane that holds spinal fluid

red blood cells to be sickle-shaped. The abnormally shaped sickle cells slow down blood flow and clog small blood vessels. In addition, sickled red blood cells have a shorter life span than normal red blood cells. Affected individuals may exhibit a number of symptoms, including severe anemia, physical weakness, poor circulation, impaired mental function, pain and high fever, rheumatism, paralysis, spleen damage, low resistance to disease, and kidney and heart failure. All of these effects are due to the tendency of sickled red blood cells to break down and to the resulting decreased oxygen-carrying capacity of the blood and the damage the body suffers as a result of the condition.

Although sickle-cell disease is a devastating disorder, from an evolutionary perspective it provides heterozygous individuals with a survival advantage. People who have sickle-cell trait are resistant to the protozoan parasite that causes malaria. The parasite spends part of its life cycle in red blood cells feeding on hemoglobin, but it cannot complete its life cycle when sickle-shaped cells form and break down earlier than usual. Because of this survival benefit, the sickle-cell allele has been maintained in the human population over evolutionary time.

Polygenic Inheritance

Polygenic inheritance [Gk. *poly*, many; L. *genitus*, producing] occurs when a trait is governed by two or more sets of alleles. Examples include human height and prevalence of diabetes. The individual has a copy of all allelic pairs, possibly located on many different pairs of chromosomes. Each dominant allele has a quantitative effect on the phenotype, and these effects are additive. Therefore, a population is expected to exhibit continuous phenotypic variations, such as a wide variation in human height and weight. In Figure 11.16, a cross between genotypes *AABBCC* and *aabbcc* yields F₁ hybrids with the genotype *AaBbCc*. A range of genotypes and phenotypes results in the F₂ generation that can be depicted as a bell-shaped curve (Fig. 11.16).

Polygenic traits are controlled by many genes and may be influenced by environmental factors. We observed previously (see Fig. 6.9) that the coat color of a Siamese cat is darker in color at the ears, nose, paws, and tail because an enzyme involved in the production of melanin is active only at a low temperature. Similarly, polygenic traits like prevalence of diabetes are influenced by environmental factors like nutrition.

Human Examples of Multifactorial Inheritance

Human skin color and height are examples of polygenic traits affected by the environment. For example, exposure to the sun can affect skin color, and nutrition can affect human height. Just how many pairs of alleles control skin color is not known, but a range in colors can be explained on the basis of just two pairs when *each capital letter contributes equally to the pigment in the skin*.

Genotypes	Phenotypes
AABB	Very dark
AABb or *AaBB*	Dark
AaBb or *AAbb* or *aaBB*	Medium brown
Aabb or *aaBb*	Light
aabb	Very light

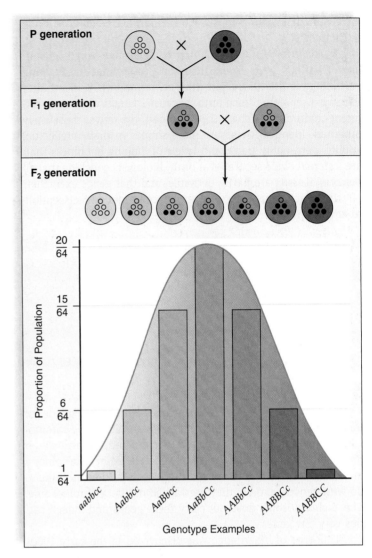

Figure 11.16 Polygenic inheritance. In polygenic inheritance, a number of pairs of genes control the trait. *Above:* Black dots and intensity of blue shading stand for the number of dominant alleles. *Below:* Orange shading shows the degree of environmental influences.

Eye color is also a polygenic trait. The amount of melanin deposited in the iris increases the darker color of the eye. Different eye colors from the brightest of blue to nearly black eyes are thought to be the result of two genes with alleles each interacting in an additive manner.

Many human disorders, such as cleft lip and/or palate, clubfoot, congenital dislocations of the hip, hypertension, diabetes, schizophrenia, and even allergies and cancers, are most likely due to the combined action of many genes plus environmental influences. In recent years, reports have surfaced that all sorts of behavioral traits, such as alcoholism, phobias, and even suicide, can be associated with particular genes.

The relative importance of genetic and environmental influences on the phenotype can vary, but in some instances the role of the environment is clear. For example, cardiovascular disease is more prevalent among those whose biological or adoptive parents have cardiovascular disease. Can you suggest environmental reasons for this correlation, based on your study of Chapter 3?

Many investigators are trying to determine what percentage of various traits is due to nature (inheritance) and what percentage is due to nurture (the environment). Some studies use twins separated since birth, because if identical twins in different environments share the same trait, the trait is most likely inherited. Identical twins are more similar in their intellectual talents, personality traits, and levels of lifelong happiness than are fraternal twins separated at birth. Biologists conclude that all behavioral traits are partly heritable, and that genes exert their effects by acting together in complex combinations susceptible to environmental influences.

Check Your Progress   11.3A

1. Interpret the genotype of the heterozygote if the inheritance pattern for a genetic disorder is shown to be incompletely dominant.
2. Examine the genotype of the child, the mother, and the possible genotypes of the father for a child with type O blood who is born to a mother with type A blood.

X-Linked Inheritance

The X and Y chromosomes in mammals determine the gender of the individual. Females are XX and males are XY. These chromosomes carry genes that control development and, in particular, if the Y chromosome contains an *SRY* gene, the embryo becomes a male. The term **X-linked** is used for genes that have nothing to do with gender, and yet they are carried on the X chromosome. The Y chromosome does not carry these genes and indeed carries very few genes.

This type of inheritance was discovered in the early 1900s by a group at Columbia University headed by Thomas Hunt Morgan. Morgan performed experiments with fruit flies, whose scientific name is *Drosophila melanogaster*. Fruit flies are even better subjects for genetic studies than garden peas. They can be easily and inexpensively raised in simple laboratory glassware; after mating, females lay hundreds of eggs during their lifetimes; and, the generation time is short, taking only about ten days from egg to adult. Fruit flies have a sex chromosome pattern similar to that of humans, and therefore Morgan's experiments with X-linked genes apply directly to humans.

Video
Why a Guy Is a Guy

Morgan's Experiment

Morgan took a newly discovered mutant male with white eyes and crossed it with a red-eyed female:

	♀		♂
P	red-eyed	×	white-eyed
F₁	red-eyed		red-eyed

From these results, he knew that red eyes are the dominant characteristic and white eyes are the recessive characteristic. He then crossed the F₁ flies. In the F₂ generation, there was the expected

3 red-eyed : 1 white-eyed ratio, but it struck him as odd that all of the white-eyed flies were males:

	♀		♂
F₁ × F₁	red-eyed	×	red-eyed
F₂	red-eyed		1 red-eyed : 1 white-eyed

Obviously, a major difference between the male flies and the female flies was their sex chromosomes. Could it be possible that an allele for eye color was on the Y chromosome but not on the X? This idea could be quickly discarded because usually females have red eyes, and they have no Y chromosome. Perhaps an allele for eye color was on the X, but not on the Y, chromosome. Figure 11.17 indicates that this explanation would match the results obtained in the experiment. These results support the chromosome theory of inheritance by showing that the

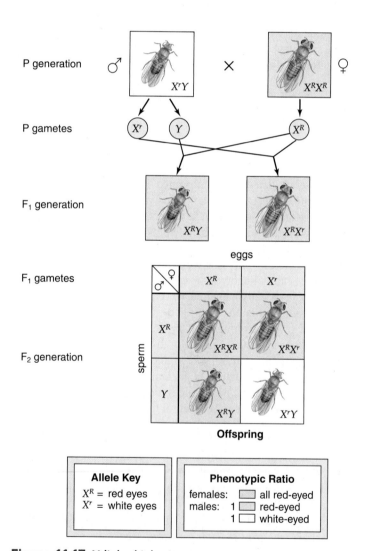

Figure 11.17 X-linked inheritance. Once researchers deduced that the alleles for red/white eye color are on the X chromosome in *Drosophila*, they were able to explain their experimental results. Males with white eyes in the F₂ generation inherit the recessive allele only from the female parent; they receive a Y chromosome lacking the allele for eye color from the male parent.

behavior of a specific allele corresponds exactly with that of a specific chromosome—the X chromosome in *Drosophila*.

Notice that X-linked alleles have a different pattern of inheritance than alleles that are on the autosomes because the Y chromosome is lacking for these alleles, and the inheritance of a Y chromosome cannot offset the inheritance of an X-linked recessive allele. For the same reason, males always receive an X-linked recessive mutant allele from the female parent—they receive only the Y chromosome from the male parent, and therefore sex-linked recessive traits appear much more frequently in males than in females.

Solving X-Linked Genetics Problems

Recall that when solving autosomal genetics problems, the allele key and genotypes can be represented as follows:

Allele key	Genotypes
L = long wings	LL, Ll
l = short wings	ll

When predicting inheritance of sex-linked traits, however, it is necessary to indicate the sex chromosomes of each individual. As noted in Figure 11.17, however, the allele key for an X-linked gene shows an allele attached to the X:

Allele key

X^R = red eyes
X^r = white eyes

The possible genotypes and phenotypes in both males and females are as follows:

Genotype	Phenotype
$X^R X^R$	red-eyed female
$X^R X^r$	red-eyed female
$X^r X^r$	white-eyed female
$X^R Y$	red-eyed male
$X^r Y$	white-eyed male

Notice that there are three possible genotypes for females but only two for males. Females can be heterozygous $X^R X^r$, in which case they are carriers. Carriers usually do not show a recessive abnormality, but they are capable of passing on a recessive allele for an abnormality. But unlike autosomal traits, males cannot be carriers for X-linked traits; if the dominant allele is on the single X chromosome, they show the dominant phenotype, and if the recessive allele is on the single X chromosome, they show the recessive phenotype. For this reason, males are considered **hemizygous** for X-linked traits, because a male only possesses one allele for the trait and, therefore, expresses whatever allele is present on the X chromosome.

We know that male fruit flies have white eyes when they receive the mutant recessive allele from the female parent. What is the inheritance pattern when females have white eyes? Females can have white eyes only when they receive a recessive allele from both parents.

Human X-Linked Disorders

Several X-linked recessive disorders occur in humans, including color blindness, Menkes syndrome, muscular dystrophy, adrenoleukodystrophy, and hemophilia.

Color Blindness. In humans, the receptors for color vision in the retina of the eyes are three different classes of cone cells. Only one type of pigment protein is present in each class of cone cell; there are blue-sensitive, red-sensitive, and green-sensitive cone cells. The allele for the blue-sensitive protein is autosomal, but the alleles for the red- and green-sensitive pigments are on the X chromosome. About 8% of Caucasian men have red-green color blindness. Most of these see brighter greens as tans, olive greens as browns, and reds as reddish browns. A few cannot tell reds from greens at all. They see only yellows, blues, blacks, whites, and grays.

Pedigrees can also reveal the unusual inheritance pattern seen in sex-linked traits. For example, the pedigree in Figure 11.18 shows the usual pattern of inheritance for color blindness. More males than females have the trait because recessive alleles on the X chromosome are expressed in males. The disorder often passes from grandfather to grandson through a carrier daughter.

Menkes Syndrome. Menkes syndrome, or kinky hair syndrome, is caused by a defective allele on the X chromosome. Normally, the gene product controls the movement of the metal

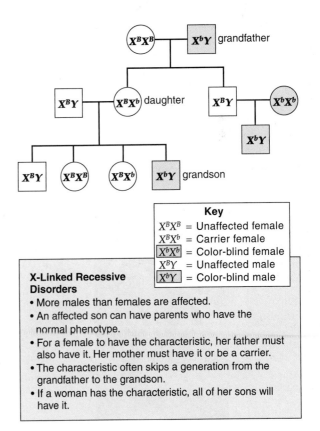

X-Linked Recessive Disorders
- More males than females are affected.
- An affected son can have parents who have the normal phenotype.
- For a female to have the characteristic, her father must also have it. Her mother must have it or be a carrier.
- The characteristic often skips a generation from the grandfather to the grandson.
- If a woman has the characteristic, all of her sons will have it.

Key
$X^B X^B$ = Unaffected female
$X^B X^b$ = Carrier female
$X^b X^b$ = Color-blind female
$X^B Y$ = Unaffected male
$X^b Y$ = Color-blind male

Figure 11.18 X-linked recessive pedigree. This pedigree for color blindness exemplifies the inheritance pattern of an X-linked recessive disorder. The list gives various ways of recognizing the X-linked recessive pattern of inheritance.

copper in and out of cells. The symptoms of Menkes syndrome are due to accumulation of copper in some parts of the body, and the lack of the metal in other parts.

Symptoms of Menkes syndrome include poor muscle tone, seizures, abnormally low body temperature, skeletal anomalies, and the characteristic brittle, steely hair associated with the disorder. Although the condition is relatively rare, affecting approximately 1 in 100,000, mostly males, the prognosis for people with Menkes syndrome is poor, and most individuals die within the first few years of life. In recent years, some people with Menkes syndrome have been treated with injections of copper directly underneath the skin, but with mixed results, and treatment must begin very early in life to be effective.

Muscular Dystrophy. Muscular dystrophy, as the name implies, is characterized by a wasting away of the muscles. The most common form, Duchenne muscular dystrophy, is X-linked and occurs in about 1 out of every 3,600 male births (Fig. 11.19). Symptoms, such as waddling gait, toe walking, frequent falls, and difficulty in rising, may appear as soon as the child starts to walk. Muscle weakness intensifies until the individual is confined to a wheelchair. Death usually occurs by age 20; therefore, affected males are rarely fathers. The recessive allele remains in the population through passage from carrier mother to carrier daughter.

The allele for Duchenne muscular dystrophy has been isolated, and it has been discovered that the absence of a protein called dystrophin causes the disorder. Much investigative work has determined that dystrophin is involved in the release of calcium from the sarcoplasmic reticulum in muscle fibers. The lack of dystrophin causes calcium to leak into the cell, which promotes the action of an enzyme that dissolves muscle fibers. When the body attempts to repair the tissue, fibrous tissue forms, and this cuts off the blood supply so that more and more cells die.

A test is now available to detect carriers of Duchenne muscular dystrophy. Also, various treatments have been tried. Immature muscle cells can be injected into muscles, and for every 100,000 cells injected, dystrophin production occurs in 30–40% of muscle fibers. The allele for dystrophin has been inserted into thigh muscle cells, and about 1% of these cells then produced dystrophin.

Adrenoleukodystrophy. Adrenoleukodystrophy, or ALD, is an X-linked recessive disorder due to the failure of a carrier protein to move either an enzyme or very long chain fatty acid (24–30 carbon atoms) into peroxisomes. As a result, these fatty acids are not broken down, and they accumulate inside the cell; the result is severe nervous system damage.

Children with ALD fail to develop properly after age 5, lose adrenal gland function, exhibit very poor coordination, and show a progressive loss of hearing, speech, and vision. The condition is usually fatal, with no known cure, but the onset and severity of symptoms in patients not yet showing symptoms may be mitigated by treatment with a mixture of lipids derived from olive oil. The disease was made well-known by the 1992 movie *Lorenzo's Oil*, detailing a mother's and father's determination to devise a treatment for their son who was suffering from ALD.

Hemophilia. About 1 in 10,000 males is a hemophiliac. There are two common types of hemophilia: Hemophilia A is due to the absence or minimal presence of a clotting factor known as factor VIII, and hemophilia B is due to the absence of clotting factor IX. Hemophilia is called the bleeder's disease because the affected person's blood either does not clot or clots very slowly. Although hemophiliacs bleed externally after an injury, they also bleed internally, particularly around joints. Hemorrhages can be stopped with transfusions of fresh blood (or plasma) or concentrates of the clotting protein. Also, clotting factors are now available as biotechnology products.

At the turn of the century, hemophilia was prevalent among the royal families of Europe, and all of the affected males could trace their ancestry to Queen Victoria of England. Of Queen Victoria's 26 grandchildren, four grandsons had hemophilia and four granddaughters were carriers. Because none of Queen Victoria's relatives were affected, it seems that the faulty allele she carried arose by mutation either in Victoria or in one of her parents. Her carrier daughters Alice and Beatrice introduced the allele into the ruling houses of Russia and Spain, respectively. Alexis, the last heir to the Russian throne before the Russian Revolution, was a hemophiliac. There are no hemophiliacs in the present British royal family because Victoria's eldest son, King Edward VII, did not receive the allele.

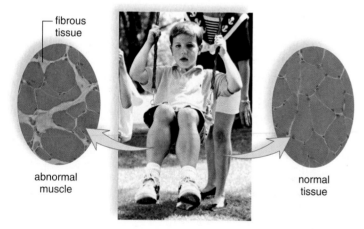

fibrous tissue

abnormal muscle

normal tissue

Figure 11.19 Muscular dystrophy. In muscular dystrophy, an X-linked recessive disorder, calves enlarge because fibrous tissue develops as muscles waste away, due to lack of the protein dystrophin.

Check Your Progress 11.3B

1. Describe the possible genotypes if a homozygous red-eyed *Drosophila* female is crossed with a red-eyed male.
2. Explain the chances that a color-blind woman who is married to a man with normal vision will produce
   a. color-blind sons b. color-blind daughters c. carrier daughters.
3. Identify the genotype of all individuals involved in a cross between a brown-haired woman and a black-haired man that produce all brown-haired male offspring and all black-haired female offspring, assuming X-linkage.

CONNECTING *the* CONCEPTS *with the* THEMES

Evolution

- Although humans usually produce small numbers of offspring, it is clear from years of research that Mendel's laws apply to humans in many instances.

- Good historical records of inheritance in large families, such as Mormon families, have shown a number of human genetic disorders are indeed controlled by a single allelic pair.

- The persistence of such genetic diseases over evolutionary time may confer some biological benefit to humans. For example, heterozygous sickle-cell anemia individuals are more resistant to malaria, one of the world's most deadly diseases.

Nature of Science

- A good experimental design and careful data analysis allowed Mendel to discover his laws of inheritance.

- Mendel was fortunate in that he chose to study an organism, namely the garden pea, whose observable traits are often determined by a single allelic pair.

- In most cases, however, traits are determined by several genes or are affected by additional factors, such as the environment.

- In the future, emerging technologies will allow humans to sequence personal genomes, showing us the entirety of individual biological potential and providing a mechanism for customized medicine.

Biological Systems

- The work of Morgan and others showed that the sex chromosomes contain genes unrelated to gender.

- Geneticists later discovered that some human genetic diseases, such as hemophilia, are caused by faulty genes on the X chromosome.

- With the help of Mendelian genetics, pedigree analysis, and statistics, scientists have been able to link many human diseases to specific genes on certain chromosomes.

- Projects like the human genome project are beginning to decipher how genes affect the whole body, not just single traits.

Media Study Tools

www.mhhe.com/maderbiology11

Enhance your study of this chapter with study tools and practice tests. Also ask your instructor about the resources available through ConnectPlus, including the media-rich eBook, interactive learning tools, and animations.

Summarize

11.1 Gregor Mendel

Gregor Mendel used the garden pea as the subject in his genetic studies. In contrast to preceding plant breeders, his study involved nonblending traits of the garden pea. Mendel applied mathematics, followed the scientific method very closely, and kept careful records. His results supported a particulate theory of inheritance, effectively disproving the blending theory of inheritance.

11.2 Mendel's Laws

When Mendel crossed heterozygous plants with other heterozygous plants, he found that the recessive phenotype reappeared in about ¼ of the F_2 plants; there was a 3:1 phenotypic ratio. This allowed Mendel to propose his law of segregation, which states that the individual has two factors for each trait, and the factors segregate with equal probability into the gametes.

Mendel conducted two-trait crosses, in which the F_1 individuals showed both dominant characteristics, but there were four phe-

notypes among the F_2 offspring. (The actual phenotypic ratio was 9:3:3:1.) This allowed Mendel to deduce the law of independent assortment, which states that the members of one pair of factors separate independently of those of another pair. Therefore, all possible combinations of parental factors can occur in the gametes.

The laws of probability can be used to calculate the expected phenotypic ratio of a cross. A large number of offspring must be counted in order to observe the expected results, and to ensure that all possible types of sperm have fertilized all possible types of eggs, as is done in a Punnett square. The Punnett square uses the product law of probability to arrive at possible genotypes among the offspring, and then the sum law can be used to arrive at the phenotypic ratio.

Mendel also crossed the F_1 plants having the dominant phenotype with homozygous recessive plants. The 1:1 results indicated that the recessive factor was present in these F_1 plants (i.e., that they were heterozygous). Today, we call this a testcross, because it is used to test whether an individual showing the dominant characteristic is homozygous dominant or heterozygous. The two-trait testcross allows an investigator to test whether an individual showing two dominant characteristics is homozygous dominant for both traits or for one trait only, or is heterozygous for both traits.

Studies have shown that many human traits and genetic disorders can be explained on the basis of simple Mendelian inheritance. When studying human genetic disorders, biologists often construct pedigrees to show the pattern of inheritance of a characteristic within a family. The particular pattern indicates the manner in which a characteristic is inherited. Sample pedigrees for autosomal recessive and autosomal dominant patterns appear in Figures 11.10 and 11.11.

11.3 Extending the Range of Mendelian Genetics

Other patterns of inheritance have been discovered since Mendel's original contribution. For example, some genes have multiple alleles, although each individual organism has only two alleles, as in the inheritance of blood type in human beings. Inheritance of blood type also illustrates codominance. With incomplete dominance, the phenotype of F_1 individuals are intermediate between the parent phenotypes; this does not support the blending theory because the parent phenotypes reappear in F_2. With incomplete penetrance, some traits that are dominant may not be expressed due to unknown reasons.

In pleiotropy, one gene has multiple effects as with Marfan syndrome and sickle-cell disease. Polygenic traits are controlled by several genes that have an additive effect on the phenotype, resulting in quantitative variations within a population. A bell-shaped curve is seen because environmental influences bring about many intervening phenotypes, as in the inheritance of height in human beings. Skin color and eye color are also examples of polygenic inheritance (multiple genes plus the environment).

In *Drosophila*, as in humans, the sex chromosomes determine the sex of the individual, with XX being female and XY being male. Experimental support for the chromosome theory of inheritance came when Morgan and his group were able to determine that the gene for a trait unrelated to sex determination, the white-eyed allele in *Drosophila*, is on the X chromosome.

Alleles on the X chromosome are called X-linked alleles. Therefore, when doing X-linked genetics problems, it is the custom to indicate the sexes by using sex chromosomes and to indicate the alleles by superscripts attached to the X. The Y is blank because it does not carry these genes. Color blindness, Menkes syndrome, adrenoleukodystrophy, and hemophilia are X-linked recessive disorders in humans.

Key Terms

allele 196	law of segregation 196
autosome 201	locus 196
carrier 202	monohybrid cross 195
codominance 205	multiple alleles 205
dihybrid cross 198	phenotype 197
dominant allele 196	pleiotropy 206
family pedigree 204	polygenic inheritance 207
genotype 196	polygenic trait 207
hemizygous 209	Punnett square 200
heterozygous 196	recessive allele 196
homozygous 196	testcross 200
incomplete dominance 205	X-linked 208
incomplete penetrance 206	
law of independent assortment 198	

Assess

Reviewing This Chapter

1. How did Mendel's procedure differ from that of his predecessors? What is his theory of inheritance called?   193
2. How does the F_2 of Mendel's one-trait cross refute the blending concept of inheritance? Using Mendel's one-trait cross as an example, trace his reasoning to arrive at the law of segregation.   195–96
3. Using Mendel's two-trait cross as an example, trace his reasoning to arrive at the law of independent assortment.   198

4. What are the two laws of probability, and how do they apply to a Punnett square?   200
5. What is a testcross, and when is it used?   200–01
6. How might you distinguish an autosomal dominant trait from an autosomal recessive trait when viewing a pedigree?   201–02
7. For autosomal recessive disorders, what are the chances of two carriers having an affected child?   202
8. For most autosomal dominant disorders, what are the chances of a heterozygote and a normal individual having an affected child?   202
9. Explain inheritance by multiple alleles. List the human blood types, and give the possible genotypes for each.   205
10. Explain the inheritance of incompletely dominant alleles and why this is not an example of blending inheritance.   205–06
11. Explain why traits controlled by polygenes show continuous variation and produce a distribution in the F_2 generation that follows a bell-shaped curve.   207
12. How do you recognize a pedigree for an X-linked recessive allele in human beings?   208–09

Testing Yourself

Choose the best answer for each question. For questions 1–4, match each item to those in the key.

KEY:
   a. 3:1
   b. 9:3:3:1
   c. 1:1
   d. 1:1:1:1
   e. 3:1:3:1

1. *TtYy* × *TtYy*
2. *Tt* × *Tt*
3. *Tt* × *tt*
4. *TtYy* × *ttyy*
5. Which of these could be a normal gamete?
   a. *GgRr*
   b. *GRr*
   c. *Gr*
   d. *GgR*
   e. None of these are correct.
6. Which of these properly describes a cross between an individual who is homozygous dominant for hairline but heterozygous for finger length, and an individual who is recessive for both characteristics? (*W* = widow's peak, *w* = straight hairline, *S* = short fingers, *s* = long fingers)
   a. *WwSs* × *WwSs*
   b. *WWSs* × *wwSs*
   c. *Ws* × *ws*
   d. *WWSs* × *wwss*
7. In peas, yellow seed (*Y*) is dominant over green seed (*y*). In the F_2 generation of a monohybrid cross that begins when a dominant homozygote is crossed with a recessive homozygote, you would expect
   a. three plants with yellow seeds to every plant with green seeds.
   b. plants with one yellow seed for every green seed.
   c. only plants with the genotype *Yy*.
   d. only plants that produce yellow seeds.
   e. Both c and d are correct.

8. In humans, pointed eyebrows (*B*) are dominant over smooth eyebrows (*b*). Mary's father has pointed eyebrows, but she and her mother have smooth. What is the genotype of the father?
   a. *BB*
   b. *Bb*
   c. *bb*
   d. *BbBb*
   e. Any one of these is correct.

9. In guinea pigs, smooth coat (*S*) is dominant over rough coat (*s*), and black coat (*B*) is dominant over white coat (*b*). In the cross *SsBb* × *SsBb*, how many of the offspring will have a smooth black coat on average?
   a. 9 only
   b. about ⁹⁄₁₆
   c. ¹⁄₁₆
   d. ⁶⁄₁₆
   e. ²⁄₆

10. In horses, *B* = black coat, *b* = brown coat, *T* = trotter, and *t* = pacer. A black trotter that has a brown pacer offspring would have which of the following genotypes?
    a. *BT*
    b. *BbTt*
    c. *bbtt*
    d. *BBtt*
    e. *BBTT*

11. In tomatoes, red fruit (*R*) is dominant over yellow fruit (*r*), and tallness (*T*) is dominant over shortness (*t*). A plant that is *RrTT* is crossed with a plant that is *rrTt*. What are the chances of an offspring possessing both recessive traits?
    a. none
    b. ½
    c. ¼
    d. ¾

12. In the cross *RrTt* × *rrtt*,
    a. all the offspring will be tall with red fruit.
    b. 75% (¾) will be tall with red fruit.
    c. 50% (½) will be tall with red fruit.
    d. 25% (¼) will be tall with red fruit.

13. A boy is color-blind (X-linked recessive) and has a straight hairline (autosomal recessive). Which could be the genotype of his mother?
    a. *bbww*   d. *XBXbWw*
    b. *XbYWw*   e. *XwXwBb*
    c. *bbXwXw*

14. Which of the following would you *not* find in a pedigree when a male has an X-linked recessive disorder?
    a. Neither parent has the disorder.
    b. Only males in the pedigree have the disorder.
    c. Only females in the pedigree have the disorder.
    d. The sons of a female with the disorder all have the disorder.
    e. Both a and c would not be seen.

For questions 15–17, match the statements to the items in the key.

KEY:
   a. multiple alleles
   b. polygenes
   c. pleiotropic gene

15. People with sickle-cell disease have many cardiovascular complications.

16. Although most people have an IQ of about 100, IQ generally ranges from about 50 to 150.

17. In humans, there are three possible alleles at the chromosomal locus that determine blood type.

18. Alice and Henry are at the opposite extremes for a polygenic trait. Their children will
    a. be bell-shaped.
    b. be a phenotype typical of a 9:3:3:1 ratio.
    c. have the middle phenotype between their two parents.
    d. look like one parent or the other.

19. Determine whether the characteristic possessed by the shaded squares (males) and circles (females) is an autosomal dominant, autosomal recessive, or X-linked recessive.

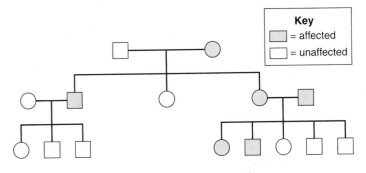

Key
■ = affected
□ = unaffected

Engage

Virtual Labs
Punnett Squares
Sex-Linked Traits

The virtual labs "Punnett Squares" and "Sex-linked Traits" both provide you with the ability to test your knowledge of Mendelian and sex-linked patterns of inheritance.

Thinking Scientifically

1. You want to determine whether a newly found *Drosophila* characteristic is dominant or recessive. Would you wait to cross this male fly with another of its own kind or cross it now with a fly that lacks the characteristic?

2. You want to test whether the leaf pattern of a plant is influenced by the amount of fertilizer in the environment. What would you do?

12

Molecular Biology of the Gene

The diversity of life is dependent on gene activity.

CHAPTER OUTLINE

12.1 The Genetic Material 215

12.2 Replication of DNA 220

12.3 The Genetic Code of Life 223

12.4 First Step: Transcription 225

12.5 Second Step: Translation 228

12.6 Structure of the Eukaryotic Chromosome 233

BEFORE YOU BEGIN

Before beginning this chapter, take a few moments to review the following discussions.

Figures 3.18 and 3.20 What are the components of a nucleotide and the structure of the DNA molecule?

Figure 11.4 How are genes organized on chromosomes, and how are alleles related to genes?

Section 11.2 What is the relationship between genotype and phenotype?

All life on Earth has the four bases of DNA—A, G, C, and T—in common. Considering up to 1.8 million different species have been discovered and named, with only a fraction of the total discovered, what makes one species different from another? It is largely due to differences in the DNA sequences that make up genes within each species.

How do DNA sequence differences determine the uniqueness of a species—for example, whether an individual is a snow leopard, a crab, or a flower? Or the variation within a species, such as whether a human has blue, brown, or hazel eyes? The diversity of life is based on the flow of genetic information from genes to proteins to observable traits, that is, from genotype to phenotype. This expression of genes is responsible for producing proteins, the molecules that carry out life functions every day.

As DNA sequences change via mutation and other mechanisms over evolutionary time, so do the proteins that are made from genes. Likewise, as proteins change, so do the life forms and diversity we see on Earth. Given that different mixtures of genes and alleles can be inherited over generations, and that life has been in existence for millions of generations, it is not surprising to see how diverse life has become.

As you read through the chapter, think about the following questions:

1. How does the flow of genetic information from DNA to protein to trait work?

2. What mechanisms are in place to ensure that genetic information is accurately expressed?

3. How might the expression of a gene change in response to environmental conditions?

FOLLOWING *the* THEMES

CHAPTER 12 MOLECULAR BIOLOGY OF THE GENE

UNIT 2 GENETIC BASIS OF LIFE		
	Evolution	Changes in DNA sequence produce different proteins that change organismal structure and function.
	Nature of Science	Research in gene expression enables scientists to discover new, effective ways to treat disease.
	Biological Systems	The flow of genetic information in biological systems is highly regulated and responsive to environmental changes.

12.1 The Genetic Material

Learning Outcomes

Upon completion of this section, you should be able to

1. Describe the properties a substance must possess in order to serve as the genetic material.
2. Examine how historical researchers demonstrated that DNA was the genetic material.
3. Explain the chemical structure of DNA as defined by the Watson and Crick model.

The middle of the twentieth century was an exciting period of scientific discovery. On one hand, geneticists were busy determining that *DNA (deoxyribonucleic acid)* is the genetic material of living things. On the other hand, biochemists were in a frantic race to describe the structure of DNA. The classic experiments performed during this era set the stage for an explosion in our knowledge of modern molecular biology.

When researchers began their work, they knew that the genetic material must be

1. able to *store information* that pertains to the development, structure, and metabolic activities of the cell or organism;
2. stable so that it *can be replicated* with high accuracy during cell division and be transmitted from generation to generation;
3. able to *undergo rare changes* called mutations [L. *muta*, change] that provide the genetic variability required for evolution to occur.

This chapter will show, as the researchers of the twentieth century did, that DNA can fulfill these functions.

Transformation of Bacteria

During the late 1920s, the bacteriologist Frederick Griffith (1879-1941) was attempting to develop a vaccine against *Streptococcus pneumoniae* (pneumococcus), which causes pneumonia in mammals. In 1931, he performed a classic experiment with the bacterium. He noticed that when these bacteria are grown on culture plates, some, called S strain bacteria, produce shiny, smooth colonies, and others, called R strain bacteria, produce colonies that have a rough appearance. Under the microscope, S strain bacteria have a capsule (mucous coat) that makes them smooth but R strain bacteria do not.

When Griffith injected mice with the S strain of bacteria, the mice died, and when he injected mice with the R strain, the mice did not die (Fig. 12.1). In an effort to determine whether the capsule alone was responsible for the virulence (ability to kill) of the S strain bacteria, he injected mice with heat-killed S strain bacteria. The mice did not die.

Finally, Griffith injected the mice with a mixture of heat-killed S strain and live R strain bacteria. Most unexpectedly, the mice died—and living S strain bacteria were recovered from the bodies! Griffith concluded that some substance necessary for the bacteria to produce a capsule and be virulent must have passed from the dead S strain bacteria to the living R strain bacteria so that the R strain bacteria were *transformed* (Fig. 12.1d). This change in the phenotype of the R strain bacteria must be due to a change in their genotype. Indeed, couldn't the transforming substance that passed from S strain to R strain be genetic material? Reasoning such as this prompted investigators at the time to begin looking for the transforming substance to determine the chemical nature of the genetic material.

DNA: The Transforming Substance

By the time the next group of investigators, led by Oswald Avery (1877-1955) in the 1940s, began their work, it was known that the genes are on the chromosomes and that the chromosomes contain both proteins and nucleic acids. Investigators were having a much heated debate about whether protein or DNA was the genetic material. Many thought that the protein component of chromosomes must be the genetic material because proteins contain up to 20 different amino acids that can be sequenced in

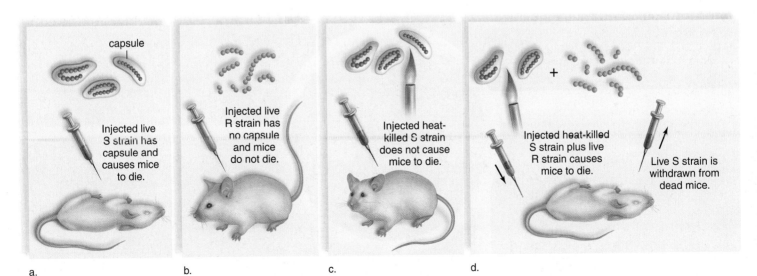

a. b. c. d.

Figure 12.1 Griffith's transformation experiment. **a.** Encapsulated S strain is virulent and kills mice. **b.** Nonencapsulated R strain is not virulent and does not kill mice. **c.** Heat-killed S strain bacteria do not kill mice. **d.** If heat-killed S strain and R strain are both injected into mice, they die because the R strain bacteria have been transformed into the virulent S strain.

any particular way. On the other hand, nucleic acids—DNA and RNA—contain only four types of nucleotides as basic building blocks. Some argued that DNA did not have enough variability to be able to store information and be the genetic material.

In 1944, after 16 years of research, Oswald Avery and his coinvestigators, Colin MacLeod and Maclyn McCarty, published a paper demonstrating that the transforming substance that allows *Streptococcus* to produce a capsule and be virulent is DNA. This meant that DNA is the genetic material. Here is what they found out:

1. DNA from S strain bacteria causes R strain bacteria to be transformed so that they can produce a capsule and be virulent.
2. The addition of DNase, an enzyme that digests DNA, prevents transformation from occurring. This supports the hypothesis that DNA is the genetic material.
3. The molecular weight of the transforming substance is large. This suggests the possibility of genetic variability.
4. The addition of enzymes that degrade proteins has no effect on the transforming substance nor does RNase, an enzyme that digests RNA. This shows that neither protein nor RNA is the genetic material.

These experiments showed that DNA is the transforming substance and, therefore, the genetic material. Although some scientists remained skeptical, many felt that the evidence for DNA being the genetic material was overwhelming.

An experiment by Alfred Hershey and Martha Chase in the early 1950s helped to firmly establish DNA as the genetic material. Hershey and Chase used a virus called a T phage, composed of radioactively labeled DNA and capsid coat proteins, to infect *E. coli* bacteria. They discovered that the radioactive tracers for DNA, but not protein, ended up inside the bacterial cells, causing them to become transformed. Since only the genetic material could have caused this transformation, Hershey and Chase determined that DNA must be the genetic material.

Animation
Hershey and Chase Experiment

Transformation of Organisms Today

Because the code for living things is based on the same four nucleic acid bases of A, G, C, and T, and genes are made from this code, it is conceivable to take genes from one organism and put them into another. Transformation of organisms, resulting in *genetically modified organisms* (GMOs), is an invaluable tool in modern biotechnology today. As discussed further in the next chapter, transformation of bacteria and other organisms has resulted in commercial products that are used every day.

Early biotechnologists seeking a dramatic way to show the possibility of gene transfer between different organisms took a jellyfish gene that codes for a green fluorescent protein (GFP) and started transforming different organisms with it. When this gene is transferred to another organism, the organism glows in the dark! (Fig. 12.2.) The basic technique is relatively simple. First, isolate the jellyfish gene and then transfer it to a bacterium, or the embryo of a plant, pig, or mouse. The result is a bioluminescent organism.

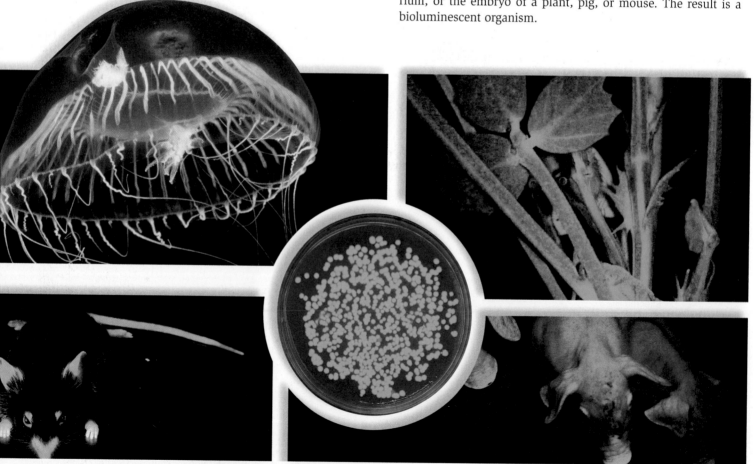

Figure 12.2 Transformation of organisms. When bacteria, plants, pigs, and mice are genetically transformed with a gene from the jellyfish *Aequorea victoria* for green fluorescent protein (GFP), these organisms glow in the dark.

Because living organisms are coded by the same four bases, genes should theoretically have no difficulty crossing the species barrier. Mammalian genes can potentially be transferred to bacteria, and an invertebrate gene, such as the GFP gene, can be transferred to a bacterium, plant, or animal. Although it is possible and relatively easy to perform, cross-species gene transfer does not always result in the host organism producing the new protein because of the innate complexity of each species.

Animation
Bacterial
Transformation

The Structure of DNA

By the early 1950s, DNA was widely accepted as the genetic material of living things. However. the structure of DNA was not known. How can a molecule with only four different nucleotides produce the great diversity of life on Earth?

To understand the structure of DNA, we need to understand how the bases in DNA are composed. Investigators knew that DNA contains four different types of nucleotides: two with *purine* bases, **adenine (A)** and **guanine (G),** which have a double ring; and two with *pyrimidine* bases, **thymine (T)** and **cytosine (C),** which have a single ring (Fig. 12.3*a, b*). Erwin Chargaff used new chemical techniques developed in the 1940s to analyze in detail the base content of DNA.

A sample of Chargaff's data is seen in Figure 12.3*c*. You can see that while some species—*E. coli* and *Zea mays* (corn), for example—do have approximately 25% of each type of nucleotide, most do not. Further, the percentage of each type of nucleotide differs from species to species. Therefore, the nucleotide content of DNA is not fixed across species, and DNA does have the *variability* between species required for it to be the genetic material.

Within each species, however, DNA was found to have the *constancy* required of the genetic material—that is, all members of a species have the same base composition. Also, the percentage of A always equals the percentage of T, and the percentage of G equals the percentage of C. It follows that if the percentage of A + G equals 40%, then the percentage of T + C would equal 60%. (Do you see why?) These relationships are called Chargaff's rules.

Chargaff's rules:

1. The amount of A, T, G, and C in DNA varies from species to species.
2. In each species, the amount of A = T and the amount of G = C.

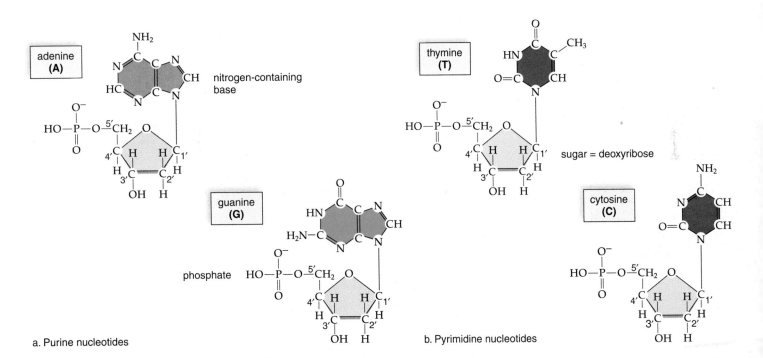

a. Purine nucleotides

b. Pyrimidine nucleotides

DNA Composition in Various Species (%)				
Species	**A**	**T**	**G**	**C**
Homo sapiens (human)	31.0	31.5	19.1	18.4
Drosophila melanogaster (fruit fly)	27.3	27.6	22.5	22.5
Zea mays (corn)	25.6	25.3	24.5	24.6
Neurospora crassa (fungus)	23.0	23.3	27.1	26.6
Escherichia coli (bacterium)	24.6	24.3	25.5	25.6
Bacillus subtilis (bacterium)	28.4	29.0	21.0	21.6

c. Chargaff's data

Figure 12.3 Nucleotide composition of DNA. All nucleotides contain phosphate, a 5-carbon sugar, and a nitrogen-containing base. In DNA, the sugar is called deoxyribose because it lacks an oxygen atom in the 2′ position, compared to ribose. The nitrogen-containing bases are **(a)** the purines adenine and guanine, which have a double ring, and **(b)** the pyrimidines thymine and cytosine, which have a single ring. **c.** Chargaff's data show that the DNA of various species differs. For example, in humans the A and T percentages are about 31%, but in fruit flies these percentages are about 27%. Note that by convention, the carbon atoms in the sugar rings are labeled with a number and a prime symbol to distinguish them from the carbon atoms in the base, which are labeled with a number only (numbers in bases not shown).

Although only one of four bases is possible at each nucleotide position in DNA, the sheer number of bases and the length of most DNA molecules is more than sufficient to provide for variability. For example, it has been calculated that each human chromosome typically contains about 140 million base pairs. This provides for a staggering number of possible sequences of nucleotides. Because any of the four possible nucleotides can be present at each nucleotide position, the total number of possible nucleotide sequences is $4^{(140 \times 10^6)}$ or $4^{140,000,000}$. No wonder each species has its own unique base percentages!

X-Ray Diffraction of DNA

Rosalind Franklin (Fig. 12.4a), a researcher at King's College in London, studied the structure of DNA using X-rays. She found that if a concentrated, viscous solution of DNA is made, it can be separated into fibers. Under the right conditions, the fibers are enough like a crystal (a solid substance whose atoms are arranged in a definite manner) that when X-rayed, an X-ray diffraction pattern results (Fig. 12.4b).

The X-ray diffraction pattern of DNA shows that DNA is a double helix. The helical shape is indicated by the crossed (X) pattern in the center of the photograph in Figure 12.4c. The dark portions at the top and bottom of the photograph indicate that some portion of the helix is repeated. Maurice H. F. Wilkins, a colleague of Franklin's, showed one of her crystallographic patterns to James Watson, who immediately grasped its significance.

Video
DNA Dark Lady

The Watson and Crick Model

James Watson, an American, was on a postdoctoral fellowship at Cavendish Laboratories in Cambridge, England, and while there he began to work with the biophysicist Francis H. C. Crick. Using the data provided from X-ray diffraction and other sources, they constructed a model of DNA for which they received a Nobel Prize in 1962.

Based on previous work of other scientists, Watson and Crick knew that DNA is a polymer of nucleotides, but they did not know how the nucleotides were arranged within the molecule. However, they deduced that DNA is a **double helix** with sugar-phosphate backbones on the outside and paired bases on the inside. This arrangement fits the mathematical measurements provided by Franklin's X-ray diffraction data for the spacing between the base pairs (0.34 nm) and for a complete turn of the double helix (3.4 nm).

According to Watson and Crick's model, the two DNA strands of the double helix are *antiparallel*, meaning the sugar-phosphate groups that are chained together to make each strand are oriented in opposite directions. As explained on page 217, each nucleotide possesses a phosphate group located at the 5′ position of the sugar. Nucleotides are joined together by linking the 5′ phosphate of one nucleotide to a free hydroxyl (–OH) located at the 3′ position on the sugar of the preceding nucleotide, giving the molecule directionality. Antiparallel simply means that while one DNA strand runs 5′ to 3′, the other strand runs in a parallel but opposite direction.

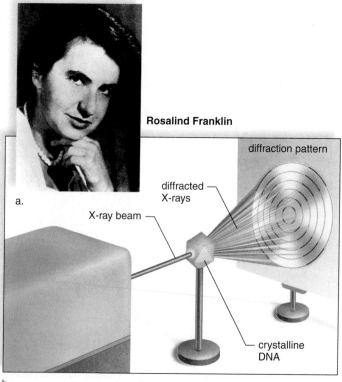

Rosalind Franklin

diffraction pattern

diffracted X-rays

X-ray beam

crystalline DNA

a.

b.

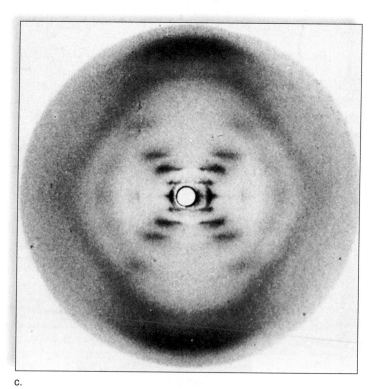

c.

Figure 12.4 X-ray diffraction of DNA. **a.** Rosalind Franklin, 1920–1958. **b.** When a crystal is X-rayed, the way in which the beam is diffracted reflects the pattern of the molecules in the crystal. The closer together two repeating structures are in the crystal, the farther from the center the beam is diffracted. **c.** The diffraction pattern of DNA produced by Rosalind Franklin. The crossed (X) pattern in the center told investigators that DNA is a helix, and the dark portions at the top and the bottom told them that some feature is repeated over and over. Watson and Crick determined that this feature was the hydrogen-bonded bases.

This model also agreed with Chargaff's rules, which states that A = T and G = C. Figure 12.5 shows that A is hydrogen-bonded to T, and G is hydrogen-bonded to C. This so-called **complementary base pairing** means that a purine (large, two-ring base) is always bonded to a pyrimidine (smaller, one-ring base). This antiparallel pairing arrangement of the two strands ensures that the bases are oriented properly so that they can interact. The consistent spacing between the two strands of the DNA was detected by Franklin's X-ray diffraction pattern, because two pyrimidines together are too narrow, and two purines together are too wide (Fig. 12.5).

3D Animation
Base Pairings

The information stored within DNA must always be read in the 5′ to 3′ direction. Thus, a DNA strand is usually replicated in a 5′ to 3′ direction.

Animation
DNA Structure

3D Animation
DNA Structure

Check Your Progress 12.1

1. Discuss how it is possible to take a gene from one organism and express it in another organism.
2. Explain the major features of DNA structure.

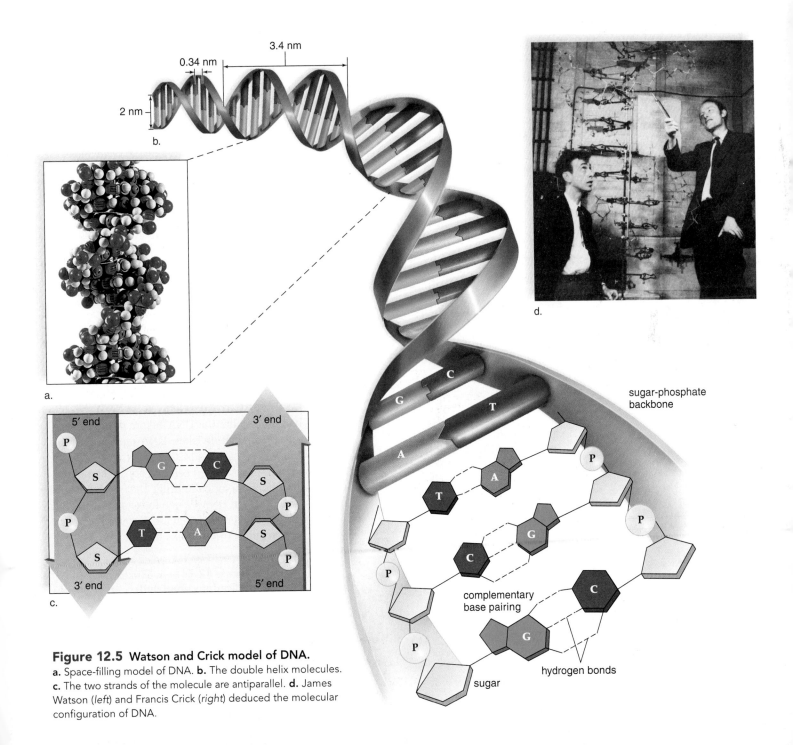

Figure 12.5 Watson and Crick model of DNA.
a. Space-filling model of DNA. **b.** The double helix molecules.
c. The two strands of the molecule are antiparallel. **d.** James Watson (*left*) and Francis Crick (*right*) deduced the molecular configuration of DNA.

12.2 Replication of DNA

Learning Outcomes

Upon completion of this section, you should be able to

1. Explain why the replication of DNA is semiconservative.
2. Examine the steps of DNA replication.
3. Contrast DNA replication in eukaryotes and prokaryotes.

The term **DNA replication** refers to the process of copying a DNA molecule. Following replication, there is usually an exact copy of the parental DNA double helix. As soon as Watson and Crick developed their double-helix model, they commented, "It has not escaped our notice that the specific pairing we have postulated immediately suggests a possible copying mechanism for the genetic material."

A **template** is most often a mold used to produce a shape complementary to itself. During DNA replication, each DNA strand of the parental double helix serves as a template for a new strand in a daughter molecule (Fig. 12.6). DNA replication is termed **semiconservative replication** because each daughter DNA double helix contains an old strand from the parental DNA double helix and a new strand.

Animation
Meselson and Stahl Experiment

Replication requires the following steps:

1. *Unwinding.* The old strands that make up the parental DNA molecule are unwound and "unzipped" (i.e., the weak hydrogen bonds between the paired bases are broken). A special enzyme called helicase unwinds the molecule.
2. *Complementary base pairing.* New free nucleotides, always present in the nucleus, are paired with nucleotides on the parental strands, A with T, and G with C.
3. *Joining.* The complementary nucleotides paired with the parental strands are connected to each other to form a connected chain. Each daughter DNA molecule now contains an old strand and a newly synthesized strand.

Steps 2 and 3 are carried out by an enzyme complex called **DNA polymerase.** DNA polymerase works in the test tube as well as in cells.

In Figure 12.6, the backbones of the parental DNA molecule are blue, and each base is given a particular color. Following replication, the daughter molecules each have a green backbone (new strand) and a blue backbone (old strand). Because A pairs with T, and G pairs with C, A daughter DNA double helix has the same sequence of bases as the parental DNA double helix had originally. Although we have described DNA replication simply here, it is actually a complicated process. Some of the more precise molecular events are discussed in the Biological Systems feature on page 221.

Animation
DNA Replication

You may recall from Chapters 10 and 11 that DNA must be copied before mitosis or meiosis can begin. Because the goal of these processes is to create either an exact cell copy (mitosis) or to make a gamete for reproduction (meiosis), in either case you have to double the DNA before you can separate it during cell division. DNA replication must occur before a cell can divide. Cancer, which is characterized by rapid, uncontrolled cell division, is sometimes treated with chemotherapeutic drugs that mimic one of the four nucleotides in DNA. When these are mistakenly used by the cancer cells to synthesize DNA, replication stops and the cells die off.

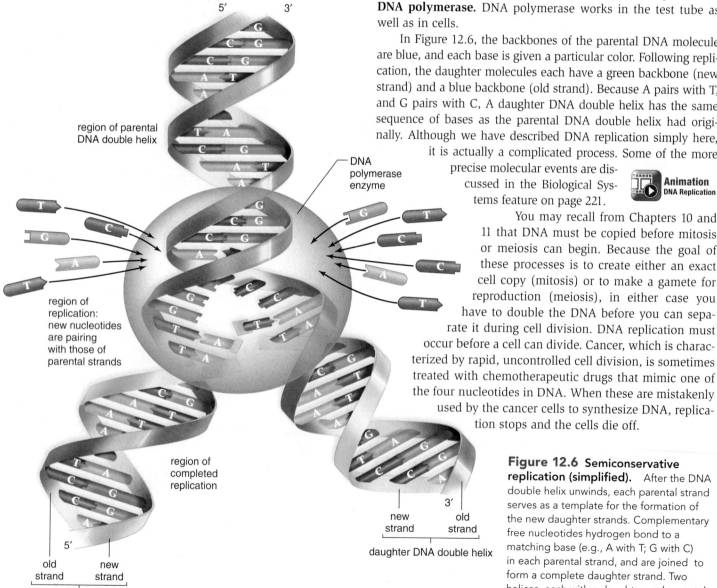

Figure 12.6 Semiconservative replication (simplified). After the DNA double helix unwinds, each parental strand serves as a template for the formation of the new daughter strands. Complementary free nucleotides hydrogen bond to a matching base (e.g., A with T; G with C) in each parental strand, and are joined to form a complete daughter strand. Two helices, each with a daughter and parental strand, are produced following replication.

THEME Biological Systems

Aspects of DNA Replication

DNA replication is an example of a complex, highly regulated biological system that requires many parts in order to function properly.

During replication, DNA polymerase needs a place to start joining new nucleotides together. In this case, it recognizes the –OH chemical group at the 3′ end of an existing nucleic acid chain, which can be DNA or RNA, and it begins synthesiz-ing from there. During DNA replication, an RNA-producing enzyme makes a short primer that has the necessary 3′ –OH group on the end. DNA polymerase recognizes that target and begins DNA synthesis, allowing new nucleotides to form complementary base pairs with the old strand and connecting the new nucleotides together in a chain.

3 As a helicase enzyme unwinds DNA, it creates two replication forks that move away from each other. Each of the parental strands in a fork is accessible for complementary base pairing with new nucleotides and therefore synthesis of a new strand. (Binding proteins coat the newly formed, single-stranded regions and prevent them from reattaching to each other.)

3D Animation
DNA Replication Fork

The parental strands are antiparallel to each other, and each of the new daughter strands must also be antiparallel to their matching parental strand—which creates a problem. **4** The new strand that gets made in the same direction as the fork is moving is called the leading strand. The other new strand in the fork must be synthesized in a direction opposite fork movement, which requires DNA polymerase to periodically start and stop. This strand is called the lagging strand. **5** Replication of this lagging strand is therefore made in segments called **6** Okazaki fragments, after the Japanese scientist Reiji Okazaki, who discovered them.

3D Animation
DNA Synthesis

Replication is complete only when the RNA primers are removed. This works out well for the lagging strand. While checking to make sure bases are properly matched up (proofreading), DNA polymerase removes the RNA primers and replaces them with the proper DNA nucleotides. **7** Another enzyme, called DNA ligase, joins the fragments, creating a seamless DNA molecule.

3D Animation
Discontinuous Synthesis

However, in eukaryotic organisms, which have linear chromosomes, there is no way for DNA polymerase to replicate all the way to the 5′ ends of both new strands after RNA primers are removed. This means that the DNA in each chromosome can get shorter for each cycle of replication. The ends of the DNA in eukaryotic chromosomes have a special nucleotide sequence called a telomere that is repeated a number of times. **Telomeres** do not code for proteins and use a repeat sequence such as TTAGGG.

Mammalian cells grown in a culture have a built-in lifespan; they can divide about 50 times before they stop. The loss of telomeres apparently signals the cell to stop dividing. Ordinarily, telomeres are maintained at their proper length by an enzyme called telomerase. Misfunctional telomerase can result in chromosome shortening, leading to premature aging and loss of cellular function. Thus, controlling telomerase activity is important to normal cell function. As you might expect, telomerase is often mistakenly turned on in cancer cells, which in effect enables them to divide indefinitely.

Questions to Consider

1. What are some potential mechanisms of regulating DNA replication?
2. How might we repair DNA when errors in replication are made?

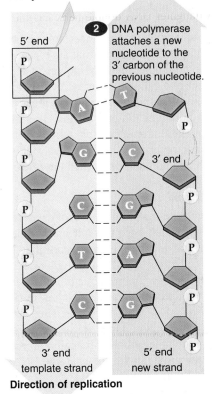

Deoxyribose molecule

2 DNA polymerase attaches a new nucleotide to the 3′ carbon of the previous nucleotide.

Direction of replication

Replication fork introduces complications

Figure 12A More detailed model of DNA replication.

Prokaryotic Versus Eukaryotic Replication

The process of DNA replication is distinctly different in prokaryotic and eukaryotic cells, although many of these organisms' basic functions are similar (Fig. 12.7).

Prokaryotic DNA Replication

Bacteria have a single circular loop chromosome whose DNA must be replicated before the cell divides. In some circular DNA molecules, replication moves around the DNA molecule in one direction only. In others, as shown in Figure 12.7a, replication occurs in two directions. The process always occurs in the 5′ to 3′ direction.

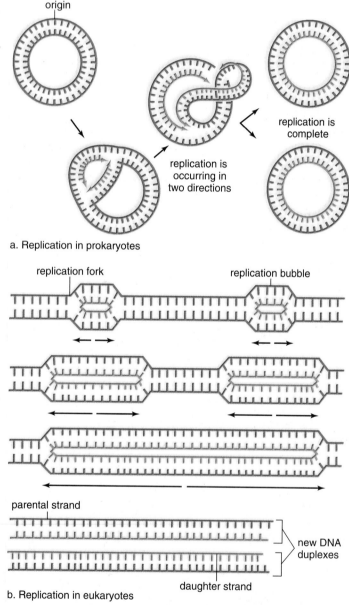

a. Replication in prokaryotes

replication fork   replication bubble

parental strand

new DNA duplexes

daughter strand

b. Replication in eukaryotes

Figure 12.7 Prokaryotic versus eukaryotic replication. **a.** In prokaryotes, replication can occur in two directions at once because the DNA molecule is circular. **b.** In eukaryotes, replication occurs at numerous replication bubbles, each with two forks. The forks move away from each other until they meet again and the two new daughter helices have been completed.

The process begins at the *origin of replication*, a specific site on the bacterial chromosome. The strands are separated and unwound, and a DNA polymerase enzyme binds to each side of the opening and begins the copying process. When the two DNA polymerases meet at a termination region, replication is halted, and the two copies of the chromosome are separated.

Bacterial cells require about 40 minutes to replicate the complete chromosome. Because bacterial cells are able to divide as often as once every 20 minutes, it is possible for a new round of DNA replication to begin even before the previous round is completed!

Eukaryotic DNA Replication

In eukaryotes, DNA replication begins at numerous origins of replication along the length of the linear chromosome, and the so-called replication bubbles spread bidirectionally until they meet. Notice in Figure 12.7b that there is a V shape wherever DNA is being replicated. This is called a **replication fork.**

The chromosomes of eukaryotes are long, making replication a more time-consuming process. Eukaryotes replicate their DNA at a slower rate—500 to 5,000 base pairs per minute—but there are many individual origins of replication to accelerate the process. Therefore, eukaryotic cells complete the replication of the diploid amount of DNA (in humans, over 6 billion base pairs) in a matter of hours!

The linear chromosomes of eukaryotes also pose another problem: DNA polymerase is unable to replicate the ends of the chromosomes. The ends of eukaryotic chromosomes are composed of telomeres, which are short DNA sequences that are repeated over and over. Telomeres are not copied by DNA polymerase; rather, they are added by an enzyme called telomerase, which adds the correct number of repeats after the chromosome is replicated. In stem cells, this process preserves the ends of the chromosomes and prevents the loss of DNA after successive rounds of replication. Unregulated telomerase activity can negatively affect cell function, as is seen with uncontrolled cell division in cancer cells.

Accuracy of Replication

A DNA polymerase is very accurate and makes a mistake approximately once per 100,000 base pairs at most. This error rate, however, would result in many errors accumulating over the course of several cell divisions. DNA polymerase is also capable of checking for accuracy, or proofreading the daughter strand it is making. It can recognize a mismatched nucleotide and remove it from a daughter strand by reversing direction and removing several nucleotides. Once it has removed the mismatched nucleotide, it changes direction again and resumes making DNA. Overall, the error rate for the bacterial DNA polymerase is only one in 100 million base pairs!

Check Your Progress   12.2

1. Explain the three major steps in DNA replication.
2. Compare DNA replication in prokaryotes and eukaryotes.
3. Examine how eukaryotic cells use telomerase to fully copy linear chromosomes.

12.3 The Genetic Code of Life

Learning Outcomes

Upon completion of this section, you should be able to

1. Explain the central dogma of molecular biology.
2. Determine the amino acid sequence specified by an mRNA sequence.

Evidence began to mount in the 1900s that metabolic disorders can be inherited. An English physician, Sir Archibald Garrod, called them "inborn errors of metabolism." Investigators George Beadle and Edward Tatum, working with red bread mold, proposed what they called the "one gene, one enzyme hypothesis," based on the observation that a defective gene caused a defective enzyme.

This and many other examples illustrate the flow of genetic information from DNA to RNA to protein to an observed trait. We now turn our attention to the transfer of information from DNA to RNA, the next component in the system.

RNA Carries the Information

Like DNA, *RNA (ribonucleic acid)* is a polymer composed of nucleotides. The nucleotides in RNA, however, contain the sugar ribose and the bases adenine (A), cytosine (C), guanine (G), and **uracil (U).** In RNA, the base uracil replaces the thymine found in DNA. Finally, RNA is single stranded and does not form a double helix in the same manner as DNA (Table 12.1 and Fig. 12.8).

Table 12.1 RNA Structure Compared to DNA Structure

	RNA	DNA
Sugar	Ribose	Deoxyribose
Bases	Adenine, guanine, uracil, cytosine	Adenine, guanine, thymine, cytosine
Strands	Single stranded	Double stranded with base pairing
Helix	No	Yes

There are three major classes of RNA. Each class of RNA has its own unique size, shape, and function in protein synthesis.

Messenger RNA (mRNA) takes a message from DNA in the nucleus to the ribosomes in the cytoplasm.

Transfer RNA (tRNA) transfers amino acids to the ribosomes.

Ribosomal RNA (rRNA), along with ribosomal proteins, makes up the ribosomes, where polypeptides are synthesized.

The Genetic Code

In the genetic flow of information, two major steps are needed to convert the information stored in DNA into a protein that supports body function (Fig. 12.9). First, the DNA undergoes **transcription** [L. *trans*, across, and *scriptio*, a writing], a process by which an RNA molecule is produced based on a DNA template. DNA is transcribed, or copied base by base, into mRNA, tRNA, and rRNA.

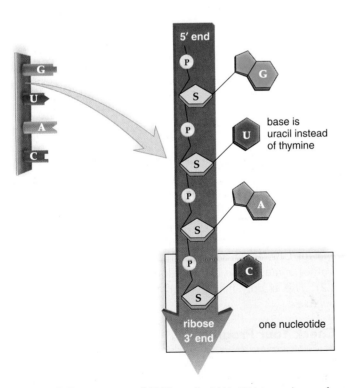

Figure 12.8 Structure of RNA. Like DNA, RNA is a polymer of nucleotides. RNA, however, is single stranded, the pentose sugar (S) is ribose, and uracil replaces thymine as one of the bases.

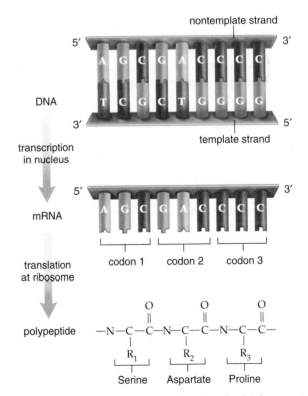

Figure 12.9 The central dogma of molecular biology. One strand of DNA acts as a template for mRNA synthesis, and the sequence of bases in mRNA determines the sequence of amino acids in a polypeptide.

Second, during **translation** [L. *trans*, across, and *latus*, carry or bear], the mRNA transcript is read by a ribosome and converted into the sequence of amino acids in a polypeptide. Like a translator who understands two languages, the cell changes a nucleotide sequence into an amino acid sequence. Together, the flow of information from DNA to RNA to protein to trait is known as the **central dogma** of molecular biology.

Now that we know that the DNA sequence within a gene is transcribed into an RNA molecule, and, for genes that code for proteins, the mRNA sequence determines the sequence of amino acids in a protein, it becomes necessary to identify the specific **genetic code** for each of the 20 amino acids found in proteins. Although scientists knew that DNA somehow directed protein production, they did not initially know specifically how the code was translated. This discovery was made in the 1960s.

Finding the Genetic Code

Logically, the genetic code would have to be at least a **triplet code**; that is, each coding unit, or **codon**, would need to be made up of three nucleotides. The reason is that fewer nucleotides would not provide sufficient variety to encode 20 different amino acids.

In 1961, Marshall Nirenberg and J. Heinrich Matthei performed an experiment that laid the groundwork for cracking the genetic code. First, they found that a cellular enzyme could be used to construct a synthetic RNA (one that does not occur in cells), and then they found that the synthetic RNA polymer could be translated in a test tube that contains the cytoplasmic contents of a cell. Their first synthetic RNA was composed only of uracil, and the protein that resulted was composed only of the amino acid phenylalanine. Therefore, the mRNA codon for phenylalanine was known to be UUU. Later, they were able to translate just three nucleotides at a time; in that way, it was possible to assign an amino acid to each of the mRNA codons (Fig. 12.10).

Like the periodic table and other major works, the genetic code seen in Figure 12.10 is a masterpiece of scientific discovery because it is a key that unlocks the very basis of biological life. Here are some of its features:

1. The genetic code is *degenerate*. This term means that most amino acids have more than one codon; leucine, serine, and arginine have six different codons, for example. The degeneracy of the code helps protect against potentially harmful mutations.
2. The genetic code is *unambiguous*. Each triplet codon has only one meaning.
3. The code has *start and stop signals*. There is only one start signal, but there are three stop signals.

The Code Is Universal

With a few exceptions, the genetic code (Fig. 12.10) is universal to all living things. In 1979, however, researchers discovered that the genetic code used by mammalian mitochondria and chloroplasts differs slightly from the more familiar genetic code.

First Base	Second Base				Third Base
	U	**C**	**A**	**G**	
U	UUU phenylalanine	UCU serine	UAU tyrosine	UGU cysteine	U
	UUC phenylalanine	UCC serine	UAC tyrosine	UGC cysteine	C
	UUA leucine	UCA serine	UAA *stop*	UGA *stop*	A
	UUG leucine	UCG serine	UAG *stop*	UGG tryptophan	G
C	CUU leucine	CCU proline	CAU histidine	CGU arginine	U
	CUC leucine	CCC proline	CAC histidine	CGC arginine	C
	CUA leucine	CCA proline	CAA glutamine	CGA arginine	A
	CUG leucine	CCG proline	CAG glutamine	CGG arginine	G
A	AUU isoleucine	ACU threonine	AAU asparagine	AGU serine	U
	AUC isoleucine	ACC threonine	AAC asparagine	AGC serine	C
	AUA isoleucine	ACA threonine	AAA lysine	AGA arginine	A
	AUG (*start*) methionine	ACG threonine	AAG lysine	AGG arginine	G
G	GUU valine	GCU alanine	GAU aspartate	GGU glycine	U
	GUC valine	GCC alanine	GAC aspartate	GGC glycine	C
	GUA valine	GCA alanine	GAA glutamate	GGA glycine	A
	GUG valine	GCG alanine	GAG glutamate	GGG glycine	G

Figure 12.10 Messenger RNA codons.   Notice that in this chart, each of the codons (in boxes) is composed of three letters representing the first base, second base, and third base. For example, find the box where C for the first base and A for the second base intersect. You will see that U, C, A, or G can be the third base. The bases CAU and CAC are codons for histidine; the bases CAA and CAG are codons for glutamine.

The universal nature of the genetic code provides strong evidence that all living things share a common evolutionary heritage. Because the same genetic code is used by all living things, it is possible to transfer genes from one organism to another. Many commercial and medicinal products, such as human insulin, can be produced in this manner. Earlier, we showed that the gene for GFP could be transferred from jellyfish to a number of other organisms to cause a fluorescent green color (see Fig. 12.2). This is only made possible because the genetic code is universal.

Check Your Progress   12.3

1. Examine the flow of genetic information in a cell.
2. Describe the three major classes of RNA; what is the function of each class?
3. Explain why the genetic code is said to be degenerate.

12.4 First Step: Transcription

Learning Outcomes

Upon completion of this section, you should be able to

1. Distinguish the events of transcription that occur during formation of an mRNA molecule.
2. Describe how eukaryotic mRNA molecules are processed and exported to the cytoplasm.

During *transcription*, a segment of the DNA serves as a template for the production of an RNA molecule. Although mRNA, tRNA, and rRNA are all produced by transcription, we focus here on transcription to make mRNA, the type of RNA that eventually leads to building a protein.

MP3
Protein Synthesis

Messenger RNA Is Produced

The sequences of bases in a gene are transcribed into an mRNA molecule based on complementary base pairing: the T base in the DNA pairs with A in the mRNA, G with C, and A with U (note that uracil replaces T in the newly formed mRNA) (Fig. 12.11). When a gene is transcribed, a segment of the DNA helix unwinds and unzips, and complementary RNA nucleotides pair with DNA nucleotides of the strand opposite the gene. This strand is known as the *template strand*; the other strand is the gene strand. An **RNA polymerase** joins the nucleotides together in the 5′ → 3′ direction. Like DNA polymerase, an RNA polymerase adds a nucleotide only to the 3′ end of the polymer under construction.

Transcription begins when RNA polymerase attaches to a region of DNA called a promoter (see Fig. 12.11). A **promoter** defines the start of transcription, the direction of transcription,

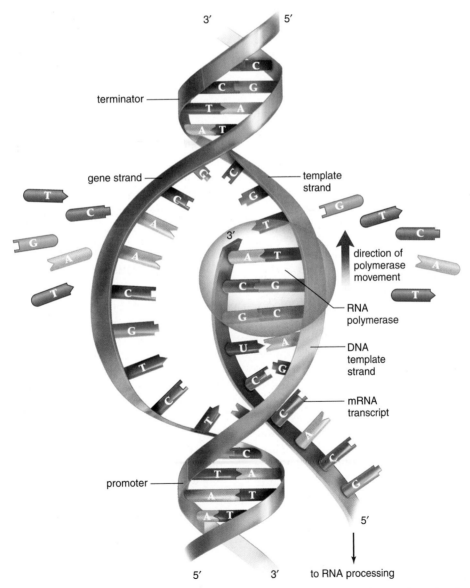

Figure 12.11 Transcription. During transcription, complementary RNA is made from a DNA template. At the point of attachment of RNA polymerase, the DNA helix unwinds and unzips, and complementary RNA nucleotides are joined together. After RNA polymerase has passed by, the DNA strands rejoin and the mRNA transcript dangles to the side.

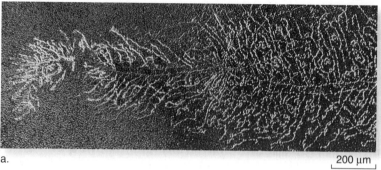

a.

200 μm

Figure 12.12 RNA polymerase.   a. Numerous RNA transcripts extend from a horizontally oriented gene in an amphibian egg cell. **b.** The strands get progressively longer because transcription begins to the left. The dots along the DNA are RNA polymerase molecules. The dots at the end of the strands are spliceosomes involved in RNA processing (see Fig. 12.13).

spliceosome

DNA

RNA polymerase

RNA transcripts

b.

and the strand to be transcribed. The binding of RNA polymerase to the promoter is the *initiation* of transcription. The RNA-DNA association is not as stable as the two strands in the DNA helix. Therefore, only the newest portion of an RNA molecule that is associated with RNA polymerase is bound to the DNA, and the rest dangles off to the side.

Elongation of the mRNA molecule occurs as the RNA polymerase reads down the DNA template strand in a 5′ to 3′ direction, and continues until RNA polymerase comes to a DNA stop sequence, where *termination* occurs. The stop sequence causes RNA polymerase to stop transcribing the DNA and to release the mRNA molecule, now called an **mRNA transcript.**

Animation
Stages of Transcription

It is not necessary for RNA polymerase to finish making one mRNA transcript before it starts another. As long as they have access to the gene's promoter, many RNA polymerase molecules can be working one after the other to produce mRNA transcripts at the same time (Fig. 12.12). This allows the cell to produce many thousands of copies of the same mRNA molecule, and eventually many copies of the same protein, within a shorter period of time than if a single mRNA copy were used to direct protein synthesis. This ability to rapidly express the gene enables the cell (and the organism) to better respond to changing environmental conditions and have a greater chance at survival.

Note that, for a given gene, either strand of the DNA can be a template strand. The example above uses one strand as the template, but for another gene, the opposite strand may be the template. Assuming both genes are on the same chromosome, and therefore the same piece of DNA, can you think what the orientation of template strand in the second gene might be? (Hint: Consider the directionality of RNA polymerase.)

3D Animation
Transcription

MP3
Transcription

RNA Molecules Undergo Processing

A newly formed RNA transcript, called a pre-mRNA, is modified before leaving the eukaryotic nucleus. For example, the molecule receives a cap at the 5′ end and a tail at the 3′ end (Fig. 12.13). The *cap* is a modified guanine (G) nucleotide that helps tell a ribosome where to attach when translation begins. The tail consists of a chain of 150–200 adenine (A) nucleotides. This *poly-A tail* facilitates the transport of mRNA out of the nucleus, helps initiate loading of ribosomes and the start of translation, and also delays degradation of mRNA by hydrolytic enzymes.

When the mRNA is first made by RNA polymerase from the gene, it is in a rough form. Called pre-mRNA, it contains a mix of **exons** (protein-coding regions) and **introns** (non-protein coding regions), particularly in multicellular eukaryotes. Because only the exons of the pre-mRNA will be contained in the mature mRNA, the introns, which occur in between the exons, must be spliced out.

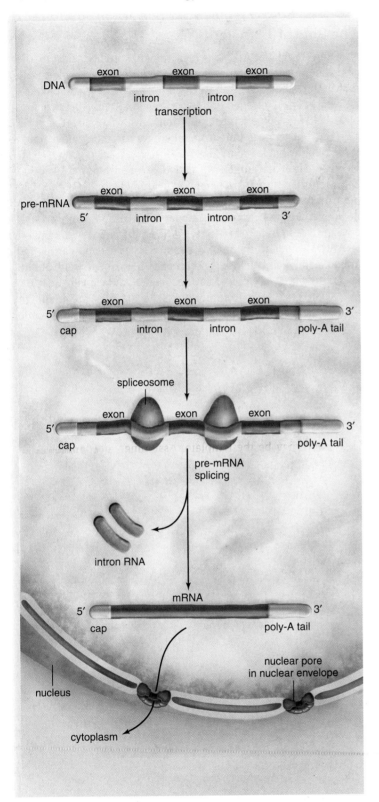

Figure 12.13 Messenger RNA (mRNA) processing in eukaryotes. DNA contains both exons (protein-coding sequences) and introns (non-protein-coding sequences). Both of these are transcribed and are present in pre-mRNA. During processing, a cap and a poly-A tail (a series of adenine nucleotides) are added to the molecule. Also, introns get cut out and the exons get spliced together by complexes called spliceosomes. Once processing is complete the mRNA molecule is ready to leave the nucleus.

In lower eukaryotes, introns are removed by "self-splicing"—that is, the intron itself has the capability of enzymatically splicing itself out of a pre-mRNA. In higher eukaryotes, the RNA splicing is done by spliceosomes, which contain *small nuclear RNAs (snRNAs)*. By means of complementary base pairing, snRNAs are capable of identifying the introns to be removed. A spliceosome utilizes a **ribozyme** (enzyme made of RNA rather than just protein) to cut and remove the introns. Following splicing of the exons together and the addition of the 5′ cap and 3′ poly-A tail, an mRNA is ready to leave the nucleus and be translated into a protein.

Animation
How Spliceosomes
Process RNA

Function of Introns

For many years, scientists thought that introns were simply wasted space within genes. Now, we realize they serve several key functions in the cell. The presence of introns allows a cell to pick and choose which exons will go into a particular mRNA (see Chapter 13). Just because an mRNA has all the exons in its pre-mRNA doesn't mean they will all make it to the final product. For example, if a gene has 3 exons, then depending on cell need and environmental conditions, it may produce an mRNA with exons 1 and 2 only, or 1 and 3 only, or 1, 2, and 3. This ability is called *alternative mRNA splicing*, and it increases the flexibility and efficiency of the cell. The snRNAs of the spliceosomes that excise the introns play an important role in alternative splicing in eukaryotes.

Some introns give rise to *microRNAs (miRNAs)*, which are small molecules involved in regulating the translation of mRNAs. These molecules bind with the mRNA through complementary base pairing and, in that way, prevent translation from occurring.

Video
Drug Discovery

Video
New Cancer Clue

It is also possible that the presence of introns encourages crossing-over during meiosis, and this permits a phenomenon termed *exon shuffling*, which can play a role in the evolution of new genes.

Animation
Exon Shuffling

3D Animation
mRNA
Modifications

Check Your Progress   12.4

1. Explain the orientation of the DNA template strand relative to both the DNA gene strand and the new mRNA molecule.
2. Describe the three major modifications that occur during the processing of an mRNA.
3. Distinguish between the introns and exons of a gene.
4. Predict the sequence of nucleotides given a strand of DNA.
5. Explain the potential evolutionary benefits of alternative mRNA splicing.

12.5 Second Step: Translation

Learning Outcomes

Upon completion of this section, you should be able to

1. Describe the roles of mRNA, tRNA, and rRNA in translating the genetic code.
2. Examine the stages of translation and the events that occur during each stage.

Translation, which takes place in the cytoplasm of eukaryotic cells, is the second step needed to express a gene into a protein. During translation, the sequence of codons (nucleotide triplets) in the mRNA is read by a ribosome, which connects the sequence of amino acids dictated by the mRNA into a polypeptide. The process is called translation because it requires the conversion of information from a nucleic acid language (DNA and RNA) into an amino acid language (protein).

The Role of Transfer RNA

Transfer RNA (tRNA) molecules transfer amino acids to the ribosomes. A tRNA molecule is a single-stranded nucleic acid that doubles back on itself to create regions where complementary bases are hydrogen-bonded to one another. The structure of a tRNA molecule is generally drawn as a flat cloverleaf (Fig 12.14a), but a space-filling model shows the molecule's actual three-dimensional shape (Fig. 12.14b).

There is at least one tRNA molecule for each of the 20 amino acids found in proteins. The amino acid binds to the 3′ end. The opposite end of the molecule contains an **anticodon,** a group of three bases that is complementary and antiparallel to a specific mRNA codon. For example, a tRNA that has the anticodon 5′ AAG 3′ binds to the mRNA codon 5′ CUU 3′ and carries the amino acid leucine. In the genetic code, 61 codons specify amino acids; the other three serve as stop sequences (see Fig. 12.10).

Approximately 40 different tRNA molecules are found in most cells. There are fewer tRNAs than codons because some

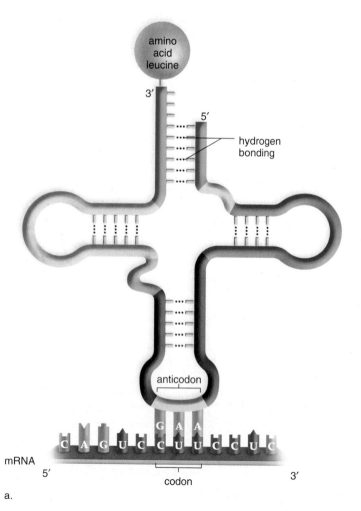

a.

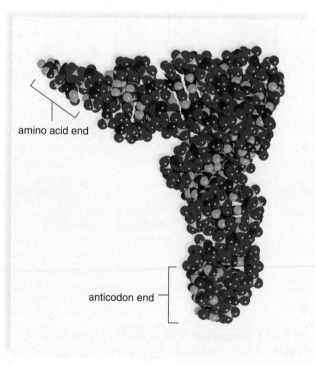

b.

Figure 12.14 Structure of a transfer RNA (tRNA) molecule. **a.** Complementary base pairing indicated by hydrogen bonding occurs between nucleotides within the molecule, and this causes it to form its characteristic loops. The anticodon that base-pairs with a particular messenger RNA (mRNA) codon occurs at one end of the folded molecule; the other two loops help hold the molecule at the ribosome. An appropriate amino acid is attached at the 3′ end of the molecule in the cytoplasm by a tRNA charging enzyme. For this mRNA codon and tRNA anticodon, the specific amino acid is leucine. **b.** Space-filling model of tRNA molecule.

tRNAs can pair with more than one codon. In 1966, Francis Crick observed this phenomenon and called it the **wobble hypothesis.** He stated that the first two positions in a tRNA anticodon pair obey the A–U/G–C configuration rule. However, the third position can be variable. Some tRNA molecules can recognize as many as four separate codons differing only in the third nucleotide. The wobble effect helps ensure that despite changes in DNA base sequences, the resulting sequence of amino acids will produce a correct protein. This is one of the reasons the genetic code is said to be degenerate.

How does the correct amino acid become attached to the correct tRNA molecule? This task is carried out by amino acid–charging enzymes, generically called aminoacyl-tRNA synthetases. Just as a key fits a lock, each enzyme has a recognition site for a particular amino acid to be joined to a specific tRNA. For example, leucine-tRNA synthetase attaches the leucine amino acid to a tRNA with the correct anticodon. This is an energy-requiring process that uses ATP. A tRNA with its amino acid attached is termed a *charged tRNA*. Once the amino acid–tRNA complex is formed, it is added to the large pool of charged tRNAs that exist in the cytoplasm, where it can now be accessed by a ribosome during protein synthesis.

The Role of Ribosomal RNA

As with so many cellular structures, the structure of a ribosome is essential to its function.

Structure of a Ribosome

In eukaryotes, ribosomal RNA (rRNA) is produced from a DNA template in the nucleolus of a nucleus. The rRNA is packaged with a variety of proteins into two ribosomal subunits, one of which is larger than the other. The subunits then move separately through nuclear envelope pores into the cytoplasm, where they join together at the start of translation (Fig. 12.15a). Once translation begins, ribosomes can remain in the cytoplasm, or they can become attached to endoplasmic reticulum.

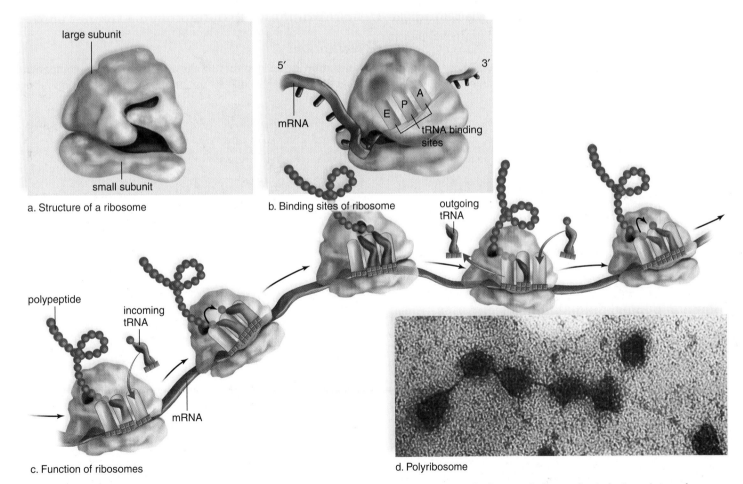

large subunit

small subunit

a. Structure of a ribosome

5′   3′

mRNA

E   P   A

tRNA binding sites

b. Binding sites of ribosome

outgoing tRNA

polypeptide

incoming tRNA

mRNA

c. Function of ribosomes

d. Polyribosome

Figure 12.15 Ribosome structure and function. **a.** Side view of a ribosome shows a small subunit and a large subunit. **b.** Frontal view of a ribosome shows its binding sites. mRNA is bound to the small subunit, and the large subunit has three binding sites for tRNAs. **c.** Overview of protein synthesis. The tRNA bearing the growing polypeptide passes the entire chain to the new amino acid carried by the tRNA occupying the A site. The ribosome shifts, and freed of its burden, the "empty" tRNA exits. The new peptide-bearing tRNA moves over one binding site, making the A site accessible once again to a new tRNA. This cycle is repeated until the ribosome reaches the termination codon. **d.** Electron micrograph of a polyribosome, a number of ribosomes all translating the same mRNA molecule.

Function of a Ribosome

Both prokaryotic and eukaryotic cells contain thousands of ribosomes per cell because they play such a significant role in protein synthesis. Ribosomes have a binding site for mRNA and three binding sites for transfer RNA (tRNA) molecules (Fig. 12.15b). The tRNA binding sites facilitate complementary base pairing between tRNA anticodons and mRNA codons. The large ribosomal subunit has enzyme activity from rRNA (i.e., a ribozyme) that creates the peptide bond between adjacent amino acids. This peptide bond is created many times to produce a polypeptide, which in turn folds into its three-dimensional shape and becomes a protein.

When a ribosome moves down an mRNA molecule, the polypeptide increases by one amino acid at a time (Fig. 12.15c). Translation terminates at a stop codon. Once translation is complete, the polypeptide dissociates from the translation complex and folds into its normal shape. Recall from Chapter 3 that a polypeptide twists and bends into a definite shape based on the makeup of its amino acids. This folding process begins as soon as the polypeptide emerges from a ribosome. Chaperone molecules that are often present in the cytoplasm and the ER ensure protein folding proceeds as it should. For proteins that contain more than one polypeptide, each subunit is folded first, and then subunits join together into a final, functional protein complex.

Like RNA polymerase during transcription, multiple ribosomes often attach and translate the same mRNA at one time. As soon as the initial portion of mRNA has been translated by one ribosome, and the ribosome has begun to move down the mRNA, another ribosome can attach to the mRNA. The entire complex of mRNA and multiple ribosomes is called a **polyribosome** (Fig. 12.15d) and it greatly increases the efficiency of translation.

Translation Requires Three Steps

During translation, the codons of an mRNA base-pair with the anticodons of tRNA molecules carrying specific amino acids. The order of the codons determines the order of the tRNA molecules at a ribosome and the corresponding sequence of amino acids in a polypeptide. The process of translation must be extremely orderly so that the amino acids of a polypeptide are sequenced correctly. Even a single amino acid change has the potential to dramatically affect a protein's function, as is the case with individuals who carry the alleles for sickle cell anemia.

> **Animation**
> How Translation Works

Protein synthesis involves three steps: initiation, elongation, and termination. Enzymes are required for each of the three steps to function properly. The first two steps, initiation and elongation, require energy.

Initiation

Initiation is the step that brings all the translation components together. Proteins called initiation factors are required to

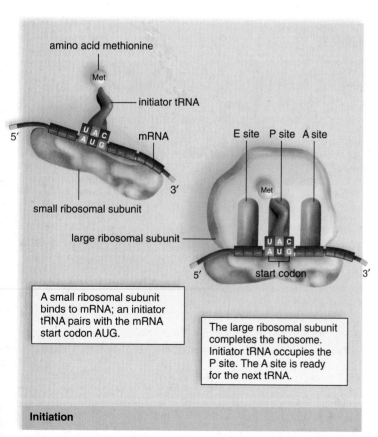

A small ribosomal subunit binds to mRNA; an initiator tRNA pairs with the mRNA start codon AUG.

The large ribosomal subunit completes the ribosome. Initiator tRNA occupies the P site. The A site is ready for the next tRNA.

Initiation

Figure 12.16 Initiation. In prokaryotes, participants in the translation process assemble as shown. The first amino acid is typically a special form of methionine.

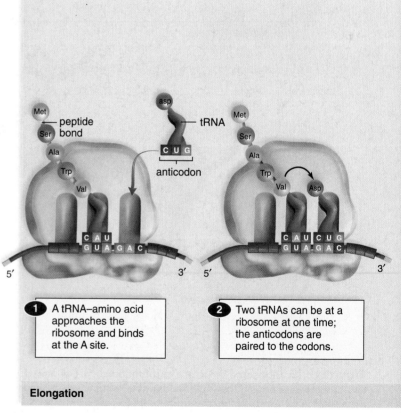

1. A tRNA–amino acid approaches the ribosome and binds at the A site.

2. Two tRNAs can be at a ribosome at one time; the anticodons are paired to the codons.

Elongation

Figure 12.17 Elongation. Note that a polypeptide is already at the P site. During elongation, polypeptide synthesis occurs as amino acids are added one at a time to the growing chain.

assemble the small ribosomal subunit, mRNA, initiator tRNA, and the large ribosomal subunit for the start of protein synthesis.

Initiation is shown in Figure 12.16. In prokaryotes, a small ribosomal subunit attaches to the mRNA in the vicinity of the *start codon* (AUG). The first or initiator tRNA pairs with this codon. Then, a large ribosomal subunit joins to the small subunit (Fig. 12.16). Although similar in many ways, initiation in eukaryotes is much more complex.

As already discussed, a ribosome has three binding sites for tRNAs. One of these is called the E (for exit) site, second is the P (for peptide) site, and the third is the A (for amino acid) site. The initiator tRNA binds to the P site, even though it carries only the amino acid methionine (see Fig. 12.10). The A site is where tRNA carrying the next amino acid enter the ribosome, and the E site is for any tRNAs that are leaving a ribosome. Following initiation, translation continues with elongation and then termination.

Elongation

Elongation is the stage during protein synthesis when a polypeptide increases in length one amino acid at a time. In addition to the necessary tRNAs, elongation requires elongation factors, which facilitate the binding of tRNA anticodons to mRNA codons within a ribosome.

1 Elongation is shown in Figure 12.17, where a tRNA with an attached peptide is already at the P site, and a tRNA

carrying its appropriate amino acid is just arriving at the A site. **2** Once a ribosome has verified that the incoming tRNA matches the codon and is firmly in place at the A site, the entire growing peptide will be transferred to the amino acid on the tRNA in the A site. A ribozyme, an rRNA-based enzyme which is a part of the large ribosomal subunit, uses energy to transfer the growing peptide and create a new peptide bond. **3** Following peptide bond formation, the peptide is one amino acid longer than it was before. **4** Next, **translocation** occurs: The ribosome moves forward, and the peptide-bearing tRNA is now in the P site of the ribosome. The spent tRNA, now at the E site, exits the ribosome. A new codon is now exposed at the A site and is ready to receive another tRNA.

The complete cycle—complementary base pairing of new tRNA, transfer of peptide chain, and translocation—is repeated at a rapid rate (about 15 times each second in the bacterium *Escherichia coli*).

Eventually, the ribosome reaches a stop codon, and termination occurs, during which the polypeptide is released.

Termination

Termination is the final step in protein synthesis. During termination, as shown in Figure 12.18, the polypeptide and the assembled components that carried out protein synthesis are separated from one another.

Termination of polypeptide synthesis occurs at a *stop codon*—that is, a codon that does not code for an amino acid.

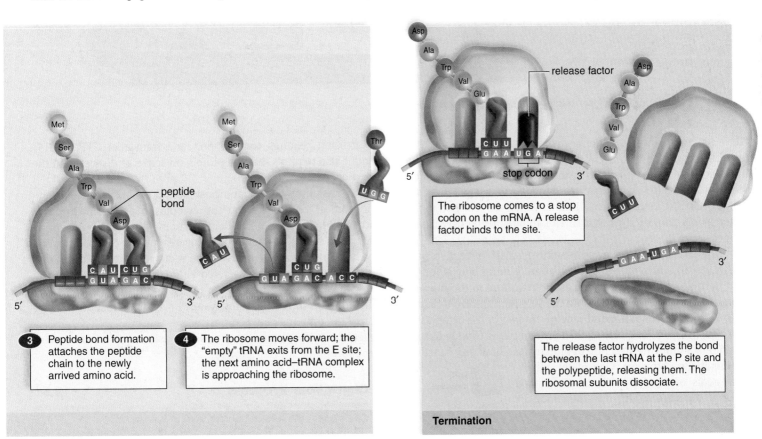

3 Peptide bond formation attaches the peptide chain to the newly arrived amino acid.

4 The ribosome moves forward; the "empty" tRNA exits from the E site; the next amino acid–tRNA complex is approaching the ribosome.

The ribosome comes to a stop codon on the mRNA. A release factor binds to the site.

The release factor hydrolyzes the bond between the last tRNA at the P site and the polypeptide, releasing them. The ribosomal subunits dissociate.

Termination

Figure 12.18 Termination. During termination, the finished polypeptide is released, as is the mRNA and the last tRNA.

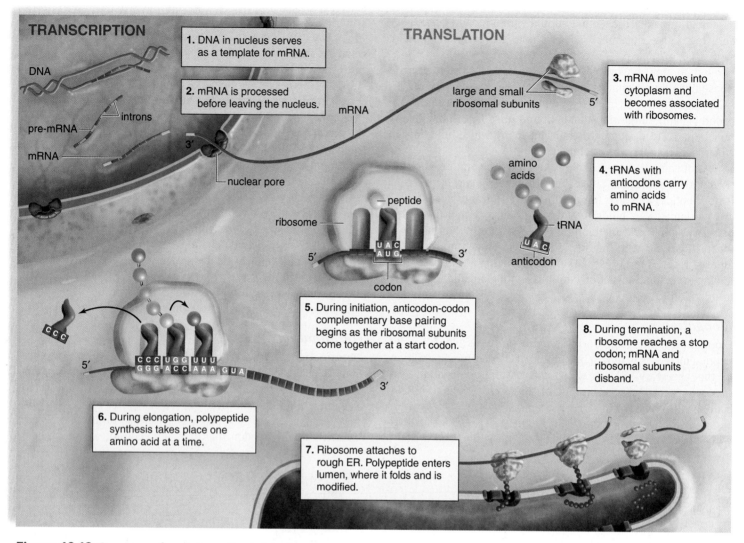

Figure 12.19 Summary of protein synthesis in eukaryotes.

Termination requires a protein called a release factor, which can bind to a stop codon and also cleave the polypeptide from the last tRNA. After this occurs, the polypeptide is set free and begins to fold and take on its three-dimensional shape. The ribosome dissociates into its two subunits, which are returned to the cytoplasmic pool of large and small subunits, to be used again as necessary.

The next section reviews the entire process of protein synthesis (recall that a protein contains one or more polypeptides) and the role of the rough endoplasmic reticulum in the production of a polypeptide. Proteins do the work of the cell, whether they reside in a cellular membrane or are free in the cytoplasm. A whole new field of biology called **proteomics** is now dedicated to understanding the structure of proteins and how they function in metabolic pathways. One of the important goals of proteomics is to understand how proteins are modified in the endoplasmic reticulum and the Golgi apparatus.

MP3 Translation

3D Animation Translation

Gene Expression

A gene has been expressed once its product, a protein (or an RNA), is made and is operating in the cell. For a protein, gene

expression requires transcription and translation (Fig. 12.19) and it also requires that the protein be active as discussed in the next chapter.

Translation occurs at ribosomes. Some ribosomes (polyribosomes) remain free in the cytoplasm, and some become attached to rough ER. The first few amino acids of a polypeptide act as a signal peptide that indicates where the polypeptide belongs in the cell or if it is to be secreted from the cell. Polypeptides that are to be secreted enter the lumen of the ER by way of a channel, and are then folded and further processed by the addition of sugars, phosphates, or lipids. Transport vesicles carry the proteins between organelles and to the plasma membrane as appropriate for that protein.

Animation Processing of Gene Information in Prokaryotes and Eukaryotes

Check Your Progress   12.5

1. Explain the role of transfer RNA in translation.
2. Describe how the structure of a ribosome contributes to polypeptide synthesis.
3. Examine the events that occur during the three major steps of translation.

12.6 Structure of the Eukaryotic Chromosome

Learning Outcomes

Upon completion of this section, you should be able to

1. Explain how DNA becomes sufficiently compacted to fit inside a nucleus.

Only in recent years have investigators been able to produce models suggesting how chromosomes are organized. A eukaryotic chromosome contains a single double helix DNA molecule, but it is composed of more than 50% protein. Some of these proteins are concerned with DNA and RNA synthesis, but a large majority, termed **histones,** play primarily a structural role.

The five primary types of histone molecules are designated H1, H2A, H2B, H3, and H4 (see Fig. 13.5*b*). Remarkably, the amino acid sequences of H3 and H4 vary little between organisms. For example, the H4 of peas is only two amino acids different from the H4 of cattle. This similarity suggests that few mutations in the histone proteins have occurred during the course of evolution and that the histones, therefore, have essential functions for survival.

A human cell contains at least 2 m of DNA. Yet, all of this DNA is packed into a nucleus that is about 5 μm in diameter. The histones are responsible for packaging the DNA so that it can fit into such a small space. First, the DNA double helix is wound at intervals around a core of eight histone molecules (two copies each of H2A, H2B, H3, and H4), giving the appearance of a string of beads (Fig. 12.20*a*). Each bead is called a **nucleosome,** and the nucleosomes are said to be joined by "linker" DNA.

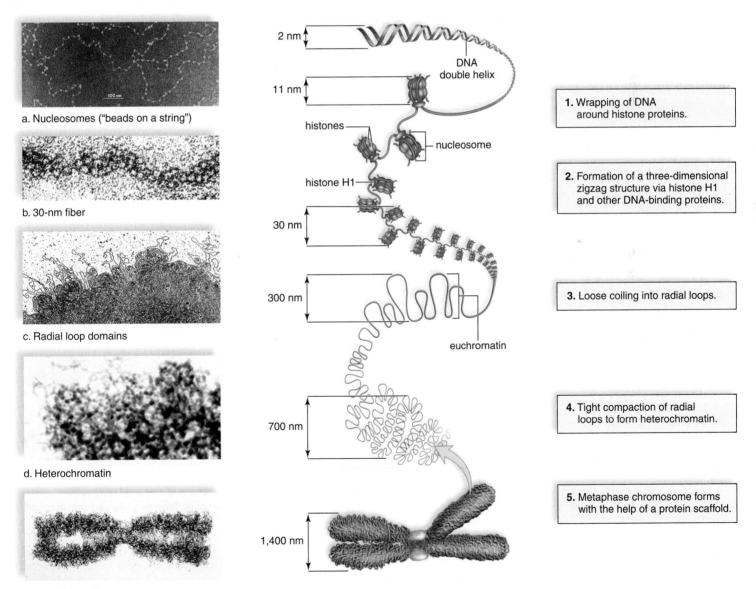

a. Nucleosomes ("beads on a string")

b. 30-nm fiber

c. Radial loop domains

d. Heterochromatin

e. Metaphase chromosome

2 nm — DNA double helix

11 nm

histones — nucleosome

histone H1

30 nm

300 nm — euchromatin

700 nm

1,400 nm

1. Wrapping of DNA around histone proteins.

2. Formation of a three-dimensional zigzag structure via histone H1 and other DNA-binding proteins.

3. Loose coiling into radial loops.

4. Tight compaction of radial loops to form heterochromatin.

5. Metaphase chromosome forms with the help of a protein scaffold.

Figure 12.20 Structure of eukaryotic chromosomes.   The DNA molecule of a chromosome is compacted at several levels. Structural changes in the DNA influence its ability to express genes. **a.** The DNA strand is wound around histones to form nucleosomes. **b.** The strand is further shortened by folding it into a zigzag structure. **c.** The fiber loops back and forth into radial loops. **d.** In heterochromatin, additional proteins further compact the radial loops. **e.** A metaphase chromosome forms.

This string is compacted by folding into a zigzag structure, further shortening the DNA strand (Fig. 12.20*b*). Histone H1 appears to mediate this coiling process. The fiber then loops back and forth into radial loops (Fig. 12.20*c*). This loosely coiled **euchromatin** represents the active chromatin containing genes that are being transcribed. The DNA of euchromatin may be accessed by RNA polymerase and other factors that are needed to promote transcription. In fact, recent research seems to indicate that regulating the level of compaction of the DNA is an important method of controlling gene expression in the cell.

Under a microscope, one often observes dark-stained fibers within the nucleus of the cell. These areas within the nucleus represent a more highly compacted form of the chromosome called **heterochromatin** (Fig. 12.20*d*). Most chromosomes exhibit both levels of compaction in a living cell, depending on which portions of the chromosome are being used more frequently. Heterochromatin is considered inactive chromatin because the genes contained on it are infrequently transcribed, if at all.

Prior to cell division, a protein scaffold helps to further condense the chromosome into a form that is characteristic of metaphase chromosomes (Fig. 12.20*e*). No doubt, compact chromosomes are easier to move about than extended chromatin.

Check Your Progress 12.6

1. Examine how regulation of gene expression might be accomplished by changing the compaction of chromatin.

CONNECTING *the* CONCEPTS *with the* THEMES

Evolution

- Genes specify proteins through the steps of transcription and translation. During transcription, a strand of DNA is used as a template for the production of an mRNA molecule.
- The actions of RNA polymerase, the enzyme that carries out transcription, and DNA polymerase, which is required for DNA replication, are similar enough to suggest that both enzymes evolved from a common ancestral enzyme.
- Specifically, it now appears that RNA may play a prominent role in the regulation of the genome. Some believe this is evidence that RNA may have preceded DNA in the evolutionary history of cells.

Nature of Science

- Early investigators who did their work between 1950 and 1990 came to the conclusion that DNA is organized into discrete units called genes.
- Scientists are now discovering that the rest of the DNA that does not specify proteins may also have valuable functions.
- Many biologists believe that we need a new definition of a gene that recognizes that much of our DNA results in RNA molecules rather than protein products.

Biological Systems

- Both protein-coding and non-protein-coding DNA provides the blueprint for building and developing an entire organism.
- But just as a blueprint is useless without a team of engineers, architects, and construction workers to execute it, the expression of genes requires a large system of proteins and other factors to control it.
- As described in the following chapter, regulatory proteins may turn genes on or off, and genes can be combined in many different ways to alter the proteins that are made. Together, these mechanisms contribute to the great complexity and diversity of living organisms.

Media Study Tools

www.mhhe.com/maderbiology11

Enhance your study of this chapter with study tools and practice tests. Also ask your instructor about the resources available through ConnectPlus, including the media-rich eBook, interactive learning tools, and animations.

3D Animations
DNA Replication
Molecular Biology
of the Gene   For an interactive examination of the processes of DNA replication and gene expression, review the 3D animations "DNA Replication" and "Molecular Biology of the Gene."

Summarize

12.1 The Genetic Material

Early work illustrated that DNA was the hereditary material. Griffith injected strains of pneumococcus into mice and observed that when heat-killed S strain bacteria were injected along with live R strain bacteria, virulent S strain bacteria were recovered from the dead mice. Griffith said that the R strain had been transformed by some substance passing from the dead S strain to the live R strain. Twenty years later, Avery and his colleagues reported that the transforming substance is DNA.

To study the structure of DNA, Chargaff performed a chemical analysis of DNA and found that A = T and G = C, and that the amount of purine equals the amount of pyrimidine. Franklin prepared an X-ray photograph of DNA that showed it is helical, has repeating structural features, and has certain dimensions. Watson and Crick built a model of DNA in which the sugar-phosphate molecules made up the sides of a twisted ladder, and the complementary-paired bases were the rungs of the ladder.

12.2 Replication of DNA

The Watson and Crick model immediately suggested a method by which DNA could be replicated. Basically, the two strands unwind and unzip, and each parental strand acts as a template for a new (daughter) strand. In the end, each new helix is like the other and like the parental helix.

The enzyme DNA polymerase joins the nucleotides together and proofreads them to make sure the bases have been paired correctly. Incorrect base pairs that survive the process are a mutation. Replication in prokaryotes typically proceeds in both directions from one point of origin to a termination region until there are two copies of the circular chromosome. Replication in eukaryotes has many points of origin and many bubbles (places where the DNA strands are separating and replication is occurring). Replication occurs at the ends of the bubbles—at replication forks. Since eukaryotes have linear chromosomes, they cannot replicate the very ends of them. Therefore, the ends (telomeres) get shorter with each replication. Telomerase enzyme helps to ensure that chromosomes maintain their proper length.

12.3 The Genetic Code of Life

The central dogma of molecular biology says that the flow of genetic information is from DNA to RNA to protein to traits. More specifically, (1) DNA is a template for its own replication and also for RNA formation during transcription, and (2) the sequence of nucleotides in mRNA directs the correct sequence of amino acids of a polypeptide during translation.

The genetic code is a triplet code, and each codon (code word) consists of three bases. The code is degenerate—that is, more than one codon exists for most amino acids. There are also one start and three stop codons. The genetic code is considered universal, but there are a few exceptions.

12.4 First Step: Transcription

Transcription to produce messenger RNA (mRNA) begins when RNA polymerase attaches to the promoter of a gene. Elongation occurs until RNA polymerase reaches a stop sequence. The mRNA is processed following transcription. A cap is put onto the 5′ end, a poly-A tail is put onto the 3′ end, and introns are removed in eukaryotes by spliceosomes.

Small nuclear RNAs (snRNAs) present in spliceosomes help identify the introns to be removed. These snRNAs play a role in alternative mRNA splicing, which allows a single eukaryotic gene to code for different proteins, depending on which segments of the gene serve as introns and which serve as exons.

Some introns serve as microRNAs (miRNAs), which help regulate the translation of mRNAs. Research is now directed to discovering the many ways small RNAs influence the production of proteins in a cell.

12.5 Second Step: Translation

Translation requires mRNA, transfer RNA (tRNA), and ribosomal RNA (rRNA). Each tRNA has an anticodon at one end and an amino acid at the other; amino acid–charging enzymes ensure that the correct amino acid is attached to the correct tRNA. When tRNAs bind with their codon at a ribosome, the amino acids are correctly sequenced in a polypeptide according to the order predetermined by DNA.

In the cytoplasm, many ribosomes move along the same mRNA at a time. Collectively, these are called a polyribosome.

Translation requires these steps: During initiation, mRNA, the first (initiator) tRNA, and the two subunits of a ribosome all come together in the proper orientation at a start codon. During elongation, as the tRNA anticodons bind to their codons, the growing pep-tide chain is transferred by peptide bonding to the next amino acid in a polypeptide. During termination at a stop codon, the polypeptide is cleaved from the last tRNA. The ribosome now dissociates.

12.6 Structure of the Eukaryotic Chromosome

Eukaryotic cells contain nearly 2 m of DNA, yet must pack it all into a nucleus no more than 20 μm in diameter. Thus, the DNA is compacted by winding it around DNA-binding proteins called histones to make nucleosomes. The nucleosomes are further compacted into a zigzag structure, which is then folded upon itself many times to form radial loops, which is the usual compaction state of euchromatin. Heterochromatin is further compacted by scaffold proteins, and further compaction can be achieved prior to mitosis and meiosis.

Key Terms

adenine (A)   217
anticodon   228
central dogma 224
codon   224
complementary base
   pairing   219
cytosine (C)   217
DNA polymerase   220
DNA replication   220
double helix   218
elongation   231
euchromatin   234
exon   226
genetic code   224
guanine (G)   217
heterochromatin   234
histone   233
initiation   230
intron   226
messenger RNA (mRNA)   223
mRNA transcript   226

nucleosome   233
polyribosome   230
promoter   225
proteomics   232
replication fork   222
ribosomal RNA (rRNA)   223
ribozyme   227
RNA polymerase   225
semiconservative
   replication   220
telomere   221
template   220
termination   231
thymine (T)   217
transcription   223
transfer RNA (tRNA)   223
translation   224
translocation   231
triplet code   224
uracil (U)   223
wobble hypothesis   229

Assess

Reviewing This Chapter

1. List and discuss the requirements for genetic material.   215
2. How did Avery and his colleagues demonstrate that the transforming substance is DNA?   215–16
3. Describe the Watson and Crick model of DNA structure. How did it fit the data provided by Chargaff and the X-ray diffraction patterns of Franklin?   218–19
4. Explain how DNA replicates semiconservatively. What role does DNA polymerase play? What role does helicase play?   220–21
5. List and discuss differences between prokaryotic and eukaryotic replication of DNA.   222
6. How did investigators reason that the code must be a triplet code, and in what manner was the code cracked? Why is it said that the code is degenerate, unambiguous, and almost universal?   224
7. What two steps are required for the expression of a gene?   225, 228
8. What specific steps occur during transcription of RNA off a DNA template?   225–26
9. How is messenger RNA (mRNA) processed before leaving the eukaryotic nucleus?   226–27

10. What is the role of snRNAs in the nucleus? 227
11. Compare the functions of mRNA, transfer RNA (tRNA), and ribosomal RNA (rRNA) during protein synthesis. What are the specific events of translation? 228–32
12. What are the various levels of chromosome structure? 233–34

Testing Yourself

Choose the best answer for each question.

1. If 30% of an organism's DNA is thymine, then
   a. 70% is purine.
   b. 20% is guanine.
   c. 30% is adenine.
   d. 70% is pyrimidine.
   e. Both c and d are correct.

2. The double-helix model of DNA resembles a twisted ladder in which the rungs of the ladder are
   a. a purine paired with a pyrimidine.
   b. A paired with G and C paired with T.
   c. sugar-phosphate paired with sugar-phosphate.
   d. a 5′ end paired with a 3′ end.
   e. Both a and b are correct.

3. DNA replication is said to be semiconservative because
   a. one of the new molecules conserves both of the original DNA strands.
   b. the new DNA molecule contains two new DNA strands.
   c. both of the new molecules contain one new strand and one old strand.
   d. DNA polymerase conserves both of the old strands.

4. If the sequence of bases in one strand of DNA is 5′ TAGCCT 3′, then the sequence of bases in the other strand will be
   a. 3′ TCCGAT 5′.
   b. 3′ ATCGGA 5′.
   c. 3′ TAGCCT 5′.
   d. 3′ AACGGUA 5′.

5. Transformation occurs when
   a. DNA is transformed into RNA.
   b. DNA is transformed into protein.
   c. bacteria cannot grow on penicillin.
   d. organisms receive foreign DNA and thereby acquire a new characteristic.

6. Pyrimidines
   a. are always paired with a purine.
   b. are thymine and cytosine.
   c. keep DNA from replicating too often.
   d. are adenine and guanine.
   e. Both a and b are correct.

7. A nucleotide
   a. is smaller than a base.
   b. is a subunit of nucleic acids.
   c. has a lot of variable parts.
   d. has at least four phosphates.
   e. always joins with other nucleotides.

8. This is a segment of a DNA molecule. What are (a) the RNA codons, (b) the matching tRNA anticodons, and (c) the sequence of amino acids in the eventual protein?

nontemplate strand

5′ ——————————————————— 3′

| G | G | A | G | G | A | C | T | T | A | C | G | T | T | T |
| C | C | T | C | C | T | G | A | A | T | G | C | A | A | A |

3′ ——————————————————— 5′

template strand

9. In prokaryotes,
   a. replication can occur in two directions at once because their DNA molecule is circular.
   b. bubbles thereby created spread out until they meet.
   c. replication occurs at numerous replication forks.
   d. a new round of DNA replication cannot begin before the previous round is complete.
   e. Both a and b are correct.

10. The central dogma of molecular biology
    a. states that DNA is a template for all RNA production.
    b. states that DNA is a template only for DNA replication.
    c. states that translation precedes transcription.
    d. states that RNA is a template for DNA replication.
    e. All of these are correct.

11. Because there are more codons than amino acids,
    a. some amino acids are specified by more than one codon.
    b. some codons specify more than one amino acid.
    c. some codons do not specify any amino acid.
    d. some amino acids do not have codons.

12. If the sequence of bases in the coding strand of a DNA is TAGC, then the sequence of bases in the mRNA will be
    a. AUCG.
    b. TAGC.
    c. UAGC.
    d. CGAU.

13. During protein synthesis, an anticodon on transfer RNA (tRNA) pairs with
    a. DNA nucleotide bases.
    b. ribosomal RNA (rRNA) nucleotide bases.
    c. messenger RNA (mRNA) nucleotide bases.
    d. other tRNA nucleotide bases.
    e. Any one of these can occur.

14. If the sequence of DNA on the template strand of a gene is AAA, the mRNA codon produced by transcription will be _____ and will specify the amino acid _____ .
    a. AAA, lysine
    b. AAA, phenylalanine
    c. TTT, arginine
    d. UUU, phenylalanine
    e. TTT, lysine

15. Euchromatin
    a. is organized into radial loops.
    b. is less condensed than heterochromatin.
    c. contains nucleosomes.
    d. All of these are correct.

Engage

Thinking Scientifically

1. How would you test a hypothesis that a genetic condition, such as cancer, is due to mistakes in transcription and translation?

2. Knowing that a plant will grow from a single cell in tissue culture, how could you transform a plant so that it glows in the dark?

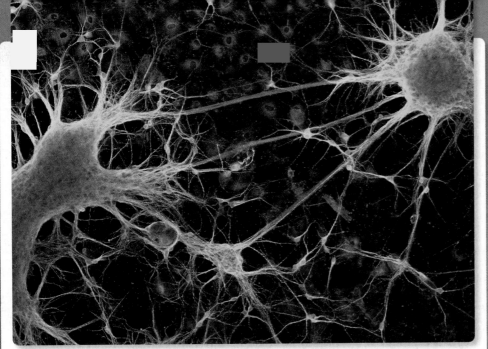

Individual neurons, shown in pink in this electron micrograph, may use unique forms of the DSCAM proteins in their plasma membranes to identify themselves.

13

Regulation of Gene Expression

It was once estimated that the human genome may contain as many as a million genes. At the start of the Human Genome Project, that number was considered to be closer to 100,000. We now know that the human genome probably contains less than 23,000 genes. So how do a mere 23,000 genes account for the variety of proteins found in human cells? The answer, surprisingly, may lie in the regulation of pre-mRNA splicing to allow the production of a myriad of proteins from a single gene. *DSCAM* is a gene associated with Down Syndrome that is present in the brain of many animals. In fruit flies *DSCAM* has four regions of alternative exons. The result is over 38,000 different possible combinations of functional mRNAs, and therefore, the *DSCAM* gene is able to specify 38,000 different proteins. Such a huge number of proteins is sufficient to provide each nerve cell with a unique identity as it communicates with others within a brain.

Complex alternative splicing, and other regulatory mechanisms, could very well account for how humans generate so many different proteins from so few genes. This chapter introduces you to regulatory mechanisms in both prokaryotes and eukaryotes, allowing you to see how these mechanisms influence the processes of transcription and translation that you learned about in the previous chapter.

As you read through this chapter, think about the following questions:

1. How does gene regulation differ between prokaryotes and eukaryotes?
2. Where in the process of gene expression does regulation occur in a eukaryotic organism?
3. How might mutations influence the ability of a cell to regulate gene expression?

CHAPTER OUTLINE

13.1 Prokaryotic Regulation 238

13.2 Eukaryotic Regulation 241

13.3 Gene Mutations 247

BEFORE YOU BEGIN

Before starting this chapter, take a few moments to review these earlier concepts

Figure 12.9 What is the central dogma of biology?

Section 12.4 What is the purpose of transcription and where does it occur in both prokaryotic and eukaryotic cells?

Section 12.5 What is the role of translation in gene expression?

FOLLOWING *the* THEMES

CHAPTER 13 REGULATION OF GENE EXPRESSION

UNIT 2 GENETIC BASIS OF LIFE		
	Evolution	Whereas prokaryotic gene regulation operates primarily at the level of the gene, eukaryotes have evolved mechanisms to regulate gene expression at multiple levels.
	Nature of Science	By understanding how cells regulate gene expression it is possible to better understand the basis of many human diseases.
	Biological Systems	Mutations in the genetic material may have a profound impact on the function of a cell or the health of an organism.

13.1 Prokaryotic Regulation

Learning Outcomes

Upon completion of this section you should be able to

1. Describe the structure of an operon and state the role of each component of the operon.
2. Explain how the *trp* and *lac* operons of prokaryotes are regulated.
3. Distinguish between positive and negative regulation of gene expression in prokaryotes.

Because their environment is ever changing, bacteria do not always need to express their entire complement of enzymes and proteins. In 1961, French microbiologists François Jacob and Jacques Monod showed that *Escherichia coli* is capable of regulating the expression of its genes. They observed that the genes for a metabolic pathway, called **structural genes,** are grouped on a chromosome and subsequently are transcribed at the same time. Jacob and Monod, therefore, proposed the **operon**

[L. *opera,* works] model to explain gene regulation in prokaryotes. They later received a Nobel Prize for their investigations.

An operon (Fig. 13.1) typically includes the following elements:

A **regulator gene**—Normally located outside the operon, this codes for a DNA-binding protein that acts as a **repressor.** The repressor controls whether the operon is active or not.

Promoter—A short sequence of DNA where RNA polymerase first attaches to begin transcription of the grouped genes.

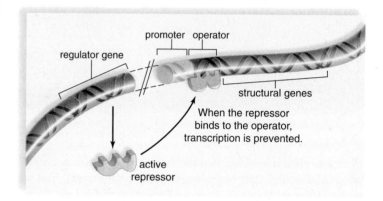

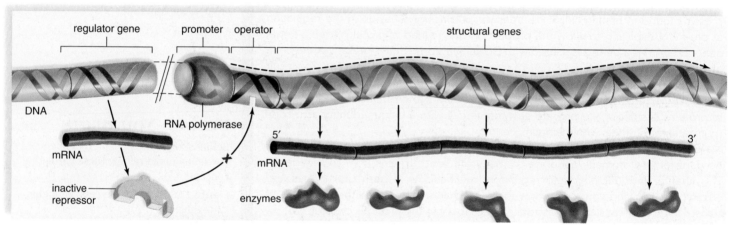

a. **Tryptophan absent.** Enzymes needed to synthesize tryptophan are produced.

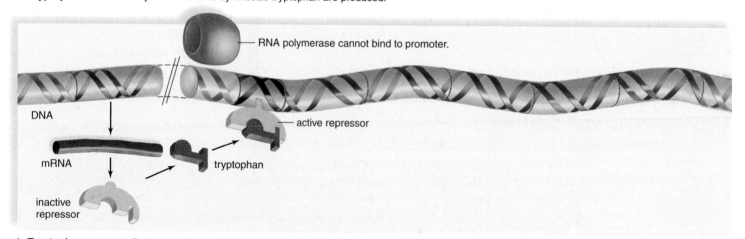

b. **Tryptophan present.** Presence of tryptophan prevents production of enzymes used to synthesize tryptophan.

Figure 13.1 The *trp* operon. **a.** The regulator gene codes for a repressor protein that is normally inactive. RNA polymerase attaches to the promoter, and the structural genes are expressed. **b.** When the nutrient tryptophan is present, it binds to the repressor, changing its shape. Now the repressor is active and can bind to the operator. RNA polymerase cannot attach to the promoter, and the structural genes are not expressed.

Basically, a promoter signals the start of the operon and the location where transcription begins.

Operator—A short portion of DNA where an active repressor binds. When an active repressor binds to the operator, RNA polymerase cannot attach to the promoter, and transcription cannot occur. In this way, the operator controls transcription of structural genes.

Structural genes—These genes code for the enzymes and proteins that are involved in the metabolic pathway of the operon. The structural genes are transcribed as a unit.

Next, we will briefly review the findings of Jacob and Monod in their studies of two *E. coli* operons: the *trp* operon and the *lac* operon.

The *trp* Operon

Many investigators, including Jacob and Monod, found that some operons in *E. coli* usually exist in the "on" rather than "off" condition. For example, in the *trp* operon, the regulator codes for a repressor that ordinarily is unable to attach to the operator. Therefore, RNA polymerase can bind to the promoter, and the structural genes of the operon are ordinarily expressed (Fig. 13.1). Their products, five different enzymes, are part of an anabolic pathway for the synthesis of the amino acid tryptophan.

If tryptophan happens to be already present in the medium, these enzymes are not needed by the cell, and the operon is turned off by the following method. Tryptophan binds to the repressor. A change in shape now allows the repressor to bind to the operator and prevent RNA polymerase from binding to the promoter, and the structural genes are not expressed. The enzymes are said to be repressible, and the entire unit is called a *repressible operon*. Tryptophan is called the **corepressor**. Repressible operons are usually involved in anabolic pathways that synthesize a substance needed by the cell.

Animation
The Tryptophan Repressor

The *lac* Operon

Bacteria metabolism is remarkably efficient; when there is no need for certain proteins or enzymes, the genes that are used to make them are usually inactive. For example, if the milk sugar lactose is not present, there is no need to express genes for enzymes involved in lactose catabolism. But when *E. coli* is denied glucose and is instead given lactose, the cell immediately begins to make the three enzymes needed for lactose metabolism.

The enzymes that break down lactose are encoded by three genes (Fig. 13.2): One gene is for an enzyme called β-galactosidase, which breaks down the disaccharide lactose to glucose and galactose; a second gene codes for a permease that facilitates the entry of lactose into the cell; and a third gene codes for an enzyme called transacetylase, which has an accessory function in lactose metabolism.

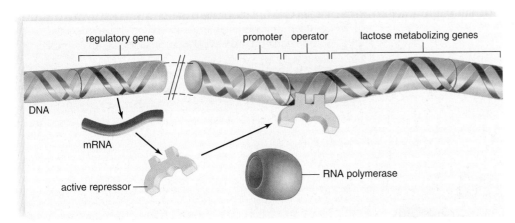

a.

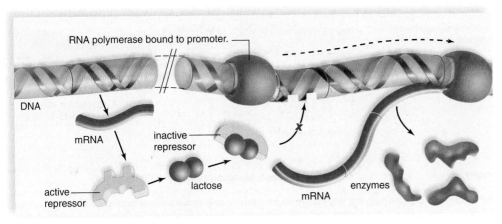

b.

Figure 13.2 The *lac* operon.
a. The regulator gene codes for a repressor that is normally active. When it binds to the operator, RNA polymerase cannot attach to the promoter, and structural genes are not expressed. **b.** When lactose is present, it binds to the repressor, changing its shape so that it is inactive and cannot bind to the operator. Now, RNA polymerase binds to the promoter, and the structural genes are expressed.

The three structural genes are adjacent to one another on the chromosome and are under the control of a single promoter and a single operator. The regulator gene codes for a *lac* operon repressor that ordinarily binds to the operator and prevents transcription of the three genes. But when glucose is absent and lactose (or more correctly, allolactose, an isomer formed from lactose) is present, lactose binds to the repressor, and the repressor undergoes a change in shape that prevents it from binding to the operator. Because the repressor is unable to bind to the operator, RNA polymerase is better able to bind to the promoter. After RNA polymerase carries out transcription, the three enzymes of lactose metabolism are synthesized.

Because the presence of lactose brings about expression of genes, it is called an **inducer** of the *lac* operon: The enzymes are said to be inducible enzymes, and the entire unit is called an *inducible operon*. Inducible operons are usually found in catabolic pathways that break down a nutrient. Why is that beneficial? Because these enzymes need to be active only when the nutrient is present.

Further Control of the lac Operon

E. coli preferentially breaks down glucose, and the bacterium has a way to ensure that the lactose operon is maximally turned on only when glucose is absent. A molecule called *cyclic AMP (cAMP)* accumulates when glucose is absent. Cyclic AMP, which is derived from ATP, has only one phosphate group, which is attached to ribose at two locations:

$$5'CH_2 \quad O \quad \text{adenine}$$
$$P \quad 3'$$
$$OH$$

cyclic AMP
(cAMP)

Cyclic AMP binds to a molecule called a *catabolite activator protein (CAP)*, and the complex attaches to a CAP binding site next to the *lac* promoter. When CAP binds to DNA, DNA bends, exposing the promoter to RNA polymerase. RNA polymerase is now better able to bind to the promoter so that the *lac* operon structural genes are transcribed, leading to their expression (Fig. 13.3).

When glucose is present, there is little cAMP in the cell; CAP is inactive, and the lactose operon does not function maximally. CAP affects other operons as well and takes its name for activating the catabolism of various other metabolites when glucose is absent. A cell's ability to encourage the metabolism of lactose and other metabolites when glucose is absent provides a backup system for survival when the preferred energy source glucose is absent.

Animation
Combination of Switches:
The *lac* Operon

The CAP protein's regulation of the *lac* operon is an example of positive control. Why? Because when this molecule is active, it promotes the activity of an operon. The use of repressors, on the other hand, is an example of negative control because when active they shut down an operon. A positive control mechanism allows the cell to fine-tune its response. In the case of the *lac* operon, the operon is only maximally active when glucose is absent and lactose is present. If both glucose and lactose are present, the cell preferentially metabolizes glucose.

Check Your Progress   13.1

1. Explain the difference between the roles of the promoter and operator of an operon.
2. Summarize how gene expression differs in an inducible operon versus a repressible operon and give an example of each.
3. Describe the difference between positive control and negative control of gene expression.

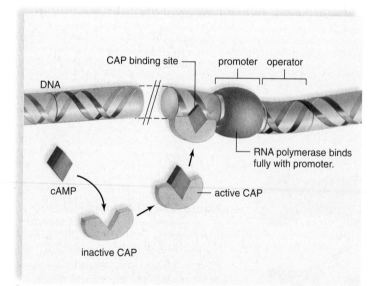

a. **Lactose present, glucose absent (cAMP level high)**

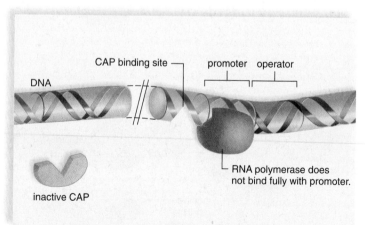

b. **Lactose present, glucose present (cAMP level low)**

Figure 13.3 Action of CAP.   When active CAP binds to its site on DNA, the RNA polymerase is better able to bind to the promoter so that the structural genes of the *lac* operon are expressed. **a.** CAP becomes active in the presence of cAMP, a molecule that is prevalent when glucose is absent. Therefore, transcription of lactose enzymes increases, and lactose is metabolized. **b.** If glucose is present, CAP is inactive, and RNA polymerase does not completely bind to the promoter. Therefore, transcription of lactose enzymes decreases, and less metabolism of lactose occurs.

13.2 Eukaryotic Regulation

Learning Outcomes

Upon completion of this section, you should be able to

1. List the levels of control of gene expression in eukaryotes.

2. Summarize how chromatin structure may be involved in regulation of gene expression in eukaryotes.

3. Identify the mechanisms of transcriptional, posttranscriptional, and translational control of gene expression.

With a few minor exceptions, each cell of a multicellular eukaryote has a complete complement of genes; the differences in cell types are determined by the different genes that are actively expressed in each cell. For example, in muscle cells a different set of genes is turned on in the nucleus and a different set of proteins is active in the cytoplasm compared to nerve cells.

Like prokaryotic cells, a variety of mechanisms regulate gene expression in eukaryotic cells. These mechanisms can be grouped under five primary levels of control; three of them pertain to the nucleus, and two pertain to the cytoplasm (Fig. 13.4). In other words, control of gene activity in eukaryotes extends from transcription to protein activity. These are the types of control in eukaryotic cells that can modify the amount of the gene product:

Animation
Control of Gene
Expression in
Eukaryotes

1. *Chromatin structure:* Chromatin packing is used as a way to keep genes turned off. If genes are not accessible to RNA polymerase, they cannot be transcribed. Chromatin structure is one method of **epigenetic inheritance** [Gk. *epi*, besides], the transmission of genetic information outside the coding sequences of a gene.

2. *Transcriptional control:* The degree to which a gene is transcribed into mRNA determines the amount of gene product. In the nucleus, transcription factors may promote or repress transcription, the first step in gene expression.

3. *Posttranscriptional control:* Posttranscriptional control involves mRNA processing and how fast mRNA leaves the nucleus.

4. *Translational control:* Translational control occurs in the cytoplasm and affects when translation begins and how long it continues. Any condition that can cause the persistence of the 5′ cap and 3′ poly-A tail can affect the length of translation. Excised introns may also have effects on the life span of mRNA.

5. *Posttranslational control:* Posttranslational control, which also takes place in the cytoplasm, occurs after protein synthesis. Only a functional protein is an active gene product.

We now explore each of these types of control in greater depth.

Chromatin Structure

The DNA in eukaryotes is always associated with a variety of proteins, and together they make up a stringy material called **chromatin.** Chromatin is most evident in the nucleus during interphase of the cell cycle.

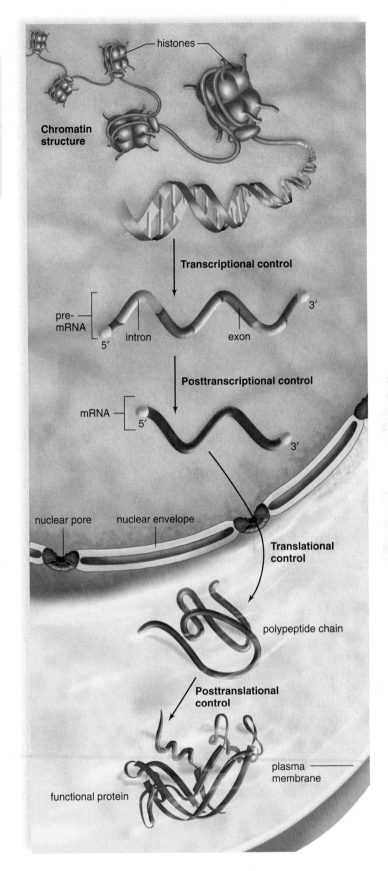

Figure 13.4 Levels at which control of gene expression occurs in eukaryotic cells.   The five levels of control are (1) chromatin structure, (2) transcriptional control, and (3) posttranscriptional control, which occur in the nucleus; and (4) translational and (5) posttranslational control, which occur in the cytoplasm.

In Chapter 12 you learned that one class of these DNA-associated proteins are the histones. Histones play an important role in the compaction of the DNA (see Figure 12.20) as well as in eukaryotic gene regulation. Without histones, the DNA would not fit inside the nucleus. Each human cell contains around 2 meters of DNA, yet the nucleus is only 5 to 8 micrometers (μm) in diameter.

The degree to which chromatin is compacted greatly affects the accessibility of the chromatin to the transcriptional machinery of the cell, and thus the expression levels of the genes. Active genes in eukaryotic cells are associated with more loosely packed chromatin called *euchromatin,* while the more tightly packed DNA, called *heterochromatin,* contains mostly inactive genes. Under a microscope, the more densely compacted heterochromatin stains darker than euchromatin (Fig. 13.5*a*).

What regulates whether chromatin exists as heterochromatin or euchromatin? In Chapter 12 you learned that a *nucleosome* consists of a portion of DNA wrapped around a group of histone molecules. Histone molecules have *tails,* strings of amino acids that extend beyond the main portion of a nucleosome (Fig. 13.5*b*). In heterochromatin, the histone tails tend to bear methyl groups ($-CH_3$); in euchromatin, the histone tails tend to be acetylated and have attached acetyl groups ($-COCH_3$).

Histones regulate accessibility to DNA; euchromatin becomes genetically active when histones no longer bar access to DNA. When DNA in euchromatin is transcribed, a so-called *chromatin remodeling complex* pushes aside the histone portion of a nucleosome so that access to DNA is not barred and transcription can begin (Fig. 13.5*c*). After *unpacking* occurs,

heterochromatin   nucleolus   euchromatin

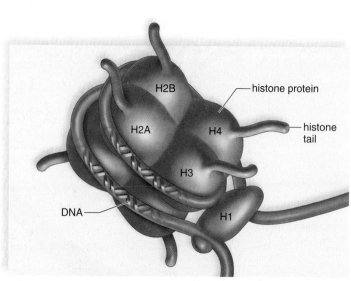

a. Darkly stained heterochromatin and lightly stained euchromatin

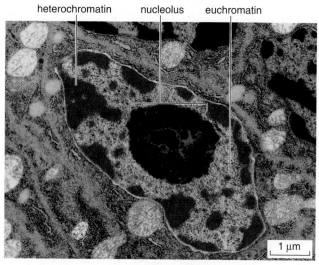

b. A nucleosome

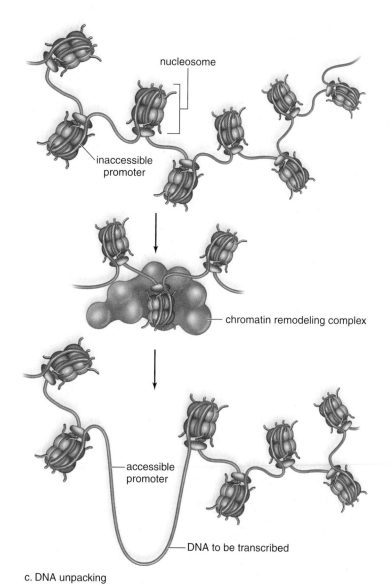

c. DNA unpacking

Figure 13.5 Chromatin structure regulates gene expression. **a.** A eukaryotic nucleus contains highly condensed heterochromatin (darkly stained) and euchromatin (lightly stained), which is not as condensed. **b.** Nucleosomes ordinarily prevent access to DNA so that transcription cannot take place. If histone tails are acetylated, access can be achieved; if the tails are methylated, access is more difficult. **c.** A chromatin remodeling complex works on euchromatin to make a promoter accessible for transcription.

many decondensed loops radiate from the central axis of the chromosome. These chromosomes have been named lampbrush chromosomes because their feathery appearance resembles the brushes that were once used to clean kerosene lamps.

In addition to physically moving nucleosomes aside to expose promoters, chromatin remodeling complexes may also affect gene expression by adding acetyl or methyl groups to histone tails.

Heterochromatin Is Not Transcribed

In general, highly condensed heterochromatin is inaccessible to RNA polymerase, and the genes contained within are seldom or never transcribed. A dramatic example of heterochromatin is the **Barr body** in mammalian females, first mentioned in Chapter 10. This small, darkly staining mass of condensed chromatin adhering to the inner edge of the nuclear membrane is an inactive X chromosome. To compensate for the fact that female mammals have two X chromosomes (XX), while males only have one (XY), one of the X chromosomes in the cells of female embryos undergoes inactivation. The inactive X chromosome does not produce gene products, allowing both males and females to produce the same amount of gene product from a single X chromosome.

Animation
X-Inactivation

How do we know that Barr bodies are inactive X chromosomes that are not producing gene products? In a heterozygous female, 50% of the cells have one X chromosome active and 50% have the other X chromosome active. The body of a heterozygous female would therefore be a mosaic, with "patches" of genetically different cells. Investigators have discovered that human females who are heterozygous for an X-linked recessive form of ocular albinism have patches of pigmented and nonpigmented cells at the back of the eye.

As other examples, women who are heterozygous for X-linked hereditary absence of sweat glands have patches of skin lacking sweat glands. And, the female tortoiseshell cat exhibits a difference in X-inactivation in its cells. In these cats, an allele for black coat color is on one X chromosome, and a corresponding allele for orange coat color is on the other. The patches of black and orange in the coat can be related to which X chromosome is in the Barr bodies of the cells found in the patches (Fig. 13.6).

Epigenetic Inheritance

Histone modification is sometimes linked to a phenomenon termed *epigenetic inheritance*, in which variations in the the pattern of inheritance is not due to changes in the sequence of the DNA nucleotides. For example, when histones are methylated, sometimes the DNA itself becomes methylated as well.

During *genomic imprinting*, either the mother's or the father's gene (but not both) is methylated during gamete formation. If an inherited allele is highly methylated, the gene is not expressed, even if it is a normal gene in every other respect. For traits that exhibit genomic imprinting, the expression of the gene depends on whether the unmethylated allele was inherited from the mother or the father.

The term *epigenetic inheritance* is now used broadly for other inheritance patterns that do not depend on the genes themselves. Epigenetic inheritance explains unusual inheritance patterns and also may play an important role in growth, aging, and cancer. Researchers are even hopeful that it will be easier to develop drugs to modify this level of inheritance rather than trying to change the DNA itself.

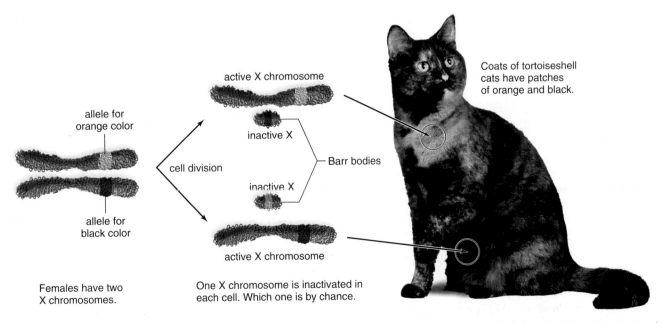

active X chromosome

allele for orange color

inactive X

cell division

Barr bodies

inactive X

allele for black color

active X chromosome

Coats of tortoiseshell cats have patches of orange and black.

Females have two X chromosomes.

One X chromosome is inactivated in each cell. Which one is by chance.

Figure 13.6 X-inactivation in mammalian females. In cats, the alleles for black or orange coat color are carried on the X chromosomes. Random X-inactivation occurs in females. Therefore, in heterozygous females, 50% of the cells have an allele for black coat color and 50% of cells have an allele for orange coat color. The result is tortoiseshell cats that have coats with patches of both black and orange.

Transcriptional Control

Although eukaryotes have various levels of genetic control (see Fig. 13.4), **transcriptional control** remains the most critical of these levels. The first step toward transcription is availability of DNA, which involves chromatin structure. Transcriptional control also involves the participation of transcription factors, activators, and repressors.

Transcription Factors, Activators, and Repressors

Although some operons like those of prokaryotic cells have been found in eukaryotic cells, transcription in eukaryotes is still controlled by DNA-binding proteins. Every cell contains many different types of **transcription factors,** proteins that help regulate transcription by assisting the binding of the RNA polymerase to the promotor. A cell has many different types of transcription factors, and often a variety of transcription factors may be active at a single promoter. Thus, the absence of one can prevent transcription from occurring.

Animation Transcription Factors

Even if all of the transcription factors are present, transcription may not begin without the assistance of a DNA-binding protein called a **transcription activator.** These bind to regions of DNA called **enhancers,** which may be located some distance from the promoter. A hairpin loop in the DNA brings the transcription activators attached to the enhancer into contact with the transcription factor complex (Fig. 13.7). Likewise, the binding of repressors to silencers within the promoter may prohibit the transcription of certain genes. Most genes are subject to regulation by both activators and repressors also.

Animation Transcription Complex and Enhancers

The promoter structure of eukaryotic genes is often very complex, and a large variety of regulatory proteins may interact with each other and with transcription factors to affect a gene's transcription level. Mediator proteins act as a bridge between transcription factors and transcription activators at the promoter. Now RNA polymerase can begin the transcription process (Fig. 13.7). Such protein-to-protein interactions are a hallmark of eukaryotic gene regulation. Together, these mechanisms can fine-tune a gene's transcription level in response to a large variety of conditions.

Transcription factors, activators, and repressors are always present in the nucleus of a cell, but they most likely have to be activated in some way before they will bind to DNA. Activation often occurs when they are phosphorylated by a kinase. *Kinases,* which add a phosphate group to molecules, and *phosphatases,* which remove a phosphate group, are known to be signaling proteins involved in a growth regulatory network that reaches from receptors in the plasma membrane to the genes in the nucleus.

Posttranscriptional Control

Posttranscriptional control of gene expression occurs in the nucleus and includes alternative mRNA splicing and controlling the speed with which mRNA leaves the nucleus.

During pre-mRNA splicing, introns (noncoding regions) are excised, and exons (expressed regions) are joined together to

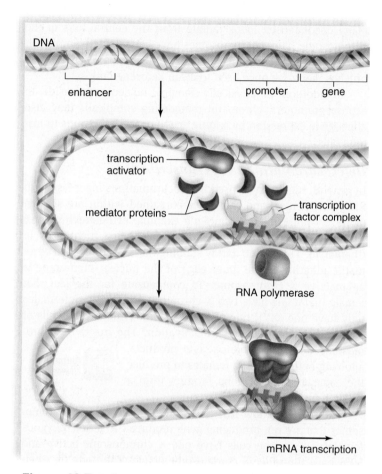

Figure 13.7 Eukaryotic transcription factors. Transcription in eukaryotic cells requires that transcription factors bind to the promoter and transcription activators bind to an enhancer. The enhancer may be far from the promoter, but the DNA loops and mediator proteins act as a bridge joining activators to factors. Only then does transcription begin.

form an mRNA (see Fig. 12.13). When introns are removed from pre-mRNA, differential splicing of exons can occur, and this affects gene expression. For example, an exon that is normally included in an mRNA transcript may be skipped, and it is excised along with the flanking introns (Fig. 13.8). The resulting mature mRNA has an altered sequence, and the protein it encodes is altered. Sometimes introns remain in an mRNA transcript; when this occurs, the protein-coding sequence is also changed.

Animation Exon-Shuffling

Examples of alternative pre-mRNA splicing abound. Both the hypothalamus and the thyroid gland produce a protein hormone called calcitonin, but the mRNA that leaves the nucleus is not the same in both types of cells. This results in the thyroid's releasing a slightly different version of calcitonin than does the hypothalamus. Evidence of alternative mRNA splicing is found in other cells, such as those that produce neurotransmitters, muscle regulatory proteins, and antibodies.

Alternative pre-mRNA splicing allows humans and other complex organisms to recombine their genes in novel ways to create the great variety of proteins found in these organisms. Researchers are busy determining how small nuclear RNAs (snRNAs) affect the splicing of pre-mRNA. They also know that, sometimes, alternative mRNA splicing can result in the inclusion

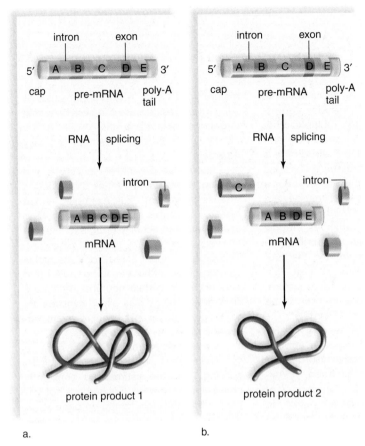

Figure 13.8 Alternative processing of pre-mRNA. Because the pre-mRNAs are processed differently in these two cells (**a** and **b**), distinct proteins result. This is a form of posttranscriptional control of gene expression.

of an intron that brings about destruction of the mRNA before it leaves the nucleus.

Further posttranscriptional control of gene expression is achieved by modifying the speed of transport of mRNA from the nucleus into the cytoplasm. Evidence indicates there is a difference in the length of time it takes various mRNA molecules to pass through a nuclear pore, affecting the amount of gene product realized per unit time following transcription.

Small RNA (sRNA) Molecules Regulate Gene Expression

For a long time, scientists were faced with a mystery: a cell appeared to contain vastly more DNA than was needed to account for the number of expressed proteins. The DNA that was not transcribed into proteins was initially termed "junk" DNA, but recently scientists have begun to understand the role of this DNA in the cell. Although only about 1.5% of the transcribed DNA codes for protein, the remainder is used to form small RNA (sRNA) molecules. We now know that these sRNA molecules represent an important form of gene regulation that functions at multiple levels of gene expression.

How do these RNA molecules regulate gene expression? Notice in Figure 13.9 that transcribed RNA can form loops as hydrogen bonding occurs between its bases. The double-stranded RNA (dsRNA) is diced up by enzymes in the cell to form sRNA molecules. Some of these sRNA molecules regulate transcription, while others are involved in the regulation of translation. Three ways have been found by which sRNA may regulate gene expression:

1. sRNA molecules have been known to alter the compaction of DNA so that some genes are inaccessible to the transcription machinery of the cell.

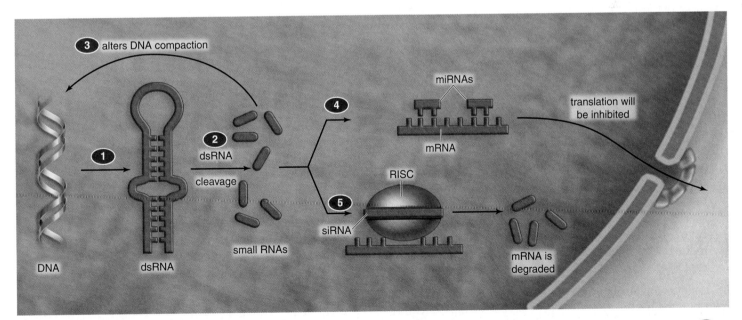

Figure 13.9 Function of small RNA molecules. Transcription of the DNA **1** may lead to looped and double-stranded RNA (dsRNA). **2** The cleavage of the dsRNA produces many small RNA (sRNA) molecules. **3** An sRNA can double-back to increase DNA compaction, or may become an miRNA or siRNA. **4** miRNA reduces translation by binding to complementary mRNA molecules. **5** siRNA forms a complex with RISC, which then degrades any mRNA with a sequence of bases that are complementary to the siRNA.

THEME Nature of Science

Alternative mRNA Splicing in Disease

The ability to combine the exons and introns of genes into new and novel combinations through alternative mRNA splicing is one of the mechanisms that allow humans to achieve a higher degree of complexity than simpler organisms without a huge increase in the number of genes. In more advanced organisms, the number of alternatively spliced mRNAs increases greatly. Recently, medical science has discovered that when this process goes awry, disease may result.

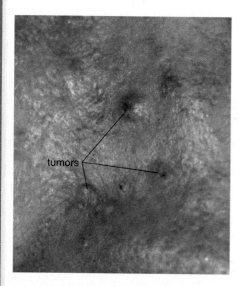

Figure 13A Skin tumors in patient with Gorlin syndrome.

Gorlin syndrome is an autosomal dominant syndrome that includes aggressive skin cancer (Fig. 13A), multiple other tumors, either benign or cancerous, and cysts in various organs. Gorlin syndrome is linked to the tumor suppressor gene called *patched* located on chromosome 9. But a recent finding demonstrated that several new mutations in *patched* were not within the gene's exons, but within its introns. These mutations caused the mRNA to be spliced incorrectly, rendering the protein nonfunctional. Because at least 95% of most human genes consists of introns, many more such mutations are likely to be discovered in other genetic disorders.

Defective pre-mRNA splicing is also a major cause of spinal muscular atrophy (SMA), an autosomal recessive disorder that is a common cause of childhood mortality. Recent research shows that exon 7 of the *SMN2* gene tends to be left out of the mature mRNA in SMA patients, rendering the protein nonfunctional. The end result is a progressive loss of spinal cord motor neurons, and eventually paralysis and skeletal muscle atrophy. Scientists at Cold Spring Harbor Laboratories turned to antisense oligonucleotide technology, a relatively new technique, in an attempt to reverse the defect. The results were stunning—several of the oligonucleotides tested were able to promote the inclusion of exon 7 in the mature mRNA both in vitro and in cultured cells. These results raise the possibility that targeting aberrant pre-mRNA splicing may ultimately be a viable treatment for many disorders.

Alternative pre-mRNA splicing is also causing scientists to rethink strategies in disease treatment. For example, recent research indicates that the common drug acetaminophen actually targets an alternative version of the COX-1 protein in neurons. This protein variant arises from alternative splicing of the mRNA encoding COX-1 that only occurs in certain neurons. Ultimately, such new findings may allow investigators to design more powerful pain relievers with fewer and less severe side effects.

Geneticists estimate that 80% or more of human genes undergo alternative mRNA splicing, and the estimate is constantly being revised upward. It is perhaps not surprising that this new frontier in gene regulation is redefining the standard approach to identifying the causes of illness and presenting new targets for the development of therapeutics.

Questions to Consider

1. What is the normal role of a tumor-suppressor gene in a cell?
2. How might the use of small RNA molecules be used to treat Gorlin syndrome?

---

2. Small RNAs are the source of **microRNAs (miRNAs),** small snippets of RNA that can bind to and dampen the translation of mRNA in the cytoplasm.

 Video Drug Discovery

3. Small RNAs are also the source of **small-interfering RNAs (siRNAs)** that join with an enzyme (an RNA-induced silencing complex, or RISC) to form an active silencing complex. This activated complex targets specific mRNAs in the cell for breakdown, preventing them from being expressed.

By using a combination of miRNA and siRNA molecules, a cell can fine-tune the amount of gene product being expressed, much like the way in which a dimmer switch on a light regulates the brightness of the room. Because both miRNA and siRNA molecules interfere with the normal gene expression pathways, the process is often referred to as **RNA interference.**

The first scientists to artifically construct miRNA and siRNA molecules to supress the expression of a specific gene were Andrew Fire and Craig Mello. Following this discovery, medical scientists recognized that it may be possible to use sRNA molecules as therapeutic agents to supress the expression of disease-causing genes. For their discovery, Fire and Mello received the 2006 Nobel Prize in Physiology and Medicine.

 Animation RNA Interference

 Video Halting Hepatitis

Video Tiny Genes Big Role

Translational Control

Translational control begins when the processed mRNA molecule reaches the cytoplasm and before there is a protein product. Translational control involves the activity of mRNA for translation at the ribosome.

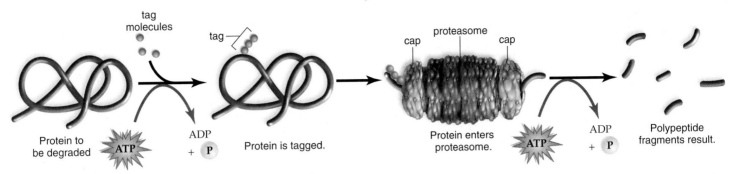

Figure 13.10 Proteasomes degrade proteins in a cell. Proteins to be degraded are first tagged with a signaling molecule. They then enter the proteasome where they are broken down to polypeptide fragments.

Presence or absence of the 5′ cap and the length of the poly-A (adenine nucleotide) tail at the 3′ end of a mature mRNA transcript can determine whether translation takes place and how long the mRNA is active. The long life of mRNAs that code for hemoglobin in mammalian red blood cells is attributed to the persistence of their 5′ end caps and their long 3′ poly-A tails. Therefore any condition that affects the length of the poly-A tail or leads to removal of the cap may trigger the destruction of an mRNA.

Posttranslational Control

Posttranslational control begins once a protein has been synthesized and has become active. Posttranslational control represents the last chance a cell has for influencing gene expression.

Some proteins are not immediately active after synthesis. For example, at first bovine proinsulin is a single, long polypeptide that folds into a three-dimensional structure. Cleavage results in two smaller chains that are bonded together by disulfide (S—S) bonds. Only then is active insulin present. This ensures that some proteins become active only when it is appropriate for them to do so.

Just how long a protein remains active in a cell is usually regulated by the use of **proteases**, enzymes that breakdown proteins. To protect the cell, proteases are typically confined to the lysosomes or special structures called **proteasomes**. For a protein to enter a proteasome, it has to be tagged with a signaling protein that is recognized by the proteasome cap (Fig. 13.10). When the cap recognizes the tag, it opens and allows the protein to enter the core of the structure, where it is digested to peptide fragments. Notice that proteasomes help regulate gene expression because they help control the amount of protein product in the cytoplasm.

Check Your Progress 13.2

1. Describe the five levels of genetic control in eukaryotes.
2. Explain how chromatin structure influences gene expression.
3. Discuss how small RNA molecules and proteasomes regulate gene expression.

13.3 Gene Mutations

Learning Outcomes

Upon completion of this section you should be able to

1. Distinguish between spontaneous and induced mutations.
2. Identify how mutations influence protein structure.
3. Summarize how mutations may cause cancer.

A **gene mutation** is a permanent change in the sequence of bases in DNA. The effect of a DNA base sequence change on protein activity can range from no effect to complete inactivity. Germ-line mutations are those that occur in sex cells and can be passed to subsequent generations. Somatic mutations occur in body cells and, therefore, they may affect only a small number of cells in a tissue. Somatic mutations are not passed on to future generations, but they can lead to the development of cancer.

Causes of Mutations

Some mutations are spontaneous—they happen for no apparent reason—while others are induced by environmental influences. In most cases, **spontaneous mutations** arise as a result of abnormalities in normal biological processes. **Induced mutations** may result from exposure to toxic chemicals or radiation, which induce (cause) changes in the base sequence of DNA.

Spontaneous Mutations

Spontaneous mutations can be associated with any number of normal processes. For example, a movable piece of DNA, termed a *transposon*, may jump from one location to another, disrupting one or more genes and leading to an abnormal product (see Chapter 14). On rare occasions, a base in DNA can undergo a chemical change that leads to a mispairing during replication. A subsequent base pair change may be carried forth in future generations. Spontaneous mutations due to DNA replication errors, however, are rare. DNA polymerase, the enzyme that carries out replication, proofreads the new strand against the old strand and detects any mismatched nucleotides, and each is usually replaced with a correct nucleotide. In the end, only about one mistake occurs for every 1 billion nucleotide pairs replicated.

Induced Mutations

Induced mutations are caused by **mutagens,** environmental factors that can alter the base composition of DNA. Among the best-known mutagens are radiation and organic chemicals. Many mutagens are also **carcinogens** (cancer-causing).

Chemical mutagens are present in many sources, including some of the food we eat and many industrial chemicals. The mutagenic potential of AF-2, a food additive once widely used in Japan, and of safrole, a flavoring agent once used to flavor root beer, caused them to be banned. Surprisingly, many naturally occurring substances like aflatoxin, produced in moldy grain and peanuts (and present in peanut butter at an average level of 2 parts per billion), and acrylamide, a natural product found in French fries, are also suspected mutagens.

Tobacco smoke contains a number of organic chemicals that are known carcinogens, and it is estimated that one-third of all cancer deaths can be attributed to smoking. Lung cancer is the most frequent lethal cancer in the United States, and smoking is also implicated in the development of cancers of the mouth, larynx, bladder, kidney, and pancreas. The greater the number of cigarettes smoked per day, the earlier the habit starts, and the higher the tar content, the greater is the possibility of these cancers. When smoking is combined with drinking alcohol, the risk of these cancers increases even more.

Scientists use the Ames test for mutagenicity to hypothesize that a chemical can be carcinogenic (Fig. 13.11). In the Ames test, a histidine-requiring strain of bacteria is exposed to a chemical. If the chemical is mutagenic, the bacteria can grow without histidine. A large number of chemicals used in agriculture and industry give a positive Ames test. Examples are ethylene dibromide (EDB), which is added to leaded gasoline (to vaporize lead deposits in the engine and send them out the exhaust), and ziram, which is used to prevent fungus disease on crops. Some drugs, such as isoniazed (used to prevent tuberculosis), are mutagenic according to the Ames test.

Aside from chemicals, certain forms of radiation, such as X-rays and gamma rays, are called ionizing radiation because they create free radicals, ionized atoms with unpaired electrons. Free radicals react with and alter the structure of other molecules, including DNA. Ultraviolet (UV) radiation is easily absorbed by the pyrimidines in DNA. Wherever there are two thymine molecules next to one another, ultraviolet radiation may cause them to bond together, forming *thymine dimers.* A kink results in the DNA. Usually, these dimers are removed by **DNA repair enzymes,** which constantly monitor DNA and fix any irregularities. One enzyme excises a portion of DNA that contains the dimer; another makes a new section by using the other strand as a template; and still another seals the new section in place.

The importance of these repair enzymes is exemplified by individuals with the condition known as xeroderma pigmentosum. They lack some of the repair enzymes, and as a consequence, these individuals have a high incidence of skin cancer because of the large number of mutations that accumulate over time. Also, repair enzymes can fail, as when skin cancer develops because of excessive sunbathing or prolonged exposure to X-rays.

Animation
Thymine Dimers:
Formation and Repair

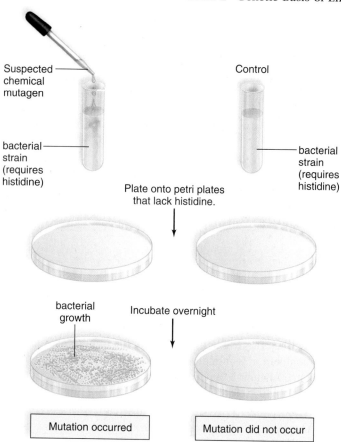

Figure 13.11 The Ames test for mutagenicity.   A bacterial strain that requires histidine as a nutrient is exposed to a suspected chemical mutagen, but a control is not exposed. The bacteria are plated on a medium that lacks histidine and only the bacteria exposed to the chemical show growth. A mutation allowed the bacteria to grow; therefore, the chemical can be carcinogenic.

Effect of Mutations on Protein Activity

Point mutations involve a change in a single DNA nucleotide and, therefore, a possible change in a specific amino acid. The base change in the second row of Figure 13.12a has no effect on the resulting amino acid in hemoglobin; the change in the third row, however, codes for the amino acid valine instead of glutamic acid. This base change accounts for the genetic disorder sickle-cell disease because the incorporation of valine instead of glutamic acid causes hemoglobin molecules to form semirigid rods, and the red blood cells to become sickle shaped. (Compare Figure 13.12b to Figure 13.12c.) Sickle-shaped cells clog blood vessels and die off more quickly than normal-shaped cells. The base change in the fourth row of Figure 13.12a may also have drastic results because the DNA now codes for a stop codon.

Animation
Mutation by Base
Substitution

Frameshift mutations occur most often when one or more nucleotides are either inserted or deleted from DNA. The result of a frameshift mutation can be a completely new sequence of codons and nonfunctional protein. Here is how this occurs: The sequence of codons is read from a specific starting point, as in this sentence, THE CAT ATE THE RAT. If the letter C is deleted from this sentence, shifting the reading frame, we read THE ATA TET HER AT—something that doesn't make sense.

Animation
Addition and
Deletion Mutations

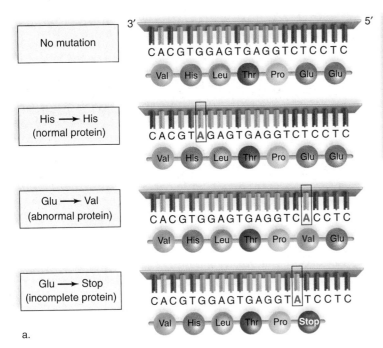

b. Normal red blood cell

c. Sickled red blood cell

Figure 13.12 Point mutations in hemoglobin. The effect of a point mutation can vary. **a.** Starting at the *top*: Normal sequence of bases in hemoglobin; next, the base change has no effect; next, due to base change, DNA now codes for valine instead of glutamic acid, and the result is that normal red blood cells **(b)** become sickle shaped **(c)**; next, a different base change causes DNA to code for termination, and the protein will be incomplete.

Nonfunctional Proteins

A single nonfunctioning protein can have a dramatic effect on the phenotype, because enzymes are often a part of metabolic pathways. One particular metabolic pathway in cells is as follows:

$$
\underset{\text{(phenylalanine)}}{A} \xrightarrow{E_A} \underset{\text{(tyrosine)}}{B} \xrightarrow{E_B} \underset{\text{(melanin)}}{C}
$$

If a faulty code for enzyme E_A is inherited, a person is unable to convert the molecule A to B. Phenylalanine builds up in the system, and the excess causes mental retardation and the other symptoms of the genetic disorder phenylketonuria (PKU). In the same pathway, if a person inherits a faulty code for enzyme E_B, then B cannot be converted to C, and the individual is an albino.

A rare condition called androgen insensitivity is due to a faulty receptor for androgens, which are male sex hormones such as testosterone. In a male with this condition, plenty of testosterone is present in the blood, but the cells are unable to respond to it. Female instead of male external genitals form, and female instead of male secondary sex characteristics occur at puberty. The individual, who appears to be a normal female, may be prompted to seek medical advice when menstruation never occurs. The karyotype is that of a male rather than a female, and the individual does not have the internal sexual organs of a female.

Mutations Can Cause Cancer

It is estimated that one in three people will develop cancer at some time in their lives. Of these affected individuals, one-third of the females and one-fourth of the males will die due to cancer. In the United States, the three deadliest forms of cancer are lung cancer, colon and rectal cancer, and breast cancer.

The development of cancer involves a series of accumulating mutations that can be different for each type of cancer. As discussed in Chapter 9, tumor suppressor genes ordinarily act as brakes on cell division, especially when it begins to occur abnormally. Proto-oncogenes stimulate cell division but are usually turned off in fully differentiated, nondividing cells. When proto-oncogenes mutate, they become oncogenes that are active all the time. Carcinogenesis begins with the loss of tumor suppressor gene activity and/or the gain of oncogene activity. When tumor suppressor genes are inactive and oncogenes are active, cell division occurs uncontrollably because a cell signaling pathway that reaches from the plasma membrane to the nucleus no longer functions as it should (Fig. 13.13 and Fig. 13.14).

It often happens that tumor suppressor genes and proto-oncogenes code for transcription factors or proteins that control transcription factors. As we have seen, transcription factors are a part of the rich and diverse types of mechanisms that control gene expression in cells. They are of fundamental importance to DNA replication and repair, cell growth and division, control of apoptosis, and cellular differentiation. Therefore, it is not surprising that inherited or acquired defects in transcription factor structure and function contribute to the development of cancer.

As examples, the major tumor suppressor gene called *p53* is more frequently mutated in human cancers than any other known gene. It has been found that the p53 protein acts as a transcription factor, and as such is involved in turning on the expression of genes whose products are cell cycle inhibitors (see Chapter 9). *p53* also promotes apoptosis (programmed cell death) when it is needed. The retinoblastoma protein (RB) controls the activity of a transcription factor for cyclin D and other genes whose products promote entry into the S stage of the cell cycle. When the tumor suppressor gene *p16* mutates, the RB

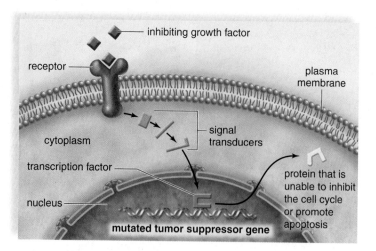

Figure 13.13 Cell signaling pathway that stimulates a mutated tumor suppressor gene. A mutated tumor suppressor gene codes for a product that directly or indirectly stimulates the cell cycle.

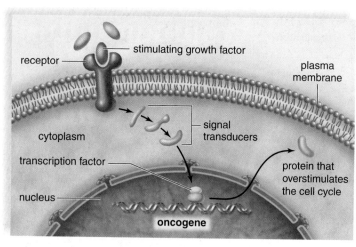

Figure 13.14 Cell signaling pathway that stimulates an oncogene. An oncogene codes for a product that either directly or indirectly overstimulates the cell cycle.

protein is always available, and the result is too much active cyclin D in the cell.

Mutations in many other genes also contribute to the development of cancer. Several proto-oncogenes code for ras proteins, which are needed for cells to grow, to make new DNA, and to not grow out of control. A point mutation is sufficient to turn a normally functioning *ras* proto-oncogene into an oncogene. Abnormal growth results.

Check Your Progress   13.3

1. List some common causes of spontaneous and induced mutations.
2. Explain how a frameshift mutation may disrupt a gene's function.
3. Discuss how a mutation in a tumor suppressor gene and in proto-oncogenes disrupts the cell cycle.

CONNECTING *the* CONCEPTS *with the* THEMES

Evolution

- In prokaryotes, regulation of gene expression occurs primarily through the regulation of the operon.
- Eukaryotes have evolved a variety of regulatory mechanisms that allows them to fine-tune gene expression and produce a large number of proteins from a relatively small number of genes.
- All living things are subject to genetic mutations or changes in the base sequence of DNA. DNA repair mechanisms have evolved to reduce the impact of mutations. Mutation is a source of genetic variability that is acted on by natural selection, allowing for evolutionary change over time.

Nature of Science

- By studying the structure of the prokaryotic operon, scientists have developed a basic understanding of gene regulation that allows them to better understand gene expression in eukaryotes.
- The discovery of small RNA molecules has caused scientists to rethink the concept of "junk" DNA. New findings may lead to development of new treatments for human diseases.

Biological Systems

- In eukaryotes, gene regulation may occur at a number of different levels, all of which influence the amount of end-product protein found in a cell.
- Mutations cause changes in the DNA and may have a significant influence on the structure and function of the cell, as is the case with cancer.

Media Study Tools

Enhance your study of this chapter with study tools and practice tests. Also ask your instructor about the resources available through ConnectPlus, including the media-rich eBook, interactive learning tools, and animations.

Summarize

13.1 Prokaryotic Regulation

Prokaryotes often organize genes that are involved in a common process or pathway into operons in which the genes are coordinately regulated. Gene expression in prokaryotes is usually regulated at the level of transcription. The operon model states that a regulator gene codes for a repressor. When the repressor binds to the operator RNA polymerase is unable to bind to the promoter, and transcription of the structural genes of the operon cannot take place. Operons may also be regulated by both activators and repressors.

The *trp* operon is an example of a repressible operon because when tryptophan, the corepressor, is present, it binds to the repressor. The repressor is then able to bind to the operator, and transcription of structural genes does not take place.

The *lac* operon is an example of an inducible operon because when lactose, the inducer, is present, it binds to the repressor. The repressor is unable to bind to the operator, and transcription of structural genes takes place if glucose is absent.

Both the *lac* and *trp* operons exhibit negative control, because a repressor is involved; however, some pathways also provide examples of positive control. The structural genes in the *lac* operon are not maximally expressed unless glucose is absent and lactose is present. At that time, cAMP attaches to a molecule called CAP, and then CAP binds to a site next to the promoter. Now RNA polymerase is better able to bind to the promoter, and transcription occurs.

13.2 Eukaryotic Regulation

The following levels of control of gene expression are possible in eukaryotes: chromatin structure, transcriptional control, posttranscriptional control, translational control, and posttranslational control.

Chromatin structure helps regulate transcription. Highly condensed heterochromatin is genetically inactive, as exemplified by Barr bodies. Less-condensed euchromatin is genetically active, as exemplified by lampbrush chromosomes in vertebrates.

Regulatory proteins called transcription factors, as well as DNA sequences called enhancers and silencers, play a role in controlling transcription in eukaryotes. Transcription factors bind to the promoter, and transcription activators bind to an enhancer. Small RNA molecules, such as microRNAs and small-interferring RNAs, are involved in RNA interference and play a role in gene expression.

Posttranscriptional control is achieved by creating variations in messenger RNA (mRNA) splicing, which may yield multiple mRNA messages from the same gene, and by altering the speed with which a particular mRNA molecule leaves the nucleus.

Translational control affects mRNA translation and the length of time it is translated, primarily by altering the stability of an mRNA.

Posttranslational control affects whether or not an enzyme is active and how long it is active. Proteasomes are specialized structures containing proteases that break down protein molecules and participate in the regulation of gene expression.

13.3 Gene Mutations

In molecular terms, a gene is a sequence of DNA nucleotide bases, and a genetic mutation is a change in this sequence. Mutations can be spontaneous or due to environmental mutagens such as radiation and organic chemicals. Carcinogens are mutagens that cause cancer.

Point mutations can have a range of effects, depending on the particular codon change. Sickle-cell disease is an example of a point mutation that greatly changes the activity of the affected gene. Frameshift mutations result when one or more bases are added or deleted, and the result is usually a nonfunctional protein. Most cases of cystic fibrosis are due to a frameshift mutation. Nonfunctional proteins can affect the phenotype drastically, as in a form of albinism that is due to a single faulty enzyme, and androgen insensitivity, which is due to a faulty receptor for testosterone.

Cancer is often due to an accumulation of genetic mutations among genes that code for regulatory proteins. The cell cycle occurs inappropriately when proto-oncogenes become oncogenes and tumor suppressor genes are no longer effective. Mutations that affect transcription factors and other regulators of gene expression are frequent causes of cancer.

Key Terms

Barr body 243	posttranscriptional control 244
carcinogen 248	posttranslational control 247
chromatin 241	promoter 238
corepressor 239	protease 247
DNA repair enzyme 248	proteasome 247
enhancers 244	regulator gene 238
epigenetic inheritance 241	repressor 238
frameshift mutation 248	RNA interference 246
gene mutation 247	small-interfering RNA
induced mutation 247	(siRNA) 246
inducer 240	spontaneous mutation 247
microRNA (miRNA) 246	structural gene 238
mutagen 248	transcription activator 244
operator 239	transcriptional control 244
operon 238	transcription factor 244
point mutation 248	translational control 246

Assess

Reviewing This Chapter

1. Name and state the function of the three components of operons.   238–39
2. Explain the operation of the *trp* operon, and note why it is considered a repressible operon.   239
3. Explain the operation of the *lac* operon, and note why it is considered an inducible operon.   239–40
4. What are the five levels of genetic regulatory control in eukaryotes?   241

UNIT 2 Genetic Basis of Life

5. Relate heterochromatin and euchromatin to levels of chromatin organization.   242–43
6. With regard to transcriptional control in eukaryotes, explain how Barr bodies show that heterochromatin is genetically inactive.   243
7. What do transcription factors do in eukaryotic cells? What are enhancers?   244
8. Explain how alternative mRNA processing may create multiple mRNAs from a single gene.   244–45
9. Describe the role of small RNA molecules in gene regulation.   245–46
10. Give examples of translational and posttranslational control in eukaryotes.   246–47
11. Name some causes of mutations.   247–48
12. What are two major types of mutations, and what effect can they have on protein activity?   247–48
13. Mutations in what types of genes, in particular, can cause cancer?   249

Testing Yourself

Choose the best answer for each question.

1. Which of the following illustrates negative control?
   a. A repressor that becomes active when bound to a corepressor and inhibits transcription.
   b. A gene that binds a repressor and becomes active.
   c. An activator that becomes active when bound to a coactivator and activates transcription.
   d. A repressor that binds a gene and becomes inactive.
2. In regulation of the *lac* operon, when lactose is present and glucose is absent,
   a. the repressor is able to bind to the operator.
   b. the repressor is unable to bind to the operator.
   c. transcription of structural genes occurs.
   d. transcription of lactose occurs.
   e. Both b and c are correct.
3. In regulation of the *trp* operon, when tryptophan is present,
   a. the repressor is able to bind to the operator.
   b. the repressor is unable to bind to the operator.
   c. transcription of the repressor in inhibited.
   d. transcription of the structural genes, operator, and promoter occurs.
4. In operon models, the function of the promoter is to
   a. code for the repressor protein.
   b. bind with RNA polymerase.
   c. bind to the repressor.
   d. code for the regulator gene.
5. Which of the following statements is/are true regarding operons?
   a. The regulator gene is transcribed with the structural genes.
   b. The structural genes are always transcribed.
   c. All genes are always transcribed.
   d. The regulator gene has its own promoter.
6. Which of the following regulate gene expression in the eukaryotic nucleus?
   a. posttranslational control
   b. transcriptional control
   c. translational control
   d. posttranscriptional control
   e. Both b and d are correct.

7. Which of the following mechanisms may create multiple mRNAs from the same gene?
   a. posttranslational control
   b. alternative mRNA splicing
   c. binding of a transcription factor
   d. chromatin remodeling
   e. miRNAs
8. Translational control of gene expression occurs within the
   a. nucleus.   c. nucleolus.
   b. cytoplasm.   d. mitochondria.
9. Alternative mRNA splicing is an example of which type of regulation of gene expression?
   a. transcriptional   c. translational
   b. posttranscriptional   d. posttranslational
10. A scientist adds radioactive uridine (label for RNA) to a culture of cells and examines an autoradiograph. Which type of chromatin is apt to show the label?
    a. heterochromatin   d. the DNA, not the histones
    b. euchromatin   e. Both a and d are correct.
    c. the histones, not the DNA
11. Barr bodies are
    a. genetically active X chromosomes in males.
    b. genetically inactive X chromosomes in females.
    c. genetically active Y chromosomes in males.
    d. genetically inactive Y chromosomes in females.
12. Which of these might cause a proto-oncogene to become an oncogene?
    a. exposure of the cell to radiation
    b. exposure of the cell to certain chemicals
    c. viral infection of the cell
    d. exposure of the cell to pollutants
    e. All of these are correct.
13. A cell is cancerous. You might find an abnormality in
    a. a proto-oncogene.   d. tumor cells.
    b. a tumor suppressor gene.   e. All of these are correct.
    c. regulation of the cell cycle.
14. A tumor suppressor gene
    a. inhibits cell division.   d. is subject to mutations.
    b. opposes oncogenes.   e. All of these are correct.
    c. prevents cancer.
15. Label this diagram of an operon.

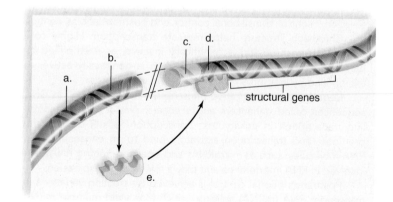

16. If the DNA codons are CAT CAT CAT, and a guanine base is added at the beginning, which would result?
    a. CAT CAT CAT G
    b. G CAT CAT CAT
    c. GCA TCA TCA T
    d. GC ATC ATC AT

17. A mutation in a DNA molecule involving the replacement of one nucleotide base pair with another is called a(n)
    a. frameshift mutation.
    b. transposon.
    c. deletion mutation.
    d. point mutation.
    e. insertion mutation.

18. Which of these is characteristic of cancer?
    a. It may involve a lack of mutations over a length of time.
    b. It cannot be tied to particular environmental factors.
    c. Apoptosis is one of the first developmental effects.
    d. Mutations in certain types of genes.
    e. It typically develops within a short period of time.

19. Which is not evidence that eukaryotes control transcription?
    a. euchromatin/heterochromatin
    b. existence of transcription factors
    c. lampbrush chromosomes
    d. occurrence of mutations
    e. All of these are correct.

Engage

Virtual Lab
DNA and Genes

The virtual lab "DNA and Genes" provides an interactive tutorial for understanding the influence of mutations on protein structure.

Thinking Scientifically

1. In patients with chronic myelogenous leukemia, an odd chromosome is seen in all the cancerous cells. A small piece of chromosome 9 is connected to chromosome 22. This 9:22 translocation has been termed the Philadelphia chromosome. How could a translocation cause genetic changes that result in cancer?

2. New findings indicate that mutations outside of genes may cause disease, such as in some cases of Hirschsprung disease and multiple endocrine neoplasia. Explain how such a mutation might alter the expression of a gene.

Bioethical Issue
Environmental Estrogens and Mutation

You have learned from this chapter that many types of carcinogens, such as those found in cigarette smoke, may alter the base sequence of DNA. However, environmental estrogens are a recently identified type of carcinogen that is generating much attention and concern in recent years. Environmental estrogens are estrogen-like compounds that can disrupt normal endocrine system function in animals by competing with normal sex hormones for receptors, inadvertently activating and inactivating transcription factors and greatly affecting gene expression. They have been linked to increased mutation rates, to deformed genitals in alligators and fish, to promotion of cell division in cultured breast cancer cells, and to inhibition of sperm development in humans.

Environmental estrogens are sometimes found naturally at low concentrations in foods such as soybeans and flax seeds. However, many of these compounds are artificial, originating from chemicals such as polychlorinated biphenyls (PCBs), phthalates (found extensively in many plastics), and atrazine, a compound found in many commercial weed killers. Many people, including scientists at the EPA, contend that these artificial compounds, even at very low doses, are a major threat to the environment, to many animal species, and to human health.

However, some critics contend that the concentrations of these compounds in the soil, air, and water are far below concentrations necessary to cause problems in most animal species, including humans. They also tout studies showing high concentrations of environmental estrogens in many grains, fruits, and vegetables, and that many of these compounds are rendered harmless by the body before they have a chance to cause mutations.

Should known environmental estrogens, such as those found in plastics, herbicides, and insecticides, be closely monitored by the government, and maximal permissible levels set for their emission into the environment? And where should money to fund these regulations be derived? Or, as some critics insist, are we worried about a problem that simply does not exist?

14

Biotechnology and Genomics

A biotechnology product derived from corn may someday replace plastics produced from oil.

CHAPTER OUTLINE

14.1 DNA Cloning   255

14.2 Biotechnology Products   258

14.3 Gene Therapy   260

14.4 Genomics   261

BEFORE YOU BEGIN

Before starting this chapter, take a few moments to review these earlier concepts.

Section 12.1 What is the basic structure of a DNA molecule?

Section 12.4 What is the difference between an intron and an exon in a gene?

Section 13.2 What is the role of microRNA molecules in a cell?

B iotechnology is the study and application of living organisms and processes to manufacture products, or improves the characteristics of bacteria, plants or animals. As a few examples, biotechnologists are actively investigating ways of making our world less dependent on fossil fuels, such as oil. Some bacteria produce biodegradable plastic granules inside of their cells. By introducing these genes into plants, such as the corn plants above, it may be possible someday to produce large quantities of biodegradable plastic. In addition to plastic-producing plants, biotechnology has made it possible for bioengineers and medical scientists to alter the genotype, and subsequently the phenotype, of other organisms—bacteria, animals, and humans. Genetically modified crops are resistant to disease and able to grow under stressful conditions. Farm animals can be made to grow larger than usual, and humans may be supplied with normal genes to make up for ones that do not function as they should.

But many people worry that genetically modified bacteria and plants might harm the environment and that the products produced by altered organisms might not be healthy for humans. Other ethical concerns abound. Is it ethical to give a cat a gene that makes it glow in the dark? To what extent would it be proper to improve the human genome? Everyone should be knowledgeable about modern genetics and biotechnology so they can participate in deciding these issues.

As you read through this chapter, think about the following questions:

1. What procedures are used to introduce a bacterial gene into a plant?
2. What is the difference between a genetically-modified and transgenic organism?
3. How are animals being genetically modified?

FOLLOWING *the* THEMES

CHAPTER 14 BIOTECHNOLOGY AND GENOMICS		
UNIT 2 GENETIC BASIS OF LIFE	**Evolution**	The comparison of the genomes of humans and model organisms, such as the mouse, is providing insights into the evolution of our species.
	Nature of Science	The development of recombinant DNA technology has enabled scientists to produce genetically-modified and transgenic organisms that benefit human society.
	Systems Biology	Recombinant DNA technology may be used to modify individual cells, as is the case in gene therapy, or produce organisms that assist in the cleanup of polluted ecosystems.

14.1 DNA Cloning

Learning Outcomes

Upon completion of this section you should be able to

1. Describe the steps involved in making a recombinant DNA molecule.
2. Explain the purpose of the polymerase chain reaction (PCR).
3. Identify how PCR may be used to analyze DNA.

In biology, **cloning** is the production of genetically identical copies of DNA, cells, or organisms through some asexual means. When an underground stem or root sends up new shoots, the resulting plants are clones of one another. The members of a bacterial colony on a petri dish are clones because they all came from the division of a single original cell. Human identical twins are also considered clones. Early in embryonic development the cells separate, and each becomes a complete individual.

DNA cloning can be done to produce many identical copies of the same gene; that is, for the purpose of **gene cloning.** Scientists clone genes for a number of reasons. They might want to determine the difference in base sequence between a normal gene and a mutated gene. Or they might use the genes to genetically modify organisms in a beneficial way. When cloned genes are used to modify a human, the process is called **gene therapy.** Otherwise, the organisms are called **transgenic organisms** [L. *trans,* across, through; Gk. *genic,* producing]. Transgenic organisms are frequently used today to produce a product desired by humans.

Recombinant DNA (rDNA) technology and the polymerase chain reaction (PCR) are two procedures that scientists can use to clone DNA.

Recombinant DNA Technology

Recombinant DNA (rDNA) contains DNA from two or more different sources, such as a human cell and a bacterial cell, as shown in Figure 14.1. To make rDNA, a technician needs a **vector** [L. *vehere,* to carry] by which rDNA will be introduced into a host cell. One common vector is a plasmid. **Plasmids** are small accessory rings of DNA found in bacteria that were first discovered in the bacterium *Escherichia coli* (*E. coli*). The ring is not part of the main bacterial chromosome, and it replicates on its own.

Two enzymes are needed to introduce foreign DNA into vector DNA: (1) a **restriction enzyme,** which cleaves DNA, and (2) an enzyme called **DNA ligase** [L. *ligo,* bind], which seals DNA into an opening created by the restriction enzyme. Hundreds of restriction enzymes occur naturally in bacteria, where they cut up any viral DNA that enters the cell. They are called restriction enzymes because they *restrict* the growth of viruses, but they also act as molecular scissors to cleave any piece of DNA at a specific site.

Notice that the restriction enzyme creates a gap in the DNA (Fig. 14.2), into which a piece of foreign DNA can be placed if it ends in bases complementary to those exposed by the restriction enzyme. The single-stranded, but complementary, ends of the two DNA molecules are called "sticky ends" because they can bind a piece of foreign DNA by complementary base-pairing. Sticky ends

Animation Restriction Endonucleases

Animation Construction of a Plasmid Vector

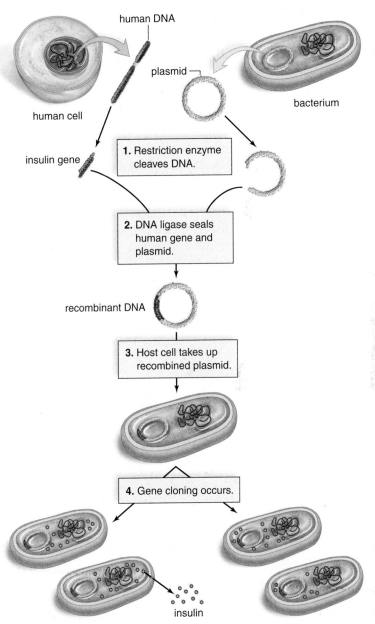

1. Restriction enzyme cleaves DNA.

2. DNA ligase seals human gene and plasmid.

recombinant DNA

3. Host cell takes up recombined plasmid.

4. Gene cloning occurs.

insulin

Figure 14.1 Cloning a human gene. This figure shows the basic steps in the cloning of a human gene. Human DNA and plasmid DNA are cleaved by a specific type of restriction enzyme. Then the human DNA, perhaps containing the insulin gene, is spliced into a plasmid by the enzyme DNA ligase. Gene cloning is achieved after a bacterium takes up the plasmid. If the gene functions normally as expected, the product (e.g., insulin) may also be retrieved.

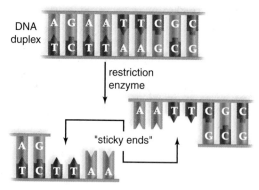

Figure 14.2 Restriction enzymes cut DNA at specific locations. Each restriction enzyme recognizes a specific sequence of nucleotides. After the enzyme cuts the DNA, "sticky ends" may be formed that are useful in the cloning of DNA sequences.

facilitate the insertion of foreign DNA into vector DNA as long as both are cleaved by the same restriction enzyme.

Next, genetic engineers use the enzyme DNA ligase to seal the foreign piece of DNA into the vector. DNA splicing is now complete; an rDNA molecule has been prepared (see Fig. 14.1). Bacterial cells take up recombinant plasmids, especially if they are treated to make their cell membranes more permeable. Thereafter, as the plasmid replicates, DNA is cloned.

For bacteria to express a human gene, the cloned gene has to be accompanied by regulatory regions unique to bacteria. Also, the gene should not contain introns because bacteria don't have introns. However, it is possible to make a human gene that lacks introns. The enzyme called reverse transcriptase can be used to make a DNA copy of human mRNA. The DNA molecule, called **complementary DNA (cDNA),** does not

contain introns. Bacteria may then transcribe and translate the cloned cDNA to produce a human protein because the genetic code is the same in humans and bacteria.

The Polymerase Chain Reaction

The **polymerase chain reaction (PCR),** developed by Kary Mullis in 1985, is widely used in research laboratories to create copies of a segment of DNA quickly in a test tube. The process mimics DNA replication in the cell (see Section 12.2), except that PCR is very specific—it amplifies (makes copies of) only a targeted DNA sequence. The targeted sequence can be less than one part in a million of the total DNA sample!

PCR requires the use of DNA polymerase, the enzyme that carries out DNA replication, and a supply of nucleotides for the new DNA strands. The DNA polymerase used in the reaction is a heat-stable (thermostable) polymerase that has been extracted from the bacterium *Thermus aquaticus,* which lives in hot springs. The enzyme can withstand the high temperature used to separate double-stranded DNA; therefore, replication does not have to be interrupted by the need to add more enzyme. PCR is a chain reaction because the targeted DNA is repeatedly replicated as long as the process continues. The colors in Figure 14.3 distinguish the old strand from the new DNA strand. Notice that the amount of DNA doubles with each replication cycle.

Analyzing DNA

DNA amplified by PCR can be analyzed for various purposes. For example, mitochondrial DNA taken from modern living populations was used to decipher the evolutionary history of

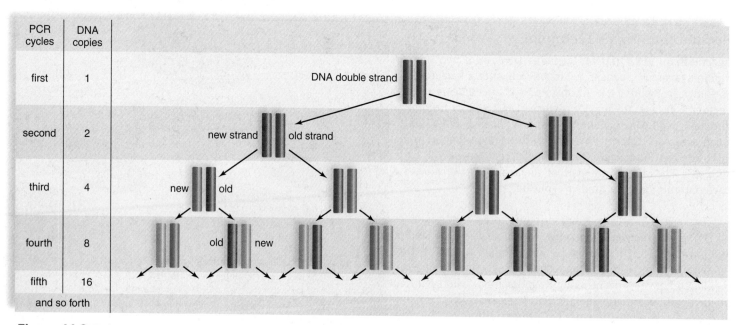

Figure 14.3 Polymerase chain reaction (PCR). PCR allows the production of many identical copies of DNA in a laboratory setting.

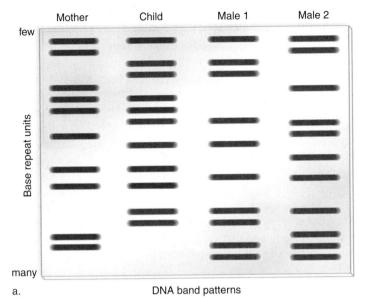

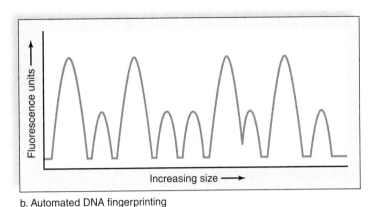

b. Automated DNA fingerprinting

Figure 14.4 **The use of STR profiling to establish paternity.**   **a.** In this method, DNA fragments containing STRs are separated by gel electrophoresis. Male 1 is the father. **b.** Each person's fingerprint pattern (only one is shown) can also be printed out by a machine that detects fluorescence.

human populations. For identification purposes, DNA taken from a corpse burned beyond recognition can be matched to that on the bristles of the person's toothbrush!

Analysis of DNA following PCR has undergone improvements over the years. At first, the entire genome was treated with restriction enzymes, resulting in a unique collection of different-sized fragments because each person has their own restriction enzyme sites. A process called **gel electrophoresis,** which separates DNA fragments according to their size, was then employed; the result of fragment sorting was a pattern of distinctive bands that identified the person.

Now, **short tandem repeat (STR) profiling** is the method of choice. STRs are short sequences of DNA bases that recur several times, as in TCGTCGTCG. STR profiling is advantageous because it doesn't require the use of restriction enzymes. The chromosomal locations for STRs are known, and therefore it is possible to subject only these locations to PCR and use gel electrophoresis to arrive at a band pattern that is different for each person. The band patterns are different because each person has their own number of repeats at the different locations. The greater the number of STRs at a location, the longer the DNA fragment amplified by PCR. The more STR locations employed, the more confident scientists can be of distinctive results for each person (Fig. 14.4a).

The newest method of producing DNA profiles, or "fingerprints," does away with the need to use gel electrophoresis: the DNA fragments are fluorescently labeled. A laser then excites the fluorescent STRs, and a detector records the amount of emission for each DNA fragment in terms of peaks and valleys. Therefore, the greater the fluorescence, the greater the number of repeats at a location. The printout, such as the one shown in

Figure 14.4b, is the DNA fingerprint, and each person has their own unique printout.

Other Applications

Applications of PCR are limited only by the imagination.

- A viral infection, a genetic disorder, or cancer can be confirmed when the DNA tested matches that of a known virus or mutated gene.
- DNA fingerprinted from blood or tissues at a crime scene has been successfully used in screening suspects, convicting criminals, and in exonerating those wrongly convicted.
- DNA fingerprinting through STR profiling has been extensively used to identify the victims of the natural disasters, such as the tsunamis in Indonesia and Japan.

  Video
  World Trade
  Center DNA

- Relatives can be found, paternity suits can be settled (Fig. 14.4a), genetic disorders can be detected, and illegally poached ivory and fish can be recognized using this technology (see Chapter 19).
- PCR has also shed new light on evolutionary studies by comparing extracted DNA from ancient specimens with that of living organisms.

Check Your Progress   14.1

1. Describe the process for creating a rDNA molecule.
2. List the scientific benefits of using the polymerase chain reaction.
3. Explain how DNA profiling can be used to analyze DNA molecules.

14.2 Biotechnology Products

Today, transgenic bacteria, plants, and animals are often called **genetically modified organisms (GMOs),** and the products they produce are called **biotechnology products.**

Genetically Modified Bacteria

Many uses have been found for genetically modified bacteria, besides the production of proteins. Biotechnology products from bacteria include insulin, clotting factor VIII, human growth hormone, t-PA (tissue plasminogen activator), and hepatitis B vaccine.

Transgenic bacteria have many other uses as well. Some have been produced to promote the health of plants. For example, bacteria that normally live on plants and encourage the formation of ice crystals have been changed from frost-plus to frost-minus bacteria. As a result, new crops such as frost-resistant strawberries are being developed. Also, a bacterium that normally colonizes the roots of corn plants has now been endowed with genes (from another bacterium) that code for an insect toxin. The toxin protects the roots from insects.

Animation
Early Genetic
Engineering Experiment

Bacteria can be selected for their ability to degrade a particular substance, and this ability can then be enhanced by bioengineering. For instance, naturally occurring bacteria that eat oil have been genetically engineered to clean up beaches (Fig. 14.5) after oil spills, such as the 2010 Deep Water Horizon spill

Figure 14.5 Genetically modified bacteria. Bacteria capable of decomposing oil have been engineered and patented. Recently, scientists used these bacteria extensively in treating the environmental impacts of the Deep Water Horizon oil spill in the Gulf of Mexico.

in the Gulf of Mexico. Bacteria can also remove sulfur from coal before it is burned and help clean up toxic waste dumps. One such strain was given genes that allowed it to clean up levels of toxins that would have killed other strains. Further, these bacteria were given "suicide" genes that caused them to self-destruct when the job had been accomplished.

Organic chemicals are often synthesized by having catalysts act on precursor molecules or by using bacteria to carry out the synthesis. Today, it is possible to go one step further and manipulate the genes that code for these enzymes. For instance, biochemists discovered a strain of bacteria that is especially good at producing phenylalanine, an organic chemical needed to make aspartame, the dipeptide sweetener better known as NutraSweet®. They isolated, altered, and formed a vector for the appropriate genes so that various other bacteria could be genetically engineered to produce phenylalanine.

Genetically Modified Plants

Techniques have been developed to introduce foreign genes into immature plant embryos or into plant cells called *protoplasts* that have had the cell wall removed. The protoplasts are treated with an electric current while they are suspended in a liquid containing foreign DNA. The current creates tiny, self-sealing holes in the plasma membrane through which the DNA can enter. These treated protoplasts go on to develop into mature plants.

Foreign genes transferred to strains of cotton, corn, potato, and even bananas, have made these plants resistant to pests such as fungi and insects, because their cells now produce a chemical that is toxic to the pest species. Similarly, soybeans have been made resistant to a common herbicide. Some corn and cotton plants are both pest- and herbicide-resistant. These and other genetically modified crops that are expected to have increased yields are now sold commercially.

Like bacteria, plants are also being engineered to produce human proteins, such as hormones, clotting factors, and antibodies, in their seeds. One type of antibody made by corn can deliver radioisotopes to tumor cells, and another made by soybeans can be used to treat genital herpes.

Video
Good Tobacco

Video
Potato Vaccine

Genetically Modified Animals

Techniques have been developed to insert genes into the eggs of animals. It is possible to microinject foreign genes into eggs by hand, but another method uses vortex mixing. The eggs are placed in an agitator with DNA and silicon-carbide needles, and the needles make tiny holes through which the DNA can enter. When these eggs are fertilized, the resulting offspring are transgenic animals. Using this technique, many types of animal eggs have taken up the gene for bovine growth hormone (bGH). The procedure has been used to produce larger fishes, cows, pigs, rabbits, and sheep.

Video
Cloned Milk

Video
Firefly Rx

Gene pharming, the use of transgenic farm animals to produce pharmaceuticals, is being pursued by a number of firms. Genes that code for therapeutic and diagnostic proteins are

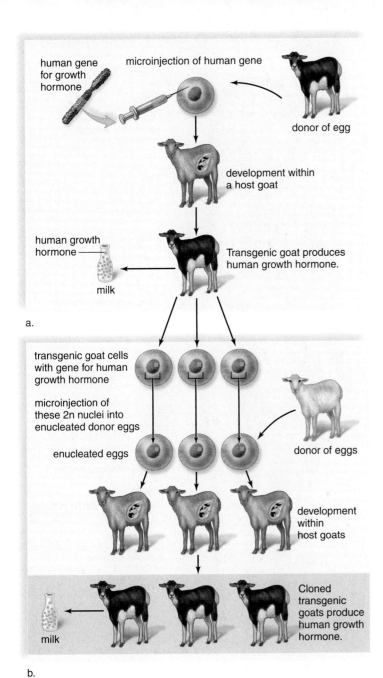

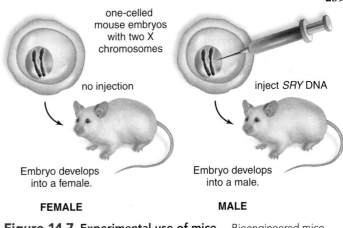

Figure 14.7 **Experimental use of mice.** Bioengineered mice showed that maleness is due to *SRY* DNA.

Figure 14.6 **Transgenic mammals produce a product.** This figure illustrates the basic procedure for generating a transgenic animal. **a.** A bioengineered egg develops in a host to create a transgenic goat that produces a biotechnology product in its milk. **b.** Nuclei from the transgenic goat are transferred into donor eggs, which develop into cloned transgenic goats.

incorporated into an animal's DNA, and the proteins appear in the animal's milk. Trials are under way for drugs that treat cystic fibrosis, cancer, blood diseases, and other disorders. Figure 14.6*a* outlines the procedure for producing transgenic mammals: DNA containing the gene of interest is injected into donor eggs. Following in vitro fertilization, the zygotes are placed in host females, where they develop. After female offspring mature, the product is secreted in their milk.

Cloning Transgenic Animals

For many years, researchers believed that adult vertebrate animals could not be cloned because cloning requires that all the

genes of an adult cell be turned on if development is to proceed normally. This had long been thought impossible.

In 1997, however, Scottish scientists announced that they had produced a cloned sheep, which they called Dolly. Since then, calves, goats, pigs, rabbits, and even cats have also been cloned. The techniques can be applied to produce populations of transgenic animals.

As shown in Figure 14.6*b*, after enucleated eggs from a donor are microinjected with 2n nuclei from a single transgenic animal, they are coaxed to begin development in vitro. Development continues in host females until the clones are born. The female clones have the same product in their milk as does the donor of the eggs. Now that scientists have a way to clone animals, this procedure will undoubtedly be used routinely to procure biotechnology products. However, animal cloning is a difficult process with a low success rate (usually 1–2 viable embryos per 100 attempts). The vast majority of cloning attempts are unsuccessful, resulting in the early death of the clone.

Applications of Transgenic Animals

Researchers are using transgenic mice for many different research projects. Figure 14.7 shows how this technology has demonstrated that a section of DNA called *SRY* (sex determining region of the *Y* chromosome) produces a male animal. The *SRY* gene was cloned, and then one copy was injected into single-celled mouse embryos. Injected embryos developed into males, but any that were not injected developed into females.

Eliminating a gene is another way to study a gene's function. A *knockout mouse* has had both alleles of a gene removed or made nonfunctional. For example, scientists have constructed a knockout mouse lacking the *CFTR* gene, the same gene mutated in cystic fibrosis patients. The mutant mouse has a phenotype similar to a human with cystic fibrosis and can be used to test new drugs for the treatment of the disease.

Check Your Progress 14.2

1. List some of the beneficial applications of transgenic bacteria, animals, and plants.
2. Distinguish between a transgenic animal and a cloned animal.

14.3 Gene Therapy

Learning Outcomes

Upon completion of this section, you should be able to

1. Distinguish between in vivo and ex vivo gene therapy in humans.
2. List examples of how in vivo and ex vivo gene therapy has been used to treat human disease.

The manipulation of an organism's genes can be extended to humans in a process called **gene therapy.** Gene therapy is an accepted therapy for the treatment of a disorder and has been used to cure inborn errors of metabolism, as well as to treat more generalized disorders such as cardiovascular disease and cancer (Fig. 14.8).

Viruses genetically modified to be safe can be used to ferry a normal gene into the body, and so can liposomes, which are microscopic globules of lipids specially prepared to enclose the normal gene. Sometimes the gene may be injected directly into a particular region of the body. Below we give examples of *ex vivo gene therapy,* in which the gene is inserted into cells that have been removed and then returned to the body, and *in vivo gene therapy,* in which the gene is delivered directly into the body.

Ex Vivo Gene Therapy

Children who have SCID (severe combined immunodeficiency) lack the enzyme ADA (adenosine deaminase), which is involved in the maturation of immune cells. Therefore, these children are prone to constant infections and may die unless they receive treatment. To carry out gene therapy, bone marrow stem cells are removed from the bone marrow of the patient and are infected with a virus that carries a normal gene for the enzyme into their DNA. Then the cells are returned to the patient, where it is hoped they will divide to produce more blood cells with the same genes.

One of the earliest uses of ex vivo gene therapy was for familial hypercholesterolemia, a condition that develops when liver cells lack a receptor protein for removing cholesterol from the blood. The high levels of blood cholesterol make the patient subject to fatal heart attacks at a young age. In this procedure, a small portion of the liver was surgically excised and then infected with a virus containing a normal gene for the receptor before being returned to the patient. Patients experienced lowered serum cholesterol levels following this procedure. Scientists are investigating using ex vivo gene therapy to treat other human diseases, including some forms of hemophilia.

In Vivo Gene Therapy

Cystic fibrosis patients lack a gene that codes for a transmembrane carrier of the chloride ion. They often suffer from numerous and potentially deadly infections of the respiratory tract. In gene therapy trials, the gene needed to cure cystic fibrosis is sprayed into the nose or delivered to the lower respiratory tract

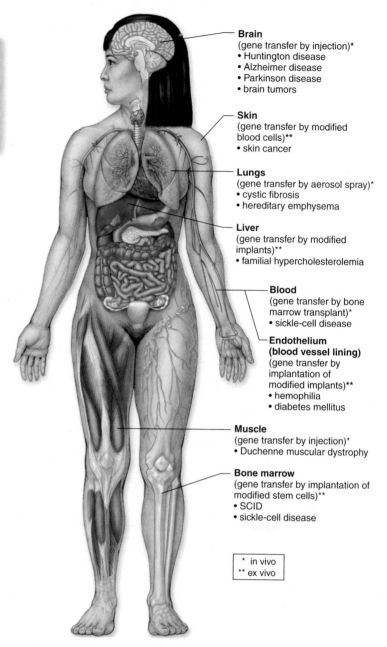

Brain
(gene transfer by injection)*
• Huntington disease
• Alzheimer disease
• Parkinson disease
• brain tumors

Skin
(gene transfer by modified blood cells)**
• skin cancer

Lungs
(gene transfer by aerosol spray)*
• cystic fibrosis
• hereditary emphysema

Liver
(gene transfer by modified implants)**
• familial hypercholesterolemia

Blood
(gene transfer by bone marrow transplant)*
• sickle-cell disease

Endothelium (blood vessel lining)
(gene transfer by implantation of modified implants)**
• hemophilia
• diabetes mellitus

Muscle
(gene transfer by injection)*
• Duchenne muscular dystrophy

Bone marrow
(gene transfer by implantation of modified stem cells)**
• SCID
• sickle-cell disease

```
 * in vivo
** ex vivo
```

Figure 14.8 Gene therapy. Sites of ex vivo and in vivo gene therapy to cure the conditions noted.

by adenoviruses or by the use of a liposome. So far, this treatment has resulted in limited success.

In cancer patients, genes are being used to make healthy cells more tolerant of chemotherapy and to make tumors more vulnerable to chemotherapy. The gene *p53* brings about apoptosis, and there is much interest in introducing it into cancer cells that no longer have the gene and in that way killing them off.

Check Your Progress   14.3

1. Describe the methods that are being used to introduce genes into human beings for gene therapy.
2. Discuss an example of ex vivo and of in vivo gene therapy.

14.4 Genomics

Learning Outcomes

Upon completion of this section, you should be able to

1. Distinguish between the sciences of genomics, proteomics, and bioinformatics.
2. Identify the function of repetitive elements, transposons, and unique noncoding RNA sequences in the human genome.
3. Explain how DNA microarrays are used in the study of genomics.

In the preceding century, researchers discovered the structure of DNA, how DNA replicates, and how DNA and RNA are involved in the process of protein synthesis. Genetics in the twenty-first century concerns **genomics,** the study of genomes—our complete genetic makeup and also that of other organisms. Knowing the sequence of bases in genomes is the first step, and thereafter we want to understand the function of our genes and their introns, as well as the intergenic sequences. The enormity of the task can be appreciated by knowing that there are approximately 6 billion base pairs in the 2n human genome. Many other organisms have a larger number of protein-coding genes but fewer noncoding regions compared to the human genome.

Sequencing the Genome

We now know the order of the base pairs in the human genome. This feat, which has been likened to arriving at the periodic table of the elements in chemistry, was accomplished by the **Human Genome Project (HGP),** a 13-year effort that involved both university and private laboratories around the world.

In the beginning, investigators developed a laboratory procedure that would allow them to decipher a short sequence of base pairs, and then instruments became available that could carry out sequencing automatically. Over the 13-year span, DNA sequencers were constantly improved, and now modern instruments can automatically analyze up to 2 million base pairs of DNA in a 24-hour period.

Sperm DNA was the material of choice for analysis because it has a much higher ratio of DNA to protein than other types of cells. (Recall that sperm do provide both X and Y chromosomes.) However, white cells from the blood of female donors were also used in order to include female-originated samples. The male and female donors were of European, African, American (both North and South), and Asian ancestry.

Many small regions of DNA that vary among individuals, termed polymorphisms, were identified during the HGP. Most of these are *single nucleotide polymorphisms (SNPs);* these vary by only one nucleotide. Many SNPs have no effect; others may contribute to enzymatic differences affecting the phenotype. It's possible that certain SNP patterns change an individual's susceptibility to disease and alter their response to medical treatments (see Chapter 16).

Determining the number of genes in the human genome required a number of techniques, many of which relied on identifying RNAs in cells and then working backward to find the DNA that can pair with that RNA. **Structural genomics**—knowing the sequence of the bases and how many genes we have—is now being followed by functional genomics.

Estimates place the number of human genes between 23,000 and 25,000. The majority of these genes are expected to code for proteins. However, much of the human genome was formerly described as "junk" because it does not specify the order of amino acids in a polypeptide. However, recall from Chapter 12 that it is possible for RNA molecules to have a regulatory effect in cells. We examine this in more detail in the next section.

Structure of the Eukaryotic Genome

Historically, genes were defined as discrete units of heredity that corresponded to a locus on a chromosome (see Fig. 11.4). Prokaryotes typically possess a single circular chromosome with genes that are packed together very closely; eukaryotic chromosomes, in contrast, are much more complex: The genes are seemingly randomly distributed along the length of a chromosome and are fragmented into exons, with intervening sequences called introns scattered throughout the length of the gene (Fig. 14.9).

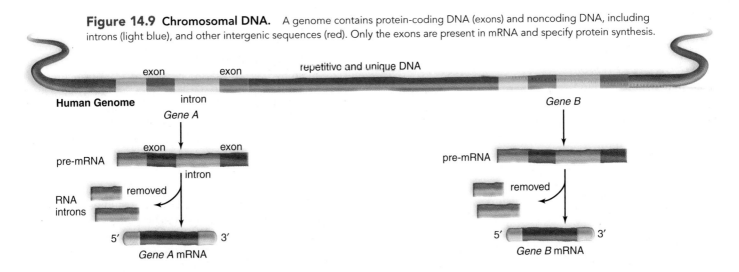

Figure 14.9 Chromosomal DNA. A genome contains protein-coding DNA (exons) and noncoding DNA, including introns (light blue), and other intergenic sequences (red). Only the exons are present in mRNA and specify protein synthesis.

In general, more complex organisms have more complex genes with more and larger introns. In humans, 95% or more of the average protein-coding gene is introns. Once a gene is transcribed, the introns must be removed and the exons joined together to form a functional mRNA transcript (see Fig. 12.13).

Once regarded as merely intervening sequences, introns are now attracting attention as regulators of gene expression. The presence of introns allows exons to be put together in various sequences so that different mRNAs and proteins can result from a single gene. Introns might also function to regulate gene expression and help determine which genes are to be expressed and how they are to be spliced. In fact, entire genes have been found embedded within the introns of other genes.

Intergenic Sequences

DNA sequences occur between genes and are referred to as **intergenic sequences.** In general, as the complexity of an organism increases, so does the proportion of its noncoding DNA sequences. Intergenic sequences are now known to comprise the vast majority of human chromosomes, and protein-coding genes represent only about 1.5 to 2% of our total DNA. The remainder of this DNA, once dismissed as "junk DNA," is now thought to serve many important functions. Several basic types of intergenic sequences are found in the human genome, including (1) repetitive elements, (2) transposons, and (3) unique noncoding DNA. The majority of intergenic sequences belong to this last class.

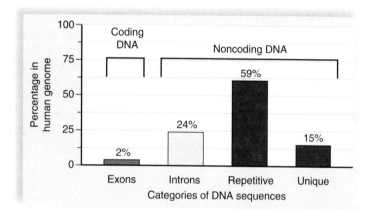

Repetitive DNA Elements

Repetitive DNA elements occur when a sequence of two or more nucleotides is repeated many times along the length of one or more chromosomes. Repetitive elements are very common—comprising nearly half of the human genome—and therefore, many scientists believe that their true significance has yet to be discovered. Although many scientists still dismiss them as having no function, others point out that the centromeres and telomeres of chromosomes are composed of repetitive elements, suggesting that repetitive DNA elements may not be as useless as once thought. For one thing, those of the centromere could possibly help with segregating the chromosomes during cell division.

Repetitive DNA elements include tandem repeats and interspersed repeats. **Tandem repeat** means that the repeated sequences are next to each other on the chromosome. Tandem repeats are often referred to as satellite DNA, because they have a different density than the rest of the DNA within the chromosome. The number and types of tandem repeats may vary significantly from one individual to another, making them invaluable as indicators of heritage. One type of tandem repeat sequence, referred to as *short tandem repeats*, or STRs, has become a standard method in forensic science for distinguishing one individual from another and for determining familial relationships (see page 257).

The second type of repetitive DNA element is called an **interspersed repeat,** meaning that the repetitions may be placed intermittently along a single chromosome, or across multiple chromosomes. For example, a repetitive DNA element, known as the *Alu* sequence, is interspersed every 5,000 base pairs in human DNA and comprises nearly 5–6% of total human DNA. Because of their common occurrence, interspersed repeats are thought to play a role in the evolution of new genes.

Transposons

Transposons are specific DNA sequences that have the remarkable ability to move within and between chromosomes. Their movement to a new location sometimes alters neighboring genes, particularly decreasing their expression. In other words, a transposon sometimes acts like a regulator gene. The movement of transposons throughout the genome is thought to be a driving force in the evolution of living things. The *Alu* repetitive element is an example of a transposon. In fact, many scientists now think that many repetitive DNA elements were originally derived from transposons.

Although Barbara McClintock first described these "movable elements" in corn over 60 years ago, it took time for the scientific community to fully appreciate this revolutionary idea. In fact, their significance was only realized within the past few decades. Transposons, sometimes termed "jumping genes," have now been discovered in bacteria, fruit flies, humans, and many other organisms. McClintock received a Nobel Prize in 1983 for her discovery of transposons and for her pioneering work in genetics.

Animation
Transposons

Unique Noncoding DNA

Genes comprise an estimated 1.5% of the human genome, and repetitive DNA elements make up about 44%; the function of the remaining half, or *unique noncoding DNA*, remains a mystery. Even though this DNA does not appear to contain any protein-coding genes, it has been highly conserved through evolution. In the many millions of years that separate humans from mice, large tracts of this mysterious DNA have remained almost unchanged. But if this DNA has no relevant function, then why has it been so meticulously maintained?

Recently, scientists observed that between 74% and 93% of the genome is transcribed into RNA, including many of these unknown sequences. Thus, what was once thought to be a vast "junk DNA" wasteland may be much more important than once thought and may play active roles in the cell. Small-sized

RNAs may be able to carry out regulatory functions more easily than proteins at times. Therefore, a previously overlooked RNA signaling network may be what allows humans, for example, to achieve structural complexity far beyond anything seen in the unicellular world. Together, these findings have revealed a much more complex, dynamic genome than was envisioned merely a few decades ago.

Revisiting the Definition of a Gene

Perhaps the modern definition of a gene should take the emphasis away from the chromosome and place it on the results of transcription. Previously, molecular genetics considered a gene to be a nucleic acid sequence that codes for the sequence of amino acids in a protein. In contrast to this definition, geneticists have known for some time that all three types of RNA are transcribed from DNA, and that these RNAs are useful products. We also know that protein-coding regions can be interrupted by regions that do not code for a protein but do produce RNAs with various functions. Taking this into consideration, an alternative definition was suggested by Mark Gerstein and associates in 2007: "A gene is a genomic sequence (either DNA or RNA) directly encoding functional products, either RNA or protein."[1]

This definition merely expands on the central dogma of genetics and recognizes that a gene product need not be a protein, and a gene need not be a particular locus on a chromosome. The DNA sequence that results in a gene product can be split and be present on one or several chromosomes. Also, any DNA sequence can result in one or more products. Furthermore, this definition recognizes that some prokaryotes have RNA genes. In other words, the genetic material need not be DNA. Again, we can view this as a simple expansion of the central dogma of genetics.

However, the definition does not spell out what is meant by functional product. It would seem, then, that sequences of DNA resulting in regulatory RNAs or proteins could be considered

---

1 Gerstein, M. B., Bruce, C., Rozowsky, J. S., et al. 2007. What is a gene, post-ENCODE? History and updated definition. *Genomic Research* 17: 669–81.

genes. According to this definition, "coding" no longer necessarily indicates a DNA sequence that codes for a sequence of amino acids. Instead, it simply means a sequence of DNA bases that are transcribed. The gene product can be RNA molecules, or it can be a protein.

Functional and Comparative Genomics

Since we now know the structure of our genome, the emphasis today is on functional genomics and also on comparative genomics. The aim of **functional genomics** is to understand the exact role of the genome in cells or organisms.

The Nature of Science feature on page 264 discusses the importance of a new technology that can be used to monitor the expression of thousands of genes simultaneously. **DNA microarrays,** also known as DNA chips or genome chips, contain microscopic amounts of known DNA sequences fixed onto a small glass slide or silicon chip in known locations (see Fig. 14A). The use of a microarray can tell you what genes are turned on in a specific cell or organism at a particular time and under what particular environmental circumstances. When mRNA molecules of a cell or organism bind through complementary base pairing with the various DNA sequences on an array, then that gene is active in the cell.

DNA microarrays are increasingly available that rapidly identify all the mutations in the genome of an individual. This information is called the person's **genetic profile.** The genetic profile can indicate if any genetic illnesses are likely and what type of drug therapy for an illness might be most appropriate for that individual.

Animation
Microarray

Aside from the protein-coding regions, researchers also want to know how SNPs and non-protein-coding regions, including repeats, affect which proteins are active in cells. As already discussed at length in Chapter 12, much research is now devoted to knowing the function of DNA regions that do not code for proteins.

The aim of **comparative genomics** is to compare the human genome to the genome of other organisms, such as the model organisms listed in Table 14.1. Model organisms are used in

Table 14.1 Comparison of Sequenced Genomes

Organism	Homo sapiens (human)	Mus musculus (mouse)	Drosophila melanogaster (fruit fly)	Arabidopsis thaliana (flowering plant)	Caenorhabditis elegans (roundworm)	Saccharomyces cerevisiae (yeast)
Estimated Size	3,200 million bases	2,500 million bases	180 million bases	125 million bases	97 million bases	12 million bases
Estimated Number of Genes	~25,000	~25,000	13,600	25,500	19,100	6,300
Chromosome Number	46	40	8	10	12	32

DNA Microarray Technology

With advances in robotic technology, it is now possible to place the entire human genome onto a single microarray (Fig. 14A). The mRNA from the organism or the cell to be tested is labeled with a fluorescent dye and added to the chip. When the mRNAs bind to the microarray, a fluorescent pattern results that is recorded by a computer. Now the investigator knows what DNA is active in that cell or organism. A researcher can use this method to determine the difference in gene expression between two different cell types, such as between liver cells and muscle cells.

Animation
DNA Microarray

Genetic Profiles

A mutation microarray, the most common type, can be used to generate a person's genetic profile. The microarray contains hundreds to thousands of known disease-associated mutant gene alleles. Genomic DNA from the individual to be tested is labeled with a fluorescent dye, and then added to the microarray. The spots on the microarray fluoresce if the individual's DNA binds to the mutant genes on the chip, indicating that the individual may have a particular disorder or is at risk for developing it later in life. This technique can generate a genetic profile much more quickly and inexpensively than older methods involving DNA sequencing.

Diseased Tissues

DNA microarrays also promise to hasten the identification of genes associated with diseased tissues. In the first instance, mRNA derived from diseased tissue and normal tissue is labeled with different fluorescent dyes. The normal tissue serves as a control.

The investigator applies the mRNA from both normal and abnormal tissue to the microarray. The relative intensities of fluorescence from a spot on the microarray indicate the amount of mRNA originating from that gene in the diseased tissue relative to the normal tissue. If a gene is activated in the disease, more copies of mRNA will bind to the microarray than from the control tissue, and the spot will appear more red than green.

Genomic microarrays are also used to identify links between disease and chromosomal variations. In this instance, the chip contains genomic DNA that is cut into fragments. Each spot on the microarray corresponds to a known chromosomal location. Labeled genomic DNA from diseased and control tissues bind to the DNA on the chip,

and the relative fluorescence from both dyes is determined. If the number of copies of any particular target DNA has increased, more sample DNA will bind to that spot on the microarray relative to the control DNA, and a difference in fluorescence of the two dyes will be detected. Researchers are currently using this technique to identify disease-associated copy number variations, such as those discussed in the Evolution feature on page 266.

Questions to Consider

1. Why might a researcher want to know what genes are being expressed in different cell types?
2. How might the information from a DNA microarray be used to develop new drugs to treat disease?

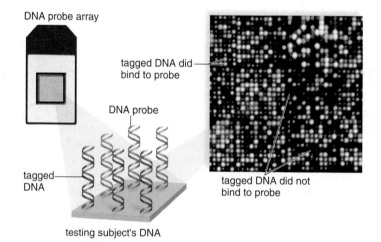

DNA probe array

tagged DNA did bind to probe

DNA probe

tagged DNA

tagged DNA did not bind to probe

testing subject's DNA

Figure 14A DNA microarray technology.
A DNA microarray contains many microscopic samples of DNA bound to known locations on a silicon chip. A fluorescently labeled mRNA from a tissue or organism binds to the DNA on the chip by complementary base pairing. The fluorescent spots indicate that binding has occurred and that the gene functions in that cell.

genetic analysis because they have many genetic mechanisms and cellular pathways in common with each other and with humans. Functional genomics has also been advanced through the study of these genomes.

Much has been learned by genetically modifying mice; however, other model organisms can also sometimes be used. Scientists inserted a human gene associated with early-onset Parkinson disease into *Drosophila melanogaster,* and the flies

showed symptoms similar to those seen in humans with the disorder. This outcome suggested that we might be able to use these organisms instead of mice to test therapies for Parkinson disease.

Comparative genomics also offers a way to study changes in a genome over time because the model organisms have a shorter generation time than humans. Comparing genomes can also help us understand the evolutionary relationships between organisms. One surprising discovery is that the genomes of all vertebrates are highly similar. Researchers were not surprised to find that the genes of chimpanzees and humans are 98% alike, but they did not expect to find that our sequence is also 85% like that of a mouse. Genomic comparisons will likely reveal evolutionary relationships between organisms never previously considered.

Proteomics

The entire collection of a species' proteins is the **proteome.** At first, it may be surprising to learn that the proteome is larger than the genome until we consider all the many regulatory mechanisms, such as alternative pre-mRNA splicing, that increase the number of possible proteins in an organism.

Proteomics is the study of the structure, function, and interaction of cellular proteins. Specific regulatory mechanisms differ between cells, and these differences account for the specialization of cells. One goal of proteomics is to identify and determine the function of the proteins within a particular cell type. Each cell produces thousands of different proteins that can vary not only between cells but also within the same cell, depending on circumstances. Therefore, the goal of proteomics is an overwhelming endeavor. Microarray technology can assist with this project and so can today's supercomputers.

Computer modeling of the three-dimensional shape of cellular proteins is also an important part of proteomics. If the primary structure of a protein is known, it should be possible to predict its final three-dimensional shape, and even the effects of DNA mutations on the protein's shape and function.

The study of protein function is viewed as essential to the discovery of new and better drugs. Also, it may be possible in the future to correlate drug treatment to the particular proteome of the individual to increase efficiency and decrease side effects. Proteomics will be a critical field of endeavor for many years to come.

Bioinformatics

Bioinformatics is the application of computer technologies, specially developed software, and statistical techniques to the study of biological information, particularly databases that contain much genomic and proteomic information (Fig. 14.10). The new, raw data produced by structural genomics and proteomics is stored in databases that are readily available to research scientists. It is called raw data because, as yet, it has little meaning. Functional genomics and proteomics are dependent on computer analysis to find significant patterns in the raw data. For example, BLAST, which stands for *basic local alignment search tool*, is a computer program that can identify homologous genes among the genomic sequences of model organisms. **Homologous genes** are genes that code for the same proteins, although the base sequences may be slightly different. Finding these differences can help trace the history of evolution among a group of organisms.

Figure 14.10 Bioinformatics.   New computer programs are being used to make sense out of the raw data generated by genomics and proteomics. Bioinformatics allows researchers to study both functional and comparative genomics in a meaningful way.

Bioinformatics also has various applications in human genetics. For example, researchers found the function of the protein that causes cystic fibrosis by using the computer to search for genes in model organisms that have the same sequence. Because they knew the function of this gene in model organisms, they could deduce the function in humans. This was a necessary step toward possibly developing specific treatments for cystic fibrosis.

The human genome has 3 billion known base pairs, and without the computer it would be almost impossible to make sense of these data. For example, it is now known that an individual's genome often contains multiple copies of a gene. But individuals may differ as to the number of copies—called *copy number variations,* as discussed in the Evolution feature on page 266. Now it seems that the number of copies in a genome can be associated with specific diseases. The computer can help make correlations between genomic differences among large numbers of people and disease.

It is safe to say that without bioinformatics, our progress in determining the function of DNA sequences, comparing our genome to model organisms, knowing how genes and proteins interact in cells, and so forth, would be extremely slow. Instead, with the help of bioinformatics, progress should proceed rapidly in these and other areas.

Check Your Progress   14.4

1. Distinguish between the genome and the proteome of a cell.
2. Summarize the difference between a short tandem repeat and a transposon.
3. Explain how the use of microarrays and bioinformatics aids in the study of genomics and proteomics.

THEME Evolution

Copy Number Variations

Geneticists have long been aware of large chromosomal duplications, deletions, and rearrangements detectable microscopically (see Fig. 10.13a, b). However, over the past decade scientists have become aware of duplications and deletions in the DNA called *copy number variations* (CNVs). Unlike shorter duplications, CNVs are sequences of DNA, usually greater than one kilobase (1,000 nucleotides) in size, that are repeated in varying numbers compared to a reference genome.

This repetition may arise from errors by the DNA polymerase during replication. For example, DNA damage or some other difficulty may cause the replication fork to stall. To continue, the replication machinery can switch to nearby chromosomal material of the same sequence. The replication fork is soon transferred back to the normal template, but the end result is extra or missing copies of small DNA segments. The fact that repetitive elements facilitate template switching suggests a new function for such sequences in our genome.

Some CNVs have known links to disease. Research shows that individuals with fewer copies of the *CCL3L1* gene are more susceptible to HIV infection than those with more copies. The disease Lupus is much more common among people with fewer copies of the complement component *C4* gene. But more surprising was a study that suggested at least some cases of autism can be linked to CNVs. The scientists who published the study examined the total chromosomal content of 1,441 autistic children and compared their DNA to more than 2,800 normal individuals. They found that in some of the autistic children, a 25-gene region of chromosome 16 was missing. Furthermore, analysis of other DNA databases revealed the same result: Approximately 1% of autism cases could be directly linked to the same deletion.[1]

CNVs are also emerging as a possible driving force in evolution. One study utilized DNA microarrays to examine the chromosomal structure of 47 individuals from many ethnic backgrounds, and found 119 regions where copy number variations existed. More surprising, none of the CNVs were found exclusively in one ethnic group,

suggesting that these variants existed well before the human population spread across the Earth. Perhaps they contributed to the phenotypic variations that developed thereafter. Furthermore, many scientists are suggesting that it may be advantageous for a species to have multiple copies of genes; if one or both normal copies of an allele fail to function properly, having a third allele available might be advantageous because it could restore normal function.

Conversely, an organism's two normal alleles would free an extra gene copy from having to maintain normal function. This situation would allow the gene to accumulate mutations without major consequence, which could ultimately lead to the formation of a new, unique gene. Copy number variations may contribute to evolution because they are yet another mechanism for organisms to achieve genetic innovation.

Questions to Consider

1. Why might a CNV in the coding region of a gene change the function of the protein?
2. From an evolutionary perspective, how might variations in CNV allow an organism to adapt to a new environment?

---

1 Weiss, L. A., et al. 2008. Association between microdeletion and microduplication at 16p11.2 and Autism. *New England Journal of Medicine*, 358: 667–75.

CONNECTING *the* CONCEPTS *with the* THEMES

Evolution

- Repetitive elements and transposons, once considered to be "junk DNA" are now believed to play a role in genome evolution.
- The field of comparative genomics is yielding valuable new insights into the relationships between species, impacting taxonomy and evolutionary biology.

Nature of Science

- Basic research into the nature and organization of genes in various organisms allowed geneticists to produce recombinant DNA molecules and transgenic organisms.
- Using model organisms as a guide, scientists are able to better understand the role of the elements of the genome.

Biological Systems

- Recombinant DNA technology is being used to generate genetically modified bacteria that can assist in protecting plants from pest species or restoring a polluted ecosystem.
- Techniques such as recombinant DNA technology, PCR, and DNA microarrays are allowing scientists to better understand the structure of the genome and to develop new treatments, such as gene therapy, for a number of human diseases.

Media Study Tools

www.mhhe.com/maderbiology11

Enhance your study of this chapter with study tools and practice tests. Also ask your instructor about the resources available through ConnectPlus, including the media-rich eBook, interactive learning tools, and animations.

Summarize

14.1 DNA Cloning

DNA cloning can isolate a gene and produce many copies of it. The gene can be studied in the laboratory or inserted into a bacterium, plant, or animal. Then, this gene may be transcribed and translated to produce a protein, which can become a commercial product or used as a medicine.

Two methods are currently available for making copies of DNA: recombinant DNA technology and the polymerase chain reaction (PCR). Recombinant DNA contains DNA from two different sources. A restriction enzyme is used to cleave plasmid DNA and to cleave foreign DNA. The resulting "sticky ends" facilitate the insertion of foreign DNA into vector DNA. The foreign gene is sealed into the vector DNA by DNA ligase. Both bacterial plasmids and viruses can be used as vectors to carry foreign genes into bacterial host cells.

PCR uses the enzyme DNA polymerase to quickly make multiple copies of a specific piece (target) of DNA. PCR is a chain reaction because the targeted DNA is replicated over and over again. Analysis of DNA segments following PCR has all sorts of uses from assisting genomic research to doing DNA fingerprinting for the purpose of identifying individuals and confirming paternity.

14.2 Biotechnology Products

Transgenic organisms have had a foreign gene inserted into them. Genetically modified bacteria, agricultural plants, and farm animals now produce commercial products of interest to humans, such as hormones and vaccines. Bacteria usually secrete the product. The seeds of plants and the milk of animals contain the product.

Transgenic bacteria have also been engineered to promote the health of plants, perform bioremediation, extract minerals, and produce chemicals. Transgenic crops, engineered to resist herbicides and pests, are commercially available. Transgenic animals have been given various genes, in particular the one for bovine growth hormone (bGH). Cloning of animals is now possible.

14.3 Gene Therapy

Gene therapy, by either ex vivo or in vivo methods, is used to correct the genotype of humans and to cure various human ills. Ex vivo gene therapy has been used to treat diseases such as SCID and cystic fibrosis. A number of in vivo therapies are being employed in the fight against cancer and other human illnesses, such as cardiovascular disease.

14.4 Genomics

Researchers now know the sequence of all the base pairs along the length of the human chromosomes. So far, researchers have identified around 25,000 human genes that code for proteins; the rest of our DNA consists of regions that do not code for a protein. Currently, researchers are placing an emphasis on functional and comparative genomics.

Genes comprise only 1.5% of the human genome. The rest of this DNA is surprisingly more active than once thought. About half of this DNA consists of repetitive DNA elements, which may be in tandem or interspersed throughout several chromosomes. Some of this DNA is made up of mobile DNA sequences called transposons, which are a driving evolutionary force within the genome. The role of the remaining portion of the genome is actively being investigated, but it is believed that these DNA sequences may play an important role in regulation of gene expression, thus challenging the classical definition of the gene. Functional genomics aims to understand the function of protein-coding regions and noncoding regions of our genome. To that end, researchers are utilizing tools such as DNA microarrays. Microarrays can also be used to create an individual's genetic profile, which is becoming helpful in predicting illnesses and how a person will react to particular medications.

Comparative genomics has revealed that little difference exists between the DNA sequence of our bases and those of many other organisms. Genome comparisons have revolutionized our understanding of evolutionary relationships by revealing previously unknown similarities between organisms.

Proteomics is the study of which genes are active in producing proteins in which cells under which circumstances. Bioinformatics is the use of computer technology to assist proteomics and functional and comparative genomics.

Key Terms

bioinformatics 265
biotechnology products 258
cloning 255
comparative genomics 263
complementary DNA
  (cDNA) 256
DNA ligase 255
DNA microarray 263
functional genomics 263
gel electrophoresis 257
gene cloning 255
gene pharming 258
gene therapy 255, 260
genetic profile 263
genetically modified organism
  (GMO) 258
genomics 261
homologous gene 265
Human Genome Project
  (HGP) 261

intergenic sequence 262
interspersed repeat 262
plasmid 255
polymerase chain reaction
  (PCR) 256
proteome 265
proteomics 265
recombinant DNA (rDNA) 255
repetitive DNA element 262
restriction enzyme 255
short tandem repeat (STR)
  profiling 257
structural genomics 261
tandem repeat 262
transgenic organism 255
transposon 262
vector 255

Assess

Reviewing This Chapter

1. What is the methodology for producing recombinant DNA? 255
2. What is the polymerase chain reaction (PCR), and how is it carried out to produce multiple copies of a DNA segment? 256
3. How does STR profiling produce a DNA fingerprint? 257

4. What are some practical applications of DNA segment analysis following PCR?   257
5. For what purposes have bacteria, plants, and animals been genetically altered?   258–59
6. Explain and give examples of ex vivo and in vivo gene therapies in humans.   260
7. What was the purpose of the Human Genome Project? What is the goal of functional genomics?   261–63
8. Describe the various types of intergenic DNA sequences found within the genome.   262–63
9. What insights into evolutionary relationships between organisms are arising from comparative genomics?   263–65
10. What are the goals of proteomics and bioinformatics?   265

Testing Yourself

Choose the best answer for each question.

1. Using this key, put the phrases in the correct order to form a plasmid-carrying recombinant DNA.

KEY:

   (1) use restriction enzymes
   (2) use DNA ligase
   (3) remove plasmid from parent bacterium
   (4) introduce plasmid into new host bacterium
   a. 1, 2, 3, 4   c. 3, 1, 2, 4
   b. 4, 3, 2, 1   d. 2, 3, 1, 4

2. Restriction enzymes found in bacterial cells are ordinarily used
   a. during DNA replication.
   b. to degrade the bacterial cell's DNA.
   c. to degrade viral DNA that enters the cell.
   d. to attach pieces of DNA together.

3. A genetic profile can
   a. assist in maintaining good health.
   b. be accomplished utilizing bioinformatics.
   c. show how many genes are normal.
   d. be accomplished utilizing a microarray.
   e. Both a and d are correct.

4. Bacteria are able to successfully transcribe and translate human genes because
   a. both bacteria and humans contain plasmid vectors.
   b. bacteria can replicate their DNA, but humans cannot.
   c. human and bacterial ribosomes are vastly different.
   d. the genetic code is nearly universal.

5. Bioinformatics can
   a. assist genomics and proteomics.
   b. compare our genome to that of a monkey.
   c. depend on computer technology.
   d. match up genes with proteins.
   e. All of these are correct.

6. The polymerase chain reaction
   a. uses RNA polymerase.
   b. takes place in huge bioreactors.
   c. uses a temperature-insensitive enzyme.
   d. makes lots of nonidentical copies of DNA.
   e. All of these are correct.

7. Which is a true statement?
   a. Genomics would be slow going without bioinformatics.
   b. Genomics is related to the field of proteomics.
   c. Genomics has now moved on to functional and comparative genomics.
   d. Genomics shows that we are related to all other organisms tested so far.
   e. All of these are correct.

8. DNA amplified by PCR and then used for fingerprinting could come from
   a. any diploid or haploid cell.
   b. only white blood cells that have been karyotyped.
   c. only skin cells after they are dead.
   d. only purified animal cells.
   e. Both b and d are correct.

9. Which was used to find the function of the cystic fibrosis gene?
   a. microarray
   b. proteomics
   c. comparative genomics and bioinformatics
   d. sequencing the gene

10. Which of these pairs is incorrectly matched?
   a. DNA ligase—mapping human chromosomes
   b. protoplast—plant cell engineering
   c. DNA fragments—DNA fingerprinting
   d. DNA polymerase—PCR

11. Which matches best to proteomics?
   a. Start with known gene sequences and build proteins.
   b. Use a microarray to discover what proteins are active in particular cells.
   c. Use bioinformatics to discover the proteins in the cells of other organisms.
   d. Match up known proteins with known genes.

12. Which is not a correct association with regard to bioengineering?
   a. plasmid as a vector—bacteria
   b. protoplast as a vector—plants
   c. RNA virus as a vector—human stem cells
   d. All of these are correct.

13. Proteomics is used to discover
   a. what genes are active in what cells.
   b. what proteins are active in what cells.
   c. the structure and function of proteins.
   d. how proteins interact.
   e. All but a are correct.

14. Which of these is an incorrect statement?
   a. Bacteria usually secrete the biotechnology product into the medium.
   b. Plants are being engineered to have human proteins in their seeds.
   c. Animals are engineered to have a human protein in their milk.
   d. Animals can be cloned, but plants and bacteria cannot.

15. Repetitive DNA elements
   a. may be tandem or spread across several chromosomes.
   b. are found in centromeres and telomeres.
   c. make up nearly half of human chromosomes.
   d. may be present just a few to many thousands of copies.
   e. All of these are correct.

16. Because of the Human Genome Project, we now know
    a. the sequence of the base pairs of our DNA.
    b. the sequence of all genes along the human chromosomes.
    c. all the mutations that lead to genetic disorders.
    d. All of these are correct.
    e. Only a and c are correct.
17. Which of the following delivery methods is not used in gene therapy?
    a. virus
    b. nasal sprays
    c. liposomes
    d. electric currents

Engage

Virtual Labs
Knocking Out Genes
Gene Splicing
Classifying Using Biotechnology

The virtual labs "Knocking Out Genes," "Gene Splicing," and "Classifying Using Biotechnology" all provide an interactive examination of the material found in this chapter.

Thinking Scientifically

1. Transposons are considered by many researchers to have played a major role in the evolution of life on Earth. Explain how the movement of genetic material within the genome may produce some organisms with a selective advantage.

2. The Evolution feature on page 266 describes copy number variations within the genome. Copy number variations do not always contain genes. How might having extra or missing copies of intergenic DNA sequences be beneficial? How might it be harmful?

Bioethical Issue

Transgenic Crops

Transgenic plants can possibly allow crop yields to keep up with the ever-increasing worldwide demand for food. And some of these plants have the added benefit of requiring less fertilizer and/or pesticides, which are harmful to human health and the environment.

Some scientists believe transgenic crops pose their own threat to the environment, however, and many activists believe transgenic plants are themselves dangerous to our health. Studies have shown that wind-carried pollen can cause transgenic crops to hybridize with nearby weedy relatives. Although it has not happened yet, some fear that characteristics acquired in this way might cause weeds to become uncontrollable pests. Or perhaps a toxin produced by transgenic crops could possibly hurt other organisms in the habitat. Many researchers are conducting tests to see if this might occur. And, although transgenic crops have not caused any illnesses in humans so far, some scientists concede the possibility that people could be allergic to a transgene's protein product.

Already, transgenic plants must be approved by the Food and Drug Administration before they are considered safe for human consumption, and they must meet certain Environmental Protection Administration standards. Some people believe safety standards for transgenic crops should be further strengthened, while others fear stricter standards would result in less food produced. Another possibility is to retain the current standards but require all biotech foods to be clearly labeled so the buyer can choose whether or not to eat them. Which approach do you prefer?

Appendix A

Answer Key

Chapter 1

Check Your Progress

1.1: 1. Populations are all of the organisms of a species in a given area, while an ecosystem contains groups of populations (a community) plus the physical environment. 2. Organization, acquisition and use of energy, homeostasis, response to the environment, reproduction and development, and adaptation. 3. Adaptations allow organisms to survive in changing environments; the changes as a result of adaptations represent evolution. **1.2:** 1. Domain, Kingdom, Phylum, Class, Order, Family, Genus, Species. 2. Protists are generally unicellular organisms; fungi are multicellular filamentous organisms that absorb food; plants are multicellular organisms that are usually photosynthetic; animals are multicellular organisms that must ingest and process their food. 3. Members of a population that have new adaptive traits reproduce more than other members, and therefore pass on these traits to the next generation in a greater proportion. **1.3:** 1. Individuals interact with members of the same species (a population), with other populations (communities), and with the physical environment (ecosystem). 2. By altering the physical environment of the ecosystem such as with pollution, increased urbanization, agriculture, etc. 3. They are more vulnerable, because high biodiversity ecosystems often depend on species with very specific roles that are more vulnerable to changes in the environment. **1.4:** 1. Experiments test the contribution of the experimental variable to a given observation. 2. Test groups are exposed to the experimental variables, while control groups are not. 3. Hypotheses are tested by designing experiments that examine the contribution of a single experimental variable to the observation, and by statistically comparing the response of a test group to that of a control group in an experiment.

Testing Yourself

1. c; **2.** The brain thinks but nerve cells do not think; **3.** b; **4.** b; **5.** d; **6.** d; **7.** b; **8.** a; **9.** c; **10.** e; **11.** b; **12.** b; **13.** Energy is brought into an ecosystem for the first time through photosynthesis. The Sun provides energy for photosynthesis. **14.** Excess carbon dioxide emitted alters its level in the atmosphere. This excess carbon dioxide is more readily available to photosynthetic plants and protists, possibly causing them to overpopulate. **15.** Not necessarily, if the new organism does not serve as prey for one species, allowing it to overpopulate, or if it does not prey on or compete with existing species in the ecosystem.

Chapter 2

Check Your Progress

2.1: 1. Atomic number is the number of protons in an atom. Atomic mass is the approximate sum of the masses of the protons and neutrons. 2. Groups indicate the number of electrons in the outer, or valence, shell of an atom. In Group VII , all the atoms including chlorine have seven electrons in the valence shell. Periods indicate the number of shells present in an atom. All atoms in Period III, including chlorine, have 3 shells. 3. Radiation can be used to kill diseased cells, such as those present in cancer. The radiation is used to damage cancer cell DNA, leading to cell death. **2.2:** 1. Ionic and covalent bonds are similar in that both involve electrons, but differ as to whether the electrons are shared or not. Ionic bonds are created when one atom gives up electron(s) and another gains electron(s) so that both atoms have outer shells filled. Covalent bonds are formed when two atoms share electrons to fill their outer shells. 2. Calcium gives away its two outer electrons in order to have a complete outer shell. Calcium then has two more protons than electrons, creating a net charge of +2. 3. By sharing with four hydrogen atoms, carbon acquires the four electrons it needs to fill its outer shell. Hydrogen has only one shell, which is complete with two electrons; therefore, each of four hydrogens can acquire a needed electron by sharing with carbon. **2.3:** 1. Water can absorb a lot of heat energy without large changes in temperature. Because of water's heat-absorbing properties, coastal cities can maintain relatively constant temperatures, even when the Sun's heat energy fluctuates. 2. Much heat energy can be put into water. As water evaporates, it takes heat energy with it, allowing a child playing in a sprinkler to dissipate body heat during a hot summer day. 3. If frozen water were heavier than liquid water, ponds and other bodies of water would freeze from the bottom up. The insulation provided by a layer of floating ice would be lost, and organisms living in aquatic environments would likely freeze to death. Water freezes from the top down because ice is less dense than water; the reason is that hydrogen bonds become more open when water freezes. **2.4:** 1. An acid dissociates in water to release hydrogen ions. A base either takes up hydrogen ions or releases hydroxide ions. 2. Living organisms require relatively narrow pH conditions to function. Both trees and fish die when their environment becomes too acidic. 3. Decreasing the blood's ability to resist large changes in pH would be catastrophic and likely cause biological malfunction or death.

Testing Yourself

1. d; **2.** e; **3.** c; **4.** c; **5.** a; **6.** d; **7.** e; **8.** b; **9.** b; **10.** Red circle is oxygen (partial negative charge). White circles are hydrogen (partial positive charge); **11.** c; **12.** a; **13.** a; **14.** e; **15.** b; **16.** d; **17.** a; **18.** c; **19.** b.

Chapter 3

Check Your Progress

3.1: 1. A carbon atom bonds with up to four different elements. Carbon–carbon bonds are stable, so long chains can be built; chains can have branching patterns, and chains can form rings. Isomers are possible. 2. 2-carbon alcohols and 2-carbon carboxylic acids are both soluble in water; however, the acid is more soluble because it easily donates its hydrogen. Both alcohols and acids become less soluble as the number of carbons increases. 3. The degradation, or hydrolysis, of a biomolecule requires water. If no water is present the molecule won't be cut into pieces without some other factor, such as heat. **3.2:** 1. Humans have no digestive enzymes capable of breaking the bonds in cellulose. 2. The monomer in cellulose is glucose; in chitin, an amino group is attached to each glucose. Cellulose is found in plant cell walls, while chitin is in the exoskeleton of some animals. **3.3:** 1. In water, oxygen and hydrogen atoms share their electrons unequally in their covalent bonds, resulting in a charge across the bonds, giving the molecule an overall polarity. In lipids, the carbon–carbon covalent bonds tend to share their electrons equally, resulting in no polarity. Because like dissolves like, these physical differences between water and lipids prevent their mixing. 2. A saturated fatty acid contains no double bonds between carbon atoms, while an unsaturated fatty acid contains one or more double bonds. Saturated fatty acids are flat and tend to stack densely in specific locations in blood vessels, reducing blood flow. Unsaturated fatty acids are kinked, and therefore do not block blood vessels to the same degree as saturated fats. 3. Because like dissolves like, phospholipids, which have hydrophilic and hydrophobic domains, arrange themselves so that their hydrophilic heads are adjacent to water, while the hydrophobic tails point inward toward each other. **3.4:** 1. A polypeptide is composed of a sequence of amino acids that are specified by the sequence of bases within a gene in the DNA. 2. Because like dissolves like, hydrophobic amino acids aggregate away from water in an aqueous environment, whereas hydrophilic amino acids associate with water. 3. Hydrophobic interactions play a major role in protein folding, as do pH, temperature, salt concentration, and other factors. **3.5:** 1. A nucleic acid stores information in the sequences of bases within a gene. Gene sequences specify amino acid sequences, thus assembling the proteins that carry out the functions of life. 2. Phosphate, 5-carbon sugar, and nitrogen-containing base. 3. ATP contains 3 phosphate molecules that are strongly negative and repel each other. The covalent bonds attaching them contain considerable potential energy, which can be captured when the bonds are broken and used to do cellular work.

Testing Yourself

1. c; 2. e; 3. e; 4. b; 5. b; 6. c; 7. d; 8. d; 9. c; 10. a. monomer; b. monomer; c. dehydration reaction; d. H_2O; e. monomer; f. monomer; g. polymer; 11. c; 12. d; 13. d; 14. a; 15. a; 16. b; 17. b; 18. d; 19. b; 20. d.

Chapter 4

Check Your Progress

4.1: 1. Living organisms are made up of one or more cells, which form the basic unit of life. New cells are produced from old cells. Energy flows within cells. 2. Organisms are composed of cells; both cells and organisms are systems in that they balance input and output and use energy to metabolize. The components of each provide structure and function that is greater than the sum of its parts. 3. The movement of materials into and out of a cell requires a sufficiently large surface area relative to cell volume. Cells that are overly large have an insufficient surface-area-to-volume ratio, thus limiting their overall size. **4.2:** 1. Prokaryotic cells lack a membrane-bounded nucleus, which is present in a eukaryotic cell. 2. Cell envelope:

mesosome, plasma membrane, cell wall, glycocalyx. Cytoplasm: inclusion bodies, nucleoid, ribosomes. Appendages: conjugation pilus, fimbriae, flagellum. **4.3:** 1. Separates various metabolic processes; localizes enzymes, substrates, and products; and allows cells to become specialized. 2. Organelles effectively divide cellular work, so that incompatible processes can occur simultaneously. This division of labor enables the cell to more quickly respond to changing environments. 3. The proportion of a given organelle can change based on cellular function. For example, a muscle cell may have a more extensive endoplasmic reticulum due to its need to regulate ions; a nerve cell has more plasma membrane to help conduct electrical signals over long distances. **4.4:** 1. Cells tightly regulate what enters and exits the nucleus by the use of nuclear pores. 2. Hereditary information encoded in genes located in the nucleus is transcribed into RNA molecules, some of which specify amino acid sequence in proteins. Amino acid sequence is determined by RNA sequence through translation. Polypeptides produced from RNA are then folded into a three-dimensional structure that has biological function. **4.5:** 1. Rough ER contains ribosomes, while smooth ER does not. Rough ER synthesizes proteins and modifies them, while smooth ER synthesizes lipids, among other activities. 2. Membrane-enclosed organelles work together as part of a larger endomembrane system within the cell. Transport vesicles from the ER proceed to the Golgi apparatus, which modifies their contents and repackages them in new vesicles to be delivered to specific locations within the cell based on a molecular address. Incoming food and other particles are packaged inside vesicles and delivered to lysosomes, which help to break down the food for energy or for building cellular structures. 3. Golgi malfunction would prevent materials from reaching their necessary destinations, disrupting cellular function and likely leading to cell death. **4.6:** 1. Both peroxisomes and lysosomes enclose enzymes; a peroxisome is a metabolic assistant to other organelles; a lysosome digests molecules and can break down cell parts and their component molecules. 2. Peroxisomal proteins are generally made in the cytoplasm and imported into the peroxisome, whereas lysosomal proteins are made in the ER and sent through the Golgi apparatus. Lysosomal proteins are made in the cytoplasm and the ER. Lysosomal proteins are sent to the lysosome via a molecular address. **4.7:** 1. Chloroplasts and mitochondria are similar in size to bacteria, also have multiple membranes, replicate via binary fission, and have circular genomes. 2. ATP is produced during photosynthesis and cellular respiration via proton gradients across

membranes. In photosynthesis, ATP provides the energy necessary to produce sugar; in respiration, ATP is the primary product and is subsequently used in many metabolic processes. **4.8:** 1. Microtubules help maintain cellular shape and provide an internal road system used to transport intracellular materials. Intermediate filaments anchor cells to each other and components in the external environment. Actin filaments are used in some forms of cellular movement. 2. Cilia and flagella are both composed of microtubules arranged in a particular pattern and enclosed by the plasma membrane. Cilia are shorter than flagella. ATP is used to produce cellular movement via microtubules. 3. Cellular movement from microtubules is accomplished via motor molecules that use ATP.

Testing Yourself

1. c; 2. c; 3. d; 4. a; 5. c; 6. c; 7. a; 8. c; 9. b. 10. b; 11. e; 12. a OR d; 13. a; 14. b, mitochondria, because both have double membranes and metabolize energy; c, flagellum, because both require the use of microtubules; d, smooth and rough, because both use membrane-embedded proteins to properly function.

Chapter 5

Check Your Progress

5.1: 1. The plasma membrane is a phospholipid bilayer with cholesterol and embedded proteins. Cholesterol helps maintain membrane fluidity across a range of temperatures. Without cholesterol, membranes would become too fluid at high temperatures and too solid at low temperatures, thus preventing necessary life processes. 2. Proteins are embedded or associated with membranes, creating a mosaic. These proteins influence membrane function. Membranes are considered a fluid mosaic because the phospholipids and membrane proteins can freely move within the membrane. 3. Membrane cores are hydrophobic due to the fatty acid tails of phospholipids. Hydrophobic substances can freely move across the membrane. In contrast, hydrophilic substances require transport mediated by membrane proteins or other mechanisms. **5.2:** 1. Hydrophilic water is able to move across hydrophobic membranes by means of an aquaporin channel protein in membranes. 2. Both move molecules from high to low concentration. Diffusion does not require a membrane or transport proteins, while facilitated transport does. **5.3:** 1. Both require a carrier protein, but active transport also requires energy because unlike facilitated diffusion it moves material against its concentration gradient. 2. Both use vesicles to transport materials across the plasma membrane. Vesicles created as materials enter the cell and reduce membrane surface area, whereas vesicles from the Golgi apparatus increase surface area. The net result of this vesicle traffic is little or no net change in the plasma membrane surface area. **5.4:** 1. The extracellular matrix is composed of polysaccharides and proteins that have a multitude of functions. In addition, the matrix in bone contains mineral salts. 2. A primary cell wall is composed of cellulose and other molecules, such as pectin. Secondary cell walls contain cellulose fibrils and lignin that adds rigidity and strength. 3. Both gap junctions in animals and plasmodesmata in plants allow water and other small molecules to freely pass between adjacent cells.

Testing Yourself

1. a. hypertonic—cell shrinks due to loss of water; **b.** hypotonic—central vacuole expands due to gain of water; **2.** b; **3.** b; **4.** b; **5.** c; **6.** c; **7.** e; **8.** e; **9.** b; **10.** b; **11.** See Figure 5.1, page 86; **12.** b; **13.** e; **14.** d; **15.** a; **16.** e.

Chapter 6

Check Your Progress

6.1: 1. Potential energy is stored in the bonds present within the glucose molecule. 2. It takes energy to clean a messy room. The input of energy helps to create the structure associated with a clean room. However, it takes little time and energy for the room to become disorganized and messy again. This is consistent with the second energy law, which states that every energy transformation increases disorder. Entropy is the tendency toward disorder. **6.2:** 1. ATP holds energy but gives it up because it is unstable and the last phosphate group can be easily removed, releasing energy. 2. ATP can donate a phosphate to energize a compound for a reaction. The addition of a high-energy negatively charged phosphate can change the molecule's shape and in that way bring about a structural change that in turn changes its function. **6.3:** 1. They bring reactants together at their active site or position a substrate so it is ready to react. Because enzymes interact very specifically with their reactants, the products produced from enzymes can be regulated, such as is seen in metabolic pathways. 2. Cofactors provide another level of control that cells use to regulate enzyme products. This control enables the cell to maximize its efficiency and ability to survive. **6.4:** 1. Plants fix carbon dioxide from the air to create carbohydrate molecules used for energy and plant structure. Animals consume plants and break these carbohydrates down to derive energy for life processes, and in so

doing produce carbon dioxide as a by-product. This cyclical relationship between plants and animals is essential to life on Earth. 2. Energized electrons are used to create ATP via proton gradients in plants and animals.

Testing Yourself

1. e; **2.** e; **3.** e; **4.** e; **5.** d; **6.** b; **7. a.** active site; **b.** substrates; **c.** product; **d.** enzyme; **e.** enzyme-substrate complex; **f.** enzyme. The shape of an enzyme is important to its activity because it allows an enzyme-substrate complex to form. **8.** a; **9.** a; **10.** c; **11.** b; **12.** c; **13.** c; **14.** c; **15.** e; **16.** c; **17.** e; **18.** c; **19.** e; **20.** See Figure 6.13, page 115.

Chapter 7

Check Your Progress

Plants, algae, and cyanobacteria. 2. Thylakoid membrane absorbs solar energy, and carbohydrate forms in stroma. **7.2:** 1. O_2 is reduced to CH_2O and when the oxygen in water gives its H_2 ($2 H^+ + 2 e^-$), it is oxidized. 2. Enzymes are used to regulate chemical reactions during photosynthesis. **7.3:** 1. Visible light is a small part of the overall electromagnetic spectrum. It ranges from purple to red light. 2. Low energy electrons within chlorophyll in Photosystem II are excited to a higher energy state by sunlight. The high potential energy of these excited electrons is siphoned off during redox reactions in the electron transport chain, creating proton gradients across the thylakoid membrane. These electrons are excited again to a higher energy state by Photosystem I, which harnesses the energy to create NADPH. **7.4:** 1. A 3-carbon G3P molecule would require 3 turns of the Calvin cycle because each turn adds a carbon molecule. RuBP must also be regenerated in order for the cycle to continue. **7.5:** 1. C_4 plants include many grasses, sugarcane, and corn; CAM plants include cacti, stonecrops, orchids, and bromeliads. 2. C_4 plants prevent oxygen from competing with carbon dioxide for an active site on the enzyme rubisco.

Testing Yourself

1. e; **2.** d; **3.** a; **4.** a, b; **5.** c; **6.** a, b, c; **7.** b; **8.** d; **9.** T; **10.** F; **11.** F; **12.** e; **13.** e; **14.** c; **15.** See Figure 7.5, page 123; **f.** thylakoid membranes; **g.** stroma; **16.** a; **17.** e; **18.** e; **19.** c; **20.** d.

Chapter 8

Check Your Progress

8.1: 1. Step-by-step breakdown allows the released energy to be captured and utilized by

the cell. Rapid breakdown would be destructive to the cell. 2. Glycolysis, the preparatory reaction, the citric acid cycle, and the electron transport chain. The prep reaction and the citric acid cycle release CO_2. ETC produces H_2O. **8.2:** 1. During the energy-investment steps, ATP breakdown provides the phosphate groups to activate substrates. During the energy-harvesting steps, NADH and ATP are produced. 2. ADP and phosphate from the cytoplasm are connected together during substrate-level ATP synthesis via enzymes from glycolysis. **8.3:** 1. In the absence of oxygen, cells derive energy through fermentation by continually regenerating NAD^+ so it can be reduced to NADH during glycolysis. **8.4:** 1. Per glucose molecule, the first 2 CO_2 molecules are produced during the preparatory reaction, and the remaining 4 CO_2 molecules are produced during the citric acid cycle. 2. The electron transport chain produces the most ATP during glycolysis breakdown. 3. A dam holds back water, just as the inner membrane holds back hydrogen ions. As water flows over a dam, electricity is produced. As hydrogen ions flow down their concentration gradient through an ATP synthase complex, ATP is produced. **8.5:** 1. Catabolic and anabolic processes are regulated by enzymes, which allow a cell to respond to environmental changes. 2. Both have an inner membrane (thylakoids in chloroplasts; cristae in mitochondria) where complexes form an ETC, and ATP is produced by chemiosmosis. Both have a fluid-filled interior (in the stroma of chloroplasts, NADPH helps reduce CO_2 to a carbohydrate; and in the matrix of mitochondria, NAD helps oxidize glucose products with the release of CO_2).

Testing Yourself

1. b; **2.** c; **3.** a; **4.** c; **5.** c; **6.** c; **7.** a; **8.** b; **9.** e; **10.** c; **11.** a; **12.** c; **13.** b; **14.** b; **15.** c; **16.** a; **17.** c; **18.** a; **19.** b; **20.** b.

Chapter 9

Check Your Progress

9.1: 1. G_1, S, G_2, and M stage. DNA is replicated during S stage, and cell division occurs during M stage. 2. DNA damage, failure to properly replicate the DNA, and failure of chromosomes to attach properly to spindle. 3. Apoptosis controls the overall density of cells by targeting excess cells, or cells with damage, for cell death.
9.2: 1. Prophase: the nuclear membrane fragments, the nucleus disappears, the chromosomes condense, and the spindle begins to form. Metaphase: the chromosomes align along a central line in the cell. Anaphase: the sister chromatids separate and

head to opposite poles. Telophase: the nuclear envelope re-forms, chromosomes decondense; the spindle disassociates. 2. Animal cells furrow and plant cells have a cell plate. Because plant cells have rigid cell walls, they cannot furrow. 3. Because the number of times most cells can divide is controlled, stem cells provide source material for tissues that need to continuously replace cells. **9.3:** 1. Cancer cells lack differentiation, have abnormal nuclei, fail to undergo apoptosis, may form tumors that may undergo angiogenesis, and may also metastasize throughout the body. 2. Malignant tumor cells enter circulation and lodge in other tissues of the body. Benign tumors remain in the tissue in which they form 3. a. Cell commits to cell division even in the absence of proper stimuli. b. Cell fails to stop dividing because the proper stimuli to stop are absent. **9.4:** 1. Binary fission involves inward growth of plasma membrane and cell wall concomitant with the separation of the duplicated chromosome attached to the plasma membrane. Mitosis always involves a mitotic spindle to distribute the daughter chromosomes. 2. Prokaryotes usually have a single, small circular chromosome with a few genes and only a few associated proteins. Eukaryotes have many long, linear chromosomes, which contain many thousands of genes and many more proteins.

Testing Yourself

1. b; **2.** e; **3.** c; **4.** a; **5.** b; **6.** b; **7.** b; **8.** e; **9.** b; **10.** c; **11.** e; **12.** b; **13.** c; **14.** c; **15.** b; **16.** d; **17.** a; **18.** c; **19.** d; **20. a.** chromatid of chromosome; **b.** centriole; **c.** spindle fiber or aster; **d.** nuclear envelope (fragment); early prophase.

Chapter 10

Check Your Progress

10.1: 1. Homologous chromosomes represent two copies of the same kind of chromosome, each containing the same genes for traits in the same order. They are also similar in length and location of the centromere. 2. Homologous chromosomes replicate prior to meiosis I, producing sister chromatids. When they separate each daughter cell receives one pair of sister chromatids, resulting in a reduction from 2n to n chromosomes. Meiosis II splits the sister chromatids, producing n chromosomes in each daughter cell. 3. A bivalent is formed between homologous chromosomes to enable crossing over and strand exchange. This increases the potential genetic variability of the offspring. **10.2:** 1. Independent assortment of chromosomes increases the number of possible combinations of chromosomes in each gamete. Crossing-over shuffles the alleles between homologous

chromosomes to create even more variation. 2. 2^4 or 16 possible combinations. 3. Genetic variability ensures that at least some individuals have traits that may allow a species to survive adverse conditions. **10.3:** 1. Two daughter cells that share the same parent cell from meiosis I are identical unless crossing-over has occurred. 2. Pairs of homologous chromosomes would not split, resulting in cells with incorrect chromosome combinations. Without proper reduction in chromosome number, offspring would have incorrect chromosome combinations and would likely not survive. **10.4:** 1. In metaphase I of meiosis, homologous chromosomes are paired at the metaphase plate with each homologue facing opposite spindle poles. In metaphase II and mitotic metaphase, homologous chromosomes are not paired, and sister chromatids are attached to spindle fibers from opposite spindle poles. 2. Meiosis II resembles mitosis because sister chromatids are separated during both processes. Meiosis II differs from mitosis because the cells are haploid and not diploid. **10.5:** 1. In males, the primary spermatocytes are located within the testes; in females, the primary oocytes are located within the ovaries. 2. Oogenesis produces a single cell, containing the bulk of the cytoplasm and other cellular contents in the one cell that will undergo embryonic development. Spermatogenesis produces four haploid cells, each of which could potentially merge with the haploid egg to create a diploid organism. **10.6:** 1. Nondisjunction in meiosis may cause aneuploidy, an extra or missing chromosome. 2. Sex chromosome aneuploidy is more common because only one of the X chromosomes is active. Any extra X chromosomes become Barr bodies. 3. An inversion involves the reversal of a piece of a chromosome from within, and normally does not cause symptoms. A translocation is swapping of two chromosome fragments from one to the other, and while not usually troublesome, may cause severe problems in offspring if the two chromosomes go into separate cells.

Testing Yourself

1. b; **2.** d; **3.** e; **4.** b; **5.** d; **6.** c; **7.** e; **8.** b; **9.** d; **10.** 24, 12; **11.** spermatogenesis, oogenesis; **12.** fertilization; **13.** diploid, haploid; **14.** b; **15.** b; **16.** a; **17.** d; **18.** a; **19.** a.

Chapter 11

Check Your Progress

11.1: 1. Mendel chose a good model organism, always followed the same well-planned procedure, kept careful records, and analyzed his data mathematically. 2. The garden pea has easily observed traits, a relatively short generation time, each plant

produces many offspring (peas), and cross pollination is only possible by hand. **11.2A:** 1.a. all W; b. 1/2 W, 1/2 w; c. 1/2 T, 1/2 t; d. all T. 2. bb. 3. 3:1, 40. **11.2B:** 1. LG, Lg, lG, lg. 2. 9:3:3:1. **11.2C:** 1. 75% yellow; 25% green. 2. 25%. 3. Tt x tt; **11.2D:** 1. cc, Cc. 2. 25%. 3. woman: Hh; husband: hh. 4. 50%. **11.3A:** 1. A_1A_2. 2. child: ii; mother: I^Ai; father: I^Ai, I^Bi, or i. **11.3B:** 1. Mother X^BX^b; father, X^BY; female offspring are X^BX^b, and males are X^bY. 2. a. 100%; b. none; c. 100%. 3. X^bX^b mother and X^BY father. Female offspring will be X^BX^b and have black hair and be carriers; male children will be X^bY and have brown hair.

Testing Yourself

1. b; **2.** a; **3.** c; **4.** d; **5.** c; **6.** d; **7.** a; **8.** b; **9.** b; **10.** b; **11.** a; **12.** d; **13.** d; **14.** c; **15.** c; **16.** b; **17.** a; **18.** c; **19.** autosomal dominant.

Answers to Figures

11.10. Individual III-1 must be heterozygous since their offspring IV-1 and IV-2 are homozygous recessive (aa).

11.11. Individual III-1 must be heterozygous since their offspring III-3 is homozygous recessive (aa).

Chapter 12

Check Your Progress

12.1: 1. All life on Earth is based on the same four bases in DNA: A, G, C, and T. Because the genetic code is universal, expressing a foreign gene in an organism is possible. 2. DNA is a right-handed double helix with two strands that run in opposite directions. The backbone is composed of alternating sugar-phosphate groups, and the molecule is held together in the center by hydrogen bonds between interacting bases. A always hydrogen-bonds to T, and G to C. **12.2:** 1. (1) The DNA strands are separated by DNA helicase, (2) new nucleotides are positioned by complementary base pairing, and (3) new nucleotides are joined together by DNA polymerase to form a new DNA strand. 2. Prokaryotic DNA replication begins at a single origin of replication and usually proceeds in both directions toward a termination region on the opposite side of the chromosome. Eukaryotic DNA replication begins at multiple origins of replication and continues until the replication forks meet. 3. Telomerase enables eukaryotic chromosomes to fully replicate by using an RNA template in the enzyme to create repeat sequences on the end of linear chromosomes. **12.3:** 1. Information from a gene coded within the DNA is copied into mRNA. mRNA sequence dictates the sequence of amino acids in a protein, which produces the observable traits for an organism. The flow of genetic information is DNA to RNA to protein to trait. 2. mRNA carries information from DNA to direct the synthesis of a protein. rRNA makes up part of the ribosomes that are used to translate messenger RNAs. tRNA transfers amino acids to the ribosome during protein synthesis. 3. Several different codons may specify the same amino acid.

12.4: 1. Transcription reads the template strand in the 3′ to 5′ direction and produces a complementary mRNA strand that is 5′ to 3′. The mRNA has the same orientation and sequence as the gene strand in the DNA and uses uracil instead of thymine. 2. During mRNA processing introns are spliced out and the exons joined together, and a 5′ guanosine cap and a 3′ poly-A tail are added. 3. A pre-mRNA transcript contains noncoding sequences called introns that are spliced out leaving coding sequences, called exons, in the mature mRNA. 4. If a gene strand in the DNA has the sequence 5′ ATGGGCATT 3′, and a template strand sequence of 5′ AATGCCCAT 3′, the mRNA sequence would be 5′ AUGGGCAUU 3′. 5. The ability to create multiple mRNA molecules from a single gene through alternative splicing enables a cell to create a wider variety of proteins whose diversity may positively affect organism survival.

12.5: 1. Transfer RNA delivers amino acids to the ribosome by binding to the appropriate codon on the mRNA being translated. 2. A ribosome consists of a small and large subunit. Each subunit is composed of a mixture of protein and rRNA. Large and small ribosomal subunits work to connect amino acids together in a sequence dictated by the mRNA. 3. Initiation: All components of the translational complex, including the first tRNA carrying methionine, are assembled. Elongation: Amino acids are delivered one by one as tRNA molecules pair with the codons on the mRNA. Termination: A stop codon is reached, a release factor binds to it, and the completed protein is cleaved from the last tRNA as the ribosomal subunits dissociate. **12.6:** 1. Euchromatin may exist in a compact or open configuration. A compact chromatin structure prevents regulatory proteins needed for gene expression from accessing gene control elements. An open configuration allows gene expression to occur.

Testing Yourself

1. c; **2.** a; **3.** c; **4.** b; **5.** d; **6.** e; **7.** b; **8. a.** GGA GGA CUU ACG UUU; **b.** CCU CCU GAA UGC AAA; **c.** glycine-glycine-leucine-threonine-phenylalanine; **9.** d; **10.** a; **11.** a; **12.** a; **13.** c; **14.** d; **15.** d.

Chapter 13

Check Your Progress

13.1: 1. An operon is a group of genes that are regulated in a coordinated manner; a promotor is a regulatory region that controls the initiation of transcription. 2. In a repressible operon, the operon is normally on and is turned off by the action of a repressor. In an inducible operon, the operon is normally off and is turned on by an environmental condition. 3. A gene under positive control is transcribed when it is regulated by a protein that is an activator and not a repressor, whereas one under negative control is not transcribed when it is regulated by a protein that is a repressor. **13.2:** 1. Chromatin, transcriptional, posttranscriptional, translational, and posttranslational. 2. Packing genes into heterochromatin inactivates a gene, whereas it is genetically active when held in loosely packed euchromatin. 3. siRNA molecules participate in posttranscriptional regulation while proteosomes are active in posttranslational regulation.

13.3: 1. Spontaneous: errors in DNA replication and natural chemical changes in the bases in DNA; Induced: organic chemicals and physical mutagens like X-rays and UV radiation. 2. Mutations in these genes disrupt the normal operation of the checkpoints in the cell cycle, allowing cell division to proceed without regulation.

Testing Yourself

1. a; **2.** e; **3.** a; **4.** b; **5.** d; **6.** e; **7.** b; **8.** b; **9.** b; **10.** b; **11.** b; **12.** e; **13.** e; **14.** e; **15. a.** DNA; **b.** regulator gene; **c.** promoter; **d.** operator; **e.** active repressor; **16.** c; **17.** d; **18.** d; **19.** d.

Chapter 14

Check Your Progress

14.1: 1. To create an rDNA molecule, a piece of foreign DNA is cut with restriction enzymes and mixed with a plasmid vector cut with the same restriction enzyme. The DNAs are mixed together and DNA ligase is added to seal the molecule. Then, it can be inserted into bacteria. 2. DNA molecules amplified by PCR can be used to create DNA profiles, or fingerprints, enabling paternity testing and forensic DNA analysis, among other applications. 3. Patterns in DNA fingerprinting can be analyzed to identify the source of a DNA sample. **14.2:** 1. Bacteria: production of medicine and drugs, bioengineering, production of organic chemicals; Animals: gene pharming, studying human disease; Plants: increased food production, production of human medicines. 2. A transgenic animal contains recombinant DNA molecules in addition to its genome, whereas a cloned animal is genetically identical to the one from which it was created, but does not contain rDNA. **14.3:** 1. Liposomes, nasal sprays, and adenoviruses are currently being used to deliver genes to cells for gene therapy. 2. Ex vivo gene therapy is being used to treat SCID and familial hypercholesterolemia. In vivo gene therapy is being used to treat cystic fibrosis. **14.4:** 1. The genome is the sum of all of the genes in a cell whereas the proteome represents the sum of all of the proteins encoded by the genome. The proteome is typically bigger than the genome. 2. A tandem repeat consists of repeated sequences that are one next to the other, whereas transposons are short sequences of DNA that may move within the genome. 3. Microarrays allow scientists to analyze the expression of genes under different environmental conditions. Bioinformatics allows scientists to rapidly analyze experimental data and generate large databases of information.

Testing Yourself

1. c; **2.** c; **3.** e; **4.** d; **5.** e; **6.** c; **7.** e; **8.** a; **9.** c; **10.** a; **11.** b; **12.** d; **13.** e; **14.** d; **15.** e; **16.** a; **17.** d.

Chapter 15

Check Your Progress

15.1: 1. Catastrophism (Cuvier) explains a change in the fossil record by mass extinctions in an area replaced by a new set of species after a catastrophe. 2. Lamarck's inheritance of acquired characteristics is flawed as an explanation of biological diversity because features acquired by an individual during his/her lifetime are not heritable to offspring. Evolution occurs only in traits that are heritable. 3. 1707-1778 Linnaeus (classification); 1731-1802 E. Darwin (first theory of evolution); 1769-1832 Cuvier (catastrophism); 1744-1829 Lamarck (acquired characteristics); 1797-1875 Lyell (uniformitarianism); 1831-1836 voyage of H.M.S *Beagle*; 1859 Darwin publishes *Origin of Species*. **15.2:** 1. Fossils, biogeography, change over time (geology). 2. Individuals have variation that is heritable; organisms compete for resources; differential reproductive success; adaptation to environmental change. 3. Evolution can occur over the span of a human lifetime. One example is artificial selection, which can modify plants and animals through selective breeding. Another are beaks of the Galápagos Islands finches, which were observed to evolve between wet and dry seasons over decades. **15.3:** 1. Biomolecules may change over time as a result of natural selection. Examples are the cytochrome *c* protein in cellular metabolism and the homeobox, or *Hox*, genes that have been shaped by natural selection to orchestrate the development of the body plan in animals. 2. Homologous structures are those that are shared because of common ancestry. Analogous structures are shared because of convergent evolution and do not tell us anything about common ancestry. 3. Transitional fossils represent intermediate evolutionary forms of life in transition from one type to another, or a common ancestor of these types. *Tiktaalik* and *Basilosaurus* are examples of intermediate fossils. 4. (One of the following) a. *Evolution is a theory about how life originated.* Evolution is concerned with how life evolved AFTER the origin of life. b. *There are no transitional fossils.* Not all fossils will ever be found because of the nature of how organisms are preserved and discovered. c. *Evolution proposes that life-forms changed as a result of random events.* New variation arises due to random processes, but natural selection is not a random process; it can only shape pre-existing variation. d. *Evolution is not observable or testable.* Evolution is both observable and testable. Many studies show how traits change in response to environmental pressures. There are examples of evolution over long periods of time, and over short periods of time.

Testing Yourself

1. d; 2. e; 3. b; 4. e; 5. e; 6. e; 7. b, c, d, e; 8. b, d, e; 9. c; 10. d, e; 11. b; 12. Life has a history, and it's possible to trace the history of individual organisms. 13. Two different continents can have similar environments, and therefore unrelated organisms that are similarly adapted. 14. All vertebrates share a common ancestor that had pharyngeal pouches during development. 15. Similarities are expected because all species share recent and distant common ancestors. DNA base difference through the occurrence of mutations accounts for the diversity of life.

Chapter 16

Check Your Progress

16.1: 1. a. Random mating, allele frequencies do not change. b. No selection, allele frequencies change. c. No mutation, allele frequencies change. d. No migration, allele frequencies change. e. Large population (no genetic drift), allele frequencies change. 2. AA = p^2 = 0.01, Aa = 2pq = 0.18, aa = q^2 = 0.81. **16.2:** 1. Females produce large gametes and have a large investment in eggs so are choosy about their mates. Males produce many small, inexpensive gametes, and value females as a resource for reproduction, resulting in competition for access to females (mates). 2. Sexual selection is a form of natural selection because traits associated with mating determine whether or not traits are passed on to the next generation. 3. See Figure 16.10 on page 297. **16.3:** 1. Mutation, sexual reproduction, genetic drift. 2. In Africa where malaria is

common, being a heterozygote for the sickle-cell trait is advantageous because it provides some resistance to malaria. Those who are homozygous for normal trait get malaria without natural resistance; those homozygous for the sickle-cell trait die young from sickle-cell disease. Heterozygotes for the cystic fibrosis trait have resistance to typhoid fever. As with sickle-cell trait, heterozygotes are maintained because of stabilizing selection that selects against homozygotes for the cystic fibrosis trait (who have the disease) and homozygous normal trait (who get typhoid fever). 3. The dominant allele (*p*) and the recessive allele (*q*) must be present in the previous generation in order for the heterozygote (*pq*) to appear in the next generation.

Testing Yourself

1. c; 2. c; 3. c; 4. c; 5. e; 6. b; 7. c; 8. e; 9. d; 10. c; 11. a; 12. e; 13. b; 14. e.

Chapter 17

Check Your Progress

17.1: 1. Pre-zygotic reproductive isolation. 2. (Three of the following) Biological species concept: Individuals of a population cannot interbreed. Phylogenetic species concept: Two populations are on different evolutionary lineages in a phylogeny that are monophyletic. Morphological species concept: A species is defined by a diagnostic trait (or traits). Evolutionary species concept: Relies on identification of certain morphological diagnostic traits that define a different evolutionary pathway. 3. If the frogs cannot recognize each other as mates, they will be reproductively isolated. **17.2:** 1. Show that each of the cats is adapted to a different environment. 2. In a newly discovered African Rift Valley lake, you would expect to see in the fishes the same shape of head and teeth for feeding in similar habitats as those observed in other lakes. Similar forms would evolve independently in this new lake—each of which would match the form of a fish that feeds in the same habitat in a different lake. 3. Allopatric speciation. **17.3:** 1. Punctuated equilibrium model proposes periods of rapid evolution and periods of little evolution (stasis). Cuvier proposed that this pattern in the fossil record was because new groups of organisms moved into an area after a mass extinction (catastrophe). 2. *Hox* genes have a powerful effect on development and offer a mechanism by which evolution could occur rapidly. 3. A change in *Pax*6 gene expression shows that changes in the genes that regulate body organization can produce rapid change in an organism, leading to speciation.

Testing Yourself

1. c; 2. e; 3. c; 4. e; 5. a. species 1; b. geographic barrier; c. genetic changes; d. species 2; e. genetic changes; f. species 3; 6. b; 7. b; 8. b; 9. d; 10. d; 11. b; 12. b; 13. b; 14. b; 15. d; 16. b; 17. c; 18. c.

Chapter 18

Check Your Progress

18.1: 1. a. Methane, ammonia, hydrogen, water environment: Recreated by Miller-Urey; b. Reducing atmosphere: Electric spark and chemical reactions. 2. a. Iron-sulfur world hypothesis: Iron-nickel sulfides at thermal vents act as catalysts to join organic molecules. b. Protein-first hypothesis: Amino acids collected in small pools and the heat of the Sun formed protenoids, small polypeptides with catalytic properties. c. RNA-first hypothesis: RNA carried out the processes commonly associated with DNA and proteins before either of these evolved. 3. Protocell: single fatty acid hydrophilic tail; modern cell: double fatty acid hydrophilic tail; Protocell: membrane of a single layer of fatty acids; modern cell: bilayer of phospholipids. **18.2A:** 1. Elements that are radioactive decay at a constant rate of time. The half-life is how long it takes for 1/2 of the number of molecules of an element to decay. If we know how much of the radioactive and decayed isotopes of an element we have left, we can estimate the number of years it took for the element to decay since the organism died. 2. Chemical evolution, evolution of first cells, evolution of eukaryotic cells by endosymbiosis, and first heterotrophic protists before photosynthetic protists. 3. DNA content and double-membrane structure of the mitochondria and chloroplasts. **18.2B:** 1. a. Eukaryote cells arise; b. Multicellular organisms arise. 2. The presence of an exoskeleton. **18.2C:** 1. a. Evolution of flowering plants; b. Reptiles undergo an adaptive radiation; c. Dinosaurs go extinct. 2. Flowering plants, conifers, birds, dinosaurs, placental mammals. **18.3:** 1. The theory of plate tectonics says that the Earth's crust is fragmented into slab-like plates that float on a lower hot mantle layer. Growth of mountains, earthquakes and the layout of the continents are all evidence. 2. Distribution of animals would be similar on continents that were once joined together. Marsupials in South America and Australia are an example. 3. Ordovician: continental drift and cooling of the Earth; Devonian: bolide, or impact of a meteorite with the Earth; Permian: excess carbon dioxide; Triassic: meteorite collision with Earth; Cretaceous: bolide, or impact of an asteroid with the Earth.

Testing Yourself

1. c; 2. d; 3. a; 4. b; 5. e; 6. b; 7. c; 8. b; 9. b;
10. e; 11. e; 12. b; 13. c; 14. d; 15. a; 16. c;
17. c; 18. e; 19. c; 20. d.

Chapter 19

Check Your Progress

19.1: 1. Domain: Eukarya; Kingdom: Animalia; Phylum: Chordata; Class: Mammalia; Order: Primates; Family: Hominidae; Genus: *Homo*; Species: *Homo sapiens*. 2. Wings in birds and bats are analogous because they have independent evolutionary origins. Thus, birds and bats are not a natural group. 3. Classification is the naming of organisms; taxonomy is the assignment of groups to a taxon; systematic biology is the study of classification and taxonomy, or more generally, the study of biodiversity. **19.2:** 1. Archaea have differences in their rRNA, in their cell wall structure, and in the lipids in their plasma membrane. 2. Molecular data (RNA/DNA sequence data) indicates that fungi are related to animals. 3. Eukarya. **19.3:** 1. Answers may vary. Refer to the material on cladistics (page 356) and Figure 19.7 for examples. 2. Ancestral traits are found in the common ancestor of a lineage and may be present in the descendants. Derived traits are found in the descendants but not in the common ancestor. 3. The phylogeny that requires the fewest number of evolutionary steps is the most parsimonious explanation of evolutionary history, and is thus the best hypothesis.

Testing Yourself

1. e; 2. e; 3. d; 4. a, b, c; 5. c, d, e; 6. b, c, d, e; 7. a; 8. c; 9. a; 10. d; 11. b; 12. e; 13. b.

Chapter 20

Check Your Progress

20.1: 1. All viruses have a nucleic acid and a capsid. 2. Viroids and prions are nonliving because, like viruses, they are noncellular and unable to reproduce without a host. 3. A virus consists of both nucleic acids and proteins, whereas a prion is composed of just protein. 4. If a virus's host survives, many more copies of the virus will be produced and spread to other hosts than if the host dies. **20.2:** 1. Bacteria exist in the air and sterilization kills bacteria. 2. The bacterial nucleoid is not surrounded by a membrane; the eukaryote nucleus has its own membrane 3. Transduction: movement of genetic material from one bacterium to another via a virus; transformation: pick up and incorporate genetic material from the

environment; conjugation: exchange genetic material between bacteria. **20.3:** 1. The peptidoglycan layer is much thicker in Gram-positive cells. In Gram-negative cells this layer is thinner and is located between layers of the plasma membrane. 2. By inhibiting protein synthesis or construction of the cell wall. 3. Endospores permit survival when environmental conditions are harsh. 4. Cyanobacteria are considered responsible for the production of an oxygen-rich atmosphere. **20.4:** 1. Archaea and bacteria differ in their rRNA base sequences, and their plasma membranes and cell walls are biochemically distinct. 2. Methanogens, halophiles, and thermoacidophiles. 3. Archaea and eukaryotes share some of the same ribosomal proteins, initiate transcription in the same way, and have similar tRNA.

Testing Yourself

1. **a.** attachment; **b.** penetration;
c. integration; **d.** prophage; **e.** biosynthesis;
f. maturation; **g.** release; 2. e; 3. e; 4. b; 5. a;
6. c; 7. d; 8. a; 9. c; 10. c; 11. c; 12. c; 13. a;
14. e; 15. e; 16. a; 17. a; 18. b; 19. d.

Chapter 21

Check Your Progress

21.1: 1. Endosymbiosis; mitochondria and chloroplasts were free-living bacteria that were engulfed and incorporated into a eukaryotic protocell. 2. Algae are photoautotrophs; they get their food from photosynthesis; protozoans are heterotrophs and ingest their food from the environment. 3. a. Archaeplastids; b. Opisthokonts. **21.2A:** 1. Haploid stage is the asexual stage of reproduction; diploid is the sexual phase. 2. Accessory pigments allow for the absorption of energy from light of different wavelengths. **21.2B:** 1. Their DNA base sequences are similar, and their ancestor had a flagellum. 2. Brown algae: *Macrocystis, Laminaria, Nereocystis;* Diatoms: *Cyclotella;* Golden brown algae: *Ochromonas.* **21.2C:** 1. Refer to the summary boxes in Fig. 21.15 on page 394. 2. Brown comes from a carotenoid pigment. 3. Aveolates possess small air sacs (alveoli) beneath their plasma membrane, all are unicellular. **21.2D:** 1. Excavates have atypical or absent mitochondria and distinctive flagella and/or deep oral grooves. 2. Parasitic: parabasalids, diplomads, kinetoplastids; free-living: euglenids. 3. Trypanosome: African sleeping sickness and Chagas disease; *Giardia:* giardiasis; *Trichomonas:* vaginitis. **21.2E:** 1. Opisthokonts move using flagella; rhizarians and amoebozoans move using pseudopods. 2. Opisthokonts are multicellular protozoans, animal-like with a flagellum.

Testing Yourself

1. f; 2. c; 3. c; 4. a; 5. b; 6. e; 7. b; 8. b; 9. e;
10. e; 11. d; 12. d; 13. b; 14. b; 15. a; 16. b;
17. c; 18. c; 19. a. sexual reproduction;
b. gametes pairing; c. zygote (2n);
d. zygospore (2n); e. asexual reproduction;
f. zoospores (n); g. nucleus with nucleolus;
h. chloroplast; i. starch granule; j. pyrenoid;
k. flagellum; l. eyespot; m. gamete formation.
See also Figure 21.5, page 388.

Chapter 22

Check Your Progress

22.1: 1. Animals are heterotrophs: they get their nutrition by consuming outside nutrients. Fungi are saprotrophs: they externally digest organic material and absorb nutrients. 2. Plant cell walls are made of cellulose; fungal cell walls are made of chitin. 3. Reproductive structure that can form a new organism without fusing with another reproductive cell. **22.2:** 1. Chitrids are the only fungi to have flagellated cells. 2. Peach leaf curl: *Taphrina;* ergot: *Claviceps;* athletes' foot: *Trichophyton* (tinea); candidiasis: *Candida;* fungal flu: *Histoplasma.* 3. Black mold: *Rhizopus;* ergot: *Claviceps;* athlete's foot: *Trichophyton* (tinea). **22.3:** 1. Lichen has a sac fungus and either a cyanobacterium or green alga. 2. Lichens reproduce asexually by releasing fragments that contain hyphae and an algal cell. In fruticose lichens, the sac fungus reproduces asexually. 3. Fungus enters the cortex of the roots of plants, giving the plants a greater absorptive surface.

Testing Yourself

1. d; 2. b; 3. c; 4. c; 5. b; 6. e; 7. e; 8. a; 9. c;
10. a; 11. c; 12. a; 13. d; 14. a. spores;
b. sporangium; c. sporangiophore; d. stolon;
e. rhizoid; 15. a; 16. e; 17. e; 18. d; 19. e;
20. a. meiosis; b. basidiospores; c. dikaryotic mycelium; d. button stage of the mushroom (basidiocarp); e. stalk; f. gill; g. cap;
h. dikaryotic; i. diploid; j. zygote. See also Figure 22.9, page 412.

Chapter 23

Check Your Progress

23.1: 1. Plentiful light and CO_2. 2. A cellulose cell wall produced in same way; apical cells that produce new tissue; plasmodesmata between cells; transfer of nutrients from haploid cells of previous generation to zygote of new generation. 3. The diploid sporophyte produces haploid spores by meiosis. The haploid gametophyte produces gametes. **23.2:** 1. Bryophytes have a dominant gametophyte generation, produce flagellated sperm that swim to the egg, and can also reproduce asexually. 2. Asexual and sexual reproduction, ability to survive in harsh environments, sporophyte is protected from drying out. 3. The gametophyte portion is most important. The sporophyte is dependent upon the gametophyte. **23.3:** 1. In lycophytes, the dominant sporophyte has vascular tissue, and therefore roots, stems, and leaves. 2. The walls of xylem contains lignin, a strengthening agent. **23.4:** 1. The independent gametophyte generation lacks vascular tissue, and it produces flagellated sperm. 2. In ferns, but not mosses, the sporophyte is dominant and separate from the gametophyte. **23.5:** 1. (1) Water is not required for fertilization because pollen grains (male gametophytes) are windblown, and (2) ovules protect female gametophytes and become seeds that disperse the sporophyte, the generation that has vascular tissue. 2. Conifers: cone bearing and evergreen; cycads: cone bearing, evergreen and wind pollinated; ginkgoes: cone bearing, deciduous; gnetophytes: cone bearing and insect pollinated. 3. The stamen contains the anther and the filament. Pollen forms in the pollen sac of the anther. The carpel contains the stigma, style, and ovary. An ovule in the ovary becomes a seed, and the ovary becomes the fruit. 4. Gymnosperms: cone-bearing, such as cycads, ginkoes, gnetophytes and pine trees. 5. Animal-pollinated flowers are showy in a variety of ways, such as color and fragrance to attract their particular pollinators. Wind-pollinated plants are not very showy.

Testing Yourself

1. e; **2.** a; **3.** b; **4.** c; **5.** b; **6.** b; **7.** e; **8.** c; **9.** c; **10.** e; **11.** d; **12.** b; **13.** a; **14.** b; **15.** b; **16.** e; **17.** c; **18. a.** sporophyte (2n); **b.** meiosis; **c.** gametophyte (n); **d.** fertilization. See also Figure 23.3, page 422.

Chapter 24

Check Your Progress

24.1: 1. Vegetative organs are the leaves (photosynthesis), the stem (support, new growth, transport), and the root (absorb water and minerals). 2. Monocots: embryo with single cotyledon; xylem and phloem in a ring in the root; scattered vascular bundles in the stem; parallel leaf veins; flower parts in multiples of three. Eudicots: embryo with two cotyledons; phloem located between arms of xylem in the root; vascular bundles in a ring in the stem; netted leaf veins; flower parts in multiples of fours or fives. **24.2:** 1. Epidermal tissue: epidermal cells; ground tissue: parenchyma, collenchyma, and sclerenchyma cells; vascular tissue: xylem (vessel elements and tracheids) and phloem (sieve-tube members). 2. Xylem transports water and

minerals usually from roots to leaves. Phloem transports organic compounds throughout the plant. **24.3:** 1. The root apical meristem is located at the tip of the root and is covered by the root cap. 2. Cortex: food storage; endodermis: control of mineral uptake; pericycle: formation of branch roots. **24.4:** 1. A vascular bundle contains xylem and phloem. 2. Vascular bundles are scattered in monocot stems and form a ring in eudicot stems. 3. Primary growth is growth in length and is nonwoody; secondary growth is growth in girth and is woody. 4. Bark is composed of cork, cork cambium, cortex, and phloem. 5. An annual ring is composed of one year's growth of wood—one layer of spring wood followed by one layer of summer wood. **24.5:** 1. Photosynthesis, which produces organic food for a plant, occurs in the mesophyll. 2. The palisade mesophyll contains elongated cells that run photosynthesis; the spongy mesophyll contains irregular cells that increase the surface area for gas exchange. 3. Leaves can be simple with a single blade or compound, which is divided into many leaflets. Pinnate leaves have leaflets occurring in pairs while palmately compound leaves have all the leaflets attached at a single point. Leaves are adapted for environmental conditions.

Testing Yourself

1. c; **2.** b; **3.** c; **4.** c; **5.** b; **6.** b; **7.** b; **8.** c; **9.** c; **10.** b; **11.** d; **12.** e; **13.** d; **14.** d; **15.** d; **16.** c; **17.** c; **18.** a; **19. a.** epidermis; **b.** cortex; **c.** endodermis; **d.** phloem; **e.** xylem. See also Figure 24.8, page 451; **20. a.** upper epidermis; **b.** palisade mesophyll; **c.** leaf vein; **d.** spongy mesophyll; **e.** lower epidermis. See also Figure 24.20, page 459.

Chapter 25

Check Your Progress

25.1: 1. a. Nitrogen and sulfur are needed to form protein. All plant roots take up nitrate (NO_3^-) and sulfate (SO_4^{2-}) from the soil. b. Nitrogen and phosphate (HPO_4^{2-}) are needed to make nucleic acids. Plant roots also take up phosphate from the soil. 2. (1) Helps prevent soil erosion; (2) helps retain moisture; and (3) as the remains decompose, nutrients are returned to the soil. 3. Humus improves soil aeration, soil texture, increases water-holding capacity, decomposes to release nutrients for plant growth, and helps retain positively charged minerals and make them available for plant uptake. **25.2:** 1. The nonpolar tails of phospholipid molecules make the center of the plasma membrane nonpolar. 2. The bacteria convert atmospheric nitrogen to nitrate or ammonium, which can be taken up by plant roots. 3. The fungus

obtains sugars and amino acids from the plant. The plant obtains inorganic nutrients and water from the fungus. **25.3:** 1. Evaporation of water from leaf surfaces causes water to be under tension in stems due to the cohesion of the water molecules. 2. When water molecules are pulled upward during transpiration, their cohesiveness creates a continuous water column. Adhesion allows water molecules to cling to the sides of xylem vessels, so the column of water does not slip down. 3. Sugars enter sieve tubes at sources, creating pressure as water flows in as well. The pressure is relieved at the other end when sugars and water are removed at the sink.

Testing Yourself

1. d; **2.** e; **3.** a; **4.** c; **5.** d; **6.** c; **7.** d; **8.** a; **9.** b; **10.** c; **11.** d; **12.** b; **13.** a; **14.** c; **15.** e; **16.** a; **17.** The diagram shows that air pressure pushing down on mercury in the pan can raise a column of mercury only to 76 cm. When water above the column is transpired, it pulls on the mercury and raises it higher than 76 cm. This suggests that transpiration would be able to raise water to the tops of trees. **18.** e; **19. a.** See Figure 25.13, page 477. **b.** After K^+ enters guard cells, water follows by osmosis and the stoma opens. **20.** There is more solute in bulb 1 than in bulb 2; therefore water enters bulb 1. This creates a positive pressure that causes water, along with solute, to flow toward bulb 2.

Chapter 26

Check Your Progress

26.1: 1. Hormones coordinate the responses of plants to stimuli. 2. You could apply gibberellins to induce growth and cytokinins to increase the number of cells. 3. ABA maintains dormancy and closes stomata. **26.2:** 1. It is adaptive for roots to grow toward water because it enhances their ability to extract water and dissolved minerals from the soil for plant tissues. 2. Positive geotropism is when part of a plant grows downward in response to gravity. Negative geotropism is when a plant grows upward against gravity. 3. Phytochrome is composed of two proteins that contain light-sensitive regions. When triggered by red light phytochrome causes various genes to become active or inactive leading to seed germination, shoot elongation and flowering responses. 4. The plant is responding to a short night, not to the length of the day. 5. Plants have (1) physical and chemical defenses (e.g., secondary metabolites); (2) wound responses (e.g., proteinase inhibitors); (3) hypersensitive responses (e.g., sealing off of infected areas);

and (4) relationships with animals (e.g., acacia with ants).

Testing Yourself

1. c; **2.** a; **3.** d; **4.** e; **5.** d; **6.** b; **7.** e; **8.** a; **9.** c; **10.** c; **11.** d; **12.** e; **13.** b **14.** e; **15.** d.

Chapter 27

Check Your Progress

27.1: 1. Male gametophytes are produced in the anther of the stamen. The female gametophyte is produced in an ovule within the ovary of the carpel. 2. Each microspore produces a two-celled pollen grain. The generative cell produces two sperm, and the tube cell produces a pollen tube. One of the four megaspores produces a seven-celled female gametophyte, called the embryo sac, within the ovule. 3. In order to accommodate the larger size of the pollinator, natural selection in the flowering plant may lead to an increase in the structural support of the part that the pollinator lands upon. It may also lead to an increase in the size of the flower to accommodate a larger pollinator. **27.2:** 1. The embryo is derived from the zygote; the stored food is derived from the endosperm; and the seed coat is derived from the ovule wall. 2. The ovule is a sporophyte structure produced by the female parent. Therefore, the wall (which becomes seed coat) is 2n. The embryo inside the ovule is the product of fertilization and is, therefore, 2n. 3. Cotyledons are embryonic leaves that are present in seeds. Cotyledons store nutrients derived from endosperm (in eudicots). **27.3:** 1. Dry fruits, with a dull, thin, and dry covering derived from the ovary, are more apt to be windblown. Fleshy fruits, with a juicy covering derived from the ovary and possibly other parts of the flower, are more apt to be eaten by animals. 2. Eudicot seedlings have a hook shape, and monocot seedlings have a sheath to protect the first true leaves. **27.4:** 1. Advantages to asexual reproduction include: (1) the newly formed plant is often supported nutritionally by the parent plant until it is established; (2) if the parent is ideally suited for the environment, the offspring will be as well; and (3) if distance between individuals make cross-pollination unlikely, asexual reproduction is a good alternative. 2. For example, stolons and rhizomes produce new shoots and roots; fruit trees produce suckers; and stem cuttings grow new roots and become a shoot system. 3. Tissue from leaves, meristem, and anthers can become whole plants in tissue culture.

Testing Yourself

1. d; **2.** a; **3.** b; **4.** a; **5.** a; **6.** a; **7.** e; **8.** d; **9.** b; **10.** e; **11.** c; **12.** a; **13.** b; **14.** e; **15. a.** diploid; **b.** anther; **c.** ovule; **d.** ovary; **e.** haploid;

f. megaspore; **g.** male; **h.** female; **i.** sperm; **j.** seed. See also Figure 27.1, page 502.

Chapter 28

Check Your Progress

28.1: 1. Multicellular, usually with specialized tissues, ingest food, diploid life cycle. 2. Animals are descended from an ancestor that resembled a hollow spherical colony of flagellated cells. Individual cells became specialized for reproduction. Two tissue layers arose by invagination. 3. Deuterostomes: blastopore becomes anus, radial cleavage, coelum forms from gut; Protostomes: blastopore becomes mouth, spiral cleavage, coelom forms from mesoderm. **28.2:** 1. Sponges are multicellular; no symmetry; no digestive cavity. Cnidarians have true tissues; radial symmetry; have a gastrovascular cavity. 2. Interior of sponges has canals lined with flagellated cells called choanocytes. Flagella produce water current that carries food particles that are filtered out. 3. Polyps have mouths directed upward, medusae are bell-shaped with tentacles around the opening of the bell and mouth downward. 4. Stinging cells called cnidocytes have a fluid-filled capsule called a nematocyst in which a hollow threadlike structure is coiled and is discharged when stimulated. Some trap prey, others contain paralyzing toxins. **28.3:** 1. They all have bilateral symmetry, three tissue layers, and protostome development. They have no body plan, coelom, or any sort of nervous tissue. 2. Annelids and molluscs have a complete digestive tract, a true coelom, and a circulatory system (closed in annelids and open in molluscs). Flatworms have a gastrovascular cavity with only one opening, no coelom, and no circulatory system. 3. Tapeworm, *Taenia*. Host ingests meat with bladder worms; worms attach to intestine and mature; proglottids mature and fill with eggs; eggs leave host in feces; eggs ingested by livestock; worms encysted in muscle of livestock and eaten by host. Blood fluke: *Schistosoma*. Larvae penetrate skin of human, mature in liver; adult worms live and mate in blood vessels of gut; eggs migrate into digestive tract, passed in feces; ciliated larvae hatch in water, enter the snail; larvae emerge from snails, enter skin of humans. 4. Bryozoa, Phoronida, Brachopoda. **28.4:** 1. Roundworms and arthropods are the molting protostomes. They both have a true coelom. 2. Crustaceans breathe by gills and have swimmerets. Insects breathe by tracheae, and they may have wings. 3. The first pair of appendages is the chelicerae (modified fangs), and the second pair is the pedipalps (hold, taste, chew food). **28.5:** 1. The larval stage is bilaterally

symmetrical. 2. The water vascular system functions in locomotion, feeding, gas exchange, and sensory reception.

Testing Yourself

1. d; **2** e; **3.** e; **4.** e; **5.** d; **6.** b; **7.** a; **8.** c; **9.** a; **10. a.** tapeworm; **b.** mollusc; **c.** sponge; **d.** cnidaria; **e.** rotifer; **f.** flatworm; **g.** arthropod; **11.** b; **12.** b; **13.** a; **14.** e; **15.** e.

Chapter 29

Check Your Progress

29.1: 1. Humans are chordates, and they have the four chordate characteristics during the embryonic period of their life cycle. Notochord: replaced by vertebral column during development. Dorsal tubular nerve cord becomes the spinal cord. Pharyngeal pouches: the first pair of pouches develops into auditory tubes. Post-anal tail: is present in developing embryo, but lost during development. 2. A sea squirt larva has the four characteristics as a larva, then undergoes metamorphosis to become an adult, which has gill slits but none of the other characteristics. **29.2:** 1. Endoskeleton protects internal organs, provides a place of attachment for muscles, permits rapid, efficient movement. 2. Four legs are useful for locomotion on land where the body is not supported by water. **29.3:** 1. All fishes are aquatic vertebrates and ectothermic. They all live in water, breathe by gills, and have a single circulatory loop (Fig. 29.11*a*, page 556). 2. Ray-finned bony fishes have fan-shaped fins supported by thin, bony rays. Lobe-finned bony fishes have fleshy fins supported by bones. **29.4:** 1. a. Paired limbs; smooth, nonscaly skin that stays moist; lungs; a three-chambered heart with a double-loop circulatory pathway; sense organs adapted for a land environment; ectothermic; and have aquatic reproduction. b. Lobe-finned fishes and amphibians both have lungs and internal nares that allow them to breathe air. The same bones are present in the front fins of the lobe-finned fishes as in the forelimbs of early amphibians. 2. Usually, amphibians carry out external fertilization in the water. The embryos develop in the eggs until the tadpoles emerge. They then undergo metamorphosis, growing legs and reabsorbing the tail, and become adults. **29.5:** 1. Alligators live in fresh water and have a thick skin, two pairs of legs, powerful jaws, and a long muscular tail that allow them to capture and eat other animals that are in the water or come to the water's edge. Snakes have no limbs and have relatively thin skin. They live close to or in the ground and can escape detection. They use smell (Jacobson's organ) and vibrations to detect prey. Some use venom to subdue prey, which they eat whole because their jaws are distensible. 2. Birds are reptiles: feathers are modified scales; birds have clawed feet and a tail that contains vertebrae. **29.6:** 1. Mammals have hair or fur and mammary glands, endothermy, limbs under body, differentiated teeth, and an enlarged brain. 2. The three groups of mammals are monotremes (have a cloaca and lay eggs), marsupials (young are born immature and finish development in a pouch), and placental (eutherians) mammals (development occurs internally and the fetus is nourished by placenta).

Testing Yourself

1. e; 2. a; 3. c; 4. e; 5. a; 6. e; 7. b; 8. b; 9. e; 10. c; 11. a; 12. a; 13. a. pharyngeal pouches; b. dorsal tubular nerve cord; c. notochord; d. postanal tail; 14. d; 15. d.

Chapter 30

Check Your Progress

30.1: 1. Refer to Figure 30.4 on page 573, focusing on the bars on the right of the figure. 2. Both humans and chimpanzees are hominines and they share similar structure of their genomes, plus the general characteristics of all primates. **30.2:** 1. Ardipithecines lived primarily in trees, whereas the australopiths lived both in and out of trees. The brain size of the australopiths was larger, and this group was better adapted for bipedalism. **30.3:** 1. Increasing size of brain cavity, increased height, eventual use of tools and fire. 2. Bipedalism allowed for organisms to move young more easily, increased brain size allowed for higher intellect and thus adaptation to non-forest environments. **30.4:** 1. The replacement model suggests that humans evolved from one group in Africa, and then migrated to other locations. This means that different groups of Cro-Magnon humans could adapt to different locations, eventually forming the major human ethnic groups. 2. Increased brain size and reliance on tool use and a hunter-gatherer lifestyle required development of communication.

Testing Yourself

1. c; 2. b; 3. b; 4. e; 5. c; 6. d; 7. b; 8. c; 9. c; 10. c; 11. T; 12. T; 13. F; 14. Africa; 15. erect, small; 16. Cro-Magnon; 17. thousands; 18. a. modern humans; b. archaic humans; c. *Homo erectus*; d. *Homo erectus*. See also Figure 30.10, page 580.

Chapter 31

Check Your Progress

31.1: 1. Squamous epithelium: flat cells that line the blood vessels and air sacs of lungs;

cuboidal epithelium: cube-shaped cells that line the kidney tubules and various glands; columnar epithelium: rectangular cells that line the digestive tract; stratified epithelium: layers of cells that protect various body surfaces; glandular epithelium: modified to secrete products, like the goblet cells of the digestive tract. 2. Fibrous connective tissue has collagen and elastic fibers in a jellylike matrix between fibroblasts; supportive connective tissue has protein fibers in a solid matrix between collagen or bone cells; fluid connective tissue lacks fibers and has a fluid matrix that contains blood cells or lymphatic cells. 3. Skeletal muscle, which is striated with multiple nuclei, causes bones to move when it contracts. Smooth muscle, which is spindle-shaped with a single nucleus, causes the walls of internal organs to constrict. Cardiac muscle, which has branching, striated cells each with a single nucleus, causes the heart to beat. 4. Dendrites conduct signals toward the cell body; the cell body contains most of the cytoplasm and the nucleus; it carries on the usual functions of the cell; the axon conducts nerve impulses. **31.2:** 1. An organ is two or more types of tissues working together to perform a function; an organ system is many organs working to perform a process. 2. The lymphatic and immune systems work together to protect the body from disease (other answers are possible). 3. The dorsal cavity contains the cranial cavity and the vertebral cavity; the ventral cavity contains the thoracic cavity and the abdominopelvic cavity. **31.3:** 1. The skin protects the deeper tissues from pathogens, trauma, and dehydration in all animals. Only birds have feathers, a derivative of skin that are involved in flying. 2. The epidermis is stratified squamous epithelium, and it protects and prevents water loss. The dermis is dense fibrous connective tissue, and it helps regulate body temperature and provides sensory reception. 3. A dark-skinned person in a low sunlight area might develop a deficiency of vitamin D, which is required for normal bone growth. 4. Nails are keratinized cells that grow from the nail root; hair is made of dead epithelial cells; sweat glands are tubules originating from the dermis; oil glands are usually associated with hair follicles. **31.4:** 1. Homeostasis, the dynamic equilibrium of the internal environment, maintains body conditions within a range appropriate for cells to continue living. 2. The circulatory system brings nutrients and removes waste from tissue fluid; the respiratory system carries out gas exchange; the urinary system excretes metabolic wastes and maintains salt-water balance and pH of blood. 3. When conditions go beyond or below a set point, a correction is made to bring conditions back to normality again.

Testing Yourself

1. b; 2. e; 3. e; 4. e; 5. b; 6. e; 7. e; 8. c; 9. a. columnar epithelium, lining of intestine (digestive tract), protection and absorption; b. cardiac muscle, wall of heart, pumps blood; c. compact bone, skeleton, support and protection. 10. e; 11. d; 12. c; 13. c; 14. a, c, g; 15. b, d, e; 16. b, c, f; 17. b; 18. d; 19. a; 20. c.

Chapter 32

Check Your Progress

32.1: 1. Circulatory systems carry nutrients and oxygen to cells and to remove their wastes. 2. Blood is always contained within blood vessels, but hemolymph (a mixture of blood and tissue fluid) flows freely in body cavities. 3. With a closed circulatory system, oxygen must diffuse across the capillary wall. **32.2:** 1. Arteries carry blood away from the heart, capillaries exchange their contents with tissue fluid, and veins return blood back to the heart. 2. Veins contain valves, because they are thin-walled and there is insufficient blood pressure in veins to return blood to the heart, so valves plus skeletal muscle contractions are needed. 3. One-circuit pathways are less efficient, because blood supplying the tissues (after leaving the gills) is under low pressure. Two-circuit pathways supply oxygen to tissues more efficiently, which helps land animals meet the increased demands of locomotion on land vs. in water. **32.3:** 1. From the body: venae cavae, right atrium, tricuspid valve, right ventricle, pulmonary semilunar valve, pulmonary trunk and arteries (carrying oxygen-poor blood). From the lungs: pulmonary veins, left atrium, bicuspid valve, left ventricle, aortic semilunar valve, aorta. 2. First the atria contract, then the ventricles contract, and then they both rest. The *lub* sound occurs when the atrioventricular valves close, and the *dub* sound occurs when the semilunar valves close. 3. The wall of the left ventricle is thicker than the wall of the right ventricle, and it generates a greater pressure than the right ventricle. The right ventricle pumps blood into the pulmonary circuit, which takes blood only to the lungs for gas exchange, while the left ventricle pumps blood into the systemic circuit, which takes blood to all the cells of the body. 4. Thromboembolism, stroke, heart attack. **32.4:** 1. Blood contains plasma and formed elements. Plasma transports many substances to and from the capillaries, helps defend against pathogen invasion, helps regulate body temperature, and helps with clotting to prevent excessive blood loss. The formed elements include red blood cells that carry oxygen to tissues and return some carbon dioxide; white blood cells that help protect the body from infections; and platelets that are involved in blood clotting. 2. Platelets accumulate at the site of injury and release a clotting factor that results in the synthesis of thrombin. Thrombin synthesizes fibrin threads that provide a framework for the clot. 3. Any fetal Rh-positive blood cells that enter the circulation of an Rh-negative mother are recognized as foreign antigens, provoking her immune system. An Rh-positive woman does not react to the Rh antigen, because her immune system does not react with "self." 4. Capillary exchange is affected by osmotic pressure (tends to cause water to enter capillaries) and blood pressure (tends to cause water to leave capillaries).

Testing Yourself

1. b; 2. a; 3. d; 4. c; 5. b; 6. b; 7. e; 8. c; 9. e; 10. b; 11. e; 12. a. superior vena cava; b. aorta; c. left pulmonary artery; d. pulmonary trunk; e. left pulmonary veins; f. right pulmonary artery; g. right pulmonary veins; h. semilunar valve; i. left atrium; j. right atrium; k. left atrioventricular (bicuspid) valve; l. right atrioventricular (tricuspid) valve; m. right ventricle; n. chordae tendinae; o. septum; p. left ventricle; q. superior vena cava (see Figure 32.7, page 611).

Chapter 33

Check Your Progress

33.1: 1. Under certain conditions, slime molds develop specialized sentinel cells that engulf pathogens and toxins. 2. PAMPs are highly conserved microbial molecules such as double-stranded viral RNA as well as carbohydrates and proteins found only in bacteria. 3. Immune cells expressing receptors for specific antigens can multiply and differentiate, resulting in immune memory. **33.2:** 1. The lymphatic system consists of the lymphatic vessels, which have the same structure as cardiovascular veins, and the lymphatic organs: red bone marrow, lymph nodes, and spleen. 2. The lymphatic system absorbs fats, returns excess tissue fluid to the bloodstream, produces lymphocytes, and helps defend the body against pathogens. 3. Red bone marrow is a spongy, semisolid red tissue located in certain bones (e.g., ribs, clavicle, vertebral column, heads of femur, and humerus), which produces all the blood cells of the body. The thymus is a soft, bilobed gland located in the thoracic cavity between the trachea and the sternum where T lymphocytes mature. Lymph nodes are small ovoid structures located along lymphatic vessels through which the lymph travels. The spleen is an oval organ with a dull purplish

color that has both immune as well as red blood cell maintenance functions. **33.3:** 1. Physical barriers include the skin, mucus membranes, and ciliated epithelia; chemical barriers include lysozyme, stomach acid, and protective proteins (e.g., complement). 2. Four cardinal signs of inflammation are heat, swelling, redness, and pain. Inflammation generally directs other components of the immune system (molecules and cells) to the inflamed area. 3. Mast cells initiate inflammation; phagocytes (dendritic cells, macrophages, neutrophils) devour pathogens; natural killer cells kill virus-infected cells and cancer cells by cell-to-cell contact. 4. Complement proteins assist other immune defenses by initiating inflammation, enhancing phagocytosis of pathogens, and forming a membrane attack complex. **33.4:** 1. B cells produce antibodies; cytotoxic T cells attack viral-infected or cancer cells, and helper T cells produce cytokines that stimulate the immune response. 2. Antigen complexes can activate the complement system and natural killer cells, or be engulfed by phagocytes. 3. Active immunity is induced in an individual by natural infection, vaccination, or exposure to a toxin; passive immunity is produced by one individual and transferred into someone else, such as maternal antibodies, administration of antibodies to treat diseases, and bone marrow transplants. **33.5:** 1. Most primary immunodeficiencies are due to a genetic defect in a component of the immune system. 2. Autoimmune diseases (e.g., rheumatoid arthritis) are generally treated with drugs that generally suppress the immune system. 3. The transplanting of animal tissues or organs into humans.

Testing Yourself

1. b; 2. e; 3. e; 4. a; 5. b; 6. c; 7. a; 8. b; 9. e; 10. b; 11. d; 12. a; 13. b; 14. e; 15. d.

Chapter 34

Check Your Progress

34.1: 1. Planarians have an incomplete digestive tract, called the gastrovascular cavity; the complete tract of earthworms has a pharynx, crop, gizzard, and intestine. 2. An incomplete tract has only one opening, with parts that cannot become very specialized, because they must serve multiple functions. 3. Carnivores tend to have pointed incisors and enlarged canine teeth to tear off pieces small enough to quickly swallow. The molars are jagged for efficient chewing of meat. Herbivores have reduced canines but sharp even incisors to clip grasses. The large flat molars grind and crush tough grasses. **34.2:** 1. Mouth, pharynx, esophagus, stomach,

duodenum, jejunum, ileum, large intestine. 2. Taste buds enable an animal to discern the difference between nutritious foods, and non-nutritious, potentially dangerous substances that should not be consumed. 3. The stomach mechanically churns food, while acid and pepsin begin protein digestion. The small intestine finishes the digestion of proteins, fats, carbohydrates, and nucleic acids. The villi and microvilli of the intestinal wall greatly enhance the surface area, thereby assisting absorption of the final products of digestion. The large intestine absorbs excess water, and its diameter is larger to permit storage of undigested food prior to defecation. 4. Bile from the liver (stored in the gallbladder) emulsifies fat, while pancreatic amylase, trypsin, and lipase digest carbohydrates, proteins, and lipids. The liver has many other functions, such as the storage of glucose as glycogen. **34.3:** 1. Starch digestion begins in the mouth where salivary amylase digests starch to maltose and pancreatic amylase continues this same process in the small intestine. Maltase and brush-border enzymes digest maltose to glucose, which enters a blood capillary. Protein digestion starts in the stomach where pepsin digests protein to peptides and continues in the small intestine in which trypsin carries out this same process. 2. Carbohydrates are digested to simple sugars (monosaccharides), proteins are digested to amino acids, and fats are digested to glycerol plus fatty acids. **34.4:** 1. Vegetables, if properly chosen, can supply limited calories but all necessary amino acids and vitamins. Much urea results when excess amino acids from proteins are metabolized. The loss of water needed to excrete urea can result in dehydration and loss of calcium ions. 2. A diet high in saturated fats tends to raise LDL cholesterol, which is associated with atherosclerosis. 3. A vitamin is an organic molecule that is required in the diet because it cannot be synthesized.

Testing Yourself

1. a; 2. e; 3. d; 4. b; 5. d; 6. c; 7. e; 8. a; 9. c; 10. c; 11. e; 12. c; 13. d; 14. c; 15. a; 16. b; 17. Test tube 1: no digestion—no enzyme and no HCl; Test tube 2: some digestion—no HCl; Test tube 3: no digestion—no enzyme; Test tube 4: digestion—both enzyme and HCl are present.

Chapter 35

Check Your Progress

35.1: 1. Air has a drying effect, and respiratory surfaces have to be moist. Hydras are aquatic, while earthworms live in moist earth, and salamanders have skin glands that provide this moisture. These animals also have a large surface area compared to their size, or they have many capillaries close to the skin to facilitate gas exchange. 2. When blood containing a low O_2 level flows in an opposite direction as the O_2-rich water passing over the gills, a higher percentage of oxygen is transferred than if both flowed in the same direction (the highest a concurrent mechanism could achieve would be 50% of the O_2 content in the water, because equilibration would occur). 3. Hemolymph distributes some O_2 in the hemocoel, but it is inefficient. Tracheae are air tubes that branch into ever-smaller tracheoles, which deliver oxygen to most cells. Tracheae open at spiracles, and some larger insects have air sacs that can expand and contract. Some aquatic insects have tracheal gills, expansions of the body wall to provide more oxygen-absorbing surface area. **35.2:** 1. During inspiration, the rib cage moves up and out, and the diaphragm contracts and moves down. As the thoracic cavity expands, air flows into the lungs due to decreased air pressure in the lungs. During expiration, the rib cage moves down and the diaphragm relaxes and moves up to its former position. Air flows out as a result of increased pressure in the lungs. 2. The carotid bodies and aortic bodies contain chemoreceptors that send stimulatory messages to the respiratory center if the pH or O_2 levels are too low. 3. In the lungs, oxygen entering pulmonary capillaries combines with hemoglobin (Hb) in red blood cells to form oxyhemoglobin (HbO_2). In the tissues, Hb gives up O_2, while CO_2 enters the blood and the red blood cells. Some CO_2 combines with Hb to form carbaminohemoglobin ($HbCO_2$). Most CO_2 combines with water to form carbonic acid, which dissociates into H^+ and HCO_3^-. The H^+ is absorbed by the globin portions of hemoglobin to form reduced hemoglobin HbH^+. This helps stabilize the pH of the blood. The HCO_3^- is carried in the plasma. **35.3:** 1. Penicillin is an antibiotic that kills bacteria, but most colds are caused by viruses. 2. Narrowing of the airways is seen in bronchitis and asthma; reduced lung expansion is seen in pulmonary fibrosis and emphysema. 3. Smoking causes or contributes to acute and chronic bronchitis, asthma, pulmonary fibrosis, emphysema, and lung cancer (along with many cardiovascular disorders).

Testing Yourself

1. **a.** external respiration; **b.** CO_2; **c.** CO_2; **d.** tissue cells; **e.** internal respiration; **f.** O_2; **g.** O_2; 2. b; 3. d; 4. c; 5. b; 6. c; 7. e; 8. b; 9. d; 10. b; 11. d; 12. e; 13. **a.** nasal cavity; **b.** nostril; **c.** pharynx; **d.** epiglottis; **e.** glottis;

f. larynx; **g.** trachea; **h.** bronchus; **i.** bronchiole (see also Figure 35.6a, page 668).

Chapter 36

Check Your Progress

36.1: 1. Osmoregulation involves the balance between salts and water; metabolic wastes are removed by excretion. 2. Urea is not as toxic as ammonia, and it does not require as much water to excrete; uric acid takes more energy to prepare than urea. 3. Kangaroo rats are active at night, have convoluted nasal passages to capture moisture in exhaled air, fur to prevent water loss from skin, secrete a hypertonic urine, and eliminate very dry feces. **36.2:** 1. The kidneys alone secrete nitrogenous wastes, but share responsibility for regulating blood pressure and water-salt balance. Certain hormones secreted by the kidneys, such as erythropoietin and ADH, have unique functions. 2. In response to low blood pressure, the kidneys secrete renin, which converts angiotensinogen to angiotensin I, which is converted to angiotensin II. Angiotensin II causes blood vessel constriction and stimulates the adrenal glands to release aldosterone, which acts on kidney tubules to increase salt reabsorption. 3. The kidneys maintain blood pH by secreting H^+ ions and reabsorbing bicarbonate ions, as needed.

Testing Yourself

1. d; 2. a; 3. c; 4. b; 5. e; 6. b; 7. d; 8. c; 9. c; 10. d; 11. c; 12. **a.** glomerular capsule; **b.** proximal convoluted tubule; **c.** loop of the nephron; **d.** descending limb; **e.** ascending limb; **f.** distal convoluted tubule; **g.** collecting duct; **h.** renal artery; **i.** afferent arteriole; **j.** glomerulus; **k.** efferent arteriole; **l.** peritubular capillary network; **m.** renal vein (see Figure 36.8, page 685).

Chapter 37

Check Your Progress

37.1: 1. A nerve net is a simple nervous system consisting of interconnected neurons, with no CNS. A ganglion is a cluster of neuron (nerve cell) bodies. In animals with a CNS and a PNS, it is a cluster of neurons located outside the CNS. A centrally located brain controls the ganglia and associated nerves. 2. The hindbrain controls essential functions like breathing, heart functions, and basic motor activity; the midbrain is a relay station connecting the hindbrain with the forebrain; the forebrain, which receives sensory input, includes the hypothalamus (involved with homeostasis) as well as the

cerebrum (involved with higher functions). 3. The more recently evolved parts of the brain are the outer portions, such as the cerebral cortex, and (in mammals) the neocortex. **37.2:** 1. Nerve impulses travel more quickly down myelinated axons due to saltatory conduction ("jumping"). 2. Na^+ moves from the outside of the axon membrane to the inside; K^+ moves from the inside of the axon membrane to the outside. 3. Inhibition of AChE, the enzyme that normally breaks down acetylcholine (ACh), would result in increased activity of nerves that use ACh as a neurotransmitter. **37.3:** 1. Sensory information from internal organs travels via spinal nerves, through the dorsal root ganglia to synapses on spinal cord interneurons whose axons travel in tracts to the brain. These then send motor impulses through tracts, to the ventral root ganglia, and then to the effector organ (smooth muscle in the intestine). 2. The four major lobes of the human brain are the frontal, parietal, temporal, and occipital. 3. Parkinson disease, with symptoms such as tremors, difficult speech, and trouble walking or standing, is associated with a loss of dopamine-producing cells in the basal nuclei of the forebrain (though the inciting cause is unknown); multiple sclerosis is an autoimmune disease that damages the myelin sheaths of neurons in the CNS, resulting in fatigue and in problems with visual and muscular function. **37.4:** 1. A reflex arc can travel from the sensory receptor, synapse on interneurons in the spinal cord, then travel back to the effector (muscle) without being perceived by the brain first. 2. Eating a big lunch mainly stimulates the parasympathetic branch of the autonomic nervous system, diverting blood supply to the digestive tract and away from the muscles. Jogging will engage the sympathetic system, reducing blood flow to the stomach and inhibiting its function. 3. The parasympathetic ("rest and digest") division dominates as you enjoy your meal, but your friend's "surprise" causes a sudden increase in sympathetic ("fight or flight") activity.

Testing Yourself

1. b; 2. c; 3. a; 4. a; 5. c; 6. d; 7. b; 8. b; 9. c; 10. d; 11. c; 12. c; 13. d; 14. b; 15. c; 16. b; 17. **a.** central canal; **b.** gray matter; **c.** white matter; **d.** dorsal root; **e.** cell body of sensory neuron in dorsal root ganglion; **f.** spinal nerve; **g.** cell body of motor neuron; **h.** interneuron (see Figure 37.13, page 709).

Chapter 38

Check Your Progress

38.1: 1. Sensory transduction is the conversion of some type of environmental stimulus into a nerve impulse. 2. Some snakes can perceive infrared radiation; bats, dolphins, and whales perceive very high or low frequency sound waves (echolocation); a dog's sense of smell is far more sensitive than a human's. **38.2:** 1. Both are chemical senses that use chemoreceptors to detect molecules in the environment. 2. Sweet, sour, salty, bitter, and umami. 3. Neurons transmit signals from different sensory organs to different areas of the brain, where they are interpreted as different types of information. **38.3:** 1. Rods are for peripheral vision and motion detection; they are well-suited for dim light. Cones are for color perception and fine detail, and are best-suited for bright light. Many rods may excite a single ganglion cell, but much smaller numbers of cones excite individual ganglion cells. 2. Sclera, choroid, retina. Light must pass through the ganglion and bipolar cell layers before reaching the photoreceptor cells. 3. An eyeball that is too long results in nearsightedness; an eyeball that is too short results in farsightedness; an uneven cornea results in astigmatism. **38.4:** 1. a. middle; b. outer; c. inner; d. inner; e. inner; f. outer. 2. Auditory canal, tympanic membrane (eardrum), ossicles (malleus, incus, and stapes), oval window, cochlea. 3. The utricle and saccule are responsible for gravitational equilibrium; the semicircular canals for rotational equilibrium. **38.5:** 1. A person lacking muscle spindles would have trouble walking, sitting, or doing other activities due to a lack of muscle tone. A person lacking nociceptors would be prone to injury due to an absence of warning signs associated with pain. 2. Pain is generally associated with potential harm: i.e., something to be avoided. An animal that quickly adapted to pain would have an increased chance of being injured or killed by a potentially dangerous stimulus.

Testing Yourself

1. b; **2.** c; **3.** c; **4.** e; **5.** d; **6.** c; **7.** c; **8.** b; **9.** d; **10.** a; **11.** b; **12.** c; **13.** a; **14.** d; **15.** b; **16.** d; **17. a.** retina—contains sensory receptors; **b.** choroid—absorbs stray light; **c.** sclera—protects and supports eyeball; **d.** optic nerve—transmits impulses to brain; **e.** fovea centralis—makes acute vision possible; **f.** muscle in ciliary body—holds lens in place, accommodation; **g.** lens—refracts and focuses light rays; **h.** iris—regulates light entrance; **i.** pupil—admits light; **j.** cornea—refracts light rays (see Figure 38.5, page 721).

Chapter 39

Check Your Progress

39.1: 1. Exoskeleton, endoskeleton, exoskeleton, exoskeleton, endoskeleton.

2. The tongue is a muscular hydrostat. 3. Because the muscle layers surrounding the coelom no longer contract, the hydrostatic skeleton cannot provide support for the body. **39.2:** 1. Osteoblasts build bone and osteoclasts break it down. Osteocytes occupy lacunae. 2. Compact bone, which serves mainly to support the body, contains many osteons, in which central canals are surrounded by a hard matrix with lacunae. Spongy bone is lighter, with numerous bars and plates as well as spaces filled with red bone marrow, which produces the blood cells. 3. Axial, axial, appendicular, appendicular, axial, appendicular, axial, appendicular, axial. **39.3:** 1. A pair of muscles that work opposite to one another; for example, if one muscle flexes (bends) the joint the other extends (straightens) it. 2. Myofibrils are tubular contractile units that are divided into sarcomeres. Each sarcomere contains actin (thin filaments) and myosin (thick filaments). 3. Cleavage of ATP allows myosin heads to bind to actin filaments, pulling them toward the center of the sarcomere.

Testing Yourself

1. b; **2.** f; **3.** c; **4.** e; **5.** e; **6.** e; **7.** b; **8.** b; **9.** c; **10.** b; **11.** e; **12.** e; **13.** c; **14.** b; **15. a.** T tubule; **b.** sarcoplasmic reticulum; **c.** myofibril; **d.** Z line; **e.** sarcomere; **f.** sarcolemma of muscle fiber (see Figure 39.13, page 745).

Chapter 40

Check Your Progress

40.1: 1. The nervous system tends to respond rapidly to both external and internal stimuli, while the endocrine system responds more slowly, but often has longer-lasting effects. Both systems use chemicals to communicate with other body systems; the nervous system at synapses, the endocrine system via hormones secreted mainly into the bloodstream. 2. Peptide hormones have receptors in the plasma membrane. Steroid hormones have receptors that are generally in the nucleus, sometimes in the cytoplasm. 3. Since peptide hormones usually bind to receptors on the outside of the cell; they must communicate with the inside of the cell via second messengers. **40.2:** 1. The hypothalamus communicates with the endocrine system via the pituitary gland: two hormones produced by the hypothalamus are stored in the posterior pituitary; several others are produced by the anterior pituitary in response to hypothalamic releasing factors that reach the anterior pituitary via a portal system. 2. ADH conserves body water by causing reabsorption of water by the kidneys; oxytocin causes uterine contractions during

labor and milk letdown during nursing. 3. Thyroid stimulating hormone (TSH) stimulates release of thyroid hormones; adrenocorticotropic hormone (ACTH) stimulates the adrenal glands to produce glucocorticoids, prolactin (PRL) causes breast development and milk production; growth hormone (GH) promotes bone and muscle growth; the gonadotropic hormones FSH and LH stimulate the testes or ovaries to produce gametes and sex hormones; and melanocyte-stimulating hormone (MSH) causes skin color changes in some animals. **40.3:** 1. Angiotensin II causes arterioles to constrict; aldosterone causes reabsorption of Na$^+$, accompanied by water, in the kidneys. 2. Adrenal cortex, pineal gland, adrenal medulla, kidneys, adipose tissue, pancreas, heart, adrenal cortex, thyroid gland. 3. PTH stimulates osteoclasts and calcitonin inhibits them.

Testing Yourself

1. f; **2.** b; **3.** c; **4.** a; **5.** e; **6.** d; **7.** b; **8.** d; **9.** a; **10.** a; **11.** e; **12.** b; **13.** d; **14.** b; **15.** a; **16.** b; **17.** c; **18.** e; **19.** d; **20.** c.

Chapter 41

Check Your Progress

41.1: 1. Asexual reproduction allows organisms to reproduce rapidly and colonize favorable environments quickly. Sexual reproduction produces offspring with a new combination of genes that may be more adaptive to a changed environment. 2. An oviparous animal lays eggs that hatch outside the body. A viviparous animal gives birth after the offspring have developed within the mother's body. Ovoviviparous animals retain fertilized eggs within a parent's body until they hatch; the parent then gives birth to the young. 3. A shelled egg contains extraembryonic membranes which keep the embryo moist, carry out gas exchange, collect wastes, and provide yolk as food. **41.2:** 1. Seminiferous tubule, epididymis, vas deferens, ejaculatory duct, urethra. 2. Seminal vesicles, prostate gland, and bulbourethral glands. 3. In males, FSH stimulates spermatogenesis and LH stimulates testosterone production. **41.3:** 1. Ovary, oviduct, uterus, cervix, vagina. 2. During the follicular phase, FSH stimulates ovarian follicles to produce primarily estrogen. A surge of LH (and FSH) also triggers ovulation. During the luteal phase, LH stimulates the corpus luteum to produce primarily progesterone. 3. Estrogen secreted by the developing follicle inhibits FSH secretion by the anterior pituitary, ending the follicular phase. Progesterone secreted by the developing corpus luteum inhibits LH secretion by the anterior pituitary, ending the luteal phase. Rising estrogen levels cause the endometrium to thicken (proliferative phase), and progesterone causes uterine glands to mature (secretory phase). If no pregnancy occurs, low levels of estrogen and progesterone initiate menstruation. **41.4:** 1. Male and female condoms and the diaphragm prevent sperm from coming in contact with the egg. 2. Abstinence (100%) and vasectomy (nearly 100%) are the most effective, the birth control pill and condoms are the next most effective, and natural family planning is least effective. 3. In AID, sperm are placed in the vagina or sometimes the uterus. In IVF, conception takes place in laboratory glassware and embryos are transferred to the woman's uterus. In GIFT, eggs and sperm are brought together in laboratory glassware, and placed in the oviducts immediately afterward. In ICSI, one sperm is injected directly into an egg. **41.5:** 1. Antiretroviral drug categories include entry inhibitors (viral attachment to host receptor), reverse transcriptase inhibitors (production of DNA from viral RNA), integrase inhibitors (insertion of viral DNA into host DNA), and protease inhibitors (processing of viral proteins). 2. HPV-induced genital warts can be painful and disfiguring, and some strains cause cancer of the cervix, vagina, vulva, penis, and anus. 3. Chlamydia and gonorrhea are associated with pelvic inflammatory disease and infertility.

Testing Yourself

1. b; **2.** e; **3.** c; **4.** e; **5.** c; **6.** c; **7.** c; **8.** c; **9.** a; **10.** a; **11.** c; **12.** c; **13.** b; **14.** e; **15.** c; **16.** a; **17.** c; **18.** b; **19.** c.

Chapter 42

Check Your Progress

42.1: 1. The fast block is the depolarization of the egg's plasma membrane that occurs upon initial contact with a sperm. The slow block occurs when the secretion of cortical granules converts the zona pellucida into the fertilization membrane. 2. Mesoderm, endoderm, ectoderm, ectoderm, mesoderm, mesoderm, mesoderm, endoderm. 3. Neurula stage. **42.2:** 1. Cytoplasmic segregation is the parceling out of maternal determinants as mitosis occurs. Induction is the influence of one embryonic tissue on the development of another. 2. A morphogen is a transcription factor that is distributed along a concentration gradient in the embryo and helps direct morphogenesis. 3. The homeobox encodes the homeodomain region of the protein product of the gene. The homeodomain is the DNA-binding region of the protein, which is a transcription factor. **42.3:** 1. oviduct.

2. Allantois, yolk sac, and chorion. 3. Structures that begin to develop between the third and fifth weeks include the nervous system, heart, chorionic villi, umbilical cord, and limb buds. **42.3:** 1. The thymus is the site where T cells finish their development; T cells are needed to stimulate other types of immune cells, including B cells that produce antibodies. 2. Menopause is the time when ovarian and uterine cycles cease. 3. Preprogrammed theories suggest aging is partly genetically programmed; single gene mutations influence aging in *C. elegans*. Damage accumulation theories suggest aging is due to an accumulation of cellular damage: e.g., DNA mutations, cross-linking of proteins, or oxidation by free radicals.

Testing Yourself

1. b; **2.** b; **3.** a; **4.** e; **5.** b; **6.** e; **7.** e; **8.** d; **9. a.** chorion: contributes to forming placenta where wastes are exchanged for nutrients and oxygen; **b.** amnion: protects and prevents desiccation; **c.** embryo; **d.** allantois: blood vessels become umbilical blood vessels; **e.** yolk sac: first site of blood cell formation; **f.** chorionic villi: embryonic portion of placenta; **g.** maternal portion of placenta; **h.** umbilical cord: connects developing embryo to the placenta (see also Figure 42.11, page 805); **10.** c; **11.** a; **12.** d; **13.** b; **14.** e; **15.** b; **16.** c; **17.** b; **18.** a; **19.** c; **20.** e.

Chapter 43

Check Your Progress

43.1: 1. Fisher lovebird (carry nesting material in beak) mated to Peach-faced lovebird (carry nesting material in rump feathers) result in offspring with intermediate behavior. Offspring of inland garter snakes (do not eat slugs) and coastal garter snakes (eat slugs) show an intermediate liking for slugs. 2. Gene for egg-laying hormone in *Aplysia* was isolated and its protein product controls egg-laying behavior. The gene *fosB* has been found to control maternal behavior in mice. **43.2:** 1. Associative learning. 2. Just hatched, laughing gull chicks instinctively peck at parents' bill to be fed but their accuracy improves after a few days. 3. Chimpanzees pile up boxes to reach food and ravens use their beaks and feet to bring up food attached to a string. **43.3:** 1. Pheromones are used to mark a territory so other individuals of that species will stay away; honeybees do a waggle dance to guide other bees to a food source; vervet monkeys have calls that make other vervets run away. 2. Chemical (effective all the time, not as fast as auditory); auditory (can be modified but the recipient has to be present when message is sent); visual (need not be

accompanied by chemical or auditory, needs light in order to receive); tactile (permits bonding; recipient must be close). 3. chemical: taste buds and olfactory receptors; auditory: ears; visual: eyes; tactile: touch receptors in skin. **43.4:** 1. One benefit of territoriality is to ensure a source of food. 2. Both an animal's reproductive strategy and sexual selection favors features that increase an animal's chance of leaving offspring. 3. Altruistic behavior is supposed to be selfless but when, for example, an offspring helps its parents raise siblings, the helper may be increasing some of its own genes in the next generation.

Testing Yourself

1. c; **2.** a; **3.** d; **4.** b; **5.** c; **6.** d; **7.** e; **8.** c; **9.** d; **10.** c; **11.** c; **12.** a; **13.** c; **14.** d; **15.** a; **16.** c; **17.** b; **18.** a; **19.** c; **20.** b.

Chapter 44

Check Your Progress

44.1: 1. A population is all the members of one species that inhabit a particular area and a community is all the populations that interact within that area. 2. To develop models that explain and predict the distribution and abundance of organisms. 3. Abiotic means the nonliving aspects of an environment such as rainfall and temperature. **44.2:** 1. Population density is the number of individuals per unit area and population distribution is the pattern of dispersal of individuals across an area of interest. 2. In a type I survivorship curve, most individuals survive well past the midpoint of the life span and death does not come until near the end of the life span. In type II, survivorship decreases at a constant rate throughout the life span. In type III, most individuals die young. 3. In a bell-shaped age pyramid, the pre-reproductive members represent the largest portion of the population. **44.3:** 1. An environment in which the weather, food supply, etc., remains stable favors iteroparity. 2. Exponential growth ceases when the environment cannot support a larger population size; that is, the point at which the size of the population has reached the environment's carrying capacity. **44.4:** 1. As population density increases, competition and predation become more intense. 2. If a flash flood occurs, mice that can stay afloat will survive and reproduce whereas those that quickly sink will not survive and will not reproduce. In this way the ability to stay afloat will be more prevalent in the next generation. **44.5:** 1. A *K*-strategist species: allocate energy to their own growth and survival and to the growth and survival of their limited number of offspring. *r*-strategist species: allocate energy to producing a large number of offspring and little or no energy goes into parental care. 2. Populations may vary between K and r strategies based upon environmental conditions. **44.6:** 1. Less-developed countries have a high population growth while more-developed countries have a low rate of population growth. 2. The parents don't immediately die after they have had their child which causes the population to increase. 3. Since resources are in limited supply an increase in consumption by the LDC will cause more competition for resources.

Testing Yourself

1. d; **2.** c; **3.** e; **4.** e; **5.** b; **6.** e; **7.** c; **8.** e; **9.** c; **10.** e; **11.** c; **12.** e; **13.** b; **14.** e; **15.** e.

Chapter 45

Check Your Progress

45.1: 1. An organism's habitat is the place where it lives and reproduces. The niche is the role it plays in its community such as whether it is a producer or consumer. 2. The two factors are (1) the predator causes the prey population to decline which leads to a decline in the predator population; later when the prey population recovers so does the predator population; (2) lack of food causes the prey population to decline followed by the predator population; later when food is available to the prey population they both recover. 3. Acacias feed the ants that protect them from herbivores; Clark's nutcrackers feed on the seeds of whitebark pine trees but also disperse the seeds; pollinators take nectar from flowers and carry their pollen to other flowers of the same species. **45.2:** 1. Environmental disturbances, fire, flood, etc., lead to succession. 2. The facilitation model predicts that a community will grow toward becoming a climax community. The inhibition model predicts that colonists will inhibit the growth of a community. **45.3:** 1. A producer of food (photosynthesizer) is at the base of an ecological pyramid. 2. Energy passes from one population to the next, and at each step more is converted to heat until all of the original input has become heat. Therefore energy flows though an ecosystem.

Chemicals pass from one population to the next and then recycle back to the producer populations again. 3. Return of CO_2 to the atmosphere because humans burn fossil fuels and destroy forests that take up CO_2.

Testing Yourself

1. c; **2.** e; **3.** e; **4.** a; **5.** c; **6.** b; **7.** d; **8.** b; **9.** c; **10.** d; **11.** e; **12. a.** producers; **b.** consumers; **c.** inorganic nutrient pool; **d.** decomposers; **13.** a; **14.** e; **15.** c; **16.** d; **17.** c; **18.** b; **19.** c; **20.** d.

Chapter 46

Check Your Progress

46.1: 1. Because the Earth is a sphere, the Sun's rays hit the equator straight on but are angled to reach the poles. 2. The windward side of the mountain receives more rainfall than the other side. Winds blowing over bodies of water collect moisture that they lose when they reach land. **46.2:** 1. A tropical rain forest has a canopy (tops of great variety of tall evergreen hardwood trees) with buttressed trunks at ground level. Long lianas (hanging vines) climb into the canopy. Epiphytes grow on the trees. The understory consists of smaller plants and the forest floor is very sparse. A temperate deciduous forest contains trees (oak, beech, sycamore, and maple) that lose their leaves in the fall. Enough light penetrates the canopy to allow a layer of understory trees. Shrubs, mosses, and ferns grow at ground level. 2. The savanna is an expansive grassland that has a moderate climate. Therefore, the grasses keep producing throughout the year and provide plentiful food for a great variety of and number of herbivores that provide food for carnivores. The tundra is cold much of the year and has a limited growing season; therefore, its productivity is low and it supports only small populations of a few types of herbivores. **46.3:** 1. The cooling and warming of the epilimnion causes the layers of water to change position. 2. Most of the open ocean is the pelagic zone (open waters) divided into the epipelagic zone (contains phytoplankton, zooplankton, many types of fishes and also dolphins and whales); the mesopelagic zone (contains only carnivores adapted to the

absence of light); and the bathypelagic zone (in complete darkness that contains strange-looking fishes and invertebrates). Few vertebrates but many invertebrates (echinoderms, tube worms) exist on the abyssal plain and feed on debris that floats down from above.

Testing Yourself

1. b; **2.** d; **3.** c; **4.** d; **5.** a; **6.** b; **7.** e; **8.** e; **9.** a; **10.** a; **11.** b; **12.** d; **13.** b; **14.** a; **15.** c; **16.** b; **17.** a; **18.** d; **19.** c.

Chapter 47

Check Your Progress

47.1: 1. Many disciplines provide data that support conservation biology. 2. Biodiversity includes the number of species on Earth; genetic diversity (variations in a species); ecosystem diversity (interactions of species); and landscape diversity (interactions of ecosystems). A hotspot is a specific region with a large amount of biodiversity. **47.2:** 1. Direct value is a service that is immediately recognizable, while indirect values may not be as noticeable. 2. Direct values include medicine, food, or commercial products. Indirect values include assisting biogeochemical cycles, waste disposal, providing fresh water, preventing soil erosion, regulating climate, or providing a place for recreation. **47.3:** 1. Habitat loss, exotic species, pollution, overexploitation, disease. 2. Exotic plants displace native plants; predators introduced to kill pests also kill native animals; escaped animals may compete with, prey on, hybridize with, or introduce diseases into native populations. **47.4:** 1. A landscape involves more than one ecosystem and sometimes keystone species move between ecosystems. 2. Begin as soon as possible, mimic natural processes, and strive for sustainable development while providing services to humans.

Testing Yourself

1. e; **2.** b; **3.** e; **4.** e; **5.** e; **6.** b; **7.** e; **8.** e; **9.** c; **10.** c; **11.** e; **12.** e; **13.** e; **14.** b, c; **15. a.** habitat loss; **b.** introduction of exotic species; **c.** pollution; **d.** overexploitation; **e.** disease.

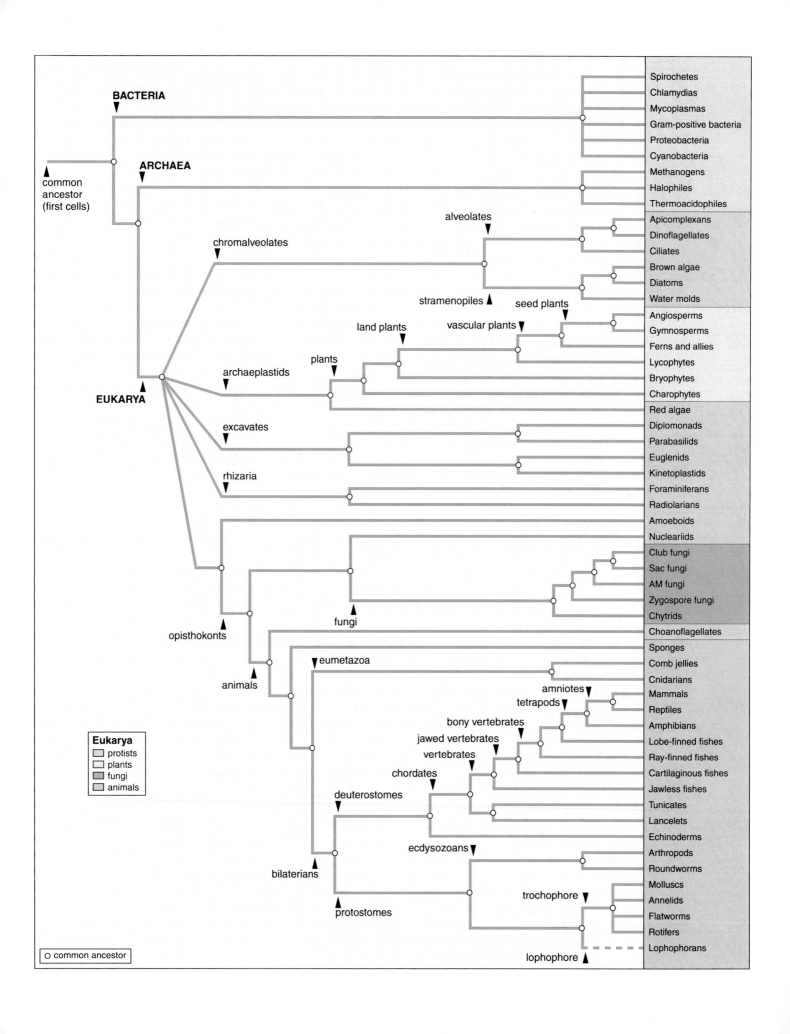

Appendix B

Tree of Life

The tree of life depicted in this appendix is based on the phylogenetic (evolutionary) trees presented in the text. Figure 1.5 showed how the three domains of life—Bacteria, Archaea, and Eukarya—are related. This relationship is also apparent in the tree of life, which combines the individual trees given in the text for eukaryotic protists, plants, fungi, and animals. In combining these trees, we show how all organisms may be related to one another through the evolutionary process.

Prokaryotes

Domains Bacteria and Archaea (Chapter 20) constitute the prokaryotic organisms that are characterized by their simple structure but a complex metabolism. The chromosome of a prokaryote is not bounded by a nuclear envelope, and therefore, these organisms do not have a nucleus. Prokaryotes carry out all the metabolic processes performed by eukaryotes and many others besides. However, they do not have organelles, except for multiple ribosomes.

Domain Bacteria

Bacteria are the most plentiful of all organisms, capable of living in most habitats, and they can carry out many different metabolic processes. Most bacteria are aerobic heterotrophs, but some are photosynthetic, and some are chemosynthetic. Motile forms move by flagella consisting of a single filament. Their cell wall contains peptidoglycan, and they have distinctive RNA sequences.

Domain Archaea

Archaean cell walls lack peptidoglycan, their lipids have a unique branched structure, and their ribosomal RNA sequences are distinctive. Examples are methanogens and the extremophiles.

Domain Eukarya

Eukarya have a complex cell structure with a nucleus and several types of organelles that compartmentalize the cell. Mitochondria that produce ATP and chloroplasts that produce carbohydrates are derived from prokaryotes that took up residence in a larger, nucleated cell. They may be unicellular (the majority of the protists), or multicellular (the plants, fungi, animals). Each multicellular group is characterized by a particular mode of nutrition. Flagella, if present, have a 9 + 2 organization.

Protists

The protists (Chapter 21) represent a group containing those eukaryotes that are not classified as a plant, fungus, or animal. The protists are members of six supergroups whose evolutionary relationships are being actively investigated. A supergroup is a major eukaryotic group, and six supergroups encompass all members of the domain Eukarya, including all protists, plants, fungi, and animals. Examples of protists include amoebas, the brown algae, and the paramecia.

Plants

Plants (Chapter 23) are multicellular photosynthetic eukaryotes that became adapted to living on land. This group includes aquatic green algae called charophytes, which have a haploid life cycle and share certain significant traits with the land plants.

The land plants exhibit an alternation-of-generations life cycle; protect a multicellular sporophyte embryo; produce gametes in gametangia; have apical meristem that produces differentiated tissues and have a waxy cuticle that prevents water loss. Examples include mosses, ferns, conifers, and flowering plants.

Fungi

Fungi (Chapter 22) have multicellular bodies composed of hyphae that absorb nutrients from the environment. They have a haploid life cycle and usually produce nonmotile spores during both asexual and sexual reproduction. Chytrids are aquatic fungi with flagellated spores and gametes. Examples include the mushrooms, cup fungi, and molds.

Animals

Animals (Chapters 28 and 29) are multicellular and have a diploid life cycle. Most have specialized tissues and ingest their food in a digestive cavity. Examples include invertebrate organisms such as sponges, earthworms, molluscs, insects, and vertebrates such as fishes, reptiles, and humans.

Glossary

A

abiogenesis Origin of life from nonliving matter, such as occurred on the early Earth. 329

abiotic synthesis Process of chemical evolution that resulted in the formation of organic molecules (amino acids, monosaccharides, etc.) from inorganic material. 329

abscisic acid (ABA) Plant hormone that causes stomata to close and initiates and maintains dormancy. 488

abscission Dropping of leaves, fruits, or flowers from a land plant. 488

absolute dating (of fossils) Determining the age of a fossil by direct measurement, usually involving radioisotope decay. 334

absorption spectrum For photosynthetic pigments, a graph of how much solar radiation is absorbed versus the wavelength of light. 124

accessory pigment Proteins that assist in the photosynthetic process by transferring energy from the photons to the central chlorophyll molecules. 389

acid Molecules tending to raise the hydrogen ion concentration in a solution and thus to lower its pH numerically. 32

acid deposition The return to Earth in rain or snow of sulfate or nitrate salts of acids produced by commercial and industrial activities. 878

acquired immunodeficiency syndrome (AIDS) Disease caused by the HIV virus that destroys helper T cells and macrophages of the immune system, thus preventing an immune response to pathogens; caused by sexual contact with an infected person, intravenous drug use, and transfusions of contaminated blood (rare). 787

actin One of two major proteins of muscle; makes up thin filaments in myofibrils of muscle fibers. *See also* myosin. 745

actin filament Component of the cytoskeleton; plays a role in the movement of the cell and its organelles; a protein filament in a sarcomere of a muscle, its movement shortens the sarcomere, yielding muscle contraction. 78

action potential Electrochemical changes that take place across the axon membrane; the nerve impulse. 699

active immunity Ability to produce antibodies due to the immune system's response to a microorganism or a vaccine. 637

active site Region of an enzyme where the substrate binds and where the chemical reaction occurs. 110

active transport Use of a plasma membrane carrier protein to move a molecule or ion from a region of lower concentration to one of higher concentration; it opposes equilibrium and requires energy. 95

adaptation Species's modification in structure, function, or behavior that makes a species more suitable to its environment. 278

adaptive immunity Type of immunity that is characterized by the action of lymphocytes to specific antigens. 627

adaptive radiation Rapid evolution of several species from a common ancestor into new ecological or geographical zones. 316

adenine (A) One of four nitrogen-containing bases in nucleotides composing the structure of DNA and RNA. Pairs with uracil (U) and thymine (T). 217

adenosine Portion of ATP and ADP that is composed of the base adenine and the sugar ribose. 54

adhesion junction Junction between cells in which the adjacent plasma membranes do not touch but are held together by intercellular filaments attached to buttonlike thickenings. 99

adipose tissue Connective tissue in which fat is stored. 590

ADP (adenosine diphosphate) Nucleotide with two phosphate groups that can accept another phosphate group and become ATP. 56, 107

adrenal cortex Outer portion of the adrenal gland; secretes mineralocorticoids, such as aldosterone, and glucocorticoids, such as cortisol. 762

adrenal gland Gland that lies atop a kidney; the *adrenal medulla* produces the hormones epinephrine and norepinephrine, and the *adrenal cortex* produces the glucocorticoid and mineralocorticoid hormones. 762

adrenal medulla Inner portion of the adrenal gland; secretes the hormones epinephrine and norepinephrine. 762

adrenocorticotropic hormone (ACTH) Hormone secreted by the anterior lobe of the pituitary gland that stimulates activity in the adrenal cortex. 757

aerobic A chemical process that requires air (oxygen); phase of cellular respiration that requires oxygen. 137

age structure diagram In demographics, a display of the age groups of a population; a growing population has a pyramid-shaped diagram. 842

agglutination Clumping of red blood cells due to a reaction between antigens on red blood cell plasma membranes and antibodies in the plasma. 619

agnathan Fishes that lack jaws; namely, the lampreys and hagfishes. 553

agranular leukocyte Form of white blood cell that lacks spherical vesicles (granules) in the cytoplasm. 620

aldosterone Hormone secreted by the adrenal cortex that regulates the sodium and potassium ion balance of the blood. 690, 763

alkaloid Bitter-tasting nitrogenous compounds that have a basic pH (e.g., caffeine). 497

allantois Extraembryonic membrane that accumulates nitrogenous wastes in the eggs of reptiles, including birds; contributes to the formation of umbilical blood vessels in mammals. 805

allele Alternative form of a gene; alleles occur at the same locus on homologous chromosomes. 196

allele frequency Relative proportion of each allele for a gene in the gene pool of a population. 290

allergy Immune response to substances that usually are not recognized as foreign. 641

allopatric speciation Model that proposes that new species arise due to an interruption of gene flow between populations that are separated geographically. 313

alloploidy Polyploid organism that contains the genomes of two or more different species. 315

allosteric site Site on an allosteric enzyme that binds an effector molecule; binding alters the activity of the enzyme. 112

alpine tundra Tundra near the peak of a mountain. 887

alternation-of-generations Life cycle, typical of land plants, in which a diploid sporophyte alternates with a haploid gametophyte. 176, 422

altruism Social interaction that has the potential to decrease the lifetime reproductive success of the member exhibiting the behavior. 833

alveolates A group of protists that includes unicellular dinoflagellates, apicomplexans, and ciliates; alveoli support plasma membrane. 392

alveolus (pl., alveoli) In humans, terminal, microscopic, grapelike air sac found in lungs. 668

Alzheimer disease Disease of the central nervous system (brain) that is characterized by an accumulation of beta amyloid protein and neurofibrillary tangles in the hippocampus and amygdala. 707

AM fungi (Glomeromycota) Fungi with branching invaginations (arbuscular mycorrhizae or AM) used to invade plant roots. 408

amino acid Organic molecule composed of an amino group and an acid group; covalently bonds to produce peptide molecules. 50

ammonia Nitrogenous end product that takes a limited amount of energy to produce but requires much water to excrete because it is toxic. 681

amnion Extraembryonic membrane of birds, reptiles, and mammals that forms an enclosing, fluid-filled sac. 805

amniote Vertebrate that produces an egg surrounded by four membranes, one of which is the amnion; amniote groups are the reptiles, (including birds), and mammals. 553

amniotic egg Egg that has an amnion, as seen during the development of reptiles, (including birds), and mammals. 558

amoeboid Cell that moves and engulfs debris with pseudopods. 396

amoebozoan Supergroup of eukaryotes that includes amoebas and slime molds and is characterized by lobe-shaped pseudopodia. 396

amphibian Member of vertebrate class Amphibia that includes frogs, toads, and salamanders; they are tied to a watery environment for reproduction. 556

amygdala Part of the limbic system of the brain; associated with emotional experiences. 707

amyotrophic lateral sclerosis (ALS) Neurodegenerative disease affecting the motor neurons in the brain and spinal cord resulting in paralysis and death; also known as Lou Gehrig's disease. 703

anabolic steroid Synthetic steroid that mimics the effect of testosterone. 767

anabolism Chemical reaction in which smaller molecules (monomers) are combined to form larger molecules (polymers); anabolic metabolism. 147

anaerobic A chemical reaction that occurs in the absence of oxygen; an example is the fermentation reactions. 137

analogous, analogous structure Structure that has a similar function in separate lineages but differs in anatomy and ancestry. 284, 317, 357

analogy Similarity of function but not of origin. 357

anaphase Fourth phase of mitosis; chromosomes move toward the poles of the spindle. 160

anaphylactic shock Severe systemic form of anaphylaxis involving bronchiolar constriction, impaired breathing, vasodilation, and a rapid drop in blood pressure with a threat of circulatory failure. 641

anapsid Characteristic of a vertebrate skull in which there is no opening in the skull behind the eye socket (orbit). 558

ancestral traits Traits that are found in a common ancestor and its descendants. 354

androgen Male sex hormone (e.g., testosterone). 767

aneuploidy Condition in which a cell does not contain the correct number, or combinations, of chromosomes. 183

angina pectoris Condition characterized by thoracic pain resulting from occluded coronary arteries; may precede a heart attack. 616

angiogenesis Formation of new blood vessels; rapid angiogenesis is a characteristic of cancer cells. 164

angiosperm Flowering land plant; the seeds are borne within a fruit. 430, 433

angiotensin II Hormone produced from angiotensinogen (a plasma protein) by the kidneys and lungs; raises blood pressure. 690

animals Multicellular, heterotrophic eukaryote that undergoes development to achieve its final form. In general, animals are mobile organisms, characterized by the presence of muscular and nervous tissue. 8

annelid The segmented worms, such as the earthworm and the clam worm. 536

annual ring Layer of wood (secondary xylem) usually produced during one growing season. 456

anterior pituitary Portion of the pituitary gland that is controlled by the hypothalamus and produces six types of hormones, some of which control other endocrine glands. 757

antheridium (pl., antheridia) Sperm-producing structures, as in the moss life cycle. 422

anthropoid Group of primates that includes monkeys, apes, and humans. 572

antibody Protein produced in response to the presence of an antigen; each antibody combines with a specific antigen. 618

antibody-mediated immunity Specific mechanism of defense in which plasma cells derived from B cells produce antibodies that combine with antigens. 634

anticodon Three-base sequence in a transfer RNA molecule base that pairs with a complementary codon in mRNA. 228

antidiuretic hormone (ADH) Hormone secreted by the posterior pituitary that increases the permeability of the collecting ducts in a kidney. 688, 757

antigen Foreign substance, usually a protein or a polysaccharide, that stimulates the immune system to react, such as to produce antibodies. 627

antigen-presenting cell (APC) Cell that displays an antigen to certain cells of the immune system so they can defend the body against that particular antigen. 635

antigen receptor Receptor proteins in the plasma membrane of immune system cells whose shape allows them to combine with a specific antigen. 633

anus Outlet of the digestive tube. 653

aorta In humans, the major systemic artery that takes blood from the heart to the tissues. 614

aortic body Sensory receptor in the aortic arch sensitive to the O_2, CO_2, and H^+ content of the blood. 671

apical Directional term that refers to the tip of a filament or branch of a plant. 421

apical dominance Influence of a terminal bud in suppressing the growth of axillary buds. 485

apical meristem In vascular land plants, masses of cells in the root and shoot that reproduce and elongate as primary growth occurs. 447

apicomplexan Parasitic protozoans, formerly called sporozoans that lack mobility and form spores; now named for a unique collection of organelles. 394

apoptosis Programmed cell death; involves a cascade of specific cellular events leading to death and destruction of the cell. 155, 800

appendicular skeleton Part of the vertebrate skeleton comprising the appendages, shoulder girdle, and hip girdle. 742

appendix (vermiform appendix) In humans, small, tubular appendage that extends outward from the cecum of the large intestine. 653

aquaporin Channel protein through which water can diffuse across a membrane. 91, 688

arboreal Living in trees. 571

archaeans (archaea) Prokaryotic organisms that are members of the domain Archaea. 65, 378

archaeplastid Supergroup of eukaryotes that includes land plants and red and green algae. Developed from endosymbiotic cyanobacteria. 387

archegonium Egg-producing structures, as in the moss life cycle. 422

Arctic tundra Biome that encircles the Earth just south of ice-covered polar seas in the Northern Hemisphere. 888

arteriole Vessel that takes blood from an artery to capillaries. 608

artery Blood vessel that transports blood away from the heart. 608

arthritis Condition characterized by an inflammation of the joints; two common forms are osteoarthritis and rheumatoid arthritis. 743

arthropod Invertebrates, with an exoskeleton and jointed appendages, such as crustaceans and insects. 539

artificial selection Intentional breeding of certain traits, or combinations of traits, over others to produce a desirable outcome. 278

ascus Fingerlike sac in which nuclear fusion, meiosis, and ascospore production occur during sexual reproduction of sac fungi. 409

asexual reproduction Reproduction that requires only one parent and does not involve gametes. 166, 513

associative learning Acquired ability to associate two stimuli or between a stimulus and a response. 824

assortative mating Mating of individuals with similar phenotypes. 295

aster Short, radiating fibers produced by the centrosomes in animal cells. 159

asthma Condition in which bronchioles constrict and cause difficulty in breathing. 673

astigmatism Uneven shape of the cornea or lens of the eye; causes a distortion in the light reaching the retina of the eye. 724

astrocyte Nervous system cell that provides metabolic and structural support to the neurons. 697

asymmetry Lack of any symmetrical relationship in the morphology of an organism. 522

atherosclerosis Form of cardiovascular disease characterized by the accumulation of fatty materials (usually cholesterol) in the arteries. 616

atom Smallest particle of an element that displays the properties of the element. 22

atomic mass Average of atom mass units for all the isotopes of an atom. 23

atomic number Number of protons within the nucleus of an atom. 23

atomic symbol One or two letters that represent the name of an element—e.g., H stands for a hydrogen atom, and Na stands for a sodium atom. 22

ATP (adenosine triphosphate) Nucleotide with three phosphate groups. The breakdown of ATP into ADP + P makes energy available for energy-requiring processes in cells. 54, 107

ATP synthase Complex of proteins in the cristae of mitochondria and thylakoid membrane of chloroplast that produces ATP from the diffusion of hydrogen ions across a membrane. 114, 126

atrial natriuretic hormone (ANH) Hormone secreted by the heart that increases sodium excretion. 690, 763

atrioventricular valve Heart valve located between an atrium and a ventricle. 611

atrium Chamber; particularly an upper chamber of the heart lying above a ventricle. 610

auditory communication Sound that an animal makes for the purpose of sending a message to another individual. 828

auditory tube Also called the eustachian tube; connects the middle ear to the nasopharynx for the equalization of pressure. 727

australopithecine (australopith) One of several species of *Australopithecus*, a genus that contains the first generally recognized humanlike hominins. 577

autoimmune disease Disease that results when the immune system mistakenly attacks the body's own tissues. 642

autonomic system Portion of the peripheral nervous system that regulates internal organs. 708

autoploidy Polyploid organism with multiple chromosome sets all from the same species. 315

autosome Chromosome pairs that are the same between the sexes; in humans, all but the X and Y chromosomes. 201

autotroph Organism that can capture energy and synthesize organic molecules from inorganic nutrients. 120, 870

auxin Plant hormone regulating growth, particularly cell elongation; also called indoleacetic acid (IAA). 485

axial skeleton Part of the vertebrate skeleton forming the vertical support or axis, including the skull, the rib cage, and the vertebral column. 740

axillary bud Bud located in the axil of a leaf. 445

axon Elongated portion of a neuron that conducts nerve impulses, typically from the cell body to the synapse. 697

B

Bacillus A rod-shaped bacterium; also a genus of bacteria, *Bacillus*. 65

bacteriophage Virus that infects bacteria. 367

bacterium (pl., bacteria) Member of the domain Bacteria. 374

bark External part of a tree, containing cork, cork cambium, and phloem. 456

Barr body Dark-staining body in the cell nuclei of female mammals that contains a condensed, inactive X chromosome; named after its discoverer, Murray Barr. 185, 243

basal body A cytoplasmic structure that is located at the base of—and may organize—cilia or flagella. 80

basal nuclei Subcortical nuclei deep within the white matter that serve as relay stations for motor impulses and produce dopamine to help control skeletal muscle activities. 704

base Molecules tending to lower the hydrogen ion concentration in a solution and thus raise the pH numerically. 32

basidium Clublike structure in which nuclear fusion, meiosis, and basidiospore production occur during sexual reproduction of club fungi. 412

basophil White blood cell with a granular cytoplasm; able to be stained with a basic dye. 620

B cell Lymphocyte that matures in the bone marrow and, when stimulated by the presence of a specific antigen, gives rise to antibody-producing plasma cells. 629

B-cell receptor (BCR) Molecule on the surface of a B cell that binds to a specific antigen. 633

behavior Observable, coordinated responses to environmental stimuli. 820

behavioral ecology Study of how natural selection shapes behavior. 830

beneficial nutrient In plants, a molecule or element that is either required or enhances the growth and production of a plant. 465

benign Mass of cells derived from a single mutated cell that has repeatedly undergone cell division but has remained at the site of origin. 163

bicarbonate ion Ion that participates in buffering the blood, and the form in which carbon dioxide is transported in the bloodstream. 672

bilateral symmetry Body plan having two corresponding or complementary halves. 522

bile Secretion of the liver that is temporarily stored and concentrated in the gallbladder before being released into the small intestine, where it emulsifies fat. 652

binary fission Splitting of a parent cell into two daughter cells; serves as an asexual form of reproduction in bacteria. 166, 373

binomial nomenclature Scientific name of an organism, the first part of which designates the genus and the second part of which designates the specific epithet. 8, 349

biocultural evolution Phase of human evolution in which cultural events affect natural selection. 581

biodiversity Total number of species, the variability of their genes, and the communities in which they live. 10, 908

biodiversity hotspot Region of the world that contains unusually large concentrations of species. 909

biogeochemical cycle Circulating pathway of elements such as carbon and nitrogen involving exchange pools, storage areas, and biotic communities. 874

biogeography Study of the geographical distribution of organisms. 275

bioinformatics Area of scientific study that utilizes computer technologies to analyze large sets of data, typically in the study of genomics and proteomics. 265, 908

biological clock Internal mechanism that maintains a biological rhythm in the absence of environmental stimuli. 494

biological species concept The concept that defines species as groups of populations that have the potential to interbreed and that are reproductively isolated from other groups. 310

biology The branch of science that is concerned with the study of life and living organisms. 2

biomagnification The accumulation of pollutants as they move up the food web. 902

biomass The number of organisms multiplied by their weight. 873

biome One of the biosphere's major communities, characterized in particular by certain climatic conditions and particular types of plants. 887

biomolecule Organic molecules such as proteins, nucleic acids, carbohydrates, and fats. 38, 328

biosphere Zone of air, land, and water at the surface of the Earth in which living organisms are found. 9, 839

biotechnology products Commercial or agricultural products that are made with or derived from transgenic organisms. 258

biotic potential Maximum population growth rate under ideal conditions. 841

bird Endothermic reptile that has feathers and wings, is often adapted for flight, and lays hard-shelled eggs. 562

bivalent Homologous chromosomes, each having sister chromatids that are joined by a nucleoprotein lattice during meiosis; also called a tetrad. 173

bivalve Type of mollusc with a shell composed of two valves; includes clams, oysters, and scallops. 534

blade Broad, expanded portion of a land plant leaf that may be single or compound leaflets. 445

blastocoel Fluid-filled cavity of a blastula. 797

blastocyst Early stage of human embryonic development that consists of a hollow, fluid-filled ball of cells. 806

blastopore Opening into the primitive gut formed at gastrulation. 798

blastula Hollow, fluid-filled ball of cells occurring during animal development prior to gastrula formation. 523, 797

blind spot Region of the retina, lacking rods or cones, where the optic nerve leaves the eye. 721

blood Fluid circulated by the heart through a closed system of vessels; type of connective tissue. 591, 606

blood pressure Force of blood pushing against the inside wall of blood vessels. 615

body cavity In vertebrates, defined regions of the body in which organs reside. 596

bog Wet, spongy ground in a low-lying area, usually acidic and low in organic nutrients. 897

bolide Term for a large, crater-forming meteorite that strikes the Earth's surface. 343

bone Connective tissue having protein fibers and a hard matrix of inorganic salts, notably calcium salts. 591

bony fishes Vertebrates belonging to the class of fish called Osteichthyes that have a bony, rather than cartilaginous, skeleton. 554

bottleneck effect Type of genetic drift; occurs when a majority of genotypes are prevented from participating in the production of the next generation as a result of a natural disaster or human interference. 295

brachiopod Lophophorans in the phyla Brachiopoda that are characterized by two shells, one on the top and one on the bottom. 530

brain Ganglionic mass at the anterior end of the nerve cord; in vertebrates, the brain is located in the cranial cavity of the skull. 703

brain stem In mammals; portion of the brain consisting of the medulla oblongata, pons, and midbrain. 704

bronchiole In terrestrial vertebrates, small tube that conducts air from a bronchus to the alveoli. 668

bronchus (pl., bronchi) In terrestrial vertebrates, branch of the trachea that leads to the lungs. 668

brown algae Marine photosynthetic protists with a notable abundance of xanthophyll pigments; this group includes well-known seaweeds of northern rocky shores. 390

bryophyte A nonvascular land plant—including the mosses, liverworts, and hornworts—in which the gametophyte is dominant. 423

bryozoan Lophophorans of the phylum Bryozoa that are characterized as being aquatic and colonial that form colonies called zooids. 53

budding Asexual form of reproduction whereby a new organism develops as an outgrowth of the body of the parent. 406

buffer Substance or group of substances that tend to resist pH changes of a solution, thus stabilizing its relative acidity and basicity. 33

bulbourethral glands Male sex glands that produce pre-ejaculate fluid that neutralizes acid in the urethra. 777

bulk transport Movement of substances, usually large particles, across the plasma membrane using vesicles. 91

C

C_3 plant Plant that fixes carbon dioxide via the Calvin cycle; the first stable product of C_3 photosynthesis is a 3-carbon compound. 130

C_4 plant Plant that fixes carbon dioxide to produce a C_4 molecule that releases carbon dioxide to the Calvin cycle. 130

calcitonin Hormone secreted by the thyroid gland that increases the blood calcium level. 761

calorie Amount of heat energy required to raise the temperature of one gram of water 1°C. 29

Calvin cycle reaction Portion of photosynthesis that takes place in the stroma of chloroplasts and can occur in the dark; it uses the products of the light reactions to reduce CO_2 to a carbohydrate. 123

calyx The sepals collectively; the outermost flower whorl. 503

CAM Crassulacean-acid metabolism; a form of photosynthesis in succulent plants that separates the light-dependent and Calvin reactions by time. 130

camera-type eye Type of eye found in vertebrates and certain molluscs; a single lens focuses an image on closely packed photoreceptors. 720

camouflage Process of hiding from predators in which an organism's behavior, form, and pattern of coloration allow it to blend into the background and prevent detection. 863

cancer Malignant tumor whose nondifferentiated cells exhibit loss of contact inhibition, uncontrolled growth, and the ability to invade tissue and metastasize. 163

capillary Microscopic blood vessel; gases and other substances are exchanged across the walls of a capillary between blood and tissue fluid. 608

capsid Protective protein containing the genetic material of a virus. 366

capsule A form of glycocalyx that consists of a gelatinous layer; found in blue-green algae and certain bacteria. 65

carbaminohemoglobin Hemoglobin carrying carbon dioxide. 672

carbohydrate Class of organic compounds that typically contain carbon, hydrogen, and oxygen in a 1:2:1 ratio; includes the monosaccharides, disaccharides, and polysaccharides. 41

carbon dioxide fixation Process by which carbon dioxide gas is attached to an organic compound; in photosynthesis, this occurs in the Calvin cycle reactions. 128

carbonic anhydrase Enzyme in red blood cells that speeds the formation of carbonic acid from water and carbon dioxide. 672

carcinogen Environmental agent that causes mutations leading to the development of cancer. 248

cardiac cycle One complete cycle of systole and diastole for all heart chambers. 612

cardiac muscle Striated, involuntary muscle tissue found only in the heart. 593

cardiac output Blood volume pumped by each ventricle per minute (not total output pumped by both ventricles). 612

carnivore Consumer in a food chain that eats other animals. 870

carotenoid An accessory photosynthetic pigment of plants and algae that are often yellow or orange in color; consist of two classes—the xanthophylls and the carotenes. 124

carotid body Structure located at the branching of the carotid arteries; contains chemoreceptors sensitive to the O_2, CO_2, and H^+ content in blood. 671

carpel Ovule-bearing unit that is a part of a pistil. 503

carrier Heterozygous individual who has no apparent abnormality but can pass on an allele for a recessively inherited genetic disorder. 202

carrier protein Protein in the plasma membrane that combines with and transports a molecule or ion across the plasma membrane. 88

carrying capacity (K) Largest number of organisms of a particular species that can be maintained indefinitely by a given environment. 845

cartilage Connective tissue in which the cells lie within lacunae embedded in a flexible, proteinaceous matrix. 590

cartilaginous fish Vertebrates that belong to the class of fish called the Chondrichthyes: possess a cartilaginous, rather than bony, skeleton; includes sharks, rays, and skates. 554

Casparian strip Layer of impermeable lignin and suberin bordering four sides of root endodermal cells; prevents water and solute transport between adjacent cells. 451

catabolism Metabolic process that breaks down large molecules into smaller ones; catabolic metabolism. 147

cataracts Condition where the lens of the eye becomes opaque, preventing the transmission of light to the retina. 724

catastrophism Belief, proposed by Georges Cuvier, that periods of catastrophic extinctions occurred, after which repopulation of surviving species took place, giving the appearance of change through time. 273

cell The smallest unit of life that displays all the properties of life; composed of cytoplasm surrounded by a plasma membrane. 2, 61

cell body Portion of a neuron that contains a nucleus and from which dendrites and an axon extend. 697

cell cycle An ordered sequence of events in eukaryotes that involves cell growth and nuclear division; consists of the stages G_1, S, G_2, and M. 154

cell envelope In a prokaryotic cell, the portion composed of the plasma membrane, the cell wall, and the glycocalyx. 65

cell-mediated immunity Specific mechanism of defense in which T cells destroy antigen-bearing cells. 636

cell plate Structure across a dividing plant cell that signals the location of new plasma membranes and cell walls. 161

cell recognition protein Glycoproteins in the plasma membrane that identify self and help the body defend itself against pathogens. 89

cell suspension culture Small clumps of naked plant cells grown in tissue culture that produce drugs, cosmetics, or agricultural chemicals, among others. 514

cell theory One of the major theories of biology, which states that all organisms are made up of cells; cells are capable of self-reproduction and come only from preexisting cells. 61

cell wall Cellular structure that surrounds a plant, protistan, fungal, or bacterial cell and maintains the cell's shape and rigidity; composed of polysaccharides. 65, 100

cellular differentiation Process and developmental stages by which a cell becomes specialized for a particular function. 800

cellular respiration Metabolic reactions that use the energy from carbohydrate, fatty acid, or amino acid breakdown to produce ATP molecules. 136

cellular response Response to the transduction pathway in which proteins or enzymes change a signal to a format that the cell can understand, resulting in the appropriate response. 484

cellular slime mold Free-living amoeboid cells that feed on bacteria and yeasts by phagocytosis and aggregate to form a plasmodium that produces spores. 397

cellulose Polysaccharide that is the major complex carbohydrate in plant cell walls. 44

centipede Elongated arthropod characterized by having one pair of legs to each body segment; they may have 15 to 173 pairs of legs. 541

central dogma Processes that dictate the flow of information from the DNA to RNA to protein in a cell. 224

central nervous system (CNS) Portion of the nervous system consisting of the brain and spinal cord. 696

central vacuole In a plant cell, a large, fluid-filled sac that stores metabolites. During growth, it enlarges, forcing the primary cell wall to expand and the cell surface-area-to-volume ratio to increase. 75

centriole Cell structure, existing in pairs, that occurs in the centrosome and may help organize a mitotic spindle for chromosome movement during animal cell division. 79, 158

centromere Constriction where sister chromatids of a chromosome are held together. 157

centrosome Central microtubule organizing center of cells. In animal cells, it contains two centrioles. 78, 157

cephalization Having a well-recognized anterior head with a brain and sensory receptors. 522, 694

cephalochordate Small, fishlike invertebrate that is a member of the phylum Chordata. Probably the closest living relative to vertebrates. 550

cephalopod Type of mollusc in which the head is prominent and the foot is modified to form two arms and several tentacles; includes squids, cuttlefish, octopuses, and nautiluses. 536

cerebellum In terrestrial vertebrates, portion of the brain that coordinates skeletal muscles to produce smooth, graceful motions. 704

cerebral cortex Outer layer of cerebral hemispheres; receives sensory information and controls motor activities. 704

cerebral hemisphere Either of the two lobes of the cerebrum in vertebrates. 703

cerebrospinal fluid Fluid found in the ventricles of the brain, in the central canal of the spinal cord, and in association with the meninges. 702

cerebrum Largest part of the brain in mammals. 703

cervix Narrow end of the uterus, which leads into the vagina. 779

channel protein Protein that forms a channel to allow a particular molecule or ion to cross the plasma membrane. 88

chaparral Biome characterized by broad-leafed evergreen shrubs forming dense thickets. 894

chaperone protein Molecule that directs the proper folding of polypeptides. 53

character displacement Tendency for characteristics to be more divergent when similar species belong to the same community than when they are isolated from one another. 860

charophyte Type of living green algae that on the basis of nucleotide sequencing and cellular features is most closely related to land plants. 387, 421

chelicerate Arthropods (e.g., horseshoe crabs, sea spiders, arachnids), that exhibit a pair of pointed appendages used to manipulate food. 543

chemical energy Energy associated with the interaction of atoms in a molecule. 105

chemical signal Molecule that brings about a change in a cell, tissue, organ, or individual when it binds to a specific receptor. 755

chemiosmosis Process by which mitochondria and chloroplasts use the energy of an electron transport chain to create a hydrogen ion gradient that drives ATP formation. 126, 145

chemoautotroph Organism able to synthesize organic molecules by using carbon dioxide as the carbon source and the oxidation of an inorganic substance (such as hydrogen sulfide) as the energy source. 375

chemoheterotroph Organism that is unable to produce its own organic molecules, and therefore requires organic nutrients in its diet. 375

chemoreceptor Sensory receptor that is sensitive to chemical stimulation—for example, receptors for taste and smell. 717

chitin Strong but flexible nitrogenous polysaccharide found in the exoskeleton of arthropods and in the cell walls of fungi. 44, 405

chlorophyll Green photosynthetic pigment of algae and plants that absorbs solar energy; occurs as chlorophyll *a* and chlorophyll *b*. 121

chlorophyte Most abundant and diverse group of green algae, including freshwater, marine, and terrestrial forms that synthesize. Chlorophytes share chemical and anatomical characteristics with land plants. 387

chloroplast Membrane-bounded organelle in algae and plants with chlorophyll-containing membranous thylakoids; where photosynthesis takes place. 76, 121

choanoflagellate Unicellular choanoflagellates have one and colonial forms have many collar cells like those of sponges; choanoflagellates are the protists most closely related to animals. 397

cholesterol A steroid found in the plasma membrane of animal cells and from which other types of steroids are derived. 86

chordate Animals that have a dorsal tubular nerve cord, a notochord, pharyngeal gill pouches, and a postanal tail at some point in their life cycle; includes a few types of invertebrates (e.g., sea squirts and lancelets) and the vertebrates. 356, 550

chorion Extraembryonic membrane functioning for respiratory exchange in birds and reptiles; contributes to placenta formation in mammals. 805

chorionic villus In placental mammals treelike extension of the chorion, projecting into the maternal tissues at the placenta. 809

choroid Vascular, pigmented middle layer of the eyeball. 721

chromalveolate Supergroup of eukaryotes that includes alveolates and stramenopiles. 390

chromatid Following replication, a chromosome consists of a pair of sister chromatids, held together at the centromere; each chromatid is comprised of a single DNA helix. 154

chromatin Network of DNA strands and associated proteins observed within a nucleus of a cell. 70, 157, 241

chromoplast Plastid in land plants responsible for orange, yellow, and red color of plants, including the autumn colors in leaves. 77

chromosome The structure that transmits the genetic material from one generation to the next; composed of condensed chromatin; each species has a particular number of chromosomes that is passed on to the next generation. 70

chyme Thick, semiliquid food material that passes from the stomach to the small intestine. 652

chytrid (Chytridiomycota) Mostly aquatic fungi with flagellated spores that may represent the most ancestral fungal lineage. 406

cilia (sing., cilium) Short, hairlike projections from the plasma membrane, occurring usually in larger numbers. 80

ciliary muscle Within the ciliary body of the vertebrate eye, the ciliary muscle that controls the shape of the lens. 722

ciliate Complex unicellular protist that moves by means of cilia and digests food in food vacuoles. 393

circadian rhythm Biological rhythm with a 24-hour cycle. 494, 768

circulatory system In animals, an organ system that moves substances to and from cells, usually via a heart, blood, and blood vessels. 606, 608

cirrhosis Chronic, irreversible injury to liver tissue; commonly caused by frequent alcohol consumption. 656

citric acid cycle Cycle of reactions in mitochondria that begins with citric acid. This cycle breaks down an acetyl group and produces CO_2, ATP, NADH, and $FADH_2$; also called the Krebs cycle. 137, 143

clade Evolutionary lineage consisting of an ancestral species and all of its descendants, forming a distinct branch on a cladogram. 356

cladistics Method of systematics that uses derived characters to determine monophyletic groups and construct cladograms. 356

cladogram In cladistics, a branching diagram that shows the relationship among species in regard to their shared derived characters. 356

class One of the categories, or taxa, used by taxonomists to group species; the taxon above the order level. 6, 349

classification Process of naming organisms and assigning them to taxonomic groups (taxa). 348

classical conditioning Type of learning whereby an unconditioned stimulus that elicits a specific response is paired with a neutral stimulus so that the response becomes conditioned. 824

cleavage Cell division without cytoplasmic addition or enlargement; occurs during the first stage of animal development. 523, 797

cleavage furrow Indentation in the plasma membrane of animal cells during cell division; formation marks the start of cytokinesis. 160

climate Generalized weather patterns of an area, primarily determined by temperature and average rainfall. 884

climate change Recent changes in the Earth's climate; evidence suggests that this is primarily due to human influence, including the increased release of greenhouse gases. 127, 877, 915

climax community In ecology, community that results when succession has come to an end. 868

clonal selection theory States that the antigen selects which lymphocyte will undergo clonal expansion and produce more lymphocytes bearing the same type of receptor. 633

cloning Production of identical copies. In organisms, the production of organisms with the same genes; in genetic engineering, the production of many identical copies of a gene. 255

closed circulatory system A type of circulatory system where blood is confined to vessels and is kept separate from the interstitial fluid. 607

clotting Also called coagulation, the response of the body to an injury in the vessels of the circulatory system; involves platelets and clotting proteins. 620

club fungi (Basidiomycota) Fungi that produce spores in club-shaped basidia within a fruiting body; includes mushrooms, shelf fungi and puffballs. 412

cnidarian Invertebrates existing as either a polyp or medusa with two tissue layers and radial symmetry. 528

coacervate droplet An aggregate of colloidal droplets held together by electrostatic forces. 331

coccus A spherical-shaped bacterium. 65

cochlea Spiral-shaped structure of the vertebrate inner ear containing the sensory receptors for hearing. 727

codominance Inheritance pattern in which both alleles of a gene are equally expressed in a heterozygote. 205

codon Three-base sequence in messenger RNA that during translation directs the addition of a particular amino acid into a protein or directs termination of the process. 224

coelom Body cavity of an animal; the method by which the coelom is formed (or lack of formation) is an identifying characteristic in animal classification. 523

coenzyme Nonprotein organic molecule that aids the action of the enzyme to which it is loosely bound. 112

coevolution Mutual evolution in which two species exert selective pressures on the other species. 506, 866

cofactor Nonprotein assistant required by an enzyme in order to function; many cofactors are metal ions, others are coenzymes. 112

cohesion-tension model Explanation for upward transport of water in xylem based upon transpiration-created tension and the cohesive properties of water molecules. 476

cohort Group of individuals having a statistical factor in common, such as year of birth, in a population study. 841

coleoptile Protective sheath that covers the young leaves of a seedling. 485

collagen fiber White fiber in the matrix of connective tissue giving flexibility and strength. 589

collecting duct Duct within the kidney that receives fluid from several nephrons; the reabsorption of water occurs here. 686

collenchyma Plant tissue composed of cells with unevenly thickened walls; supports growth of stems and petioles. 448

colonial flagellate hypothesis Hypothesis that all animals are descended from an ancestor that resembled a hollow colony of flagellated cells, most likely resembling modern choanoflagellates. 521

colony Loose association of cells each remaining independent for most functions. 388

columnar epithelium Type of epithelial tissue with cylindrical cells. 589

comb jelly Invertebrates that resemble jelly fishes and are the largest animals to be propelled by beating cilia. 528

commensalism Symbiotic relationship in which one species is benefited, and the other is neither harmed nor benefited. 375, 865

common ancestor Ancestor common to at least two lines of descent. 354

communication Signal by a sender that influences the behavior of a receiver. 826

community Assemblage of species interacting with one another within the same environment. 9, 839, 858

compact bone Type of bone that contains osteons consisting of concentric layers of matrix and osteocytes in lacunae. 591, 739

comparative genomics Study of genomes through the direct comparison of their genes and DNA sequences from multiple species. 263

competition Results when members of a species attempt to use a resource that is in limited supply. 847

competitive exclusion principle Theory that no two species can occupy the same niche in the same place and at the same time. 860

competitive inhibition Form of enzyme inhibition where the substrate and inhibitor are both able to bind to the enzyme's active site. Only when the substrate is at the active site will product form. 113

complement Collective name for a series of enzymes and activators in the blood, some of which may bind to antibody and may lead to rupture of a foreign cell. 632

complementary base pairing Hydrogen bonding between particular purines and pyrimidines; responsible for the structure of DNA, and some RNA, molecules. 55, 219

complementary DNA (cDNA) DNA that has been synthesized from mRNA by the action of reverse transcriptase. 256

complete digestive tract Digestive tract that has both a mouth and an anus. 647

complex tissue In plants, tissue composed of two or more kinds of cells (e.g., xylem, containing tracheids and vessel elements; phloem, containing sieve-tube members and companion cells). 449

compound Substance having two or more different elements in a fixed ratio. 26

compound eye Type of eye found in arthropods; it is composed of many independent visual units. 720

concentration gradient Gradual change in chemical concentration between two areas of differing concentrations. 89

conclusion Statement made following an experiment as to whether or not the results support the hypothesis. 12

cone Reproductive structure in conifers made up of scales bearing sporangia; pollen cones bear microsporangia, and seed cones bear megasporangia. 430

cone cell Photoreceptor in vertebrate eyes that responds to bright light and makes color vision possible. 721

conidiospore Spore produced by sac and club fungi during asexual reproduction. 409

conifer Member of a group of cone-bearing gymnosperm land plants that includes pine, cedar, and spruce trees. 430

conjugation Transfer of genetic material from one cell to another. 388

conjugation pilus (pl., conjugation pili) In a bacterium, elongated, hollow appendage used to transfer DNA to other cells. 66, 373

conjunctiva Delicate membrane that lines the eyelid protecting the sclera. 721

connective tissue Type of animal tissue that binds structures together, provides support and protection, fills spaces, stores fat, and forms blood cells; adipose tissue, cartilage, bone, and blood are types of connective tissue; living cells in a nonliving matrix. 589

conservation biology Discipline that seeks to understand the effects of human activities on species, communities, and ecosystems and to develop practical approaches to preventing the extinction of species and the destruction of ecosystems. 908

consumer Organism that feeds on another organism in a food chain generally; primary consumers eat plants, and secondary consumers eat animals. 870

continental drift The movement of the Earth's crust by plate tectonics resulting in the movement of continents with respect to one another. 342

contraceptive vaccine Under development, this birth control method immunizes against the hormone HCG, crucial to maintaining implantation of the embryo. 784

control Sample that goes through all the steps of an experiment but does not contain the variable being tested; a standard against which the results of an experiment are checked. 12

convergent evolution Similarity in structure in distantly related groups generally due to similiar selective pressures in like environments. 357

copulation Sexual union between a male and a female. 774

coral reef Coral formations in shallow tropical waters that support an abundance of diversity. 901

corepressor Molecule that binds to a repressor, allowing the repressor to bind to an operator in a repressible operon. 239

cork Outer covering of the bark of trees; made of dead cells that may be sloughed off. 447

cork cambium Lateral meristem that produces cork. 447

cornea Transparent, anterior portion of the outer layer of the eyeball. 721

corolla The petals, collectively; usually the conspicuously colored flower whorl. 503

corpus luteum Follicle that has released an egg and increases its secretion of progesterone. 780

cortex In plants, ground tissue bounded by the epidermis and vascular tissue in stems and roots; in animals, outer layer of an organ, such as the cortex of the kidney or adrenal gland. 451

cortisol Glucocorticoid secreted by the adrenal cortex that responds to stress on a long-term basis; reduces inflammation and promotes protein and fat metabolism. 763

cost-benefit analysis A weighing-out of the costs and benefits (in terms of contributions to reproductive success) of a particular strategy or behavior. 298

cotyledon Seed leaf for embryo of a flowering plant; provides nutrient molecules for the developing plant before photosynthesis begins. 433, 508

countercurrent exchange Fluids flow side-by-side in opposite directions, as in the exchange of fluids in the kidneys. 666

coupled reactions Reactions that occur simultaneously; one is an exergonic reaction that releases energy, and the other is an endergonic reaction that requires an input of energy in order to occur. 108

covalent bond Chemical bond in which atoms share one pair of electrons. 27

cranial nerve Nerve that arises from the brain. 707

crenation In animal cells, shriveling of the cell due to water leaving the cell when the environment is hypertonic. 94

cristae (sing., crista) Short, fingerlike projections formed by the folding of the inner membrane of mitochondria. 77

Cro-Magnon Common name for the first fossils to be designated *Homo sapiens*. 580

crossing-over Exchange of segments between nonsister chromatids of a bivalent during meiosis. 174

crustacean Member of a group of aquatic arthropods that contains, among others, shrimps, crabs, crayfish, and lobsters. 540

cryptic species Species that are very similar in appearance but are considered separate species based on other characteristics, such as behavior or genetics. 307

cuboidal epithelium Type of epithelial tissue with cube-shaped cells. 588

cutaneous receptor Sensory receptors of the dermis that are activated by touch, pain, pressure, and temperature. 730

cuticle Waxy layer covering the epidermis of plants that protects the plant against water loss and disease-causing organisms. 422

cyanobacterium (pl., cyanobacteria) Photosynthetic bacterium that contains chlorophyll and releases oxygen; formerly called a blue-green alga. 66, 377

cyanogenic glycoside Plant compound that contains sugar; produces cyanide. 497

cycad Type of gymnosperm with palmate leaves and massive cones; cycads are most often found in the tropics and subtropics. 432

cyclic adenosine monophosphate (cAMP) ATP-related compound that acts as the second messenger in peptide hormone transduction; it initiates activity of the metabolic machinery. 755

cyclin Protein that cycles in quantity as the cell cycle progresses; combines with and activates the kinases that function to promote the events of the cycle. 155

cyst In protists and invertebrates, resting structure that contains reproductive bodies or embryos. 384, 533

cystic fibrosis (CF) Genetic disease caused by a defect in the *CFTR* gene, which is responsible for the formation of a transmembrane chloride ion transporter; causes the mucus of the body to be viscous. 675

cytochrome Any of several iron-containing protein molecules that are members of the electron transport chain in photosynthesis and cellular respiration. 144

cytokine Type of protein secreted by a T lymphocyte that attacks viruses, virally infected cells, and cancer cells. 633

cytokinesis Division of the cytoplasm following mitosis or meiosis. 155

cytokinin Plant hormone that promotes cell division; often works in combination with auxin during organ development in plant embryos. 487

cytoplasm Region of a cell between the nucleus, or the nucleoid region of a bacterium, and the plasma membrane; contains the organelles of the cell. 65

cytoplasmic segregation Process that parcels out the maternal determinants, which play a role in development, during mitosis. 800

cytosine (C) One of four nitrogen-containing bases in the nucleotides composing the structure of DNA and RNA; pairs with guanine. 217

cytoskeleton Internal framework of the cell, consisting of microtubules, actin filaments, and intermediate filaments. 68

cytotoxic T cell T lymphocyte that attacks and kills antigen-bearing cells. 635

D

data (sing., datum) Facts or information collected through observation and/or experimentation. 12

day-neutral plant Plant whose flowering is not dependent on day length—e.g., tomato and cucumber. 496

deamination Removal of an amino group (—NH$_2$) from an amino acid or other organic compound. 147

deciduous Land plant that sheds its leaves annually. 445

decomposer Organism, usually a bacterium or fungus, that breaks down organic matter into inorganic nutrients that can be recycled in the environment. 871

deductive reasoning The use of general principles to predict specific outcomes. Often uses "if . . . then" statements. 11

dehydration reaction Chemical reaction in which a water molecule is released during the formation of a covalent bond. 40

delayed allergic response Allergic response initiated at the site of the allergen by sensitized T cells, involving macrophages and regulated by cytokines. 642

deletion Change in chromosome structure in which the end of a chromosome breaks off or two simultaneous breaks lead to the loss of an internal segment; often causes abnormalities—e.g., cri du chat syndrome. 187

demographic transition Due to industrialization, a decline in the birthrate following a reduction in the death rate so that the population growth rate is lowered. 851

demography Properties of the rate of growth and the age structure of populations. 840

denatured Loss of a protein's or enzyme's normal shape so that it no longer functions; usually caused by a less than optimal pH and temperature. 53, 111

dendrite Part of a neuron that sends signals toward the cell body. 697

dendritic cell Antigen-presenting cell of the epidermis and mucous membranes. 632

denitrification Conversion of nitrate or nitrite to nitrogen gas by bacteria in soil. 878

dense fibrous connective tissue Type of connective tissue containing many collagen fibers packed together; found in tendons and ligaments, for example. 590

density-dependent factor Biotic factor, such as disease or competition, that affects population size in a direct relationship to the population's density. 847

density-independent factor Abiotic factor, such as fire or flood, that affects population size independent of the population's density. 847

deoxyribose Pentose sugar found in DNA. 42

derived trait Structural, physiological, or behavioral trait that is present in a specific lineage and is not present in the common ancestor for several related lineages. 354

dermis In mammals, thick layer of the skin underlying the epidermis. 598

desert Ecological biome characterized by a limited amount of rainfall; deserts have hot days and cool nights. 896

desmosome(s) Intercellular junctions that connect cytoskeletons of adjacent cells. 99

detritivore Any organism that obtains most of its nutrients from the detritus in an ecosystem. 870

deuterostome Group of coelomate animals in which the second embryonic opening is associated with the mouth; the first embryonic opening, the blastopore, is associated with the anus. 523

development Process of regulated growth and differentiation of cells and tissues. 508, 797

diabetic retinopathy Complication of diabetes that causes the capillaries in the retina to become damaged, potentially causing blindness. 724

diagnostic traits Characteristics that distinguish species from one another. 307

diaphragm In mammals, dome-shaped muscularized sheet separating the thoracic cavity from the abdominal cavity; contraceptive device that prevents sperm from reaching the egg. 669

diapsid Characteristic of a vertebrate skull in which there are two openings in the skull behind the eye socket (orbit). 558

diarrhea Excessively frequent and watery bowel movements. 653

diastole Relaxation period of a heart chamber during the cardiac cycle. 612

diatom Golden-brown alga with a cell wall in two parts, or valves; significant component of phytoplankton. 391

differentiation Specialization in the structure or function of a cell typically caused by the activation of specific genes. 508

diffusion Movement of molecules or ions from a region of higher to lower concentration; it requires no energy and tends to lead to an equal distribution (equilibrium). 91

dihybrid cross Cross between parents that differ in two traits. 198

dikaryotic Having two haploid nuclei that stem from different parent cells; during sexual reproduction, sac and club fungi have dikaryotic cells. 406

dinoflagellate Photosynthetic unicellular protist with two flagella, one whiplash and the other located within a groove between protective cellulose plates; significant part of phytoplankton. 392

dinosaur General term used to describe the large reptiles that existed prior to the start of the Cretaceous period. 559

dioecious Having unisexual flowers or cones, with the male flowers or cones confined to certain land plants and the female flowers or cones of the same species confined to other different plants. 432

diploid (2n) Cell condition in which two of each type of chromosome are present. 157, 172

diplomonad Protist that has modified mitochondria, two equal-sized nuclei, and multiple flagella. 395

directional selection Outcome of natural selection in which an extreme phenotype is favored, usually in a changing environment. 296

disaccharide Sugar that contains two monosaccharide units; e.g., maltose. 42

disruptive selection Outcome of natural selection in which the two extreme phenotypes are favored over the average phenotype, leading to more than one distinct form. 297

distal convoluted tubule Final portion of a nephron that joins with a collecting duct; associated with tubular secretion. 686

diverge Process by which a new evolutionary path begins; on a phylogenetic tree this is indicated by branching lines. 354

DNA (deoxyribonucleic acid) Nucleic acid polymer produced from covalent bonding of nucleotide monomers that contain the sugar deoxyribose; the genetic material of nearly all organisms. 54

DNA ligase Enzyme that links DNA fragments; used during production of recombinant DNA to join foreign DNA to vector DNA. 255

DNA microarray Glass or plastic slide containing thousands of single-stranded DNA fragments arranged in an array (grid); used to detect and measure gene expression; also called gene chips. 263

DNA polymerase During replication, an enzyme that joins the nucleotides complementary to a DNA template. 220

DNA repair enzyme One of several enzymes that restore the original base sequence in an altered DNA strand. 248

DNA replication Synthesis of a new DNA double helix prior to mitosis and meiosis in eukaryotic cells and during prokaryotic fission in prokaryotic cells. 220

domain Largest of the categories, or taxa, used by taxonomists to group species; the three domains are Archaea, Bacteria, and Eukarya. 6, 349

domain Archaea One of the three domains of life; contains prokaryotic cells that often live in extreme habitats and have unique genetic, biochemical, and physiological characteristics; its members are sometimes referred to as *archaea*. 7, 351

domain Bacteria One of the three domains of life; contains prokaryotic cells that differ from archaea because they have their own unique genetic, biochemical, and physiological characteristics. 7, 351

domain Eukarya One of the three domains of life, consisting of organisms with eukaryotic cells; includes protists, fungi, plants, and animals. 7, 351

dominance hierarchy Organization of animals in a group that determines the order in which the animals have access to resources. 298

dominant allele Allele that exerts its phenotypic effect in the heterozygote; it masks the expression of the recessive allele. 196

dormancy In plants, a cessation of growth under conditions that seem appropriate for growth. 487

dorsal root ganglion Mass of sensory neuron cell bodies located in the dorsal root of a spinal nerve. 707

double fertilization In flowering plants, one sperm nucleus unites with the egg nucleus, and a second sperm nucleus unites with the polar nuclei of an embryo sac. 437, 505

double helix Double spiral; describes the three-dimensional shape of DNA. 218

doubling time Number of years it takes for a population to double in size. 851

dryopithecine Tree dwelling primate existing 12–9 MYA; ancestral to apes. 574

duodenum First part of the small intestine, where chyme enters from the stomach. 652

duplication Change in chromosome structure in which a particular segment is present more than once in the same chromosome. 187

E

ecdysozoan Protostome characterized by periodic molting of their exoskeleton. Includes the roundworms and arthropods. 538

echinoderm Invertebrates such as sea stars, sea urchins, and sand dollars; characterized by radial symmetry and a water vascular system. 544

ecological niche Role an organism plays in its community, including its habitat and its interactions with other organisms. 859

ecological pyramid Visual depiction of the biomass, number of organisms, or energy content of various trophic levels in a food web—from the producer to the final consumer populations. 873

ecological release In an ecosystem, the freedom of a species to expand its use of available resources due to an elimination of competition. 316

ecological succession The gradual replacement of communities in an area following a disturbance (secondary succession) or the creation of new soil (primary succession). 868

ecology Study of the interactions of organisms with other organisms and with the physical and chemical environment. 839

ecosystem Biological community together with the associated abiotic environment; characterized by a flow of energy and a cycling of inorganic nutrients. 9, 839, 870

ecosystem diversity Variety of species in a particular locale, dependent on the species interactions. 909

ectoderm Outermost primary tissue layer of an animal embryo; gives rise to the nervous system and the outer layer of the integument. 798

ectotherm Organism having a body temperature that varies according to the environmental temperature. 553

edge effect Phenomenon in which the edges around a landscape patch provide a slightly different habitat than the favorable habitat in the interior of the patch. 919

effector Muscle or gland that receives signals from motor fibers and thereby allows an organism to respond to environmental stimuli. 708

egg Also called an ovum; haploid cell that is usually fertilized by a sperm to form a diploid zygote. 779

elastic cartilage Type of cartilage composed of elastic fibers, allowing greater flexibility. 591

elastic fiber Yellow fiber in the matrix of connective tissue, providing flexibility. 589

electrocardiogram (ECG) Recording of the electrical activity associated with the heartbeat. 613

electron Negative subatomic particle, moving about in an energy level around the nucleus of an atom. 22

electronegativity The ability of an atom to attract electrons toward itself in a chemical bond. 27

electron shell The average location, or energy level, of an electron in an atom. Often drawn as concentric circles around the nucleus. 23

electron transport chain (ETC) Process in a cell that involves the passage of electrons along a series of membrane-bound electron carrier molecules from a higher to lower energy level; the energy released is used for the synthesis of ATP. 137, 144

element Substances that cannot be broken down into substances with different properties; composed of only one type atom. 22

El Niño–Southern Oscillation Warming of water in the Eastern Pacific equatorial region such that the Humboldt Current is displaced, with possible negative results such as reduction in marine life. 904

elongation Middle stage of translation in which additional amino acids specified by the mRNA are added to the growing polypeptide. 231

embryo Stage of a multicellular organism that develops from a zygote before it becomes free-living; in seed plants, the embryo is part of the seed. 797

embryo sac Female gametophyte (megagametophyte) of flowering plants. 504

embryonic development In humans, the first two months of development following fertilization during which the major organs are formed. 805

embryonic disk During human development, flattened area during gastrulation from which the embryo arises. 808

embryophyta Bryophytes and vascular plants; both of which produce embryos. 422

emergent property A function or trait that appears as biological complexity increases. 2

emerging viruses Newly identified viruses that are becoming more prominent usually because they cause serious disease. 369

emphysema Disorder of the respiratory system, specifically the lungs, that is characterized by damage to the alveoli, thus reducing the ability to exchange gases with the external environment. 675

endangered species A species that is in peril of immediate extinction throughout all or most of its range (e.g., California condor, snow leopard). 908

endergonic reaction Chemical reaction that requires an input of energy; opposite of exergonic reaction. 107

endocrine gland Ductless organ that secretes hormone(s) into the bloodstream. 589, 753

endocrine system Organ system involved in the coordination of body activities; uses hormones as chemical signals secreted into the bloodstream. 753

endocytosis Process by which substances are moved into the cell from the environment; includes phagocytosis, pinocytosis, and receptor-mediated endocytosis. 97

endoderm Innermost primary tissue layer of an animal embryo that gives rise to the linings of the digestive tract and associated structures. 798

endodermis Internal plant root tissue forming a boundary between the cortex and the vascular cylinder. 451

endomembrane system Cellular system that consists of the nuclear envelope, endoplasmic reticulum, Golgi apparatus, and vesicles. 72

endometrium Mucous membrane lining the interior surface of the uterus. 779

endoplasmic reticulum (ER) System of membranous saccules and channels in the cytoplasm, often with attached ribosomes. 72

endoskeleton Protective internal skeleton, as in vertebrates. 737

endosperm In flowering plants, nutritive storage tissue that is derived from the union of a sperm nucleus and polar nuclei in the embryo sac. 505

endospore Spore formed within a cell; certain bacteria form endospores. 375

endosymbiosis *See* endosymbiotic theory.

endosymbiotic theory Explanation of the evolution of eukaryotic organelles by phagocytosis of prokaryotes. 67, 335

endotherm Organism in which maintenance of a constant body temperature is independent of the environmental temperature. 563

energy Capacity to do work and bring about change; occurs in a variety of forms. 4, 105

energy of activation Energy that must be added in order for molecules to react with one another. 109

enhancer DNA sequence that acts as a regulatory element to increase the level of transcription when regulatory proteins, such as transcription activators, bind to it. 244

entropy Measure of disorder or randomness in a system. 106

enzymatic protein Protein that catalyzes a specific reaction; may be found in the plasma membrane or the cytoplasm of the cell. 89

enzyme Organic catalyst, usually a protein, that speeds a reaction in cells due to its particular shape. 41, 109

enzyme inhibition Means by which cells regulate enzyme activity; may be competitive or noncompetitive inhibition. 112

eosinophil White blood cell containing cytoplasmic granules that stain with acidic dye. 632

epidermal tissue Exterior tissue, usually one cell thick, of leaves, young stems, roots, and other parts of plants. 447

epidermis In mammals, the outer, protective layer of the skin; in plants, tissue that covers roots, leaves, and stems of nonwoody organisms. 447, 451, 598

epididymis Location of sperm maturation in an adult human; located in the testis. 775

epigenetic inheritance An inheritance pattern in which a nuclear gene has been modified but the changed expression of the gene is not permanent over many generations; the transmission of genetic information by means that are not based on the coding sequences of a gene. 241

epiglottis Structure that covers the glottis, the air-tract opening, during the process of swallowing. 668

epinephrine Hormone secreted by the adrenal medulla in times of stress; adrenaline. 762

epiphyte Plant that takes its nourishment from the air because its placement in other plants gives it an aerial position. 428, 892

epithelial tissue Tissue that lines hollow organs and covers surfaces. 588

erythropoietin (EPO) Hormone produced by the kidneys that speeds red blood cell formation. 688

esophagus Muscular tube for moving swallowed food from the pharynx to the stomach. 651

essential nutrient In plants, substance required for normal growth, development, or reproduction; in humans, a nutrient that cannot be produced in sufficient quantities by the body and must be obtained from the diet. 465

estrogen Female sex hormone that helps maintain sexual organs and secondary sex characteristics. 779

estuary Portion of the ocean located where a river enters and fresh water mixes with salt water. 900

ethylene Plant hormone that causes ripening of fruit and is also involved in abscission. 488

etiolate Changes to a plant, such as yellowing of leaves and increase in shoot length, that occur when it is grown in darkness. 495

euchromatin Chromatin with a lower level of compaction and therefore accessible for transcription. 234

eudicot (Eudicotyledone) Flowering plant group; members have two embryonic leaves (cotyledons), net-veined leaves, vascular bundles in a ring, flower parts in fours or fives and their multiples, and other characteristics. 433, 446

euglenid Flagellated and flexible freshwater unicellular protist that usually contains chloroplasts and has a semirigid cell wall. 395

eukaryotic cell (eukaryote) Type of cell that has a membrane-bounded nucleus and membranous organelles; found in organisms within the domain Eukarya. 7, 65

euploidy Condition in which a cell contains the correct number, and combinations, of chromosomes. 183

eutrophication Enrichment of water by inorganic nutrients used by phytoplankton. Often, overenrichment caused by human activities leads to excessive bacterial growth and oxygen depletion. 877, 898

evergreen Land plant that sheds leaves over a long period, so some leaves are always present. 445

evolution Genetic change in a species over time resulting in the development of genetic and phenotypic differences that are the basis of natural selection; descent of organisms from a common ancestor. 5, 272

evolutionary species concept Every species has its own evolutionary history, which is partly documented in the fossil record. 307

excavate Supergroup of eukaryotes that includes euglenids, kinetoplastids, parabasalids, and diplomonads. 395

excretion Elimination of metabolic wastes by an organism at exchange boundaries such as the plasma membrane of unicellular organisms and excretory tubules of multicellular animals. 681

exergonic reaction Chemical reaction that releases energy; opposite of endergonic reaction. 107

exocrine gland Gland that secretes its product to an epithelial surface directly or through ducts. 589, 753

exocytosis Process in which an intracellular vesicle fuses with the plasma membrane so

that the vesicle's contents are released outside the cell. 95

exon Segment of mRNA containing the protein-coding portion of a gene that remains within the mRNA after splicing has occurred. 226

exophthalmos Condition associated with an enlargement of the thyroid gland accompanied by an abnormal protrusion of the eyes. 761

exoskeleton Protective external skeleton, as in arthropods. 736

exotic species Nonnative species that migrate or are introduced by humans into a new ecosystem; also called alien species. 913

experiment A test of a hypothesis that examines the influence of a single variable. Often involves both control and test groups. 11

experimental design Methodology by which an experiment will seek to support the hypothesis. 11

experimental variable Factor of the experiment being tested. 12

expiration Act of expelling air from the lungs; exhalation. 656

exponential growth Growth, particularly of a population, in which the increase occurs in the same manner as compound interest. 844

extant Species, or other levels of taxa, that are still living. 272

external respiration Exchange of oxygen and carbon dioxide between alveoli of the lungs and blood. 664

extinct; extinction Total disappearance of a species or higher group. 10, 338

extracellular matrix (ECM) Nonliving substance secreted by some animal cells; is composed of protein and polysaccharides. 87

extraembryonic membrane Membrane that is not a part of the embryo but is necessary to the continued existence and health of the embryo. 774, 805

ex vivo gene therapy Gene therapy in which cells are removed from an organism, and DNA is injected to correct a genetic defect; the cells are returned to the organism to treat a disease or disorder. 256

F

facilitated transport Passive transfer of a substance into or out of a cell along a concentration gradient by a process that requires a protein carrier. 94

facultative anaerobe Prokaryote that is able to grow in either the presence or the absence of gaseous oxygen. 374

FAD Flavin adenine dinucleotide; a coenzyme of oxidation-reduction that becomes $FADH_2$ as oxidation of substrates occurs in the mitochondria during cellular respiration, FAD then delivers electrons to the electron transport chain. 136

fall overturn Mixing process that occurs in fall in stratified lakes, whereby oxygen-rich top waters mix with nutrient-rich bottom waters. 898

family One of the categories, or taxa, used by taxonomists to group species; the taxon located above the genus level. 6, 349

family pedigree Chart of genetic relationship of family individuals across generations. 204

farsighted (hyperopic) Condition in which an individual cannot focus on objects closely; caused by the focusing of the image behind the retina of the eye. 724

fat Organic molecule that contains glycerol and three fatty acids; energy storage molecule. 46

fatty acid Molecule that contains a hydrocarbon chain and ends with an acid group. 46

fermentation Anaerobic breakdown of glucose that results in a gain of two ATP and end products such as alcohol and lactate; occurs in the cytoplasm of cells. 137, 140

fern Member of a group of land plants that have large fronds; in the sexual life cycle, the independent gametophyte produces flagellated sperm, and the vascular sporophyte produces windblown spores. 428

fertilization Fusion of sperm and egg nuclei, producing a zygote that develops into a new individual. 175, 796

fibroblast Cell found in loose connective tissue that synthesizes collagen and elastic fibers in the matrix. 590

fibrocartilage Cartilage with a matrix of strong collagenous fibers. 591

fibrous protein A protein that has only a secondary structure; generally insoluble; includes collagens, elastins, and keratins. 51

fibrous root system In most monocots, a mass of similarly sized roots that cling to the soil. 452

filament End-to-end chains of cells that form as cell division occurs in only one plane; in plants, the elongated stalk of a stamen. 388

fimbria (pl., fimbriae) Small, bristlelike fiber on the surface of a bacterial cell, which attaches bacteria to a surface; also fingerlike extension from the oviduct near the ovary. 66, 372

fin In fishes and other aquatic animals, membranous, winglike, or paddlelike process used to propel, balance, or guide the body. 553

first messenger Chemical signal such as a peptide hormone that binds to a plasma membrane receptor protein and alters the metabolism of a cell because a second messenger is activated. 755

fishes Aquatic, gill-breathing vertebrate that usually has fins and skin covered with scales; fishes were among the earliest vertebrates that evolved. 553

fitness Ability of an organism to reproduce and pass its genes to the next fertile generation; measured against the ability of other organisms to reproduce in the same environment. 297

five-kingdom system System of classification that contains the kingdoms Monera, Protista, Plantae, Animalia, and Fungi. 351

fixed action pattern (FAP) Innate behavior pattern that is stereotyped, spontaneous, independent of immediate control, genetically encoded, and independent of individual learning. 822

flagellum (pl., flagella) Long, slender extension used for locomotion by some bacteria, protozoans, and sperm. 66, 80, 372

flagship species Species that evoke a strong emotional response in humans; charismatic, cute, regal (e.g., lions, tigers, dolphins, pandas). 918

flatworm Invertebrates such as planarians and tapeworms with extremely thin bodies; a three-branched gastrovascular cavity and a ladder type nervous system. 531

flower Reproductive organ of a flowering plant, consisting of several kinds of modified leaves arranged in concentric rings and attached to a modified stem called the receptacle. 434, 502

fluid-mosaic model Model for the plasma membrane based on the changing location and pattern of protein molecules in a fluid phospholipid bilayer. 87

follicle Structure in the ovary of animals that contains an oocyte; site of oocyte production. 780

follicular phase First half of the ovarian cycle, during which the follicle matures and much estrogen (and some progesterone) is produced. 780

food chain The order in which one population feeds on another in an ecosystem, thereby showing the flow of energy from a detritivore (detrital food chain) or a producer (grazing food chain) to the final consumer. 873

food web In ecosystems, a complex pattern of interlocking and crisscrossing food chains. 873

foraminiferan A protist bearing a calcium carbonate test with many openings through which pseudopods extend. 398

formed elements Portion of the blood that consists of erythrocytes, leukocytes, and platelets (thrombocytes). 618

formula A group of symbols and numbers used to express the composition of a compound. 26

fossil Any past evidence of an organism that has been preserved in the Earth's crust. 280, 333

founder effect Cause of genetic drift due to colonization by a limited number of individuals who, by chance, have different genotype and allele frequencies than the parent population. 295

fovea centralis Region of the retina consisting of densely packed cones; responsible for the greatest visual acuity. 721

frameshift mutation Insertion or deletion of at least one base so that the reading frame of the corresponding mRNA changes. 248

free energy Energy in a system that is capable of performing work. 107

frond Leaf of a fern, palm, or cycad. 428

fruit Flowering plant structure consisting of one or more ripened ovaries that usually contain seeds. 437, 511

fruiting body Spore-producing and spore-disseminating structure found in sac and club fungi. 409

functional genomics Study of gene function at the genome level. It involves the study of many genes simultaneously and the use of DNA microarrays. 263

functional group Specific cluster of atoms attached to the carbon skeleton of organic molecules that enters into reactions and behaves in a predictable way. 39

fungus (pl., fungi) Eukaryotic saprotrophic decomposer; the body is made up of filaments called hyphae that form a mass called a mycelium. 8, 404

G

gallbladder Organ attached to the liver that serves to store and concentrate bile. 656

gametangia Cell or multicellular structure in which gametes are formed. 408

gamete Haploid sex cell; e.g., egg or sperm. 172, 785

gametogenesis Development of the male and female sex gametes. 180

gametophyte Haploid generation of the alternation of generations life cycle of a plant; produces gametes that unite to form a diploid zygote. 180, 422, 504

ganglion (pl., ganglia) Collection or bundle of neuron cell bodies usually outside the central nervous system. 531, 694

gap junction Junction between cells formed by the joining of two adjacent plasma membranes; it lends strength and allows ions, sugars, and small molecules to pass between cells. 100

gastropod Mollusc with a broad, flat foot for crawling (e.g., snails and slugs). 535

gastrovascular cavity Blind digestive cavity in animals that have a sac body plan. 528

gastrula Stage of animal development during which the germ layers form, at least in part, by invagination. 798

gastrulation Formation of a gastrula from a blastula; characterized by an invagination to form cell layers of a caplike structure. 798

gel electrophoresis Process that separates molecules, such as proteins and DNA, based on their size and electrical charge by passing them through a matrix. 257

gene Unit of heredity existing as alleles on the chromosomes; in diploid organisms, typically two alleles are inherited—one from each parent. 5, 70

gene cloning DNA cloning to produce many identical copies of the same gene. 255

gene flow Sharing of genes between two populations through interbreeding. 294

gene mutation Altered gene whose sequence of bases differs from the original sequence. 247

gene pharming Production of pharmaceuticals using transgenic organisms, usually agricultural animals. 258

gene pool Total of all the alleles of all the individuals in a population. 290

gene therapy Correction of a detrimental mutation by the insertion of DNA sequences into the genome of a cell. 255, 260

genetically modified organisms (GMO) Organism whose genetic material has been altered or enhanced using DNA technology. 258

genetic code Universal code that has existed for eons and allows for conversion of DNA and RNA's chemical code to a sequence of amino acids in a protein. Each codon consists of three bases that stand for one of the 20 amino acids found in proteins or directs the termination of translation. 224

genetic diversity Variety among members of a population. 908

genetic drift Mechanism of evolution due to random changes in the allelic frequencies of a population; more likely to occur in small populations or when only a few individuals of a large population reproduce. 294

genetic profile An individual's genome, including any possible mutations. 263

genetic recombination Process in which chromosomes are broken and rejoined to form novel combinations; in this way offspring receive alleles in combinations different from their parents. 175

genomics Area of study that examines the genome of a species or group of species. 261

genotype Genes of an organism for a particular trait or traits; often designated by letters—for example, *BB* or *Aa*. 196

genus One of the categories, or taxa, used by taxonomists to group species; contains those species that are most closely related through evolution. 6, 349

geologic timescale History of the Earth based on the fossil record and divided into eras, periods, and epochs. 334

germ cell During zygote development, cells that are set aside from the somatic cells and that will eventually undergo meiosis to produce gametes. 773

germinate Beginning of growth of a seed, spore, or zygote, especially after a period of dormancy. 512

germ layer Primary tissue layer of a vertebrate embryo—namely, ectoderm, mesoderm, or endoderm. 522, 798

gibberellin Plant hormone promoting increased stem growth; also involved in flowering and seed germination. 486

gills Respiratory organ in most aquatic animals; in fish, an outward extension of the pharynx. 550, 664

ginkgo Member of phylum Ginkgophyte; maidenhair tree. 432

girdling Removing a strip of bark from around a tree. 478

gland Epithelial cell or group of epithelial cells that are specialized to secrete a substance. 589

glaucoma Condition in which the fluid in the eye (aqueous humor) accumulates, increasing pressure in the eye and damaging nerve fibers. 724

global warming Predicted increase in the Earth's temperature due to human activities that promote the greenhouse effect. 877

globular protein Most of the proteins in the body; soluble in water or salt solution; includes albumins, globulins, histones. 52

glomerular capsule Cuplike structure that is the initial portion of a nephron. 685

glomerular filtration Movement of small molecules from the glomerulus into the glomerular capsule due to the action of blood pressure. 686

glomerulus Capillary network within the glomerular capsule of a nephron. 686

glottis Opening for airflow in the larynx. 668

glucagon Hormone produced by the pancreas that stimulates the liver to break down glycogen, thus raising blood glucose levels. 765

glucocorticoid Type of hormone secreted by the adrenal cortex that influences carbohydrate, fat, and protein metabolism; *See also* cortisol. 763

glucose Six-carbon monosaccharide; used as an energy source during cellular respiration and as a monomer of the structural polysaccharides. 42

glycerol Three-carbon carbohydrate with three hydroxyl groups attached; a component of fats and oils. 46

glycocalyx Gel-like coating outside the cell wall of a bacterium. If compact, it is called a capsule; if diffuse, it is called a slime layer. 65

glycogen Storage polysaccharide found in animals; composed of glucose molecules joined in a linear fashion but having numerous branches. 43

glycolipid Lipid in plasma membranes that contains an attached carbohydrate chain; assembled in the Golgi apparatus. 88

glycolysis Anaerobic breakdown of glucose that results in a gain of two ATP and the production of pyruvate; occurs in the cytoplasm of cells. 137, 138

glycoprotein Protein in plasma membranes that has an attached carbohydrate chain; assembled in the Golgi apparatus. 88

gnathostome Term used to describe any vertebrates with jaws. 552

gnetophyte Member of one of the four phyla of gymnosperms; Gnetophyta has only three living genera, which differ greatly from one another—e.g., *Welwitschia* and *Ephedra*. 432

golden brown algae Unicellular organism that contains pigments, including chlorophyll *a* and *c* and carotenoids, that produce its color. 391

Golgi apparatus Organelle consisting of sacs and vesicles that processes, packages, and distributes molecules about or from the cell. 72

gonad Organ that produces gametes; the ovary produces eggs, and the testis produces sperm. 773

gonadotropic hormone Substance secreted by the anterior pituitary that regulates the activity of the ovaries and testes; principally, follicle-stimulating hormone (FSH) and luteinizing hormone (LH). 757

granular leukocyte Form of white blood cell that contains spherical vesicles (granules) in its cytoplasm. 620

granum (pl., grana) Stack of chlorophyll-containing thylakoids in a chloroplast. 76, 121

grassland Biome characterized by rainfall greater than 25 cm/yr, grazing animals, and warm summers; includes the prairie of the U.S. midwest and the African savanna. 894

gravitational equilibrium Maintenance of balance when the head and body are motionless. 728

gravitropism Growth response of roots and stems of plants to the Earth's gravity; roots demonstrate positive gravitropism, and stems demonstrate negative gravitropism. 491

gray matter Nonmyelinated axons and cell bodies in the central nervous system. 702

green algae Members of a diverse group of photosynthetic protists; contain chlorophylls *a* and *b* and have other biochemical characteristics like those of plants. 387

greenhouse effect Reradiation of solar heat toward the Earth, caused by an atmosphere that allows the Sun's rays to pass through but traps the heat in the same manner as the glass of a greenhouse. 877

greenhouse gases Gases in the atmosphere such as carbon dioxide, methane, water vapor, ozone, and nitrous oxide that are involved in the greenhouse effect. 876

ground tissue Tissue that constitutes most of the body of a plant; consists of parenchyma, collenchyma, and sclerenchyma cells that function in storage, basic metabolism, and support. 447

growth factor A hormone or chemical, secreted by one cell, that may stimulate or inhibit growth of another cell or cells. 155

growth hormone (GH) Substance secreted by the anterior pituitary; controls size of an individual by promoting cell division, protein synthesis, and bone growth. 758

guanine (G) One of four nitrogen-containing bases in nucleotides composing the structure of DNA and RNA; pairs with cytosine. 217

guard cell One of two cells that surround a leaf stoma; changes in the turgor pressure of these cells cause the stoma to open or close. 477

guttation Liberation of water droplets from the edges and tips of leaves. 475

gymnosperm Type of woody seed plant in which the seeds are not enclosed by fruit and are usually borne in cones, such as those of the conifers. 430

H

habitat Place where an organism lives and is able to survive and reproduce. 839, 859

hair follicle Tubelike depression in the skin in which a hair develops. 599

halophile Type of archaean that lives in extremely salty habitats. 379

haploid (n) Cell condition in which only one of each type of chromosome is present. 157, 172

Hardy-Weinberg principle (equilibrium) Mathematical law stating that the gene frequencies in a population remain stable if evolution does not occur due to nonrandom mating, selection, migration, and genetic drift. 290,291

heart Muscular organ whose contraction causes blood to circulate in the body of an animal. 610

heart attack Damage to the myocardium due to blocked circulation in the coronary arteries; myocardial infarction. 616

heat Type of kinetic energy associated with the random motion of molecules. 105

helper T cell Secretes lymphokines, which stimulate all kinds of immune cells. 635

heme Iron-containing group found in hemoglobin. 672

hemizygous Possessing only one allele for a gene in a diploid organism; males are hemizygous for genes on the X chromosome. 209

hemocoel Residual coelom found in arthropods, which is filled with hemolymph. 534

hemoglobin (Hb) Iron-containing respiratory pigment occurring in vertebrate red blood cells and in the blood plasma of some invertebrates. 49, 618, 672

hemolymph Circulatory fluid that is a mixture of blood and interstitial fluid; seen in animals that have an open circulatory system, such as molluscs and arthropods. 606

hepatitis Inflammation of the liver. Viral hepatitis occurs in several forms. 654

herbaceous stem Nonwoody stem; herbaceous plants tend to die back to ground level at the end of the growing season. 454

herbivore Primary consumer in a grazing food chain; a plant eater. 870

hermaphroditic Type of animal that has both male and female sex organs. 531, 773

heterochromatin Highly compacted chromatin that is not accessible for transcription. 234

heterosporous Seed plant that produces two types of spores—microspores and megaspores. A plant that produces only one type of spore is *homosporous*. 426

heterotrophy Organism that cannot synthesize needed organic compounds from inorganic substances and therefore must take in organic food. 120, 870

heterozygote advantage Situation in which individuals heterozygous for a trait have a selective advantage over those who are homozygous dominant or recessive; an example is sickle-cell disease. 302

heterozygous Possessing unlike alleles for a particular trait. 196

hexose Any monosaccharide that contains six carbons; examples are glucose and galactose. 42

hippocampus Region of the central nervous system associated with learning and memory; part of the limbic system. 705

histamine Substance, produced by basophils in blood and mast cells in connective tissue, that causes capillaries to dilate. 631

histone A group of proteins involved in forming the nucleosome structure of eukaryote chromatin. 157, 233

homeobox 180-nucleotide sequence located in all homeotic genes. 804

homeodomain Conserved DNA-binding region of transcription factors encoded by the homeobox of homeotic genes. 804

homeostasis Maintenance of normal internal conditions in a cell or an organism by means of self-regulating mechanisms. 4, 599

homeothermic Ability to regulate the internal body temperature around an optimum value. 599

homeotic genes Genes that control the overall body plan by controlling the fate of groups of cells during development. 803

hominid Taxon that includes humans, chimpanzees, gorillas, and orangutans. 572

hominin Taxon that includes humans and species very closely related to humans plus chimpanzees. 572

hominine Taxon that includes humans, chimpanzees, and gorillas. 572

hominoid Taxon that includes the hominids plus the gibbons. 572

homologous chromosome Member of a pair of chromosomes that are alike and come together in synapsis during prophase of the first meiotic division; a *homologue*. 172

homologous gene Gene that codes for the same protein, even if the base sequence may be different. 265

homologous, homologous structure A structure that is similar in different types of organisms because these organisms descended from a common ancestor. 283, 317, 357

homologue Member of a homologous pair of chromosomes. 172

homology Similarity of parts or organs of different organisms caused by evolutionary derivation from a corresponding part or organ in a remote ancestor, and usually having a similar embryonic origin. 357

homosporous A plant that produces only one type of asexual spore. 426

homozygous Possessing two identical alleles for a particular trait. 196

hormone Chemical messenger produced in one part of the body that controls the activity of other parts. 484, 753

hornwort A bryophyte of the phylum Anthocerophyta with a thin gametophyte and tiny sporophyte that resembles a broom handle. 424

horsetail A seedless vascular plant having only one genus (*Equisetum*) in existence today;

characterized by rhizomes, scalelike leaves, strobili, and tough, rigid stems. 427

host Organism that provides nourishment and/or shelter for a parasite. 865

human chorionic gonadotropin (HCG) Gonadotropic hormone produced by the chorion that functions to maintain the uterine lining. 782, 806

Human Genome Project (HGP) Initiative to determine the complete sequence of the human genome and to analyze this information. 261

human immunodeficiency virus (HIV) Virus responsible for the disease AIDS. 637, 787

humus Decomposing organic matter in the soil. 467

hunter-gatherer A hominin that hunted animals and gathered plants for food. 580

hyaline cartilage Cartilage whose cells lie in lacunae separated by a white translucent matrix containing very fine collagen fibers. 591

hybridization Interbreeding between two different species; typically prevented by prezygotic isolation mechanisms. 310

hydrogen bond Weak bond that arises between a slightly positive hydrogen atom of one molecule and a slightly negative atom of another molecule or between parts of the same molecule. 28

hydrogen ion (H^+) Hydrogen atom that has lost its electron and therefore bears a positive charge. 32

hydrolysis reaction Splitting of a chemical bond by the addition of water, with the H^+ going to one molecule and the OH^- going to the other. 41

hydrophilic Type of molecule, often polar, that interacts with water by dissolving in water and/or by forming hydrogen bonds with water molecules. 40

hydrophobic Type of molecule, that is typically nonpolar, and therefore does not interact easily with water. 40

hydroponics Technique for growing plants by suspending them with their roots in a nutrient solution. 465

hydrostatic skeleton Fluid-filled body compartment that provides support for muscle contraction resulting in movement; seen in cnidarians, flatworms, roundworms, and segmented worms. 528, 736

hydrothermal vent Hot springs in the seafloor along ocean ridges where heated sea water and sulfate react to produce hydrogen sulfide; here, chemosynthetic bacteria support a community of varied organisms. 902

hydroxide ion (OH^-) One of two ions that results when a water molecule dissociates; it has gained an electron and therefore bears a negative charge. 32

hypersensitive response (HR) Plants respond to pathogens by selectively killing plant cells to block the spread of the pathogen. 498

hyperthyroidism Caused by the over-secretion of hormones from the thyroid gland; symptoms include hyperactivity, nervousness, and insomnia. 761

hypertonic solution Higher solute concentration (less water) than the cytoplasm of a cell; causes cell to lose water by osmosis. 94

hypha Filament of the vegetative body of a fungus. 405

hypertension Form of cardiovascular disease characterized by blood pressure over 140/95 (over 45 years of age) or 130/90 (under 45 years of age). 616

hypothalamic-inhibiting hormone One of many hormones produced by the hypothalamus that inhibits the secretion of an anterior pituitary hormone. 757

hypothalamic-releasing hormone One of many hormones produced by the hypothalamus that stimulates the secretion of an anterior pituitary hormone. 757

hypothalamus In vertebrates, part of the brain that helps regulate the internal environment of the body—for example, heart rate, body temperature, and water balance. 704, 757

hypothesis Supposition established by reasoning after consideration of available evidence; it can be tested by obtaining more data, often by experimentation. 11

hypothyroidism Caused by the under-secretion of hormones from the thyroid gland; symptoms include weight gain, lethargic behavior, and depression. 761

hypotonic solution Solution that contains a lower solute (more water) concentration than the cytoplasm of a cell; causes cell to gain water by osmosis. 93

I

immediate allergic response Allergic response that occurs within seconds of contact with an allergen; caused by the attachment of the allergen to IgE antibodies. 641

immune system System associated with protection against pathogens, toxins, and some cancerous cells; in humans this is an organ system. 627

immunity Ability of the body to protect itself from foreign substances and cells, including disease-causing agents. 630

immunization Strategy for achieving immunity to the effects of specific disease-causing agents. 639

immunoglobulin (Ig) Globular plasma protein that functions as an antibody. 634

implantation In placental mammals, the embedding of an embryo at the blastocyst stage into the endometrium of the uterus. 806

imprinting Learning to make a particular response to only one type of animal or object. 823

inbreeding Mating between closely related individuals; influences the genotype ratios of the gene pool. 295

inclusive fitness Fitness that results from personal reproduction and from helping nondescendant relatives reproduce. 834

incomplete digestive tract Digestive tract that has a single opening, usually called a mouth. 647

incomplete dominance Inheritance pattern in which an offspring has an intermediate phenotype, as when a red-flowered plant and a white-flowered plant produce pink-flowered offspring. 205

incomplete penetrance Dominant alleles that are either not always, or partially expressed. 206

independent assortment Alleles of unlinked genes segregate independently of each other during meiosis so that the gametes could contain all possible combinations of alleles. 175

index fossil Deposits found in certain layers of strata; similar fossils can be found in the same strata around the world. 334

induced fit model Change in the shape of an enzyme's active site that enhances the fit between the active site and its substrate(s). 110

induced mutation Mutation that is caused by an outside influence, such as organic chemicals or ionizing radiation. 247

inducer Molecule that brings about activity of an operon by joining with a repressor and preventing it from binding to the operator. 240

induction Ability of a chemical or a tissue to influence the development of another tissue. 800

inductive reasoning Using specific observations and the process of logic and reasoning to arrive at general scientific principles. 11

infertility Inability to have as many children as desired. 784

inflammatory response Tissue response to injury that is characterized by redness, swelling, pain, and heat. 631

ingroup In a cladistic study of evolutionary relationships among organisms, the group that is being analyzed. 356

inheritance of acquired characteristics Lamarckian belief that characteristics acquired during the lifetime of an organism can be passed on to offspring. 273

initiation First stage of translation in which the translational machinery binds an mRNA and assembles. 230

innate immunity An immune response that does not require a previous exposure to the pathogen. 627

inner ear Portion of the ear consisting of a vestibule, semicircular canals, and the cochlea where equilibrium is maintained and sound is transmitted. 727

inorganic chemistry Branch of science that studies the chemical reactions and properties of all of the elements, except hydrogen and carbon. 38

insect Type of arthropod. The head has antennae, compound eyes, and simple eyes; the thorax has three pairs of legs and often wings; and the abdomen has internal organs. 541

insight learning Ability to apply prior learning to a new situation without trial-and-error activity. 825

inspiration Act of taking air into the lungs; inhalation. 669

insulin Hormone released by the pancreas that serves to lower blood glucose levels by stimulating the uptake of glucose by cells, especially muscle and liver cells. 765

integration Summing up of excitatory and inhibitory signals by a neuron or by some part of the brain. 701

interferon Antiviral agent produced by an infected cell that blocks the infection of another cell. 633

intergenic sequence Region of DNA that lies between genes on a chromosome. 262

interkinesis Period of time between meiosis I and meiosis II during which no DNA replication takes place. 176

intermediate filament Ropelike assemblies of fibrous polypeptides in the cytoskeleton that provide support and strength to cells; so called because they are intermediate in size between actin filaments and microtubules. 78

internal respiration Exchange of oxygen and carbon dioxide between blood and tissue fluid. 664

interneuron Neuron located within the central nervous system that conveys messages between parts of the central nervous system. 698

internode In vascular plants, the region of a stem between two successive nodes. 445

interphase Stages of the cell cycle (G_1, S, G_2) during which growth and DNA synthesis occur when the nucleus is not actively dividing. 154

interspersed repeat Repeated DNA sequence that is spread across several regions of a chromosome or across multiple chromosomes. 262

intertidal zone Region along a coastline where the tide recedes and returns. 900

intron Intervening sequence found between exons in mRNA; removed by RNA processing before translation. 226

inversion Change in chromosome structure in which a segment of a chromosome is turned around 180°; this reversed sequence of genes can lead to altered gene activity and abnormalities. 187

invertebrate Animal without a vertebral column or backbone. 521

ion Charged particle that carries a negative or positive charge. 26

ionic bond Chemical bond in which ions are attracted to one another by opposite charges. 26

iris Muscular ring that surrounds the pupil and regulates the passage of light through this opening. 721

iron-sulfur world Hypothesis that ocean thermal vents provided all of the materials needed for abiotic synthesis of the first molecules. 329

island biogeography model Proposes that the biodiversity on an island is dependent on its distance from the mainland, with islands located a greater distance having a lower level of diversity. 859

isomer Molecules with the same molecular formula but a different structure, and therefore a different shape. 40

isotonic solution Solution that is equal in solute concentration to that of the cytoplasm of a cell; causes cell to neither lose nor gain water by osmosis. 93

isotope Atoms of the same element having the same atomic number but a different mass number due to a variation in the number of neutrons. 24

iteroparity Repeated production of offspring at intervals throughout the life cycle of an organism. 843

J

jaundice Yellowish tint to the skin caused by an abnormal amount of bilirubin (bile pigment) in the blood, indicating liver malfunction. 654

jawless fishes Type of fishes that lack jaws (agnathan); includes hagfishes and lampreys. 553

joint Articulation between two bones of a skeleton. 742

junction protein(s) Proteins in the cell membrane that assist in cell-to-cell communication. 89

K

karyotype Chromosomes arranged by pairs according to their size, shape, and general appearance in mitotic metaphase. 184

keystone species Species whose activities significantly affect community structure. 918

kidneys Paired organs of the vertebrate urinary system that regulate the chemical composition of the blood and produce a waste product called urine. 684

kinetic energy Energy associated with motion. 105

kinetochore An assembly of proteins that attaches to the centromere of a chromosome during mitosis. 157

kinetoplastid Unicellular, flagellate protist characterized by the presence in their single mitochondrion of a kinetoplast (a structure containing a large mass of DNA). 396

kingdom One of the categories, or taxa, used by taxonomists to group species; the taxon above phylum. 6, 349

kin selection Indirect selection; adaptation to the environment due to the reproductive success of an individual's relatives. 834

K-selection Favorable life-history strategy under stable environmental conditions characterized by the production of a few offspring with much attention given to offspring survival. 849

L

lactation Secretion of milk by mammary glands, usually for the nourishment of an infant. 782

lacteal Lymphatic vessel in an intestinal villus; aids in the absorption of fats. 653

lacuna Small pit or hollow cavity, as in bone or cartilage, where a cell or cells are located. 590

lake Body of fresh water, often classified by nutrient status, such as oligotrophic (nutrient-poor) or eutrophic (nutrient-rich). 898

landscape A number of interacting ecosystems. 909

landscape diversity Variety of habitat elements within an ecosystem (e.g., plains, mountains, and rivers). 909

large intestine In vertebrates, portion of the digestive tract that follows the small intestine; in humans, consists of the cecum, colon, rectum, and anal canal. 653

larynx Cartilaginous organ located between the pharynx and the trachea; in humans, contains the vocal cords; sometimes called the voice box. 668

last universal common ancestor (LUCA) The first living organism on the planet, from which all life evolved. 328

lateral line Canal system containing sensory receptors that allow fishes and amphibians to detect water currents and pressure waves from nearby objects. 726

law Universal principle that describes the basic functions of the natural world. 12

law of independent assortment Mendelian principle that explains how combinations of traits appear in gametes; *see also* independent assortment. 198

law of segregation Mendelian principle that explains how, in a diploid organism, alleles separate during the formation of the gametes. 196

laws of thermodynamics Two laws explaining energy and its relationships and exchanges. The first, also called the "law of conservation," says that energy cannot be created or destroyed but can only be changed from one form to another; the second says that energy cannot be changed from one form to another without a loss of usable energy. 105

leaf Lateral appendage of a stem, highly variable in structure, often containing cells that carry out photosynthesis. 445

leaf vein Vascular tissue within a leaf. 450

learning Relatively permanent change in an animal's behavior that results from practice and experience. 823

lens Transparent, disclike structure found in the vertebrate eye behind the iris; brings objects into focus on the retina. 721

leptin Hormone produced by adipose tissue that acts on the hypothalamus to signal satiety (fullness). 768

less-developed country (LDC) Country that is becoming industrialized; typically, population growth is expanding rapidly, and the majority of people live in poverty. 851

leucoplasts Plastid, generally colorless, that synthesizes and stores starch and oils. 77

leukocyte Another name for a white blood cell (WBC). 620

lichen Symbiotic relationship between certain fungi and either cyanobacteria or algae, in which the fungi possibly provide inorganic food or water and the algae or cyanobacteria provide organic food. 377, 414

life cycle Recurring pattern of genetically programmed events by which individuals grow, develop, maintain themselves, and reproduce. 180

ligament Tough cord or band of dense fibrous tissue that binds bone to bone at a joint. 590, 742

light reaction Portion of photosynthesis that captures solar energy and takes place in thylakoid membranes of chloroplasts; it produces ATP and NADPH. 122

lignin Chemical that hardens the cell walls of land plants. 426, 449

limbic system In humans, functional association of various brain centers, including the amygdala and hippocampus; governs learning and memory and various emotions such as pleasure, fear, and happiness. 705

limiting factor Resource or environmental condition that restricts the abundance and distribution of an organism. 840

lineage Line of descent represented by a branch in a phylogenetic tree. 354

lipase Fat-digesting enzyme secreted by the pancreas. 657

lipid Class of organic compounds that tends to be soluble in nonpolar solvents; includes fats and oils. 45

liposome Droplet of phospholipid molecules formed in a liquid environment. 331

liver Large, dark red internal organ that produces urea and bile, detoxifies the blood, stores glycogen, and produces the plasma proteins, among other functions. 654

liverwort Bryophyte with a lobed or leafy gametophyte and a sporophyte composed of a stalk and capsule. 424

lobe-finned fishes Type of fishes with limblike fins; also called the sarcopterygians. 555

locus Physical location of a trait (or gene) on a chromosome. 196

logistic growth Population increase that results in an S-shaped curve; growth is slow at first, steepens, and then levels off due to environmental resistance. 844

long-day plant Plant that flowers when day length is longer than a critical length; e.g., wheat, barley, clover, and spinach. 496

loop of the nephron Portion of a nephron between the proximal and distal convoluted tubules; functions in water reabsorption. 686

loose fibrous connective tissue Tissue composed mainly of fibroblasts widely separated by a matrix containing collagen and elastic fibers. 590

lophophoran A general term to describe several groups of lophotrochozoans that have a feeding structure called a lophophore. 530

lophotrochozoa Main group of protostomes; widely diverse. Includes the flatworms, rotifers, annelids, and molluscs. 530

lumen Cavity inside any tubular structure, such as the lumen of the digestive tract. 651

lung cancer Uncontrolled cell growth that affects any component of the respiratory system. 675

lungs Internal respiratory organ containing moist surfaces for gas exchange. 665

lungfishes Type of lobe-finned fishes that utilize lungs in addition to gills for gas exchange. 555

luteal phase Second half of the ovarian cycle, during which the corpus luteum develops and much progesterone (and some estrogen) is produced. 781

lycophyte Club mosses, among the first vascular plants to evolve and to have leaves. The leaves of the lycophytes are microphylls. 426

lymph Fluid, derived from tissue fluid, that is carried in lymphatic vessels. 592, 622, 629

lymphatic capillary Smallest vessels of the lymphatic system; closed-ended; responsible for the uptake of fluids from the surrounding tissues. 629

lymphatic system Organ system consisting of lymphatic vessels and lymphatic organs; transports lymph and lipids, and aids the immune system. 628

lymphatic vessel Vessel that carries lymph. 628

lymph node Mass of lymphatic tissue located along the course of a lymphatic vessel. 629

lymphocyte Specialized white blood cell that functions in specific defense; occurs in two forms—T lymphocytes and B lymphocytes. 620

lymphoid (lymphatic) organ Organ other than a lymphatic vessel that is part of the lymphatic system; the lymphatic organs are the lymph nodes, tonsils, spleen, thymus gland, and bone marrow. 629

lysogenic cell Cell that contains a prophage (virus incorporated into DNA), which is replicated when the cell divides. 368

lysogenic cycle Bacteriophage life cycle in which the virus incorporates its DNA into that of a bacterium; occurs preliminary to the lytic cycle. 368

lysosome Membrane-bounded vesicle that contains hydrolytic enzymes for digesting macromolecules and bacteria; used to recycle worn-out cellular organelles. 73

lytic cycle Bacteriophage life cycle in which the virus takes over the operation of a bacterium immediately upon entering it and subsequently destroys the bacterium. 368

M

macroevolution Large-scale evolutionary change, such as the formation of new species. 307

macronutrient Essential element needed in large amounts for plant growth, such as nitrogen, calcium, or sulfur. 465

macrophage In vertebrates, large phagocytic cell derived from a monocyte that ingests microbes and debris. 632

macular degeneration Condition in which the capillaries supplying the retina of the eye become damaged resulting in reduced vision and blindness. 724

malignant The power to threaten life; cancerous. 163

maltase Enzyme produced in small intestine that breaks down maltose to two glucose molecules. 656

mammal Endothermic vertebrate characterized especially by the presence of hair and mammary glands. 564

mantle In molluscs, an extension of the body wall that covers the visceral mass and may secrete a shell. 534

marsh Soft wetland, that is treeless. 897

marsupial Member of a group of mammals bearing immature young nursed in a marsupium, or pouch—for example, kangaroo and opossum. 564

mass extinction Episode of large-scale extinction in which large numbers of species disappear in a few million years or less. 338

mass number Mass of an atom equal to the number of protons plus the number of neutrons within the nucleus. 23

mast cell Connective tissue cell that releases histamine in allergic reactions. 631

maternal determinant One of many substances present in the egg that influences the course of development. 800

matrix Unstructured semifluid substance that fills the space between cells in connective tissues or inside organelles. 77

matter Anything that takes up space and has mass. 22

mechanical energy A type of kinetic energy associated with the position, or motion (such as walking or running) of an object. 105

mechanoreceptor Sensory receptor that responds to mechanical stimuli, such as pressure, sound waves, or gravity. 717

medulla oblongata In vertebrates, part of the brain stem that is continuous with the spinal cord; controls heartbeat, blood pressure, breathing, and other vital functions. 705

medusa Among cnidarians, bell-shaped body form that is directed downward and contains much mesoglea. 528

megafauna Large animals, such as humans, bears, and deer. Often defined as those over 100 pounds (44 kg) in adult size. 341

megaphyll Large leaf with several to many veins. 427

megaspore One of the two types of spores produced by seed plants; develops into a female gametophyte (embryo sac). 426, 502

meiosis Type of nuclear division that reduces the chromosome number from 2n to n; daughter cells receive the haploid number of chromosomes in varied combinations; also called reduction division. 172

melanocyte Specialized cell in the epidermis that produces melanin, the pigment responsible for skin color. 598

melanocyte-stimulating hormone (MSH) Substance that causes melanocytes to secrete melanin in most vertebrates. 757

melatonin Hormone, secreted by the pineal gland, that is involved in biorhythms. 768

membrane-first hypothesis Proposes that the plasma membrane was the first component of the early cells to evolve. 331

memory Capacity of the brain to store and retrieve information about past sensations and perceptions; essential to learning. 707

memory B cell Forms during a primary immune response but enters a resting phase until a secondary immune response occurs. 634

memory T cell T cell that differentiated during an initial infection and responds rapidly during subsequent exposure to the same antigen. 636

meninges Protective membranous coverings around the central nervous system. 702

meningitis A condition that refers to inflammation of the brain or spinal cord meninges (membranes). 702

menopause Termination of the ovarian and uterine cycles in older women. 782, 813

menstruation Periodic shedding of tissue and blood from the inner lining of the uterus in primates. 781

meristem Undifferentiated embryonic tissue in the active growth regions of plants. 447

mesoderm Middle primary tissue layer of an animal embryo that gives rise to muscle, several internal organs, and connective tissue layers. 798

mesoglea Transparent jellylike substance located between the endoderm and ectoderm of some sponges and cnidarians. 528

mesophyll Inner, thickest layer of a leaf consisting of palisade and spongy mesophyll; the site of most of photosynthesis. 459

mesosome In a bacterium, plasma membrane that folds into the cytoplasm and increases surface area. 65

messenger RNA (mRNA) Type of RNA formed from a DNA template and bearing coded information for the amino acid sequence of a polypeptide. 223

metabolic pathway Series of linked reactions, beginning with a particular reactant and terminating with an end product. 109

metabolic pool Metabolites that are the products of and/or the substrates for key reactions in cells, allowing one type of molecule to be changed into another type, such as carbohydrates converted to fats. 147

metabolism The sum of the chemical reactions that occur in a cell. 4, 107

metamorphosis Change in shape and form that some animals, such as insects, undergo during development. 521, 540

metaphase Third phase of mitosis; chromosomes are aligned at the metaphase plate. 159

metaphase plate A disk formed during metaphase in which all of a cell's chromosomes lie in a single plane at right angles to the spindle fibers. 159

metapopulation Population subdivided into several small and isolated populations due to habitat fragmentation. 919

metastasis Spread of cancer from the place of origin throughout the body; caused by the ability of cancer cells to migrate and invade tissues. 164

methanogen Type of archaean that lives in oxygen-free habitats, such as swamps, and releases methane gas. 378

MHC (major histocompatibility complex) protein Protein marker that is a part of cell-surface markers anchored in the plasma membrane, which the immune system uses to identify "self." 635

micelle Single layer of fatty acids (or phospholipids) that orientate themselves in an aqueous environment. 331

microevolution Change in gene frequencies between populations of a species over time. 290

microglia Supportive cells of the nervous system that help remove bacteria and debris, thus supporting the activity of the neurons. 697

micronutrient Essential element needed in small amounts for plant growth, such as boron, copper, and zinc. 465

microphyll Small leaf with one vein. 426

microRNA (miRNA) Short sequences of RNA, usually less than 22 nucleotides, that are involved in posttranscriptional regulation of gene expression. These molecules either inhibit, or reduce, the expression of specific genes. 246

microsphere Formed from proteinoids exposed to water; has properties similar to those of today's cells. 330

microspore One of the two types of spores produced by seed plants; develops into a male gametophyte (pollen grain). 426, 502

microtubule Small, cylindrical organelle composed of tubulin protein around an empty central core; present in the cytoplasm, centrioles, cilia, and flagella. 78

midbrain In mammals, the part of the brain located below the thalamus and above the pons. 704

middle ear Portion of the ear consisting of the tympanic membrane, the oval and round windows, and the ossicles, where sound is amplified. 727

migration Regular back-and-forth movement of animals between two geographic areas at particular times of the year. 825

millipede More-or-less cylindrical arthropod characterized by having two pairs of short legs on most of its body segments; may have 13 to almost 200 pairs of legs. 541

mimicry Superficial resemblance of two or more species; a survival mechanism that avoids predation by appearing to be noxious. 864

mineral Naturally occurring inorganic substance containing two or more elements; certain minerals are needed in the diet. 465

mineralocorticoid Hormones secreted by the adrenal cortex that regulate salt and water balance, leading to increases in blood volume and blood pressure. 763

mitochondria (sing., mitochondrion) Membrane-bounded organelle in which ATP molecules are produced during the process of cellular respiration. 76, 142

mitosis The stage of cellular reproduction in which nuclear division occurs; process in which a parent nucleus produces two daughter nuclei, each having the same number and kinds of chromosomes as the parent nucleus. 155

mitotic spindle A complex of microtubules and associated proteins that assist in separating the chromatids during cell division. 155

mixotrophic Organism that can use autotrophic and heterotrophic means of gaining nutrients. 384

model Simulation of a process that aids conceptual understanding until the process can be studied firsthand; a hypothesis that describes how a particular process could possibly be carried out. 12

mold Various fungi whose body consists of a mass of hyphae (filaments) that grow on and receive nourishment from organic matter such as human food and clothing. 410

mole The molecular weight of a molecule expressed in grams; contains 6.023×10^{23} molecules. 107

molecular clock Idea that the rate at which mutational changes accumulate in certain genes is constant over time and is not involved in adaptation to the environment. 359

molecule Union of two or more atoms of the same element; also, the smallest part of a compound that retains the properties of the compound. 26

mollusc Invertebrates including squids, clams, snails, and chitons; characterized by a visceral mass, a mantle, and a foot. 534

monoclonal antibody One of many antibodies produced by a clone of hybridoma cells that all bind to the same antigen. 635

monocot (Monocotyledone) Flowering plant group; members have one embryonic leaf (cotyledon), parallel-veined leaves, scattered vascular bundles, flower parts in threes or multiples of three, and other characteristics. 433, 446

monocyte Type of agranular leukocyte that functions as a phagocyte, particularly after it becomes a macrophage, which is also an antigen-presenting cell. 620

monoecious Having male flowers or cones and female flowers or cones on a single plant. 430

monogamous Breeding pair of organisms that reproduce only with each other through their lifetime. 831

monohybrid cross Cross between parents that differ in only one trait. 195

monomer Small molecule that is a subunit of a polymer—e.g., glucose is a monomer of starch. 40

monophyletic Group of species including the most recent common ancestor and all its descendants. 308, 384

monosaccharide Simple sugar; a carbohydrate that cannot be broken down by hydrolysis—e.g., glucose; also, any monomer of the polysaccharides. 41

monosomy Chromosome condition in which a diploid cell has one less chromosome than normal; designated as 2n-1. 183

monotreme Egg-laying mammal—e.g., duckbill platypus or spiny anteater. 564

monsoon Climate in India and southern Asia caused by wet ocean winds that blow onshore for almost half the year. 885

montane coniferous forest Coniferous forest of a mountain. 887

more-developed country (MDC) Country that is industrialized; typically, population growth is low, and the people enjoy a good standard of living overall. 851

morphogenesis Emergence of shape in tissues, organs, or entire embryo during development. 800

morphological species concept Definition of a species that defines species by specific diagnostic traits. 307

morphology Physical characteristics that contribute to the appearance of an organism. 307

morula Spherical mass of cells resulting from cleavage during animal development prior to the blastula stage. 797

mosaic evolution Concept that human characteristics did not evolve at the same rate; for example, some body parts are more humanlike than others in early hominins. 577

moss Bryophyte that is typically found in moist habitats. 424

motor molecule Protein that moves along either actin filaments or microtubules and translocates organelles. 78

motor (efferent) neuron Nerve cell that conducts nerve impulses away from the central nervous system and innervates effectors (muscle and glands). 697

mouth In humans, organ of the digestive tract where food is chewed and mixed with saliva. 650

mRNA transcript mRNA molecule formed during transcription that has a sequence of bases complementary to a gene. 226

mucosa Epithelial membrane containing cells that secrete mucus; found in the inner cell layers of the digestive (first layer) and respiratory tracts. 651

multicellular Organism composed of many cells; usually has organized tissues, organs, and organ systems. 2

multiple alleles Inheritance pattern in which there are more than two alleles for a particular trait; each individual has only two of all possible alleles. 205

multiple sclerosis Disease of the central nervous system characterized by the breakdown of myelin in the neurons; considered to be an autoimmune disease. 705

muscularis Smooth muscle layer found in the digestive tract. 651

muscular (contractile) tissue Type of animal tissue composed of fibers that shorten and lengthen to produce movements. 592

mutagen Chemical or physical agent that increases the chance of mutation. 248

mutualism Symbiotic relationship in which both species benefit in terms of growth and reproduction. 375, 866

mycelium Tangled mass of hyphal filaments composing the vegetative body of a fungus. 405

mycorrhizae (sing., mycorrhiza) Mutualistic relationship between fungal hyphae and roots of vascular plants. 414, 472

myelin sheath White, fatty material—derived from the membrane of neurolemmocytes—that forms a covering for nerve fibers. 697

myofibril Specific muscle cell organelle containing a linear arrangement of sarcomeres, which shorten to produce muscle contraction. 745

myosin Muscle protein making up the thick filaments in a sarcomere; it pulls actin to shorten the sarcomere, yielding muscle contraction. 745

N

NAD⁺ (nicotinamide adenine dinucleotide)
Coenzyme in oxidation-reduction reactions that accepts electrons and hydrogen ions to become NADH + H⁺ as oxidation of substrates occurs. During cellular respiration, NADH carries electrons to the electron transport chain in mitochondria. 114, 136

NADP⁺ (nicotinamide adenine dinucleotide phosphate) Coenzyme in oxidation-reduction reactions that accepts electrons and hydrogen ions to become NADPH + H⁺. During photosynthesis, NADPH participates in the reduction of carbon dioxide to a carbohydrate. 113

nail Flattened epithelial tissue from the stratum lucidum of the skin; located on the tips of fingers and toes. 598

natural killer (NK) cell Lymphocyte that causes an infected or cancerous cell to burst. 632

natural group In systematics, groups of organisms that possess a shared evolutionary history. 348

natural selection Mechanism of evolutionary change caused by environmental selection of organisms most fit to reproduce; results in adaptation to the environment. 8, 277

navigate To steer or manage a course by adjusting one's bearings and following the result of the adjustment. 825

Neandertal Hominin with a sturdy build that lived during the last Ice Age in Europe and the Middle East; hunted large game and left evidence of being culturally advanced. 580

nearsighted (myopic) Condition in which an individual cannot focus on objects at a distance; caused by the focusing of the image in front of the retina of the eye. 724

negative feedback Mechanism of homeostatic response by which the output of a system suppresses or inhibits activity of the system. 600, 757

nematocyst In cnidarians, a capsule that contains a threadlike fiber, the release of which aids in the capture of prey. 528

nephridium (pl., nephridia) Segmentally arranged, paired excretory tubules of many invertebrates, as in the earthworm. 536

nephron Microscopic kidney unit that regulates blood composition by glomerular filtration, tubular reabsorption, and tubular secretion. 685

nerve Bundle of long axons outside the central nervous system. 593, 707

nerve fiber Axon; conducts nerve impulses away from the cell. Axons are classified as either myelinated or unmyelinated based on the presence or absence of a myelin sheath. 697

nerve net Diffuse, noncentralized arrangement of nerve cells in cnidarians. 529, 694

nervous tissue Tissue that contains nerve cells (neurons), which conduct impulses, and neuroglia, which support, protect, and provide nutrients to neurons. 593

neural plate Region of the dorsal surface of the chordate embryo that marks the future location of the neural tube. 799

neural tube Tube formed by closure of the neural groove during development. In vertebrates, the neural tube develops into the spinal cord and brain. 799

neurodegenerative disease Disease, usually caused by a prion, virus, or bacterium, that damages or impairs the function of nervous tissue. 371

neuroglia Nonconducting nerve cells that are intimately associated with neurons and function in a supportive capacity. 593, 697

neuromuscular junction Region where an axon bulb approaches a muscle fiber; contains a presynaptic membrane, a synaptic cleft, and a postsynaptic membrane. 747

neuron Nerve cell that characteristically has three parts: dendrites, cell body, and an axon. 593, 697

neurotransmitter Chemical stored at the ends of axons that is responsible for transmission across a synapse. 700

neutron Neutral subatomic particle, located in the nucleus and assigned one atomic mass unit. 22

neutrophil Granular leukocyte that is the most abundant of the white blood cells; first to respond to infection. 631

nitrification Process by which nitrogen in ammonia and organic compounds is oxidized to nitrites and nitrates by soil bacteria. 878

N₂ (nitrogen) fixation Process whereby free atmospheric nitrogen is converted into compounds, such as ammonium and nitrates, usually by bacteria. 878

node In plants, the place where one or more leaves attach to a stem. 421, 445

nodes of Ranvier Gaps in the myelin sheath around a nerve fiber. 697

noncompetitive inhibition Form of enzyme inhibition where the inhibitor binds to an enzyme at a location other than the active site; while at this site, the enzyme shape changes, the inhibitor is unable to bind to its substrate, and no product forms. 112

noncyclic pathway Light-dependent photosynthetic pathway that is used to generate ATP and NADPH; because the pathway is noncyclic, the electrons must be replaced by the splitting of water (photolysis). 124

nondisjunction Failure of the homologous chromosomes or sister chromatids to separate during either mitosis or meiosis; produces cells with abnormal chromosome numbers. 183

nomenclature In systematics, the process of assigning names to taxonomic groups; usually determined by governing organizations. 350

nonpolar covalent bond Bond in which the sharing of electrons between atoms is fairly equal. 27

nonrandom mating Mating among individuals on the basis of their phenotypic similarities or differences, rather than mating on a random basis. 295

nonseptate Lacking cell walls; some fungal species have hyphae that are nonseptate. 405

nonvascular plants Bryophytes, such as mosses and liverworts, that have no vascular tissue and either occur in moist locations or have special adaptations for living in dry locations. 423

norepinephrine Neurotransmitter of the postganglionic fibers in the sympathetic division of the autonomic system; also, a hormone produced by the adrenal medulla. 762

notochord Cartilage-like supportive dorsal rod in all chordates at some time in their life cycle; replaced by vertebrae in vertebrates. 550, 799

nuclear envelope Double membrane that surrounds the nucleus in eukaryotic cells and is connected to the endoplasmic reticulum; has pores that allow substances to pass between the nucleus and the cytoplasm. 70

nucleariid Protist that may be related to fungi although nucleariids lack the same type of cell wall and have threadlike pseudopods. 398

nuclear envelope Name for the phospholipid double membrane that separates the contents of the nucleus from the cytoplasm. 71

nuclear pore Opening in the nuclear envelope that permits the passage of proteins into the nucleus and ribosomal subunits out of the nucleus. 71

nucleic acid Polymer of nucleotides; both DNA and RNA are nucleic acids. 54

nucleoid Region of prokaryotic cells where DNA is located; it is not bounded by a nuclear envelope. 65, 166, 372

nucleolus Dark-staining, spherical body in the nucleus that produces ribosomal subunits. 70

nucleoplasm Semifluid medium of the nucleus containing chromatin. 70

nucleosome In the nucleus of a eukaryotic cell, a unit composed of DNA wound around a core of eight histone proteins, giving the appearance of a string of beads. 233

nucleotide Monomer of DNA and RNA consisting of a 5-carbon sugar bonded to a nitrogenous base and a phosphate group. 54

nucleus Membrane-bounded organelle within a eukaryotic cell that contains chromosomes and controls the structure and function of the cell. 64

O

obligate anaerobe Prokaryote unable to grow in the presence of free oxygen. 374

observation Initial step in the scientific method that often involves the recording of data from an experiment or natural event. 11

octet rule The observation that an atom is most stable when its outer shell is complete and contains eight electrons; an exception is hydrogen which requires only two electrons in its outer shell to have a completed shell. 25

oil Triglyceride, usually of plant origin, that is composed of glycerol and three fatty acids and is liquid in consistency due to many unsaturated bonds in the hydrocarbon chains of the fatty acids. 46

oil gland Gland of the skin, associated with a hair follicle, that secretes sebum; sebaceous gland. 599

olfactory cell Modified neuron that is a sensory receptor for the sense of smell. 719

oligodendrocyte Type of glial cell that forms myelin sheaths around neurons in the CNS. 697

omnivore Organism in a food chain that feeds on both plants and animals. 870

oncogene Cancer-causing gene formed by a mutation in a proto-oncogene; code for proteins that stimulate the cell cycle and inhibit apoptosis. 164

oocyte Immature egg that is undergoing meiosis; upon completion of meiosis, the oocyte becomes an egg. 779

oogenesis Production of eggs in females by the process of meiosis and maturation. 180

open circulatory system Arrangement of internal transport in which blood bathes the organs directly, and there is no distinction between blood and interstitial fluid. 606

operant conditioning Learning that results from rewarding or reinforcing a particular behavior. 824

operator In an operon, the sequence of DNA that serves as a binding site for a repressor, and thereby regulates the expression of structural genes. 239

operon Group of structural and regulating genes that function as a single unit. 238

opisthokont Supergroup of eukaryotes that choanoflagellates animals, nucleariids and fungi. 397

opposable thumb Fingers arranged in such a way that the thumb can touch the ventral surface of the fingertips of all four fingers. 571

optimal foraging model Analysis of behavior as a compromise of feeding costs versus feeding benefits. 831

order One of the categories, or taxa, used by taxonomists to group species; the taxon located above the family level. 6, 349

organ Combination of two or more different tissues performing a common function. 444, 596

organelle Small, membranous structures in the cytoplasm having a specific structure and function. 67

organic chemistry Branch of science that deals with organic molecules including those that are unique to living things. 38

organic molecule Molecule that always contains carbon and hydrogen, and often contains oxygen as well; organic molecules are associated with living things. 38

organ of Corti Structure in the vertebrate inner ear that contains auditory receptors (also called spiral organ). 727

organ system Group of related organs working together; examples are the digestive and endocrine systems. 596

orientation In birds, the ability to know present location by tracking stimuli in the environment. 825

osmoregulation Regulation of the salt water balance to maintain a normal balance within internal fluids. 681

osmosis Diffusion of water through a selectively permeable membrane. 92

osmotic pressure Measure of the tendency of water to move across a selectively permeable membrane; visible as an increase in liquid on the side of the membrane with higher solute concentration. 93

ossicle One of the small bones of the vertebrate middle ear—malleus, incus, and stapes. 727

osteoblast Bone-forming cell. 738

osteoclast Cell that is responsible for bone resorption. 738

osteocyte Mature bone cell located within the lacunae of bone. 738

osteoporosis Condition characterized by a loss of bone density; associated with levels of sex hormones and diet. 738

ostracoderm Earliest vertebrate fossils of the Cambrian and Devonian periods; these fishes were small, jawless, and finless. 553

otolith Calcium carbonate granule associated with sensory receptors for detecting movement of the head; in vertebrates, located in the utricle and saccule. 728

outer ear Portion of the ear consisting of the pinna and the auditory canal. 726

outgroup In a cladistic study of evolutionary relationships among organisms, a group that has a known relationship to, but is not a member of, the taxa being analyzed. 356

ovarian cycle Monthly changes occurring in the ovary that determine the level of sex hormones in the blood. 780

ovary In flowering plants, the enlarged, ovule-bearing portion of the carpel that develops into a fruit; female gonad in animals that produces an egg and female sex hormones. 434, 503, 773, 779

overexploitation When the number of individuals taken from a wild population is so great that the population becomes severely reduced in numbers. 916

oviparous Type of reproduction in which development occurs in an egg, laid by mother, in reptiles. 774

ovoviviparous Animals that produce eggs that develop internally and hatch at around the same time as they are released to the environment; mostly aquatic. 774

ovulation Bursting of a follicle when a secondary oocyte is released from the ovary; if fertilization occurs, the secondary oocyte becomes an egg. 780

ovule In seed plants, a structure that contains the female gametophyte and has the potential to develop into a seed. 430

oxidation Loss of one or more electrons from an atom or molecule; in biological systems, generally the loss of hydrogen atoms. 113

oxidation-reduction reaction A paired set of chemical reactions in which one molecule gives up electrons (oxidized) while another molecule accepts electrons (reduced); commonly called a redox reaction. 113

oxygen debt Amount of oxygen required to oxidize lactic acid produced anaerobically during strenuous muscle activity. 747

oxyhemoglobin Compound formed when oxygen combines with hemoglobin. 672

oxytocin Hormone released by the posterior pituitary that causes contraction of the uterus and milk letdown. 757

ozone shield Accumulation of O_3, formed from oxygen in the upper atmosphere; a filtering layer that protects the Earth from ultraviolet radiation. 335

P

p53 The protein produced from a tumor suppressor gene that (1) attempts to repair DNA damage or (2) stops the cell cycle, or (3) initiates apoptosis. 155

pacemaker Cells of the sinoatrial node of the heart; electrical device designed to mimic the normal electrical patterns of the heart. 613

paleontology Study of fossils that results in knowledge about the history of life. 272, 333

palisade mesophyll Layer of tissue in a plant leaf containing elongated cells with many chloroplasts. 459

pancreas Internal organ that produces digestive enzymes and the hormones insulin and glucagon. 654, 765

pancreatic amylase Enzyme that digests starch to maltose. 656

pancreatic islet Masses of cells that constitute the endocrine portion of the pancreas. 765

panoramic vision Vision characterized by having a wide field of vision; found in animals with eyes to the side. 721

parabasalid Unicellular protist that lacks mitochondria; possesses flagella in clusters near the anterior of the cell. 395

parasite Species that is dependent on a host species for survival, usually to the detriment of the host species. 865

parasitism Symbiotic relationship in which one species (the *parasite*) benefits in terms of growth and reproduction to the detriment of the other species (the *host*). 375, 865

parasympathetic division Division of the autonomic system that is active under normal conditions; uses acetylcholine as a neurotransmitter. 713

parathyroid gland Gland embedded in the posterior surface of the thyroid gland; it produces parathyroid hormone. 761

parathyroid hormone (PTH) Hormone secreted by the four parathyroid glands that increases the blood calcium level and decreases the phosphate level. 761

parenchyma Plant tissue composed of the least-specialized of all plant cells; found in all organs of a plant. 448

Parkinson disease (PD) Progressive deterioration of the central nervous system due to a deficiency in the neurotransmitter dopamine. 704

parsimony In systematics, the simplest solution in the analysis of evolutionary relationships. 356

partial pressure Pressure exerted by each gas in a mixture of gases. 671

parthenogenesis Development of an egg cell into a whole organism without fertilization. 773

passive immunity Protection against infection acquired by transfer of antibodies to a susceptible individual. 639

pathogen Disease-causing agent such as viruses, parasitic bacteria, fungi, and animals. 375, 592

pattern formation Positioning of cells during development that determines the final shape of an organism. 800

pectoral girdle Portion of the vertebrate skeleton that provides support and attachment for the upper (fore) limbs; consists of the scapula and clavicle on each side of the body. 742

peduncle Flower stalk; expands into the receptacle. 434

pelagic zone Open portion of the ocean. 901

pelvic girdle Portion of the vertebrate skeleton to which the lower (hind) limbs are attached; consists of the coxal bones. 742

penis Male copulatory organ; in humans, the male organ of sexual intercourse. 777

pentose Five-carbon monosaccharide. Examples are deoxyribose found in DNA and ribose found in RNA. 42

pepsin Enzyme secreted by gastric glands that digests proteins to peptides. 656

peptidase Intestinal enzyme that breaks down short chains of amino acids to individual amino acids that are absorbed across the intestinal wall. 657

peptide Two or more amino acids joined together by covalent bonding. 50

peptide bond Type of covalent bond that joins two amino acids. 50

peptide hormone Type of hormone that is a protein, a peptide, or derived from an amino acid. 755

peptidoglycan Polysaccharide that contains short chains of amino acids; found in bacterial cell walls. 44, 374

perennial Flowering plant that lives more than one growing season because the underground parts regrow each season. 444

pericycle Layer of cells surrounding the vascular tissue of roots; produces branch roots. 451

periderm Protective tissue that replaces epidermis; includes cork, cork cambium. 447

peripheral nervous system (PNS) Nerves and ganglia that lie outside the central nervous system. 696

peristalsis Wavelike contractions that propel substances along a tubular structure such as the esophagus. 651

permafrost Permanently frozen ground, usually occurring in the tundra, a biome of Arctic regions. 888

peroxisome Enzyme-filled vesicle in which fatty acids and amino acids are metabolized to hydrogen peroxide that is broken down to harmless products. 75

petal A flower part that occurs just inside the sepals; often conspicuously colored to attract pollinators. 434, 503

petiole The part of a plant leaf that connects the blade to the stem. 445

phagocytosis Process by which cells engulf large substances, forming an intracellular vacuole. 97, 396

pharyngitis Inflammation of the pharynx; often caused by viruses or bacteria. 673

pharynx In vertebrates, common passageway for both food intake and air movement; located between the mouth and the esophagus. 668

phenomenon Observable natural event or fact. 11

phenotype Visible expression of a genotype—e.g., brown eyes or attached earlobes. 197

pheromone Chemical messenger that works at a distance and alters the behavior of another member of the same species. 755, 826

phloem Vascular tissue that conducts organic solutes in plants; contains sieve-tube members and companion cells. 426, 449

phoronids Lophophorans of the phylum Phoronida that are characterized by a long protective tube formed of chitin. 530

phospholipid Molecule that forms the bilayer of the cell's membranes; has a polar, hydrophilic head bonded to two nonpolar, hydrophobic tails. 46

photoautotroph Organism able to synthesize organic molecules by using carbon dioxide as the carbon source and sunlight as the energy source. 375

photoperiod (photoperiodism) Relative lengths of daylight and darkness that affect the physiology and behavior of an organism. 494, 495

photoreceptor Sensory receptor that responds to light stimuli. 717, 720

photorespiration Series of reactions that occurs in plants when carbon dioxide levels are depleted but oxygen continues to accumulate, and the enzyme RuBP carboxylase fixes oxygen instead of carbon dioxide. 130

photosynthesis Process, usually occurring within chloroplasts, that uses solar energy to reduce carbon dioxide to carbohydrate. 4, 120

photosystem Photosynthetic unit where solar energy is absorbed and high-energy electrons are generated; contains a pigment complex and an electron acceptor; occurs as PS (photosystem) I and PS II. 124

phototropism Growth response of plant stems to light; stems demonstrate positive phototropism. 491

pH scale Measurement scale for hydrogen ion concentration. Based on the formula $-\log[H+]$. 32

phylogenetic species concept Definition of a species that is determined by analysis of a phylogenetic tree to determine a common ancestor. 308

phylogenetic tree Diagram that indicates common ancestors and lines of descent among a group of organisms. 348

phylogeny Evolutionary history of a group of organisms. 348

phylum One of the categories, or taxa, used by taxonomists to group species; the taxon located above the class level. 6, 349

phytochrome Photoreversible plant pigment that is involved in photoperiodism and other responses of plants, such as etiolation. 495

phytoplankton Part of plankton containing organisms that photosynthesize, releasing oxygen to the atmosphere and serving as food producers in aquatic ecosystems. 899

phytoremediation The use of plants to restore a natural area to its original condition. 470

pineal gland Gland—either at the skin surface (fish, amphibians) or in the third ventricle of the brain (mammals)—that produces melatonin. 704, 768

pinocytosis Process by which vesicle formation brings macromolecules into the cell. 98

pioneer species Early colonizer of barren or disturbed habitats that usually has rapid growth and a high dispersal rate. 868

pit Any depression or opening; usually in reference to the small openings in the cell walls of xylem cells that function in providing a continuum between adjacent xylem cells. 449

pith Parenchyma tissue in the center of some stems and roots. 452

pituitary gland Small gland that lies just inferior to the hypothalamus; consists of the anterior and posterior pituitary, both of which produce hormones. 757

placenta Organ formed during the development of placental mammals from the chorion and the uterine wall; allows the embryo, and then the fetus, to acquire nutrients and rid itself of wastes; produces hormones that regulate pregnancy. 564, 774, 809

placental mammal Also called the eutherians; species that rely on internal development whereby the fetus exchanges nutrients and wastes with its mother via a placenta. 564

placoderm First jawed vertebrates; heavily armored fishes of the Devonian period. 553

plankton Freshwater and marine organisms that are suspended on or near the surface of the water; includes phytoplankton and zooplankton. 384

plants Multicellular, photosynthetic, eukaryotes that increasingly became adapted to live on land. 8, 420

plasma In vertebrates, the liquid portion of blood; contains nutrients, wastes, salts, and proteins. 618

plasma cell Mature B cell that mass-produces antibodies. 634

plasma membrane Membrane surrounding the cytoplasm that consists of a phospholipid bilayer with embedded proteins; functions to regulate the entrance and exit of molecules from cell. 65

plasmid Extrachromosomal ring of accessory DNA in the cytoplasm of prokaryotes. 65, 255, 372

plasmodesmata In plants, cytoplasmic connections in the cell wall that connect two adjacent cells. 100

plasmodial slime mold Free-living mass of cytoplasm that moves by pseudopods on a forest floor or in a field, feeding on decaying plant material by phagocytosis; reproduces by spore formation. 396

plasmolysis Contraction of the cell contents due to the loss of water. 94

plastid Organelles of plants and algae that are bounded by a double membrane and contain internal membranes and/or vesicles (i.e., chloroplasts, chromoplasts, leucoplasts). 77

plate tectonics Concept that the Earth's crust is divided into a number of fairly rigid plates whose movements account for continental drift. 343

platelet Component of blood that is necessary to blood clotting. 592, 620

pleiotropy Inheritance pattern in which one gene affects many phenotypic characteristics of the individual. 206

pneumonia Condition of the respiratory system characterized by the filling of the bronchi and alveoli with fluid; caused by a viral, fungal, or bacterial pathogen. 674

poikilothermic Body temperature that varies depending on environmental conditions; informally termed "cold-blooded." 599

point mutation Change of only one base in the sequence of bases in a gene. 248

polar body Nonfunctional product of oogenesis produced by the unequal division of cytoplasm in females during meiosis; in humans three of the four cells produced by meiosis are polar bodies. 181

polar covalent bond Bond in which the sharing of electrons between atoms is unequal. 27

pollen grain In seed plants, structure that is derived from a microspore and develops into a male gametophyte. 430, 504

pollen tube In seed plants, a tube that forms when a pollen grain lands on the stigma and germinates. The tube grows, passing between the cells of the stigma and the style to reach the egg inside an ovule, where fertilization occurs. 430

pollination In gymnosperms, the transfer of pollen from pollen cone to seed cone; in angiosperms, the transfer of pollen from anther to stigma. 430, 505

pollution Any environmental change that adversely affects the lives and health of living things. 915

polyandrous Practice of female animals having several male mates; found in the New World monkeys where the males help in rearing the offspring. 831

polygamous Practice of males having several female mates. 831

polygenic inheritance Pattern of inheritance in which a trait is controlled by several allelic pairs. 207

polygenic trait Traits that are under the control of multiple genes as opposed to monogenic (single-gene) traits. 207, 296

polymer Macromolecule consisting of covalently bonded monomers; for example, a polypeptide is a polymer of monomers called amino acids. 40

polymerase chain reaction (PCR) Technique that uses the enzyme DNA polymerase to produce millions of copies of a particular piece of DNA. 256

polyp Among cnidarians, body form that is directed upward and contains much mesoglea; in anatomy: small, abnormal growth that arises from the epithelial lining. 528, 654

polypeptide Polymer of many amino acids linked by peptide bonds. 50

polyploidy Having a chromosome number that is a multiple greater than twice that of the monoploid number. 315

polyribosome String of ribosomes simultaneously translating regions of the same mRNA strand during protein synthesis. 71, 230

polysaccharide Polymer made from carbohydrate monomers; the polysaccharides starch and glycogen are polymers of glucose monomers. 41

pons Portion of the brain stem above the medulla oblongata and below the midbrain; assists the medulla oblongata in regulating the breathing rate. 704

population Group of organisms of the same species occupying a certain area and sharing a common gene pool. 9, 290, 839

population density The number of individuals per unit area or volume living in a particular habitat. 840

population distribution The pattern of dispersal of individuals living within a certain area. 840

population genetics The study of gene frequencies and their changes within a population. 290

portal system Pathway of blood flow that begins and ends in capillaries, such as the portal system located between the small intestine and liver. 614

positive feedback Mechanism of homeostatic response in which the output of the system intensifies and increases the activity of the system. 601, 757

posterior pituitary Portion of the pituitary gland that stores and secretes oxytocin and antidiuretic hormone produced by the hypothalamus. 757

posttranscriptional control Gene expression following transcription that regulates the way mRNA transcripts are processed. 244

posttranslational control Alternation of gene expression by changing a protein's activity after it is translated. 247

postzygotic isolating mechanism Anatomical or physiological difference between two species that prevents successful reproduction after mating has taken place. 312

potential energy Stored energy in a potentially usable form, as a result of location or spatial arrangement. 105

predation Interaction in which one organism (the predator) uses another (the prey) as a food source. 860

predator Organism that practices predation. 860

prediction Step of the scientific process that follows the formulation of a hypothesis and assists in creating the experimental design. 11

preparatory (prep) reaction Reaction that oxidizes pyruvate with the release of carbon dioxide; results in acetyl CoA and connects glycolysis to the citric acid cycle. 137, 142

pressure-flow model Explanation for phloem transport; osmotic pressure following active transport of sugar into phloem produces a flow of sap from a source to a sink. 478

prey Organism that provides nourishment for a predator. 860

prezygotic isolating mechanism Anatomical, physiological, or behavioral difference between two species that prevents the possibility of mating. 310

primary lymphoid organ Location in the lymphatic system where lymphocytes develop and mature; e.g., bone marrow and thymus. 629

primary root Original root that grows straight down and remains the dominant root of the plant; contrasts with fibrous root system. 452

primate Member of the order Primates; includes prosimians, monkeys, apes, and hominins, all of whom have adaptations for living in trees. 571

primordial soup hypothesis Another name for the hypothesis of abiogenesis proposed by Alexander Oparin and J.B.S. Haldane that the first cells evolved in the oceans from present in the early atmosphere. 329

principle Theory that is generally accepted by an overwhelming number of scientists; also called a law. 12

prion Infectious particle consisting of protein only and no nucleic acid. 53, 369

producer Photosynthetic organism at the start of a grazing food chain that makes its own food—e.g., green plants on land and algae in water. 870

product Substance that forms as a result of a reaction. 107

progesterone Female sex hormone that helps maintain sexual organs and secondary sex characteristics. 779

proglottid Segment of a tapeworm that contains both male and female sex organs and becomes a bag of eggs. 533

prokaryote Organism that lacks the membrane-bounded nucleus and the membranous organelles typical of eukaryotes. 7, 371

prokaryotic cell Cells that generally lack a membrane-bounded nucleus and organelles; the cell type within the domains Bacteria and Archaea. 65

prolactin (PRL) Hormone secreted by the anterior pituitary that stimulates the production of milk from the mammary glands. 757

prometaphase Second phase of mitosis; chromosomes are condensed but not fully aligned at the metaphase plate. 159

promoter In an operon, a sequence of DNA where RNA polymerase binds prior to transcription. 238

prophase First phase of mitosis; characterized by the condensation of the chromatin; chromosomes are visible, but scattered in the nucleus. 158

proprioceptor Class of mechanoreceptors responsible for maintaining the body's equilibrium and posture; involved in reflex actions. 730

prosimian Group of primates that includes lemurs and tarsiers, and may resemble the first primates to have evolved. 575

prostaglandin Hormone that has various and powerful local effects. 768

prostate gland Gland in male humans that secretes an alkaline, cloudy, fluid that increases the motility of sperm. 777

proteasome Cellular structure containing proteases that is involved in the destruction of tagged proteins; used by cells for posttranslational control of gene expression. 247

protease Enzyme that breaks the peptide bonds between amino acids in proteins, polypeptides, and peptides. 247

protein Polymer of amino acids; often consisting of one or more polypeptides and having a complex three-dimensional shape. 49

protein-first hypothesis In chemical evolution, the proposal that protein originated before other macromolecules and made possible the formation of protocells. 330

proteinoid Abiotically polymerized amino acids that, when exposed to water, become microspheres having cellular characteristics. 330

proteome Sum of the expressed proteins in a cell. 265

proteomics Study of the complete collection of proteins that a cell or organism expresses. 232, 265

protists The group of eukaryotic organisms that are not a plant, fungus, or animal. Protists are generally a microscopic complex single cell; they evolved before other types of eukaryotes in the history of Earth. 7, 384

protobiont (protocell) In biological evolution, a possible cell forerunner that became a cell once it acquired genes. 330

proton Positive subatomic particle located in the nucleus and assigned one atomic mass unit. 22

proto-oncogene Gene that promotes the cell cycle and prevents apoptosis; may become an oncogene through mutation. 164

protostome Group of coelomate animals in which the first embryonic opening (the blastopore) is associated with the mouth. 523

protozoan Heterotrophic, unicellular protist that moves by flagella, cilia, or pseudopodia. 374

proximal convoluted tubule Portion of a nephron following the glomerular capsule where tubular reabsorption of filtrate occurs. 686

pseudocoelom Body cavity lying between the digestive tract and body wall that is incompletely lined by mesoderm. 538

pseudopod Cytoplasmic extension of amoeboid protists; used for locomotion and engulfing food. 78, 396

pteridophyte Ferns and their allies (horsetail and whisk ferns). 427

pulmonary circuit Circulatory pathway between the lungs and the heart. 609

pulmonary fibrosis Respiratory condition characterized by the buildup of connective tissue in the lungs; typically caused by inhalation of coal dust, silica, or asbestos. 675

pulmonary tuberculosis Respiratory infection caused by the bacterium *Mycobacterium tuberculosis*. 674

pulse Vibration felt in arterial walls due to expansion of the aorta following ventricle contraction. 613

Punnett square Visual representation developed by Reginald Punnett that is used to calculate the expected results of simple genetic crosses. 200

pupil Opening in the center of the iris of the vertebrate eye. 721

R

radial symmetry Body plan in which similar parts are arranged around a central axis, like spokes of a wheel. 522

radiolarian Protist that has a glassy silicon test, usually with a radial arrangement of spines; pseudopods are external to the test. 398

rain shadow Leeward side (side sheltered from the wind) of a mountainous barrier, which receives much less precipitation than the windward side. 885

rate of natural increase (r) Growth rate dependent on the number of individuals that are born each year and the number of individuals that die each year. 841

ray-finned bony fishes Group of bony fishes with fins supported by parallel bony rays connected by webs of thin tissue. 554

RB The protein of a tumor suppressor gene; interprets growth signals and nutrient availability before allowing the cell cycle to proceed. 155

reactant Substance that participates in a reaction. 107

receptacle Area where a flower attaches to a floral stalk. 434, 484

receptor Type of membrane protein that binds to specific molecules in the environment, providing a mechanism for the cell to sense and adjust to its surroundings. 474

receptor-mediated endocytosis Selective uptake of molecules into a cell by vacuole formation after they bind to specific receptor proteins in the plasma membrane. 98

receptor protein Proteins located in the plasma membrane or within the cell; bind to a substance that alters some metabolic aspect of the cell. 89

recessive allele Allele that exerts its phenotypic effect only in the homozygote; its expression is masked by a dominant allele. 196

reciprocal altruism The trading of helpful or cooperative acts, such as helping at the nest, by individuals—the animal that was helped will repay the debt at some later time. 834

recombinant DNA (rDNA) DNA that contains genes from more than one source. 255

red algae Marine photosynthetic protists with a notable abundance of phycobilin pigments; includes coralline algae of coral reefs. 389

red blood cell Erythrocyte; contains hemoglobin and carries oxygen from the lungs or gills to the tissues in vertebrates. 591, 618

red bone marrow Vascularized, modified connective tissue that is sometimes found in the cavities of spongy bone; site of blood cell formation. 740

radiocarbon dating Process of radiometric dating the measures the decay of ^{14}C to ^{14}N. 334

red tide A population bloom of dinoflagellates that causes coastal waters to turn red. Releases a toxin that can lead to paralytic shellfish poisoning. 392

redox reaction A paired set of chemical reactions in which one molecule gives up electrons (oxidized) while another molecule accepts electrons (reduced); also called an oxidation-reduction reaction. 113

reduction Gain of electrons by an atom or molecule with a concurrent storage of energy; in biological systems, the electrons are accompanied by hydrogen ions. 113

reflex action Automatic, involuntary response of an organism to a stimulus. 702

refractory period Time following an action potential when a neuron is unable to conduct another nerve impulse. 700

regulator gene Gene that controls the expression of another gene or genes; in an operon, regulator genes code for repressor proteins. 238

reinforcement Connection between natural selection and reproductive isolation that occurs when two closely related species come back into contact after a period of isolation. 314

relative dating (of fossils) Determining the age of fossils by noting their sequential relationships in strata; *absolute dating* relies on radioactive dating techniques to assign an actual date. 334

renin Enzyme released by the kidneys that leads to the secretion of aldosterone and a rise in blood pressure. 690, 763

repetitive DNA element Sequence of DNA on a chromosome that is repeated several times. 262

replacement reproduction Population in which each person is replaced by only one child. 852

replication fork In eukaryotic DNA replication, the location where the two parental DNA strands separate. 222

repressor In an operon, protein molecule that binds to an operator, preventing transcription of structural genes. 238

reproduce To produce a new individual of the same kind. 5

reproductive cloning Used to create an organism that is genetically identical to the original individual. 161

reproductive isolation Model by which new species arise when gene flow is disrupted between two populations, genetic changes accumulate, and the populations are subsequently unable to mate and produce viable offspring. 310

reproductively isolated Descriptive term that indicates that a population is incapable of interbreeding with another population. 294

reptile Terrestrial vertebrate with internal fertilization, scaly skin, and an egg with a leathery shell; includes snakes, lizards, turtles, crocodiles, and birds. 558

resource Abiotic and biotic components of an environment that support or are needed by living organisms. 840

resource partitioning Mechanism that increases the number of niches by apportioning the supply of a resource such as food or living space between species. 860

respiration Sequence of events that results in gas exchange between the cells of the body and the environment. 674

respiratory center Group of nerve cells in the medulla oblongata that send out nerve impulses on a rhythmic basis, resulting in involuntary inspiration on an ongoing basis. 670

responding variable Result or change that occurs when an experimental variable is utilized in an experiment. 14

resting potential Membrane potential of an inactive neuron. 698

restriction enzyme Bacterial enzyme that stops viral reproduction by cleaving viral DNA; used to cut DNA at specific points during production of recombinant DNA. 255

reticular activating system (RAS) Area of the brain that contains the reticular formation; acts as a relay for information to and from the peripheral nervous system and higher processing centers of the brain. 705

reticular fiber Very thin collagen fiber in the matrix of connective tissue, highly branched and forming delicate supporting networks. 589

retina Innermost layer of the vertebrate eyeball containing the photoreceptors—rod cells and cone cells. 721

retinal detachment Condition characterized by the separation of the retina from the choroid layer of the eye. 724

retrovirus RNA virus containing the enzyme reverse transcriptase that carries out RNA/ DNA transcription. 368

reverse transcriptase Viral enzyme found in retroviruses that is capable of converting their RNA genome into a DNA copy. 368

rhizarian Supergroup of eukaryotes that includes foraminiferans and radiolarians. 398

rhizoid Rootlike hair that anchors a plant and absorbs minerals and water from the soil. 424

rhizome Rootlike underground stem. 426, 458, 513

rhodopsin Light-absorbing molecule in rod cells and cone cells that contains a pigment and the protein opsin. 722

ribose Pentose sugar found in RNA. 42

ribosomal RNA (rRNA) Structural form of RNA found in the ribosomes. 223

ribosome Site of protein synthesis in a cell; composed of proteins and ribosomal RNA (rRNA). 66, 71

ribozyme RNA molecule that functions as an enzyme that can catalyze chemical reactions. 109, 227

RNA (ribonucleic acid) Nucleic acid produced from covalent bonding of nucleotide monomers that contain the sugar ribose; occurs in many forms, including: messenger RNA, ribosomal RNA, and transfer RNA. 54

RNA-first hypothesis In chemical evolution, the proposal that RNA originated before other macromolecules and allowed the formation of the first cell(s). 330

RNA interference Cellular process that utilizes miRNA and siRNA molecules to reduce, or inhibit, the expression of specific genes. 246

RNA polymerase During transcription, an enzyme that creates an mRNA transcript by joining nucleotides complementary to a DNA template. 225

rod cell Photoreceptor in vertebrate eyes that responds to dim light. 721

root apical meristem Meristem tissue located under the root cap; the site of the majority of cell division in the root. 450

root cap Protective cover of the root tip, whose cells are constantly replaced as they are ground off when the root pushes through rough soil particles. 450

root hair Extension of a root epidermal cell that collectively increases the surface area for the absorption of water and minerals. 447

root nodule Structure on plant root that contains nitrogen-fixing bacteria. 452, 471

root pressure Osmotic pressure caused by active movement of mineral into root cells; serves to elevate water in xylem for a short distance. 475

root system Includes the main root and any and all of its lateral (side) branches. 444

rotational equilibrium Maintenance of balance when the head and body are suddenly moved or rotated. 728

rotifer Microscopic invertebrates characterized by ciliated corona that when beating looks like a rotating wheel. 533

rough ER (endoplasmic reticulum) Membranous system of tubules, vesicles, and sacs in cells; has attached ribosomes. 72

roundworm Invertebrates with nonsegmented cylindrical body covered by a cuticle that molts; some forms are free-living in water and soil, and many are parasitic. 538

r-selection Favorable life history strategy under certain environmental conditions; characterized by a high reproductive rate with little or no attention given to offspring survival. 849

RuBP carboxylase An enzyme that starts the Calvin cycle reactions by catalyzing attachment of the carbon atom from CO_2 to RuBP. 128

rumen The first chamber in the digestive tract of a ruminant mammal; microorganisms here break down complex carbohydrates. 649

S

saccule Saclike cavity in the vestibule of the vertebrate inner ear; contains sensory receptors for gravitational equilibrium. 728

sac fungi (Ascomycota) Fungi that produce spores in fingerlike sacs called asci within a fruiting body; includes morels, truffles, yeasts, and molds. 408

salivary amylase In humans, enzyme in saliva that digests starch to maltose. 651, 656

salivary gland In humans, gland associated with the mouth that secretes saliva. 651

salt Solid substances formed by ionic bonds that usually dissociate into individual ions in water. 27

saltatory conduction Movement of nerve impulses from one node to another along a myelinated axon. 699

saprotroph Organism that secretes digestive enzymes and absorbs the resulting nutrients back across the plasma membrane. 375, 404

sarcolemma Plasma membrane of a muscle fiber; also forms the tubules of the T system involved in muscular contraction. 744

sarcomere One of many units, arranged linearly within a myofibril, whose contraction produces muscle contraction. 745

sarcoplasmic reticulum Smooth endoplasmic reticulum of skeletal muscle cells; surrounds the myofibrils and stores calcium ions. 744

saturated fatty acid Fatty acid molecule that lacks double bonds between the carbons of its hydrocarbon chain. The chain bears the maximum number of hydrogens possible. 46

savanna Terrestrial biome that is a grassland in Africa, characterized by few trees and a severe dry season. 895

Schwann cell Cell that surrounds a fiber of a peripheral nerve and forms the myelin sheath. 697

scientific method Process by which scientists formulate a hypothesis, gather data by observation and experimentation, and come to a conclusion. 11

scientific theory Concept, or a collection of concepts, widely supported by a broad range of observations, experiments, and data. 12

sclera White, fibrous, outer layer of the eyeball. 721

sclerenchyma Plant tissue composed of cells with heavily lignified cell walls; functions in support. 449

scolex Tapeworm head region; contains hooks and suckers for attachment to host. 533

sea star An echinoderm with noticeable 5-pointed radial symmetry; found along rocky coasts where they feed on bivalves. 544

secondary lymphoid organ Location in the lymphatic system where lymphocytes are activated by antigens; example is the lymph nodes. 629

secondary metabolite Molecule not directly involved in growth, development, or reproduction of an organism; in plants, these molecules, which include nicotine, caffeine, tannins, and menthols, can discourage herbivores. 496

secondary oocyte In oogenesis, the functional product of meiosis I; becomes the egg. 181

second messenger Chemical signal such as cyclic AMP that causes the cell to respond to the first messenger—a hormone bound to plasma membrane receptor protein. 755

secretion Release of a substance by exocytosis from a cell. 73

sediment Particulate material (sand, clay, etc.) that is carried by streams and rivers and deposited in areas of slow water movement. 333

sedimentation Process by which particulate material accumulates and forms a stratum. 333

seed Mature ovule that contains an embryo, with stored food enclosed in a protective coat. 430, 502

seed plant Vascular plants that disperse seeds; the gymnosperms and angiosperms. 430

seedless vascular plant Collective name for club mosses (lycophytes) and ferns (pteridophytes) Characterized by windblown spores. 426

segmentation Repetition of body units as seen in the earthworm. 536

selectively permeable Property of the plasma membrane that allows some substances to pass, but prohibits the movement of others. 89

semelparity Condition of having a single reproductive effort in a lifetime. 843

semen (seminal fluid) Thick, whitish fluid consisting of sperm and secretions from several glands of the male reproductive tract. 777

semicircular canal One of three half-circle-shaped canals of the vertebrate inner ear; contains sensory receptors for rotational equilibrium. 727

semiconservative replication Process of DNA replication that results in two double helix molecules, each having one parental and one new strand. 220

semilunar valve Valve resembling a half moon located between the ventricles and their attached vessels. 611

seminal vesicles Glands in male humans that secrete a viscous fluid that provides nutrition to the sperm cells. 777

seminiferous tubule Long, coiled structure contained within chambers of the testis where sperm are produced. 776

senescence Sum of the processes involving aging, decline, and eventual death of a plant or plant part. 487

sensory (afferent) neuron Nerve cell that transmits nerve impulses to the central nervous system after a sensory receptor has been stimulated. 697

sensory receptor Structure that receives either external or internal environmental stimuli and is a part of a sensory neuron or transmits signals to a sensory neuron. 717

sensory transduction Process by which a sensory receptor converts an input to a nerve impulse. 717

sepal Outermost, leaflike covering of the flower; usually green in color. 434, 503

septate Having cell walls; some fungal species have hyphae that are septate. 405

septum Partition or wall that divides two areas; the septum in the heart separates the right half from the left half. 405, 610

serosa Outer embryonic membrane of birds and reptiles; chorion. 651

seta (pl., setae) A needlelike, chitinous bristle in annelids, arthropods, and others. 536

severe combined immunodeficiency (SCID) Immune disease characterized by the impairment, or lack of, T or B cells in the body. 641

sexual dimorphism Species that have distinct differences between the sexes resulting in male and female forms. 297

sexual reproduction Reproduction involving meiosis, gamete formation, and fertilization; produces offspring with chromosomes inherited from each parent with a unique combination of genes. 172

sexual selection Changes in males and females, often due to male competition and female selectivity, leading to increased fitness. 297, 831

shoot apical meristem Group of actively dividing embryonic cells at the tips of plant shoots. 453

shoot system Aboveground portion of a plant consisting of the stem, leaves, and flowers. 444

short-day plant Plant that flowers when day length is shorter than a critical length—e.g., cocklebur, poinsettia, and chrysanthemum. 495

short tandem repeat (STR) profiling Procedure of analyzing DNA in which PCR and gel electrophoresis are used to create a banding pattern; these are usually unique for each individual; process used in DNA barcoding. 257

shrubland Arid terrestrial biome characterized by shrubs and tending to occur along coasts that have dry summers and receive most of their rainfall in the winter. 894

sieve-tube member Member that joins with others in the phloem tissue of plants as a means of transport for nutrient sap. 450

sign stimulus The environmental trigger that causes a fixed action pattern or unchanging behavioral response. 822

signal Molecule that stimulates or inhibits an event in the cell. 155

signal peptide Sequence of amino acids that binds with a signal recognition particle (SRP), causing a ribosome to bind to the endoplasmic reticulum (ER). 71

signal transduction Process that occurs within a cell when a molecular signal (protein, hormone, etc.) initiates a response within the interior of the cell. 484

sink In the pressure-flow model of phloem transport, the location (roots) from which sugar is constantly being removed. Sugar will flow to the roots from the source. 479

sink population Population that is found in an unfavorable area where at best the birthrate equals the death rate; sink populations receive new members from source populations. 919

sister chromatid One of two genetically identical chromosomal units that are the result of DNA replication and are attached to each other at the centromere. 154

skeletal muscle Striated, voluntary muscle tissue that comprises skeletal muscles; also called striated muscle. 592

skin Outer covering of the body; can be called the integumentary system because it contains organs such as sense organs. 597

sliding filament model An explanation for muscle contraction based on the movement of actin filaments in relation to myosin filaments. 745

small interfering RNAs (siRNA) Short sequences of RNA, typically less than 25 nucleotides, that are involved in posttranscriptional control of gene expression through a process called RNA interference. 246

small intestine In vertebrates, the portion of the digestive tract that precedes the large intestine; in humans, consists of the duodenum, jejunum, and ileum. 652

smooth (visceral) muscle Nonstriated, involuntary muscles found in the walls of internal organs. 592

smooth ER (endoplasmic reticulum) Membranous system of tubules, vesicles, and sacs in eukaryotic cells; site of lipid synthesis; lacks attached ribosomes. 72

society Group in which members of species are organized in a cooperative manner, extending beyond sexual and parental behavior. 826

sodium-potassium pump Carrier protein in the plasma membrane that moves sodium ions out of and potassium ions into cells; important in the function of nerve and muscle cells in animals. 95

soil Accumulation of inorganic rock material and organic matter that is capable of supporting the growth of vegetation. 467

soil erosion Movement of topsoil to a new location due to the action of wind or running water. 468

soil horizon Major layer of soil visible in vertical profile; for example, topsoil is the A horizon. 468

soil profile Vertical section of soil from the ground surface to the unaltered rock below. 468

solute Substance that is dissolved in a solvent, forming a solution. 30, 91

solution Fluid (the solvent) that contains a dissolved solid (the solute). 30, 91

solvent Liquid portion of a solution that serves to dissolve a solute. 91

somatic cell Body cell; excludes cells that undergo meiosis and become sperm or eggs. 155

somatic system Portion of the peripheral nervous system containing motor neurons that control skeletal muscles. 708

source In the pressure-flow model of phloem transport, the location (leaves) of sugar production. Sugar will flow from the leaves to the sink. 479

source population Population that can provide members to other populations of the species because it lives in a favorable area, and the birthrate is most likely higher than the death rate. 919

speciation Origin of new species due to the evolutionary process of descent with modification. 307, 313

species Group of similarly constructed organisms capable of interbreeding and producing fertile offspring; organisms that share a common gene pool; the taxon at the lowest level of classification. 6, 349

species concepts Models that describe the process by which new species arise. 307

species diversity Variety of species that make up a community. 858

species richness Number of species in a community. 858

specific epithet In the binomial system of taxonomy, the second part of an organism's name; it may be descriptive. 349

sperm Male gamete having a haploid number of chromosomes and the ability to fertilize an egg, the female gamete. 777

spermatogenesis Production of sperm in males by the process of meiosis and maturation. 180

spicule Skeletal structure of sponges composed of calcium carbonate or silicate. 527

spinal cord In vertebrates, the nerve cord that is continuous with the base of the brain and housed within the vertebral column. 702

spinal nerve Nerve that arises from the spinal cord. 707

spirillum (pl., spirilla) Long, rod-shaped bacterium that is twisted into a rigid spiral; if the spiral is flexible rather than rigid, it is called a spirochete. 65

spirochete Long, rod-shaped bacterium that is twisted into a flexible spiral; if the spiral is rigid rather than flexible, it is called a spirillum. 65

spleen Large, glandular organ located in the upper left region of the abdomen; stores and filters blood. 629

sponge Invertebrates that are pore-bearing filter feeders whose inner body wall is lined by collar cells that resemble a unicellular choanoflagellate. 527

spongy bone Type of bone that has an irregular, meshlike arrangement of thin plates of bone. 591, 740

spongy mesophyll Layer of tissue in a plant leaf containing loosely packed cells, increasing the amount of surface area for gas exchange. 459

spontaneous mutation Mutation that arises as a result of anomalies in normal biological processes, such as mistakes made during DNA replication. 247

sporangium (pl., sporangia) Structure that produces spores. 422

spore Asexual reproductive or resting cell capable of developing into a new organism

without fusion with another cell, in contrast to a gamete. 176, 406, 422

sporophyll Modified leaf that bears a sporangium or many sporangia. 426

sporophyte Diploid generation of the alternation-of-generations life cycle of a plant; produces haploid spores that develop into the haploid generation. 180, 422

spring overturn Mixing process that occurs in spring in stratified lakes whereby oxygen-rich top waters mix with nutrient-rich bottom waters. 899

squamous epithelium Type of epithelial tissue that contains flat cells. 588

stabilizing selection Outcome of natural selection in which extreme phenotypes are eliminated and the average phenotype is conserved. 296

standard deviation A statistical analysis of data from an observation or experiment; measures how much the data varies. 12

stamen In flowering plants, the portion of the flower that consists of a filament and an anther containing pollen sacs where pollen is produced. 434, 503

starch Storage polysaccharide found in plants that is composed of glucose molecules joined in a linear fashion with few side chains. 43

statolith Sensors found in root cap cells that cause a plant to demonstrate gravitropism. 491

stem Usually the upright, vertical portion of a plant that transports substances to and from the leaves. 445

stereoscopic vision Vision characterized by depth perception and three-dimensionality. 572, 721

steroid Type of lipid molecule having a complex of four carbon rings—e.g., cholesterol, estrogen, progesterone, and testosterone. 46

steroid hormone Type of hormone that has the same complex of four carbon rings, but each one has different side chains. 755

stigma In flowering plants, portion of the carpel where pollen grains adhere and germinate before fertilization can occur. 434, 503

stolon Stem that grows horizontally along the ground and may give rise to new plants where it contacts the soil—e.g., the runners of a strawberry plant. 456, 513

stomach In vertebrates, muscular sac that mixes food with gastric juices to form chyme, which enters the small intestine. 652

stomata (sing., stoma) Small openings between two guard cells on the underside of leaf epidermis through which gases pass. 121, 422, 447

stramenopile Group of protists that includes water molds, diatoms, and golden brown algae and is characterized by a "hairy" flagellum. 390

strata (sing. stratum) Ancient layer of sedimentary rock; results from slow deposition of silt, volcanic ash, and other materials. 273, 333

striated Having bands; in cardiac and skeletal muscle, alternating light and dark bands produced by the distribution of contractile proteins. 592

strobilus In club mosses, terminal clusters of leaves that bear sporangia. 426

stroke Condition resulting when an arteriole in the brain bursts or becomes blocked by an embolism; cerebrovascular accident. 616, 704

stroma Region within a chloroplast that surrounds the grana; contains enzymes involved in the synthesis of carbohydrates during the Calvin cycle of photosynthesis. 76, 121

stromatolite Domed structure found in shallow seas consisting of cyanobacteria bound to calcium carbonate. 335

structural gene Gene that codes for the amino acid sequence of a peptide or protein. 238

structural genomics Study of the sequence of DNA bases and the amount of genes in organisms. 261

style Elongated, central portion of the carpel between the ovary and stigma. 434, 503

submucosa Tissue layer just under the epithelial lining of the lumen of the digestive tract (second layer). 651

substrate Reactant in an enzyme-controlled reaction. 109

substrate-level ATP synthesis Process in which ATP is formed by transferring a phosphate from a metabolic substrate to ADP. 138

supergroup Systematic term that refers to the major groups of eukaryotes. 384

surface-area-to-volume ratio Ratio of a cell's outside area to its internal volume; the relationship limits the maximum size of a cell. 62

surface tension Force that holds moist membranes together due to the attraction of water molecules through hydrogen bonds. 31

survivorship Probability of newborn individuals of a cohort surviving to particular ages. 841

suture Line of union between two nonarticulating bones, as in the skull. 740

swamp Wet, spongy land that is saturated and sometimes partially or intermittently covered with water. 897

sweat gland Skin gland that secretes a fluid substance for evaporative cooling; sudoriferous gland. 599

swim bladder In fishes, a gas-filled sac whose pressure can be altered to change buoyancy. 554

symbiosis Relationship that occurs when two different species live together in a unique way; it may be beneficial, neutral, or detrimental to one or both species. 865

symbiotic relationship *See also* symbiosis. 375

symmetry Pattern of similarity in an object. 522

sympathetic division Division of the autonomic system that is active when an organism is under stress; uses norepinephrine as a neurotransmitter. 709

sympatric speciation Origin of new species in populations that overlap geographically. 314

synapse Junction between neurons consisting of the presynaptic (axon) membrane, the synaptic cleft, and the postsynaptic (usually dendrite) membrane. 700

synapsid Characteristic of a vertebrate skull in which there is a single opening in the skull behind the eye socket (orbit). 558

synapsis Pairing of homologous chromosomes during meiosis I. 173

synaptic cleft Small gap between presynaptic and postsynaptic cells of a synapse. 700

synaptonemal complex Protein structure that forms between the homologous chromosomes of prophase I of meiosis; promotes the process of crossing-over. 173

synovial joint Freely moving joint in which two bones are separated by a cavity. 742

systematics Study of the diversity of life for the purpose of understanding the evolutionary relationships between species. 6, 348

systemic circuit Circulatory pathway of blood flow between the tissues and the heart. 609

systemin In plants, an 18-amino-acid peptide that is produced by damaged or injured leaves that leads to the wound response. 497

systole Contraction period of the heart during the cardiac cycle. 612

T

tactile communication Communication through touch; for example, when a chick pecks its mother for food, chimpanzees groom each other, and honeybees "dance." 829

taiga Terrestrial biome that is a coniferous forest extending in a broad belt across northern Eurasia and North America. 890

tandem repeat Repetitive DNA sequence in which the repeats occur one after another in the same region of a chromosome. 262

taproot Main axis of a root that penetrates deeply and is used by certain plants (such as carrots) for food storage. 452

taste bud Structure in the vertebrate mouth containing sensory receptors for taste; in humans, most taste buds are on the tongue. 718

taxon (pl., taxa) Group of organisms that fills a particular classification category. 348

taxonomist Scientist that investigates the identification and naming of new organisms. 307, 348

taxonomy Branch of biology concerned with identifying, describing, and naming organisms. 6, 348

T cell Lymphocyte that matures in the thymus and exists in four varieties, one of which kills antigen-bearing cells outright. 629

T-cell receptor (TCR) Molecule on the surface of a T cell that can bind to a specific antigen fragment in combination with an MHC molecule. 635

telomere Tip of the end of a chromosome that shortens with each cell division and may thereby regulate the number of times a cell can divide. 164, 221

telophase Final phase of mitosis; daughter cells are located at each pole. 160

temperate deciduous forest Forest found south of the taiga; characterized by deciduous trees such as oak, beech, and maple, moderate climate, relatively high rainfall, stratified plant growth, and plentiful ground life. 891

temperate grassland Grasslands characterized by very cold winters and dry, hot summers; examples are the North American prairies and Russian steppes. 894

temperate rain forest Coniferous forest—e.g., that running along the west coast of Canada and the United States—characterized by plentiful rainfall and rich soil. 890

template Parental strand of DNA that serves as a guide for the complementary daughter strand produced during DNA replication. 220

tendon Strap of fibrous connective tissue that connects skeletal muscle to bone. 590, 744

terminal bud Bud that develops at the apex of a shoot. 453

termination End of translation that occurs when a ribosome reaches a stop codon on the mRNA that it is translating, causing release of the completed protein. 231

territoriality Marking and/or defending a particular area against invasion by another species member; area often used for the purpose of feeding, mating, and caring for young. 299, 830

territory Area occupied and defended exclusively by an animal or group of animals. 299, 830

test Loose-fitting shell of a foraminiferan or a radiolarian; made of calcium carbonate or silicon, respectively. 398

testcross Cross between an individual with a dominant phenotype and an individual with a recessive phenotype to determine whether the dominant individual is homozygous or heterozygous. 200

testes Male gonads that produce sperm and the male sex hormones. 773, 775

testosterone Male sex hormone that helps maintain sexual organs and secondary sex characteristics. 778

tetany Severe spasm caused by involuntary contraction of the skeletal muscles due to a calcium imbalance. 744

tetrapod Four-footed vertebrate; includes amphibians, reptiles, birds, and mammals. 552

thalamus In vertebrates, the portion of the diencephalon that passes on selected sensory information to the cerebrum. 704

therapeutic cloning Used to create mature cells of various cell types. Facilitates study of specialization of cells and provide cells and tissue to treat human illnesses. 161

thermoacidophile Type of archaean that lives in hot, acidic, aquatic habitats, such as hot springs or near hydrothermal vents. 379

thermoreceptor Sensory receptor that detects heat. 717

thigmotropism In plants, unequal growth due to contact with solid objects, as the coiling of tendrils around a pole. 491

threatened species Species that is likely to become an endangered species in the foreseeable future (e.g., bald eagle, gray wolf, Louisiana black bear). 908

thylakoid Flattened sac within a granum of a chloroplast; membrane contains chlorophyll; location where the light reactions of photosynthesis occur. 66, 76, 121

thymine (T) One of four nitrogen-containing bases in nucleotides composing the structure of DNA; pairs with adenine. 217

thymus gland Lymphoid organ involved in the development and functioning of the immune system; T lymphocytes mature in the thymus gland. 629,768

thyroid gland Large gland in the neck that produces several important hormones, including thyroxine, triiodothyronine, and calcitonin. 762

thyroid-stimulating hormone (TSH) Substance produced by the anterior pituitary that causes the thyroid to secrete thyroxine and triiodothyronine. 760

thyroxine (T_4) Hormone secreted from the thyroid gland that promotes growth and development; in general, it increases the metabolic rate in cells. 760

tight junction Junction between cells when adjacent plasma membrane proteins join to form an impermeable barrier. 99

tissue Group of similar cells combined to perform a common function. 588

tissue culture Process of growing tissue artificially, usually in a liquid medium in laboratory glassware. 513

tissue fluid Fluid that surrounds the body's cells; consists of dissolved substances that leave the blood capillaries by filtration and diffusion. 591, 621

tone Continuous, partial contraction of muscle. 744

tonicity The solute concentration (osmolarity) of a solution compared to that of a cell. If the solution is isotonic to the cell, there is no net movement of water; if the solution is hypotonic, the cell gains water; and if the solution is hypertonic, the cell loses water. 93

topography Surface features of the Earth. 885

totipotent Cell that has the full genetic potential of the organism, including the potential to develop into a complete organism. 514, 800

toxin Poisonous substance produced by living cells or organisms. Toxins are often proteins that are capable of causing disease on contact with or absorption by body tissues. 376

trachea (pl., tracheae) In insects, air tubes located between the spiracles and the tracheoles. In tetrapod vertebrates, air tube (windpipe) that runs between the larynx and the bronchi. 542, 664, 668

tracheid In vascular plants, type of cell in xylem that has tapered ends and pits through which water and minerals flow. 449

tract Bundle of myelinated axons in the central nervous system. 703

trait A characteristic of an organism; may be based on the physiology, morphology, or the genetics of the organism. 348

transcription First stage of gene expression; process whereby a DNA strand serves as a template for the formation of mRNA. 223

transcription activator Protein that participates in the initiation of transcription by binding to the enhancer regulatory regions. 244

transcriptional control Control of gene expression by the use of transcription factors, and other proteins, that regulate either the initiation of transcription or the rate at which it occurs. 244

transcription factor In eukaryotes, protein required for the initiation of transcription by RNA polymerase. 244

transduction Exchange of DNA between bacteria by means of a bacteriophage. 373

transduction pathway Series of proteins or enzymes that change a signal to one understood by the cell. 484

trans-fats Unsaturated fatty acid chains in which the configuration of the carbon-carbon double bonds is such that the hydrogen atoms are across from each other, as opposed to being on the same side (cis). 658

transfer rate Amount of a substance that moves from one component of the environment to another within a specified period of time. 875

transfer RNA (tRNA) Type of RNA that transfers a particular amino acid to a ribosome during protein synthesis; at one end, it binds to the amino acid, and at the other end it has an anticodon that binds to an mRNA codon. 223

transformation Taking up of extraneous genetic material from the environment by bacteria. 373

transgenic organism An organism whose genome has been altered by the insertion of genes from another species. 255

transitional fossil Fossil that bears a resemblance to two groups that in the present day are classified separately. 280

translation During gene expression, the process whereby ribosomes use the sequence of codons in mRNA to produce a polypeptide with a particular sequence of amino acids. 224

translational control Gene expression regulated by influencing the interaction of the mRNA transcripts with the ribosome. 246

translocation Movement of a chromosomal segment from one chromosome to another nonhomologous chromosome, leading to abnormalities—e.g., Down syndrome. 187, 231

transpiration Plant's loss of water to the atmosphere, mainly through evaporation at leaf stomata. 476

transposon DNA sequence capable of randomly moving from one site to another in the genome. 262

trichocyst Found in ciliates; contains long, barbed threads useful for defense and capturing prey. 393

trichomes In plants, specialized outgrowths of the epidermis (e.g., root hairs). 447

triglyceride Neutral fat composed of glycerol and three fatty acids; typically involved in energy storage. 46

triplet code During gene expression, each sequence of three nucleotide bases stands for a particular amino acid. 224

trisomy Chromosome condition in which a diploid cell has one more chromosome than normal; designated as 2n + 1. 183

trochozoan Type of protostome that produces a trochophore larva; also has two bands of cilia around its middle. 530

trophic level Feeding level of one or more populations in a food web. 873

trophoblast Outer membrane surrounding the embryo in mammals; when thickened by a layer of mesoderm, it becomes the chorion, an extraembryonic membrane. 806

tropical rain forest Biome near the equator in South America, Africa, and the Indo-Malay regions; characterized by warm weather, plentiful rainfall, a diversity of species, and mainly tree-living animal life. 892

tropism In plants, a growth response toward or away from a directional stimulus. 490

true coelom Body cavity completely lined with mesoderm; found in certain protostomes and all deuterostomes. 523

trypsin Protein-digesting enzyme secreted by the pancreas. 656

tubular reabsorption Movement of primarily nutrient molecules and water from the contents of the nephron into blood at the proximal convoluted tubule. 686

tubular secretion Movement of certain molecules from blood into the distal convoluted tubule of a nephron so that they are added to urine. 686

tumor Cells derived from a single mutated cell that has repeatedly undergone cell division; benign tumors remain at the site of origin, while malignant tumors metastasize. 164

tumor suppressor gene Gene that codes for a protein that ordinarily suppresses the cell

cycle; inactivity due to a mutation can lead to a tumor. 164

turgor movement In plant cells, pressure of the cell contents against the cell wall when the central vacuole is full. 493

turgor pressure Pressure of the cell contents against the cell wall; in plant cells, determined by the water content of the vacuole; provides internal support. 93

tympanic membrane Membranous region that receives air vibrations in an auditory organ; in humans, the eardrum. 727

U

umbilical cord Cord connecting the fetus to the placenta through which blood vessels pass. 809

unicellular An organism comprised of a single cell, as in the bacteria. 2

uniformitarianism Belief, supported by James Hutton, that geological forces act at a continuous, uniform rate. 274

unsaturated fatty acid Fatty acid molecule that contains double bonds between some carbons of its hydrocarbon chain; thus contains fewer hydrogens than a saturated hydrocarbon chain. 46

upwelling Upward movement of deep, nutrient-rich water along coasts; it replaces surface waters that move away from shore when the direction of prevailing wind shifts. 904

uracil (U) Pyrimidine base that occurs in RNA, replacing thymine. 223

urea Main nitrogenous waste of terrestrial amphibians and most mammals. 681

ureter Tubular structure conducting urine from the kidney to the urinary bladder. 684

urethra Tubular structure that receives urine from the bladder and carries it to the outside of the body. 684

uric acid Main nitrogenous waste of insects, reptiles, and birds. 681

urinary bladder Organ where urine is stored. 684

urine Liquid waste product made by the nephrons of the vertebrate kidney through the processes of glomerular filtration, tubular reabsorption, and tubular secretion. 682

urochordate Group of aquatic invertebrate chordates that consists of the tunicates (sea squirts). 551

uterine cycle Cycle that runs concurrently with the ovarian cycle; it prepares the uterus to receive a developing zygote. 781

uterus In mammals, expanded portion of the female reproductive tract through which eggs pass to the environment or in which an embryo develops and is nourished before birth. 779

utricle Cavity in the vestibule of the vertebrate inner ear; contains sensory receptors for gravitational equilibrium. 728

V

vacuole Membrane-bounded sac, larger than a vesicle; usually functions in storage and can contain a variety of substances. In plants, the central vacuole fills much of the interior of the cell. 75

vagina Component of the female reproductive system that serves as the birth canal; receives the penis during copulation. 779

valence shell The outer electron shell of an atom. Contains the valence electrons, which determine the chemical reactivity of the atom. 25

vas deferens Also called the ductus deferens; storage location for mature sperm before they pass into the ejaculatory duct. 775

vascular bundle In plants, primary phloem and primary xylem enclosed by a bundle sheath. 450

vascular cambium In plants, lateral meristem that produces secondary phloem and secondary xylem. 454

vascular cylinder In eudicots, the tissues in the middle of a root, consisting of the pericycle and vascular tissues. 450

vascular plant Plant that has xylem and phloem. 426

vascular tissue Transport tissue in plants, consisting of xylem and phloem. 423, 447

vector In genetic engineering, a means to transfer foreign genetic material into a cell—e.g., a plasmid. 66, 255, 394

vein Blood vessel that arises from venules and transports blood toward the heart. 608

vena cava Large systemic vein that returns blood to the right atrium of the heart in tetrapods; either the superior or inferior vena cava. 614

ventilation Process of moving air into and out of the lungs; breathing. 664

ventricle Cavity in an organ, such as a lower chamber of the heart or the ventricles of the brain. 611, 702

venule Vessel that takes blood from capillaries to a vein. 608

vertebral column Portion of the vertebrate endoskeleton that houses the spinal cord; consists of many vertebrae separated by intervertebral disks. 741

vertebrate Chordate in which the notochord is replaced by a vertebral column. 520

vertigo Equilibrium disorder that is often associated with problems in the receptors of the semicircular canals in the ear. 730

vesicle Small, membrane-bounded sac that stores substances within a cell. 67, 331

vessel element Cell that joins with others to form a major conducting tube found in xylem. 449

vestibule Space or cavity at the entrance to a canal, such as the cavity that lies between the semicircular canals and the cochlea. 727

vestigial structure Remnant of a structure that was functional in some ancestor but is no longer functional in the organism in question. 272

villus Small, fingerlike projection of the inner small intestinal wall. 652

viroid Infectious strand of RNA devoid of a capsid and much smaller than a virus. 369

virus Noncellular parasitic agent consisting of an outer capsid and an inner core of nucleic acid. 364

visual accommodation Ability of the eye to focus at different distances by changing the curvature of the lens. 722

visual communication Form of communication between animals using their bodies, includes various forms of display. 828

vitamin Organic nutrient that is required in small amounts for metabolic functions. Vitamins are often part of coenzymes. 112

viviparous Animal that gives birth after partial development of offspring within mother. 774

vocal cord In humans, fold of tissue within the larynx; creates vocal sounds when it vibrates. 668

W

water column In plants, water molecules joined together in xylem from the leaves to the roots. 476

water (hydrologic) cycle Interdependent and continuous circulation of water from the ocean, to the atmosphere, to the land, and back to the ocean. 875

water mold Filamentous organisms having cell walls made of cellulose; typically decomposers of dead freshwater organisms, but some are parasites of aquatic or terrestrial organisms. 391

water potential Potential energy of water; a measure of the capability to release or take up water relative to another substance. 473

water vascular system Series of canals that takes water to the tube feet of an echinoderm, allowing them to expand. 544

wax Sticky, solid, water-repellent lipid consisting of many long-chain fatty acids usually linked to long-chain alcohols. 48

wetland Area that is covered by water at some point in the year. (*See also* bog, marsh, or swamp.) 897

whisk fern Common name for seedless vascular plant that consists only of stems and has no leaves, or roots. 428

white blood cell Leukocyte, of which there are several types, each having a specific function in protecting the body from invasion by foreign substances and organisms. 620

white matter Myelinated axons in the central nervous system. 703

whorl Cluster of branches, or other plant structures, that occurs in a circular pattern. 421

wobble hypothesis Ability of the tRNAs to recognize more than one codon; the codons differ in their third nucleotide. 229

wood Secondary xylem that builds up year after year in woody plants and becomes the annual rings. 456

X

X-linked Allele that is located on an X chromosome; not all X-linked genes code for sexual characteristics. 208

xylem Vascular tissue that transports water and mineral solutes upward through the plant body; it contains vessel elements and tracheids. 426, 449

Y

yeast Unicellular fungus that has a single nucleus and reproduces asexually by budding or fission, or sexually through spore formation. 408

yolk Dense nutrient material in the egg of a bird or reptile. 774, 797

yolk sac One of the extraembryonic membranes that, in shelled vertebrates, contains yolk for the nourishment of the embryo, and in placental mammals is the first site for blood cell formation. 805

Z

zero population growth No growth in population size. 852

zooflagellate Nonphotosynthetic protist that moves by flagella; typically zooflagellates enter into symbiotic relationships, and some are parasitic. 395

zooplankton Part of plankton containing protozoans and other types of microscopic animals. 899

zoospore Spore that is motile by means of one or more flagella. 407

zygospore Thick-walled resting cell formed during sexual reproduction of zygospore fungi. 408

zygospore fungi (Zygomycota) Fungi such as black bread mold that reproduces by forming windblown spores in sporangia; sexual reproduction involves a thick-walled zygospore. 407

zygote Diploid cell formed by the union of two gametes; the product of fertilization. 172, 310

Credits

© David Sieren/Visuals Unlimited; 24.14(left): © Ed Reschke; 24.14(right): Courtesy Ray F. Evert/University of Wisconsin Madison; 24.15(top): © CABISCO/Phototake; 24.15(bottom): © Kingsley Stern; 24.17(circular cross section): © Ed Reschke/Peter Arnold/Photolibrary; 24.18a: © Ardea London Limited; 24.19a: © The McGraw-Hill Companies Inc./Evelyn Jo Johnson, photographer; 24.19b: © Science Pictures Limited/Photo Researchers, Inc.; 24.19c: © The McGraw Hill Companies, Inc./Carlyn Iverson, photographer; 24.19d: © The McGraw Hill Companies, Inc. Carlyn Iverson, photographer; 24B(flooring): © Alamy RF; 24B(shoots): © Getty RF; 24B(bamboo grove): © Michele Westmorland/Getty Images; 24.20: © Jeremy Burgess/SPL/Photo Researchers, Inc.; 24.22a: © Patti Murray Animals Animals; 24.22b: © Gerald & Buff Corsi/Visuals Unlimited; 24.22c: © P. Goetgheluck/Peter Arnold/Photolibrary.

CHAPTER 25 Openers (left): © Kit R. Roane/age fotostock; (right): © The Nug/Alamy; 25.2a(all): Courtesy Mary E. Doohan; 25.5a: © CABISCO/Phototake; 25A: © Yann Arthus-Bertrand/Corbis; 25.6(top): © Dwight Kuhn; 25.6(circle): © E.H. Newcomb & S.R. Tardon/Biological Photo Service; 25.7(left): © Runk Schoenberger/Grant Heilman; 25.7(circle): © Dana Richter/Visuals Unlimited; 25.8a: © Kevin Schafer/Corbis; 25.8b(sundew plant): © Barry Rice/Visuals Unlimited; 25.8b(sundew leaf): © Dr. Jeremy Burgess/Photo Researchers, Inc.; 25C(both): © The McGraw Hill Companies, Inc./Ken Cavanagh, photographer; 25.1(all): Courtesy Wilfred A. Cote, from H.A. Core, W.A. Cote, and A.C. Day, Wood: Structure and Identification 2/e; 25.11: © Ed Reschke/Peter Arnold/Photolibrary; 25.13(both): © Jeremy Burgess/SPL/Photo Researchers, Inc.; 25.14a: © M. H. Zimmermann, Courtesy Dr. P. B. Tomlinson, Harvard University; 25.14b: © Steven P. Lynch.

CHAPTER 26 Opener: Courtesy USDA/photo by Bruce Fritz; 26.4a: © Robert E. Lyons/Visuals Unlimited; 26.4b: © Sylvan Whittwer/Visuals Unlimited; 26.5a–d: Courtesy Alan Darvill and Stefan Eberhard, Complex Carbohydrate Research Center, University of Georgia; 26.6: © John Solden/Visuals Unlimited; 26.7: Courtesy Dr. Donald R. McCarty, University of Florida; 26.9(both), 26.11a: © Kingsley Stern; 26.11b: Courtesy Malcolm Wilkins, Glascow University; 26.11c: Micrographs courtesy of Randy Moore; 26.13: © John D. Cunningham/Visuals Unlimited; 26A: Courtesy Elliot Meyerowitz/California Institute of Technology; 26.14(both): © John Kaprielian/Photo Researchers, Inc.; 26.15a(both): © Tom McHugh/Photo Researchers, Inc.; 26.15b(left): © BIOS A. Thais/Peter Arnold/Photolibrary; 26.15b(right): © BIOS Pierre Huguet/Peter Arnold/Photolibrary; 26.17(both): © Nigel Cattlin/Visuals Unlimited; 26.19(bug): Courtesy USDA/Agricultural Research Service, photo by Scott Bauer; 26.19(fungus): © Kingsley Stern; 26.19(caterpillar): © The McGraw Hill Companies, Inc. Ken Cavanagh, photographer; 26.19(butterfly): © Dwight Kuhn.

CHAPTER 27 Opener: © Corbis RF; 27.3a: © Farley Bridges; 27.3b: © Pat Pendarvis; 27.4a: © Radius Images/Getty RF; 27.4b: © Garden World Images/age fotostock; 27.5(pollen grain): Courtesy Graham Kent; 27.5(embryo sac): © Ed Reschke; 27.6a: © George Bernard/Animals Animals; 27.6b: © Simko/Visuals Unlimited; 27.6c: © Dwight Kuhn; 27Aa: © Steven P. Lynch; 27Ab: © Robert Maier/Animals Animals; 27Ba: © Anthony Mercieca/Photo Researchers, Inc.; 27Bb: © Merlin D. Tuttle/Bat Conservation International; 27.7(proembryo, globular, heart): Courtesy Dr. Chun-Ming Liu; 27.7(torpedo): © Biology Media/Photo Researchers, Inc.; 27.7(mature embryo): © Jack Bostrack/Visuals Unlimited; 27.8a(bean): © Dwight Kuhn; 27.8b(corn): Courtesy Ray F. Evert/University of Wisconsin Madison; 27.9a, b: © Kingsley Stern; 27.9c: © Dr. James Richardson/Visuals Unlimited; 27.9d: © James Mauseth; 27.9e: Courtesy Robert A. Schlising; 27.9f: © Ingram Publishing/Alamy RF; 27.10a: © Marie Read/Animals Animals; 27.10b: © Scott Camazine/Photo Researchers, Inc.; 27.11a(bean): © Ed Reschke; 27.11b(corn): © James Mauseth; 27.12: © G.I. Bernard/Animals Animals; 27.13a(all): Courtesy Prof. Dr. Hans-Ulrich Koop, from Plant Cell Reports, 17:601-604; 27.14: © Kingsley Stern.

CHAPTER 28 Opener: © James H. Robinson/Photo Researchers, Inc.; 28.1(all top row, zygote to embryo): © Cabisco/Phototake; 28.1(adult frog and all bottom row): © Dwight Kuhn; 28A(phase I): © Christiane Nusslein-Volhard, Development, Supplement 1, 1991, reproduced with permission, website: http://dev.biologists.org; 28A(phase II, all): Courtesy Jim Langeland, Steve Paddock, and Sean Carroll/University of Wisconsin, Madison; 28B(chicken): © Photodisc/Getty RF; 28B(mouse): © Alamy RF; 28B(python): © IT Stock/PunchStock RF; 28.6a: © Andrew J. Martinez/Photo Researchers, Inc.; 28.7a: © Jeff Rotman; 28.7b: © J. McCollugh/Visuals Unlimited; 28.8a: © Azure Computer & Photo Services/Animals Animals; 28.8b: © Ron Taylor/Bruce Coleman/Photoshot; 28.8c: © Image courtesy of Islands in the Sea 2002, NOAA/OER; 28.8d: © Amos Nachoum/Corbis; 28.9: © CABISCO/Visuals Unlimited; 28.10a: © Robert Brons/Biological Photo Service; 28.11: © Diane R. Nelson; 28.12e: © Tom E. Adams/Peter Arnold/Photolibrary; 28.13a: © SPL/Photo Researchers, Inc.; 28.14(proglottid): © John D. Cunningham/Visuals Unlimited; 28.14(scolex): © James Webb/Phototake; 28.16b: © Kjell Sandved/Butterfly Alphabet; 28.17a: Courtesy Larry S. Roberts; 28.17b: © Fred Whitehead/Animals Animals; 28.18a: © M. Gibbs/OSF/Animals Animals; 28.18b: © Farley Bridges; 28.18c: © Douglas Faulkner/Photo Researchers, Inc.; 28.18d: © Georgette Douwma/Photo Researchers, Inc.; 28.19c: © Roger K. Burnard/Biological Photo Service; 28.20b: © James H. Carmichael; 28.20c: © St. Bartholomews Hospital/SPL/Photo Researchers, Inc.; 28.21a: © Lauritz Jensen/Visuals Unlimited; 28.21b: © James Solliday/Biological Photo Service; 28.21c: © Vanessa Vick/The New York Times/Redux; 28.22c: © OSF/London Scientific Films/Animals Animals; 28.23a: © Michael Lustbader/Photo Researchers, Inc.; 28.23b: © Bruce Robinson/Corbis; 28.23c: © Kjell Sandved/Butterfly Alphabet; 28.25a: © Larry Miller/Photo Researchers, Inc.; 28.25b: © David Aubrey/Corbis; 28.26(mealybug): © Farley Bridges; 28.26(beetle): © Wolfgang Kaehler/Corbis; 28.26(leafhopper): © Farley Bridges; 28.26(louse): © Darlyne A. Murawski/Peter Arnold/Photolibrary; 28.26(wasp): © Johnathan Smith/LatitudeStock; 28.26(dragonfly): © Farley Bridges; 28.28a: © Jana R. Jirak/Visuals Unlimited; 28.28b: © Tom McHugh/Photo Researchers, Inc.; 28.28c: © Ken Lucas; 28.29b : © Randy Morse, GoldenStateImages.com; 28.29c: © Alex Kerstitch/Visuals Unlimited; 28.29d: © Randy Morse/Animals Animals.

CHAPTER 29 Opener: © 2003 Monty Sloan/Wolf Photography; 29.2(bottom): © Heather Angel/Natural Visions; 29.3: © Corbis RF; 29.6: © Heather Angel/Natural Visions; 29.8a: © James Watt/Animals Animals; 29.8b: © Fred Bavendam/Minden Pictures; 29.9b: © Hal Beral/Visuals Unlimited; 29.9c: © Jane Burton/Bruce Coleman/Photoshot; 29.9d: © Photos by Team Hymas/Getty RF; 29.9e: © Franco Banfi/SeaPics.com; 29.10: © Peter Scoones/SPL/Photo Researchers, Inc.; 29.13a: © Suzanne L. Collins & Joseph T. Collins/Photo Researchers, Inc.; 29.13b: © Joe McDonald/Visuals Unlimited; 29.13c: © Juan Manuel Renjifo/Animals Animals; 29Aa: © MedioImages/SuperStock RF; 29Ab: © Allan Friedlander/SuperStock; 29Ac: © Account Phototake/Phototake; 29.16a: © H. Hall/OSF/Animals Animals; 29.16b: © Joe McDonald/Visuals Unlimited; 29.16c: © Joel Sartorie/National Geographic/Getty Images; 29.16d: © Nathan W. Cohen/Visuals Unlimited; 29.16e: © Martin Harvey/Gallo Images/Corbis; 29.18a: © Thomas Kitchin/Tom Stack & Associates; 29.18b: © Joel McDonald/Corbis; 29.18c: © IT Stock/PunchStock RF; 29.18d: © Kirtley Perkins/Visuals Unlimited; 29.20a: © D. Parer & E. Parer-Cook/Ardea; 29.20b: © Fritz Prenzel/Animals Animals; 29.20c: © Leonard Lee Rue/Photo Researchers, Inc.; 29.2(whale): © Mike Bacon; 29.2(deer): © Stephen J. Krasemann/Photo Researchers, Inc.; 29.2(horse): © Juniors Bildarchiv/Alamy RF; 29.2(lioness): © John Downer/Getty Images; 29.2(pangolin): © Nigel G. Dennis/Photo Researchers, Inc.; 29.2(bat): © Corbis RF; 29.2(hedgehog): © 1996 PhotoDisc, Inc./Getty RF; 29.2(mole): © Digital Vision/Getty RF; 29.2(squirrel): © Nature Picture Library/Alamy RF; 29.2(rabbit): © Rubberball/Getty RF; 29.2(flying lemur): © Getty RF; 29.2(tree shrew): © Correia Patrice/Photolibrary; 29.2(monkey): © Gerald Lacz/Animals Animals; 29.2(armadillo): © Photodisc/Getty RF; 29.2(tenrec): © Martin Harvey/Gallo Images/Getty Images; 29.2(elephant shrew): © Oxford Scientific/Photolibrary/Getty Images; 29.2(aardvark): © National Geographic/Getty RF; 29.2(manatee): © Keith Ramos/USFWS; 29.2(hyrax): © PhotoLink/Getty RF; 29.2(elephant): © Purestock RF.

CHAPTER 30 Opener: © Frank Vinken/Max Planck Institute for Evolutionary Anthropology, Leipzig, Germany; 30.1(tarsier): © Doug Wechsler; 30.1(monkey): © Paul Souders/Corbis; 30.1(baboon): © St. Meyers/Okapia/Photo Researchers, Inc.; 30.1(orangutan): © Tim Davis/Photo Researchers, Inc.; 30.1(chimpanzee): © Martin Harvey/Peter Arnold/Photolibrary; 30.1(humans): © Comstock Images/JupiterImages RF; 30.5: © National Museums of Kenya; 30.6(*S. tchadensis*): © Prof. Michel Brunet; 30.6(*A. afarensis*): © Friedrich Saurer/Alamy; 30.6(*A. boisei*): © Science VU/NMK/Visuals Unlimited; 30.6(*H. habilis*): © Herve Conge/ISM/Phototake; 30.6(*H. sapiens*): © 2007 Educational Images Ltd./Custom Medical Stock Photo; 30.8a: © Dan Dreyfus and Associates; 30.8b: © John Reader/Photo Researchers, Inc.; 30.9: © National Museums of Kenya; 30.11: Transp. #608 Courtesy Dept. of Library Services, American Museum of Natural History; 30.12a: © PhotoDisc/Getty RF; 30.12b: © Sylvia S. Mader; 30.12c: © B & C Alexander/Photo Researchers, Inc.

CHAPTER 31 Opener: © Science Photo Library/Photo Researchers, Inc.; 31.1(all): © Ed Reschke; 31.3a, b, d, e: © Ed Reschke; 31.3c: © The McGraw-Hill Companies, Inc. Dennis Strete, Photographer; 31.5a, c: © Ed Reschke; 31.5b: © The McGraw-Hill Companies, Inc. Dennis Strete, Photographer; 31.6b: © Ed Reschke; 31A(both): © Courtesy Justin Rosenberg; 31.9a: © John D. Cunningham/Visuals Unlimited; 31.9b: © Ken Greer/Visuals Unlimited; 31.9c: © James Stevenson/SPL/Photo Researchers, Inc.

CHAPTER 32 Opener: © AF archive/Alamy RF; 32.1a: © CABISCO/Visuals Unlimited; 32.1b: © Lester V. Bergman/Corbis; 32.1c: © Randy Morse, GoldenStateImages.com; 32.6b: © SIU/Visuals Unlimited; 32.7b: © Dr. Don W. Fawcett/Visuals Unlimited; 32.8d: © Biophoto Associates/Photo Researchers, Inc.; 32.9b, c: © Ed Reschke; 32.9d: © David Joel/MacNeal Hospital/Getty Images; 32A: © Biophoto Associates/Photo Researchers, Inc.; 32.15, 32.16: © J. C. Revy/Phototake; 32.17: © Eye of Science/Photo Researchers, Inc.; 32B: © Andrew J. Martinez/Photo Researchers, Inc.

CHAPTER 33 Opener: © Courtesy Baylor College of Medicine Photo Archives; 33.1a: © Stephen Durr; 33.1b: © Dr. Owen Gilbert, Rice University; 33.3a: © R. Calentine/Visuals Unlimited; 33.3b, d: © Ed Reschke/Peter Arnold/Photolibrary; 33.3c: © Fred E. Hossler/Visuals Unlimited; 33.6: © Dennis Kunkel/Phototake; 33.12b: © Steve Gschmeissner/Photo Researchers, Inc.; p. 638(patient): © A. Ramey/PhotoEdit; p. 638(shingles): © CDC; p. 638(candidiasis): © Everett S. Beneke/Visuals Unlimited; p. 638(pneumonia): © Dr. Dennis Kunkel/Visuals Unlimited; 33.13: © Michael Newman/PhotoEdit; 33.14: © Digital Vision/Getty RF; 33.15(girl): © Damien Lovegrove/SPL/Photo Researchers, Inc.; 33.15(allergens): © David Scharf/SPL/Photo Researchers, Inc.; 33.16: © Southern Illinois University/Photo Researchers, Inc.; 33.17: © Dr. Ken Greer/Visuals Unlimited.

CHAPTER 34 Opener: © Goodshoot/PunchStock RF; 34.9b: © Ed Reschke/Peter Arnold/Photolibrary; 34.10(villi): © Manfred Kage/Peter Arnold/Photolibrary; 34.10(microvilli): This photo was published in Medical Cell Biology, Charles Flickinger, photo by Susumu Ito, Copyright Elsevier, 1979; 34.14: © Amiard/photocuisine/Corbis; 34.15: © Ryan McVay/Getty RF.

CHAPTER 35 Opener: © Timothy A. Clary/AFP/Getty Images; 35.4a(fish): © Dr. Jeffrey Isaacson, Nebraska Wesleyan University; 35.4c(gills): © David M. Phillips/Photo Researchers, Inc.; 35.5, 35.6b: © Ed Reschke; 35.13: © Andrew Syred/Photo Researchers, Inc.; 35.14: © Dr. P. Marazzi/Photo Researchers, Inc.; 35.16a: © Matt Meadows/Peter Arnold/Photolibrary; 35.16b: © SIU/Visuals Unlimited; 35.16c: © Biophoto Associates/Photo Researchers, Inc.; 35A: Courtesy The Wyss Institute, Harvard University.

CHAPTER 36 Opener: © Georgette Douwma/Photo Researchers, Inc.; 36.4: © Bob Calhoun/Bruce Coleman/Photoshot; 36.5: © Eric Hosking/Photo Researchers, Inc.; 36.6a: © James Cavallini/Photo Researchers, Inc.; 36.8b: © Science Photo Library/Getty RF; 36.8c, d: © Ed Reschke/Peter Arnold/Photolibrary; 36.9b: © Joseph F. Gennaro, Jr./Photo Researchers, Inc.; 36A: © AFP/Getty Images.

CHAPTER 37 Opener: © Time & Life Pictures/Getty Images; 37.4a: © M.B. Bunge/Biological Photo Service; 37.4c: © Manfred Kage/Peter Arnold/Photolibrary; 37.7a: Courtesy Dr. E.R. Lewis, University of California Berkeley; 37.8: © Colin Chumbley/Science Source/Photo Researchers, Inc.; 37.12c: © Karl E. Deckart/Phototake; 37B: © Science VU/Visuals Unlimited.

LINE ART & TEXT

Index

Note: This text contains a substantial number of supporting graphics. To ease index use, regular page numbers indicate *both* discussion and figure(s) on the same page; page numbers with *f* indicate additional figures on a different page; *t* indicates a table

A

A. *See* Adenine (A)
A band, 745
A horizon soil, 468
ABA (abscisic acid), 477, 488, 489*t*
Abalone, 534
ABC Islands, brown bears of, 889
Abdomen
   crustacean, 541f
   insect, 542, 543f
Abdominal cavity organs, 596
Abiogenesis, 329
Abiotic agents, of natural selection, 8
Abiotic synthesis, 328*f*, 329
ABO blood types, 205, 619
Abortion, 783–84
Aboveground vertical stems, 457*f*, 458
Abscisic acid (ABA), 477, 488, 489*t*
Abscission, 488, 489*f*, 489*t*
Absolute dating of fossils, 334
Absorption spectrum, 124
Abstinence, 783
Abulocetus natans, 281
Abyssal plain, 902
Acacia tree, 498, 866, 895
Accessory organs, digestive tract, 654–55
Accessory pigments, red algae, 389
Accessory structures, skin, 598–99
Accidental transport of alien species, 914
Accommodation, visual, 722
Acetaminophen, 246
Acetic acid bacteria, 141
Acetobacter aceti, 141
Acetyl CoA, 142–43, 147
Acetylcholine (ACh), 700, 708, 713, 747
Acetylcholinesterase (AChE), 701, 748
Acetylene, 39
ACh (acetylcholine), 700, 708, 713, 747
AChE (acetylcholinesterase), 701, 748
Achromatopsia (color blindness), 209,
   300–301, 723
Acid deposition, 878, 915
Acid rain, 33, 467, 878
Acid reflux, 651
Acid-base balance, 690
Acidosis, 33
Acids, chemistry of, 32–34
Acinonyx jubatus, 895*f*
Acne, 599
Acquired characteristics, inheritance
   of, 273–74
Acquired immunity. *See* Adaptive
   immunity
Acquired immunodeficiency syndrome.
   See AIDS
Acrocephalus, 867*f*
Acromegaly, 759
Acrosome, 775*f*, 776*f*, 777, 796–97
Acrylamide, 248
ACTH (adrenocorticotropic hormone),
   754*f*, 757, 758*f*, 764, 810
Actin, 49, 108, 592, 745
Actin filaments
   cell structure and function, 68f–69f
   cytoskeleton, 78, 79f
   in extracellular matrix, 99f
   in muscle contraction, 745–46, 747t,
     748–49
Actinopterygii, 554, 555*f*
Action potentials, 698*f*, 699–700, 744
Active immunity, 637–39
Active site, of enzyme, 110
Active transport, 95–98
   carrier proteins and energy needed,
     95, 96f

   defined, 89t, 95
   endocytosis, 97–98
   exocytosis, 95, 96f
   phagocytosis, 97–98
   plasma membrane, 91
Acute bronchitis, 673, 674*f*
Acute phase proteins, 631
AD (Alzheimer disease), 53, 184, 701, 707
Adam's apple, 668, 778
Adaptation
   behavioral, 830–34
   defined, 5, 278
   to diet, digestive tracts, 648–49
   evolutionary theory, 278
   Lamarck and, 273
   photosynthesis, 131
   plants, 420
Adaptive immunity, 633–39
   active vs. passive, 637–39
   antibody-mediated, 633–35
   cell-mediated, 633, 635–37
   defined, 630
   evolution of, 627–28
   generally, 633–34
Adaptive radiation mode of speciation,
   316–17
Addiction to drugs, 710–11
Addison disease, 764
Adductor longus muscle, 744*f*
Adenine (A)
   complimentary base pairing, 55
   DNA structure, 55f, 217–20, 223, 223t
   molecular structure of, 217f
   mRNA codons, 224f
   as nucleotide, 54f
   RNA structure, 220, 223t
Adenosine, 55, 755. *See also* Ribose
Adenosine deaminase deficiency, gene
   therapy for, 260
Adenosine diphosphate (ADP), 56,
   107, 748
Adenosine triphosphate. *See* ATP
Adenovirus, 364*f*
ADH (antidiuretic hormone), 688, 754*f*,
   757, 758*f*
Adhesion, 30, 476
Adhesion junctions, 98, 99*f*, 588, 593
Adiantum pedatum, 428*f*
Adipocytes, 590
Adipose tissue
   aging process, 811
   blood glucose regulation, 765
   functions of, 590
   leptin produced by, 768
   skin, 597f
   subcutaneous layer, 598
ADP (adenosine diphosphate), 56,
   107, 748
Adrenal cortex, 754*f*, 756, 758*f*, 762–64
Adrenal glands, 754*f*, 758*f*, 762–64
Adrenal medulla, 754*f*, 755, 762–63
Adrenaline, 613, 754*f*, 755–56, 762
Adrenocorticotropic hormone (ACTH),
   754*f*, 757, 758*f*, 764, 810
Adrenoleukodystrophy (ALD), 75, 210
Adult stem cells. *See* Stem cells
Adventitious roots, 452, 457*f*
AEDs (automatic external
   defibrillators), 614
Aequorea victoria, 216*f*
Aerial roots, 461*f*
Aerial stems, 428
Aerobic bacteria, 335
Aerobic reactions, in cellular
   respiration, 137
Aerotropism, 491
AF-2 (food additive), 248
Afferent (sensory) neurons, 697–98, 717
Aflatoxin, 248
Africa
   convergent evolution Rift Valley, 317
   evolutionary hypotheses, 579
   savanna, 895
African sleeping sickness, 396, 398–99

Afrocoricida, 566*t*
Agapornis, 820
Agar, 389
Agaricus bisporus, 406*t*
Age distribution, 842–43, 852–53
Age of Amphibians, 339
Age of Cycads, 340
Age of Fishes, 339
Age spots, 811
Agent Orange, 485
Agglutination, 619
Aggregate fruits, 510*f*, 511, 511*t*
Aging process, 811–14
   cardiovascular systems, 811–12
   digestive systems, 812
   endocrine systems, 813
   excretory systems, 812
   hypotheses about, 813–14
   immune systems, 812
   integumentary systems, 811
   musculoskeletal systems, 737, 738,
     812–13
   nervous systems, 812
   organ systems, 811–13
   reproductive systems, 813
   respiratory systems, 812
   sensory systems, 722, 724, 728, 812
Agnathans (jawless fish), 339, 526*t*, 552,
   553
Agranular leukocytes, 620
Agriculture
   alien species introduced by, 914
   biodiversity, 910–11
   evolution of, 581
   livestock as tapeworm host, 533
   pollution from, 14–15, 877, 878, 915
   swidden (slash-and-burn), 893
AID (artificial insemination), 785
AIDS (acquired immunodeficiency
   syndrome). *See also* HIV
   electron micrograph of, 289f
   epidemiology of, 787
   microevolution, 289
   opportunistic infections in, 626, 638,
     674, 787
   retrovirus, 368
   stages and symptoms of, 787
   treatment of, 788
   virus, 364
Air
   movements of, 884–85, 902
   nutritional function of soil, 467
   pollution of, 33, 414, 878
   temperature of, 902
Air bladder, brown algae, 390*f*
Air sacs, 667, 670*f*
Alagille syndrome, 188
Albumin, 618
ALD (adrenoleukodystrophy), 75, 210
Aldosterone, 690, 763
Alexandrium catanella, 392–93
Alexis (son of Tzar Nicolas I of Russia), 210
Algae
   blue-green. See Cyanobacteria
   brown, 385t, 386f, 390, 900
   classification of, 354
   colonial, 2, 385t, 388
   in coral reefs, 901
   as decomposers in soil, 468
   filamentous, 388
   in food chain, 383
   golden brown, 385t, 386f, 390, 391
   green. See Green algae
   multicellular, 388, 389, 390
   photosynthesis by, 76

   protist diversity, 385t
   red, 385t, 386f, 389
   size variety of, 384
   sperm production in, 422
Algae blooms, 392–93
Algin, 390
Ali, Muhammad, 693
Alien species, 838, 861, 909, 913–15
Alkaloids, 497
Alkalosis, 33
Allantois, 805, 808*f*, 809
Alleles. *See also* Gene(s)
   defined, 172, 196
   dominant, 290
   frequencies, and microevolution,
     290–95, 292t
   in homologous chromosomes, 196f
   multiple, 205
Allelic traits, multiple, 205
Allen's rule, 583
Allergy(ies), 641–42, 642*t*
Alligators, 558*f*, 561–62, 918
Allopatric speciation mode of speciation,
   313–14
Alloploidy, 315–16
Allosteric site, 112
Alouatta pigra, 893*f*
α-helix, 51, 52*f*
Alpine tundra, 887, 888
ALS (amyotrophic lateral sclerosis), 703
Alternate leaves, 460
Alternation of generations, 176, 388,
   407, 422
Alternative splicing, 237
   mRNA, 227, 244–46
Altitude, and biomes, 887
Altman, Sidney, 330
Altruism, 833–34
Alu sequence, 262
Aluminum, in plants, 465
Alvarez, Luis, 343
Alvarez, Walter, 343
Alveolates, 385*t*, 392–94
Alveoli (sing., alveolus)
   mammary, 782, 783f
   pulmonary, 668
Alyces obstetricans, 848*f*
Alzheimer disease (AD), 53, 184, 701, 707
AM fungi, 404*f*, 406*t*, 408
Amanita phalloides, 411
Amborella trichopoda, 433
Ambulocetus natans, 281*f*, 310*f*
Ambystoma tigrinum, 557*f*
Amebic dysentery, 396
Amebocytes, 622
Amenorrhea, 782
American Cancer Society, 675
American Dietetic Association, 658, 659
American goldfinch, 774*f*
American Heart Association, 659
Ames test, 248
Amine group, polarity of, 27
Amino acids. *See also* Adenine (A);
   Cytosine (C); Guanine (G);
   Thymine (T); *specific amino acid*
   cellular respiration, 147
   codons for, 224
   essential, 658–59
   with ionized R groups, 51f
   metabolism of, 681
   protein digestion, 657
   as protein monomer, 50
   sequencing, and phylogeny, 358
   synthesis of, 129
   and tRNA, 223, 228–29
Amino functional groups, 39*t*
Aminoacyl-tRNA synthetases, 229
Ammonia
   as atmospheric gas, 329
   as buffer, 690
   in nitrogenous waste, 681
   photosynthesis vs. cellular respiration,
     148
   water as solvent for, 30

Ammonium, 878
Amniocentesis, 807
Amnion, 805, 808
Amniotes
    defined, 553
    evolution of, 558–59
    fossil, 334
    timeline of evolution, 559f
Amniotic cavity, 808f
Amniotic eggs, reptile, 552–53, 558
Amniotic fluid, 808, 810f, 811
Amoeba, 4f, 97, 627
Amoeba proteus, 63f, 385t, 396
Amoeboid(s), 385t, 386f, 396
Amoeboid cells, 97–98
Amoebozoa, 385t, 386f, 396–97
    amoeboids, 385t, 386f, 396
    defined, 396
    slime molds, 396–97
Amphibians. See also specific animal
    amniote evolution, 558–59
    characteristics, 556
    circulatory system, 556, 609
    classification, 557f
    defined, 556
    diversity of living, 556–57
    evolution of, 552–53, 556–59
    hearing, 726
    hormones, 755, 758
    limbs, 552
    metamorphosis, 520f, 521, 556, 755
    pineal gland, 768
    reproduction, 552, 556
    respiration, 556, 665
    skeleton of, 737
Amphibians, Age of, 339
Amphipathic molecules, 86
Amphipods, 901
Ampulla (pl., ampullae), semicircular
    canals, 728, 729f
AMU (atomic mass unit), 23
Amygdala, 705, 705f, 707
Amylase
    pancreatic, 654
    salivary, 651, 656
Amyloid plaque, 707
Amyloplasts, 490f, 491
Amylose, 43
Amyotrophic lateral sclerosis (ALS), 703
Anabaena, 429
Anabolic steroids, 767, 778
Anabolism, 147–48
Anaerobes, 374, 375
Anaerobic reactions, cellular
    respiration, 137
Anal pore, of ciliates, 393
Analogous structures, 284, 357, 358
Analogous traits, 317
Analogy, 357
Anaphase
    meiosis, 177t
    mitosis, 158f, 160, 180f
Anaphase I, 176, 177t, 178f, 180f
Anaphase II, 176, 177t, 178f
Anaphylactic shock, 641–42
Anapsid, 558
Anartia amalthea linnaeus, 893f
Anatomical evidence supporting
    evolution, 283–84
Ancestor, common, 328, 348, 349, 351f,
    354–58
Ancestral traits, 354
Anchor cell, 802
Andes Mountains, 273f, 275
Androgen(s), 754f, 767
Androgen insensitivity, 249, 754f
Anencephaly, 807
Aneuploidy, 183–87
    defined, 183
    Jacobs syndrome, 186–87
    Klinefelter syndrome, 184, 185–86
    monosomy, 183–84
    poly-X females (superfemale), 186
    sex chromosome number changes,
        184–85
    trisomy, 183–84
    trisomy 21 (Down syndrome), 184, 187
    Turner syndrome, 184, 185
Angina pectoris, 616
Angiogenesis, cancer, 164
Angioplasty, 616

Angiosperms. See also Flowering plant(s)
    characteristics, 421t
    defined, 430, 433
    dominant generation in, 422
    flowers, 433–34
    fossil, 357, 433
    gametophytes vs. sporophyte size, 423f
    life cycle of, 502
    life history strategy of, 849
    monocots and eudicots, 433, 433t
    origin and radiation of, 433–34
Angiotensin, 690, 690f
Angiotensin I, 763
Angiotensin II, 763
Angiotensinogen, 763
ANH (atrial natriuretic hormone), 690, 763
Animal(s). See also Invertebrates;
        Vertebrates; specific animal
    ancestry, 521
    animal-pollinated flowers, 505, 911f
    artificial selection of, 278f
    body plan evolution, 521, 522f, 524–25
    cells. See Animal cells
    characteristics, 526t
    classification, 354, 522f
    communication by. See Communication
    defined, 8
    development of. See Animal
        development
    diploid chromosome numbers, 157t
    embryonic development of, 522–23,
        797–804
    emotions in, 826, 827, 828
    evolution of, 6f, 335f, 520–26. See also
        Invertebrate evolution; Vertebrate
        evolution
    excretory system, 680, 681–84
    eyes, 720–21
    fruit dispersal by, 511
    vs. fungi, 520
    genetically modified, 258–59
    geologic timescale, 336t
    glucose metabolism, 42
    glucose storage, 43, 657
    hearing, 726
    hormones, 753, 754f, 755–56. See also
        specific hormone
    life cycle of, 180, 182f, 520
    mammals. See Mammals
    organic molecules in, 38
    organization of systems, 587–604
    parasitic, 865
    phylogenetic tree of, 521–22, 525f
    plant responses to, 498
    plants vs., 520
    reproduction. See Reproduction
    seed dispersal by, 511
    symmetry, 522
    virus reproduction, 368
    vision, 720–21
Animal cells. See also Eukaryotic cells
    anatomy of, 68f
    cytokinesis, 160
    division in, 167, 167t
    meiosis I and II, 178f–179f
    mitosis, 158f–159f
    organelle origin, 67f
    osmosis, 93–94
    plasma membrane, 86f
    rabbit intestine, 61f
    surfaces, 98–100
Animal development, 795–804
    aging process, 811–14
    cellular differentiation process, 800–802
    cellular stages, 797–98. See also
        Embryonic development
    defined, 797
    early developmental stages, 796–99
    fertilization, 796–97, 806f
    human embryonic and fetal
        development, 804–10, 811f
    model organisms, 800
    morphogenesis, 802–4
    organ stages, 799
    processes of, 800–804
    review and exercises, 814–17
    stages of, 797–99
    tissue stages, 798
Animal pole, 797, 798, 801f
Animal systems, organization of, 587–604
    homeostasis, 599–601

    integumentary system, 595–99
    organs and organ systems, 595–96
    review and exercises, 602–4
    tissue types, 588–95
Animalcules, wheel, 543
Animalia (kingdom)
    characteristics, 526t
    classification, 351
    defined, 8
    evolution of, 520
    Linnaean classification, 349–50
Ankle, bones of, 742
Annelids, 536–37. See also Earthworms
    characteristics, 526t
    circulatory system of, 607
    defined, 536
    digestive tract, 647–48
    eyes, 720
    hydrostatic skeleton of, 736
    locomotion, 736
    nervous system of, 694–95
    polychaete, 537–38
    reproduction, 773
Annual rings, 456, 457f
Anodonta, 535
Anolis lizard, 314
Anopheles mosquito, 394
Anoplura, 542f
Anosmia, 812
Ant(s)
    coevolution of, 867
    mutualism, 498, 866
    pheromones in, 826
    social behavior in, 847
    in soil, 468
Antagonistic hormones, 762
Antagonistic muscles, 744, 745f
Antelopes, 864, 894
Antennae, crustaceans, 540
Antennules, crustaceans, 540
Anterior compartment, of eye, 721
Anterior pituitary gland, 757–59, 778,
    780–81
Anteroposterior polarity, 802, 804
Anther of flower, 434f, 436–37, 502f,
    503–5
Anther tissue culture, 514
Antheridium (pl., antheridia), 422,
    424, 425t
Anthoceros, 424f
Anthrax, 353, 376
Anthropoids, 572
Antibiotics
    for bacterial infections, 376–77
    derivation of, 910
    resistance to, 280, 376–77
Antibody(ies)
    anti-Rh, 620
    defined, 618
    immunoglobulin, 634–35, 641–42
    maternal, 810
    monoclonal, 635, 642, 783
    production of, 620
    proteins and, 49
    structure of, 634–35
Antibody titers, 639
Antibody-mediated immunity, 633–35
Anticodons
    defined, 228
    translation, 229, 230, 231, 232f
Antidepressant drugs, 701
Antidiuresis, 688
Antidiuretic hormone (ADH), 688, 754f,
    757, 758f
Antigen(s), 49, 619, 620, 627
Antigen receptors, 627, 633–34
Antigen-presenting cells (APCs), 635–36
Antihistamines, 642
Anti-inflammatory drugs, 631
Anti-obesity drugs, 655
Antioxidants, 814
Antiretroviral drugs, 637, 638, 788
Antithrombin, bioengineered, 560
Anus, 523, 647, 650f, 653
Anvil (incus), 726f, 727
Aorta, 614
Aortic bodies, 671, 690
Aortic dissection, 605
Aortic semilunar valve, 611, 612f
Apatosaurus, 340
APCs (antigen-presenting cells), 635–36

Apes. See also specific animal
    brain, 572
    classification, 571
    evolution of, 341
    genomics, 574
    locomotion, 737
Aphids, 478, 843f, 911
Apical cells, in green algae, 421
Apical dominance, 485
Apical meristem
    defined, 447, 453
    root, 450, 451f
    shoot, 453, 462f
Apical tissue, of plants, 421
Apicomplexans, 385t, 386f, 394
Apis mellifera, 911
Aplysia, 821–22
Aplysina fistularis, 527f
Apoptosis
    cancer cells, 163–64
    and cell division, 153
    defined, 153
    G_1 checkpoint, 156
    in immune response, 632, 634, 636
    in morphogenesis, 800, 804
    mutation, 249
Appendages. See also Limb(s)
    bacterial, 66
    biramous, of crustaceans, 540
    of crustaceans, 540
    jointed, 737
    as vertebrate characteristic, 552
Appendicitis, 653
Appendicular skeleton, 740f, 742
Appendix, 630, 653
Aquaculture, 911, 917
Aquaporins, 91, 688
Aquatic animals. See also specific animal
        or fish
    evolution of, 339
    habitats, 901–2
    osmoregulation, 680, 682–84, 683–84
    reproduction, 556, 773, 774
    skeleton of, 737
Aquatic ecosystems, 897–904
    biomass, 874
    carbon cycle in, 876
    classification of, 897
    coastal, 9–10, 885, 900–901
    lakes, 33, 898–900, 912, 915
    nitrogen cycle, 878
    oceans, 900f, 901–2
    phosphorus cycle in, 877
    water cycle, 897, 912
    wetlands, 468–69, 897, 912, 913, 921
Aquatic insect respiration, 667
Aquatic plants, 899, 900
Aquatic reproduction, 556
Aqueous humor, 721, 721f
Aquifers, 875, 897
Ara ararauna, 563f
Ara macao, 893f
Arabidopsis thaliana, 402, 491, 494, 495,
    508f–509f
Arachidonate, 768
Arachnids (spiders), 526t, 543, 649,
    682, 736
Arboreal life, 571
Arboreal lizard, 893f
Arbuscular mycorrhizal (AM) fungi, 404f,
    406t, 408
Archaea
    cell division, 167, 167t
    defined, 378
    domain, 7
    evolution of, 335f
    evolutionary tree, 6f
    extreme habitats, 378–79
    halophiles, 335f, 354, 379
    methanogens, 335f, 354, 378–79
    moderate habitats, 379
    in moderate habitats, 379
    prokaryotic cells, 65
    review and exercises, 379–82
    structure of, 378
    three system domain, 351
    three-domain system of classification,
        351, 352t, 353–54
    Tree of Life project, 282f
    types of, 378–79
Archaebacteria, evolution of, 335f

Archaefructus liaoningensis, 357, 357*f*
Archaeopteryx, 280–81, 340
Archaeplastida, 385*t*, 386*f*, 387–89. *See also* Charophytes
    chlorophytes, 385*t*, 386*f*, 387–88
    defined, 387
    green algae, 387
    red algae, 389
Archegonium (pl., archegonia), 422, 424, 425*t*
Archenteron, 523, 798–99
Arctic, oil drilling in, 19
Arctic tundra, 888
Ardipithecines, 576–77
Ardipithecus kadabba, 576
Ardipithecus ramidus, 576, 577
Arginine, 51*f*
Argon, 23
Argus II (retinal prosthesis), 725
Aristotle, 272, 348, 351
Arm, bones of, 740*f*, 742
Armadillo, 910
Armstrong, Lance, 689
Army ants, 833–34
Arrector pili muscle, 597*f*, 599
Arrhythmias, 613–14
Arrow cichlid fish, 314
Arteries
    aging process, 811–12
    coronary, 610, 614, 616, 617*f*
    pulmonary, 611–12
    renal, 684*f*, 686, 687*f*
    in skin, 597*f*
    structure and function, 608
Arterioles
    renal, 685*f*, 686, 687*f*
    structure and function, 608, 609*f*, 614
Arteriosclerosis (atherosclerosis), 616, 617*f*, 811
Arthritis, 743
    rheumatoid, 642, 642*f*, 743
Arthropod(s), 539–43
    centipedes, 526*t*, 541, 542*f*
    characteristics, 526*t*, 539–40
    circulatory system, 606, 607*f*, 667
    crustaceans. *See* Crustaceans
    evolution of, 338, 339, 539–43
    excretory system, 682
    exoskeleton, 539*f*
    eyes, 539*f*, 720
    gravitational equilibrium organs in, 728
    insects. *See* Insect(s)
    millipedes, 468, 526*t*, 541, 542*f*
    nervous system, 539*f*, 540, 694–95
    nutrition of, 649
    respiratory system, 666–67
    skeleton, 736, 737*f*
    vision, 539*f*, 720
Arthropoda, 539
Articular cartilage, 743
Artificial insemination (AID), 785
Artificial joints, 743
Artificial lung, 676
Artificial selection, evolutionary theory, 278–80
Artiodactyla, 566*t*
ARTs (assisted reproductive technologies), 785
Ascaris, 172, 526*t*, 538–39
Ascocarp, 408*f*, 409, 415
Ascomycota, 404*f*, 406*t*, 408–10, 412
Ascus (pl., asci), 408, 409
Asexual reproduction. *See also specific organism*
    bacteria, 166–67, 167*t*, 373
    cellular, 61. *See also Cell division*
    defined, 166, 513, 773
    flowering plants, 513–14. *See also specific plants*
    invertebrates, 773
    prokaryotic cells, 166–67, 167*t*, 373
    reproductive isolation, 310
    vs. sexual reproduction, 175, 176, 773
Asian carp, 838
Asian turtles, overexploitation of, 917
Asparagine, 51*f*
Aspartic acid, 51*f*
Aspergillus, 409, 410
Aspirin, 768

Assisted reproductive technologies (ARTs), 785
Association areas, 703*f*, 707
Association neurons (interneurons), 697*f*, 698
Associative learning, 824
Assortative mating, 295, 300
Asteroid, 343
Asteroidea, 544
Asters, 159
Asthma, 641, 673–74
Astigmatism, 724
Astrocytes, 593
Atelopus, 407
Atherosclerosis, 616, 617*f*, 811
Athlete's foot, 410
Atmosphere
    carbon cycle, 876–77
    mass extinction, 344
    and origins of life, 329, 333*f*, 335
    ozone shield, 335, 915
Atom(s)
    biological organization, 3*f*
    Bohr model of, 25
    chemical elements, 22–23
    defined, 2, 22
    structure of, 22–23
Atomic mass, 23, 24–25
Atomic mass unit (AMU), 23
Atomic number, 23
Atomic symbol, 22, 23
ATP (adenosine triphosphate)
    active transport, 95
    in Calvin cycle, 129
    in cellular respiration, 42, 135
    in citric acid cycle, 143
    in coupled reactions, 108
    cycle of, 107
    defined, 54, 55
    in glycolysis, 137, 138
    mitochondrial production of, 77
    in muscle contraction, 746–49
    as nucleotides, 55–56, 76, 107–8
    in photosynthesis, 122, 131
    protocells, 332
    structure of, 56*f*, 107
    substrate-level synthesis of, 138, 146
ATP (adenosine triphosphate) production
    in cellular respiration, 136
    electron transport chain, 144–45
    fermentation, 140
    mitochondrial, 77
    noncyclic electron pathway, 125–26
    organelles and energy flow, 76, 113, 114–15, 144–45
    in thylakoid space, 126
ATP synthase, 114, 115*f*
ATP synthase complex, 126, 144–45
ATP-driven proton pump, 469*f*, 470, 477–79
Atrial natriuretic hormone (ANH), 690, 763
Atriopore, 550
Atrioventricular (AV) node, 613, 613*f*
Atrioventricular (VA) valves, 611, 612*f*, 613
Atrium (pl., atria), 550
    cardiac, 608–10, 612–13
Attachment, in lytic cycle, 367*f*, 368
Auditory area, primary, 703*f*, 704
Auditory association area, 703*f*
Auditory canal, 726*f*, 727
Auditory communication, 828
Auditory tube, 726*f*, 727
Auricles
    cardiac, 610
    ear, 718
Australia
    alien species in, 915
    marsupials of, 283, 342–43
    Precambrian fossils in, 335, 337*f*
Australopithecines, 577, 578
Australopithecus aethiopicus, 576*f*, 577
Australopithecus afarensis, 576*f*, 577, 578*f*
Australopithecus africanus, 576*f*, 578
Australopithecus anamensis, 576*f*
Australopithecus boisei, 576*f*, 577
Australopithecus robustus, 576*f*, 578
Australopithecus sediba, 578

Autoimmune diseases, 642, 642*f*
Automatic external defibrillators (AEDs), 614
Autonomic nervous system
    defined, 708
    human, 696*f*
    motor pathways of, 709*t*
    parasympathetic divisions, 708–9, 709*t*, 712*f*, 713
    structure and function, 712*f*
    sympathetic divisions, 708–9, 709*t*, 712*f*, 713
Autoploidy, 315
Autosomal patterns of inheritance, 201–4
    disorders of, 202–3, 202*f*
    pedigree analysis, 204
    testing for, 204
Autosomes, 201
Autotroph(s), 120, 586, 870–73
Autotrophic bacteria, 375
Auxins, 483–87
    asexual reproduction, 514
    commercial uses, 489*t*
    and cytokinins, 487
    defined, 485
    and ethylene production, 489
    gravitropism, 485–86
    growth and development, 485–86, 489*t*
    phototropism, 483, 485–86
    signal transduction, 484*f*
    stem curvature, 486
    synthetic, 485
AV (atrioventricular) node, 613, 613*f*
AV (atrioventricular) valves, 611, 612*f*, 613
Avery, Oswald, 215–16
Aves. *See* Bird(s)
Avian influenza (bird flu), 369, 370
Axial skeleton, 740–41
Axillary bud
    dormant, 453, 461*f*
    inhibition of, ethylene and, 489
    plant structure, 444*f*
    of stem, 445
Axillary lymph nodes, 628*f*, 629
Axon(s), 593, 697, 697*f*, 753. *See also* Nerve fibers
    motor, 747–48
Axon terminals, 700, 701*f*
Azalea, 5032*f*
Azolla, 429
AZT, 788

B

B cells
    aging process, 812
    clonal selection theory, 633–34
    formation, 629, 633
    function, 620, 633–35
B horizon soil, 468
Baboons
    classification, 571*f*
    predator detection, 864
    sexual selection, 298–99
    social behavior in, 826, 828*f*, 833
Bacillus (pl. bacilli), 65, 374
Bacillus anthracis, 353, 374*f*
Bacteria, 374–77. *See also specific bacterium*
    aerobic, 335
    antibiotic resistance in, 280
    appendages of, 66
    autotrophic, 375, 870
    blue-green, 66
    cell characteristics, 374
    cell division, 167, 167*t*
    cell envelope of, 65
    chemoautotrophic, 332, 902
    classification of, 351, 352*t*, 353
    commensalism in, 375
    contamination, LAL test for, 622
    cyanobacteria, 377
    cytoplasm, 65–66
    as decomposer, 375, 468, 871
    defined, 374
    denitrifying, 878
    diseases caused by, 376–77, 376*t*
    DNA nucleotide composition in, 217*f*
    DNA replication in, 222
    domain, 7

    evolution of, 6*f*, 335, 335*f*
    fermentation, 140–41
    genetically modified, 258
    Gram-negative/Gram-positive, 374, 376
    heterotrophic, 352*f*, 353, 375
    in large intestine, 653–54
    life span of, 2
    metabolism, 374–75
    mutualism, 375, 866
    nitrogen-fixing, 375, 452, 471, 878
    organic molecules in, 38
    organization of life, 2*f*
    parasitism, 375–76, 865
    peptidoglycan in, 44
    photoautotrophic, 375
    photosynthetic, 335, 351–52, 375
    in Precambrian time, 335
    reproduction, 166–67, 167*t*, 373
    review and exercises, 379–82
    sexually transmitted diseases, 790–91
    shapes of, 374
    structure of, 65–66
    symbiotic, 375–77
    transformation experiments, 215–17
    transgenic, 258
    Tree of Life project, 282*f*
Bacterial vaginosis (BV), 790–91
Bacteriophage
    defined, 367
    life cycle of, 367*f*
    lysogenic cycle, 368
    lytic cycle, 368
    reproduction of, 367–68
    T-even, 364*f*
Baker's yeast, 141
Balance, sense of, 728–30
Balanced translocation, 187–88
Balanus, 860
Bald eagles, 562*f*, 563*f*, 909*f*
Baldness, 767
Baleen, 648
Baleen whale, 648, 827, 901
Ball-and-socket joints, 743
Ball-and-stick model of water, 28*f*
Bamboo, 454, 458
Bang, Frederick, 622
Banting, Frederick, 766
Bangham, Alec, 331
Bañuelos, Gary, 471
Barash, David, 15–16
Barcoding DNA, 350, 352–53
Bariatric surgery, 655
Bark, 456
Barnacles, 540*f*, 860, 861*f*, 865
Barr, Murray, 185
Barr body, 185, 243
Barracuda, 901
Barred tiger salamanders, 557*f*
Bartholin (vestibular) glands, 780
Basal body, flagellum, 66, 80, 81*f*, 797
Basal cell carcinoma, 598
Basal ganglia, 704, 705
Basal nuclei, 704, 705
Base(s)
    chemistry of, 32–34
    defined, 32
    DNA vs. RNA, 55*t*
    pairing in DNA structure, 217–19. *See also Complementary base pairing*
Basement membrane, 588
Basidiocarp, 412, 413
Basidiomycota, 404*f*, 406*t*, 412–13
Basidiospores, 412, 413
Basidium (pl., basidia), 412–13
Basilar membrane, 727–28
Basilosaurus, 281
Basking sharks, 554
Basophils, 620
Bat(s)
    echolocation by, 717, 826
    as keystone species, 918
    as pollinators, 507, 911*f*
    reciprocal altruism in, 834
Bates, Henry, 864
Batesian mimicry, 864
Bathypelagic zone, 901*f*, 902
Batrachochytrium dendrobatidis, 407
B-cell receptor (BCR), 633–34
BCR (B-cell receptor), 633–34
Beadle, George, 223

HMS *Beagle*, 272, 273*f*, 275–77
Beak(s)
    diversity of, 563*f*
    in Galápagos finches
        genetic basis of shape, 318–19
        size of, 273*f*, 276–77, 279–80,
            302, 860
Beaked whale, 889
Bean seed, 509*f*, 510*f*, 512
Bears, 849*f*, 866
    brown, 889
    grizzly, 889, 909*f*, 918–19
    polar, 888
Beaumont, William, 652
Beavers, 918
Becquerel, Antoine-Henri, 24
Bedstraw, 460
Bee(s). *See also* Honeybee(s)
    eyes, 720
    inclusive fitness in, 834
    mimicry in, 864*f*
    as pollinators, 437, 501*f*, 506–7, 911
    vision, 720
Beech, 460, 916
Beef, 647
Beer, 410
Beeswax, 49
Beet(s), 452
Beetles, 542*f*, 864*f*
Behavior, 819–37
    animal communication, 826–30. *See
        also* Communication
    courtship. *See* Courtship behavior
    defined, 820
    environmental influence on, 822–26
    feeding. *See* Feeding behavior
    fitness (adaptive), 830–34
    genetic basis for, 820–22
    human, heritability of, 207
    of living organisms, 5
    mating. *See* Mating behavior
    nature vs. nurture question, 208,
        820–26
    review and exercises, 835–37
    social. *See* Social behavior
Behavioral data and phylogeny, 358
Behavioral ecology, 830
Behavioral isolation, 311*f*, 312
Bekoff, Marc, 827
Bellows function of lungs, 669–70
Beltian bodies, 866
Beneficial nutrients, defined, 465
Benign cancer, 163
Benign positional vertigo (BPV), 730
Benign prostatic hypertrophy (BPH), 777
Benthic species, 900
Benthic zone, 899–900
Berger, Lee, 578
Bergmann's rule, 581, 583
Berry(ies), true, 510*f*
Best, Charles, 766
β-galactosidase, 239
β-sheet, 51, 52*f*
bGH (bovine growth hormone), 258
Bicarbonate buffer system, 690
Bicarbonate ions, 672, 876
Biceps brachii muscle, 744*f*
Bicoid protein, 802
Bicuspid valve, 611, 612*f*, 613
Bigfin reef squid, 536*f*
Bilateral symmetry, 522, 526*t*
Bile, 652, 654
Bile ducts, 654
Bile pigments, 619
Bile salts, 654
Bilirubin, 618, 654
Binary fission
    ciliate, 393
    prokaryotic cell division, 166–67,
        167*t*, 373
Binge drinking, 710
Binomial nomenclature, 8, 349–50
Bioaccumulation, 903
Biochemical evidence supporting
    evolution, 284, 285*f*
Biocultural evolution, 581, 582
Biodiversity
    conservation biology, 907–24
    defined, 10, 908
    distribution of, 909

island biogeography, 862
organization of life, 2
species diversity, 858–59
value of, 910–13
Biodiversity hotspots, 909
Bioengineering, 258
Bioethical issues
    oil drilling in Arctic, 19
    organic pollutants, 59
    right to refuse and IV, 36
    stem cells, 84
    world food supply, 134
Biogeochemical cycles. *See* Chemical
    cycling
Biogeography
    defined, 275
    evidence supporting evolution, 283
    island model, 862
    observation and evolutionary theory,
        271, 275–77
Bioinformatics, 265, 908
Biological clock
    defined, 494, 768, 830
    honeybees, 830
    plants, 478, 494–95
Biological organization, 2–4
Biological pest control, 910–11
Biological species concept, 310
Biology, defined, 2, 11. *See also specific
    topics*
Bioluminescence, 392, 528
Biomagnification, 902, 903
Biomass, 435, 873
Biomes. *See also specific biome*
    climate and, 887
    coniferous forests, 890
    defined, 887
    deserts, 896
    distribution of, 886*f*, 887
    migration and, 883, 887
    shrublands, 894–95
    temperate deciduous forests, 891
    terrestrial ecosystems, 887–96
    tropical forests, 892–93
    tundra, 888
Biomolecules
    carbohydrates, 40*f*, 41–44
    carbon bonding in, 38–39
    defined, 38, 40, 328
    degradation of, 40–41
    evolution of, 282, 328–32
    lipids, 40*f*, 45–49
    nucleic acids, 40*f*, 54–56
    polymers, 40–41
    proteins, 40*f*, 49–53
    synthesis of, 40–41
Biosphere, 883–906. *See also* Ecosystems
    aquatic ecosystems, 897–904
    biological organization, 2, 3*f*, 9–10
    biome distribution, 886*f*, 887
    climate, 884–85
    defined, 9, 818, 839
    diversity in, 909
    ocean currents, 902–4
    review and exercises, 904–6
    terrestrial ecosystems, 887–96
Biosynthesis, in lytic cycle, 367*f*, 368
Biotechnology, 254–69
    defined, 254
    DNA cloning, 255–57
    gene therapy, 260
    genomics, 261–66
    products of, 254, 258–59, 419
    review and examples, 267–69
Biotic agents, of natural selection, 8
Biotic community, 875
Biotic potential, 841, 863
Bipedalism, evolution of, 341,
    575–77, 578*f*
Bipolar cells, of eye, 723
Biramous appendages, crustaceans, 540
Birch tree, 476
Bird(s). *See also specific bird*
    anatomy, 562*f*, 563
    auditory communication by, 807, 828
    beaks of. *See* Beak(s)
    characteristics, 562–63
    circulatory system, 609
    cognitive learning, 825–26
    defined, 562

diversity of living, 563
embryonic development, 797–99
evolution of, 283, 327, 340, 562–63
excretory system, 681
eyes, 720
fat storage in, 46
habitat preservation, 919–20
hormones in, 755
illegal trade of, 916
imprinting in, 823–24
lungs, 665, 670*f*
mating behavior, 297, 312, 828, 831–32
migratory behavior, 825
mutualism, 866*f*
nest-building behavior, 774*f*,
    820–21, 847
niche specialization in, 860, 861*f*
osmoregulation, 680, 683–84
parenting in, 774*f*, 823–24
as pollinators, 437, 505, 507
population density, 847*f*
reciprocal altruism in, 834
reproduction, 773–74, 805
respiration, 562, 665, 670*f*
seed dispersal by, 511
skeleton of, 562, 737
song learning, 824
species identification, 358
territoriality in, 830
vision, 720
Bird flu, 369, 370
Bird of paradise, 297–98, 828
Bird's-nest fungi, 412, 413
Birth (human)
    oxytocin in, 757
    positive feedback mechanisms,
        601, 757
    stages of, 810, 811*f*
Birth control, 783–84, 852
Birth defects, 807
Birth weight, human, 296, 297*f*
Birthrate, 842–43, 852–53
Bison, 894, 895*f*, 918
Biston betularia, 279–80, 290–92
Bitter taste, 718
Bivalent chromosomes, 173, 176
Bivalves, 534–35
Black bread mold, 406*t*, 407–8
Black Death (plague), 848
Black howler monkey, 893*f*
Black mangroves, 452, 461*f*
Black mold, 410
Black walnut, 460
Black widow spider, 543*f*
Blackberry fruit, 510*f*
Black-footed ferret, 909
Blackman, F. F., 122
Bladder, 684, 684*f*
Blade of leaf, 444*f*, 445
Blaine, David, 663
BLAST (computer program), 265
Blastocoel, 797
Blastocyst, 806*f*, 808*f*
Blastopore, 523, 798
Blastula, 523, 797
Blaylock, Mike, 471
Bleeder's disease (hemophilia), 210
Blending concept, of inheritance, 193
Blepharisma, 385*t*
Blind spot, 721, 723*f*
Blindness, 723, 725
Blood, 618–23. *See also* Red blood cells
        (RBCs); White blood cells
        (WBCs)
    capillary exchange, 621–23
    circulatory pathways of. *See* Circulation
    components, 591
    composition and functions of, 618–19
    defined, 606
    glucose levels in, 654, 765, 766
    lipid levels, 659–60
    osmolarity of, 686
    pH of, 32–33, 690
    respiratory gas exchange, 672
    sickle cell disease, 206–7
    transfusions, 619
    transport of. *See* Circulatory system
    water in, 30
Blood clotting, 620, 621*f*
Blood doping, 768

Blood fluke, 532–33
Blood glucose levels, 654, 765, 766
Blood pressure
    aging process, 811
    in capillary exchange, 621
    high, 616, 812
    measurement, 615
    regulation, 615, 690, 763
Blood transfusions, 619
Blood types, 205, 619–20
Blood vessels. *See also* Arteries;
        Capillary(ies); Circulation; Veins
    aging process, 811–12
    structure and function, 608
Blood volume
    defined, 686
    regulation of, 690, 763
Blooms
    algae or dinoflagellates, 392–93
    cyanobacteria, 377
    plants. *See* Flowering plant(s)
Blubber, 46
Blue columbine, 130*f*
Blue crab, 897*f*
Blue Fugates of Troublesome Creek, 202
Blue light and phototropism, 491, 492
Blue whale, 564, 648
Bluebirds, 15–16, 847
Blue-footed booby, 312
Bluegrass mortality patterns, 841–42, 841*t*
Blue-green algae. *See* Cyanobacteria
Blue-green bacteria, 66
Blue-spotted stingrays, 554*f*
BMP4 gene, 318*f*, 319
Bobcat, 891*f*
Body (somatic) cells, 155
Body cavities, in mammals, 596
Body fluid regulation, 680–92
    animals, 681–84
    excretory system, 680–92
    flatworms, 531
    human urinary system, 596, 684–90
    insect, 542
    invertebrates, 681–82
    nitrogenous waste, 681
    osmoregulation, 680–90, 757, 758*f*, 763
    review and exercises, 691–92
Body language, 827, 828
Body plan, evolution of animal, 521, 522*f*,
    524–25
Body shape, human variation, 581, 583
Body stalk, 808*f*, 809
Body temperature
    fever, 631
    regulation of, 599, 600*f*, 601
    and water, 29*f*
Bogs, 897
Bohr, Niels, 25
Bohr model, of atoms, 25
Boiling point of water, 29
Boletus, 413*f*
Bolides, 343
Bolus, 651
Bombus, 864*f*
Bonds and bonding
    carbon, for biomolecules, 38–39
    chemical, 26–31
    covalent, 27
    disulfide, 52*f*
    double, 7, 39
    hydrogen, 50, 51*f*
    hydrogen bonds, 28–29
    ionic, 26–27
    peptide, 50, 51*f*
    triple, 27, 39
Bone(s) (human). *See also* Human
        skeleton; *specific bone*
    aging process, 812–13
    compact, 591, 739–40
    dermal, 738
    growth and renewal of, 738
    hormonal action on, 761–62
    long, 738–40
    spongy, 591, 739–40
Bone marrow
    in long bones, 591
    red, 591, 628*f*, 629, 740
    transplantation of, 639
    yellow, 739
Bone mass, loss of, 738, 812–13

Bony fishes
  characteristics, 526t, 554–55
  circulatory system, 554
  defined, 554
  gas exchange, 666
  gills, 666f
  osmoregulation, 680, 682–83
  ray-finned, 554, 555f
  skeleton of, 553, 737
Boreal forest (taiga), 890
Borneo, 306
Boron, in plants, 466t
Botox®, 746
Bottleneck effect, 295
Bottlenose dolphins, 21, 828
Botulinum toxin, 746
Botulism, 376, 746
Bovine growth hormone (bGH), 258
Bovine spongiform encephalopathy
    (BSE), 371
Bowerbirds, 297, 832
Bowman's capsule, 685, 685f
BPG in glycolysis, 138f, 139f
BPH (benign prostatic hypertrophy), 777
BPV (benign positional vertigo), 730
Brachiation, 576, 577
Brachiopoda, 530
Brachioradialis muscle, 744f
Brachiosaurus, 559
Brackish water, 897, 900
Brain, 703–7. See also Nervous system
  aging process, 812
  australopithecines, 577, 578
  in central nervous system, 696,
      702f, 703–7
  cephalopod, 536
  Cro-Magnons, 580
  embryonic development of, 799, 809
  in homeostatic regulation, 600
  Homo ergaster, 578
  Homo rudolfensis, 578
  human, 696f, 702f, 703–7, 812
  learning and memory, 707
  nervous tissue, 593
  prosimians, 572
  vertebrates, 695–96
Brain stem, 702f, 704, 740
Brain tumors, 594
Branch roots, 444f, 452, 461f
Branchiostoma, 550–51
Branta canadensis, 883
Brassica oleracea, 278–79
BRCA1 gene, 164
Bread, yeasts and, 141
Bread mold, 406f, 407–8
Breast(s), 782–83
Breast cancer, 782–83
Breastbone (sternum), 740f, 741
Breast-feeding, 639, 757, 782
Breath-holding champions, 663
Breathing. See also Respiration
  diaphragmatic action, 669
  during exercise, 747
  gas exchange, 668f, 669–70, 671f
  modifications of, in humans, 670–71
  respiratory system, 668f, 669–71
Breeding. See Reproduction
Bright-field microscopy, 64f
Bristlecone pine, 430
British land snails, 297, 298f
Brittle stars, 544
Broad-tailed hummingbird, 46
Broca's area, 703f, 704
Bronchioles, 668
Bronchitis
  acute, 673, 674f
  chronic, 673, 675
Bronchus (pl., bronchi)
  disorders affecting, 673–74
  human lung, 668
Broomrapes, 452, 472
Brown, Robert, 61
Brown algae, 385t, 386f, 390, 900
Brown bear, 888
Brown planthopper, 910–11
Brown tree snake, 915
Brush border, intestinal, 652
Brush-footed butterfly, 893f
Bryophytes
  defined, 423

    land colonization by, 420f, 423–25
    reproduction, 422–24, 425f
    uses of, 425
Bryozoa, 526t, 530
BSE (bovine spongiform
    encephalopathy), 371
Buckeye, 460
Bud(s)
  axillary, 444f, 445, 453, 461f
  dormant, 487, 488
  ethylene inhibition, 489
  terminal, 444f, 453, 461f
Bud scales, 453
Budding
  fungi, 406
  reproduction by, 773
  sponge, 527
  yeasts, 408f
Buffers, 33–34, 690
Buffon, Count (Georges-Louis
    Leclerc), 272
Bulb(s), 445, 457f, 458
Bulbourethral glands, 775f, 775t, 777
Bulk (active) transport, 95–98
  carrier proteins and energy needed,
      95, 96f
  defined, 89t, 95
  endocytosis, 97–98
  exocytosis, 95, 96f
  phagocytosis, 97–98
  plasma membrane, 91
Bullhorn acacia tree, 866
Bumblebee, 864f
Bundle scars, 453, 461f
Bundle sheath cells, 455f
Bupropion hydrochloride
    (Wellbutrin), 701
Burgess Shale, 338f
Burkett lymphoma, 188
Bursae (pl., bursa), 743
Bursitis, 743
Butterflies
  homologous traits, 317
  indirect defenses of plants, 498
  migration, 825
  mimicry in, 864
  as pollinators, 506–7, 867
Button mushrooms, 406t
BV (bacterial vaginosis), 790–91

C

C. See Cytosine (C)
C horizon soil, 468
C_3 plants, 130, 131
C_4 photosynthesis, 130, 131
C_4 plants, 130–31
Cabanac, Michel, 827
Cabbage, 460
Cactornis scandens, 279f, 318, 319
Cactus (pl., cacti)
  fossil, 357
  habitat, 896
  illegal trade in, 916
  leaves of, 460, 461f
  population dynamics, 861
Cactus finch, 279f, 318, 319
Caecilia nigracans, 557f
Caecilians, 557
Caenorhabditis elegans, 538, 800, 802,
    804, 813
Cairns-Smith, Graham, 332
Calcitonin, 738, 754f, 760–62
Calcium
  blood level of, regulation of, 738,
      761–62
  dietary requirement for, 660
  ions, 26
  in muscle contraction, 738, 745, 747t,
      748–49
  in nerve impulse transmission,
      700, 738
  nutritional function of soil, 467
  in ossification, 738
  in plants, 466f
Calcium carbonate, 33, 728, 736–37, 901
Callinectes sapidus, 897f
Callus, 487, 514f
Calment, Jeanne, 814
Calorie, of heat, 29

Calotes calotes, 893f
Caltha howellii, 891f
Calvatiga gigantea, 413f
Calvin, Melvin, 24, 123, 128
Calvin cycle, 123, 128–29
Calyx, 552
CAM (crassulacean-acid metabolism),
    130–31
CaM gene, 318f, 319
CAM photosynthesis, 130–31
Cambarus, 541f
Cambium
  cork, 447, 456, 456f
  vascular, 453
Cambrian period
  "Cambrian explosion," 338
  chordates, 552
  geologic timescale, 336t
  mass extinctions, 338, 343f
  sea life, 338
  vertebrate evolution, 552
Camera-type eye, 720–21
Camouflage, 863–64
cAMP (cyclic adenosine monophosphate),
    240, 255–56
Campylonerurum scolopendrium, 428f
Canada, acid rain in, 33
Canada geese, 883
Canada lynx, 863
Canadian Dietetic Association, 659
Canadian goldenrod, 505f
Canaliculi, 591
Cancer
  angiogenesis in, 164
  breast, 782–83
  causes of, 153, 164, 165f
  cervical, 788
  chemotherapy, 220
  colon, 654
  defined, 163
  gene therapy, 260
  lung, 248, 675
  metastasis of, 163–64
  mutations causing, 249–50
  origin of, 164
  progression of, 163f
  prostate, 777
  radiation therapy, 24–25
  testicular, 776
  thyroid, 761
  translocations, 188
  tumors, 163–64, 594
  vaccines for, 640
  viruses and, 368
Cancer cells
  characteristics, 163–64
  division, mutations, 249
  vs. normal cells, 163t
Candida, 409
Candida albicans, 410, 791
Candidiasis, 410, 638
Canis familiaris hallstromi, 549
Canis lupus, 278f
Canola plants, 470–71
Canopy, 891, 892
Cap, RNA molecules, 226, 247
CAP (catabolite activator protein), 240
Cape sundew, 472
Capillary(ies)
  artificial lung on computer chip, 676
  body temperature regulation, 601
  closed circulatory systems, 607
  gas exchange, 668
  human lung, 668f
  lymphatic, 629
  peritubular, 685f, 686, 687f
  skin, 597f
  structure and function of, 608
Capillary beds
  blood, 608, 609f, 614, 622–23
  lymph, 622
Capillary exchange, 621–23
Capsid, of viruses, 364f, 365f, 366
Capsule, of bacteria, 65, 372
Capuchin monkeys, 572, 573f
Carapace, crayfish, 541
Carbaminohemoglobin, 672
Carbohydrates
  as biomolecule, 40f, 41–44
  chains in plasma membrane, 88

    in common foods, 40t
    defined, 41, 657
    digestion of, 656, 657–58
    disaccharides, 42
    metabolism of, 147
    monosaccharides, 41, 42
    nutrition and human health, 657–58
    organic chemistry, 41–44
    as organic compound class, 38
    polysaccharides, 41, 42–44
    production of, in photosynthesis,
        120–22
    as structural material, 41f
    synthesis of, in plants, 105–6
Carbon. See also under Organic
  atom of, 38–39
  in biomolecules, 38–39
  Bohr model of, 25f
  as essential plant nutrient, 465
  isotopes of, 24
  plant acquisition of, 466
  in plants, 443, 466t
  radioactive tracer studies, phloem
      transport, 478–79
  radiocarbon dating, 334
Carbon chain (skeleton) of functional
    groups, 39–40
Carbon cycle, 876–77
Carbon dating of fossils, 334
Carbon dioxide
  Calvin cycle, 128–29
  in carbon cycle, 876–77
  cellular respiration, 136
  and climate change, 127, 344, 879,
      912, 915
  as essential plant nutrient, 465
  excess, and mass extinctions, 344
  gas exchange, 671
  photosynthesis, 121–23, 443
  in plants, 443
  production of, 143
  proton pump, 477
  respiratory gas exchange, 664f,
      670–71, 690
  transport of, 669, 672
Carbon dioxide fixation, 128–31
Carbon monoxide, 672
Carbon skeleton of functional groups,
    39–40
Carbonic anhydrase, 672
Carboniferous period
  amniotes, 558
  amphibians, 556
  forests, 435
  geologic timescale, 336t
  mass extinctions, 343f
  swamp forests, 339, 427
Carboxyl functional groups, 39t, 40
Carcharias taurus, 554f
Carcinogen, 248
Carcinogenesis, 164, 249
Cardiac arrhythmias, 613–14
Cardiac conduction system, 613
Cardiac cycle, 612–14
Cardiac glycosides, 497
Cardiac muscle, 593, 612–13, 744
Cardiac output, 612
Cardiac pacemaker, 613
Cardiac veins, 614
Cardinal, 563f
Cardinalis cardinalis, 563f
Cardiovascular disease (CVD), 616–17,
    659–60. See also specific disease
Cardiovascular system, 605–25. See also
    specific organ
  aging process, 811–12
  blood, 618–23
  functions of, 596
  human, 610–17, 811–12
  invertebrate, 606–7
  review and exercises, 623–25
  vertebrates, 552, 556, 608–9
Carduelis tristis, 774f
Caretta caretta, 889f
Caribou, 888
Carnivores
  characteristics, 566t
  defined, 648, 870
  dentition of, 649
  as discontinuous feeders, 648

in food web, 871-74
locomotion, 737
mammals, 341
planaria, 647
plants, 472
Carotenoids, 124, 391, 392, 723
Carotid body(ies), 671
Carp, 838, 840, 897f
Carpal bones, 740f, 742
Carpel(s), 434, 436f, 502f, 503
Carpellate flowers, 503
Carrageenin, 389
Carrier proteins, 88, 89, 95-96
Carriers
  in electron transport chain, 144
  of genetic disorders, 202
Carroll, Sean, 279
Carrots, 444, 452
Carruthers, Jean, 746
Carrying capacity, 845-46, 863
Cartilage (human)
  articular, 743
  costal, 740f, 741
  facial, 741
  hyaline, 591, 739
  ossification of, 738
  structure, 590
  types, 591
  vertebral, 741
Cartilaginous endoskeleton, 553
Cartilaginous fishes, 554, 682
Cartilaginous joints, 742-43
Casella, 509f
Casparian strip, 451, 469
Caspases, 155
Cat(s). See also specific animal
  coat color, 111, 243
  nervous system, 695
Catabolism, 147
Catabolite activator protein (CAP), 240
Catalase, 75
Cataracts, 724
Catastrophism, 273
Categories of classification, 348-54
  Linnaean hierarchy, 349-50
  nested, 349, 350f
Caterpillars, 498, 762, 860
Catfish, 840
Catharanthus roseus, 910f
Cat's cry (cri du chat) syndrome, 188
Cattle, 646
Cattle egrets, 865
Cave paintings, Cro-Magnon, 581
CBOL (Consortium for the Barcode of
  Life), 352
CDC (Centers for Disease Control and
  Prevention), 370
CDK (cyclin-dependent kinase), 156
CDKNA gene, 153
cDNA (complementary DNA), 256
Cebus capucinus, 571f
Cech, Thomas, 330
Cecum, 648, 653
Celery, 460
Cell(s). See also Animal cells; specific
    type of cell
  apoptosis. See Apoptosis
  basic chemistry, 21-36
  biological organization, 3f
  biomolecules. See Biomolecules
  cancer. See Cancer cells
  cellular respiration, 135-51
  defined, 2, 61
  energy flow, 105-6
  and entropy, 106
  eukaryotic. See Eukaryotic cells
  evolution of living, 328, 330-32
  in immune response, 632, 634, 636
  junctions between, 99-100
  membrane structure and function,
    85-103
  metabolism, 104-18
  nerve. See Neurons
  organic chemistry, 37-59
  origin of, 328, 330-32
  photosynthesis, 119-31
  plant. See Plant cells
  prokaryotic. See Prokaryotic cells
  reproduction of. See Meiosis; Mitosis
  size of, 62

structure and function, 60-84
surfaces of, modification of, 98-100
Cell body, 593, 697, 701f, 707
Cell cycle, 154-55, 164
Cell division. See also Meiosis; Mitosis
  aging process and, 813
  apoptosis, 153, 155
  cancer, and mutations, 249
  in cell cycle, 154-55
  centrioles, 80
  eukaryotic, 167, 167t
  during fertilization, 797
  generally, 588
  neuroglia, 594
  prokaryotic, 166-67
  promotion and cytokinins, 487, 489t
  root zone of, 450, 451f
Cell envelope, of prokaryotes, 65
Cell plate, 161
Cell recognition proteins, 88
Cell signaling, 90
Cell structure and function, 60-84
  cellular level of organization, 61-62
  cytoskeleton, 78-81
  endomembrane system, 72-74
  energy-related organelles, 76-77
  eukaryotic cells, 67-81
  microscopy, 63-64
  nucleus, 70-71
  peroxisomes (vesicles), 75
  photosynthesis vs. cellular
    respiration, 148
  prokaryotic cells, 65-66
  review and exercises, 82-84
  ribosomes, 71
  vacuoles, 75-76
  vesicles, 75
Cell surface modification, 98-100
  in animals, 98-100
  in plants, 100
Cell suspension culture, 514
Cell theory, 12, 61
Cell walls
  auxin-induced expansion of, 486f
  bacteria, 374
  carbohydrates in, 41f
  charophyte, 421
  eukaryotic cells, 67, 82t
  plant cells, 69f, 100
  prokaryotes, 65, 66f, 82t, 372
  three-domain system of
    classification, 352t
Cell-mediated immunity, 633, 635-37
Cellular damage accumulation theories of
    aging, 813-14
Cellular differentiation, 508, 588, 800-802
Cellular level of organization, 61-62
Cellular reproduction. See Cell division
Cellular respiration, 135-51
  adenosine triphosphate in, 133
  ATP production in, 136
  cell structure and function, 76
  citric acid cycle, 137, 143-44
  defined, 136
  efficiency of, 146
  electron transport chain, 137, 144-46
  fermentation, 140-41
  glucose in, 42, 136
  glycolysis, 137, 138-39
  metabolic pool, 147-49
  mitochondrial, 142-46
  organelles and energy flow, 114
  outside the mitochondria, 138-41
  oxygen in, 136
  phases of, 137
  vs. photosynthesis, 148
  plants, 465
  preparatory (prep) reaction, 137,
    142-43
  review and exercises, 149-51
Cellular response, signal transduction in
    plants, 484
Cellular slime molds, 386f, 397, 627
Cellular stages of development,
    797-98
Cellulose
  Calvin cycle, 129
  carbohydrates in, 41f
  in cell walls, 100
  charophyte cell walls, 421

defined, 44
digestion of, 43, 646
fibers of, 44f
plant defense mechanism, 448
ruminant digestion of, 646
Cellulose plates, dinoflagellates, 391f
Cenozoic period
  continental drift, 342, 342f
  generally, 341
  geologic timescale, 336t
  mammalian diversification, 341
  mass extinctions, 343f
  primate evolution, 572
Centers for Disease Control and
    Prevention (CDC), 370
Centipedes, 526t, 541, 542f
Central canal
  bone, 740
  spinal cord, 708f
Central dogma
  of genetics, 332
  of molecular biology, 223f, 224, 263
Central nervous system (CNS), 702-7. See
    also Brain; Spinal cord
  defined, 696, 702
  functions, 702
  human, 696f
  vertebrates, 696
Central sulcus, 703f, 704
Central vacuoles, of plant cells, 69f,
    75-76
Centrioles
  defined, 158
  eukaryotic cell, 68f, 79-80
  meiosis, 157
  prokaryotic vs. eukaryotic cells, 82t
Centromere, 80f, 157, 172, 173f
Centrosomes
  eukaryotic cell, 68f-69f, 78, 80
  during fertilization, 797
  in mitosis, 157-58
Cephalization. See also Brain
  defined, 694
  embryonic development, 522
  nervous system evolution, 694-95
  as vertebrate characteristic, 552
Cephalochordates, 540f, 550
Cephalopods, 536, 695
Cephalothorax, 541, 543
Ceratium, 385t
Cercopithecus aethiops, 828f
Cerebellum, 702f, 704, 708f
Cerebral cortex, 695, 704
Cerebral hemispheres, 703-4
Cerebral ventricles, 702, 703, 704
Cerebrospinal fluid (CSF), 702
Cerebrum, 695, 702f, 703-5
Certhidea olivacea, 279f, 318, 319
Cerumen, 49, 727
Cervical cancer, 788
Cervical nerves, 696f
Cervical vertebrae, 741
Cervix, 601, 779, 810, 811f
Cervus elaphus, 299, 833
Cestodes, 532
Cetacea, 566t
CF. See Cystic fibrosis (CF)
CFCs (chlorofluorocarbons), 915
CFTR (cystic fibrosis transmembrane
    regulator), 203, 259, 675
CFTR gene, 203, 259, 675
CGMP (cycline guanosine
    monophosphate), 777, 778
Chagas disease, 396
Chambered nautilus, 536f
Chameleon, 79f, 561
Channel proteins, 88
Chaos, 848
Chaparral, 894
Chaperone proteins, 53
Chara, 79f, 388-89, 421
Character displacement, 860
Charales, 421
Chargaff, Erwin, 217
Chargaff's rules for DNA, 217, 218
Charged tRNA, 229
Charophytes
  ancestry of plants, 421
  characteristics, 421-22, 421t
  evolutionary history of plants, 420f

as protist supergroup, 385t, 386f,
    388-89
reproduction, 422
Chase, Martha, 216
CHD (coronary heart disease), 45
Cheek, cells of, 64f
Cheese, 410
Cheetah
  coevolution, 867
  energy transformation, 104
  evolution of, 564
  habitat, 895
  pheromones in, 826
  territoriality in, 830
Chelicerae, 543
Chelicerates, 543
Chemical barriers, 630
Chemical communication, 826-28
Chemical cycling, 9, 874-78
  biodiversity and, 912
  carbon cycle, 876-77
  nitrogen cycle, 878
  phosphorus cycle, 877
  water cycle, 875, 897, 912
Chemical defenses, plant, 496-97
Chemical elements, 22-25
  atomic number, 23
  atoms, 22-23
  defined, 2, 22
  electrons and energy, 25
  isotopes, 24-25
  mass number, 23
  periodic table, 23
Chemical energy, 105
Chemical evolution, 328f
Chemical mediators, 631
Chemical messengers, 90, 755, 777
Chemical senses (smell and taste), 718-19
Chemical signals, 753, 755
Chemiosmosis
  ATP production, 114, 115f
  ATP-driven proton pump, 470
  defined, 126
  in electron transport chain, 144, 145
  glucose metabolism, 146
Chemistry, 21-36
  acids and bases, 32-34
  bonds and bonding, 26-31, 50, 51f
  chemical elements, 2, 22-25
  compounds, 26-29
  inorganic, 38
  molecules, 26-31. See also Molecules
  organic. See Organic chemistry
  review and exercises, 34-36
  of water, 28-31
Chemoautotrophs, 332, 375, 870, 902
Chemoheterotrophs, 375, 379
Chemoreceptors, 671, 690, 717, 718
Chemosynthesis, 332, 375, 870
Chemotherapy, 220, 675
Chemotropism, 491
Chest cavity, organs in, 596
Chestnut blight, 410
Chiasma (pl., chiasmata), 175, 176
Chicken
  embryonic development of, 797-99
  extraembryonic membranes, 805
  Hox genes, 322f, 524, 525
Chicken pox, 365
Chicxulub crater, 344
Childhood diseases, viral, 364t
Chimaeras, classification, 554
Chimpanzee
  classification, 571f, 572
  communication by, 828
  emotions in, 827
  evolution of, 573f
  genome of vs. human genome, 265
  genomics, 574
  inclusive fitness in, 834
Chinese liver fluke, 533
Chipmunk, 891f
Chiroptera, 566t
Chitin, 41f, 44, 405, 539, 736
Chitons, 526t, 534
Chlamydia, 790
Chlamydia trachomatis, 790
Chlamydomonas, 385t, 387-88
Chlorophytes, 387
Chlorarachniophytes, 385t

Chloride ions, in cystic fibrosis, 203
Chlorine, 26, 466t, 915
Chlorofluorocarbons (CFCs), 915
Chlorophyll
    ancestry of plants, 420
    in brown algae, 390
    in cyanobacteria, 66
    in dinoflagellates, 392
    in eukaryotic cells, 76
    in green algae, 387
    in green plants, 119, 121
    magnesium in, 465
    types of, 124
Chlorophyll a, 124
Chlorophyll b, 124
Chlorophytes, 385t, 386f, 387–88
Chloroplasts. See also Photosynthesis
    ATP production in, 113
    in dinoflagellates, 392
    as energy-related organelle, 76–77
    of euglenids, 395
    eukaryotic cells, 67, 69f
    evolution of, 335–36, 337
    genetic code used by, 224
    in green plants, 121
    leaves and photosynthesis, 121, 445
    vs. mitochondria, 148
    photosynthesis, 130
    prokaryotic vs. eukaryotic cells, 82t
    in protists, 384
    structure of, 76f
CHNOPS, 22, 38
Choanocytes, 527
Choanoflagellates, 385t, 386f, 397
Choice, as female mating behavior,
    297–98
Choking, 673
Cholesterol
    defined, 658
    dietary, 658, 659
    familial hypercholesterolemia, 98
    as lipid, 45
    liver regulation on, 654
    in plasma membrane, 86
    recommended intake, 659
Cholinesterase inhibitors, 701
Chondrichthyes, 554
Chordae tendineae, 611
Chordates, 349–50, 550–51. See also
    specific animal
    characteristics, 526t, 550
    in cladistics, 356
    defined, 550
    embryonic development, 523
    evolution of, 550–51
    nonvertebrate, 550–51
    phylogenetic tree of, 561f
Chorion, 774, 805, 806f, 808, 809
Chorionic villi, 808f, 809, 810f
Chorionic villi sampling (CVS), 907
Choroid, 721, 723
Christmas tree worms, 537f
Chromalveolata, 385t, 386f, 387, 390–94
    alveolates, 392–94
    apicomplexans, 385t, 386f, 394
    brown algae, 385t, 386f, 390
    ciliates, 393–94
    defined, 390
    diatoms, 385t, 386f, 390–91
    dinoflagellates, 385t, 386f, 392–93
    golden brown algae, 385t, 386f,
        390, 391
    stramenopiles, 385t, 390–92
    water molds, 7, 385t, 386f, 391–92
Chromatids. See also Sister chromatids
    chiasmata of, 175
    defined, 154, 157
    electron micrograph, 157f
Chromatin
    of animal cells, 68f
    defined, 157
    eukaryotic chromosome structure,
        233–34
    eukaryotic regulation, 241–43
    gene regulation, 241–42
    in nucleus, 70
    of plant cells, 69f
    from sperm nucleus, 797
    structure of, 241–43
Chromatin remodeling complex, 242, 243

Chromoplasts, 77
Chromosomes
    in chimpanzees, 574
    crossing-over of, 174–75
    daughter cells, 157, 160, 173–75, 179f
    diploid number of, 172
    DNA of, 233–34, 261–62
    duplication of, 157, 158f
    eukaryotic, 157, 158t, 167, 233–34
    haploid number of, 172
    homologous, 172–73, 175, 196
    human life cycle, 181–82, 574
    inactive X chromosome, 243
    independent assortment of, 198–99
    in meiosis (halving the number),
        172–73
    mutations of, 187
    nondisjunction of, 183–84
    in nucleus, 70
    number of, changes in, 172–74, 183–88
    prokaryotic, 166, 261
    sex, 184–85, 208
    in sexual reproduction, 171, 780
    structure of, 187–88, 233–34
Chronic bronchitis, 673, 675
Chronic myelogenous leukemia, 188
Chronic obstructive pulmonary disease
    (COPD), 673
Chrysotoxum, 864f
Chthamalus, 860
Chylomicrons, 657
Chyme, 652
Chytridiomycota, 404f, 406–7, 406t
Chytrids, 404f, 406–7, 406t
Chytriomyces hyalinus, 406t
Cicada, 737f
Cichlid fish, 314, 317f
Cilia (sing. cilium)
    in equilibrium organs, 728, 729f
    eukaryotic cells, 80, 82t
    evolution of, 337
    in oviducts, 779
    rotifers, 533
    tracheal, 589
Ciliary body, 721
Ciliary muscle, 721
Ciliates, 385t, 393–94
Cinchona, 458
Cinchona ledgeriana, 514
Cinnamomum verum, 458
Cinnamon, 458
Cinnamon fern, 428f
Circadian rhythms
    human, 768
    plants, 478, 494–95
Circular muscles, and locomotion, 736
Circulation
    coronary, 611–12
    invertebrate, 606–7
    pulmonary, 609, 614
    renal, 684f, 685–86
    systemic, 609, 614–15
    vertebrate, 552, 556, 608–9
Circulatory system, 605–25
    blood, 618–23
    closed, 607
    components of, 587
    defined, 606
    disorders of, 45
    human heart, 610–17
    invertebrate, 606–7
    open, 606
    review and exercises, 623–25
    vertebrates, 552, 556, 608–9
Circumcision, 777
Cirrhosis, 656
Cirri, 541
Citellum, 537
CITES (Convention of International Trade
    of Endangered Species), 916
Citric acid cycle, 137, 143–44
Clade, 356
Cladistics, 356, 357f
Cladogram, 356, 357f
Cladosporium, 409
Clam
    anatomy, 648f
    as bivalve, 534–35
    as continuous feeders, 648
    gas exchange in, 666

    habitats, 900, 901
    muscular hydrostat, 736
    nutrition of, 648
    population distribution, 840
    skeleton, 736
Clam worms, 537–38
Clarkia concinna, 315
Clarkia pulchella, 315
Clarkia virgata, 315f
Clark's nutcrackers, 866
Class (taxonomic), 6, 349. See also
    specific class
Classical conditioning, 824
Classification, 347–61
    of animals, 522f
    categories of, 348–54
    defined, 348
    DNA, 358–59
    five-kingdom system of, 351
    of leaves, 460, 461f
    Linnean hierarchy, 349–50, 356
    of living things, 6, 6t, 7
    molecular data, 358–59
    nested, 349, 350f
    phylogeny, 354–59
    protein comparisons, 359
    of protostomes, 523
    review and exercises, 359–61
    systematic biology, 348–50
    taxonomic, 6–8, 6t, 348–50
    three-domain system, 351–54, 352t
Claviceps purpurea, 411
Clavicle, 738, 740f, 742
Clay, 343, 467
Cleaner wrasse, 866f
Cleaning symbiosis, 866
Cleavage, 523, 523f, 797, 806f
Cleavage furrow, cytokinesis, 160
Clements, F. E., 868
Climate
    biomes, 887
    biosphere and, 884–85, 886f
    defined, 884
    regulation of, 912
Climate change
    biodiversity and, 916
    Cro-Magnons affected by, 581
    defined, 127, 877, 915
    deforestation and, 127, 912
    documentation of, 879, 915–16
    mass extinction, 344
    models of, 879, 916
    plant storage, 443
    prevention of, 879
Climax community, 868
Clitoris, 779f, 780
Cloaca, 557, 681, 774
Clonal plants, 514
Clonal selection theory
    B cells, 633–34
    T cells, 636
Cloning
    defined, 255
    of DNA, 255–57
    polymerase chain reaction, 256–57
    recombinant DNA technology, 255–56
    reproductive, 161, 162
    therapeutic, 161, 162
    tissue culture for plant
        propagation, 514
    transgenic animals, 259
Clonorchis sinensis, 533
Closed circulatory system, 607
Closterium, 385t
Clostridium botulinum, 746
Clostridium tetani, 353, 374, 376
Clothing, bamboo for, 458
Clover, 496
Clownfish, 865
Club drugs, 710
Club fungi, 404f, 406t, 412–13
Club mosses, 421t, 426
Clubbing, nail, 599
Clumped distribution, 840, 841
CMV (cytomegalovirus), 638
Cnidarians, 528–29
    body of, 528
    characteristics, 526t
    comb jellies v., 528
    defined, 528

    diversity of, 528, 529f
    embryonic development, 523–24
    eyes, 720
    gas exchange, 655f
    gravitational equilibrium organs
        in, 728
    Hox genes in body plan evolution, 525
    hydrostatic skeleton, 736
    nervous system, 694, 694f
    reproduction, 773
    transport in, 606
CNS. See Central nervous system (CNS)
CNVs (copy number variations), 265, 266
CoA (coenzyme A) , 142–43
Coacervate droplets, 331
Coagulation, 620, 621f
Coal, 120, 435
Coastal ecosystems
    climate of, 885
    estuary, 900
    human impact on, 9–10, 912
    intertidal zone, 900
    loss of habitat, 913
Coastal redwood, 430
Coat color, cat, 111, 243
Coated pit, 97f, 98
Coated vesicle, 97f, 98
Cobras, 561
Cocaine
    abuse of, 710–11
    during pregnancy, 807
    psychosis caused by, 710
Cocci (sing., coccus), 65, 374
Coccinella, 911f
Coccobacilli, 374
Coccyx, 740–41
Cochlea, 726f, 727, 729f
Cochlear canal, 727
Cochlear implants, 730
Cochlear nerve, 726f, 727–28
Cocklebur, 496
Cocksfoot grass, 505f
Cocoon, of insects, 542
Cod, 849, 918
Codominance, 205
Codonosiga, 397
Codons
    defined, 224
    stop, 120
    translation, 229–32
Coelacanths, 555
Coelom
    of annelids, 536, 537f
    crayfish, 541
    defined, 523
    development of, 798–99
    hydrostatic skeleton, 736
    lophoporans, 530
    mollusc, 534, 535f
    structure, 596
    true, 523
Coelomic fluid, 606
Coenzyme(s)
    cellular respiration, 142–43
    defined, 54, 112
    electron transport chain, 144, 145f
    in glycolysis, 138, 139f
    in photosynthesis, 122
    vitamins, 660
Coenzyme A (CoA), 142–43
Coenzyme Q, 144, 145f
Coevolution
    defined, 505, 506, 867
    plants and pollinators, 506–7, 866, 867
Cofactors, 112
Cognitive learning, 825–26
Cohesion, 30, 476
Cohesion-tension model of xylem
    transport, 476–77
Cohort, 841
Colchicine, 79
Cold receptors, 730
Cold-blooded animals, 599
Coleochaete, 421
Coleoptera, 542f
Coleoptile, 485, 509, 512
Coleorhiza, 509, 512
Coleus, 490f
Collagen
    in blood vessels, 608, 811

in connective tissue, 589, 590*f*
in extracellular matrix, 99*f*
osteogenesis imperfecta, 203
as protein, 50
in skin, 598
Collar cells, sponges, 527, 773
Collarbone (clavicle), 738, 740*f*, 742
Collecting duct, 685*f*, 686, 687*f*, 688
Collenchyma cells, 448–49, 454*f*
Colloblasts, 528
Colon, 653
Colon cancer, 654
Colonial flagellate hypothesis, 521
Colonization
  by alien species, 914
  of land, by plants, 420*f*, 423–25
Colony(ies)
  of green algae, 388
  opisthokonta, 397
Colony-stimulating factors, 631
Color blindness, 209, 300–301, 723
Color vision, 720, 723
Coloration
  in cats, 111, 243
  cryptic, 863–64
  of flowers, 437, 464
  of hair, 811
  of skin, 207, 758
  warning, 864
Colostrum, 782
Columnar epithelium, 589
Comb jellies, 523, 526*t*, 528
Comets
  Earth impact and mass extinction, 343–44
  extraterrestrial origins hypothesis, 330
Commensalism, 375, 865, 865*t*, 867
Common ancestors, 328, 348, 349, 351*f*, 354–58
Common cold, 673
Communication, 826–30
  auditory, 828
  chemical, 826–28
  defined, 826
  tactile, 829–30
  visual, 828–29
Community(ies), 858–69
  biodiversity benefits, 913
  biological organization, 3*f*
  biotic, 875
  climax, 868
  coevolution, 867
  defined, 2, 9, 839, 858
  development of, 868–69
  ecologies of, 858–68
  interactions within, 859–64
  predator-prey interactions, 860–64
  review and exercises, 880–82
  structure of, 858–59
  symbiotic relationships, 864–66
Compact bone, 591, 739–40
Companion cells, plants, 450, 453, 455*f*, 473
Comparative anatomy, 272, 357
Comparative genomics, 263–65
Competition
  as mating behavior, 298–99, 831–33
  population density and, 847
  between populations, 859–60, 861*f*
Competitive exclusion principle, 860
Competitive inhibition, 112
Complement, 632
Complementary base pairing. *See also*
  Adenine (A); Cytosine (C);
  Guanine (G); Thymine (T)
  defined, 219
  in DNA double helix, 55, 219*f*
  DNA replication, 220, 221
Complementary DNA (cDNA), 256
Complete digestive tract, 531, 647–48
Complete flowers, 434*t*, 503
Complex tissues, xylem and phloem as, 449–50
Composite flower, 434*t*
Compound, molecular, 26–31
Compound eyes, 539*f*, 540, 541, 720
Compound fruit, 511, 511*t*
Compound leaves, 460
Compound light microscope, 63
Compound tools, Cro-Magnons, 580

Computer chip, artificial lung on, 676
Concentration gradient
  ATP-driven proton pump, 469*f*, 470, 477–79
  defined, 89
Conchs, 534, 535
Conclusion, scientific method, 11*f*, 12, 14–15, 16
Condensation, 40–41, 875
Conditioning
  classical, 824
  operant, 824–25
Condoms, 784*f*
Conduction system, of heart, 613
Cone(s)
  conifer, 430, 431*f*
  cycad, 432
  pollen cones, 430*f*, 431*f*, 432
  seed cones, 430*f*, 431*f*, 432
Cone cells, 721–23
Cone-headed katydid, 893*f*
Confocal microscopy, 64
Confuciusornis, 281
Congenital hypothyroidism, 760
Conidia, 409
Conidiosphores, 409, 410*f*
Conifer(s), 421*t*, 430, 431
Coniferous forests
  montane, 887, 890
  seed plant development, 430–31
  species composition, 858
  taiga, 890
  temperate, 890
Conjugation
  in ciliates, 393–94
  prokaryotes, 373
  in ***Spirogyra***, 388, 389*f*
Conjugation pili, 66, 373
Conjunctiva, 721
Connective tissue, 588–92
  components, 589–90
  defined, 588
  fibrous, 590
  fluid, 591–92
  ligaments, 590, 742–43
  matrix, 590
  in the subcutaneous layer, 598
  supportive, 590–91
  tendons, 590, 743, 744
  types of, 590
  vascular, 608, 608*f*
Connell, Joseph, 860
Consanguineous reproduction (inbreeding), 202, 295, 300–301, 819
Conservation biology, 907–24
  biodiversity, 908–13
  defined, 908
  DNA analysis in, 889
  extinction, causes of, 913–18
  review and exercises, 920, 922–24
  study of, 10
  techniques of, 918–20
Conservation of energy, law of, 105
Consortium for the Barcode of Life (CBOL), 352
Construction, bamboo for green, 458
Consumers, 870
Consumption, endomembrane system, 74*f*
Consumptive use value, 911
Contact dermatitis, 642
Continental drift, 342–43, 344, 868
Continental shelf, 900*f*, 901
Continuous feeders, 648
Contraception, 783–84, 852
Contraceptive vaccines, 784
Contractile ring, cytokinesis, 160
Contractile tissue, 592–93. *See also*
  Muscle
Contractile vacuoles, 384, 395, 396
Contraction of muscles
  in coelom, 736
  as metabolic reaction, 108
  skeletal muscle, 744–49
Contrast, microscope, 64
Control groups, 12
Controlled study, example of, 14–15
Convention of International Trade of Endangered Species (CITES), 916

Convergent evolution, 317, 357, 720
Convergent evolution mode of speciation, 317
Cooksonia, 426
COPD (chronic obstructive pulmonary disease), 673
Copepods, 540–41
Copper, in plants, 466*t*
Copperheads, 561
Copulation, 774
Copy number variations (CNVs), 265, 266
Coral
  characteristics, 526*t*
  cnidarians as, 528
  formation of, 392
Coral reefs
  biodiversity in, 862, 901, 909
  as community, 839, 862
  described, 528, 901
  destruction of, 913, 916
  formation of, 389
  human impact on, 10
  symbiosis in, 866
Coralline algae, 385*t*
Corepressor, 239
Corey, Robert, 51
Cork, 455*f*, 456, 475*f*
Cork cambium, 447, 455*f*, 456
Cork cells, 447, 456, 457*f*
Corms, 457*f*, 458
Corn
  adventitious roots, 452
  cytokinins, 487
  DNA nucleotide composition in, 217*f*
  evolution of maize, 438–39
  genome sizes, 492
  germination and growth, 488, 512
  indirect defenses of, 498
  kernels, 510*f*
  maize, 433
  as monocot, 454
  monocot seed, 509
  monoecious plants, 503
  photosynthesis, 130*f*
  root system, 444
  taxonomic classification of, 6*t*
  transpiration in, 476
Corn smut, 413
Cornea, 721
Corolla, 434, 503
Corona, rotifer, 533
Corona radiata, 796, 806*f*
Coronary arteries
  plaque in, 616, 617*f*
  structure and function, 610, 614
Coronary bypass, 616
Coronary circulation, 611–12
Coronary heart disease (CHD), 45
Corpus callosum, 702*f*, 703, 705*f*
Corpus luteum, 780–82, 808
Cortex
  plant transport, 469
  of roots, 451
  of stems, 454*f*, 455, 457*f*, 462*f*
  woody twig, 456*f*
Cortical granules, 797
Cortisol, 763
Cortisone, 763, 764
Corynactis, 529*f*
Costal cartilages, 740*f*, 741
Cost-benefit analysis, in sexual selection, 298
Cotton, 498
Cotton aphid, 911
Cotyledons
  defined, 433
  eudicot development, 508
  germination, 512
  of monocot seed, 509
  monocot vs. eudicot, 433*t*, 446

Convergent evolution, 317, 357, 720
Coxal bones, 740*f*, 742, 743*f*
Coxal glands, 682
Crabs
  chemoreceptors in, 718
  as crustaceans, 540
  as decapods, 540*f*
  foraging for food, 831
  habitats, 897*f*, 901
  mutualism, 866
  nervous system of, 694, 695*f*
  population density, 848
Crambionella, 529*f*
Cranial bones, 740–42
Cranial cavity, organs in, 596*f*
Cranial nerves, 696*f*, 707, 708*f*
Cranium, 740–41
Crassulacean-acid metabolism (CAM), 130–31
Crayfish
  as crustaceans, 540–41
  gas exchange in, 666
  male anatomy, 541*f*
  reproduction, 774
C-reactive protein, 631
Creatine phosphate, 746
Crenation, 94
Creosote bush, 840*f*
Cretaceous period
  dinosaurs, 340
  geologic timescale, 336*t*
  gymnosperm, 433
  mass extinction in, 343–44
Cretinism, 760
Cri du chat (cat's cry) syndrome, 188
Crick, Francis H. C., 218–19, 229
Crickets, 312, 828
Crinoids, 344, 544, 902
Cristae, of mitochondria, 77, 142, 144, 145*f*
Critical length, day light, 495–96
Crocodilians. *See also specific animal*
  characteristics, 561–62
  circulatory system, 609
  classification of, 356, 526*t*
  common ancestors, 358
  origin of, 559
Cro-Magnons humans, 580–81, 583
Crop, of earthworm, 647–48
Crops, genetically modified, 254
Cross-fertilization
  defined, 773
  dihybrid, 198–99, 200
  monohybrid, 195, 196
  reciprocal, 195
Crossing-over, 174–75, 176
Cross-linking of proteins, 814
Cross-pollination
  flowering plants, 505–7
  gene flow through, 294*f*
  Mendel's garden pea experiments, 193–201
Crotalus atrox, 278
Crust of Earth, 22, 22*t*, 342, 343
Crustaceans, 540–41. *See also specific animal*
  characteristics, 526*t*
  chemoreceptors, 718
  digestion, 541
  evolution of, 540–41
  excretory system, 682
  gravitational equilibrium organs in, 728
  nervous system, 541
  reproduction, 773
  respiratory system, 541
Crustose lichens, 414
Cryptic coloration, 863–64
Cryptic species, 307
CSF (cerebrospinal fluid), 702
Ctenophora, 528
CTLs (cytotoxic T cells), 620, 633*f*, 635–36
Cuboidal epithelium, 588–89
Cuckoo, 867
Cuculus, 867*f*
Cucumber, 460, 461*f*
Cucumis, 461*f*
Cud, 649
Culture, defined, 582
Cunnilingus, 773

Cup coral, 529f
Cup fungi, 406t, 408f
Cupula, 728, 729f
Curie, Marie, 24
Cuscuta, 472f
Cushing syndrome, 764
Cutaneous receptors, 730
Cutaneous respiration, 556
Cuticle
  plant, 422, 423, 447, 453, 459, 476
  skin, 598
Cuttings, asexual reproduction from, 513–14
Cuvier, Georges, 272–73
CVD (cardiovascular disease), 616–17, 659–60. *See also specific disease*
CVS (chorionic villi sampling), 907
Cyanide, 112, 144
Cyanobacteria
  blooms of, 377
  defined, 377
  described, 351–52
  endosymbiosis of, 384
  evolution of, 335
  in nitrogen cycle, 878
  photosynthesis, 66, 76, 120f, 377
Cyanogenic glycosides, 497
Cycads, 340, 421t, 430, 432
Cycads, Age of, 340
Cycas revoluta, 432
Cyclamen, 486f
Cyclic adenosine monophosphate (cAMP), 240, 755–56
Cyclin(s), 155, 249
Cyclin D, 249
Cyclin-dependent kinase (CDK), 156
Cyclohexane, 39
Cyclooxygenase, COX-1, alternative version of, 246
Cyclospora cayetanensis, 394
Cyclosporine, 410
Cyclotella, 391f
Cynognathus, 342
Cyphoma gibbosum, 536f
Cyprinus carpio, 897f
Cyst(s)
  diplomonad, 395
  protist, 384
  tapeworm, 533
Cysteine, 50, 51f
Cystic fibrosis (CF)
  bioinformatics, 265
  CFTR gene, 203, 259, 675
  faulty chloride channel proteins, 88f, 95
  gene therapy, 260
  heterozygote advantage, 303
  as protein-folding disease, 53
  recessive disorder, 202–3
Cystic fibrosis transmembrane regulator (CFTR), 203, 259, 675
Cysticercosis, 519, 533
Cytochrome, 144, 465
Cytochrome c, 146f, 284, 285f
Cytochrome c protein, 359
Cytochrome complex, 126
Cytochrome oxidase, 144
Cytochrome reductase, 145f
Cytokines, 631, 633, 637
Cytokinesis
  animal cells, 160
  defined, 155
  eukaryotes vs. prokaryotes, 167, 167t
  meiosis, 176
  mitosis, 157–61
  plant cells, 160
Cytokinins, 487–88, 489t
Cytologists, 172
Cytology, 61
Cytolysis, 93
Cytomegalovirus (CMV), 638
Cytoplasm
  bacterial, 65–66
  cell structure and function, 68f–69f
  eukaryotic cell, 78
Cytoplasmic segregation, 800, 801f
Cytoplasmic streaming, 78
Cytosine (C)
  complimentary base pairing, 55
  DNA structure, 55f, 217–19, 223
  DNA vs. RNA, 223t

  molecular structure of, 217f
  mRNA codons, 224f
  as nucleotide, 54f
  RNA structure, 223
Cytoskeleton
  actin filaments, 78, 79f
  eukaryotic cells, 78–80
  intermediate filaments, 78, 79f
  microtubules, 78–79
  structure and function, 68f, 78–81, 82t
Cytotoxic T cells (CTLs), 620, 633f, 635–36

D

2,4-D, 485
Dactylus glomerata, 505f
Dalton, John, 22
Damage accumulation theories of aging, 813–14
Damselflies, 774
Dandelion, 849f
Dark-field microscopy, 64f
Darwin, Charles
  on animal emotions, 827
  blending concept, 193
  evolutionary theory of, 8, 275–80
  on first living organisms, 328
  on gravitropism, 491
  microevolution, 290
  nomenclature, 350
  On the Origin of Species, 282
  on phototropism, 485
  on population ecology, 845, 846
  speciation, 307
  and voyage of HMS Beagle, 272
Darwin, Erasmus, 272
Darwin, Francis, 485, 491
Darwin's finches. *See* Galápagos finches
Dasypus novemcinctus, 910f
Data
  bluebird mating behavior, 16
  defined, 12
  legumes and wheat rotation study, 14
  scientific method, 11–12, 14
Date rape drugs, 710, 789
Dating, of fossils, 334
Daughter cells, 157, 160, 173–75, 179f, 800, 801f
Daylily, 503f
Day-neutral plants, 496
de la Chapelle syndrome, 184
Deafness, 728–30
Deamer, David, 331
Deamination, 147, 654, 659
"Death cap" mushroom, 412
Death rate, 841–43, 852–53
Decapods, 540
Deceleration phase, of logistic growth, 845
Deciduous forests, 891
Deciduous plants, 445, 448
Decomposers
  bacterial, 375, 871
  detritivores, 870–71
  fungi as, 403, 871
  in lakes, 898, 900, 915
  in waste recycling, 912
Deductive reasoning, 11
Deep Water Horizon oil spill clean-up, 258, 469
Defenses
  against disease. See Immune system
  of plants, 447–48, 483, 484f, 496–98
  of prey, 863–64
  and protein, 49
Deforestation
  biodiversity and, 911, 912
  carbon cycle and, 876
  climate change caused by, 912
  habitat loss from, 913, 914f, 919
  soil profiles, 468
  of tropical rain forests, 127, 893, 913
Degenerate, genetic code as, 224
Degradation
  of biomolecules, 40–41
  enzymatic, 110f
  of maltose, 42f
  of peptides, 50f
Dehiscent fruit, 510f, 511t, 512
Dehydration reaction, 40–41, 46

Delayed allergic response, 642, 642t
Deletion, 188
Deletion syndromes, 188
Deltoid muscle, 744f
Demographic transition, 851
Demography, 840–43
Denatured enzymes, 111
Denatured proteins, 53
Dendrites, 593, 697, 700
Dendritic cells, 631–32, 636
Dendrobates azureus, 893f
Dendrobates pumilio, 848f
Denitrification, 878
Dense fibrous connective tissue, functions of, 590
Density
  population, 840, 846–49
  of water, temperature and, 31
Density-dependent factors, 846f, 847
Density-independent factors, 846f, 847
Dentition, of mammals, 649
Deoxyribonucleic acid. *See* DNA
Deoxyribose, 42, 54
Dependent variable, 14
Depolarization, 698–99
Depression, 701
Derived traits, 354, 422–23
Dermal bones, 738
Dermal denticles, 554
Dermatitis, contact, 642
Dermis, 597f, 598
Dermoptera, 566t
Descent, with modification, 8, 275
Desert(s), 840, 896
Desertification, 468
Deterministic chaos, 848
Detrital food chains/webs, 872f, 873
Detritivores, 870–71
Detritus, 873, 898, 900, 901
Deuteromycota, 408
Deuterostomes, 544–45
  characteristics, 526t
  echinoderms, 544–46
  embryonic development, 523
  evolution of, 544–45
  protostomes vs., 523f
Development
  animal. See Animal development
  animal development, 795–804
  biological evidence of, supporting evolution, 284–85
  cellular stages, 797–98
  community, 868–69
  defined, 508, 797
  of embryo. See Embryonic development
  human. See Human development
  of life, 5
  macroevolution and genes, 320–22
  of nervous system, 799, 800, 801f, 808–9
  seed and seed plant development, 42f, 421t, 430–39, 508–9
  sustainable, 920
Devonian period
  amphibians, 552, 556
  fishes, evolution of, 553–54
  geologic timescale, 336t
  mass extinction in, 343, 344
  placoderms, 553
  seed plants, 430
  vascular plants, 426
  vertebrates, 339
Dewlap, *Anolis* lizard, 314
DHT (dihydrotestosterone), 778
Diabetes insipidus, 757
Diabetes mellitus, 765–67
  insulin, 90
  symptoms of, 765
  type 1, 766–67
  type 2, 659, 767
  urinary glucose in, 686
Diabetic retinopathy, 724, 765
Diagnostic traits, 307
Diamond, 38f
Diaphragm (respiration), 669–71
Diapsid, 558
Diarrhea, 653
Diastole, 612, 615
Diatom(s)
  fossilized, 385t

  as photosynthetic organism, 120f
  supergroup chromalveolata, 385t, 386f, 390–91
Diatomaceous earth, 391
Dickinsonia, 338f
Dicots, 433. *See also* Eudicots
Dictyostelium discoideum, 627
Didelphis virtinianus, 565f
Didinium nasutum, 861
Diencephalon, 702f, 704, 705
Diet. *See also* Nutrition
  adaptation to, 648–49
  human health, 655, 659–60, 812
  obesity, 658, 659–60
Differential interference contrast microscopy, 64
Differential reproductive success, 278
Differentiation, cellular, 508, 588, 800–802
Diffusion, 89t, 91–92
Digestion
  of cellulose, 43, 646
  of food, 40
  of nutrients, 656–57
Digestive enzymes, 656–57
Digestive system, 646–62. *See also specific organs*
  accessory organs of, 654, 656
  adaptation to diet, 648–49
  aging process, 812
  complete, 531, 647–48
  components of, 647
  continuous feeders, 648
  defined, 647
  discontinuous feeders, 648
  diseases of, bacterial, 376t
  epithelium of, 589
  flatworms, 531
  functions of, 596
  homeostatic regulation, 599
  human, 650–57, 809f, 812
  nutrition and, 657–60
  incomplete, 531, 647
  review and exercises, 660–62
  as vertebrate characteristic, 552
  viral diseases of, 364t
  wall of, 651–52
Digestive tract
  accessory organs, 654–55
  adaptation to diet, 648–49
  complete, 531, 647–48
  human, 650f, 652–54
  incomplete, 531, 647
Digitalis, 514
Digitalis purpurea, 497
Digitoxin, 514
Digits, 742
Digoxin, 514
Dihybrid cross, 198–99, 200
Dihydrotestosterone (DHT), 778
Dihydroxyacetone, 40f
Dikaryotic hyphae, 406, 408f, 409
Dimorphism, 297, 298, 528
Dinoflagellate(s), 385t, 386f, 391f, 392–93
Dinoflagellate blooms, 392–93
Dinosaurs
  adaptive radiation among, 317
  evolution of, 327
  fossil footprint, 334f
  generally, 559
  mass extinction, 343–44
  in Mesozoic period, 340
  origin of, 559
Dioecious organisms, 773
Dioecious plants, 432, 503
Dionnaea, 461f
Diploblastic animals, 523, 526t, 528f
Diplococci, 374
Diploid (2n) number, 157, 172, 436f–437f
Diploid chromosomes, 157, 157t, 176, 796–97
Diplomonads, 385t, 386f, 395–96
Diplydium, 519
Dipodomys spectabilis, 896f
Direct selection, 834
Directional natural selection, 296–97
Dirofilaria immitis, 865f
Disaccharides, 42, 657
Discontinuous feeders, 648
Disease. *See also specific disorders*
  autoimmune, 642, 642f

bacterial, 376t
bacterial parasitic, 375–76
caused by protists, 383, 384, 393–400
copy number variations, 265, 266
defenses against. See Immunity
emerging, 369, 371f
fungal, 410–11
genetic. See Genetic disorders
hearing disorders, 728–30
immune system, 638, 640–43
inbreeding, 300–301
infectious. See Infections
liver, 654
mitochondrial, 77
Neglected Tropical Diseases (NTD), 383, 398–99, 519, 532
population density and, 848
protists causing, 383, 384
respiratory, 376t
sexually transmitted, 787–91
viral, 364, 364t, 365
Disruptive natural selection, 296f, 297
Distal convoluted tubule, 685f, 686, 687f
Distribution
biodiversity, 909
population, 840
Disulfide bonds, 52f
Diuresis, 688
Diversification, flowers, 437
Diversity. See also Biodiversity
ecosystem, 2, 909, 913
of flowers, 437
of fungi, 406–13
genetic, 908–9
landscape, 909
of leaves, 460, 461f
of life, 2
maintaining, and microevolution, 300–303
of plants, 420–39
of protists, 384–400, 385t, 386f
of roots, 452, 461f
of species, 858–59
of stems, 456, 457f, 458
"Diving response," 663
DNA (deoxyribonucleic acid), 214–36
analysis of, 256–57
apoptosis, 153f
barcoding, 350, 352–53
and cancer, 164
cell cycle, 154–55
Chargaff on base content of, 217–18
chimpanzees, 574
chloroplast, 337
chromosomal, 261–62
classification, 6, 358–59
cloning, 255–57
complementary DNA, 256
constancy within species, 217
damage and repair, 155, 156
defined, 54
double helix model, 54–55, 218–19
enhancer regions, 244
eukaryotic chromosome structure, 233–34
evolutionary hypotheses, 579
fingerprinting of, 257
Franklin's X-ray diffraction of, 217
functions of, 215
genetic code of life, 215–19, 223–24
genomic microarray technology, 264
Griffith's experiments, 215–17
hormone synthesis, 756
human, 574
hydrogen bonding, 28
integrity assessment, 156
"linker," 233
meiosis, 172–74
mitochondrial, 337, 359, 579, 583
molecular clock, 338
naming, 350, 352–53
nucleic acids, 54–55, 217f
in nucleus, 70
origin of, 330, 332
of prokaryotes, 65
recombinant, 255
repeated sequences, 214
replication, 220–22, 332
in reproduction, 5
review and exercises, 234–36
vs. RNA, 55t, 223

sequence alignment, 358f
structure of, 54–55, 217–19
transcription, 223, 225–27
transformed, 492
as transforming substance, 215–16
translation, 223f, 228–32
unique noncoding, 262–63
unpacking, 242–43
variability among species, 217
viral, 365, 366
wildlife conservation and, 889
X-ray diffraction of, 217
DNA chips, 263
DNA ligase, 221, 255
DNA microarrays, 264, 265
DNA polymerase, 220, 247, 256
DNA repair enzymes, 248
DNA replication, 220–22, 332
Dodders, 452, 472
Dog(s)
conditioning experiments in, 824
dentition of, 649
evolution of, 278
play behavior, 827
sense of smell, 717
territoriality in, 830
Dogfish, 918
Doldrums, 885
Dolichotis patagonium, 276, 283
Dolly (cloned sheep), 162, 259
Dolphins
auditory communication by, 828
bottle-nosed, 21
dentition of, 636
echolocation by, 717
habitat, 901
as keystone species, 918
tuna fishing and, 916
Domain (taxonomic), 7–8. See also
Archaea; Bacteria; Eukarya
classification of living things, 6, 6t
Linnean, 349, 350f
three-domain system, 351–54, 352t
Dominance
allele, 196, 197f, 290
codominance, 205
incomplete, Mendelian patterns of
inheritance, 205–6
Dominance hierarchies, 298, 833, 848
Dominant alleles, 196, 197f, 290
Donkey, 312, 313f, 314
Dopamine, 700, 812, 827
Dormancy
and abscisic acid (ABA), 488, 489t
of buds, 487, 488
of plants, 448, 488, 489t
of seeds, 448, 488, 510
Dorsal cavity, organs in, 596
Dorsal root ganglion, 707, 708f
Dorsal tubular nerve cord, 550, 551
Double covalent bonding, 27, 39
Double fertilization, 436f, 437, 504f, 505
Double helix model of DNA, 54–55, 218–19
Doubling time, 851
Down syndrome (trisomy 21), 184, 187
Drag net fishing, 916–18
Dragonfly
anatomy, 539f, 542f
fossil, 339f
habitat, 859
mechanical isolation, 312
modern, 339f
Drifting, of plasma membrane proteins, 87f
Drosera capensis, 472
Drosophila biarmipes, 279, 280f
Drosophila melanogaster
DNA nucleotide composition in, 217f
genomics, 264
immunity in, 627
as model organism, 800
morphogenesis in, 802–4
natural selection, 279, 280f
X-linked inheritance, 208–9
Drugs. See also Medicine; specific drug
abuse of, 706, 710–11, 789
aging process and, 812
anti-obesity, 655
birth defects caused by, 807
club, 710

date rape, 710
and neurotransmitters, 701
organisms producing, 910
predatory, 710
Drupe, 510f
Dry fruits, 511, 511t, 512
Dryocopus pileatus, 563f
Dryopithecines, 574–75, 576
DSCAM mRNA, 237
Duchenne muscular dystrophy, 210
Duck, 824
Duckbill platypus, 565f, 774
Ductus deferens, 775–76
Dugesia, 531
Dungeness crab, 848
Duodenum, 652
Duplication, chromosomal, 157, 187
Dutch elm disease, 410
Dwarfism, pituitary, 758, 759f
Dynein, 78, 81f
Dysentery
amebic, 396
bacterial, 376
Dystrophin, 210

E

E. coli. See Escherichia coli
E2F protein, 156
E_a (energy of activation), 109
Eagles, 562f, 563f, 841, 909f
Ear(s), 726–30, 741. See also Hearing
Eardrum, 726f, 727
Earlobes, 200, 726f
Early gastrula stage, 798
Earth. See also Biomes; Ecosystems
atmosphere origins, 329, 330
climate. See Climate
continental drift, 342–43
crust, 22, 22t, 342, 343
formation of, 328–29
history through fossils, 333–34
meteorite impact and mass extinction, 343–44
number of flowering plants on, 443
orbit and tilt of, 884
plate tectonics, 343
Earthquakes, 343
Earthworms
characteristics, 526t
circulatory system, 536–37, 607
as decomposers, in soil, 468
digestive tract, 536, 537f, 647–48
evolution of, 536–37
excretory system, 682
gas exchange, 665f
locomotion, 736
nervous system, 536, 537f, 694
reproduction, 773
segmented, fossil, 338f
Earwax, 49, 727
East African australopithecines, 577
Easterly winds, 883–84
Eastwood, Clint, 889
Eating, to maintain life, 4. See also
Digestion
Ebola hemorrhagic fever, 368, 369
Ecdysis, 539
Ecdysone, 752
Ecdysozoans, 538–43
arthropods, 539–43
characteristics, 526t
defined, 538
roundworms, 538–39
ECG (electrocardiogram), 613–14
Echinoderms, 544–46
characteristics, 526t
evolution of, 544–46
nutrition of, 649
reproduction, 773
skeleton of, 736–37
transport in, 606
Echinoidea, 544, 545f
Echolocation, 717, 826
ECM (extracellular matrix), 87, 99f
Ecological niche, 859–60
Ecological pyramids, 873
Ecological release, 316
Ecological succession, 868–69
Ecology
acid deposition, 33

behavioral. See Behavior
community. See Community
defined, 818, 839
ecosystem. See Ecosystems
population. See Population(s)
restoration, 920–21
scope of, 839
Ecosystems, 870–78. See also Biosphere
abiotic components of, 859
aquatic, 897–904
biological organization, 3f
biosphere diversity, 909
biotic components, 859, 870–71
chemical cycles in. See Chemical cycling
defined, 9, 839, 870
diversity, 2, 909, 913
dynamics, 870–71, 872f, 873–78
energy flow in, 9, 871–74, 902, 912
fungi as decomposer, 403
human impact on, 9–10
population in, 9. See also Community
review and exercises, 880–82
terrestrial, 887–996
theory of, 12
Ecotourism, 912–13
Ecovative design, 403
Ecstasy (drug), 710
ECT. See Electron transport chain (ETC)
Ectoderm, 523, 797–99, 798t, 808
Ectomycorrhizae, 415
Ectoparasites, 865
Ectopic pregnancy, 779
Ectothermy (ectotherms)
amphibians, 556
animals, 111f
dinosaurs, 340
fishes, 339, 553
reptiles, 558
EDB (ethylene dibromide), 248
Edema, 629
Edenspace, 471
Ediacaran fossils, 337, 338f
Edge effect, 919–20
Effectors, 708
Efferent (motor) neurons, 697f, 698
Egg(s)
amniotic, 553
fertilization of. See Fertilization
in plant reproduction, 436, 438
polarity in, 802
in sexual reproduction, 172, 773–74, 779, 796
shelled, 774, 797, 798, 805
Egg-laying hormone (ELH), 822
Ejaculation, 777–78
Ejaculatory ducts, 776, 777
El Niño-Southern Oscillation (ENSO), 904
Elastic cartilage, 591
Elastic fibers
in blood vessels, 608
in connective tissue, 589–90
in skin, 598
Elastin, 99f
Elbow joint, 742–43
Electrical charges, soil, 467
Electrocardiogram (ECG), 613–14
Electromagnetic energy, 716
Electromagnetic spectrum, 124
Electron(s)
in Bohr model of atom, 25
defined, 22
and energy, 25
in helium, 23f
Electron acceptors, 26
Electron donors, 26
Electron microscopes, 62, 63–64, 365
Electron model of water, 28f
Electron pathway, noncyclic, 124–25
Electron sharing, covalent bonds, 27
Electron shell, 22, 23f, 25
Electron transport chain (ETC)
cellular respiration, 137, 144–46
chemiosmosis, 146
defined, 14, 137
evolution of, 335–36
noncyclic electron pathway, 125–26
organelles and energy flow, 114, 144–45
photosynthesis vs. cellular
respiration, 148
structure and function of, 144, 145f
Electronegativity, 27

Elements, defined, 2, 22. *See also* Chemical elements
Elephant
emotions in, 807
as keystone species, 918
population growth, 845
trunk of, muscular hydrostat of, 736
Elephantiasis, 538f, 539
ELH (egg-laying hormone), 822
Elk, 299, 833
Elm, 859
Elodea, 122
Elongated tortoises, 916f
Elongation
DNA translation, 230f–231f, 231, 232f
mRNA transcription, 226
root zone of, 450, 451f
in translation, 230f–231f, 231
Embolus, 616
Embryo
defined, 797
development of. See Embryonic development
flowering plant, 436f
human, 782
shelled, nitrogenous wastes of, 681
somatic, 504
Embryo sac, flowering plant, 436, 504f, 505
Embryonic development
of animals, 522–23, 797–804
body plan, 524f
chicks, 797–99, 805
eudicots, 508–9
evolution of, 284
flowering plants, 504f, 505
human, 797–99, 805–10
lancelet, 797–99
mammals, 803–4
Embryonic disk, 808
Embryonic germ layers, 798, 808
Embryonic stem cells (ESC), 84, 162
Embryophytes, 421t, 422
Emergency contraception (morning-after pill), 783–84
Emergent properties, 2
Emerging virus and disease, 369, 371f
Emiquon floodplain restoration, 921
Emission phase, of ejaculation, 777
Emotions
in animals, 826, 827, 828
smell and, 719
Emphysema, 674f, 675
Encephalartos transvenosus, 432f
Encephalitis, toxoplasmic, 638
Endangered species, 908, 916
Endergonic reactions, metabolism as, 107
Endocardium, 610
Endocarp, of fruit, 510f, 511
Endochondral ossification, 738
Endocrine system, 752–71. *See also* Hormones; *specific gland or hormone*
aging process, 813
behavioral influence of, 821–22
functions of, 596, 752–53
glands of, 753, 754f
nervous system, interaction with, 753
Endocytosis, 91, 97–98
Endoderm, 523, 797–99, 798t, 808
Endodermal cells, plant transport, 469
Endodermis, 451, 469
Endolymph, 728, 729f
Endomembrane system, 67, 72–74
Endometrium, 779, 782, 808, 809, 810f
Endomycorrhizae, 415
Endoparasites, 865
Endoplasmic reticulum (ER)
defined, 67, 71
endomembrane system, 72, 74
prokaryotic vs. eukaryotic cells, 82t
rough, 68f–69f, 72, 74f
in skeletal muscle, 744–45
smooth, 68f–69f, 72, 74f
structure and function, 68f–69f, 72f
Endorphins, 701
Endoskeleton. *See also* Skeleton
defined, 737
of echinoderms, 544, 736–37
fish, 553
as vertebrate characteristic, 552, 736–37

Endosperm
double fertilization, 504f, 505
eudicot development, 508, 508f–509f
flowering plant reproduction, 437
of monocot seed, 509
Endospores, 376
Endosymbiosis, 384, 392
Endosymbiotic theory, 67, 335–36, 384
Endothelium, vascular, 608, 608f
Endotherms (endothermy)
animals, 111f, 340
birds, 563
dinosaurs, 340
Energy. *See also* Photosynthesis; Solar energy
acquisition of, 4
of activation (E_a), 109
in ADP and ATP, 56, 76
bulk transport, 95, 96f
chemical, 105
of chemical bonds, 26
conservation of, law of, 105
conversion of, 106
defined, 4, 105
electrons, 25
in fermentation, 140
forms of, 105, 107
from glucose, 42
in glucose metabolism, 146
kinetic, 105
laws of thermodynamics, 105–6
in muscular contraction, 746–47
organelles, 76–77, 113–14
photosynthesis vs. cellular respiration, 148
polysaccharides, 41, 42–44
production of, 104, 146
storage of, 46
transformations of, 107–8
Energy flow
cells and, 105–6
cycle of, 105f
in ecosystems, 9, 871–74, 902, 912
organelles, 113–14
photosynthesis vs. cellular respiration, 148
Energy of activation (E_a), 109
English ivy, 452, 461f
Enhancers, 244
Ensatina, 313–14, 313f
ENSO (El Niño-Southern Oscillation), 904
Entamoeba histolytica, 396
Entropy, 106
Envelope, viral, 365f, 366, 368
Environment. *See also* Ecosystems
behavioral influence, 822–26
human impact on, 9–10
and phenotype, 207
plant responses, 460, 483, 496–98
population growth and, 853
population polymorphism, 301–2
respiratory tract disorders, 673–74
responses to, 4–5, 460, 483, 496–98
Enzymatic proteins, 88f, 89
Enzymatic speed
cofactors, 112
factors affecting, 110–13
pH and, 111
substrate concentration, 110
temperature, 111
Enzyme(s). *See also specific enzyme*
action and degradation, 110f
active site, 110
coenzymes. See Coenzyme(s)
cofactors, 112
defined, 109
denatured, 111
digestive, 656–57
DNA repair, 248
energy of activation (E_a), 109
enzyme-substrate complex, 109–10
function of, 41
as globular proteins, 53
induced fit model of, 110
inhibition of, 112, 113f
and metabolic pathways, 109–13
metabolism, 49
"one gene–one enzyme hypothesis," 223
optimal pH for, 111
origin of, 330, 332

restriction, 255
speed of actions, 110–13
Enzyme cascade (signaling cascade), 755
Enzyme-substrate complex, 109–10
Eocene period, 296, 336t, 341
Eosinophils, 620, 632
Ephedra, 432f, 433
Ephedrine, 433
Ephemeroptera, 897f
Epicotyl, 508, 509f, 512f
Epidermal tissue, flowering plants, 447
Epidermis. *See also* Skin
anatomy, 597f
components, 598
of leaves, 459, 459f
plant, 447
of roots, 451
of stems, 453, 454f, 455f, 456, 462f
Epididymis (pl., epididymides), 775, 775t, 777
Epigenetic inheritance, 241
Epiglottis, 651, 668
Epilimnion, 898
Epinephrine, 613, 754f, 755–56, 762
Epipelagic zone, 901
Epiphysis (pineal gland), 702f, 704, 768
Epiphytes, 428, 865, 892
Episodic memory, 707
Epithelial tissue, 588–89. *See also* Skin
Epitheliomuscular cells, 529
Epithelium, 588–89
EPO (erythropoietin), 619, 688, 689, 768
Eponyms, 349
Equatorial regions, 884, 887
Equilibrium
gravitational, 728, 729f
rotational, 728, 729f
Equilibrium species, 849
Equisetum, 427–28
Equus, 296, 297f, 322–23
Equus quagga, 895f
ER. *See* Endoplasmic reticulum
Erectile dysfunction (ED), 778
Erection, penile, 777
Ergot, 411
Ergotism, 411
Erinaceomorpha, 566t
Erosion of soil, 468–69, 912
Erythrocytes. *See* Red blood cells
Erythromycin, 376–77
Erythropoietin (EPO), 619, 688, 689, 768
Erythroxylon coca, 710
ESC (embryonic stem cells), 84, 162
Escherichia coli
binary fission, 166
commensalism, 375
DNA research, 216, 217f
domain of, 7f
gene regulation in, 238–40
as heterotrophic, 353
in human intestine, 653
prokaryotic gene regulation, 238–40
recombinant DNA, 255
Eskimos, 581f, 583
Esophagus, 650f, 651–52
Esox lucius, 899f
An Essay on the Principle of Population (Malthus), 274
Essential amino acids, 148, 658–59
Essential nutrients, plants, 465–66
Estrogen(s)
functions of, 754f, 767–68, 782
in ovarian cycle, 780–81
postmenopausal replacement therapy, 738, 813
during pregnancy, 782, 809
secretion of, 45, 754f, 767, 779
as steroid, 46, 48
structure of, 48f
in uterine cycle, 781
Estuaries, 900, 913
ETC. *See* Electron transport chain (ETC)
Ethane, 40
Ethnic group evolution, 581, 583
Ethyl alcohol, 141
Ethylene
abscission promotion, 488, 489f, 489t
bud inhibition, 489
commercial uses, 489t
defined, 488
fruit ripening, 489

Ethylene dibromide (EDB), 248
Eucalyptus, 433
Euchromatin, 233f, 234, 242
Eudicots
defined, 433
embryonic development, 508–9
flowers of, 503
herbaceous vs. woody stem, 454
leaves of, 459f, 460
vs. monocots, 433t, 446, 510f
roots, 445f, 446, 450–52, 461f
seeds, 509, 509f, 512
stems of, 454–55
vascular bundle, 446
Eudicotyledones, 433. *See also* Eudicots
Eugenics, 786
Euglena, 120f, 384, 385t, 395
Euglena deses, 395
Euglenids, 385t, 386f, 395
Eukarya
characteristics of Animalia, 515
domain, 6t, 7, 421t
evolution of, 6f, 335f
three-domain system of classification, 351, 352t, 354
Tree of Life project, 282f
Eukaryotes
animal evolution, 520–26
cell division, 152–61, 167, 167t
chromosomes of, 157, 233–34
classification of, 351f, 354
defined, 7
diploid numbers of chromosomes, 157t
DNA and chromosomes in, 222, 233–34
fungi, 403–17
gene expression in, 233
genome structure, 261–62
mitosis, 157, 167, 167t
nutrition, 354
protein synthesis in, 233
protists, 383–402
ribosomes of, 229–30
RNA processing in, 226–27
supergroups, 384–400, 385t, 386f
Eukaryotic cells, 67–81
centrioles, 79–80
chloroplasts, 76–77
cilia, 80, 82t
cytoskeleton, 78–81
defined, 65
endomembrane system, 67, 72–74
endoplasmic reticulum, 72
energy-related organelles, 76–77
evolution of, 335, 337
flagella, 80, 81f
Golgi apparatus, 72–73
lysosomes of, 73
mitochondria, 77
nucleus of, 70–71
origin of, 67, 384
peroxisomes of, 75
plasma membrane, 85f
vs. prokaryotic cells, 82t
ribosomes of, 71
structure of, 67–68, 68f–69f
vacuoles of, 75–76
Eukaryotic regulation, 241–47
chromatin structure and control, 241–43
levels of control, 241
posttranscriptional control, 241, 244–46
posttranslational control, 241, 247
transcriptional control, 241, 244
translational control, 241, 246–47
Euphotic zone, 900f, 901
Euploidy, 183
Eustachian tube, 726f, 727
Eutrophic lakes, 898
Eutrophication, 877, 898, 915
Evaporation, 29, 875
Evening primrose *(Oenothera)*, 720f
Evergreen forests. *See* Coniferous forests
Evolution, 271–88. *See also* Macroevolution; Microevolution; *specific organisms*
artificial selection, 278, 278f
biocultural, 581, 582
biological, 328f
as biological unifying concept, 6–8
biomolecules, 328–32

chemical, 328f
continental drift, 342–43
convergent, 357, 720
copy number variations, 266
criticism of, 285–86
defined, 5, 272
evidence supporting, 280–85
  anatomical, 283–84
  biochemical, 284, 285f
  biogeographical, 283
  biomolecular, 282
  developmental biological, 284–85
  fossil, 280–81
geological factors that influence
  evolution, 342–44
gradualistic model of, 319, 320f
history of evolutionary thought, 272–74
immune systems, 627–28
invertebrates, 519–48
law of, 12
of mammals, 340–43, 564–65, 566t
monomers, 328, 329–30
mosaic, 577
natural selection, 8, 277–80, 285–86
population genetics definition, 290
in populations. See Microevolution
principle of, 12
punctuated equilibrium model, 319–20
review and exercises, 286–88
self-replication system, 328, 332
taxonomic organization, 6–8
theory of, 275–80
  adaptation, 278
  biogeographical observation, 275–77
  change over time, observation of, 275
  early-nineteenth century
    contributions to, 272–74
  evidence supporting, 280–85
  evolutionary hypotheses, 579–80
  history of evolutionary thought,
    272–74
  late-eighteenth century contributions
    to, 272–73
  mid-eighteenth century contributions
    to, 272
  natural selection, 277–80
  and scientific method, 12
vertebrates, 549–69
Evolutionary species concept, 307–8
Evolutionary tree, 6. *See also* Phylogeny
Ex vivo gene therapy, 260
Excavata, 385t, 386f, 395–96
defined, 395
diplomonads, 385t, 386f, 395–96
euglenids, 385t, 386f, 395
kinetoplastids, 385t, 386f, 396
parabasalids, 385t, 386f, 395
Excavates, 395
Exchange pool, 874–75
Excitatory signals, 701
Excretion, 681
Excretory system, 680–92
aging process, 812
animals, 681–84
exercises and review, 691–92
flatworms, 531
human, 684–90, 812
insect, 542
invertebrates, 681–82
nitrogenous waste, 681
osmoregulation, 680–90, 757, 758f, 763
review and exercises, 691–92
Exercise
diabetes prevention, 659
lactate metabolism during, 747
Exergonic reactions, metabolism as, 107
Exhalation. *See* Expiration
Exocarp, 510f, 511
Exocoetus volitans, 555f
Exocrine glands, 589, 654, 753
Exocytosis, 73, 74, 91, 95, 96f
Exons
alternative mRNA splicing, 246
defined, 226
genomes sequencing, 261f
mRNA processing, 226
posttranscriptional control, 244
shuffling, 227
Exophthalmos, 760f, 761
Exoskeleton
of arthropods, 539–40, 539f

of crustaceans, 540
defined, 736
evolution of, 338
molting, 736, 737f
Exotic species, 838, 861, 909, 913–15
Experiment(s)
field, 14, 15–16
scientific method, 11–12, 14–15
Experimental design, 11–12
Experimental variable, 12, 14–15
Expiration, respiratory, 669–70
Exponential growth, 844
Expulsion phase, of ejaculation, 778
Extant species, 272
Extensor digitorum longus muscle, 744f
External auditory canal, 741f
External fertilization, 773
External oblique muscle, 744f
External respiration, 671, 672
Extinction
causes of, 913–18
climate change, 915–16
continental drift and, 868
conversation biology and, 908
defined, 10, 338
exotic species, 913–15
fossil record, 272
habitat loss, 913
human population growth and, 853
island biogeography and, 862
mass. See Mass extinctions
overexploitation, 916–18
phylogenetic tree, 309
pollution, 915
rate of, 908
speciation, 307
in tropical rain forests, 893
Extracellular matrix (ECM), 87, 99f
Extraembryonic membranes, 774, 805,
  808–9, 810f
Eye(s). *See also* Vision
animals, 720–21
arthropods, 539f, 540
camera-type, 720–21
color of, as inherited trait, 207, 208–9
compound, 539f, 540, 720
human, 721–25
  aging process, 812
  anatomy, 721f
  disorders of, 724–25
  focusing, 722, 724
  photoreceptors, 722–23
  visual signal integration, 723
Pax6 gene and formation of, 320–21
simple, 543
Eyespots
Chlamydomonas, 387
euglenids, 395
false, 864
invertebrates, 720
planarian, 531f, 532, 694
sea star, 544
Eyestalks, of crayfish, 541
Eyestrain, 722

F

F_1 generation, Mendel's experiments,
  195–96, 198f
F_2 generation, Mendel's experiments,
  195–96, 197f, 198f
F_2 generation fitness, 311f
Facial bones, 740–41
Facilitated transport, 89t, 94
Facilitation model of succession, 868
Facultative anaerobes, 374
FAD (flavin adenine dinucleotide),
  136–37, 143, 660
FADH2, 143, 144
Fairy ring, mushrooms, 413
Fall overturn, 898–99
Fallopian tubes (oviducts), 589, 779, 806f
False ribs, 741
Familial hypercholesterolemia, 98,
  205, 260
Family (taxonomic). *See also specific*
  family
classification of living things, 6, 6t
Linnean, 349, 350f
Family pedigree, 204
FAP (fixed action patterns), 822–23

Far-red light, phytochrome conversion
  cycle, 495
Farsightedness, 724
FAS (fetal alcohol syndrome), 807
"Fast block," 797
Fat. *See also* Lipids
defined, 46
dietary, 654, 658
digestion, 652, 654, 656, 657f
functions of, 45t
metabolism of, 147
molecule structure, 47f
polyps growth, 654
Fate maps, 802, 804
Fatty acids
defined, 46
essential, 658
lipids, 46, 47f
omega-3, 617, 659
saturated, 46, 47f, 658, 659
synthesis, 129
unsaturated, 46, 47f, 658
Feather(s), 562, 562f, 597
Feather stars, 544
Feces, 653
Feedback mechanisms
negative. See Negative feedback
positive, 601, 757, 781, 916
Feeders, continuous *vs.* discontinuous,
  648
Feeding behavior. *See also* Carnivores;
  Herbivores; Omnivores;
  Predation
foraging, 830–31
grazing, 649, 872f, 873, 895
niche specialization, 860
omnivores, 649, 870, 871–74
snakes, 821
vegetarian, 658–59
Fellatio, 789
Female(s)
choice, as female mating behavior,
  297–98
human
  hormonal regulation in, 767–68,
    780–81
  infertility, 784–85
  orgasm, 780
  reproductive system of, 779–83,
    779t, 813. See also Pregnancy
  secondary sex characteristics,
    767, 782
inactive X chromosome, 243
mating behaviors, 297–98, 831–33
Female condoms, 784f
Female gametophyte, flowering plants,
  504–5
Femur, 740f, 742, 743f
Fermentation
advantages and disadvantages, 140
cellular respiration, 140–41
defined, 137
efficiency, 140
food production, 141
muscles, 747
yeast, 410
Fern(s)
carboniferous forests, 435
characteristics, 421t
described, 428
dominant generation in, 422
evolutionary history of plants, 420f
gametophytes vs. sporophyte size, 423f
life history strategy of, 849
reproduction, 428, 429f
uses of, 429
whisk ferns, 427
Fertilization. *See also* Reproduction
defined, 175, 778
double, 436f, 437, 504f, 505
external, 773
in flowering plants, 436–37, 502
in humans, 182f, 779–80, 782,
  796–97, 806
internal, 774
isolating mechanism, 311f, 312
in mammals, 796
in mosses, 425t
oogenesis, 181–82
self-fertilization, 773

Fertilization membrane, 797
Fertilizers, pollution from, 14–15, 877,
  878, 915
Fetal alcohol syndrome (FAS), 807
Fetal development, 805, 810
Fever, 631
Fiber, dietary, 657–58
Fibers
nerve, 697
postganglionic, 709, 712f
preganglionic, 709, 712f
schlerenchyma cells, 449
skeletal muscle, 744–45
Fibrillin, 206
Fibrin, 620
Fibrinogen, 620
Fibrinolysin, 782
Fibroblasts, 590
Fibrocartilage, 591, 741
Fibronectin, 99f
Fibrous connective tissue, 590, 608
Fibrous joints, 742–43
Fibrous proteins, 51, 53f
Fibrous root system, 452, 461f
Fibula, 740f, 742, 743f
Fiddlehead, 429
Field study, 15–16
Fight or flight reaction, 713, 762–63
Filament(s)
actin. See Actin filaments
cell structure and function, 68f–69f
defined, 388
of flower, 434f, 502f, 503
intermediate, 68f, 78, 79f
myosin. See Myosin
of Spirogyra, 388, 389f
Filamentous algae, 388
Filarial worms, 526t, 538f, 539
Filiariasis, 539
Filopodia, 400
Filter feeders
digestive system, 648–49
molluscs, 535
in oceans, 901
sponges, 527
Fimbriae (sing., fimbria)
bacterial, 66, 372, 373f, 376
human, 779, 806f
Fin whale, 889
Finch(es)
adaptive radiation among, 316
beak size, 273f, 276–77, 279–80,
  302, 860
genetic basis of beak shape, 318–19
niche specialization, 859–60
sexual selection in, 831
Fingerprinting DNA, 257
Fins, 553, 554
Fire, Andrew, 246
Firefly, 312, 828, 829f
First messenger, 755
Fish, 553–55. *See also specific type of fish*
Age of, 339
bony. See Bony fishes
cartilaginous, 526t, 554, 682
characteristics, 526t, 553
chemoreceptors, 718
circulatory system, 553–54, 608, 609f
defined, 553
evolution of, 339, 552–56, 557f
eyes, 720
freshwater, 899
gas exchange, 664, 665f, 666
gills. See Gill(s)
human consumption of, 901, 911
illegal trade of, 916
jawed, 339, 526t, 552, 553–55
jawless, 339, 526t, 552, 553
lateral line system, 726
lobe-finned, 555, 556, 557f
marine, 901–2
mercury contamination in, 903
nervous system, 554
osmoregulation, 680, 682–83
reproduction, 773
sex reversal, 773
symbiosis, 865–66
vision, 720
Fish kills, 392–93, 878, 915
Fish odor syndrome, 192
Fishapod, 271, 280, 281f, 285

Fishing, 911, 916–18
Fitness
 behaviors that increase, 830–34
 natural selection, 297
 reproductive success, 278
Five-kingdom system of classification, 351
Fixation
 carbon dioxide, 128–31
 nitrogen, 375, 878
Fixed action patterns (FAP), 822–23
Flagella (sing., flagellum)
 bacterial, 66
 chytrids, 407
 defined, 80
 eukaryotic, 81f, 82t
 evolution of, 337
 excavata, 395
 opisthokonta, 397
 prokaryotic, 82t, 372, 373f
 sperm, 777, 797
 sponges, 527
 stramenopiles, 391, 392
 structure, 81
Flagellates, colonial hypothesis, 520
Flagship species, 918
Flame cells, 682
Flamingo tongue shell, 536f
Flat feet, 742
Flatworms, 531–43. See also Planarians
 characteristics, 526t
 digestive tract, 531, 647
 flukes, 532–43
 free-living, 531–32
 hydrostatic skeleton, 736
 nervous system, 531, 694
 parasitic, 532–34
 planaria, 531–32
 reproduction, 773
 tapeworm. See Tapeworm
 transport in, 606
Flavin adenine dinucleotide (FAD),
 136–37, 143, 660
Flax fibers, 449
Flemming, Alexander, 11
Fleshy fruits, 510f, 511t, 512
Flexor carpi muscles, 744f
Flies. See Fruit flies
Flight, bird, 562–63
Floating ribs, 741
Flores island, 579
Florida panther, 849
Florida scrub jay, 834
Flounder, 863, 864f
Flower(s)
 anatomy and structure of, 502–3
 artificial color, 464
 characteristics, 433–34
 composite, 434t
 defined, 433, 502
 diversification, 437
 evolution of, 420f, 502, 518–19
 flowering and photoperiodism, 495–96
 monocots vs. eudicots, 446f
 pollination, 437
 structure and function, 433–34, 502–3
Flower fly, 864f
Flowering plant(s). See also Plant(s);
  specific type of plant
 ancestral, 357
 angiosperms. See Angiosperms
 animal-pollinated, 505
 bat-pollinated, 507, 911f
 bee-pollinated, 437, 506–7, 911
 bird-pollinated, 437, 505, 507
 butterfly-pollinated, 506–7, 867
 characteristics, 421t
 circadian rhythm in, 478
 dicot. See Dicots
 eudicot. See Eudicots
 evolution of, 341, 420
 female gametophyte, 504–5
 fertilization of, 502
 flowers of, 433–34
 gametophytes, 436f, 502, 504–5
 genome of, 263t
 growth response controls, 483–500
 inorganic nutrients, essential, 466t
 insect-pollinated, 437, 505–7
 life cycle of, 502
 male gametophyte, 504–5
 mineral uptake in, 469–72

 minerals, 465, 466t
 mitosis, 161
 monocot. See Monocots
 moth-pollinated, 506–7
 number, on Earth, 443
 nutrition, 465–66, 478–79
 organs of, 444–45, 446f
 origin and radiation of, 433–34
 photosynthesis in, 121
 reproduction, 501–17
 review and exercises, 461–63, 480–82,
  498–500, 515–17
 soil, 466–69
 stomata opening and closing, 477–78
 structure and organization, 443–63.
  See also Additional details at
  specific topic
 transport mechanisms, 469, 472–79
 water potential, 474
 water transport, 469, 475–77
 wind-pollinated, 505
Flowering plant reproduction, 501–17
 asexual reproductive strategies, 513–14
 cross-pollination, 505–7
 flowers, 502–12
 fruit types, 510f, 511, 511t, 512f
 gametophyte, 436f, 502, 504–5
 life cycle, 502, 504–7
 pollinators, 501, 506–7
 review and exercises, 515–17
 seed and seed plant development, 42f,
  421t, 430–39, 508–9
 seed dispersal, 511
 sexual reproduction, 502–7
 structure and function, 436–37
 survival mechanism, 448
Flowering plant structure and
  organization, 443–63. See also
  Additional details at specific topic
 leaves, 445, 446, 459–60
 monocot vs. eudicot, 446
 organs, 444–46
 review and exercises, 461–63
 roots, 444, 445f, 446, 450–52, 453f
 stems, 445, 446, 453–56, 457f, 458
 tissues, 446, 447–50
Flu. See Influenza
Flu shot, 366
Fluid connective tissue, 591–92
Fluid-mosaic model, plasma membrane,
 87–88
Flukes, 526t, 532–43, 907
Fluoxetine (Prozac), 701
Fly agaric, 411
Flycatchers, 310, 314
Focus, eye, 722, 724
Folic acid, 807
Foliose lichens, 414
Follicles, ovarian, 780
Follicle-stimulating hormone (FSH)
 in males, 778
 in ovarian cycle, 780–81, 782t
 secretion of, 754f, 758f, 767
Follicular phase, of ovarian cycle,
 780–81, 782t
Fontanels, 740
Food
 bamboo for, 458
 biomolecules in, 40t
 competition for, 847
 digestion of, 40
 fermentation, 140–41
 foraging for, 830–31
 preferences, 821
Food chains, 9, 383, 873
Food poisoning, 376
Food supply, 134, 438–39
Food vacuoles, 393, 396
Food webs, 9, 872f, 873
Foot
 human, 740f, 742
 mollusc, 534, 535
Foraging, food, 830–31
Foramen magnum, 740
Foraminiferans, 385t, 386f, 398–99
Forebrain, 695, 696
Forelimbs, vertebrate, evolution of,
 283, 737
Forensic phylogeny, 347
Forensics, in wildlife conservation, 889

Foreskin, 777
Forest(s). See also Tree(s)
 acid deposition, 33
 boreal, 890
 in carbon cycle, 876
 of Carboniferous period, 339
 climate regulation by, 912
 coniferous. See Coniferous forests
 destruction of. See Deforestation
 ecological succession, 868–69
 species composition, 858–59
 sponge effect of, 912
 temperate, 884, 887, 890–91
 tropical. See Tropical rain forests
Forest floor, 890, 892, 893
Fork stalling, 266
Formed elements, of blood, 618–19
Formula, for molecules, 26
FosB gene, 822
Fossil(s)
 absolute dating of, 334
 of angiosperms, 433
 in Burgess Shale, 338f
 continental drift, 332
 Cooksonia, 426f
 Darwin's observations, 275
 dating, 334
 defined, 280, 333
 of diatoms, 385t
 and Earth history, 333–34
 Ediacaran, 337, 338f
 evolutionary evidence, 280–81
 evolutionary hypotheses, 579–80
 of fungi, 405
 generally, 333–34
 from Mars, 330
 Precambrian, 337f
 of prokaryotes, 372
 relative dating of, 334
 of rhizarians, 399
 sources of, 333
 transitional, 280–81, 285
Fossil fuels, 435, 876
Fossil record
 of bryophytes, 423
 extinctions, 272–73
 macroevolution, 333–34
 morphological species concept, 307
 phylogeny, 356–57
 punctuated equilibrium models of
  macroevolution, 319
 transitional fossils, 280–81, 285
Founder effect, 295
Four-o'clock flowers, 205
Fourth ventricle, 702f
Fovea centralis, 721, 723
Fox, 888, 896f
Fox, George, 378
Fox, Sidney, 330
Foxglove, 497
Fragaria, 513f
Frameshift mutations, 248
Franklin, Rosalind, 217
Free energy, 107
Free nerve endings, 597f
Free radicals, 814
Free-living flatworms, 531–32
Freeze-fracture, of plasma membranes, 87
Freezing temperature of water, 29
"French paradox," 617
Freon, 915
Fresh water
 ecosystems, 897–904, 912
 green algae, in land plant evolution,
  420–22, 423f
 osmoregulation in fish, 683
 sources of, 912
Frogs
 characteristics, 526t, 557
 courtship behavior, 307, 308f
 deformed, 907
 development of, 520f, 521,
  797–800, 801f
 gastric-brooding, 2
 harlequin, 407
 leopard, 307, 308f
 life history patterns, 848
 metamorphosis of, 520f, 521, 755
 microfrog macroevolution, 306
 prey defenses of, 864f
 temporal isolation, 312

Fronds, ferns, 428, 429f
Frontal bone, 740–41
Frontal cortex, human, 696
Frontal lobe, 703–4, 708f
Frontalis muscle, 744f
Fructose, 657
Fruit
 aggregate, 510f
 auxins, 485
 classification of, 511, 511t
 defined, 437, 511
 dehiscent, 510f
 development of, 434
 dispersal of, 511
 dry, 510f
 fleshy, 510f
 flowering plant reproduction, 436f,
  502, 510f, 511–12, 511t
 human consumption of, 911
 indehiscent, 510f
 multiple, 510f
 plant diversification, 437
 ripening, 488–89
 ripening and ethylene, 489
 types of, 511t, 512
 waxy coating on, 47, 48f
Fruit flies. See also Drosophila
  melanogaster
 body plan evolution, 524–25
 embryonic development, 524f, 802–4
 eyes and vision, 720
 genome of, 263t
 immunity in, 627
 as model organism, 800
Fruiting body, 397, 409
Fruticose lichens, 414
FSH. See Follicle-stimulating hormone
 (FSH)
Fucoxanthin, 391f
Fucus, 390
Fugate family of Troublesome Creek, 202
Functional genomics, 263
Functional groups, organic molecules,
 39–40, 39t
Fundamental niche, 859
"Fungal flu," 412
Fungi (sing., fungus), 403–17. See also
  Mycorrhizae
 vs. animals, 520
 asexual reproduction, 406, 408–9
 cell division in, 167, 167t
 characteristics, 404
 classification of, 351f, 354
 as decomposers, in soil, 468, 871
 defined, 8, 404
 diploid chromosome numbers, 157t
 diversity of, 406–13
 DNA nucleotide composition in, 217f
 energy acquisition by, 4f
 evolution of, 335f, 404–5
 evolutionary tree, 6f
 fungal, 410–11
 as kingdom, 8
 mutualism, 866
 organization of life, 2
 parasitic, 496, 497f, 865
 phyla
  Ascomycota (sac fungi), 404f, 406t,
   408–10, 412
  Basidiomycota (club fungi), 404f,
   406t, 412–13
  Chytridomycota (chytrids), 404f,
   406t–7, 406t
  Glomeromycota (AM fungi), 404f,
   406t, 408
  Zygomycota (zoospore fungi), 404f,
   406t, 407–8
 poisonous, 411
 protist, 385t
 reproduction, 405–9, 406t, 412–13
 review and exercises, 415–17
 spores, 406, 407, 408, 409, 412–13
 structure of, 405
 symbiotic relationships, 408, 414–15
Fungicides, 412
Fusiform bacteria, 374

G

G. See Guanine (G)
G_0 checkpoint, interphase, 154, 156

G_1 checkpoint, interphase, 154, 155, 156
G_2 checkpoint, interphase, 154, 155
G3P
    in Calvin cycle, 128f, 129
    in glycolysis, 138, 139f
GA3 (gibberellic acid), 486
Galápagos finches
    adaptive radiation among, 316
    beak size, 273f, 276–77, 279–80, 302, 860
    genetic basis of beak shape, 318–19
    niche specialization, 859–60
Galápagos Islands, 273f, 276–77, 915
Galápagos tortoises, 276
Gallbladder, 650f, 654, 656
Gallstones, 656
Gametangium (pl. gametangia), 407f, 408
Gamete(s)
    defined, 172, 785
    formation of, 176, 180
    isolation of, 311f, 312
    meiosis, 172–74
    production of, 182, 773
Gamete intrafallopian transfer (GIFT), 768, 785
Gametocytes, of Plasmodium, 394f
Gametophytes
    bryophytes, 424
    conifers (pine), 431f
    defined, 422
    ferns, 429f
    flowering plants, 436f, 502, 504–5
    mosses, 424, 425t
    plants, 180
    pollen grain as, 430
    size of, 423f
Gamma-hydroxybutyric acid, 710
Ganglion (pl. ganglia), 694, 707, 708f
Ganglion cells, eye, 723
Gap genes, 524, 802–3
Gap junctions
    cardiac muscle, 593, 611
    between cells, 100
    defined, 588
Gardasil, 788
Garden pea
    cross-pollination, 193–94
    gene flow through cross-pollination, 294f
    Mendel's cross-pollination experiments, 193–201
    structure of, 194f
    tendrils, 460
Gardnerella vaginalis, 790–91
Garrod, Archibald, 223
Garter snakes, 821
Gas exchange. See also Respiration
    artificial lung, 676
    respiration, 596, 664–70, 671f
        birds, 670f
        fish, 608, 609f, 664–66
        humans, 92, 668f, 669–70, 671f
    surfaces for, 664–68
    through skin, 597, 607
    and transport, 671–72
Gaseous cycles, 874
Gastric ceca, insects, 542
Gastric glands, 652
Gastric juice, 652
Gastric mill, crayfish, 541
Gastric pits, 652
Gastric ulcers, 652
Gastric-brooding frogs, 2
Gastrocnemius muscle, 743f, 744f
Gastrointestinal tract. See Digestive system
Gastropods, 535–36
Gastrovascular cavity, 528, 529f, 736
Gastrula, 798
Gastrulation, 798, 800
Gause, G. F., 859, 861
Geckos, 561
Gehring, Walter, 320
Geiger counter, 24
Gel electrophoresis, 257
Geldsetzer, Helmont, 344
Gelidium, 389
Gemma cups, 424
Gemmae, 424
Gene(s). See also DNA (deoxyribonucleic acid); specific gene
    body plan evolution in animals, 521, 522f, 524–25

cloning, 255. See also Cloning
    cystic fibrosis, 675
    defined, 5, 261, 263
    developmental, and macroevolution, 320–22
    eukaryotic, structure of, 261–62
    expression and regulation, 237–53
    homeotic, 528, 803–4
    homologous, 265
    microevolution, 290–95
    molecular biology of, 214–36. See also DNA
    mutations, 247. See also Mutation
    in nucleus, 70
    protein-first hypothesis, 330
    regulator, 238, 239, 240
    RNA-first hypothesis, 330, 332
    segment-polarity, 803
    in sexual reproduction, 171
    structural, 238, 239–40
    tumor-suppressor, 153, 164, 165f, 249
    X-linked, 208
Gene expression and regulation, 237–53
    eukaryotic, 233, 241–47
    Galápagos finch beak shape, 318–19
    mutations, 247–50
    prokaryotic, 238–40
    review and exercises, 250–53
Gene flow, 294, 310
Gene locus, 196
Gene migration (flow), 294, 310
Gene pharming, 258–59
Gene pool, 290, 291f, 292, 292t
Gene theory, 12
Gene therapy, 203, 255, 260, 725
Generalist species, 859
Generations, alternation of, 176, 388, 407, 422
Genetic(s). See also Inheritance
    aging process and, 813
    behavioral influence, 820–22
    and environment, 207–8, 301–2
    inclusive fitness and, 834
    laws of probability, 200, 201f
    population polymorphism, 301–2
    study of Arabidopsis thaliana, 402, 491, 495
    variation in, 174–75, 277. See also Mutation
    wildlife conservation and, 889
    X-linked, 208–10
Genetic code
    defined, 224
    DNA as, 223–24
    evolution, 332
    finding, 224
    immunity, 627–28
    universal features, 224
Genetic disorders
    autoimmune, 642
    autosomal inheritance patterns, 201–4
    cancer, 165f
    generally, 192
    genetic profile, 263–64
    hearing loss, 730
    human, 201–4, 208–10, 263–64
    immunodeficiency, 641
    preimplantation diagnosis of, 786
    testing for, 204, 807
    X-linked, in humans, 208–10
Genetic diversity, 908–9
Genetic drift, 294–95, 307, 309f
Genetic engineering, 372, 439
Genetic profile, 263–64
Genetic recombination, 174–75
Genetic testing, 204, 807
Genetically modified animals, 258–59
Genetically modified bacteria, 258
Genetically modified organisms (GMOs), 216, 254, 258–59
Genetically modified plants, 254, 258, 419
Genital herpes, 788–90
Genital warts, 788
Genome
    chimpanzees, 574
    comparisons of, 263, 264–65
    humans, 570, 574
    sequencing of, 261, 263t
    size of, in Arabidopsis thaliana, 492
    virus, 365, 366
Genome chips, 263

Genome sequencing, 261, 264
Genomic imprinting, 243
Genomic microarrays, 264
Genomics, 261–66
    bioinformatics, 265
    comparative, 263–65
    copy number variations (CNVs), 266
    defined, 261
    definitions of genes, 263
    DNA microarray technology, 264
    functional, 263
    genome sequencing, 261, 264
    intergenic sequences, 262
    proteomics, 265
    repetitive DNA elements, 262
    structure of eukaryotic genome, 261–62
    transposons, 262
    unique noncoding DNA, 262–63
Genotype
    defined, 196
    frequencies of, and microevolution, 290, 291–95, 292t, 300
    vs. phenotype, 196–97
Genus (taxonomic). See also specific genus
    classification of living things, 6, 6t
    Linnean, 349, 350f
Geococcyx californianus, 896f
Geographic isolation, 313–14, 316
Geographic speciation, 313–14
Geographic timescale, 334–35, 336t. See also specific time periods
Geology. See also Fossil(s)
    continental drift, 342–43
    evolutionary theory, 274, 275
    factors that influence evolution, 342–44
    mass extinctions, 343–44
    plate tectonics, 343
Geometric ratio of increase, 277
Geospiza fortis, 279
Geospiza magnirostris, 279f, 318, 319
Germ cells, 773
Germ layers, embryonic, 522, 798, 798t, 808
    ectoderm, 523, 797–99, 798t, 808
    endoderm, 523, 797–99, 798t, 808
    mesoderm, 523, 798–99, 798t, 808–9
German measles (rubella), 730, 807
Germination, seeds, 488, 502, 512
Gerontology, 813
Gerris, 902f
Gerstein, Mark, 263
Gestation. See Pregnancy
GFP (green fluorescent protein), 216, 594
GH growth hormone, 738, 754f, 758–59, 813
Ghost crabs, 901
Ghost shrimp, 901
Giant ground sloth (extinct), 269
Giantism, 759
Giardia lamblia, 60, 395–96
Gibberella fujikuroi, 486
Gibberellic acid (GA3), 486
Gibberellins, 486–87, 489t
Gibbons
    classification, 571f, 572
    evolution of, 573f
    locomotion, 575
    reproductive strategies, 830, 831
    territoriality, 830
GIFT (gamete intrafallopian transfer), 768, 785
Gila monsters, 561
Gill(s)
    anatomy of, 666f
    bony fishes, 554
    cartilaginous fishes, 554
    chordates, 540–51
    crayfish, 540, 541
    defined, 550
    fishes, 553
    gas exchange in, 608, 609f, 664–66, 665f
    lancelets, 550
    mushroom, 413
    nitrogenous waste removal by, 682
Gill arches, 550, 553
Gill slits, 550, 551

Ginkgo biloba, 432
Ginkgoes, 421t, 430, 432
Giomerales, 406t

Giraffa camelopardalis, 310, 311f
Giraffa tippelskirchi, 311f
Giraffe
    habitat, 895f
    neck length, 274
    species concept, 308, 310, 311f
Girdling of trees, 456, 478
Gizzard, earthworm, 647
Gladiolus corms, 458
Glands. See also specific gland
    defined, 589
    endocrine, 753, 754f. See also Endocrine system
    exocrine, 589, 654, 753
Glandular epithelium, 589
Glans clitoris, 779f, 780
Glans penis, 777
Glaucoma, 724
Glial cell-derived growth factor, 593
Glial cells (neuroglia), 697–98
Global warming, 877, 879. See also Climate change
Globigerina, 400f
Globin, 592
Globular proteins, 52–53
Globular stage of eudicot embryonic development, 508, 509f
Gloeocapsa, 377f
Glomeromycota, 404f, 406t, 408
Glomerular capsule, 685, 685f, 687f
Glomerular filtrate, 686
Glomerular filtration, 686, 687f
Glomerulus, 685f, 686, 687f
Glossina, 396, 398–99
Glossopteris, 342
Glottis, 651, 668
Glucagon, 654, 754f, 765
Glucocorticoids, 754f, 762f, 763–64
Glucose
    blood levels of, 654, 765, 766
    breakdown of. See Glycolysis
    as carbohydrate, 657
    in cellular respiration, 136
    defined, 42
    digestion and absorption of, 656
    in fermentation, 140
    metabolism of, energy yield from, 146
    photosynthesis, 122
    renal metabolism of, 686
    storage in plants and animals, 657
    structure of, 42f
Glucose phosphate, Calvin cycle, 129
Glutamic acid, 51f
Glutamine, 51f
Glyceraldehyde, 40f
Glycerol, 46, 47f, 129, 654
Glycocalyx, 65, 66f, 88
Glycocalyx, 372
Glycogen
    defined, 43
    digestion, 654
    energy production from, 755, 756f
    fungal energy storage, 405
    storage in liver, 657, 753f, 765
    structure and function, 43f
Glycolipids, 88
Glycolysis
    cellular respiration, 137, 138–39
    defined, 137, 138
    diagram, 139f
    energy-harvesting steps of, 138, 139f
    energy-investment steps of, 138, 139f
    fermentation, 140
    protocell evolution, 332
Glycoproteins, 88
Glycosides, 497
Glyptodon (extinct), 275
GMOs (genetically modified organisms), 216, 254, 258–59
Gnathostomes, 553
Gnetophytes, 421t, 430, 432–33
Gnetum, 432–33
GnRH (gonadotropin-releasing hormone), 767, 778, 781
Goal-orientation, and macroevolution, 322–23
Goblet cells, 589
Goddard, Ken, 889
Goiter, 760
Golden brown algae, 385t, 386f, 390, 391
Golgi, Camillo, 72

Golgi apparatus
  cytokinesis, 161
  endomembrane system, 74
  eukaryotic cells, 67, 82t
  prokaryotic cells, 82t
  structure and function, 68f–69f, 72–73
Golgi tendon organs, 730, 731f, 744
Gonad(s), 773
  human. See Ovaries; Testes
Gonadotropic hormones, 754f, 757, 758f, 767-68. *See also specific hormone*
Gonadotropin-releasing hormone (GnRH), 767, 778, 781
Gondwana, 342, 344
Gonorrhea, 790, 791f
Gonyaulax, 391f
Good genes hypothesis, female choice, 297
Goose, Canada, 883
Gooseneck barnacles, 540f
Gore, Al, 125f
Gorillas, 572, 573f
Gorlin syndrome, 246
Graafian (vesicular) follicle, 780
Gracilaria, 389
Gracilis muscle, 744f
Gradualist models of macroevolution, 318–19, 320f
Grain(s)
  as dry fruits, 511, 512
  refinement of, 658
  world supply of, 134
Gram, Hans Christian, 374
Gram-negative bacteria, 374, 376, 377
Gram-positive bacteria, 374
Granite mosses, 424
Grant, Peter and Rosemary, 279
Granular leukocytes, 620
Granum (pl., grana), 69f, 76, 121
Granzymes, 636
Grapsus grapsus, 540f
Grass(es), 452, 458, 461f
Grasshoppers
  circulatory system of, 606, 607f
  female anatomy, 543f
  nutrition of, 649
  tracheal system of, 667f
  as typical insect, 542–43
Grasslands, 9, 894–95
Graves disease, 761
Gravitational equilibrium, 728, 729f
Gravitropism
  auxins, 485–86
  defined, 490
  tropisms, 490f, 491
Gray crescent, 800, 801f
Gray matter
  brain, 704
  spinal cord, 702–3, 708
Grazers, 649, 895
Grazing food web, 872f, 873
Great white sharks, 554
Greater Yellowstone Ecosystem, 919
Green algae
  colonial, 388
  in coral reefs, 901
  land plant evolution from, 420–22, 423f
  multicellular, 388
  supergroup archaeplastida, 385t, 387
Green construction, bamboo for, 458
Green fluorescent protein (GFP), 216, 594
Green glands, 682
Green sulfur bacteria, 375
Greenhouse effect, 877
Greenhouse gases, 127, 876–77, 879, 912, 915
Greenland, Precambrian fossils in, 335
Griffith, Frederick, 215–17
Grizzly bear, 889, 909f, 918–19
Ground finches, 279f, 318, 319
Ground meristem, 447, 453, 462f
Ground pine, 426
Ground substance connective tissue, 589
Ground tissue, 447, 448–49, 455f
Groundwater mining, 875
Groundwater table, 875, 897
Group living, 833, 864

Growth
  animal. See Animal development
  population. See Population growth
  response controls in flowering plants, 483–500
Growth factors
  and cancer, 165f
  cell cycle, 155
  cell signaling, 90
Growth plate, 738
Grubs, 468
Guam, alien species on, 915
Guanine (G)
  complimentary base pairing, 55
  in DNA structure, 55f, 217–19, 223
  DNA vs. RNA, 223t
  molecular structure of, 217f
  mRNA codons, 224f
  as nucleotide, 54f
  in RNA structure, 223
Guano, 904
Guard cells, 447, 477
Gulf Stream, 902f, 904
Gullet, of ciliates, 393
Gulls, 683–84, 823, 829
Gulper, 901f
Gut. *See Digestive system*
Guttation, 475
Gycolysis, cellular respiration, 146
Gymnosperms
  characteristics, 421t, 430
  conifers, 430–32
  cycades, 432
  defined, 430
  dominant generation in, 422
  evolution of, 340
  evolutionary history of plants, 420f
  gametophytes vs. sporophyte size, 423f
  ginkgoes, 432
  gnetophytes, 432–33
  life history strategy of, 849
Gypsy moths, 312

H

H zone, 745
H1N1 ("swine flu") virus, 363, 369, 370
HAART (highly active antiretroviral therapy), 788
HAB (Harmful Algal Bloom), 392–93
Habitat
  defined, 839, 859
  isolation of, 310, 311f, 312
  loss of, 913, 914f, 916, 919
  preservation of, 918–20
  restoration of, 920
Habituation, 823
Haddock, 918
Haeckel, Ernst, 351, 839
Hagfish, 553, 901f
Hair, 597, 599, 811
Hair cells, 726, 728, 729f
Hair follicles, 597f, 599
Hair root, 597f
Haldane, J. B. S., 329
Haliaetus leucocephalus, 562f, 563f
Hallucinogenic mushrooms, 411
Halocynthia, 551f
Halophiles, 335f, 354, 378f, 379
Halophilic archaea, 378f
Halorhodopsin, 379
Halteres, 803
Hamilton, Tyler, 689
Hamm, Paul, 735
Hammer (malleus), 726f, 727
Hand
  bones of, 740f, 742
  evolution of, 572f
Hantavirus pulmonary syndrome (HPS), 369
Haploid (n) number, 157, 172, 436f–437f
Haploid cells, 176, 177, 797
Haploid life cycle, 387–88, 389
Hard palate, 650, 651f
Hardwoods, 431, 433
Hardy, Godfrey H., 290–91
Hardy-Weinberg equilibrium, 290–96
  allele and genotype frequencies, 291–95, 292t
  inbreeding, 300

  migration (gene flow), 292, 292t, 294
  mutation, 292, 292t, 293–94
  natural selection, 292, 292t, 295
  random mating, 292, 292t, 295, 300
  small population (genetic drift), 294–95
Hardy-Weinberg principle, 291
Hare, snowshoe, 863, 888
Harem masters, red deer stags, 299
Harlequin frogs, 407
Harmful Algal Bloom (HAB), 392–93
Hart's tongue fern, 428
Harvestmen, 543
Hatchet fish, 902
Haustoria (sing., haustorium), 452, 472
Haversian systems, 591
Hawaiian honeycreepers, 316–17
Hawaiian islands, alien species on, 915
Hawk, 847f, 848, 860, 896
Hay fever, 641
Hb. *See Hemoglobin*
HCG (human chorionic gonadotropin), 782, 784, 806-8
Hcl (hydrochloric acid), 32, 652
HDL (high-density lipoproteins), 659-60
HDN (hemolytic disease of the newborn), 620
Head. *See also Brain; Cephalization; Skull*
  insect, 542, 543f
Head louse, 542f
Hearing, 726–30
  in animals, 726
  ears, 726–30, 741
  in humans, 727–30, 812
Heart. *See also Cardiovascular system*
  in closed circulatory system, 607–9
  human, 610–17
    aging process, 811
    blood pressure, 615
    cardiovascular disease, 616, 617
    circulation in, 611–12, 614–15
    conduction system of, 613
    contraction, 612–14
    embryonic development of, 799, 809
    structure, 610–11
  in open circulatory system, 606, 607f
  respiratory gas exchange, 671f
Heart attack, 616
Heart murmur, 613
Heart stage of eudicot embryonic development, 508, 509f
Heartbeat, 612–14
  fetal, 810
Heartburn, 651
Heartwood, 456, 457f
Heartworm, 865
Heat
  in biosphere, 9, 902–4
  defined, 105
  laws of thermodynamics, 105–6
Heat capacity, of water, 29
Height, in humans, 207
Heimlich manueveur, 673
Helicase, 221
Helicobacter pylori, 652
Heliconius, 498
Helium, 22–23
Helix, DNA, 54-55, 218–19
  vs. RNA, 55t
Helix aspersa, 536f
Helper T cells, 620, 633f, 635
Hemagglutinin (H) spike, 370
Heme, 592, 672
Heme group, 672f
Hemitrichia, 397f
Hemizygous males, 209
Hemocoel
  circulatory system, 606, 607f
  crayfish, 541
  insect, 542, 666
  mollusc, 524, 534, 535f
Hemocyanin, 534
Hemoglobin
  components, 592
  defined, 672
  in earthworms, 607
  globular protein, 50, 53
  heme, 672f
  in red blood cells, 591–92
  structure and function of, 618–19

Hemolymph
  crayfish, 541
  defined, 606
  horseshoe crabs, 622
  insect, 542, 606, 607f, 666
Hemolytic disease of the newborn (HDN), 620
Hemophilia, 210
Hendry, Andrew, 314
Henslow, John, 275
Hepatic artery, 654
Hepatic portal system, 614
Hepatitis, 366, 368, 656, 790
Herbaceous perennial plants, 444
Herbaceous stems, 454
Herbicides, 165f, 280, 877
Herbivores
  of African savanna, 895
  defined, 648, 870
  dentition of, 649f
  as discontinuous feeders, 648
  in food web, 871–74
  mammals, 341
  vegetarian diet, 658–59
Herceptin (trastuzumab), 635, 783
Hereditary spherocytosis, 203
Heredity. *See Genetic(s); Inheritance*
Hermaphroditic organisms, 531, 536, 537, 543, 773
Herpes, genital, 788–90
Herpes simplex virus (HSV-1), 365
Herpes virus 3 (HHV-3), 365
Herrings, 554
Hershey, Alfred, 216
Heterocephalus glaber, 819
Heterochromatin, 233f, 234, 242
Heterocysts, 377
Heterosporous plants, 426, 504
Heterotroph(s)
  animals as, 404, 520, 870–73
  bacteria, 352f, 353, 375
  defined, 120, 332, 586, 870
  fungi as, 520
Heterotrophic bacteria, 375
Heterozygote advantage, 302–3
Heterozygous organism, 196
Hevea, 911f
Hexose, 42
HFCS (high-fructose corn syrup), 658
HGH (human growth hormone), 738, 754f, 758–59, 813
HGP (Human Genome Project), 237, 261
HHV-3 (herpes virus 3), 365
High-density lipoproteins (HDL), 659-60
High-fructose corn syrup (HFCS), 658
Highly active antiretroviral therapy (HAART), 788
Hindbrain, 695
Hindlimb reduction, in vertebrate evolution, 321–22
Hinge joints, 743
Hip bones (coxal bones), 740f, 742, 743f
Hip joint, 743
Hippocampus, 705-6
Hippocampus kuda, 555f
Hippopotamus, 8
Hirudo medicinalis, 537
Histamine, 631, 641–42
Histidine, 51f
Histone(s), 157, 233–34, 242–43
Histone tails, 242
Histoplasma capsulatum, 410, 412
Histoplasmosis, 412
History of life, 333–42
  continental drift, 342f
  fossils, 333–34
  geographic timescale, 334–35, 336t. See also specific time periods
  mass extinctions, 343–44
HIV (human immunodeficiency virus). *See also AIDS*
  and coevolution, 867
  electron micrograph of, 289f
  gene of, phylogeny, 347
  microevolution, 289
  parasitic nature of, 366, 867
  pathophysiology of, 637, 787
  during pregnancy, 788
  prevention of, 788
  research cure for, 366

retrovirus, 368, 369f
T cells, 347
transmission of, 787
Hodgkin disease, 910
Holdfasts, brown algae, 390
Holly trees, 503, 503f
Holocene period, 336t
Holothurians, 544, 545f
Homeobox, 804
Homeobox genes, 284–85
Homeodomain, 804
Homeostasis, 599–601
defined, 4, 587, 599
kidneys in, 688–90
mechanisms in, 600
negative feedback, 600–601, 757
positive feedback, 601, 757
regulation, 599–600, 753
review and exercises, 602–4
for space walks, 587
theory of, 12
Homeostatic regulation, 599–600
Homeothermic animals, 599
Homeotic genes, 528, 803–4
Homeotic transformations, 803
Hominids
ardipithecines, 576–77
australopithecines, 577–78
classification, 575f
defined, 572
evolution of, 341
Hominines, 572
Hominins, 572, 575–78
Hominoids, 572
Homo species
early, evolution of, 578–79
late, evolution of, 579–83
timeline of evolution, 576f
Homo erectus
characteristics, 578
hunter-gatherers, 582f
timeline of evolution, 576f
tool use by, 582
Homo ergaster, 576f, 578, 579f
Homo floresiensis, 579
Homo habilis, 576f, 578, 582
Homo heidelbergensis, 576f
Homo neandertalensis, 576f, 580
Homo rudolfensis, 576f, 578, 582
Homo sapiens. See also Human(s)
Cro-Magnons, 580–81
genomics of, 570
skeleton, 577
timeline of evolution, 576f
Homologous chromosomes, 172, 175, 196
Homologous genes, 265
Homologous structures, 283–84, 357
Homologous traits, 317
Homologues, 172, 176, 196
Homology, 357
Homoptera, 542f
Homosporous plants, 426
Homozygous organism, 196
Honeybee(s)
biological clock of, 830
communication among, 829–30
and plants, mutualism of, 501
as pollinator, 501f, 911
reproduction, 773
wax production, 49
Honeycreepers, Hawaiian, 316–17
Hookworms, 526t
Horizons of soil, 468
Horizontal stems, 457f, 458
Hormones, 752–71. See also Endocrine
system; specific hormone
action of, 755–56
aging process and, 813
animal, 753, 754f, 755–56
antagonistic, 762
in bone growth, 738
as chemical signals, 755
in childbirth, 601
defined, 484, 752
functions of, 49, 600, 753–55
gland production. See specific glands
in osmoregulation, 688–90, 757, 758f,
763
peptide, 755–56
plant. See Plant hormones

proteins as, 49
review and exercise, 769–71
secretion of, 589, 753
steroid, 756
Hornworts, 420f, 421t, 423, 424, 425
Horses
dentition, 649
directional selection, 296–97
evolution of, 296–97, 322–23
locomotion, 737
mule sterility, 312, 313f, 314
Horseshoe crabs, 543, 622, 910
Horsetails, 409f, 427–28, 465
Horticulture, and alien species, 914
Host, 543, 865. See also Parasitism
Host cells, of viruses, 366
Host-specific viruses, 366
"Hot flashes," 813
Hotspots, biodiversity, 909
House mouse, 350
Hox genes
body plan evolution, 524–25
cnidarian, 528
genetic variation, 284–85
macroevolution, 320, 321–22
mutations of, 803, 804
pattern formation in mice and fruit
flies, 803f
Hox6 genes, 322f
HPS (hantavirus pulmonary
syndrome), 369
HPV (human papillomavirus), 788
HR (hypersensitive responses),
plants, 498
HRT (hormone replacement therapy),
738, 813
HSV-1 (herpes simplex virus), 365
Huber, Claudia, 330
Human(s). See also Homo sapiens
acid deposition, 33
aging in. See Aging process
bacterial diseases in, 376, 376t
birth weight, stabilizing selection,
296, 297f
brain, 572, 702f, 703–7
cardiovascular system of, 610–17
circulatory system, 610–17
classification, 571
communication by, 828–29
dentition of, 649
development of. See Human
development
digestion, 650–57, 809f, 812
DNA nucleotide composition in, 217f
ears, 726–30
effects on biosphere, 9–10
endocrine system. See Endocrine
system; Hormones
evolution of, 322, 341, 570–85
eyes, 572, 720, 721–24
female. See Female(s)
genome of, 261, 263t, 265, 574. See
also Human Genome Project
health. See Human health
hearing, 727–30
heart, 610–17
Hox genes, 804
incomplete dominance in, 205–6
life cycle of, 181–82
life expectancy in, 813–14
locomotion, 737, 741
lungs, 668, 668f
male. See Male(s)
Mendel's laws and genetic disorders,
201–4
muscular system, 744–49. See also
Muscle(s), specific muscle
nature vs. nurture studies, 821
nervous system, 696f
oogenesis, 181–82
parenting behavior, 825
pH balance, 32–33
pheromones, 826–28
population growth, 851–53
reproduction, 775–91
respiratory tract, 667–68
senses. See Sense organs
skeletal system, 738–43. See also
Bone(s); Human skeleton
spermatogenesis in, 181

taxonomic classification of, 6t
urinary system of, 684–90. See also
Kidneys
vertebrate evolution, 560
vision, 572, 720, 721–24
X-linked genetic disorders, 208–10
Human chorionic gonadotropin (HCG),
782, 784, 806–8
Human development
embryonic, 797–99, 805–10
before implantation, 796–97, 806
first week, 806, 808f
second week, 806–8
third week, 808–9
fourth and fifth week, 808f, 809
extraembryonic membranes, 805,
808–9, 810f
fetal, 805, 810
Human evolution, 570–85
genes and, 322
hominins, 575–78
Homo species, 578–83
human variation, 581, 583
life history, 341
primates, 571–75
review and exercises, 583–85
Human Genome Project (HGP), 237, 261
Human growth hormone (HGH), 738,
754f, 758–59, 813
Human health. See also Disease
biodiversity and, 911–12
cardiovascular, 617
health care costs, 168
healthy lifestyle, 612
lungs, 668, 668f
nutrition, 657–60
obesity treatments, 655
respiratory, 364t, 376t, 667–76
Human immunodeficiency virus. See HIV
Human papillomavirus (HPV), 788
Human reproduction, 775–91
aging process, 813
control of, 783–85
female system, 779–83, 779t, 813. See
also Pregnancy
fertilization, 182f, 779–80, 782,
796–97, 806
male system, 775–78, 775t
oogenesis, 181–82
sexually transmitted diseases, 787–91.
See also specific disease
zygote, 181–82, 780, 796–97, 806f
Human skeleton, 738–43
aging process, 812–13
appendicular, 742
axial, 740–41
bone growth and renewal, 738
evolution of, 576–78, 580
functions of, 738
joint classification, 742–43
long bone anatomy, 738–40
Human variation, evolution of, 581, 583
Humboldt Current, 902f, 904
Humerus, 742
Hummingbird, 46, 507, 562, 830
Humoral (antibody-mediated) immunity,
633–35
Humpback whales, 314, 889
Humus, 464–68
Hunger, obesity and, 655
Hunter-gatherer humans, 439, 580, 582
Hunting, 911, 916
Huntington disease, 204, 704
Hurricane Katrina, 469
Hutton, James, 274
Hyaline cartilage, 591, 739
Hybrid inviability, 312
Hybrid sterility, 311f, 312
Hybridization, 310
Hybridomas, 635
Hydra
anatomy of, 529
characteristics, 526t
gas exchange, 665f
hydrostatic skeleton of, 736
hydrozoa polyp stage, 528
nerve net of, 694
reproduction, 773
transport in, 606
Hydrocarbons, 38–39

Hydrochloric acid (HCl), 32, 652
Hydrogen
as atmospheric gas, 329
Bohr model of atom, 25f
as essential plant nutrient, 465
in plants, 466t
respiratory center, 670–71
Hydrogen bonding
covalent, 27
defined, 28
peptides, 50, 51f
water, 28–29
Hydrogen ions
in acid-base balance, 690
in acids, 32, 34
ATP-driven proton pump, 469f, 470,
477–79
cells and entropy, 105
in chemiosmosis, 114, 115f
in cristae of mitochondria, 145f
in thylakoid, 126
transport, in plants, 469f
Hydrogen peroxide, 75
Hydrogen sulfide, 332, 902
Hydrologic (water) cycle, 875, 897, 912
Hydrolysis reaction, 41, 46, 108
Hydrophilic molecules, 30, 40
Hydrophilic region, in plasma
membrane, 86
Hydrophobic interactions, 51f
Hydrophobic molecules, 30, 40
Hydrophobic region, in plasma
membrane, 86
Hydroponics, 465–66
Hydrostat, muscular, 736
Hydrostatic skeletons, 528, 536, 736
Hydrothermal vents, 330f, 332, 902
Hydroxide ions (OH⁻), 32, 34
Hydroxyl functional groups, 39–40, 39t
Hydrozoa, 528–29
Hyenas, 895
Hyla andersoni, 557f
Hylobates syndactylus, 830f
Hyman, Flo, 206
Hymenoptera, 542f
Hypercholesterolemia, familial, 98,
205, 260
Hyperglycemia, 766
Hyperopia, 724
Hyperparathyroidism, 762
Hypersensitive responses (HR), in
plants, 498
Hypersensitivity (allergy), 641–42
Hypertension, 616, 812
Hyperthyroidism, 761
Hypertonic solution, 93f, 94, 101t
Hyphae (sing. hypha)
dikaryotic, 406, 408f, 409
septate, 405
Hypocotyl, 509, 512f
Hypodermis, 597, 598
Hypoglycemia, 766
Hypolimnion, 898
Hypoparathyroidism, 762
Hypophysis. See Pituitary gland
Hypothalamic-inhibiting hormones, 757
Hypothalamic-releasing hormones, 757
Hypothalamus
hormones secreted by, 754f, 762f, 763,
778, 781
human, 704, 705f
structure and function, 757, 758f
temperature regulation, 601
vertebrate, 695f, 696
Hypothesis, in scientific method, 11,
14, 16
Hypothyroidism, 760–61
Hypotonic solution, 93, 101t
Hyracoidea, 566t
Hyracotherium, 296, 297f, 323

I

I band, 745
IAA (indoleacetic acid), 485
Iberomesornis, 281
Ice, 31, 888, 898–99
Ice ages, 341, 868
Ichthyophthirius, 393
Ichthyosaurs, 334f, 559

"Ick," 393
ICSI (intracytoplasmic sperm injection), 785
ICTV (International Committee on Taxonomy of Viruses), 365
ICZN (International Code of Zoological Nomenclature), 351
Igs (immunoglobulins), 634–35, 641–42
Iguanas, 314, 561, 827
Iliopsoas muscle, 744f
Illinois River floodplains, 921
Illumination, for microscopy, 64
Immediate allergic response, 641–42, 642t
Immigration
  island biogeography, 862
  population growth, 851–52
Immune complex, 634
Immune system, 626–45
  adaptive (acquired and specific) defenses, 633–39
  adverse reactions, 641–42, 643
  aging process, 812
  defined, 630
  disorders, 638, 640, 641–43
  evolution of, 627–28
  function, 596, 627
  innate (nonspecific) defenses, 627, 630–33
  lymphatic system, 596, 628–30
  review and exercises, 643–46
Immunity, defined, 630
Immunizations, 639, 639f, 640
Immunodeficiency disorders, 626, 641
Immunofluorescence microscopy, 78
Immunoglobulins (Igs), 634–35, 641–42
Immunokine, cobra-derived, 560
Imperfect flower, 434t, 503
Implantation, 806
Impotency (erectile dysfunction), 778
Imprinting, 823–24
In vitro fertilization (IVF), 785, 786
In vivo gene therapy, 260
Inbreeding (consanguineous reproduction), 202, 295, 300–301, 819
Inclusion bodies, bacterial, 66
Inclusive fitness, 834
Incomplete digestive tracts, 531, 647
Incomplete dominance, Mendelian patterns of inheritance, 205–6
Incomplete flowers, 434t, 503
Incomplete penetrance, Mendelian patterns of inheritance, 206
Incus, 726f, 727
Indehiscent fruit, 510f, 511t, 512
Independent assortment
  of homologous chromosomes, 175
  Mendel's law of, 198–99
Independent variable, 12, 14–15
Index fossils, 334, 399
Indirect defenses, plant responses, 498
Indirect selection, 834
Indoleacetic acid (IAA), 485
Indotestudo elongata, 916f
Induced fit model, of enzymes, 110
Induced mutations, 248
Inducer, 240
Inducible operon, 240
Induction, 800
Inductive reasoning, 11
Industrial melanism, 279–80, 290–92
Infections. *See also specific infection*
  bacterial, 376, 376t
  defense against. See Immunity
  fungal, 410–11, 412
  opportunistic, AIDS-related, 638, 787
  respiratory tract, 673–74
  sexually transmitted, 787–91
  viral, 369, 370
Inferior vena cava, 611, 614
Infertility, 775, 784–85
Inflammatory response, 631, 763
Inflorescence (cluster) of flower, 434t
Influenza
  bird flu, 369, 370
  flu shot, 366
  H1N1 ("swine flu") virus, 363, 369, 370
  pandemic, 363, 370, 371
  vaccines, 366, 370
  virus, 365f, 370

Infrared spectrum, 716
Ingroup, in cladistics, 356
Inguinal lymph nodes, 628f, 629
Inhalation. *See* Inspiration
Inheritance. *See also* Genetic(s)
  of acquired characteristics, 273–74
  autosomal patterns of, 201–4
  behavioral influences of, 820–22
  blending concept of, 193
  of blood types, 205
  epigenetic, 241
  Mendelian patterns of, 192–213
  multifactorial, 207–8
  particulate theory of, 193
  polygenic, 207–8
Inhibin, 778
Inhibition model of succession, 868–69
Inhibitors, of enzymes, 112, 113f
Inhibitory signals, 701, 701f
Initiation
  DNA translation, 230–31, 232f
  mRNA transcription, 226
Innate immunity, 627, 630–33
Inner cell mass, 806, 808
Inner ear, 726f, 727
Inner membrane, nuclear envelope, 70f
Inorganic chemistry, defined, 38
Inorganic molecules, 38t
Inorganic nutrients, plants, 465, 466t
Insect(s), 541–43. *See also specific insect*
  characteristics, 526t
  circulatory system, 543, 606, 607f
  desert, 896
  digestion, 542, 543f
  evolution of, 541–43
  excretory system, 682
  eye, 720
  flying, 339
  fossil, 339
  gas exchange, 664–65
  hearing, 726
  metamorphosis, 542, 543, 752–54
  mimicry, 864
  pheromones used by, 826
  as plant predators, 496, 497f
  as pollinators, 437, 505–7
  population growth, 844
  reproduction, 773
  respiratory system, 542, 543
  social, 543, 833–34
  in soil, 468
  tracheal system, 666–67
  vision, 720
Insectivorous plants, 460–61, 472
Insight learning, 825
Instinct, 823
Insulation, made from fungi, 403
Insulin
  bulk transport, 95
  and diabetes mellitus, 90
  discovery of, 766
  evolutionary origin of, 753
  functions of, 754f, 765
  glucose storage, 43
  pig-derived, 560
  for regulation, 49
  secretion of, 654, 753, 754f, 765
  therapeutic use of, 766
Insulin resistance, 767
Integrase inhibitors, 788
Integration
  as central nervous system function, 702
  in lysogenic cycle, 367f, 368
  synaptic, 701
  of visual signals, 723
Integrin, 99f
Integumentary system, 597–99. *See also* Epidermis; Skin
  accessory structures, 598–99
  aging process, 811
  components and function, 597
  regions, 597–98
Intercalary meristem, 447
Intercalated disks, 593, 610, 611
Intercostal nerves, respiration, 670
Interferons, 633, 637
Intergenic sequences, genomics, 262
Interkinesis (meiosis), 176, 179f
Interleukins, 637

Intermediate filaments, 68f, 78, 79f
Internal fertilization, 774
Internal organs, as vertebrate characteristic, 552
Internal respiration, 671, 672
International Code of Zoological Nomenclature (ICZN), 351
International Committee on Taxonomy of Viruses (ICTV), 365
Interneurons, 697f, 698
Internodes, stem, 444f, 445, 453, 461f
Interphase, mitosis, 154, 157, 158f
Interspersed repeats, DNA, 262
Interstitial cells, 776f, 778
Intertidal zone, 900–901
Intervertebral disks, 741–42
Intestinal lumen, 592
Intestine
  bacteria in, 375
  human digestive tract, 650f, 652–54
  large, 650f, 653–54
  pH, 652
  small, 650f, 652–53
Intracytoplasmic sperm injection (ICSI), 785
Intrauterine device (IUD), 784
Intrauterine insemination (IUI), 785
Intravenous (IV) infusions, right to refuse, 36
Introns
  alternative mRNA splicing, 246
  cloning, 256
  defined, 226
  genomes sequencing, 261f
  mRNA processing, 226
  posttranscriptional control, 244
  three-domain system of classification, 352t
Invagination, 798, 808
Inversion, chromosomal, 187
Invertebrates. *See also specific animal*
  aquatic, gas exchange in, 664, 666
  circulatory system of, 606–7
  defined, 521
  evolution of, 519–48
  excretory system, 681–82
  eyes, 720
  fossils, 337
  gravitational equilibrium organs in, 728
  hormones, 753–55
  marine, 902
  nervous system, 694–95
  reproduction, 773–74
  transport in, 606–7
  vision, 720
Invertebrate evolution, 519–48
  animal evolution, 520–26
  Cambrian period, 339
  characteristics, 526t
  defined, 521
  Deuterostomes, 523, 526t, 544–45
  Ecdysozoan diversity, 538–43
  fossils, 337
  Lophotrochozoan diversity, 530–38
  nervous system, 694–95
  review and exercises, 545–48
  simplest varieties, 527–29. *See also* Cnidarians; Comb jellies; Sponge(s)
Inverted pyramids, 874
Iodine, 24, 760
Ion, defined, 26
Ion transport, ATP-driven proton pump, 469f, 470, 477–79
Ionic bond, 26–27
Ionizing radiation, 248
Ipomoea, 491f
Ipomoea leptophylla, 494
Iridium, 343, 344, 559
Iris
  eye, 721
  plant, 448
Iron
  dietary requirement, 660
  Earth atmosphere origins, 329, 330
  in plants, 465, 466t
Iron-sulfur world, 329, 330
Irruptive growth, 846
Islands
  adaptive radiation, 316–17

  biogeography, 862
  exotic species on, 915
Islets of Langerhans, 765, 766
Isoetes, 426
Isolation mechanisms, species, 310, 311f, 312
Isomers, 39
Isoniazid, 248
Isotonic solution, 93, 101t
Isotopes, 24–25
Iteroparity, 843
IUD (intrauterine device), 784
IUI (intrauterine insemination), 785
IV infusion, right to refuse, 36
Ivanowsky, Dimitri, 365
Ivar the Boneless (Ivar Ragnarsson), 203
IVF (in vitro fertilization), 785, 786

J

Jackal, 834
Jacob, François, 238, 239
Jacobs syndrome, 186–87
Jacobson's organ, 561, 718
Jaguar, 892
Jasmonic acid, 498
Jaundice, 654
Jaws
  evolution of, 553
  fish with, 339, 526t, 552, 553–55
  fish without, 339, 526t, 552, 553
Jeholodens, 340
Jelly fungi, 412
Jellyfish, 216f, 526t, 694. *See also* Comb jellies; Sea jellies
Jerne, Niels, 635
Jogi, Nanu Ram, 171
Jointed appendages, 737
Joints, classification of, 742–43
"Jumping genes," 262
Junction proteins, 88f, 89
Junctions between cells, 99–100
Junipers, 430
Juniperus, 430f
"Junk" DNA, 261
Jurassic period, 336t, 343

K

Kangaroo, 283f, 564, 737, 840
Kangaroo rat, 683, 896f
Kaposi's sarcoma, 638
Karyotype, 172f, 184
Kelp, 120f, 384, 390
Kenyan giant scorpion, 543f
Keratin
  defined, 589
  protein, 49, 78
  skin hardening, 598
  structure of, 51, 53f
Kerner, Justinus, 746
Ketamine, 710
Keystone species, 918
Kidneys, 682–90
  aging process, 812
  blood supply, 684f, 685–86
  functions of, 596
  in homeostatic regulation, 599, 688–90
  location of, 684
  osmoregulation by, 682–84, 686, 687f, 688–90, 757, 758f, 763
  structure of, 685, 685f
  urine formation by, 682, 683, 686, 687f
Kidston, Barry, 706
Kin selection, 834
Kinases, 244
Kinesin, 78
Kinetic energy, 105
Kinetochore
  electron micrograph, 157f
  meiosis, 176, 178f
  mitosis, 157, 159
Kinetochore spindle fibers, 159
Kinetoplastids, 385t, 386f, 396
Kinetoplasts, 396
Kingdom (taxonomic). *See also specific kingdom*
  classification of living things, 6, 6t
  Linnean, 349, 350f
Kinky hair (Menkes) syndrome, 209–10
Kinocilium, 728, 729f

Kit fox, 896f
Kitti's bats, 564
Klinefelter syndrome (KS), 184, 185–86
Klipspringers, 826
Knee joint, 743
Kneecap (patella), 740f, 743f
Knockout mouse, 259
Knop, Wilhem, 465
Koala, 564, 565f, 649
Köhler, George, 635
Kovalick, Walter W., 471
Krause end bulbs, 730
Krebs, Hans, 143
Krebs cycle. *See* Citric acid cycle
Krill
evolution of, 540–41, 554
as food source, 648
Krypton, 23
KS Klinefelter syndrome (KS), 184, 185–86
K-selection, 849
Kudzu, 914, 915f
Kurosawa, Ewiti, 486
Kyoto Protocol, 879

L

Labia majora, 779f, 780
Labia minora, 779f, 780
Labor, obstetric. *See* Birth
Labroides dimidiatus, 866f
Lac operon, 239–40
Lactate, 140, 747
Lactation, 639, 757, 782
Lacteals, 592, 628, 653, 657
Lactic acid bacteria, 141
Lactic acid fermentation, 140
Lactobacillus, 141
Lactose, 42, 657
Lactose metabolism, 239–40
Lacuna (pl., lacunae), 591, 740
Ladderlike nervous system, 531, 694
Ladybugs, 911f
Laetoli footprints, 577
Lag phase of population growth, 844
Lagging strand, DNA replication, 221
Lagomorpha, 566t
Lake(s), 33, 898–900, 912, 915
Lake effect, 885
Lake Malawi and Tanganyika cichlids, 317
LAL test, 622
Lamarck, Jean-Baptiste de, 273–74
Lamella, 69f, 666f
Laminaria, 390
Lamprey, 553
Lampshells, 526t
Lance fluke, 867
Lancelet
characteristics, 526t
embryonic development of, 797–99
evolution of, 540–51
Land plants. *See also* Plant(s); *specific plant*
adaptations of, 420, 430–39
algal relatives of, 421–22
alternation of generations in, 422
characteristics, 421t
colonization by nonvascular plants, 420f, 423–25
derived traits of, 422–23
dominant generation in, 422
evolution of, 420–39
from freshwater to land, 420–22, 423f
gametophytes vs. sporophyte size, 423f
seed plant development, 42f, 421t, 430–39
Land snails
disruptive selection, 297, 298f
as gastropod, 536f
hermaphroditic, 536
nutrition of, 648–49
Landscape
diversity, 909
preservation of, 919–20
topography, 885
Language, 828
Lantern fish, 901f, 902
Lantern fly, 864f
Lanugo, 810
Lap-Band, 655
Larch (tree), 457f

Large intestine, 650f, 653–54
Larix decidua, 457f
Larson, Gary, 349
Larva
defined, 521, 774
frog metamorphosis, 521
insect, 542
trochophore, 530
Larynx, 668
Laser-assisted in situ keratomileusis (LASIK), 724
Last universal common ancestor (LUCA), 328, 351
Late gastrula stage, 798
Latency, in lysogenic cycle, 368
Lateral line, fish, 554, 726
Lateral meristems, 453
Lateral roots, 445f, 452, 461f
Lateral sulcus, 703f
Lateral ventricles, 702f, 703
Laterite, 893
Latex, 911
Latimeria chalumnae, 555f
Latin language, 349
Latissimus dorsi muscle, 744f
Latitude and biomes, 887
Latrodectus, 543f
Laughing gulls, 823
Laurasia, 342
Laws
of conservation of energy, 105
defined, 12
of evolution, 12
Mendel's
independent assortment, 198–99
probability, 200–201
segregation, 195–96
of thermodynamics, 105–6, 871–73
LDCs (less-developed countries), 851–53
LDL (low-density lipoprotein), 98, 659–60
Leaching, 467, 468
Leading strand, DNA replication, 221
Leaf (pl., leaves)
alternate, 460
classification, 460
club mosses, 408
compound, 460
cross-sectional structure of, 121f
defined, 445
epidermal tissue of, 447
eudicot, 446, 459f, 460
flowering plants, 445, 446, 459, 461f
generally, 445
of horsetail, 427
monocot, 446
morphology, 459
opposite, 460
organization and diversity of, 445, 446, 459–60, 461f
palmate compound, 460
and photosynthesis, 121, 445
pinnate compound, 460
plant structure, 444f
simple, 460
specialized, 445
structure of, 459f, 460
transport system, 473f, 476–79, 476t
vascular plants, 423f
veins of, 450
whorled, 460
Leaf axil, 445
Leaf curl fungi, 410
Leaf primordia, 453, 462f
Leaf scars, 453, 461f
Leafhopper, 542f
Leafy liverworts, 424
Learning, 823–26
associative, 824
brain, 707
cognitive, 825–26
defined, 823
imprinting, 823–24
insight, 825
instinct, 823
in octopus, 536
social interactions, 824
Leclerc, Georges-Louis, 272
Leeches
characteristics, 526t
medicinal, 537f, 538
as parasites, 865

Leeuwenhoek, Antonie van, 60, 371, 533
Leeward side, 885
Leg, bones of, 740f, 742, 743f
Legumes
as dry fruit, 510f, 511, 512
nitrogen-fixing bacteria, 375, 452, 471, 878
nutritional function of soil, 467
wheat rotation study, 14–15
Leishmania, 398f
Leishmaniasis, 398f
Lemming, 888
Lemurs
brain, 572
evolution of, 573f, 575
habitat, 892
Lens
corrective, 724
of eye, 720–21
Lenticels, 447, 455f, 456, 461f
Leopard, 829, 895
Leopard frog, 307, 308f, 310
Lepas anatifera, 540f
Lepidoptera. *See* Butterflies
Leprosy, 910
Leptonycteris curasoae, 911f
Lepus americanus, 863
Lepus europaeus (Patagonian hare), 276
Less-developed countries (LDCs), 851–53
Leucine, 51f
Leucochloridium, 867
Leucoplasts, 77
Leukemia, 910
Leukocytes. *See* White blood cells (WBCs)
Lewontin, Richard, 581, 583
Leydig (interstitial) cells, 776f, 778
LH. *See* Luteinizing hormone (LH)
Lianas, 892
Lichens
in archaeplastida, 387
cyanobacteria, 377
sac fungi, 410
soil formation, 467
symbiosis, 414, 866
Licht, Louis, 470
Lidy Hot Springs, 378–79
Life, 1–19, 327–46
adaptations, 5
biological organization, 2–4
biosphere organization, 9–10
defining, 2–5
evolution, as biological unifying concept, 6–8
geologic timescale, 336t. *See also specific periods of time*
geological factors that influence evolution, 342–44
history of, 333–41, 342f
homeostasis, 4
need for materials and energy, 4
organization of, 3f
origin of, 328–32
reproduction and development, 5
as responsive, 4–5
review and exercises, 17–19, 344–46
scientific method, 11–16
Life cycle, 180, 520. *See also* Reproduction
Life expectancy, human, 813–14
Life history patterns, 842–43, 848–49
Life tables, 841–42
Life zones, aquatic, 899–902
Ligaments, 590, 742–43
Light
infrared spectrum, 716
phototropism, 491, 492
phytochrome conversion cycle, 495
reception of, 716, 720, 722–23
ultraviolet spectrum, 720
visible, 124, 716, 720
Light microscope, 62, 63–64
Light reactions, 124–25
Lignin, 100, 426, 449, 451, 469
Lilac plant, 61f
Lilium bulbiferum, 349
Lilium canadense, 349
Lily, 349
Lima beans, 498
Limb(s). *See also* Appendages; *specific limbs*
amphibian, 552, 556

development, and Tbx5 gene, 321
human, 740f, 742, 743f
primates, 571, 737
regeneration, 594–95
reptile, 558
salamanders, 594
vertebrate, 552, 737
Limb buds, 809
Limbic system, 705–6
Limestone, 33, 901
Limiting factors, 840, 844, 846, 849–50, 859
Limnetic zone, 899
Limpets, 534, 535
Limulus, 543, 910
Limulus amoebocyte lysate, 910
Limulus polyphemus, 622
Linen, 449
"Linker" DNA, 233
Linnaeus, Carolus, 272, 307, 349, 350
Linnean binomial classification hierarchy, 8, 349–50
Linnean classification, 356
Linnean taxonomy, 349
Lion, 649, 895, 918
Lionfishes, 555f
Lipase, 655, 657
Lipids, 45–49
in common foods, 40t
defined, 45
dietary, 658
fat and fatty acids, 46, 47f
functions of, 45t
nutrition and human health, 658
as organic compound class, 38
plasma membrane, 87
plasma membrane origin, 331
steroids, 46, 48
triglycerides, 46, 47f
types and functions, 45t
waxes, 48–49
Lipopolysaccharide (LPS), 376
Lipoproteins, 618
Liposomes, 331
Litter, as soil layer, 468
Littoral zone, 899
Liver
aging process, 812
bile production, 652, 654, 656
blood glucose regulation, 765
disorders of, 654, 656
embryonic development, 809f
glycogen storage, 657, 753f, 765
in homeostatic regulation, 599
human, 650f, 654, 656, 809f, 812
portal system, 614
protein digestion, 659
structure and function, 654
transplantation of, 656
Liverworts
as bryophyte, 423
characteristics, 421t
described, 424
evolutionary history of plants, 420f
uses of, 425
Living things, classification of, 6, 6t, 7
Lizards, 561, 773, 842f
Lobaria, 414f
Lobe-finned fishes, 555, 556, 557f
Lobsters, 540, 718, 901
Lobules, of liver, 654f
Locomotion. *See also* Movement
human, 737, 741
mammal, 737
muscular system in, 744. *See also* Muscle(s)
skeletal support for, 736–37. *See also* Skeleton
Locoweed, 465
Locus, gene, 196
Locusts, 649
Lodgepole pine, 430f
Loggerhead turtles, 825, 889
Logistic growth, 844–45, 848–49
Loligo, 698
Long bones, 591, 738–40
Long-day plants, 496
Longhorn beetle, 864f
Longitudinal fissure, cerebrum, 703
Longitudinal muscles, 736

Long-term memory, 707
Loop of the nephron (loop of Henle),
    685f, 686, 687f, 688
Loose fibrous connective tissue, 590
Lophophorans, 530
Lophophore, 530
Lophotrochozoa, 530–38
    characteristics, 526t, 530
    defined, 530
    diversity of, 530–38
    lophophorans, 530
    trochozoans, 530, 531–38
Lorenz, Konrad, 823
Lorenzo's Oil (film), 75, 210
Lou Gehrig disease (amyotrophic lateral
    sclerosis), 703
Louisiana wetlands, 469, 921
Lovebirds, 820–21
Low-density lipoprotein (LDL), 98,
    659–60
Lower gastroesophageal sphincter, 651
Lower respiratory tract disorders,
    673–74
LPS (lipopolysaccharide), 376
LSD (lysergic acid diethylamide), 411
LUCA (last universal common ancestor),
    328, 351
"Lucy" (Australopithecus afarensis),
    577, 578f
Lumbar nerves, 696f
Lumbar vertebrae, 741
Lumbricu terrestris, 536, 537f
Lumen, digestive tract, 651
Lung(s)
    acid-base regulation by, 690
    aging process, 812
    anatomy, 668f
    artificial, 676
    bellows function of, 669–70
    bird, 665, 670f
    chemoreceptors in, 718
    disorders affecting, 674–75
    gas exchange, 92, 665, 665f
    human, 668–76, 812
    mammals, 665
Lung cancer, 248, 675
Lungfish, 555
Lunula, 598–99
Lupus, 642, 642f
Luteal phase, of ovarian cycle, 781, 782t
Luteinizing hormone (LH)
    in males, 778, 780
    in ovarian cycle, 780–81, 782t
    secretion of, 754f, 758f, 767
Lycophytes
    Carboniferous forests, 435
    characteristics, 421t
    defined, 426
    evolutionary history of
        plants, 420f
    plant evolution, 420f, 426
    reproduction, 426
Lycopodium, 426
Lyell, Charles, 274
Lyme disease, 543, 850
Lymnaea, 755
Lymph, 592, 622, 629
Lymph nodes, 592, 628f, 629
Lymphatic (lymphoid) organs, 628f,
    629–30
Lymphatic capillaries, 629
Lymphatic duct, right, 628f, 629. See also
    Immune system
Lymphatic system, 596, 628–30. See also
    Immune system
Lymphatic vessels, 592, 628–29
Lymphocytes, 592, 620, 629. See also B
    cells; T cells
Lynx, 863, 888
Lynx canadensis, 863
Lysergic acid, 411
Lysergic acid diethylamide (LSD), 411
Lysine, 51f
Lysis, 367
Lysmata grasbhami, 540f
Lysogenic cells, 368
Lysogenic cycle, bacteriophage, 368
Lysosomal storage diseases, 73
Lysosomes, 68f, 73, 74, 82t
Lysozyme, 368
Lystrosaurus, 342
Lytic cycle, bacteriophage, 368

M

M (mitotic) stage of cell cycle, 155. See
    also Mitosis
Maasai tribe, 581f, 583
MAC (Mycobacterium avium complex),
    638
Macaques, 825
MacArthur, Robert, 860, 862
Macaws, 22, 563f, 893f, 914f
Mackerel, 901f
MacLeod, Colin, 216
Macleod, J. J., 766
Macrocystis, 390
Macroevolution, 318–26
    defined, 307
    developmental genes, 320–22
    goal-orientation, 322–23
    gradualist models, 318–19, 320f
    microfrog, 306
    phylogenetic tree, 309
    principles of, 318–23
    punctuated equilibrium models, 319–20
    review and exercises, 324–26
Macromolecules, 37
Macronutrients, in plants, 465, 466t
Macrophages, 620, 631–32
Macropus, 283f
Macroscelidia, 566t
Macular degeneration, 724
"Mad cow disease," 53, 371
Madreporite, 544f, 545
Magnesium, 26, 465, 660
Magnification, microscopic, 63–64
Magnolia, 460
Maiasaura, 327
Maidenhair fern, 428
Maize, 433, 438–39. See also Corn
Major histocompatibility complex (MHC)
    proteins, 632, 635, 643, 755
Malaria, 207, 303, 394, 865, 867
Malate, 130–31
Male(s)
    human
        hormonal birth control for, 784
        hormonal regulation in, 767, 778
        infertility, 784–85
        orgasm, 777–78
        reproductive system of, 775–78,
            775t, 813
        secondary sex characteristics,
            767, 778
    mating behaviors of, 298–99, 831–33
    pregnancy in seahorses, 772, 774
Male condoms, 784f
Male gametophyte, flowering plants,
    504–5
Malignant cancer, 163
Malleus, 726f, 727
Malpighi, Marcello, 478
Malpighian tubules, 542, 682
Maltase, 656
Malthus, Thomas, 274, 277, 846
Malthusian growth, 846
Maltose, 42, 656
Mambas, 561
Mammalia (class), 349–50
Mammals. See also specific animal
    adaptive radiation among, 317
    characteristics, 526t, 564
    circulatory system, 564, 609
    defined, 564
    dentition of, 649
    diversification, Cenozoic period, 341
    embryonic development, 803–4
    evolution of, 340–43, 564–65, 566t
    eye, 720
    flying. See Bat(s)
    gas exchange, 665f
    habitats, 565
    hormones, 755
    locomotion, 737
    lungs, 665
    marsupials. See Marsupials
    monotremes, 564, 565f
    nervous system, 696
    oogenesis, 181, 182f
    orders of placental, 566t
    origin, 281
    osmoregulation, 683–84

    placental, 526t, 564–65, 566t, 774
    with pouches, 283
    reciprocal altruism, 834
    reproduction, 774, 796. See also Sexual
        reproduction
    respiration, 564, 665, 669–70
    skeleton, 737
    spermatogenesis, 181, 182f
    timeline of evolution, 565f
    vision, 720
    viviparous, 774
Mammary glands, 564, 758f, 782–83
Mammography, 783
Mammoths, 341
Manatees, 322
Mandible, 738, 740f, 741
Manduca sexta, 752
Manganese, 466t
Mangrove swamps, 900, 912
Mangrove trees, 452, 461f, 913
Manta rays, 554
Mantle, mollusc, 534, 535f
Mantle cavity, mollusc, 534, 535, 774
Mantle layer, Earth, 343
Manubrium, 741
Maple (tree), 460, 510f
Maranta leuconeura, 494
Marchantia, 424
Marfan syndrome, 206
Marine animals. See Aquatic animals;
    specific animal or fish
Marine ecosystems, 897, 900f, 901–2
Marine polychaetes, 537–38
Mars meteorite, 330
Marsh marigold, 891f
Marshes, 897, 900, 912
Marsupials. See also specific animal
    characteristics, 526t
    evolution of, 283, 342–43
    generally, 564
    reproduction, 566t, 774
Mass, atomic, 23
Mass extinctions
    continental drift, 342, 344, 868
    defined, 338
    described, 10, 343–44
    dinosaurs, 559
    geologic timescale, 336t
Mass number, 23
Masseter muscle, 744f
Mast cells, 631
Mastoid sinuses, 740
Mastoiditis, 740
Maternal antibodies, 810
Maternal determinants, 800, 802
Mathematical data
    in experiments, 12
    in population growth models, 844–45
Mating behavior. See also Sexual
    reproduction
    assortative, 295, 300
    birds, field study of, 15–16
    female choice in, 297–98
    fitness strategies, 831
    isolating mechanism, 311f, 312
    male competition in, 298–99
    nonrandom, 295, 300
    random, 292, 292t, 295, 300
    sexual selection, 297–99, 831–32
Matrix
    blood, 591f
    bone, 591
    connective tissue, 590
    mitochondrial, 77, 142
Matter, defined, 22
Matteuccia truthiopteris, 429
Matthei, J. Heinrich, 224
Maturation
    in lytic cycle, 367f, 368
    root zone of, 450, 451f
    of sperm, 775
Maxilla, 740f, 741
Maxillary glands, 682
Mayfly, 542f
Mayr, Ernst, 313
McCarty, Maclyn, 216
McClintock, Barbara, 262
MDCs (more-developed countries),
    851–53
MDMA, 710
Mealybug, 542f

Mechanical energy, 105
Mechanical isolation, 311f, 312
Mechanoreceptors, 717, 726–30, 727f
Median nerve, 696f
Mediastar, 544f
Medicine. See also Human health
    biodiversity and, 910
    ferns, 429
    fungi, 403
    radioactive isotopes, 24–25
    vertebrate-derived, 560
Medulla oblongata
    human, 702f, 705, 708f
    respiratory center, 670
    vertebrate, 695, 696
Medullary cavity, 739
Medusa, 528, 529
Meerkat, 834f
Megafauna, 341
Megaphyll, 427, 428
Megasporangium, 431f, 437f
Megaspores
    conifers (pine), 431f
    defined, 426, 502
    flowering plant reproduction, 436,
        437f, 504, 505
    seed plants, 430
Meiosis, 171–91
    chromosome number and structure,
        changes in, 172–74, 183–88
    defined, 172
    gametogenesis, 773, 776f, 777,
        780, 797
    generally, 173–74
    independent assortment, 198, 199f
    land plants, 422
    life cycle, 180–82
    Mendel's cross, 196
    vs. mitosis, 177, 177t, 180f–181f
    phases of, 176
    review and exercises, 189–91
Meiosis I
    animal and plant cells, 178f–179f
    generally, 173–74, 173f
    independent assortment, 198, 199f
    Mendel's cross, 196
    vs. mitosis, 177, 177t
    nondisjunction of chromosomes, 183f
    oogenesis, 181, 182f
    spermatogenesis, 180, 182f
Meiosis II
    animal and plant cells, 178f–179f
    gamete formation, 176
    generally, 171f, 173–74, 173f
    vs. mitosis, 177, 177t
    nondisjunction of chromosomes, 183f
    oogenesis, 181, 182f
    spermatogenesis, 180, 182f
Meissner corpuscles, 730
Melanin, 598, 599, 764
Melanism, industrial, 279–80, 290–92
Melanocytes, 597f, 598, 811
Melanocyte-stimulating hormone (MSH),
    757–58
Melanoma, 153, 165f, 598
Melanophores, 758
Melatonin, 704, 754f, 768
Mello, Craig, 246
Membrane attack complexes, 632
Membrane potential, 698
Membrane structure and
        function, 85–103
    active transport across a membrane,
        89t, 91, 95–99
    cell surface modification, 98–100
    passive transport across a membrane,
        91–94
    phospholipids in, 46, 48f
    plasma membrane structure and
        function, 86–91
    review and exercises, 101–3
Membrane-bounded organelles, three-
        domain system of
        classification, 352t
Membrane-first hypothesis, 331
Memory, 707, 719
Memory B cells, 634
Memory T cells, 636, 642
Menarche, 782
Mendel, Gregor, 193–201, 282
Mendeleev, Dmitri, 23

Mendelian patterns of inheritance, 192–213
  application extension, 205–10
  garden pea cross-pollination, 193–201
  incomplete dominance, 205–6
  incomplete penetration, 206
  multiple allelic traits, 205
  pleiotropic effects, 206–7
  polygenic inheritance, 207–8
  review and exercises, 211–13
  X-linked inheritance, 208–10
Mendel's laws, 195–204
  human genetic disorders and, 201–4
  independent assortment, 198–99
  probability, 200–201
  segregation, 195–96
Meniere's disease, 730
Meninges, 702
Meningitis, 702
Meniscus (pl., menisci), 743
Menkes (kinky hair) syndrome, 209–10
Menopause, 738, 782, 813
Menstrual cycle, 781–82
Menstrual pain, 768–69
Menstrual phase, of uterine cycle, 781, 782*t*
Menstruation, 781, 782
Mercury, 903
Meristem
  apical, 447
  in flowering plants, 447
  ground, 453
  intercalary, 447
  lateral, 453
  root apical, 450, 451f
Meristematic tissue, 161, 514
Merkel disks, 730
Merozoites, 394*f*
Merychippus, 297f, 323
Mesocarp, 510*f*, 511
Mesoderm, 523, 798–99, 798*t*, 808–9
Mesoglea, 528, 529*f*
Mesopelagic zone, 901*f*, 902
Mesophyll, 459
Mesosomes, 65, 66*f*
Mesozoic period
  continental drift, 342f
  generally, 340
  geologic timescale, 336t
  gymnosperm, 433
  mammalian diversification, 341
  mass extinctions, 343f
  movement from water to land, 339
Mesquite tree, 444
Messenger RNA. *See* mRNA
Metabolic pathways, 109
Metabolic pool, 147–49
Metabolic reactions, 107–8
Metabolism, 104–18
  aging process, 813
  amino acids, 681, 681f
  bacteria, 374–75
  cells and energy flow, 105–6
  defined, 4, 107
  hormones regulating, 760
  inborn error of, 223
  lactose, 239–40
  metabolic pathways and enzymes, 109–13
  metabolic reactions and energy transformations, 107–8
  organelles and energy flow, 113–15
  proteins, 49
  review and exercises, 116–18
Metacarpal bones, 740*f*, 742
Metamorphosis
  amphibian, 520f, 521, 556, 755
  arthropods, 540
  defined, 556
  frog, 520f, 521
  insects, 542, 543, 752–54
  urochordate, 551
Metaphase (mitosis)
  eukaryotic chromosome structure, 233f, 234
  generally, 158f, 159–60
  vs. meiosis, 177t, 180f
Metaphase I (meiosis), 176, 177, 177*t*, 178*f*, 180*f*
Metaphase II (meiosis), 176, 177*t*, 178*f*
Metaphase plate, 159, 173, 176

Metapopulations, 919
Metastasis, 164
Metatarsal bones, 740*f*, 742, 743*f*
Meteorites
  extraterrestrial origins hypothesis, 330
  impact on Earth, and mass extinction, 343–44
  primordial soup hypothesis, 329
Methamphetamine, 710
Methane, 27, 329, 876
Methanogen(s)
  archaea, 378–79
  classification, 354
  evolution of, 335f
Methanogenesis, 378
Methanosarcina mazei, 7f
Methemoglobinemia, 202, 203*f*
Methicillin-resistant *Staphylococcus aureus* (MRSA), 377
Methionine, 51*f*
Methoprene, 907
MHC (major histocompatibility complex) proteins, 632, 635, 643, 755
Mice. *See* Mouse
Microarrays, DNA, 264, 265
Microevolution, 289–305
  allele frequencies, 290–95, 292t
  defined, 289, 290
  diversity, maintaining, 300–303
  gene flow, 294
  genetic change, 290–95
  genetic drift, 294–95
  Hardy-Weinberg equilibrium, 290–96, 292t
  heterozygote advantage, 302–3
  HIV/AIDS, 289
  inbreeding, 202, 295, 300–301
  mutations, 292, 292t, 293–94
  natural selection, 292, 295–302
  in peppered moth, 290–92
  phylogenetic tree, 309
  review and exercises, 303–5
Microglia, 593
Micrometers, 62
Micronutrients, plants, 465, 466*t*
Microorganisms, 468. *See also* Bacteria; Virus(es); Yeast; *specific microorganism*
Microphyla nepenthicola, 306
Microphylls, 426, 427*f*
Micropores, 436
Micropyle, 437
Microraptor, 327
microRNA (miRNA), 227, 246
Microscopy, 60, 62, 63–64
Microspheres, 330, 331
Microsporangia, 431*f*, 437*f*
Microspores
  conifers (pine), 431f
  defined, 426, 502
  flowering plant reproduction, 437f, 504, 505
  seed plants, 430
Microtubule(s)
  in centriole, 79–80
  eukaryotic chromosomes, 157
  in flagella, 81f
  in sperm, 777
  structure and function, 68f–69f, 78–79
Microtubule organizing center (MTOC), 78
Microvilli (sing., microvillus)
  intestinal, 78, 652, 653f
  renal, 685f, 686, 687f
  taste buds, 718
Midas cichlid fish, 314
Midbrain, 695, 702*f*, 704
Middle ear, 726*f*, 727
Midshipman, 901*f*
Midwife toad, 848*f*
Mifepristone, 783–84
Migration
  biomes, 883, 887
  defined, 825
  of exotic species, 914
  gene flow and, 292, 292t, 294
  macroevolution, 307
  orientation in, 825
  phylogenetic tree, 309f
  population density and, 848
Mildew, 410
Milk, human, 782

Miller, Stanley, 329
Miller-Urey experiment, 329
Millipedes, 468, 526*t*, 541, 542*f*
Milstein, César, 635
Mimicry, 864
Mimosa pudica, 493
Mineral(s)
  defined, 465
  dietary requirement for, 660
  flowering plant nutrition, 465f
  in flowering plants, 465, 466t
  nutrition and human health, 660
  plant uptake of, 469–72
  in soil, 467
Mineralocorticoids, 754*f*, 762*f*, 763–64
Minke whale, 889
Miocene period, 296, 336*t*, 341
miRNA (microRNA), 227, 246
Misoprostol, 768
Mitchell, Peter, 114
Mites, 543, 911
Mitochondria
  in active tissues, 145
  of animal cell, 68f
  ATP production, 114–15
  cellular respiration, 76, 135, 137–46
  vs. chloroplasts, 148
  cristae of, 144, 145f
  diseases, 77
  from endosymbiosis, 384
  in eukaryotic cell, 67
  evolution of, 335f, 337
  genetic code used by, 224
  in lysosome, 73f
  of plant cell, 69f
  prokaryotic vs. eukaryotic cells, 82t
  in sperm, 777
  structure and function of, 77, 142, 145
Mitochondrial DNA (mtDNA), 337, 359, 579
Mitochondrial Eve hypothesis, 579
Mitosis, 152–61
  animal cells, 158f–159f
  cytokinesis, 160–61
  cytoplasmic segregation during, 800
  eukaryotes, 157, 167, 167t
  functions of, 161
  interphase preceding, 154, 158f
  in land plants, 422
  vs. meiosis, 177, 177t, 180f–181f
  phases of, 158–60
  plant cells, 158f–159f
  preparation for, 157–58
  prokaryotes, 167, 167t
  review and exercises, 168–70
  in spermatogenesis, 776f
  stem cells, 161
Mitotic spindle, 79, 80*f*, 155
Mitral valve, 611, 612*f*, 613. *See also* Bicuspid valve
Mixed nerves, 707
Mixotrophic protists, 384, 391, 395
Model(s)
  atom, 25
  chemical cycling, 874f
  climate change, 879, 916
  DNA, 54–55, 218–19
  ecological succession, 868–69
  enzymes, 110
  evolution of, 319, 320f
  in experimentation, 12
  island biogeography, 862
  muscle contraction, 745–46
  optimal foraging, 831
  plasma membrane, 87–88
  population growth, 843–46
  prokaryotic gene regulation, 238–39
  proteins, 265
  transport in leaves, 476f, 478–79
  water, 28f
Model organisms, 264, 800
Modification
  of cell surface, 98–100
  descent with, 8, 275
Molds
  as asexual sac fungi, 409
  classification of, 8
  as Eukarya, 354
  in human life, 410–11
  slime. See Slime molds
  water molds, 7, 385t

Molecular biology. *See* DNA; Gene(s)
Molecular clock, 338, 359
Molecular compound, 26–31
Molecular traits, phylogeny, 358–59
Molecules, 26–31
  biological organization, 3f
  bonding, 26–27
  defined, 2, 26
  inorganic, 38t
  organic, 38–41
  polar, 27
  water, 28–31
Moles (unit), 107
Molluscs, 534–36
  bivalve, 534–35
  cephalopod, 536
  characteristics, 526t
  circulatory system, 534, 535, 606–7
  digestion, 534, 535, 648–49
  gastropod, 535–36
  gravitational equilibrium organs in, 728, 728f
  nervous system, 534, 535, 694, 695, 696f
  reproduction, 774
  skeleton, 736
  vision, 720
Molting
  by arthropods, 539f, 540
  of exoskeleton, 736, 737f
  during metamorphosis, 752–54
  of protostomes, 523
Molybdenum, 466*t*
Monarch butterfly, 497*f*, 498, 825, 918
Mongoose, 915
Monitor lizards, 561
Monkeys
  auditory communication of, 828
  classification, 571
  hands, evolution of, 572f
  New World, 571f, 572, 573f, 574
  Old World, 571f, 572, 573f, 574
Monoclonal antibodies, 635, 642, 783
Monocot seeds, 509, 512
Monocots
  defined, 433
  vs. eudicots, 433t, 446, 510f
  flowers of, 503
  leaf, 459
  root diversity, 452, 461f
  roots of, 452
  stem, 455f
  stems of, 454
Monocotyledones, 433. *See also* Monocots
Monocytes, 620, 631
Monod, Jacques, 238, 239
Monoecious organisms, 773
Monoecious plants, 430, 503
Monogamy, 831
Monohybrid cross, 195, 196
Monomers, 40, 328, 329–30
Mononuclear cells (agranular leukocytes), 620
Monophyletic groupings, 308, 309, 384, 558
Monophyly, 309
Monosaccharides, 41, 42, 657
Monosomy, 183–84
Monotremes, 526*t*, 564, 565*f*, 566*t*
Mons pubis, 779*f*, 780
Monsoon climate, 885
Montane coniferous forests, 887, 890
Moose, 890*f*
Moray eel, 901
Morchlla, 406t, 409f
More-developed countries (MDCs), 851–53
Morels, 2, 406*t*, 408, 409*f*
Morgan, Thomas Hunt, 208–9
Morning glory, 458, 491, 494
Morning-after pill, 783–84
Morphogenesis, 800, 802–4
Morphogens, 802
Morphological data, phylogeny, 357–58
Morphological species concept, 307, 308*f*
Morphology, 307
Mortality patterns, 841–42, 841*t*, 851–52
Morula, 797, 806*f*
Mosaic evolution, 577
Mosquito, 394, 720, 842*f*

Moss(es)
  as bryophyte, 423
  characteristics, 421t
  described, 424
  dominant generation in, 422
  evolutionary history of plants, 420f
  gametophytes vs. sporophyte size, 423f
  as photosynthetic organism, 120f
  reproduction, 424, 425t
  soil formation, 467
  uses of, 425
Moths
  camouflage of, 864
  echolocation detected by, 826
  metamorphosis in, 752
  peppered, and industrial melanism,
    279–80, 290–92
  pheromones in, 826
  as pollinators, 518–19
  population dynamics, 846, 861
Motion of proteins, 49
Motor (efferent) neurons, 697f, 698
Motor area, primary, 703f, 704
Motor cells, in pulvinus, 493
Motor molecules, 78, 81f
Motor nerves, 707, 747–48
Motor output, as central nervous system
  function, 702
Motor speech area, 703f, 704
Mountains, 343, 885, 887
Mouse
  biotic potential, 841f
  genome of, 263t, 265
  Griffith's DNA and bacterial
    transformation experiments,
    215–17
  Hox genes, 524, 525, 803f, 804
  nurturing behavior in, 822
  population density, 846f, 847–48
  transgenic, experimental use of, 259
Mouth
  annelid, 647
  human, 650–51
  protostome, 523
Mouthbrooders, 773
Mouth-brooding frog, 848f
Movement. *See also* Locomotion
  fetal, 810
  nastic (turgor) movements, 493–95
  of organisms, water to land, 339, 423
  in response to environment, 4–5
MPPP, 706
MPTP, 112, 706
mRNA (messenger RNA)
  alternative splicing of, 244–45, 246
  anteroposterior polarity and, 802
  codons, 224
  defined, 223
  DSCAM mRNA, 237
  genomic structure, 261f, 262
  in hormone synthesis, 756
  in nucleus, 70
  in posttranscriptional control, 244–45
  pre-mRNA, 225–26, 237, 244–45
  production of, 225–26
  transcription, 223, 226
  translation, 229f, 230
MRSA (methicillin-resistant
  Staphylococcus aureus), 377
MS (multiple sclerosis), 705
MSH (melanocyte-stimulating hormone),
  757–58
mtDNA (mitochondrial DNA), 337,
  359, 579
MTOC (microtubule organizing center), 78
Mucosa, of digestive tract, 651
Mucus, 630, 651
Mudflats, 900
Mule, 312, 313f, 314
Müller, Fritz, 864
Müllerian mimicry, 864
Mullis, Kary, 256
Multicellular organisms
  algae, 388, 389, 390
  cell division, 167, 167t
  defined, 2
  domains, 7f
  fungi, 404
  origins of, 337
  reproduction, 5
  water in, 30

Multifactorial inheritance, human
  examples of, 207–8
Multifactorial traits, 207
Multiple alleles, 205
Multiple fruits, 510f, 511, 511t
Multiple sclerosis (MS), 705
Multipolar neurons, 697f, 698
Multiregion continuity hypothesis, 579–80
Mumps, 730
Mus musculus, 350
Muscaridine, 411
Muscle(s). *See also specific muscle*
  aging process, 812
  anatomy and physiology of, 744–49
  animal evolution, 520
  antagonistic, 744, 745f
  cardiac, 593, 612–13, 744
  circular, 736
  components, 592
  contraction of, 108, 744–49
  defined, 588
  epinephrine receptors in, 755–56
  fiber components, 592
  functions of, 592, 744
  glycogen storage, 657
  human, 744–49
  innervation of, 747–48
  longitudinal, 736
  mitochondria in, 145
  skeletal (striated). See Skeletal muscle
  smooth, 592–93, 608, 744
  tetany of, 744, 762
Muscle spindles, 730, 731f, 744
Muscle tone, 744
Muscular dystrophy, 210
Muscular hydrostat, 736
Muscular system (human), 744–49
  aging process, 812
  functions of, 596, 744
Muscularis, of digestive tract, 651
Mushrooms
  basidiomycota, 412–13
  classification of, 8
  club fungi, 404f, 406t, 412–13
  domain of, 7f
  as Eukarya, 354
  hallucinogenic, 411
  poisonous, 411, 412
Musk ox, 888
Mussels, 534, 535f, 914
Mutagens, 248, 293
Mutation, 247–50
  in Arabidopsis thaliana, 402
  carcinogenesis, 153, 163–64, 248–50
  causes of, 247–48
  chromosomal, 187
  defined, 247
  and evolution, 285–86
  Hardy-Weinberg equilibrium, 292, 292t,
    293–94
  of homeotic genes, 803, 804
  human evolution, 322
  induced, 248
  macroevolution, 307
  microevolution, 292, 292t, 293–94
  natural selection, 8
  phylogenetic tree, 309f
  in prokaryotes, 373
  protein activity effects, 248–49
  spontaneous, 247
  viruses, 365, 366, 370
Mutation microarray, 264
Mutualism
  bacteria, 375, 452, 471, 866
  and coevolution, 866–67
  defined, 865t, 866
  fungi, 408, 414–15, 866
  insects, 498, 501, 866
  plants, 471–72, 498, 501, 866–67
  protists, 384
Myasthenia gravis, 642
Mycelium, 403, 405
Mycobacterium tuberculosis, 642
Mycobond, 403
Mycologists, 404
Mycorrhizae
  fungal structure, 405
  in glomeromycota, 408
  mutualism, 866
  plant symbiosis, 414–15, 452, 472
  root specialization, 452

  as sac fungi, 410
  soil fertility, 414, 415f
Myelin, 593
Myelin sheath, 593, 697, 708f
Mylodon darwinii (extinct), 275
Myocardial infarction, 616
Myocardium, 610
Myofibrils, 745, 747f, 748
Myoglobin, 746
Myopia, 724
Myosin
  cytoskeleton, 78
  defined, 745
  functions of, 592
  in muscle contraction, 108, 745–46,
    747f, 748–49
  protein metabolism, 49
Myrica faya, 915
Myripristis jacobus, 555f
Myrtle trees, 915
Mysis relicta, 909
Mytilus edulis, 535f
Myxedema, 761

N

NAD⁺ (nicotinamide adenine
    dinucleotide)
  in cellular respiration, 114, 136–37
  in citric acid cycle, 143
NADH
  in citric acid cycle, 143
  in electron transport chain, 144, 145f
NADH-Q reductase, 144, 145f
NADP⁺ (nicotinamide adenine
    dinucleotide phosphate) DP
  energy transformation, 113
  in photosynthesis, 122–23
NADPH DP
  noncyclic electron pathway, 125–26
  in photosynthesis, 122–23
Nail(s), 598–99
Nail root, 598
Naked mole rats, 819, 826
Naming, scientific, 8, 349–50
Nanometers, 62
Nanos protein, 802
Nasal bones, 741
Nasal cavity, 667–68, 719
Nasal septum, 741
Nasopharynx, 651
Nastic (turgor) movements, 493–95
  biological clock, 494–95
  circadian rhythms, 494–95
  defined, 493
  responses to touch, 493–94
  sleep movements, 494
National Sleep Foundation, 655
Natriuresis, 690, 763
Natural groups, phylogeny, 348–49
Natural increase, rate of, 841
Natural killer (NK) cells, 632, 812
Natural selection
  vs. artificial selection, 278–80
  Darwin on, 277, 282
  defined, 277
  directional selection, 296–97
  disruptive selection, 296f, 297
  for diversity maintenance, 300–302
  in evolutionary theory, 8, 277–80
  Hardy-Weinberg equilibrium, 292,
    292t, 295
  inbreeding, 202, 295, 300–301
  life history patterns, 848
  macroevolution, 307
  mutation, 285–86
  niche specialization and, 860
  phylogenetic tree, 309f
  sexual selection, 297–99, 831–32
  stabilizing selection, 296
  survivorship curve and, 842
  types of, 296–97
Nature *vs.* nurture question, 208,
    820–26
Nautilus belauensis, 536f
Navigation, 825
Neander Valley, 580
Neandertals, 570, 580
Nearsightedness, 724
Nectar, 437
Nectar guides, 720

Needle sharing, diseases transmitted
    by, 789
Negative feedback
  defined, 600
  operation of, 600–601
  in osmoregulation, 757, 758f
  in reproductive cycles, 778, 780–81, 809
Neglected Tropical Diseases (NTD), 383,
    398–99, 519, 532, 539
Neisseria gonorrhoeae, 372, 790
Nematocyst, 528–29
Nematoda, 538. *See also* Roundworms
Neocortex, 696
Neogene period, 341
Neon, 23
Nepenthes ampullaria, 306
Nephridium (pl., nephridia), 536,
    537f, 682
Nephrons, 685–88
Nereis succinea, 537–38
Nereocystis, 390
Nerve(s)
  animal evolution, 520
  cranial, 696f, 708f
  defined, 707
  functions of, 593
  in skin, 597f
  spinal, 708f
  types of, 707
Nerve cells. *See* Neurons
Nerve cord, dorsal tubular, 550
Nerve fibers, 697, 707, 708f
Nerve impulses
  at neuromuscular junctions, 747–48
  sensory, 717
  synaptic integration of, 701
  transmission of, 698–701, 698f, 753
Nerve net, of hydra, 529, 694
Nervous system, 693–715. *See also*
    specific components; specific
    organisms
  aging process, 812
  autonomic, 696f, 708–9, 709t, 712f, 713
  bacterial diseases, 376t
  body temperature regulation, 601
  central, 696, 702–7. See also Brain;
    Spinal Cord
  components, 587
  drug abuse, 710–11
  embryonic development of, 799, 800,
    801f, 808–9
  endocrine system interaction, 753
  evolution of, 694–96
  functions of, 593, 596
  in homeostatic regulation, 600
  human, 696f, 812
  invertebrate, 694–95
  ladderlike, 531, 694
  nervous tissue, 697–701
  notochord, 550–52, 799, 800, 801f, 809
  peripheral, 696f, 707–9, 712f, 713
  reflex arc, 708, 709f
  respiratory center, 670–71
  review and exercises, 713–15
  somatic, 696f, 707, 708, 709t
  vertebrate, 552, 695–96
  viral diseases, 364t
Nervous tissue, 697–701
  components, 593
  defined, 588
  neuroglia, 697–98
  neurons, 697–98. See also Neurons
  transmission across synapse, 700–701
  transmission of nerve impulses,
    698–700
Nest-building behavior
  birds, 774f, 820–21, 847
  fish, 773
Nested categories of classification,
    349, 350f
Netted venation in eudicot leaf, 446, 458
Neural crest, 799
Neural plate, 799, 801f
Neural tube, 799, 807, 809
Neural tube defects, 807
Neuraminidase (N) spike, 370
Neurofibril nodes (nodes of Ranvier), 697
Neurofibrillary tangles, in Alzheimer
    disease, 707
Neuroglia, 593, 594, 697–98
Neurolemmocytes, 697

Neuromodulators, 701
Neuromuscular junction, 747–48
Neurons. *See also* Nervous system
  aging process, 812
  components, 593
  defined, 697
  motor (efferent), 697f, 698
  multipolar, 697f
  neuroglia vs., 594
  in retina, 723
  sensory (afferent), 697–98, 717
  types of, 697–98
  unipolar, 697f
  vertebrates, 695
Neurospora, 408
Neurotransmitters, 700–701, 747–48, 753
Neurula, 799
Neurulation, 799, 801f
Neutrons, 23
Neutrophils, 620, 631–32
New Guinea singing dog, 549
New World monkeys, 571f, 572, 573f, 574
Newborns, skull of, 740
Newts, 556–57
Niacin, 111, 660
Niche specialization, 859–60
Nickel, in plants, 465
Nickel sulfide, 329, 330
Nicotinamide adenine dinucleotide. *See*
  NAD$^+$
Nicotine, 710
Night blindness, 660
Night vision, 723
Night-blooming flowers, 437
Nine-banded armadillo, 910
Nirenberg, Marshall, 224
Nitrates
  ATP-driven proton pump, 470
  marine, 379
  in nitrogen cycle, 878
Nitric oxide (NO), 777
Nitrification, 878
Nitrifying bacteria, 375
Nitrogen
  ATP-driven proton pump, 470
  Bohr model of atom, 25f
  in fertilizer, 14–15, 877, 878
  legumes and wheat rotation study, 14–15
  nutritional function of soil, 467, 468
  in plants, 465, 466f, 466t
  pollution caused by, 878, 915
Nitrogen cycle, 452, 878
Nitrogen fixation, 375, 878
Nitrogen-fixing bacteria, 375, 452, 471, 878
Nitrogenous waste products, 681
Nitrous oxide, 876
NK (natural killer) cells, 632, 812
Noble gases, 23, 25
Nociceptors, 731
Noctiluca, 392
Nodes
  green algae, 421
  horsetails, 427
  phylogenetic tree, 309f
  of Ranvier, 697
  stems, 444f, 445, 462f
Nodules, root
  legumes, 14–15, 452
  nitrogen-fixing bacteria, 375, 452, 471, 878
Noise-induced hearing loss, 728–30
Nomenclature, binomial, 8, 349–50
Noncompetitive inhibition, 112, 113f
Noncyclic electron pathway, 124–25
Nondisjunction, 183
Nonessential amino acids, 148
Nonfunctional proteins, frameshift
  mutations, 248, 249
Nonionina, 385t
Nonmotile (sessile) organisms, 526t, 744
Nonrandom mating, 295, 300
Nonseptate fungi, 405
Nonspecific (innate) immunity, 627,
  630–33
Nonvascular plants, 420f, 423–25
Nonvertebrate chordates, 550–51
Nonwoody plants, 430
Nonylphenols, 915
Norepinephrine
  functions of, 613, 700–701, 754f, 762

  secretion of, 754f, 762
  sympathetic division, 713
North American bullfrog, 350f
Northern Leopard Frog, 308f
Northern spotted owl, 890, 909, 919
Nose
  anatomy of, 741
  human respiration, 667, 668f
  olfactory cells in, 719, 719f
Notochord, 550–52, 799, 800, 801f, 809
NTD (Neglected Tropical Diseases), 383,
  398–99, 519, 532, 539
Nuclear envelope
  cell structure and function, 68–69f,
    70f, 71
  during fertilization, 797
  three-domain system of
    classification, 352t
Nuclear pores, 69f, 70f, 71
Nucleariids, 385t, 386f, 398
Nucleic acids. *See also* DNA; RNA
  ATP, 55–56
  in common foods, 40t
  defined, 54
  organic chemistry, 38, 54–56
  viral, 366
Nucleoid, 65, 66f, 166, 372
Nucleolus
  cell structure and function, 68f–69f
  defined, 70
  meiosis, 173f
  prokaryotic vs. eukaryotic cells, 82t
Nucleoplasm, 70
Nucleosomes, 233, 242
Nucleotides
  defined, 54
  in DNA, 215, 217–19, 223t
  phylogenetic species concept, 308, 309
  in RNA, 223, 223t
  structure of, 54f
Nucleus (pl. nuclei)
  animal cell, 68f
  cancer cell, 163
  cell structure and function, 61f, 65,
    68–69f
  ciliates, 393–94
  eukaryotic cells, 67, 70–71, 82t
  plant cell, 69f
  prokaryotic cells, 82t
  sperm, 777, 796–97
Nudibranch, 534, 535
Nummulites, 399, 400f
Nutrients
  acquisition of, 4
  beneficial, defined, 465
  digestion of, 656–57
Nutrition
  bacteria, 353
  eukaryotes, 353, 354
  fungi, 405
  human, 657–60, 760, 807
  plant. See Plant nutrition
  protists, 384
  protocell, 332
Nymphs, 667

O

Obesity, 655, 658, 659–60
Obligate anaerobes, 374, 375
Obligate intracellular parasites, viruses
  as, 366
Observation
  evolution as, 285
  scientific method, 11, 14–16
Occipital bone, 740
Occipital lobe, 703f, 704
Ocean(s)
  animals in. See Aquatic animals;
    specific animal or fish
  as ecosystem, 897, 900f, 901–2
  temperature of, 885
Ocean currents, 344, 902–4
Ocean ridges, 330f, 332
Oceanic ridges, 902
Ochromonas, 391
Ocotillo, 896
Octet rule, atom electron shells, 25
Octopus
  circulatory system of, 607

  eye, 720
  learning, 536
  as mollusc, 534, 535
  organization of life, 2
  vision, 720
Odocoileus virginianus, 850
Odonata, 542f
Odor, 719
Oenothera (evening primrose), 720f
Oil(s)
  defined, 46
  dietary, 658
  functions of, 45t
  plant, synthesis of, 129
Oil drilling, Arctic, 19
Oil glands, 597f, 599, 630
Oil spills, clean-up, genetically modified
  bacteria for, 258
Okazaki, Reiji, 221
Okazaki fragments, 221
Old World monkeys, 298, 571f, 572,
  573f, 574
Oldowan tools, 582
Olfaction, 719
Olfactory bulb, 708f, 719
Olfactory cells, 719
Olfactory epithelium, 719
Olfactory nerve, 708f
Olfactory tract, 708f
Oligocene period, 336t, 341
Oligochaetes, 536
Oligodendrocytes, 593, 697
Oligotrophic lakes, 898
Oligozoospermia, 778
Omega-3 fatty acids, 617, 659
Ommatidium (pl., ommatidia), 720
Omnivores, 649, 870, 871–74
Oncogenes, 164, 165f, 249
"One gene–one enzyme hypothesis," 223
One-trait testcross, 201
One-way ventilation mechanism, 670
Onion, 458
Onion bulb, 460
Onychodromus, 385t
Oocyte(s), 182f, 779, 796–97, 806f
Oocyte donors, 785
Oogenesis, 181–83, 780
Oogonia, 181, 392
Oomycetes (water molds), 7, 385t, 386f,
  391–92
Opabinia, 338f
Oparin, Alexander, 329
Oparin-Handane hypothesis, 329
Open circulatory system, 606
Operant conditioning, 824–25
Operator, 238f, 239
Operculum (pl., opercula), 554, 666
Operon
  inducible, 240
  lac, 239–40
  repressible, 239
  trp, 238f, 239
Operon models of prokaryotic gene
  regulation, 238–39
Ophiuroidea, 544
Ophrys, 506
Opisthokonta
  choanoflagellates, 385t, 386f
  and fungi, 406, 407
  nucleariids, 385t, 386f
  protist supergroup, 385t, 386f, 397–98
Opossum, 564, 565f
Opossum shrimp, 909, 914
Opportunistic infections, AIDS-related,
  638, 787
Opportunistic species, 849
Opposable thumbs, 571
Opposite leaves, 460
Oprah Winfrey Show (TV program), 663
Opsin, 722–23
Optic chiasma, 708f
Optic lobes, 695
Optic nerve, 721, 723f
Optic vesicle, 809f
Optimal foraging model, 831
Opuntila, 461f
Oral cavity, human, 650–51, 650f
Oral groove of ciliates, 393f
Oral thrush (candidiasis), 410, 638
Orangutans, 571f, 572, 573f
Orbicularis oculi muscle, 744f

Orbicularis oris muscle, 744f
Orchid, 2, 472
Orchid seeds, 472
Orcinus orca (toothed whale), 308, 310f
Order (taxonomic). *See also* specific order
  classification of living things, 6, 6t
  Linnean, 349, 350f
  of placental mammals, 566t
Ordovician period
  geologic timescale, 336t
  mass extinction, 343, 344
  movement from water to land, 339, 423
  vertebrate evolution, 552
  vertebrates, 552
Organ(s). *See also* specific organ or system
  aging process, 811–13
  biological organization, 3f
  classification of life, 2
  defined, 2, 596
  of flowering plants, 444–46
  functions of, 595
  generally, 595
  internal. See Internal organs
  regeneration, 594–95
  stages of development, 799
  transplantation of, 643
  vegetative, 145, 444f
  vestigial, 272
Organ of Corti, 727–28
Organelles
  defined, 67
  energy flow, 76–77, 113–14
  origin of, 67f, 337
Organic chemicals, pollution from, 915
Organic chemistry, 37–59
  carbohydrates, 41–44
  defined, 38
  lipids, 45–49
  molecules, 38–41
  nucleic acids, 54–56
  proteins, 49–53
  review and exercises, 57–59
Organic molecules, 38–41
  biomolecules, 40–41
  carbon atom, 38–39
  carbon skeleton, 39–40
  chemistry of, 38–41
  classes of, 38
  defined, 38
  functional groups, 39–40, 39t
  vs. inorganic molecules, 38t
Organic nutrients, transport of, in plants,
  478–79
Organic pollutants, bioethical issues, 59
Organisms
  biological organization, 3f
  defined, 2
  genetic transformation of, 216–17
  model, 264, 800
  multicellular. See Multicellular
    organisms
  photosynthetic, 120–21
  unicellular. See Unicellular organisms
Organization
  of animal systems, 587–604
  biological, 2, 3f
  of biosphere, 9–10
  cellular level of, 61–62
  of flowering plants and structures,
    443–63
  of life, 3f
Orgasm
  female, 780
  male, 777–78
Orientation, 825
Origin of life, 328–32
  stage 1: evolution of organic
    monomers, 328, 329–30
  stage 2: evolution of organic polymers,
    328, 330
  stage 3: evolution of protocells, 328,
    330–32
  stage 4: evolution of living cells and
    self-replication system, 328, 332
Origin of replication, DNA, 222
On the Origin of Species (Darwin), 282
Orlistat (Xenical), 655
Oryza sativa, 492
Oscillatoria, 377f
Osculum, 527
Osmolarity, 686

Osmoreceptors, 684
Osmoregulation
  aging process, 812
  in aquatic vertebrates, 680, 682–83, 683f
  defined, 681
  hormones in, 688–90, 757, 758f, 763
  by kidneys, 682–84, 686, 687f, 688–90,
    757, 758f, 763
Osmosis
  effect on cells, 101t
  in osmoregulation, 688
  passive transport, 92–94
  in urine formation, 686
Osmotic potential, 474
Osmotic pressure, 93, 469, 621
Osmunda cinnamomea, 428f
Ossicles, 726f, 727
Ossification, 738
Osteichthyes, 554
Osteoarthritis, 743
Osteoblasts, 738
Osteoclasts, 738, 761
Osteocytes, 738–40
Osteogenesis imperfecta, 203
Osteons, 591, 738
Osteoporosis, 660, 738, 812
Ostium (pl., ostia), 606, 607f
Ostracoderms, 553
Ostrich fern, 429
Ostriches, 562
Otolith(s), 728, 729f
Otolithic membrane, 728, 729f
Outer ear, 726–27
Outer membrane, of nuclear envelope, 70f
Outgroup, in cladistics, 356
Out-of-Africa hypothesis, 579, 583
Oval window, 726f, 727
Ovarian cycle, 780–81, 782t
Ovaries (sing., ovary), 181
  defined, 434
  flower, 436f, 502f, 503
  human
    aging process, 813
    hormonal control of, 780–81
    hormones secreted by, 754f, 756,
      758f, 767, 779
    structure and function, 767, 779,
      779t, 806f
Overexploitation, 916–18
Overturn, lake, 898–99
Oviducts, 589, 779–80, 779t, 806f
Oviparous animals, 774
Ovipositor, 772
Ovoviviparous animals, 774
Ovulation, 779, 780–81, 782t, 806f
Ovule, flowers, 430, 434, 436, 437, 502–5
Ovum (pl., ova), 779. *See also* Egg(s)
Owls
  niche specialization, 860
  northern spotted, 890, 909, 919
  snowy, 888
Oxaloacetate, 130
Oxidation
  in cellular respiration, 136
  defined, 113
Oxidation-reduction reaction, 113, 122
Oxygen
  Bohr model of atom, 25f
  in cellular respiration, 136, 144
  covalent bonding, 27
  as essential plant nutrient, 465
  gas exchange, 664f, 666f, 671
  in muscle contraction, 747
  origin of life, 332, 333f, 335, 339
  plant acquisition of, 466, 466t
  production of, in photosynthesis, 120,
    122
  respiration, 669–72
  transport of, 669–72
Oxygen debt, 140, 747
Oxygen transport, red blood cells, 592
Oxyhemoglobin, 672
Oxytocin, 601, 754f, 757, 758f
Oysters, 534, 774
Ozone depletion, 915
Ozone shield, 335, 915

P

P generation, Mendel's experiments,
  195–96, 198f

P16 gene, Peyer patches, 249–50
p53 protein, 155, 156, 164
Pacemaker, cardiac, 613
Pacific yew, 497
Pacinian corpuscles, 730
Pain receptors, 731
Pair-rule genes, 524, 803
Pakicetus, 281
Pakicetus attocki, 310f
Palate, 650, 651f
Paleocene period, 336t
Paleogene period, 341
Paleontology, 333
Paleozoic period, 338–39
  Cambrian life, 338
  chordates, 552
  continental drift, 342f
  generally, 338
  geologic timescale, 336t
  invertebrates, 339
  mass extinctions, 343–44
  movement from water to land, 339
  plants, 339
  vertebrates, 339, 552
Palisade mesophyll, 459
Palmate compound leaves, 460
Palmate netted venation, eudicot leaf, 446
Palolo worms, 773
Palumbi, Stephen, 889
Pampas, 894
PAMPs (pathogen-associated molecular
  patterns), 627
Pan troglodytes, 571f
Panacanthus cuspidatus, 893f
Pancreas
  blood glucose regulation, 765
  disorders of, 765–67. See also Diabetes
    mellitus
  hormones secreted by, 754f, 765
  human digestive tract, 650f, 652
  structure and function, 599, 654, 765
Pancreatic amylase, 654
Pancreatic exocrine glands, 589
Pancreatic islets, 765, 766
Pancreatic juice, 654
Panda, 918
Pandemics, 363, 370, 371
Pandinus, 543f
Pangaea, 342, 344, 868
Panoramic vision, 721
Panther, 849, 893f
Panthera onca, 893f
Pantheropsis obsoleta lindheimeri, 302f
Pantheropsis obsoleta obsoleta, 302f
Pantheropsis obsoleta quadrivittata, 302f
Pantheropsis obsoleta rossalleni, 302f
Pantheropsis obsoleta spiloides, 302f
Papilio memnon, 864
Papillae, of tongue, 718, 718f
Papio anubis, 571f
Papio hamadryas, 831f
Parabasalids, 385t, 386f, 395
Parallel venation, monocot leaf,
  446, 458
Paralysis, 703
Paramecium
  as Chromalveolata, 393
  classification of, 354
  competition among, 859–60
  domain of, 7f
  organization of life, 2
  phagocytosis by, 97–98
  predator-prey interactions, 861
Paramylon, 395
Paranthropus, 577
Paraphyletic group, 558
Paraplegia, 703
Parapodia, 537
Parasaurolophus, 340
Parasaurolophus wakeri, 340f
Parasitism
  bacteria, 375–76, 865
  and coevolution, 867
  defined, 861, 865
  disease caused by, 383
  flatworms, 532–34
  obligate intracellular, 366
  population density and, 848, 865
  as predation, 861, 865
  root specialization, 452
  social, 867

  as symbiosis, 865, 865t
  viruses, 366, 865
Parasympathetic division, autonomic
  nervous system, 696f, 709t,
  712f, 713
Parathyroid glands, 754f, 760, 761–62
Parathyroid hormone (PTH), 738, 754f,
  761–62
Parenchyma, 454f, 455f
Parenchyma cells, 448, 449f, 450, 459
Parent cell, chromosome duplication, 157
Parenting
  in birds, 774f, 823–24
  fitness strategies, 831
  in humans, 825
  in mice, 822
Parietal bones, 740
Parietal lobe, 703f, 704
Parkinson, James, 706
Parkinson disease (PD), 112, 264, 593,
  693, 704, 706
Parsimony, 356
Parthenogenesis, 773
Partial pressure, gas exchange, 671
Particulate theory of inheritance, 193
Parturition. *See* Birth
Passion flower, 7f
Passive immunity, 637–39
Passive transport, 91–94
  diffusion, 91–92
  facilitated, 94
  osmosis, 92–94
Pasteur, Louis, 141, 364–65, 371, 372f,
  746
Patagonian cavy, 275–76, 283
Patagonian Desert, 273f
Patched gene, 246
Patella, 740f, 743f
Pathogen(s), 376, 592, 597
Pathogen-associated molecular patterns
  (PAMPs), 627
Pattern formation, 800, 802–3
Pauling, Linus, 51
Pavlov, Ivan, 824
Pax6 gene, 320–21
PCR (polymerase chain reaction), 256–57
PD (Parkinson disease), 112, 264, 593,
  693, 704, 706
PDE-5 enzyme, 778
Pea plants
  cross-pollination, 193–94
  gene flow through cross-pollination,
    294f
  Mendel's cross-pollination experiments,
    193–201
  structure of, 194f
Pea pod, 510f, 512
Peach, 510f
Peach leaf curl, 408f, 409f
Peacocks/peahens, 79f, 831
Pear, 449
Pearl, Raymond, 844
Peat moss, 425
Pecten, 535f
Pectins, 100
Pectoral fins, 553
Pectoral girdle, 740f, 742
Pectoralis major muscle, 744f
Pedigree analysis, 201–4, 209
Pedipalps, 543
Peduncle of flower, 433, 502f, 503
Pelagic zone, 900f, 901
Pellagra, 717
Pellicle, 393, 395
Pelvic cavity, 596, 742
Pelvic fins, 553
Pelvic girdle, 740f, 742, 743f
Pelvic inflammatory disease (PID), 790
Pelvic-fin genes, in stickleback, 312
Penetration
  incomplete, Mendelian patterns of
    inheritance, 206
  in lytic cycle, 367f, 368
Penguins, 5
Penicillin, 11, 377, 410, 910
Penicillium, 11, 409, 410
Penis, 774, 777–78
Pentose sugar, 42, 54
PEP carboxylase in C4 plants, 130–31
PEPFAR (President's Emergency Plan for
  AIDS Relief) program, 788

Peppered moths, 279–80, 290–92
Pepsin, 652, 656
Peptidases, 656
Peptide bond, 50
Peptide hormones, 755–56
Peptidoglycan, 41f, 44, 65, 374
Perceptions, 717
Perennial plants, 444
Perfect flower, 434t, 503
Perforation plate, 449, 450, 473, 474, 475f
Perforin, 636
Pericardium, 610, 610f
Pericarp
  fruit, 510f, 511, 511t
  monocot seed, 509, 512
Pericycle, 451, 452f
Periderm, 447, 455f, 456
Period gene, 830
Periodic table, 23
Periosteum, 739f
Peripheral nervous system (PNS)
  autonomic system, 708–9, 709t, 712f,
    713
  defined, 696
  human, 696f
  reflex arc, 708, 709f
  somatic system, 708, 709t
Perissodactyla, 566t
Peristalsis, 651
Peritoneum, 652
Peritonitis, 653
Peritubular capillaries, 685f, 686, 687f
Permafrost, 888
Permeability of plasma membrane, 89,
  89t, 91
Permian period
  geographic timescale, 336t
  geologic timescale, 336t
  mass extinctions, 343, 344
  movement from water to land, 339
  reptiles, 340
Peroneal nerve, 696f
Peroneus longus muscle, 744f
Peroxisomes, 68f–69f, 73f, 75, 82t
Pest control, biological, 910–11
Pesticides
  as cancer cause, 165f
  deformed frogs, 907
  resistance to, 280, 911
PET (positron-emission tomography), 24
Petals, 434, 502f, 503
Petaurus breviceps, 283f
Petiole, 444f, 445, 460
Petromyzon, 553f
Peyer patches, 139f, 164, 630, 651
pH
  of acids and bases, 32–33
  of blood, 32–33, 690
  buffers, 33–34
  defined, 32
  enzymatic speed, 111
  optimal, for enzymes, 111
  of rainwater, 33
  of stomach, 652
  thermoacidophiles, 354, 378f, 379
Phagocytes, 629, 631–32
Phagocytosis, 97–98, 396
Phalanges, 740f, 742, 743f
Pharmaceutical products, vertebrate-
  derived, 560
Pharyngeal pouches, 284, 550, 809
Pharyngitis, 673
Pharynx
  earthworm, 647–48
  human, 650f, 651
  planarian, 647
Phase contrast microscopy, 64
Phenomenon, 11
Phenotype
  allele frequencies, and microevolution,
    290
  defined, 197
  vs. genotype, 196–97
  monohybrid cross results, 195
  multifactorial inheritance, 207–8
Phenylalanine, 51f, 224, 258
Pheromones, 312, 718, 755, 826–28
Philadelphia chromosome, 188
Phloem
  defined, 426, 473
  in eudicots, 451f

functions of, 473
in monocots, 452
organic nutrient transport, 478–79
pressure-flow model, 478–79
primary, 453, 455f, 462f
in stem, 453, 454f, 455, 457f
structure and function, 426f,
449–50, 473
in tree trunk, 457f
in vascular cylinder, 451–52
Phloem rays, 455f, 456
Phloem sap, 473, 478, 478f
Pholidota, 566t
Phoronidia, 530
Phoronids, 530
Phosphatases, 244
Phosphate
ATP-driven proton pump, 470
blood levels of, 761
inorganic, 107
mining of, 877
in nucleotide, 54
in osmoregulation, 690
in phosphorus cycle, 877
Phosphate functional groups, 39t
Phosphocreatine (creatine
phosphate), 746
Phospholipid(s), 45t, 46, 48f
Phospholipid bilayer, 86–87, 330–31
Phosphorus, 25f, 466f, 470
Phosphorus cycle, 877
Phosphorylation, 108, 138
Photoautotrophs, 375, 870
Photoperiod, 494
Photoperiodism, 483, 495–96
Photoreceptors, 717, 720, 722–23
Photorespiration, 130
Photosynthesis, 119–34
absorption spectrum and pigments, 124
bacteria, 335, 351–52, 375
biodiversity, 913
C$_3$, 130, 131
C$_4$, 130–31
Calvin cycle in, 123, 128–29
CAM, 130–31
carbon dioxide fixation, 128–29
vs. cellular respiration, 148
chloroplasts, 76–77
cyanobacteria, 66, 377
defined, 4, 120
domains, 7–8
in ecosystems, 9, 871–73
electrons and energy, 25
energy flow and transformation, 104,
105, 113–14, 871
equation for, 76
evolution of organisms, 335
in flowering plants, 121
leaves, 121, 445
light reactions in, 122–23, 124–25
noncyclic electron pathways, 124–26
organisms engaged in, 120–21
photosynthetic organisms, 120–21
pigments in, 124
process of, 122–23
reaction equation for, 122
review and exercises, 131–34
solar energy conversion and, 124–27
Photosynthetic pigments, 124
Photosystem, defined, 124
Photosystem I (PS I), 124–26
Photosystem II (PS II), 124–26
Phototropism
auxins, 483, 485–86
defined, 490, 491
Phrenic nerves, respiration, 670
Phylogenetic species concept, 308,
310, 311f
Phylogenetic tree
of animals, 521–22, 525f
of chordates, 551f
cladistic, 356, 357f
defined, 309f
symmetry and body plan of animals,
521–22, 525f
three-domain system, 351f
Phylogeny, 354–59
behavioral data, 358
cladistics, 356, 357f
defined, 308, 348
forensic, 347

fossil record, 356–57
of HIV gene, 347
interpreting, 354–55
molecular clock, 359
molecular traits, 358–59
morphological data, 357–58
protein comparison, 359
tracing, 356–59
Phylum (pl., phyla, taxonomic). See also
specific phyla
classification of living things, 6, 6t
Linnean, 349, 350f
Physalia, 528f
Physarum, 397f
Physical barriers, 630
Physical defenses, plant responses,
496–97
Phytochrome, 483, 495–96
Phytochrome conversion cycle, 495–96
Phytophthora infestans, 391
Phytoplankton
algae, 391, 870
estuarine, 900
lakes, 899
oceans, 901
Phytoremediation, 470–71
PID (pelvic inflammatory disease), 790
Pigeon pea plant, 14–15
Pigments, 124, 389
Pike, 902f
Pileated woodpeckers, 563f
Pili, conjugation, 66
Pillbugs, 682
Pine (tree)
as conifers, 430–31
life cycle of, 430, 431f, 432
mutualism, 866
organization of life, 2
uses of, 431
Pine nuts, 431
Pineal gland, 702f, 704, 754f, 768
Pineapple, 131f, 510f
Pinedrops, 472
Pingelap island, inbreeding, 300–301
Pinna, 726f, 727
Pinnate compound leaves, 460
Pinnate netted venation, eudicot leaf, 446
Pinocytosis, 98
Pinus contorta, 430f
Pinus longaeva, 430
Pinworms, 526t, 539
Pisum arvense, 294f
Pisum sativum. See also Garden pea
cross-pollination, 193–94
gene flow through cross-pollination, 294f
structure of, 194f
Pit(s), in tracheids, 449
Pitcher plant, 306, 461
Pith
of monocot root, 452
in stem, 453, 454f, 455f, 462f
in tree trunk, 457f
woody twig, 456f
Pituitary dwarfism, 758, 759f
Pituitary gland
anterior, 757–59, 778, 780–81
hormones secreted by, 589, 754f,
757–59
hypothalamic control of, 757, 758f
posterior, 757, 758f
structure of, 702f, 757
vertebrate, 695f, 696
Pivot joints, 743
Placenta
evolution of, 774
in green algae, 422
human, 782, 805, 809–10, 811f
in mammals, 564
structure and function of, 774, 809
Placental mammals, 564–65, 566t, 774
Placoderms, 334f, 553–54
Plague, 848
Plan B, 783
Planarians. See also Flatworms
characteristics, 526t
digestive tract, 647
evolution of, 531–32
excretory system, 682
eye, 720
hydrostatic skeleton, 736

nervous system, 694
transport in, 606
Plankton, 384, 391, 899
Plant(s)
algal relatives of, 421–22
alternation of generations in, 422
ancestry of, 420–21
vs. animals, 520
aquatic, 899, 900
artificial selection of, 278
asexual reproduction of, 513–14
body organization, 444f
C$_3$, 130, 131
C$_4$, 130–31
Cambrian period, 339
carbohydrate synthesis in, 105–6
as carbon dioxide fixers, 128–29
cells of. See Plant cells
characteristics, 421t
circadian rhythms, 494–95
classification of, 354
color of, 119
defenses of, 447–48, 483, 484f, 496–98
defined, 420
desert, 896
dicot. See Dicots
diploid chromosome numbers, 157t
diversity of, 420–39
dominant generation in, 422
ecological succession, 868–69
energy acquisition by, 4
eudicot. See Eudicots
evolution of, 419–42
flowering. See Flowering plant(s)
fungal diseases of, 410
gametophytes vs. sporophyte size, 423f
genetically modified, 254, 258, 419
geologic timescale, 336t
glucose storage in, 43, 43f, 657
growth response controls, 483–500
gymnosperms. See Gymnosperms
hormones. See Plant hormones
insectivorous, 460–61, 461f
land. See Land plants
leaves of. See Leaf (pl., leaves)
life cycle of, 180
life history strategy of, 843f, 849
medicinal, 910
monocot. See Monocots
mutualism, 866–67
in nitrogen cycle, 878
nitrogen fixation, 375
nonvascular, 420f, 423–25
nutrition. See Plant nutrition
organs of, 444–45, 446f
parasitic, 472, 865
photosynthesis. See Photosynthesis
phytoremediation, 470–71
reproduction, 501–17
responses of. See Plant responses
review and exercises, 440–42
roots of. See Root(s)
seed, 403t, 420f, 438–47. See
also Flowering plant(s);
Gymnosperms; Seed(s)
signal transduction, 484–85, 490,
492, 497f
sleep movements, 494
soil, 466–69
as solar energy converters, 124–27
stems of. See Stem(s)
tissue culture of, 513–14
transport in, 472–79
tropisms, 490–91, 493
tundra, 888
uses of, 470–71
vacuoles of, 75–76
vascular. See Vascular plants
water transport in, 30, 469, 475–77
Plant cells. See also Eukaryotic cells
anatomy of, 69f
cell surfaces, 100
cell walls of, 67, 100
cytokinesis, 160
lilac leaves, 61f
meiosis I and II, 178f–179f
mitosis, 158f–159f
organelle origin, 67f
osmosis in, 93–94, 93f
peroxisomes in, 75
turgor movement, 493–94

Plant evolution, 419–42
bryophytes (nonvascular, land
colonization), 420f, 423–25
evolutionary tree, 6f
generally, 339, 340
green algae (from freshwater to land),
420–22, 423f
lycophytes, 420f, 426
maize, 438–39
pteridophytes (megaphylls), 420f,
427–29
review and exercises, 440–42
seed plants (land adaptation), 420f,
430–39
tree of life, 335f
Plant hormones, 484–89
abscisic acid (ABA), 488
auxins, 485–86
cytokinins, 487–88
defined, 484
ethylene, 488–89
gibberellins, 486–87
phytochrome, 483
review and exercises, 498–500
signal transduction, 484–85, 490,
492, 497f
Plant nutrition, 465–82
acquisition of, 466
deficiency, 465, 466f
essential, 465–66
minerals, 469–72
review and exercises, 480–82
soil, 465–69, 466–69
transport mechanisms, 472–79
water uptake, 465, 469–72
Plant responses, 490–500
animal relationships, 498
chemical defenses, 496–97
defenses, 447–48, 483, 484f, 496–98
to environment, 460, 483, 496–98
hypersensitive, 498
indirect defenses, 498
nastic (turgor) movements, 493–95
photoperiodism, 495–96
physical defenses, 496–97
review and exercises, 498–500
sequence of events, 490
signal transduction, 484–85, 490,
492, 497f
tropisms, 490–91, 493
to wounds, 497–506
Plantae (kingdom), 8, 351, 421t
Plantlets, 514, 514f
Plaque, atherosclerotic, 616, 617f
Plasma, 591f, 618, 618f
Plasma cells, 634, 634f
Plasma membrane
active transport across, 89t, 91, 95–98
of animal cells, 68f
bulk transport, 91
carbohydrate chains, 88
cell signaling, 90
components of, 86–87
defects of, 85
of eukaryotic cell, 67, 82t, 85f
fluid-mosaic model, 87–88
invagination of, 67f
origin of, 330–31
permeability, 89, 89t, 91
phospholipids in, 46, 48f, 330–31
of plant cells, 69f
of prokaryotic cells, 65, 66f, 82t
prokaryotic vs. eukaryotic cells, 82t
protein functions, 88–89
protocell vs. modern cell, 331f
of sensory receptors, 717, 722
structure and function, 86–91, 331f
Plasma proteins, 618, 632, 654
Plasmids, 65, 255, 372
Plasmin, 620
Plasmodesmata, 100, 421, 450, 469
Plasmodial slime molds, 386f, 396–97
Plasmodium, 385t, 394, 396, 397f, 867
Plasmodium vivax, 394
Plasmolysis, 94
Plasmopara viticola, 391
Plastids, 77, 385t, 387
Plastoquinone (Pq) complex, 126
Plate tectonics, 343
Platelets, 591f, 592, 620
Plato, 272

Platyhelminthes, 531. *See also* Flatworms
Play, 827
Plectorhincus chaetodontoides, 866f
Pleiotropy, 206-7
Pleistocene overkill, 581
Pleistocene period, 336t, 341, 581
Pleurobrachia pileus, 528f
Pliocene period, 336t, 341
Plumule, 509, 512f
Pluripotent stem cells, 594
PMS (premenstrual syndrome), 782
Pneumocystis, 638, 674
Pneumonia, 638, 674
PNS. *See* Peripheral nervous
    system (PNS)
Poaching, 916
Poikilothermic animals, 599
Point mutations, 248, 250
Poison arrow frog, 848f, 864f, 893f
Polar bears, 888
Polar bodies, 181, 182f, 780
Polar easterlies, 885
Polar nuclei, 436, 437
Polar regions, 884, 887, 888
Polar spindle fibers, 158f-159f, 160
Polarity
    covalent bonding, 27
    in embryonic development, 797, 800,
      802, 804
    functional groups, 40, 42
    hydrogen bonding, 28
Polio virus, 366
Pollen allergy, 641
Pollen cones, 430f, 431f, 432
Pollen grains
    anther tissue culture, 514
    conifers (pine), 431f
    defined, 430
    examples of, 505f
    flowering plant reproduction, 436f,
      502, 503, 504f, 505
Pollen sac, 431f, 437f, 505f
Pollen tube, 430, 434f, 437, 504f, 505
Pollination. *See also* Cross-pollination
    conifers (pine), 431f
    defined, 430
    flowering plant reproduction, 437-38
Pollinators
    agricultural value of, 911
    bats, 507, 911f
    bees, 437, 501f, 506-7, 911
    birds, 437, 505, 507
    butterflies, 506-7, 867
    in flowering plant reproduction, 501,
      518-19
    moths, 518-19
    and plants, mutualism of, 501
    seed dispersal by, 437
Pollution
    air, 33, 414, 878
    atmospheric, 876-78, 915
    bioethical issues, 59
    chemical cycling, 875
    defined, 915
    extinction caused by, 915
    mercury, 903
    organic chemicals, 915
    phytoremediation, 470-71
    remediation, 912
    water, 875, 877, 915
Poly-A tail, of RNA molecules, 226, 247
Polyandry, 831
Polychaetes, 526t, 537-38
Polydactyly, 206
Polygamy, 831
Polygenic inheritance, 207-8, 296
Polymer(s), 40-41, 328, 330
Polymerase chain reaction (PCR), 256-57
Polymorphonuclear cells (neutrophils),
    620, 631-32
Polynucleotide, 54
Polyorchis penicillatus, 528f
Polyp(s), 528, 529f, 654
Polypeptides, 50, 51f
Polyploidy, 314
Polyribosomes, 68f, 71, 229f, 230
Polysaccharides, 41, 42-44
Polyspermy, 797
Polytrichum, 425t
Poly-X females (superfemale), 186

Ponds, 31f, 899
Pongo pygmaeus, 571f
Pons, 702f, 704
Poplar, 470, 859
Population(s), 838-56
    age distribution, 842-43, 852-53
    biological organization, 3f
    competition between, 859-60, 861f
    defined, 2, 290, 839
    demographics of, 840-43
    density of, 840, 846-49
    distribution in, 840, 842-43, 852-53
    ecology, scope of, 839
    in ecosystems, 9. See also Community
    environmental impact of, 301-2, 853
    evolution in. See Macroevolution;
      Microevolution
    growth of. See Population growth
    human, 9-10, 851-53
    life history patterns, 848-49
    metapopulations, 919
    models of growth, 843-46
    mortality patterns, 841-42, 841t, 851-52
    overproduction potential of, 277
    parasitism, 848, 865
    polymorphism, 301-2
    predation, 847-48, 861-63
    review and exercises, 854-56
    sink, 919
    size regulation, 846-48, 850, 851
    source, 919
    variation in, 277
Population genetics, 290. *See also*
    Microevolution
Population growth, 841-43
    carrying capacity, 845-46, 863
    environmental impact of, 853
    exponential, 844
    human, 851-53
    logistic, 844-45, 848-49
    models of, 843-46
Porcupine, 863
Pore mushrooms, 413f
Porphyra, 206, 389
Porpoise, 901
Portal system, 614, 757, 758f
Portuguese man-of-war, 528, 529f
Positive feedback, 601, 757, 781, 916
Positive reinforcement, 825
Positron, 24
Positron-emission tomography (PET), 24
Postanal tail, 550
Posterior axes, 802, 804
Posterior compartment, eye, 721
Posterior pituitary gland, 757, 758f
Postganglionic fibers, 709, 712f
Postreproductive group, 842-43, 852
Postsynaptic membrane, 700
Posttranscriptional control, 241, 244-46
Posttranslational control, 241, 247
Postzygotic species isolating mechanisms,
    310, 312, 313f
Potassium
    ATP-driven proton pump, 469f, 470,
      477-79
    ions, 26
    nutritional function of soil, 467
    in plants, 466t
    sodium-potassium pump, 95, 96f,
      698-700
Potassium-argon dating, 334
Potatoes, 448, 458
Potential energy, 105
Powdery mildew, 410
Pq (plastoquinone) complex, 126
Prairie, 894
Prawn, 901f
Prayer plant, 494
Praying mantis, 649
Precambrian period, 334-37
    eukaryotic cells arise, 335, 337
    generally, 334-35
    geologic timelines, 334-35, 336t
    multicellular protists arise, 337
    tree of life, 335f
Precapillary sphincters, 608, 609f, 622f
Precipitation, 875, 884, 897, 912
Predation
    coevolution and, 867
    defined, 860

population dynamics, 847-48, 861-63
predator-prey interactions, 860-63
Prediction, in scientific process, 11
Pre-ejaculate, 777
Prefrontal area, 703f, 705-6
Preganglionic fibers, 709, 712f
Pregnancy, human. *See also* Birth
    birth defects, 807
    development during. See Human
      development
    ectopic, 779
    fertilization, 182f, 779-80, 782,
      796-97, 806
    HIV infection during, 788
    length of, 804
    nutrition during, 760, 807
    prevention of, 783-84, 852
    Rh incompatibility during, 620
    skeletal system and, 742
    trimesters of, 805
Pregnancy in male seahorses, 772, 774
Preimplantation genetic diagnosis, 786
Premenstrual syndrome (PMS), 782
Premnas biaculeatus, 865f
Premotor area
    alternative splicing of, 244-45
    location in brain, 703f
    pre-mRNA, 225-26, 237
Pre-mRNA
    alternative pre-mRNA splicing, 244-45
    premotor area, 225-26, 237
Prenatal genetic testing, 204, 807
Preparatory (prep) reaction, 137, 142-43
Preprogrammed theories of aging, 813
Prereproductive group, 842-43, 852
Presbyopia, 812
Pressure potential, 474
Pressure receptors, 730
Pressure-flow model of phloem transport,
    478-79
Presynaptic membrane, 700
Preven, 783
Prey
    defenses of, 863-64
    defined, 860
    interactions with predators, 860-63
    population density of, 847-48, 861-63
Prezygotic isolating mechanisms, 310,
    311f, 312
Prickly-pear cactus, 861
Primaevifilum, 337f
Primary auditory area, 703f, 704
Primary growth, stem, 455
Primary lymphoid organs, 629
Primary meristem, 462f
Primary motor area, 703f, 704
Primary nondisjunction, 183
Primary organizer, 800
Primary ossification center, 738
Primary phloem, 453, 455f, 462f
Primary root, 444f, 452
Primary somatosensory area, 703f, 704
Primary structure, of proteins, 50-51, 52f
Primary succession, 868
Primary taste area, 703f, 704
Primary visual area, 703f, 704
Primary xylem, 453, 455f, 456f, 462f
Primates. *See also* Apes; Human(s);
    Monkeys; *specific animal*
    auditory communication by, 828
    characteristics, 566t, 571-72
    diversity of, 571f
    evolution of, 341, 358f, 359, 571-75
    fossils of, 572
    hands, evolution of, 572f
    molecular clock for, 358f, 359
    reproductive strategies in, 831
    social behavior in, 826, 828f, 829, 833
Primitive gut, 523, 523f, 798-99
Primitive streak, 798, 808
"Primordial soup" hypothesis, 329
Principles
    competitive exclusion, 860
    of evolution, 12, 318-23
    Hardy-Weinberg, 291
Principles of Geology (Lyell), 274
Prion, 53, 369, 371
PRL (prolactin), 754f, 755, 757, 758f, 782
Probability
    of error, in experiments, 12

Mendel's law of, 200-201
product rule of, 200
sum rule of, 200
Proboscidea, 566t
Procambium, 451f, 453, 462f, 509
Procambium meristem, 447
Proconsul, 574, 575f
Proctitis, 790
Producers, 870
Product, 107
Product rule of probability, 200
Proembryo, eudicot development, 508
Progesterone
    contraceptive use of, 783
    in ovarian and uterine cycles, 779,
      781-82
    secretion of, 767-68, 809
Proglottids, 543
Programmed cell death. *See* Apoptosis
Progymnosperms, 430, 435
Prokaryotes, 371-73. *See also* Archaea;
    Bacteria
    cell division, 167
    chromosomes, 166, 261
    classification of, 351, 353
    defined, 7, 371
    DNA replication in, 222
    evolution of, 335, 337f
    fossils of, 372
    mitosis, 167, 167t
    Pasteur's experiment, 371, 372f
    Precambrian, 337f
    reproduction, 166-67, 373
    ribosomes, 230, 231
    structure of, 372, 373f
    word meaning, 372
Prokaryotic cells
    division, 166-67
    vs. eukaryotic cells, 82t
    lac operon, 239-40
    operon models, 238-39
    protein synthesis in, 372, 373f
    regulation of, 238-40
    structure and function, 65-66, 167t,
      372, 373f
    trp operon, 238f, 239
Prolactin (PRL), 754f, 755, 757, 758f, 782
Proliferative phase, of uterine cycle,
    781, 782t
Proline, 51f
Prometaphase (late prophase), 158f, 159
Promoter
    defined, 238-39
    of eukaryotic genes, 244
    gene expression regulation, 238-40
    transcription, 225-26
Pronghorn antelope, 894
Pronucleus, 797
Proofreading, during DNA replication,
    222, 247
Prop roots, 452, 461f
Prophage, 367f, 368
Prophase (mitosis), 158-59, 158f,
    177t, 180f
Prophase I (meiosis), 176, 177, 177t,
    178f, 180f
Prophase II (meiosis), 177t, 178f
Proprioceptors, 730, 731f
Prosimians, 571, 575
Prostaglandins, 768-69, 777
Prostate cancer, 640, 777
Prostate cancer vaccine, 640
Prostate gland, 640, 775f, 775t, 777, 812
Protease(s), 247
Protease inhibitors, 788
Proteasomes, 247
Protein(s). *See also specific protein*
    active transport, 95-96
    acute phase, 631
    amino acids. See Amino acids
    carrier. See Carrier proteins
    cell recognition, 88
    channel, 88
    compared, in phylogeny, 359
    cross-linking of, 814
    defined, 47
    dephosphorylation, 78
    dietary, 40t, 658-59
    digestion of, 656, 657f

enzymatic, 88f, 89
functions in animals, 49–50
junction, 88f, 89
junctions, 88f, 89, 588
major histocompatibility complex, 632, 635, 643
membrane, 717
metabolism of, 147
in morphogenesis, 802, 803f
mutations and activity effects, 248–49
nonfunctional, 248, 249
organic chemistry, 38, 49–53
peptides, 50
phosphorylation, 78
plasma, 618, 632
plasma membrane, 86–87, 88–89
protective, 632–33
receptors, 88f, 89, 90
shape and structure, 50–53, 265
   primary, 50–51
   secondary, 51, 52f
   tertiary, 52–53
   quaternary, 52f
structural, 99f
synthesis of, 71, 228–33, 372, 373f, 756
three-dimensional modeling, 265
in viruses, 366
Proteinase inhibitors, in plants, 497, 498
Protein-first hypothesis, 330, 332
Protein-folding disease, 53
Proteinoids, 330
Proteoglycans, 99f
Proteome, 265
Proteomics, 232, 265
Proterospongia, 397
Prothrombin activator, 620
Protists, 383–402. See also specific organism
   asexual reproduction, 384
   cell division in, 167, 167t
   characteristics, 384
   classification of, 354
   defined, 2, 7
   diseases caused by, 383, 384, 393–400
   diversity of, 384–400, 385t
   ecological importance of, 384
   endosymbiotic theory, 384
   evolution of, 6f, 337, 384, 386f, 404
   general biology of, 384
   heterotrophic, 335f
   parasitic, 865
   photosynthetic, 335f
   review and exercises, 400–402
   supergroups, 384–400, 385t
Protobiont, 330
Protocells, 328, 330–32
Protochloroplasts, 67f
Protoderm, 451f, 453, 462f
Protoderm meristem, 447
Proton(s)
   atomic mass unit, 23
   in chemiosmosis, 114, 115f
   defined, 22
   in helium, 23f
   hydrogen ion as, 32
Proton pump, 469f, 470, 477–79
Protonema, 424, 425t
Protonephridia, 682
Proto-oncogenes, 164, 165f, 249
Protoplasts, 258
Protostomes, 523, 526t, 530
Protostomia, 526t
Protozoans
   classification of, 7
   as decomposers, in soil, 168
   defined, 384
   diversity of, 385t
   in food chain, 383
   population dynamics, 861
Proximal convoluted tubule, 685f, 686, 687f
Pruning, 475, 488
PS I (Photosystem I), 124–26
PS II (Photosystem II), 124–26
Pseudocoelom, 538, 736
Pseudocoelomates, 606
Pseudogenes, 574
Pseudomyrmex ferruginea, 498, 866
Pseudopods
   amoebozoan, 396

coated vesicles, 97f
cytoskeleton, 78
defined, 396
of rhizarians, 398–99, 400f
Pseudostratified epithelial tissue, 589
Psilocybe mexicana, 411
Psilocybin, 411
Psilotum, 428
Ptarmigan, 888
Pteridophytes, 420f, 427–29
Pterois volitans, 555f
Pteromyzon, 553f
Pterosaurs, 340, 559
PTH (parathyroid hormone), 738, 754f, 761–62
Ptilonorhynchus violaceus, 832
Puberty, 767
Puccinia, 413f
Puffballs, 2, 412, 413f
Pulling force, in transpiration, 476
Pulmonary arteries, 611–12
Pulmonary circuit, 609, 614
Pulmonary fibrosis, 674f, 675
Pulmonary semilunar valve, 611
Pulmonary tuberculosis, 674–75
Pulmonary veins, 611–12
Pulse, 613
Pulvinus, 493
Punctuated equilibrium models of macroevolution, 319–20
Punnett square, 200, 208f, 291, 318f
Pupa, 542
Pupil of eye, 721
Purine bases, 54, 217
Pus, 620, 632
Pussy willow, 505f
Pyramids, 874
Pyrenoid, 387, 396
Pyrimidine bases, 54, 217
Pyrogens, 768
Pyruvate, 137, 139f, 140

Q

Quadriceps femoris muscles, 743f, 744f
Quadriplegia, 703
Quadrupedalism, 575
Quaternary period, 336t, 341
Quaternary structure of protein, 52f, 53
Quetzalcoatlus, 559
Quillworts, 426
Quinine, 458, 514

R

R group, for amino acids, 50, 51f
Rabbit, 61f, 737
Rabies virus, 364, 366
Radial nerve, 696f
Radial symmetry
   animal characteristics, 514–26t
   of animals, 522f
   defined, 522
   of echinoderms, 544–45
Radiata, 526t
Radiation
   as birth defect cause, 807
   as cancer cause, 165f
   high levels of, 24–25
   ionizing, 248
   low levels of, 24
   radioactive isotopes, 24–25
   solar. See Solar energy
   ultraviolet. See Ultraviolet (UV) radiation
Radicle, eudicot vs. monocot seed, 509
"Radioactivity," as term, 24
Radiocarbon dating, 334
Radiolarians, 385t, 386f, 398–99, 400f
Radioles, 538
Radiometric fossil dating, 334
Radish, 452
Radius, 740f, 742
Radula, 534, 535f, 648
Raggiana bird of paradise, 297–98, 828
Ragnarsson, Ivar, 203
Rain forests
   HMS Beagle observation, 273f
   species composition, 858

temperate, 890
tropical. See Tropical rain forests
Rain shadow, 885
Rainbow trout, 897f
Rana, temporal isolation of, 312
Rana berlandieri, 308f
Rana catesbeiana, 350f
Rana pippiens, 308f
Rana sphenocephala, 308f
Random distribution, 840
Random mating, Hardy-Weinberg equilibrium, 292, 292t, 295, 300
Range, 840
RAS (reticular activating system), 705
Ras genes, 164, 250
Rat(s), 676, 827, 828, 915
Rat snake, 302f
Rate of natural increase, 841
Ratfish, 554
Rattlesnakes, 561
Raven, 825–26
Ray(s)
   blue-spotted stingrays, 554f
   as cartilaginous fishes, 554
   classification, 554
   manta, 554
   osmoregulation, 682
   phloem, 455f, 456
   sawfish, 554
   skeleton of, 737
   stingrays, 554
   xylem, 455f, 456
Ray-finned bony fishes, 554, 555f
RB (retinoblastoma) protein, 155, 156, 164, 249–50
RB tumor suppressor gene, 164
RBCs. See Red blood cells
rDNA (recombinant DNA) technology, 255–56
Reactants, 107, 109
Realized niche, 859
Reasoning, 11
Receptacle of flower, 433, 502f
Reception, plant response process, 490
Receptor(s)
   chemo-, 717, 718
   cutaneous, 730
   mechano-, 717, 726–30
   pain, 731
   photo-, 717, 720, 722–23
   sensory, 717
   signal transduction in plants, 484
   thermo-, 717, 730
Receptor proteins, 88f, 89, 90
Receptor-mediated endocytosis, 97–98
Recessive alleles, 196, 197f
Recessive X-linked inheritance, 209–10
Reciprocal altruism, 834
Reciprocal crosses, 195
Recombinant DNA (rDNA) technology, 255–56
Recombinant human erythropoietin (rHuEPO), 689
Recording, in microscopy, 64
Rectal gland, 682
Rectum, 650f, 653
Rectus abdominis muscle, 744f
Red algae, 385t, 386f, 389, 901
Red blood cells (RBCs)
   in blood sample, 591f
   function of, 619
   oxygen transport through, 592
   production of, 619, 768
   in sickle cell disease, 206–7
   structure of, 591–92, 618–19
Red bone marrow, 591, 628f, 629, 740
Red bread mold, 408
Red deer, 299, 826
Red fox, 7f
Red light, phytochrome conversion cycle, 495
Red pulp, 630
Red sea star, 544f
Red tide, 392–93
"Red wine effect," 617
Red-backed cleaning shrimp, 540f
Red-eared slider turtle, 917f
Redox reactions, 113, 122, 136

Reduction
   in cellular respiration, 136
   defined, 113
   in photosynthesis, 122
Redwood trees, 430, 476
Reefs. See Coral reefs
Reflex
   centers for, in medulla oblongata, 705
   defined, 708
   proprioceptive, 730, 731f
Reflex actions, 702, 708, 709
Reflex arc, 708, 709f
Refractory period, 700, 778
Regeneration, 773
Regenerative medicine, 594–95
Regulation
   cell cycle, 153
   eukaryotic, 241–47
   gene expression, 237–53
   prokaryotic, 238–40
   proteins, 49
Regulator gene, 238, 239, 240
Reindeer, 846, 888
Reinforcement of reproductive isolation, 314
Relative dating of fossils, 322
Release, in lytic cycle, 367f, 368
Remoras, 865
Renal artery, 684f, 686, 687f
Renal cortex, 685, 688
Renal medulla, 685, 688
Renal pelvis, 685
Renal vein, 684f, 685f, 686, 687f
Renin, 690, 763
Renin-angiotensin-aldosterone system, 690, 763
Repetitive DNA elements, 262
Replacement model, 579, 583
Replacement reproduction, 852
Replication fork, 221, 222
Replication of DNA, 220–22
Repolarization, 698–99
Repressible operon, 239
Repressors, 238–39, 244
Reproduction
   asexual. See Asexual reproduction
   cellular, 61. See also Cell division
   consanguineous, 202, 295, 300–301, 819
   defined, 5. See specific organisms
   eukaryotes. See specific organism
   evolution of self-replication, 328, 332
   fitness strategies, 831
   human, 775–83, 775t, 779t
   invertebrates, 773–74
   life history strategies, 774
   and natural selection, 8
   organs of. See Reproductive system
   plants, 180, 420, 501–17
   population growth, 843–44, 851–53, 863
   prokaryotes, 166–67, 373
   self-replication, 61, 328, 332
   sexual. See Sexual reproduction
   systems of, 772–94. See also specific organism
   vertebrates, 773–74
   virus, 366–69
Reproductive cloning, 161, 162
Reproductive group, 842–43, 852
Reproductive isolation
   mechanisms, 310, 311f, 312
   postzygotic, 310, 312, 313f
   prezygotic, 310, 311f, 312
Reproductive potential, 277
Reproductive speciation, 313–14
Reproductive system, 772–94
   animals, 773
   functions of, 596
   human, 775–83
      aging process, 813
      female, 779–83, 779t, 813
      male, 775–78, 775t
   mollusc, 524
   polychaetes, 538
   review and exercises, 791–94
   as vertebrate characteristic, 552
Reproductively isolated, 294

Reptiles, 558–63. *See also specific animal*
  amniotes, 558–59
  anatomy, 558f
  characteristics, 526t, 558
  circulatory system, 558, 609
  defined, 558
  desert, 896
  dinosaurs, 559
  evolution, 340, 558–59, 561–63
  excretory system, 681
  eye, 720
  hormones, 755, 758
  osmoregulation, 683–84
  pineal gland, 768
  reproduction, 558, 774, 805
  respiration, 558, 669–70
  skeleton, 737
RER (rough endoplasmic reticulum), 68f–69f, 72, 74f
Reservoirs, 874, 876
Resin, 431
Resistance, antibiotic, 376–77
Resolution, of microscopes, 64
Resource partitioning, 853, 860
Resources, 840, 847, 913
Respiration
  arthropods, 666–67
  in birds, 665, 670f
  cellular, 76. *See also Cellular respiration*
  external, 671, 672
  gas exchange, 664–70, 668f, 671f
  internal, 671, 672
  mammals, 669–70
  reptiles, 669–70
Respiratory center, 670–71
Respiratory control center, 690
Respiratory pump, 615
Respiratory syncytial virus (RSV), 635
Respiratory system, 663–79. *See also specific organism*
  acid-base regulation by, 690
  functions of, 596
  gas exchange in, 664–68, 671–72
  in homeostatic regulation, 599
  human, 364t, 376f, 667–76, 668f, 812
    breathing, 669–71
    disorders of, 673–74
    gas exchange, 671–72
  review and exercises, 677–79
  vertebrate, 552
Responding (dependent) variable, 14
Resting potential, nerve impulse transmission, 698–99
Restoration ecology, 920–21
Restriction enzymes, 255
Resvertrol, 617
Reticular activating system (RAS), 705
Reticular fibers, 589
Reticular formation, 705
Retina, 721, 723, 724, 725
Retinal, 722–23
Retinal detachment, 724
Retinoblastoma, 155
Retinoblastoma (RB) protein, 155, 156, 164, 249–50
Retinopathy, diabetic, 724, 765
Retroviruses, 368, 369f
Reverse transcriptase, 256, 332, 368, 369f
Reverse transcriptase inhibitors, 788
Rh factor, 619–20
Rhea, 273f, 276
Rhesus monkeys, 573f
Rheumatic fever, 642
Rheumatoid arthritis, 642, 743
Rhiniophytes, 426f
Rhinoceros, 841f
Rhinoderma darwinii, 848f
Rhizaria
  foraminiferans, 385t, 386f, 398–99, 400f
  protist supergroup, 385t, 386f, 398–400
Rhizobium bacteria, 471
Rhizoids, 389, 408, 424
Rhizomes
  asexual reproduction, 448
  defined, 426, 458, 513
  fern, 428
  as specialized leaf, 445
  stem diversity, 457f

Rhizopus stolonifer, 406t, 407–8
Rhodoglossum affine, 389f
Rhodopsin, 722, 722f
Rhubarb, 460
RHuEPO (recombinant human erythropoietin), 689
Rib(s), 740f, 741
Rib cage, 669f, 740f, 741
Riboflavin, 111, 660
Ribonucleic acid. *See* RNA
Ribose, 42, 54
Ribosomal RNA. *See* rRNA
Ribosomes
  animal cells, 68f
  binding sites of, 229f, 230, 231
  eukaryotic cells, 71, 82t
  plant cells, 69f
  prokaryotic cells, 65–66, 82t
  in protein synthesis, 756
  structure and function, 229–30
  subunits of, 229, 230–32
  three-domain system of classification, 352t
Ribozymes, 109, 227, 332
Rice, 492, 910
Rieppel, Olivier C., 357
Right whale, 281f
Rigor mortis, 749
Ringworm, 410
Rio Grande Leopard Frog, 308f
RISC (RNA-induced silencing complex), 245f, 246
Ritter, John, 605
Rivers, 896, 897, 900, 912
RNA (ribonucleic acid)
  classes of, 223
  defined, 54
  vs. DNA, 55t, 223, 223t
  evolution of, 330–31, 332
  information carried by, 223
  messenger. *See* mRNA
  microRNA (miRNA), 227, 246
  nucleotides in, 223
  in nucleus, 70
  processing, in eukaryotes, 226–27
  ribosomal RNA. *See* rRNA
  snRNA (small nuclear RNA), 227, 244
  sRNA (small RNA), 245–46
  structural genomics, 261
  structure of, 54–55, 223, 223t
  synthetic, 224
  transfer RNA. *See* tRNA
  viral, 365, 366
RNA polymerase
  as operator, 239
  prokaryotic gene regulation, 239–40
  transcription, 221, 225–26
  transcription factors, 244
RNA primer, 221
"RNA world," 330
RNA-first hypothesis, 330, 332
RNA-induced silencing complex (RISC), 245f, 246
Roadrunner, 894f, 896f
Rockweed, 390, 900
Rocky Mountain spotted fever, 543
Rocky shores, 900
Rod cells, 721–23
Rodentia, 566t
Rodhocetus, 281, 310f
Rodhocetus kasrani, 310f
Rohypnol, 710
Romalea, 543f
Room temperature regulation, 600f, 601
Root(s)
  adventitious, 457f
  asexual reproduction from, 513
  auxins, and growth, 485
  branch, 452, 461f
  of club mosses, 426
  defined, 444
  diversity of, 452, 461f
  epidermal tissue of, 447
  ethylene and elongation of, 489
  eudicot, 445f, 446, 450–52, 461f
  flowering plants, 444, 445f, 446, 450–52, 453f
  fungal symbiosis. *See* Mycorrhizae
  generally, 444, 445f
  lateral, 445f

  mineral uptake by, 469–72
  monocot, 446, 452
  organization of, 444, 445f, 446, 450–52, 453f
  phylogenetic tree, 309
  specialization of, 452, 461f
  transport system in, 473f, 475–79
Root apical meristem, 450, 451f
Root cap, 450, 451f
Root hairs
  defined, 444
  epidermal tissue of, 447
  nutritional function of soil, 467f
  plant structure, 444f
  plexus, 730
  structure and function, 451f
  transport, 469
Root nodules, 14–15, 375, 452, 471
Root pressure, 475
Root systems
  defined, 444
  plant body organization, 444f, 445f
  root diversity, 452, 461f
Rosy periwinkle, 910
Rotational equilibrium, 728, 729f
Rotifers, 526t, 533–34
Rough endoplasmic reticulum (RER), 68f–69f, 72, 74f
Round window, 726f, 727
Roundworms
  aging studies in, 813
  characteristics, 526t
  embryonic development, 802, 804
  evolution of, 538–39
  genome, 263t
  hydrostatic skeleton, 736
  as model organisms, 800
  parasitic, 539
  reproduction, 773
  transport in, 606
rRNA (ribosomal RNA)
  amino acids and, 223
  in nucleus, 70
  prokaryotes, 351, 378
  translation of DNA, 229–31
R-selection, 849
RSV (respiratory syncytial virus), 635
RU-486, 783–84
Rubber, 911
Rubella, 730, 807
RuBP carboxylase, 128
RuBP regeneration, Calvin cycle, 128–29
Ruffini endings, 730
Rumen, 649
Ruminants, 646, 649
Runaway hypothesis, female choice, 297
Rusts, 413
Rye, 411, 444

S

S layer, prokaryote, 372
S stage, interphase, 154
SA (sinoatrial) node, 613
Sac fungi, 404f, 406t, 408–10, 412
Saccharomyces, 408, 410
Saccharomyces cerevisiae, 141
Saccules, 72, 73f, 728, 729f
Sachs, Julius von, 465
Sacral nerves, 696f
Sacral vertebrae, 741
Sacrum, 740f, 742
Safrole, 248
Sagebrush, 896
Saguaros, 916
Sahara Desert, 896
Sahelanthropus tchadensis, 576
St. Anthony's Fire, 411
Salamanders
  allopatric speciation in, 313–14
  characteristics, 526t, 556–57
  gas exchange, 665
  regenerative ability, 594
  transgenic, 594, 595f
Salicylic acid, 498
Salivary amylase, 651, 656
Salivary glands, 651, 812

Sally lightfoot crab, 540f
Salmo gairdneri, 897f
Salmon, 314, 315f, 909f, 915
Salmonella, 376
Salt(s)
  active transport, 95
  body fluid balance. *See* Osmoregulation
  defined, 27
  iodized, 760
  in water, 30
Salt environments, halophiles, 335f, 354, 378f, 379
Salt marshes, 900
Saltatory conduction, 699
Salt-excreting glands, 684
Saltwater ecosystems, 897–904
Salty taste, 718
Samara, 510f
San Andreas fault, 343
Sand (ghost) shrimp, 901
Sand dollar, 526t, 544
Sand shark, 2, 554f
Sandhoppers, 901
Sandworms, 901
Sandy shores, 900–901
Sandy soil, 467
Sanger, Frederick, 50
Sap, 478
Saprolegnia, 391, 392f
Saprotrophs, 375, 404, 412, 520
Sapwood, 456, 457f
SAR (systemic acquired resistance), 498
Sarcolemma, 744–45, 746f, 747–48
Sarcomeres, 745–46
Sarcoplasmic reticulum, 744–45, 748–49
Sarcopterygii (lobe-finned fishes), 555, 556, 557f
Sarcoscypha, 406t, 408f
Sarin, 112
SARS (severe acute respiratory syndrome), 369
Sartorius muscle, 744f
Satin bowerbirds, 297, 832
Saturated fatty acids, 46, 47f, 658, 659
Saturation zone, 875
Savannas, 895
Sawfish rays, 554
Scala naturae, 272
Scales, fish, 553, 554, 597
Scallops, 534, 535f
Scalp, human, 599
Scandentia, 566t
Scanning electron microscope (SEM), 63
Scapula, 740f, 742
Scarification, seed, 448
Scavengers, 901–2
Schistosoma, 532–33
Schistosomiasis, 532–33
Schleiden, Matthias, 61
Schwann, Theodor, 61
Schwann cells, 697
Schwarz, Stefan, 186
Sciatic nerve, 696f
SCID (severe combined immunodeficiency), 260, 264, 626, 641
Scientific method, 11–16
Scientific names, 8, 349–50
Scientific process/method
  conclusion, 12, 14–15
  data, 11–12, 14
  defined, 11
  experiments, 11–12, 14
  field study, 15–16
  flow diagram, 11f
  hypothesis, 11, 14
  observation, 11, 14
  scientific theory, 12
  statistical studies, 13
Scientific theory, 11f, 12
Sclera, 721, 723f
Sclereids, 449
Sclerenchyma cells, 449, 450
Scolex, 543
Scorpions, 526t, 543, 682
Scotch pine, 431
"Scouring rushes," 428
Scrotum, 775
Scrub jay, 834

Sea anemones
    characteristics, 526t
    cnidarian, 528, 529f
    nerve nets of, 694
    symbiotic relationships, 865, 866
Sea cucumber, 526t, 544, 545f, 902
Sea horses, 555f, 772, 774
Sea jellies, 528, 529f
Sea lettuce, 388
Sea lilies, 902
Sea otters, 826, 918
Sea snakes, 684
Sea squirts, 551
Sea stars
    characteristics, 526t
    as echinoderms, 544–46
    habitats, 900f, 901
    muscular hydrostat of, 736
    nutrition of, 649
    transport in, 606
Sea turtles, 680, 684, 825, 889, 901f
Sea urchins
    characteristics, 526t
    evolution of, 544, 545f
    habitats, 901, 902
    population control, 918
Seabird territoriality, 830
Seafloor spreading, 343
Seagulls, 683–84, 823, 829
Seahorses, 772, 774
Seashores, 900–901. See also Coastal
        ecosystems
Seasons, 884, 898–99
Seaweed, 383, 389, 390, 900, 901
Sebaceous glands, 599
Sebum, 599
Second messengers, 755, 777
Secondary growth, stem, 455
Secondary lymphoid organs, 629–30
Secondary metabolites, in plant
        defenses, 496
Secondary nondisjunction, 183
Secondary oocyte, 181
Secondary ossification centers, 738
Secondary sex characteristics, 767,
        778, 782
Secondary structure of proteins, 51, 52f
Secondary succession, 868–69
Secondary xylem, 455f, 456, 457f
Secretion, 73, 74
Secretory phase, of uterine cycle,
        782, 782t
Secretory vesicles, 72, 74
Sedgewick, Adam, 275
Sediment, 333
Sedimentary cycles, 874
Sedimentation, 333
Seed(s)
    auxins, 488
    defined, 430
    development, 508–9
    dispersal, 437, 511
    dormant, 448, 488, 512
    eudicot, 446, 509
    evolutionary history of plants, 420f
    flowering plant reproduction, 436f,
        437, 446, 504f, 505
    gametophytes vs. sporophyte size, 423f
    germination and growth, 488, 502, 512
    monocots, 446, 509
    scarification, 448
Seed coat, 430, 509f, 512f
Seed cones, 430f, 431f, 432
Seed ferns, 430, 435
Seed plants. See also Flowering plant(s);
        Gymnosperms
    characteristics, 421t
    defined, 430
    evolution of, 420f, 430–39
    spores retained by, 430
Seedless vascular plant, 420f, 426
Seedling germination and growth, 512
Segmentation
    of annelids, 536, 537f
    of arthropods, 540
    pattern of, 802–3
Segment-polarity genes, 803
Segregation
    cytoplasmic, 800, 801f
    Mendel's law of, 195–96

Selaginella, 426
Selam (australopith), 577
Selection
    artificial, 278
    natural. See Natural selection
Selective permeability, 89
Selenium, 465, 470–71
Self-fertilization, 773
Self-interest vs. altruism, 833–34
Self-replication, 61, 328, 332
SEM (scanning electron microscope), 63
Semantic memory, 707
Semelparity, 843, 844
Semen (seminal fluid), 777, 778
Semicircular canals, 726f, 727–28, 729f
Semiconservative replication, DNA, 220
Semidesert, 885
Semilunar valves, 611, 612f, 613
Seminal vesicles, 775f, 775t, 777
Seminiferous tubules, 776, 778
Senescense, cytokinin prevention of,
        487–88, 489t
Sense organs, 716–34
    aging process, 722, 724, 728, 812
    arthropods, 540
    balance, 728–30
    cartilaginous fishes, 554
    chemical senses, 718–19
    eyes, 720–25
    hearing, 726–30
    review and exercises, 731–34
    smell, 719
    somatic, 730–31
    taste, 718, 812
    touch, 730
    vertebrate development of, 552
    vision, 720–25
Sensitive period, 824
Sensitive plant, 493
Sensory (afferent) neurons, 697–98, 717
Sensory apparatus, paired, vertebrate
        nervous system, 695
Sensory association areas, 707
Sensory input, as central nervous system
        function, 702
Sensory nerves, 707
Sensory receptors
    anatomy, 597f
    defined, 598, 717
    endocrine system interaction, 753
    muscle tone, 744
    peripheral nervous system (PNS), 708
Sensory speech area, 703f
Sensory transduction, 717
Sentinel cells, 627
Sepals, 434, 502f, 503
Sepioteuthis lessoniana, 536f
Septate fungi, 405
Septate hyphae, 405
Septum (pl., septa), 405
    cardiac, 610
Sequential hermaphroditism, 773
Sequoia sempervirens, 430
Serine, 51f
Serosa, of digestive tract, 651–52
Serotonin, 700–701
Sertoli cells, 776f, 777
Sessile organisms, 526t, 744
Set point, 601
Setae, annelid, 536, 537f
Severe acute respiratory syndrome
        (SARS), 369
Severe combined immunodeficiency
        (SCID), 260, 264, 626, 641
Sewage treatment, 912, 915
Sex chromosomes
    Drosophila melanogaster, 208–9
    number of, changes in, 184–85
Sex hormones. See also Estrogen(s);
        Testosterone
    and bone growth, 738
    functions of, 767–68
    secretion of, 754f, 756, 758f, 767
    synthesis of, 756, 775
Sex reversal, 773
Sexual dimorphism, 297, 298f
Sexual intercourse (copulation), 774
Sexual reproduction, 773–74. See also
        Mating; specific organism
    vs. asexual reproduction, 175, 176, 773

defined, 172, 773
flowering plants, 502–7. See also
        specific types of plants
    of fungi, 406
    genetic variation, 174–75
    life cycle, 180–82
    meiosis, 171–91
    origins of, 337
    of sac fungi, 408, 409
    seahorses, 772, 774
    sponges, 527
Sexual selection, 297–99, 831–32
Sexually transmitted diseases (STDs),
        787–91. See also specific disease
    bacterial, 376t, 790–91
    prevention of, 789
    viral, 364t, 787–90
Shared derived traits, 356
Sharks
    as cartilaginous fishes, 554
    classification, 554
    commensalism, 865
    evolution of, 339
    fetal, 2
    habitat, 901
    osmoregulation, 682
    skeleton of, 737
Sheep cloning, 162
Shelf fungus, 412, 413f
Shellfish poisoning, 392
Shields, Gerald, 889
Shiga toxin, 376
Shigella dysentariae, 376
Shingles, 638
Shivering, 601
Shock, anaphylactic, 641–42
Shoot apical meristem, 453, 462f
Shoot elongation, 495
Shoot system, 444, 445f
Shoot tip, 462f
Shores, 900–901. See also Coastal
        ecosystems
Short tandem repeat (STR)
        profiling, 257
Short tandem repeats (STRs), 262
Short-day plants, 495, 496f
Short-term memory, 707
Shoulder blade (scapula), 740f, 742
Shoulder joint, 742–43
Shrimp
    as decapods, 540f
    excretory system of, 682
    habitat, 901f, 902
    introduced species, 909, 914
Shrublands, 894
Shrubs, 455, 868–69, 894
Sialia mexicana, 847
Siamese cat, 111
Sick building syndrome, 410
Sickle cell disease, 206–7, 248, 302–3
Sieve plate, 450, 544f, 545
Sieve tube, 473, 479
Sieve-tube members, 450, 453,
        455f, 473
Sign stimulus, 822, 823
Signal(s)
    in cell cycle, 155
    signal transduction in plants, 484–85,
        490, 492, 497f
    visual, 828–29
Signal peptide, 71
Signal recognition particle (SRP), 71
Signaling cascade (enzyme cascade), 755
Signaling molecules, 90
Silicon, in plants, 465
Silk, 51, 53f, 543
Silurian period, 336t, 339, 426, 552
Simple epithelium, 588–89
Simple eye, 543
Simple fruits, 511, 511t
Simple goiter, 760
Simple leaves, 460
Simplexvirus, 365
Single nucleotide polymorphisms (SNPs),
        261, 263
Sink, sieve tube flow, 479
Sink population, 919
Sinoatrial (SA) node, 613
Sinornis, 280–81
Sinus, 740

Sirenia, 566t
Sister chromatids
    chromosome duplication, 157
    defined, 154, 157
    electron micrograph, 157f
    homologous chromosomes, 196f
    meiosis, 172–73, 174f
    metaphase, 159f
    prophase, 158
Skates, 554, 682, 918
Skeletal muscle
    in blood pressure regulation, 615
    in body temperature regulation, 601,
        744
    defined, 744
    structure and function, 592, 744–48
Skeleton. See also Endoskeleton;
        Exoskeleton
    appendicular, 740f, 742
    axial, 740–41
    diversity of, 736–37
    functions of, 596, 736–37
    human, 738–43. See also Bone(s);
        specific bone
    hydrostatic, 528, 536, 736
    monkeys, 575f
    review and exercises, 749–51
    sponges, 527
    vertebrate evolution, 552–54, 562, 564
Skill memory, 707
Skin. See also Integumentary system
    accessory structures, 598–99
    aging process, 811
    amphibians, 556, 597
    anatomy, 597–98
    bacterial diseases, 376t
    color of, 207, 758
    derivatives, 597
    epithelium of, 589
    fishes, 553, 597
    functions of, 597, 630
    gas exchange through, 597, 607
    human, 581, 597
    reptiles, 558, 597
    sensory receptors in, 730
    thick or thin, 598
    vertebrates, 553
    viral diseases, 364t
    wrinkling of, 598, 744, 746, 811
Skin cancer, 598
Skin tanning, 598
Skinks, 561
Skinner, B. F., 825, 827
Skototropism, 491
Skull
    evolution of, 552
    human skeletal system, 740–41
    ossification in, 738, 740
Sleep
    melatonin, 768
    obesity, 655
    plant movements, 494
Sleeping sickness, 396, 398–99
Sliding filament model of muscle
        contraction, 745–46
Slime layer, prokaryote, 372
Slime molds
    cellular, 397, 627
    classification of, 354
    plasmodial, 386f, 396–97
    supergroup amoebozoa, 385t,
        396–97
Sloths, 892
"Slow block," 797
Slugs, 534, 535
SMA (spinal muscular atrophy), 246
Small intestine, 650f, 652–53
Small nuclear RNA (snRNA), 227, 244
Small RNA (snRNA), 245–46
Smell, sense of, 719, 812
SMN2 gene, 246
Smoking
    birth defects caused by, 807
    general health effects, 710
    lung cancer, 675
    respiratory impact, 675f
Smooth endoplasmic reticulum, 68f–69f,
        72, 74f
Smooth muscle, 592–93, 608, 744
Smuts, 413

Snails. *See also* Land snails
  characteristics, *526t*
  coevolution, *867*
  disruptive selection, *297, 298f*
  egg-laying behavior in, *821–22*
  hormones in, *755*
  as mollusc, *534*
  regenerative ability, *594*
  skeleton of, *736*
Snakes
  characteristics, *526t, 561*
  chemoreceptors, *718*
  feeding behavior, *526t*
  hearing, *726*
  Hox genes, *322f, 524, 525*
  infrared detection, *716, 717*
  osmoregulation in marine, *684*
Snow goose, *2*
Snowshoe hare, *863, 888*
Snowy owl, *888*
SNPs (single nucleotide polymorphisms), *261, 263*
snRNA (small nuclear RNA), *227, 244*
Social amoebas, *627*
Social behavior
  in ants, *847*
  communication, *826–30*
  fitness, *833*
  learning, *824*
  in primates, *826, 828f, 829, 833*
Social parasitism, *867*
Societies, *543, 826, 833*
Sockeye salmon, *314, 315f*
Sodium
  intake, excessive, *660*
  regulation of. *See* Osmoregulation
  in sodium chloride formation, *26–27*
Sodium bicarbonate, *652, 656*
Sodium chloride, *26–27, 30*
Sodium hydroxide, *32*
Sodium-potassium pump, *95, 96f, 698–700*
Soft palate, *651, 668*
Softwoods, *431*
Soil
  defined, *467*
  ecological succession, *868*
  erosion of, *468–69, 912*
  flowering plants, *466–69*
  formation of, *467*
  humus, *464–68*
  microorganisms in, *468*
  minerals in, *467*
  in nitrogen cycle, *878*
  nutritional function, *467–68*
  in tropical rain forests, *468, 893, 913*
  zone of leaching, *468f*
Soil horizons, *468*
Soil profile, *468*
Solar energy
  climate, *884–85*
  distribution on Earth, *884f*
  in ecosystems, *9, 871*
  plants as converters, *104, 105, 124–27.*
    See also Photosynthesis
  in water cycle, *875, 897*
Soldierfishes, *555f*
Solidago canadensis, *505f*
Soluble fiber, *658*
Solute concentration, water potential, *474*
Solutes, *30, 91, 474*
Solutions
  acidic, *32*
  basic, *32*
  defined, *30, 91*
  hypertonic, *93f, 94, 101t*
  hypotonic, *93, 101t*
  isotonic, *93, 101t*
Solvent, *29–30, 91*
Somatic cells, *155*
Somatic embryogenesis, *514*
Somatic nervous system, *696f, 707, 708, 709t*
Somatic senses, *730–31*
Somatosensory area, primary, *703f, 704*
Somatosensory association area, *703f*
Somatotropic hormone, *738, 754f, 758–59*
Somites, *799, 809f*
Song learning, birds, *824*
Songbirds, *299*

Sori (sing., sorus), *428, 429f*
Soricomorpha, *566t*
Sound wave detection, *726-28. See also* Hearing
Sour taste, *718*
Source, sieve tube flow, *479*
Source population, *919*
South African australopithecines, *578*
Southern Leopard Frog, *308f*
Southern Oscillation, *904*
Southern yellow pine, *431*
Soy sauce, *141*
Space-filling model, *28f, 55f*
Spacing between children, statistical studies, *13*
Sparrows, *824*
Specialist species, *859–60*
Speciation, *306–26. See also* Evolution
  adaptive radiation mode, *316–17*
  allopatric speciation mode, *313–14*
  anatomy of, *309*
  convergent evolution mode, *317*
  defined, *313*
  geographic and reproductive speciation, *313–14*
  modes of, *313–17*
  review and exercises, *324–26*
  species, described, *307–12*
  sympatric speciation mode, *314–16*
Species (taxonomic), *307–13. See also* specific species
  benthic, *900*
  binomial naming of, *8, 349–50*
  classification of living things, *6, 6t*
  composition of, *858–59*
  defined, *6, 307*
  described, *307–12, 908f*
  endangered, *908, 916*
  equilibrium, *849*
  exotic (alien), *838, 861, 909, 913–15*
  flagship, *918*
  generalist, *859*
  identification of, *349*
  isolating mechanisms, *310, 311f, 312*
  keystone, *918*
  Linnean, *349, 350f*
  number of, *908f*
  opportunistic, *849*
  overproduction potential of, *277*
  pioneer, *868*
  postzygotic isolating mechanisms, *310, 312, 313f*
  prezygotic isolating mechanisms, *310, 311f, 312*
  specialist, *859–60*
  threatened, *908*
Species concept, *307–11*
  biological, *310*
  defined, *307*
  evolutionary, *307–8*
  morphological, *307, 308f*
  phylogenetic, *308, 310, 311f*
Species diversity, *858–59. See also* Biodiversity
Species richness, *858, 862*
Specific epithet, *8, 349*
Spectrophotometer, *124*
Sperm (spermatozoa)
  donors of, *785*
  flowering plant reproduction, *436, 438*
  human, *773–78*
    during fertilization, *796–97, 806f*
    infertility, *775, 784–85*
    structure of, *777, 796*
  sexual reproduction, *172, 774, 780, 796*
  spermatogenesis, *181, 182f, 776–77*
  structure of, *81f, 777, 796*
Sperm whale, *901f*
Spermatids, *181, 776f, 777*
Spermatocytes, *181, 182f, 776–77*
Spermatogenesis
  in algae, *422*
  in bryophytes, *422*
  in humans, *181, 182f, 776–77*
Spermatogonia, *181, 776*
Sphagnum, *425*
Sphenoid bones, *740–41*
Sphincter, *651, 652*
Sphinx moth, *752*
Sphygmomanometer, *615*

Spicules, of sponges, *527*
Spider(s), *526t, 543, 649, 682, 736*
Spider monkeys, *572*
Spike mosses, *426*
Spinal cord
  in central nervous system, *702–3, 708f*
  defined, *702*
  embryonic development of, *799, 809*
  injury to, *703*
  mammals, *696f*
  nervous tissue, *593*
  in vertebral column, *740*
  as vertebrate key characteristic, *520–21*
Spinal muscular atrophy (SMA), *246*
Spinal nerves, *682, 696f, 707, 708f*
Spinal reflex, *708, 709f*
Spindle, *176, 797*
Spines, plants, *447, 448, 461f*
Spinks, Lorna, *710*
Spiny anteater, *774*
Spiracles, insect, *542, 667*
Spirillum (pl., spirilla), *65, 374*
Spirillum volutans, *374f*
Spirobranchus giganteus, *537f*
Spirochetes, *65*
Spirogyra, *384, 388, 389f, 421*
Spleen, *628f, 629–30*
Spliceosomes, *226f, 227*
Sponge(s)
  characteristics, *526t*
  as diploblastic, *523*
  embryonic development, *523*
  opisthokonta, *397*
  reproduction, *527, 773*
  as simplest invertebrate, *527*
  skeleton of, *736*
Sponge effect, *912*
Spongin, *527*
Spongy bone, *591, 739–40*
Spongy mesophyll, *459*
Spontaneous generation, *371, 372f*
Spontaneous mutations, *247*
Sporangia (sing., sporangium)
  ferns, *422, 428, 429f*
  fungi, *407f, 408*
  mosses, *424, 425t*
  slime molds, *397*
  water molds, *392*
Sporangiospores, *408*
Spores
  defined, *176, 422*
  fern, *422*
  fungi, *406, 407, 408, 409, 412–13*
  gametophytes vs. sporophyte size, *423f*
  moss, *424, 425t*
  plant, *422*
  protist, *384*
  seed plant, *430, 431f*
  slime mold, *397*
  sporozoan, *394*
Sporophylls, *426*
Sporophyte
  bryophyte, *424*
  conifers, *431f*
  defined, *422*
  fern, *429f*
  flowering plants, *436f, 437, 502, 504f, 505*
  moss, *424, 425t*
  plant, *180*
  size of, *422, 423f*
Sporopollenin, *422*
Sporozoans, *394*
Sporozoites, of *Plasmodium*, *394f*
Sports, erythropoietin in, *689*
Spotted sweetlip, *866f*
Spriggina, *338f*
Spring overturn, *898–99*
Spring wood, *456, 457f*
Springbok, *864*
Spurge, *357*
Squamous epithelium, *588, 598*
Squid
  anatomy, *648f*
  characteristics, *526t*
  circulatory system of, *607*
  digestive system of, *648*
  eyes, *720*
  habitat, *901f, 902*
  as mollusc, *534, 535, 536f*

nerve impulse transmission, *698*
nervous system of, *694, 695f*
organization of life, *2*
vision, *720*
sRNA (small RNA), *245–46*
SRP (signal recognition particle), *71*
SRY gene, *184, 259*
Stabilizing natural selection, *296*
Stable equilibrium phase, of logistic growth, *845*
Stachybotrys chartarum, *410*
Stamens, *434, 436f, 502f, 503*
Staminate flowers, *503*
Standard deviation, *12*
Stapes, *726f, 727*
Staphylococci, *374*
Staphylococcus aureus, *377*
Starch
  defined, *43, 656*
  digestion of, *656, 657f*
  sources of, *657*
  structure and function, *43f*
  synthesis of, *129*
Starfish. *See* Sea stars
Starlings, *296, 825*
Start and stop, genetic code as, *224*
Start codons, *230f, 231*
Startle response, *864*
Statistical studies, *13*
Statocysts, *541, 728*
Statoliths, *490f, 491, 728*
STDs. *See* Sexually transmitted diseases
Stegosaurus, *340*
Stem(s)
  asexual reproduction, *513*
  auxins and curvature, *486*
  bark, *456*
  defined, *445*
  diversity of, *456, 457f, 458*
  elongation of, *486, 489, 489t, 495*
  epidermal tissue of, *447*
  of eudicots, *445f, 446, 454–55*
  of flowering plants, *445, 446, 453–58*
  generally, *445*
  growth of, *455*
  herbaceous, *454*
  horizontal, *457f*
  of monocots, *446, 454, 455f*
  organization of, *445, 446, 453–56, 457f, 458*
  plant structure, *444f*
  primary meristems, *462f*
  shoot tip, *462f*
  transport system, *473f, 476–79*
  vertical, *457f*
  woody, *455–56, 457f, 458, 461f*
Stem cells
  bioethical issues, *84*
  in body part regeneration, *594*
  cloning, *162*
  described, *161*
  embryonic, *162*
  mitosis, *161*
  research, *84, 162*
  skin derived from, *598*
Stentor, *393*
Stents, *616, 616f*
Steppe tortoises, *916f*
Steppes, *894*
Stereocilia, *728, 729f*
Stereoscopic vision, *571–72, 721*
Sterilization, radiation for, *25*
Sternocleidomastoid muscle, *744f*
Sternum, *740f, 741–42*
Steroid(s)
  anabolic, *767, 778*
  defined, *46*
  functions of, *45t*
  fungal production of, *410*
  lipids, *46, 48*
Steroid glycosides, *497*
Steroid hormones, *756*
Stickleback fish, *322, 822–23*
"Sticky ends," of DNA, *255*
Stigma, flower, *434, 436f, 437, 502f, 503*
Stimulatory pathway, and protooncogenes, *164*
Stimulus, *717*
Stinging nettle, *447*
Stingrays, *554*

Stinkhorns, 412, 413
Stirrup (stapes), 726, 727
Stoeckle, Kate, 352, 353*f*
Stolon
    asexual reproduction, 448, 514
    defined, 407, 456
    of Rhizopus, 407
    stem diversity, 457f
Stoma (pl., stomata)
    C₃ and C₄ plants, 130
    closing, and abscisic acid (ABA), 488
    epidermal tissue of, 447
    leaf, 121, 422, 423, 459
    opening and closing, 477–78, 488–89
Stomach, 649, 651, 655
Stone tools, 578, 580–81
Stonefly, 667
Stonewort, 388–89, 421
Stop codons, 120, 231–32
STR (short tandem repeat) profiling, 257
Stramenopiles, 385t, 390–92
    brown algae, 385t, 386f, 390–92
    diatoms, 385t, 386f, 390–91
    golden brown algae, 385t, 386f, 390, 391
    water molds, 7, 385t, 386f, 391–92
Strands, DNA *vs.* RNA, 55t
Stratified epithelium, 589, 598
Stratum (pl., strata), 333–34
Strauss, Louisa, 352, 353*f*
Strawberry
    autoploidy, 315
    reproduction, 448, 514
    stem diversity, 456, 457f, 458
Strawberry poison arrow frog, 848*f*
Streams, 896, 897, 900
Strep throat, 673
Streptococci, 215, 374, 673
Streptococcus pneumoniae, 215
Streptococcus pyogenes, 673
Streptococcus thermophilus, 374*f*
Streptomycin, 910
Stress response, 762*f,* 763
Stretch marks, 598
Striae, skin, 598
Striations, muscular, 745. *See also*
    Skeletal muscle
Strigophilus garylarsonii, 349
Strix occidentalis caurina, 890, 919*f*
Strobilus (pl., strobili), 426, 432
Stroke, 616
Stroma, 76, 121
Stromatolites, 336, 337*f*
Strophiona, 864*f*
STRs (short tandem repeats), 262
Structural genes, 238, 239–40
Style of flower, 434, 436*f,* 502*f,* 503
Subatomic particles of helium, 22–23
Subclavian veins, 628*f,* 629
Subcutaneous layer of skin, 597, 598
Subduction zones, 343
Suberin, 456, 469
Submucosa, digestive tract, 651
Subsoil, 468*f*
Subspecies, natural selection, 301–2
Substance P, 701
Substantia nigra, 706
Substrate-enzyme complex, 109–10
Substrate-level ATP synthesis, 138, 146
Substrate-level phosphorylation, 138
Succinea, 867
Succulents, 896
Sucrose, 42, 129, 657
Suctoria, 393
Sudoriferous glands. *See* Sweat glands
Sugar(s). *See also* Carbohydrates
    as biomolecule, 41
    digestion of, 657–58
    DNA vs. RNA, 55t
    pentose, 54
    transport, in plants, 479
Sugar glider, 283*f,* 564
Sugarcane, 458
"Suicide" genes, 258
Sulci (sing., sulcus), 703, 703*f*
Sulfhydryl functional groups, 39t
Sulfur, 25, 466t
Sulfur dioxide, 878, 915
Sum rule of probability, 200
Summer wood, 456, 457*f*

Sun, 884, 902. *See also* Solar energy
Sundew, 460, 472
Sunflowers, 2, 483
Superfemale (poly-X females), 186
Supergroups, eukaryotes (protists),
    384–400, 385t
Superior vena cava, 611, 614
Support systems. *See* Muscular system;
    Skeleton
Supportive connective tissue, 590–91
Supraorbital ridges, 741
Surface tension of water, 30
Surface-area-to-volume ratio, 62
Surrogate mothers, 785
Survivorship, 841–42
Suspension feeders, 527
Sustainable development, 920
Sustenacular (Sertoli) cells, 776*f,* 777
Sutures, cranial, 740, 742
Swallowing, 651, 668
Swamp(s), 897, 912
Swamp forests, of Carboniferous period,
    339, 427
Sweat glands
    aging process, 811
    anatomy, 597f
    functions of, 599, 601
    secretion, 589
Sweat pore, 597*f*
Sweet potatoes, 444, 452
Sweet taste, 718
Swidden (slash-and-burn) agriculture, 893
Swim bladder, 554
Swimmerets, 541
"Swine flu" virus, 363, 369, 370
Swiss starlings, 296
Swordfishes, 555*f*
Swyer syndrome, 184
Symbiosis
    bacteria, 375–77
    cleaning, 866
    and coevolution, 866–67
    defined, 375, 865
    in fungi, 408, 414–15. See also
        Mycorrhizae
    nitrogen-fixing bacteria, 375, 452,
        471, 878
    in protists, 384
    types of, 864–65, 865t
Symmetry
    of animals, 522
    body plan evolution in animals, 521,
        522f, 524–25
Sympathetic division of autonomic
    nervous system, 696*f,* 708–9,
    709*t,* 712*f,* 713
Sympatric speciation mode, 314–16
Synapses, 700–701, 753
Synapsids, 281, 558
Synapsis, 173, 176
Synaptic cleft, 700, 701, 747
Synaptic integration, 701
Synaptic transmission, 700–701
Synaptic vesicles, 747
Syndromes. *See also specific syndrome*
    aneuploidy, 184–87
    changes in chromosomal
        structure, 188
    deletion, 188
Synergids, 504*f,* 505
Synovial fluid, 743
Synovial joints, 742–43
Synovial membrane, 743
Synpolydactyly, 804
Synthetic auxins, 485
Syphilis, 790, 791*f*
Systematic biology (systematics),
    348–50
    defined, 6, 348
    Linnaean, 349–50
    and phylogeny, 347
    taxonomy, 348–50
Systematics and the Origin of Species
    (Mayr), 313
Systemic acquired resistance (SAR), 498
Systemic circuit, 609, 614–15
Systemic diseases, bacterial, 376t
Systemic lupus erythematosus, 642
Systemin, 497, 498
Systole, 612, 615

T

T. *See* Thymine (T)
T cells (T lymphocytes)
    aging process, 812
    clonal selection theory, 636
    function of, 620, 633, 635–37
    HIV infection and, 347, 637, 787
    production of, 629, 633, 768, 812
    types of, 635
T tubules, 744–45, 748
Tactile communication, 829–30
Taenia solium, 533
Taiga, 890
Tail
    human, 809f
    postnatal, 550
Tailbone (coccyx), 740–41
Talbot, Sandra, 889
Tamarins, 831
Tamias striatus, 891*f*
Tandem repeats, 262
Tanning, skin, 598
Tannins, 496–97
Tapetum lucidum, 721
Tapeworm
    characteristics, 526t
    digestive tract, 647
    evolution, of, 519, 532, 534
    self-fertilization, 773
"Tapeworm diet," 519
Taphrina, 409*f*
Taproot, 452, 461*f*
Tarbela Dam, 912
Target cells, 755
Tarsal bones, 740*f,* 742, 743*f*
Tarsiers, 571*f,* 572, 573*f,* 575
Tarsius bancanus, 571*f*
Tasmanian devils, 564
Taste, sense of, 718, 812
Taste area, primary, 703*f,* 704
Taste buds, 651, 718, 718*f*
Tatum, Edward, 223
Taxa, 6
Taxol, 497
Taxon (pl., taxa), 348
Taxonomist, 307
Taxonomy, 348–50
    defined, 6, 348
    evolutionary, 272
    levels of, 6t
    Linnaean, 349–50
    of living things, 6–8
    phylogeny, 354–59
    systematic biology, 348–50
    three-domain system of, 351–54, 352t
Taxus brevifolia, 497
Tay-Sachs disease, 73
TB (tuberculosis), 642, 672, 674–75
Tbx5 gene, and limb development, 321
T-cell receptor (TCR), 635–36
TCR (T cell receptor), 635–36
T-DNA (transformed DNA), 492
Technology. *See* Biotechnology
Tectorial membrane, 727
Teeth, 649
Telencephalon (cerebrum), 695, 702*f,*
    703–5
Telomerase, 221, 222
Telomeres, 164, 221, 222, 813
Telophase (mitosis), 158*f,* 160, 177t
Telophase I (meiosis), 176, 177t, 179*f*
Telophase II (meiosis), 176, 177t, 179*f*
Telson, 541
TEM (transmission electron
    microscope), 63
Temperate forests, 884, 887, 890–91
Temperate grasslands, 894, 895*f*
Temperate regions, 884, 887
Temperate zone, 898
Temperature
    air, 902
    body, 29f, 599, 600f, 601, 631
    boiling point of water, 29
    enzymatic speed, 111
    freezing point of water, 29
    global. See Climate
    homeostasis, 599–601
    lakes, 898–99
    ocean, 885, 902

testicular, 775
    of water, 29, 31
Template, DNA strand, 220
Template strand, 221, 225
Template switching, 266
Temporal bones, 740
Temporal isolation, 211*f,* 312
Temporal lobe, 703*f,* 704, 708*f*
Tendons, 590, 743, 744
Tendrils, 445, 458, 460, 461*f,* 491
Tension, in transpiration, 476
Tentacles, 528, 529*f,* 648
Teosinte, 278–79, 438, 439
Terminal bud, 444*f,* 453, 461*f*
Termination
    DNA translation, 231–32, 232f
    mRNA transcription, 226
    of translation, 231–32
Termites, 826, 866, 892, 895
Terrestrial ecosystems, 887–96. *See also*
        specific ecosystem
    climate and, 897
    coniferous forests, 890. See also
        Coniferous forests
    deserts, 896
    grasslands, 894–95
    shrublands, 894
    temperate deciduous forests, 891
    tropical forests, 892–93. See also
        Tropical rain forests
    tundra, 888
Territoriality, 299, 830, 848
Territory, 299, 830
Tertiary period, 336t, 341, 433
Tertiary structure, of proteins, 52–53
Test (skeleton), of rhizarians, 398–99
Testable, evolution as, 285
Testcrosses, 200–201
Testes (sing., testis)
    development of, 775
    hormonal control of, 778
    hormones secreted by, 754f, 755, 756,
        758f, 767, 775
    structure and function, 181, 767,
        775–77, 775t
Testicular cancer, 776
Testis-determining factor, 184
Testosterone
    aging process, 813
    secretion of, 45, 754f, 755, 767, 778
    as steroid, 46, 48
    structure and function, 48f, 754f, 767,
        778
Testudo horsefieldii, 916*f*
Tetanus, 376, 746
Tetany, 744, 762
Tetracyclines, 376, 910
Tetrad chromosomes, 173
Tetrapods
    amphibians, 552, 556
    in cladistics, 356
    defined, 552
    fishapod, 271, 280, 281f, 285
T-even bacteriophage, 364*f*
Thalamus, 695, 702*f,* 704, 705
Thallose liverworts, 424
Thallus, 424
Thamnophis elegans, 821*f*
Thaumaptilon, 338*f*
Thecodonts, 559
Theory
    defined, 12, 285
    of evolution, 275–80
    scientific, 11f, 12
Therapeutic cloning, 161, 162
Therapsids, 340
Thermoacidophiles, 354, 378*f,* 379
Thermocline, 898
Thermodynamics, laws of, 105–6, 871–73
Thermophiles, evolution of, 335*f*
Thermoreceptors, 717, 730
Thermostat, 601
Thermus aquaticus, 256
Theropods, 340
Thick skin, 598
Thighbone (femur), 740*f,* 742
Thigmomorphogenesis, 493
Thigmotropism, 490, 491, 493
Thin skin, 598
Third ventricle, 702*f,* 704

Thistle tube, 92*f*, 93
Thompson, D'Arcy, 320
Thoracic cage, 740
Thoracic cavity, 596, 667, 668*f*
Thoracic duct, 628*f*, 629
Thoracic nerves, 696*f*
Thoracic vertebrae, 741
Thorax
    crayfish, 541
    insects, 542, 543*f*
Thorns, of plants, 448
Threatened species, 908
3PG molecules, in Calvin cycle, 128*f*, 129
Three-domain system of classification,
        351–54
    Archaea, 352*t*, 353–54
    Bacteria, 351, 352*t*, 353
    Eukarya, 352*t*, 354
    vs. five-kingdom system, 351
    tree of life with, 351*f*
Three-spined stickleback fish, 322
Threonine, 51*f*
Thrombin, 620
Thrombocytes. See Platelets
Thrombus, 616
Thrush (bird), 297
Thrush (candidiasis), 410, 638
Thylakoids, 66, 76, 121, 126
Thymine (T)
    complimentary base pairing, 55
    in DNA composition, 55*f*, 217–19, 223
    as nucleotide, 54*f*, 217*f*
Thymine dimers, 248
Thymosins, 754*f*, 768
Thymus
    involution of, 812
    structure and function, 628*f*, 629, 754*f*
    T cell maturation in, 629, 768, 812
Thyroid cancer, 761
Thyroid gland
    aging process, 813
    disorders of, 760–61
    hormone secretion, 589, 754*f*, 758*f*, 760
    radioactive iodine uptake, 24
    structure and function of, 760, 761*f*
Thyroid hormones, 754*f*, 755, 760–61
Thyroxine (T4), 754*f*, 757, 760–61
Tibia, 740*f*, 742, 743*f*
Tibial nerve, 696*f*
Tibialis anterior muscle, 744*f*
Tibicen, 737*f*
Tick, 543, 848
Tidal pools, 900*f*
Tidal ventilation mechanism, 670
Tidal zone, 900–901
Tiger, 918
Tiger shark, 554
Tight junctions, 99–100, 588, 594
Tiktaalik roseae, 271, 280, 281*f*, 285, 556
Timber industry, 911
Timberline, 840
Time, change over, observation of, and
        evolutionary theory, 275
Timelines
    of evolution, 559*f*, 565*f*, 576*f*
    geologic, 334–35, 336*t*
Tineas, 410
Tinnitus, 728, 730
Tissue
    biological organization, 2, 3*f*
    complex, xylem and phloem as, 449–50
    connective tissue, 588–92
    defined, 2
    epithelial, 588–89. See also Skin
    fat. See Adipose tissue
    of flowering plants, 446, 447–50
    meristematic, 161
    monocot vs. eudicot, 446
    muscular tissue. See Muscle(s)
    nervous tissue. See Nervous tissue
    organization and diversity of, 2, 3*f*,
        446, 447–50
    types of, 588–94
    vascular. See Vascular tissue
Tissue culture, plant, 513–14
Tissue engineering, 643
Tissue fluid, 621
Tissue stages of development, 797
Tmesipteris, 428
TNF (tumor necrosis factor), 637
Toads, 526*t*, 557, 848

Toadstools, 412
Tobacco hornworm, 752
Tobacco mosaic virus, 365, 366
Tobacco smoke, 248. See also Smoking
Tolerance model of succession, 869
Tomato, 510*f*
Tone, muscle, 744
Tongue, 651, 718
Tonicity, 93, 101*t*
Tonsils, 628*f*, 630
Tool use, by early humans, 578, 580–82
Toothed whale, 308, 310*f*
Topography, 885
Topsoil, 468*f*
Torpedo stage, eudicot embryonic
        development, 508, 509*f*
Tortoises, 276, 917
Tortoises, 276, 917
Totipotent cells, 514, 800
Touch
    plant responses to, 493–94
    receptors for, 598
    sense of, 730
Tourism, 912–13
Toxins, bacterial, 376
Toxoplasma gondii, 394
Toxoplasmic encephalitis, 638
Toxoplasmosis, 394
Tracer, 24
Trachea (pl., tracheae)
    arthropod, 540
    ciliary actions, 589
    defined, 667
    disorders affecting, 673–74
    epithelium of, 589
    gas exchange, 665
    human, 668
    insect, 542, 667
Tracheal gills, 667
Tracheids
    defined, 449
    in plant transport system, 473
    stem structure and function, 453, 456
    water transport, 475
    in xylem, 449–50, 475
Trachemys scripta elegans, 916*f*
Tracheole, 665, 667
Tracheostomy, 673
Trade winds, 885
Traits
    ancestral, 354
    behavioral, in humans, heritable, 207
    derived, 354
        of land plants, 422, 423*f*
    diagnostic, 307
    multifactorial, 207
    multiple allelic, 205
    shared derived, 356
    systematic biology, 348
Transacetylase, 239
Transamination, 147
Transcription
    defined, 223, 225–27
    eukaryotic chromosome structure, 233
    genomic sequence, 261*f*, 262
    introns, 227
    mRNA production, 225–27
    pre-mRNA, 226–27
    process of, 225*f*
Transcription activators, 244
Transcription factors, 244, 249, 804
Transcriptional control, eukaryotic
        regulation, 241, 244
Transduction
    in prokaryotes, 373
    of signals, plants, 484–85, 490,
        492, 497*f*
Transduction pathway, 90
Trans-fatty acids, 658
Transfer rate, 875
Transfer RNA. See tRNA
Transform boundary, 343
Transformation
    of bacteria, experiments on, 215–17
    of organisms, genetic, 216–17
    in prokaryotes, 373
Transformed DNA (T-DNA), 492
Transfusions, blood, 619, 619*f*
Transgenic organisms
    animals, 258–59
    bacteria, 258
    defined, 255

plants, 258
    salamanders, 594, 595*f*
Transitional fossils, 280–81, 285
Translation, 228–32
    defined, 228
    elongation, 230*f*–231*f*, 231, 232*f*
    eukaryotic chromosome structure, 233
    initiation, 230–31, 230*f*, 232*f*
    process of, 223*f*, 230–32
    rRNA in, 229–31
    termination, 231–32, 232*f*
    tRNA in, 228–29
Translational control, eukaryotic
        regulation, 241, 246–47
Translocation, 187–88, 231
Transmissible spongiform encephalopathy
        (TSE), 53, 371
Transmission electron microscope
        (TEM), 63
Transpiration, 476–77, 875
Transplantation
    bone marrow, 639
    liver, 656
    pancreatic, 767
    of plants, 444
    rejection, 643
Transport
    active, 89*t*, 91, 95–98
    bulk, 95–98, 96*f*
    by carrier proteins, 95–96
    of exotic species, 914
    facilitated, 89*t*, 94
    in invertebrates, 606–7
    passive, across a membrane, 91–94
    in plants, 472–79
    proteins and, 49
    in vertebrates, 608–9
Transport medium, water as, 30
Transport vesicles, 67, 74
Transposons, 262, 574, 627
Trapezius muscle, 744*f*
Trastuzumab (Herceptin), 635, 783
Traumotropism, 491
Trawling, 916–18
Tree(s). See also Forest(s)
    advantages and disadvantages, 456
    annual rings, 456, 457*f*
    vs. bamboo uses, 458
    growth of, 455–56
    mutualism, 848
    oldest living, 430
    as photosynthetic organisms, 120*f*
    in phytoremediation, 470–71
    population distribution, 840–41
    trunk of, 455–56, 457*f*
    as woody stem, 455
Tree frogs, 557*f*
Tree of life
    Darwin's, 282
    Precambrian period, 335*f*
    three-domain system of
        classification, 351*f*
Tree of Life project, 282
Trematodes, 532, 907
Treponema pallidum, 790
Triads, 527
Triassic period, 336*t*, 340, 343, 344
Triceps brachii muscle, 744*f*
Triceratops, 340
Trichinella, 538*f*, 539
Trichinosis, 539
Trichocysts, 393
Trichomes, 447, 458, 461
Trichomonas vaginalis, 395, 791
Trichomoniasis, 791
Trichophyton, 410
Tricuspid valve, 611
Triglycerides, 46, 47*f*, 658
Triiodothyronine (T3), 757, 760–61
Trilobites, 338, 344
Trimesters, pregnancy, 805
Trimethylaminuria, 192
Triple covalent bonding, 27, 39
Triplet code, 224
Triploblastic animals, 523
Trisomy, 183–84
Trisomy 21 (Down syndrome), 184, 187
Triticum aestivum, 492
tRNA (transfer RNA)
    charged tRNA, 229
    in nucleus, 70

structure and function, 223, 228–29
    translation, 228–31, 232*f*
Trochophores, 530
Trochozoans, 530–38
    annelids, 536–37
    characteristics, 526*t*
    defined, 530
    flatworms, 531–33
    marine polychaetes, 537–38
    molluscs, 534–36
    rotifers, 533–34
Trophic levels, 873
Trophoblast, 808
Tropical rain forests
    climate, 887, 892, 893
    destruction of, 127, 893, 913
    habitat loss in, 913, 914*f*
    human impact on, 10
    soil in, 468, 893, 913
    species composition, 858
    structure of, 892
Tropisms
    defined, 490
    gravitropism, 485–86, 490*f*, 491
    phototropism, 483, 485–86, 490, 491
    thigmotropism, 490, 491, 493
Troponin, 748
Trout, 554, 840, 897*f*
Trp operon, 238*f*, 239
True coelom, 523
True mosses, 424
True ribs, 741
True-breeding, 194
Truffles, 408, 415
Trypanosoma brucei, 396, 398, 399*f*
Trypanosoma cruzi, 396
Trypanosomes, 396
Trypanosomiasis, 398
Trypsin, 110, 656
Tryptophan, 238*f*, 239
TSE (transmissible spongiform
        encephalopathy), 53, 371
Tsetse fly, 396, 398–99
TSH (thyroid-stimulating hormone), 754*f*,
        757, 758*f*, 760–61
2,4,5-T, 485
Tuataras, 1, 561
Tubal ligation, 779
Tubastrea, 529*f*
Tube cell, 436
Tube feet, 544
Tube worms, 648, 902
Tuberculosis (TB), 642, 672, 674–75
Tubers, 445, 448, 457*f*, 458
Tubular reabsorption, 686, 687*f*
Tubular secretion, 686, 687*f*
Tubulidentata, 566*t*
Tubulin, 78–79, 158
Tumor, 163–64, 594. See also Cancer
Tumor necrosis factor (TNF), 637
Tumor suppressor genes, 153, 164,
        165*f*, 249
Tuna, 901*f*, 916
Tundra, 887, 888
Tunicates, 526*t*, 551
Turgor, 493
Turgor (nastic) movements, 493–95
    biological clock, 494–95
    circadian rhythms, 494–95
    defined, 493
    responses to touch, 493–94
    sleep movements, 494
Turgor pressure, 93, 474, 477, 486*f*
Turkeys, 773
Turner syndrome, 184, 185
Turnips, 452
Turpentine, 431
Turtles
    characteristics, 526*t*, 561
    fossil, 356–57
    marine, osmoregulation in, 680, 684
    overexploitation of, 917
    tortoises, 276, 917
Twin studies, on nature vs. nurture,
        208, 821
Twining shoots, 458
Two-trait testcross, 201
Tympanal organs, insect, 726
Tympanic membrane, 726*f*, 727
Type 1 diabetes mellitus, 766–67
Type 2 diabetes mellitus, 659, 767

Typhlosole, 536, 537f, 647
Typhoid fever, 376
Tyrannosaurus rex, 340, 559
Tyrosine, 51f, 760

U

Ulcer, gastric, 652
Uliprystal acetate, 783
Ulna, 740f, 742
Ulnar nerve, 696f
Ultraviolet (UV) radiation
　bee-pollinated flowers, 506–7
　induced mutations, 248
　melanoma, 153
　ozone shield, 335
　vitamin D conversion, 597, 598
Ultraviolet (UV) spectrum, 720
Ulva, 388
Umami taste, 718
Umbilical cord, 805, 808f, 809–10, 811f
Unambiguous, genetic code as, 224
Unbalanced translocation, 188
Underground horizontal stems, 457f, 458
Understory, 890, 891, 892, 894
Unicellular organisms, 2, 167, 167t
Uniform distribution, 840
Uniformitarianism, 274
Unipolar neurons, 697–98
Unique noncoding DNA, 262–63
Unknown sequences of DNA, 262
Unsaturated fatty acids, 46, 47f, 658
Upper respiratory tract disorders, 673
Upwelling, 904
Uracil, 54f, 223, 223t, 224f
Urea, 147, 659, 681, 686
Ureter, 684, 684f
Urethra
　defined, 684
　female, 779f
　male, 775f, 775t, 777f, 778
Urey, Harold, 329
Uric acid, 681
Urinary bladder, 684
Urinary bladder sphincter, 778
Urinary incontinence, 812
Urinary system, 596, 684–90, 812
Urine, 682, 683, 686, 687f
Urochordates, 551
Uropods, 541
Ursus arctos, 889f
Ursus arctos horribilis, 919f
Ustilago, 413f
Uterine cycle, 781–82, 782t
Uterine tubes (oviducts), 589, 779, 806f
Uterus
　effect of prostaglandins on, 768–69
　implantation in, 806
　during pregnancy, 809, 810, 811f
　structure and function, 779, 779t, 781–82
Utricle, 728, 729f
UV radiation. *See* Ultraviolet (UV)
　radiation
Uvula, 651f

V

Vaccines
　aging process, 812
　cancer, 640
　contraceptive, 784
　diabetes, 767
　HIV, 788
　and immunity, 639
　influenza, 366, 370
　prostate cancer, 640
Vacuoles
　central, of plant cells, 69f, 75–76
　ciliates, 393
　contractile, 384, 395, 396
　euglenids, 395
　food, 396
　protist, 384, 385t
Vagina, 774, 779, 779t
Vaginal infections, 790–91
Vaginitis, 790–91
Valence shell, 25
Valine, 51f
Valves
　heart, 611–13
　veins, 608, 615

Vampire bat, 834
van Beneden, Pierre-Joseph, 172
Van Ermengem, Emile Pierre, 746
Van Helmont, Jean-Baptiste, 465
van Niel, C. B., 122
Vaporization of water, 29, 875
Variables
　experimental (independent), 12, 14–15
　responding (dependent), 14
Variation
　environment and population
　　polymorphism, 301–2
　genetic, and meiosis, 174–75
　inheritable, 277
　in populations, 277
Varicellovirus, 365
Vas deferens (pl., vasa deferentia),
　775–77, 775t
Vascular bundle, stem, 450, 453, 454f, 455
Vascular cambium
　stem, 454, 455
　tree trunk, 457f
　woody twig, 456f
Vascular cylinder, 450, 451–52, 451f
Vascular endothelium, 608, 608f
Vascular plants
　adaptation to land, 420
　characteristics, 421t
　defined, 426
　evolution of, 420
　leaves of, 423f
　seedless, 426
　tallest living, 430
　transport mechanisms in, 472–79
Vascular rays, 450
Vascular system (human). *See*
　Cardiovascular system
Vascular tissue (plant)
　cambium, 453–54, 462f
　defined, 423
　evolutionary history of plants, 420f
　flowering plants, 447
　leaf and stem structure, 444f
　lycophytes, 426
　monocot vs. eudicot, 446
　roots, 451–52
　in stem, 445
　structure and function, 449–50
Vasectomy, 776
Vauxia, 338f
VE (vessel element), 449, 453, 455f, 473
Vectors
　African sleeping sickness, 398, 399
　defined, 394
　gene cloning, 255
　neglected tropical diseases, 398
　parasitic, 865
Vegans, 658–59
Vegetal pole, 797, 801f
Vegetarian diet, 658–59. *See also*
　Herbivores
Vegetation. *See* Plant(s)
Vegetative cells, in *Chlamydomonas*, 387
Vegetative organs, of flowering
　plants, 444
Veins
　cardiac, 614
　leaf structure, 444f
　leaves, 446
　pulmonary, 611–12
　renal, 684f, 685f, 686, 687f
　in skin, 597f
　structure and function of, 608, 615
　subclavian, 628f, 629
　valves of, 608, 615
Vena cavae, 611, 614
Ventilation
　one-way mechanism, 670
　respiratory center, 670–71
　tidal mechanism, 670
Ventral cavity, 596
Ventral root, spinal nerves, 707, 708f
Ventricles
　cardiac, 609, 610f, 611, 612–13
　cerebral, 702, 703, 704
Ventricular fibrillation, 613–14
Venules
　in circulatory system, 608, 614
　renal, 685f, 686, 687f
Venus flytrap
　carnivorous, 472

as modified leaf, 460–61
　modified leaves of, 461f
　turgor movement, 493–94
Vermiform appendix, 630, 653
Vernix caseosa, 810
Vertebrae (pl., vertebra), 708f, 741–42
Vertebral cavity, 596f
Vertebral column
　embryonic development of, 809
　evolution of, 552
　human, 740–42
Vertebrates. *See also specific organisms*
　amphibians, 552–53, 556–57
　birds, 562–63
　body plan evolution, 524–25
　brain of, 695–96, 695f
　Cambrian period, 339
　characteristics, 526t, 552–53
　chordates, 550–51
　circulatory system of, 552, 556, 608–9
　defined, 520–21
　embryonic development of, 797–99
　evolution of, 549–69
　eyes, 720
　fishes, 553–55, 556
　forelimbs of, evolution of, 283, 737
　gas exchange in, 665–66
　generally, 552–53
　genome of, 263t, 265
　hormones in, 753, 755. *See also*
　　Hormones
　human, 460, 560
　human evolution, 560
　mammals, 564–65, 566t
　nervous system, 695–96
　osmoregulation, 680, 682–84
　pineal gland in, 768
　reproduction, 773–74. *See also*
　　Reproduction
　reptiles, 558–59, 561–63
　respiration, 665–66
　skeletal system of, 736–37
　transport in, 606–7
　vision, 720
Vertebrate evolution, 549–69
　amphibians, 552–53, 556–57
　birds, 562–63
　Cambrian period, 339
　characteristics, 340–43, 564–65, 566t
　chordates, 550–51
　fishes, 553–55, 556
　generally, 552–53
　human, 460, 560
　mammals, 564–65, 566t
　reptiles, 558–59, 561–63
　review and exercises, 567–69
Vertical stems, 457f, 458
Vertigo, 730
Vervet monkeys, 828
Vesicles
　animal cell, 68f
　coated, 97f, 98
　defined, 67
　endocytic, 98
　formation of, 91, 95
　intracellular movement, 68
　optic, 809f
　peroxisomes, 75
　pinocytic, 98
　secretory, 73, 74, 96f
　seminal, 777
　synaptic, 747
　transport, 67, 74
Vesicular follicle, 780
Vespula, 864f
Vessel element (VE), 449, 453, 455f, 473
Vestibular canal, 727
Vestibular glands, 780
Vestibular nerve, 726f, 728, 729f
Vestibule, 726f, 727
Vestigial structures, 272, 284
Vetter, David, 626, 641
Vibrio cholerae, 353, 374
Video-enhanced contrast microscopy, 64
Viewing, in microscopy, 64
Villus. *See* Microvilli
Vinegar, 141
Viperfish, 901f
Virchow, Rudolph, 61
Virology, 365
Virulence factors, 376–77

Virus(es), 364–69. *See also specific virus*
　as cancer cause, 165f
　classification, 365
　defined, 364
　discovery of, 364–65
　disease caused by, 364t
　emerging, 369, 371f
　evolution of, 366
　flu pandemics, 363, 370, 371
　laboratory culturing, 366
　mutation of, 365, 366, 370
　parasitic nature of, 366, 865
　reproduction, 366–69
　retroviruses, 368, 369f
　review and exercises, 379–82
　sexually transmitted diseases, 787–90
　structure, 365–66
Visceral (smooth) muscle, 592–93,
　608, 744
Visible light, 124, 716, 720
Vision, 720–25. *See also* Eye(s)
　aging process, 812
　color, 720, 723
　disorders of, 724–25
　night, 723
　panoramic, 721
　stereoscopic, 721
Visual accommodation, 721
Visual area, primary, 703f, 704
Visual association area, 703f
Visual communication, 828–29
Visual focus disorders, 724
Vitamin(s)
　deficiencies of, 112, 660
　defined, 112
　dietary, 660
Vitamin A, 654, 660, 723
Vitamin B$_{12}$, 654
Vitamin D, 597, 598, 654, 738, 761
Vitamin E, 654
Vitamin K, 653
Vitreous humor, 721
Viviparous mammals, 774
VNO (vomeronasal organ), 828
Vocal cords, 668
Vocalization, territoriality and, 299
Voles, 888
Voltage, 698–99
Voluntary muscle, 592
Volvox, 2, 384, 388
Vombatus, 283f
Vomeronasal organ (VNO), 828
Vomiting, 651
von Linne, Karl, 349f
Vulpes velox, 896f
Vulva, 780

W

Wachtershäuser, Gunter, 329
Wallace, Alfred Russel, 277
Warbler(s), 318, 319, 860, 861f, 867f
Warbler finch, 279f
Warfarin, 112
Warm receptors, 730
Warm-blooded animals, 599
Warning coloration, 863
Warts, genital, 788
Wasps, 498, 506, 542f, 834, 864
Waste, metabolic. *See* Excretory system
Waste recycling, 912
Water
　acid rain, 33
　adhesion, 30–31
　body fluid balance. *See* Osmoregulation
　boiling point, 29
　brackish, 897, 900
　chemistry of, 28–31
　density and temperature, 31
　"diving response," 663
　ecosystems in. *See* Aquatic ecosystems
　evolution of life on Earth, 329
　freezing point, 29
　fresh. *See* Fresh water
　heat of evaporation, 29
　models of, 28f
　molecular polarity, 27
　molecules of, 27, 28–29, 30
　nutritional function of soil, 467
　ocean, 885, 902
　in photosynthesis, 122

Water, *continued*
  phytoremediation of, 470–71
  plant transport systems, 469,
    475–77
  pollution of, 875, 877, 915
  properties of, 29–31
  as solvent, 29–30
  as transport medium, 30
  transportation in sponges, 527f
Water column, 476, 477
Water culture (hydroponics), 465–66
Water cycle, 875, 897, 912
Water hyacinth, 914
Water molds (oomycetes), 7, 385t, 386f,
    391–92
Water potential, 473, 474
Water striders/spiders, 31, 667, 899
Water table, 875, 897
Water vascular system, 544
Watson, James, 218–19
Waxes (lipids), 45t, 48–49
WBCs. *See* White blood cells
Weather. *See* Climate
Weathering, soil formation, 467
Wegener, Alfred, 342
Weight
  human
    birth, 296, 297f
    obesity treatment, 655
  vs. mass, in atomic particles, 23
Weinberg, Wilhelm, 291
Weisheit, Chris, 206
Welwitschia, 433
Welwitschia mirabillis, 432f
Went, Frits W., 485
Wernicke's area, 703f
West Nile encephalitis, 369
Westerly winds, 885
Wetlands, 468–69, 897, 912, 913
Whale(s)
  allopatric speciation in, 314
  auditory communication by, 828
  conservation of, 889
  courtship behavior of, 827
  dentition in, 648
  echolocation by, 717
  evolution of, 281f, 283f, 322
  evolutionary species concept, 308, 310f
  habitat, 901
  osmoregulation, 684
Whale sharks, 554
Wheat, 492
Wheat rust, 413
"Wheel animalcules," 543
Wheel animals, 526t
Whelks, 535
Whisk ferns, 427, 428
White blood cells (WBCs)
  in blood sample, 591f

functions of, 592, 620
  inflammatory response, 631
  structure, 592
  types of, 620
White Cliffs of Dover, 399, 400f
White matter
  brain, 704
  spinal cord, 703, 708f
White pulp, 630
Whitebark pine trees, 866
White-crowned sparrows, 824
White-faced monkeys, 571f
White-tailed deer, 849–50
Whittaker, R. H., 351, 406
WHO. *See* World Health Organization
    (WHO)
Whorls
  green algae, 421
  horsetails, 427
  leaves, 460
Wickramsinghe, Chandra, 330
Wildebeest, 895f
Wildlife conservation, 889
Wildlife species, trade in, 916–18
Wilkins, Maurice H. F., 218
Williams syndrome, 187f, 188
Willow, 452f
Wilson, E. O., 862
Wilting, 474
Wind(s), 884–85, 902
Wind-pollinated flowers, 437, 505
Windward side, 885
Wine, fungi and, 410
Wings
  bird, 283
  evolution of, 283, 339
  insect, 339, 542
Winter buds, 488
Witchcraft, 411
Wiwaxia, 338f
Wobble hypothesis, 229
Woese, Carl, 351, 378
Wolf (pl., wolves)
  body language, 807
  and dogs, 278
  reintroduction of, 857, 889
  tundra, 888
Womb. *See* Uterus
Wombat, 283f, 564
Woodruff, David, 889
Woody plants, 430
Woody stems, 453–58
  advantages and disadvantages, 456
  bark, 456
  diversity of, 456, 457f, 458
  generally, 455
  wood, 456, 457f
Woody twig, 456f
Woolly mammoth, 341f

World Health Organization (WHO)
  Neglected Tropical Diseases (NTD),
    383, 398–99, 519, 532, 539
  "swine flu" pandemic, 363
World population growth, 851–53
Worms. *See* Earthworms; Flatworms;
    Roundworms
Wounds, plant responses to, 497–98
Wrasses, 773, 866f
Wrinkling, skin, 598, 744, 746, 811
Wuchereria bancrofti, 539
Würsig, B., 827

X

X chromosome, inactive, 243
Xanthoparmelia, 414f
Xanthoria, 414f
Xenarthra, 566t
Xenical (orlistat), 655
Xenotransplantation, 560, 643, 767
Xeroderma pigmentosum, 248
Xiphias gladius, 555f
Xiphoid process, 741f
XLA (X-linked agammaglobulinemia), 641
X-linked agammaglobulinemia (XLA), 641
X-linked genes, 208
X-linked inheritance, 208–10
Xolair, 642
X-rays
  birth defects caused by, 807
  DNA diffraction, 217
Xylem
  cohesion-tension transport model,
    476–77
  conducting cells, 475f
  defined, 426, 449
  in eudicots, 451f, 454f
  functions of, 473
  mineral uptake, 469–70
  in monocots, 452
  primary, 453, 455f, 462f
  secondary, 455f, 456, 457f
  in stem, 453, 454f, 455f
  structure of, 426f, 449, 449f, 473
  in tree trunk, 457f
  in vascular cylinder, 451f, 452
  water transport, 475
Xylem rays, 455f, 456
Xylem sap, 473

Y

Yeast
  budding of, 408f
  cell division, 167, 167t
  as Eukarya, 354
  fermentation, 140–41

genome of, 263t
  population growth, 845f
  reproduction of, 408–9
  vaginal infection with, 791
Yellow bone marrow, 739
Yellow jacket wasp, 864
Yellowstone National Park, 919
Yersinia pestis, 848
Yew, 497
Yogurt, 141
Yolk, 774, 797, 798, 805
Yolk plug, 798
Yolk sac, 805, 808

Z

Z lines, 745
Zamia pumila, 432
Zea mays, 433, 476, 487, 492
Zebra, 895f
Zebra finch, 831
Zebra mussel, 914
Zero population growth, 851, 852
Zinc, 466t, 660
Ziram, 248
Zona pellucida, 796–97, 806f
Zone
  of cell division, 450, 451f
  of elongation, 450, 451f
  of leaching, 468
  of maturation, 450, 451f
Zooflagellates, 395
Zooids, 530
Zooplankton, 899, 902, 909
Zoosporangia, 392
Zoospore, 388, 407
Zoospore fungi, 404f, 406t, 407–8
Zooxanthellae, 392, 901
Zygomatic bone, 740f, 741
Zygomaticus muscle, 744f
Zygomycota, 404f, 406t, 407–8
Zygospore, 388, 407–8
Zygospore fungi, 407–8
Zygote
  in animals, 588, 796–97
  conifers, 431f
  eudicot, 508
  ferns, 429f
  genetic variation, 175
  human, 181–82, 780, 796–97, 806f
  hybrid, 312
  meiosis, 176
  mortality of, 311f
  mosses, 425t
  paired chromosomes, 172–73
  reproductive isolation, 310
  totipotency of, 800

A Brief History of Biology

Year	Name	Contribution
1628	William Harvey	Demonstrates that the blood circulates and the heart is a pump.
1665	Robert Hooke	Uses the word cell to describe compartments he sees in cork under the microscope.
1668	Francesco Redi	Shows that decaying meat protected from flies does not spontaneously produce maggots.
1673	Antonie van Leeuwenhoek	Uses microscope to view living microorganisms.
1735	Carolus Linnaeus	Initiates the binomial system of naming organisms.
1809	Jean B. Lamarck	Supports the idea of evolution by the inheritance of acquired characteristics.
1825	Georges Cuvier	Founds the science of paleontology and shows that fossils are related to living forms.
1828	Karl E. von Baer	Establishes the germ layer theory of development.
1838	Matthias Schleiden	States that plants are multicellular organisms.
1839	Theodor Schwann	States that animals are multicellular organisms.
1851	Claude Bernard	Concludes that a relatively constant internal environment allows organisms to survive under varying conditions.
1858	Rudolf Virchow	States that cells come only from preexisting cells.
1858	Charles Darwin, Alfred Wallace	Independently present evidence that natural selection guides the evolutionary process.
1865	Louis Pasteur	Disproves the theory of spontaneous generation for bacteria; shows that infections are caused by bacteria.
1866	Gregor Mendel	Proposes basic laws of genetics based on his experiments with garden peas.
1882	Robert Koch	Establishes the germ theory of disease and develops many techniques used in bacteriology.
1902	Walter S. Sutton, Theodor Boveri	Suggest that genes are on the chromosomes, after noting the similar behavior of genes and chromosomes.
1904	Ivan Pavlov	Shows that conditioned reflexes affect behavior, based on experiments with dogs.
1910	Thomas H. Morgan	States that each gene has a locus on a particular chromosome, based on experiments with Drosophila.
1924	Hans Spemann, Hilde Mangold	Show that induction occurs during development, based on experiments with frog embryos.
1929	Sir Alexander Fleming	Discovers the toxic effect of a mold product he called penicillin on certain bacteria.
1937	Konrad Z. Lorenz	Founds the study of ethology and shows the importance of imprinting in learning.
1937	Sir Hans A. Krebs	Discovers the reactions of a cycle that produces carbon dioxide during cellular respiration.
1940	George Beadle, Edward Tatum	Develop the one gene—one enzyme theory, based on red bread mold studies.
1944	O. T. Avery, Colin MacLeod, Maclyn McCarty	Demonstrate that DNA alone from virulent bacteria can transform nonvirulent bacteria.
1945	Melvin Calvin, Andrew A. Benson	Discover the individual reactions of a cycle that reduces carbon dioxide during photosynthesis.
1950	Barbara McClintock	Discovers transposons (jumping genes) while doing experiments with corn.
1952	Alfred D. Hershey, Martha Chase	Find that only DNA from viruses enters cells and directs the reproduction of new viruses.
1953	James Watson, Francis Crick, Rosalind Franklin	Establish that the molecular structure for DNA is a double helix.
1953	Harold Urey, Stanley Miller	Demonstrate that the first organic molecules may have arisen from the gases of the primitive atmosphere.
1954	Linus Pauling	States that disease-causing abnormal hemoglobins are due to mutations.
1954	Jonas Salk	Develops a vaccine that protects against polio.
1958	Matthew S. Meselson, Franklin W. Stahl	Demonstrate that DNA replication is semiconservative.
1961	Francois Jacob, Jacques Monod	Discover that genetic expression is controlled by regulatory genes.
1964	Marshall W. Nirenberg, Philip Leder	Produce synthetic RNA, enabling them to break the DNA code.
1973	Stanley Cohen	Uses recombinant DNA technique (genetic engineering) to place plant and animal genes in Escherichia coli.
1977	Carl Woese	Based on differences in ribosomal RNA sequences, proposes the three domain system of classifications.
1978	Peter Mitchell	Determines chemiosmotic mechanism by which ATP is produced in chloroplasts and mitochondria.
1989	Sidney Altman, Thomas R. Check	Independently discover that some RNA molecules can act as enzymes.
1990	R. Michael Blaese, W. French Anderson, Kenneth W. Culver	Develop procedure to infuse genetically engineered blood cells for treatment of immune system disorder—first gene therapy used in a human.
1997	Ian Wilmut	Clones an adult mammal for the first time.
2003	Human Genome Project	Complete human genome sequenced, creating push to discover genomic links to health and disease.
2010	Craig Venter	Leads team that develops the first synthetic life form.

Metric System

Unit and Abbreviation	Metric Equivalent	Approximate English-to-Metric Equivalents	Units of Temperature
Length			
nanometer (nm)	$= 10^{-9}$ m $(10^{-3}$ μm$)$		
micrometer (μm)	$= 10^{-6}$ m $(10^{-3}$ mm$)$		
millimeter (mm)	$= 0.001$ (10^{-3}) m		
centimeter (cm)	$= 0.01$ (10^{-2}) m	1 inch = 2.54 cm 1 foot = 30.5 cm	
meter (m)	$= 100$ (10^{2}) cm $= 1,000$ mm	1 foot = 0.30 m 1 yard = 0.91 m	
kilometer (km)	$= 1,000$ (10^{3}) m	1 mi = 1.6 km	
Weight (mass)			
nanogram (ng)	$= 10^{-9}$ g		
microgram (μg)	$= 10^{-6}$ g		
milligram (mg)	$= 10^{-3}$ g		
gram (g)	$= 1,000$ mg	1 ounce = 28.3 g 1 pound = 454 g	
kilogram (kg)	$= 1,000$ (10^{3}) g	= 0.45 kg	
metric ton (t)	$= 1,000$ kg	1 ton = 0.91 t	
Volume			
microliter (μl)	$= 10^{-6}$ l $(10^{-3}$ ml$)$		
milliliter (ml)	$= 10^{-3}$ liter $= 1$ cm^3 (cc) $= 1,000$ mm^3	1 tsp = 5 ml 1 fl oz = 30 ml	
liter (l)	$= 1,000$ ml	1 pint = 0.47 liter 1 quart = 0.95 liter 1 gallon = 3.79 liter	
kiloliter (kl)	$= 1,000$ liter		

Temperature scale:

°F — °C

230	110
220	
212° — 210	100 — 100°
200	90
190	
180	80
170	
160° — 160	70 — 71°
150	
140	60
134° ; 131° — 130	57°
120	50
110	
105.8° ; 98.6° — 100	40 — 41° ; 37°
90	30
80	
70	20
56.66° — 60	13.7°
50	10
40	
32° — 30	0 — 0°
20	
10	-10
0	-20
-10	
-20	-30
-30	
-40	-40

To convert temperature scales:

$$°C = \frac{(°F - 32)}{1.8}$$

$$°F = 1.8\,(°C) + 32$$

°C	°F	
100	212	Water boils at standard temperature and pressure.
71	160	Flash pasteurization of milk
57	134	Highest recorded temperature in the United States, Death Valley, July 10, 1913
41	105.8	Average body temperature of a marathon runner in hot weather
37	98.6	Human body temperature
13.7	56.66	Human survival is still possible at this temperature.
0	32.0	Water freezes at standard temperature and pressure.

Periodic Table of Elements

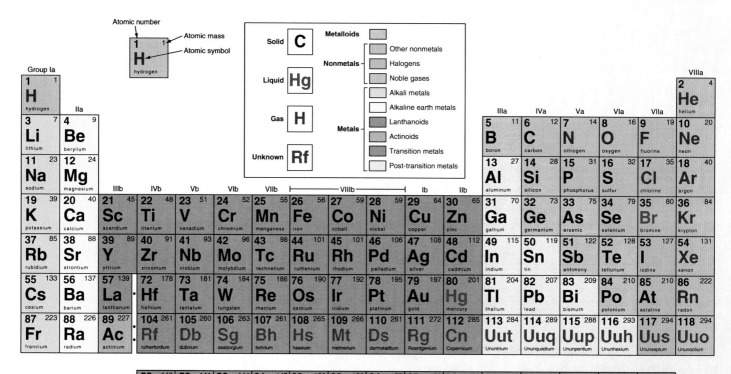

Atomic number
Atomic mass
Atomic symbol

1	1
H	
hydrogen	

Solid **C**

Liquid **Hg**

Gas **H**

Unknown **Rf**

Metalloids

Nonmetals
- Other nonmetals
- Halogens
- Noble gases

Metals
- Alkali metals
- Alkaline earth metals
- Lanthanoids
- Actinoids
- Transition metals
- Post-transition metals

Group Ia

Ia	IIa												IIIa	IVa	Va	VIa	VIIa	VIIIa
1 1 **H** hydrogen																		**2** 4 **He** helium
3 7 **Li** lithium	**4** 9 **Be** berylium												**5** 11 **B** boron	**6** 12 **C** carbon	**7** 14 **N** nitrogen	**8** 16 **O** oxygen	**9** 19 **F** fluorine	**10** 20 **Ne** neon
11 23 **Na** sodium	**12** 24 **Mg** magnesium	IIIb	IVb	Vb	VIb	VIIb		VIIIb		Ib	IIb		**13** 27 **Al** aluminum	**14** 28 **Si** silicon	**15** 31 **P** phosphorus	**16** 32 **S** sulfur	**17** 35 **Cl** chlorine	**18** 40 **Ar** argon
19 39 **K** potassium	**20** 40 **Ca** calcium	**21** 45 **Sc** scandium	**22** 48 **Ti** titanium	**23** 51 **V** vanadium	**24** 52 **Cr** chromium	**25** 55 **Mn** manganese	**26** 56 **Fe** iron	**27** 59 **Co** cobalt	**28** 59 **Ni** nickel	**29** 64 **Cu** copper	**30** 65 **Zn** zinc		**31** 70 **Ga** gallium	**32** 73 **Ge** germanium	**33** 75 **As** arsenic	**34** 79 **Se** selenium	**35** 80 **Br** bromine	**36** 84 **Kr** krypton
37 85 **Rb** rubidium	**38** 88 **Sr** strontium	**39** 89 **Y** yttrium	**40** 91 **Zr** zirconium	**41** 93 **Nb** niobium	**42** 96 **Mo** molybdium	**43** 98 **Tc** technetium	**44** 101 **Ru** ruthenium	**45** 101 **Rh** rhodium	**46** 106 **Pd** palladium	**47** 108 **Ag** silver	**48** 112 **Cd** cadmium		**49** 115 **In** indium	**50** 119 **Sn** tin	**51** 122 **Sb** antimony	**52** 128 **Te** tellurium	**53** 127 **I** iodine	**54** 131 **Xe** xenon
55 133 **Cs** cesium	**56** 137 **Ba** barium	**57** 139 **La** lanthanum	**72** 178 **Hf** hafnium	**73** 181 **Ta** tantalum	**74** 184 **W** tungsten	**75** 186 **Re** rhenium	**76** 190 **Os** osmium	**77** 192 **Ir** iridium	**78** 195 **Pt** platinum	**79** 197 **Au** gold	**80** 201 **Hg** mercury		**81** 204 **Tl** thalium	**82** 207 **Pb** lead	**83** 209 **Bi** bismuth	**84** 210 **Po** polonium	**85** 210 **At** astatine	**86** 222 **Rn** radon
87 223 **Fr** francium	**88** 226 **Ra** radium	**89** 227 **Ac** actinium	**104** 261 **Rf** rutherfordium	**105** 260 **Db** dubnium	**106** 263 **Sg** seaborgium	**107** 262 **Bh** bohrium	**108** 265 **Hs** hassium	**109** 266 **Mt** meitnerium	**110** 281 **Ds** darmstadtium	**111** 272 **Rg** Roentgenium	**112** 285 **Cn** Copernicum		**113** 284 **Uut** Ununtrium	**114** 289 **Uuq** Ununquadium	**115** 288 **Uup** Ununpentium	**116** 293 **Uuh** Ununhexium	**117** 294 **Uus** Ununseptium	**118** 294 **Uuo** Ununoctium

58 140 **Ce** cerium	**59** 141 **Pr** praseodymium	**60** 144 **Nd** neodymium	**61** 147 **Pm** promethium	**62** 150 **Sm** samarium	**63** 152 **Eu** europium	**64** 157 **Gd** gadolinium	**65** 159 **Tb** terbium	**66** 163 **Dy** dysprosium	**67** 165 **Ho** holmium	**68** 167 **Er** erbium	**69** 169 **Tm** thulium	**70** 173 **Yb** ytterbium	**71** 175 **Lu** lutetium
90 232 **Th** thorium	**91** 231 **Pa** protactinium	**92** 238 **U** uranium	**93** 237 **Np** neptunium	**94** 242 **Pu** plutonium	**95** 243 **Am** americium	**96** 247 **Cm** curium	**97** 247 **Bk** berkelium	**98** 249 **Cf** californium	**99** 254 **Es** einsteinium	**100** 253 **Fm** fermium	**101** 256 **Md** mendelevium	**102** 254 **No** nobelium	**103** 257 **Lr** lawrencium